A HISTORY OF CHEMISTRY

A HISTORY OF CHEMISTRY

BY

J. R. PARTINGTON

M.B.E., D.Sc.

EMERITUS PROFESSOR OF CHEMISTRY IN THE UNIVERSITY OF LONDON
FELLOW OF QUEEN MARY COLLEGE, LONDON

VOLUME THREE

LONDON
MACMILLAN & CO LTD
NEW YORK · ST MARTIN'S PRESS
1962

MACMILLAN AND COMPANY LIMITED
St Martin's Street London WC2
also Bombay Calcutta Madras Melbourne

THE MACMILLAN COMPANY OF CANADA LIMITED
Toronto

ST MARTIN'S PRESS INC
New York

PRINTED IN GREAT BRITAIN

PREFACE

THE present volume deals with topics detailed in the table of Contents. The chapters on earlier French chemistry point out the influence of Paracelsus and a little later that of Boyle. The phlogiston theory was not first introduced by Macquer, and normal, acid, and basic salts were recognised before Rouelle; an attempt is made to separate the contributions of the two Rouelles. The chapters on chemistry in Scandinavia include material not easily accessible elsewhere; it is pointed out that Bergman gave a little-known summary of Scheele's work in 1775, when Priestley's discovery of oxygen and Lavoisier's claim to such discovery were published.

The discovery of oxygen is taken to mean the isolation of the pure gas, and a statement of such properties as distinguish it from other gases, as happened with Priestley in 1774. Although he says he did not appreciate its 'true nature' until 1775, this meant his 'discovery' then that it was a compound of nitric acid and earth. Whether Priestley was sure his original mercuric oxide was made *per se* or not has little significance; he also used red-lead and thought it had absorbed nitric acid from the atmosphere in the preparation. If the recognition of the true nature of a substance constitutes its discovery, then Dalton, and not the Dutch chemists, discovered ethylene, and Chevreul or Berthelot, and not Scheele, discovered glycerol. A little-known remark of Priestley in 1774 that he had found no change in weight on heating tin in a closed vessel is quoted.

Priestley was a likeable man and a clever experimenter, but his obstinate retention of theoretical (and some experimental) errors retarded the progress of chemistry. The account of his incorrect but influential views is dreary but necessary. It is once again pointed out that Cavendish, before Priestley, first collected a gas over mercury. The discussion of the claims made for Cavendish, Watt, and Lavoisier for the determination of the composition of water is tedious, but this could hardly have been avoided.

Lavoisier has mostly been allowed to speak for himself, attention being directed to the studied ambiguity of some of his statements which has misled so many who have read them. Otherwise, Meldrum, Speter, and Guerlac, all very well-informed, have been followed in matters of fact. Lavoisier's theory of combustion, which had to provide an alternative to the theory of phlogiston, combined his chemical views (not always correct) with his false theory of caloric, and differs from that popularly presented. Lavoisier's caloric theory is given in detail, because (as Hartog almost alone of recent writers on Lavoisier pointed out) it is an integral part of his new theory. His *Reflexions on Phlogiston*, supposed to have demolished the phlogiston theory, did nothing of the kind; the theory flourished for some time afterwards, as is shown in a separate chapter.

Writing on German chemistry is difficult, since many important German books are lacking in English libraries (the same is true of English books in Germany). Since all Richter's writings are exceedingly scarce, a fairly comprehensive account of his work is given, and the attribution of his achievements to Wenzel may in time die out.

Bryan and William Higgins are treated on the basis of their own writings, the claims of the first in relation to the second being pointed out. The claims of William Higgins have been intemperately asserted, mostly in ignorance of the prior contributions of Bryan. William Higgins has been given credit for all that he is entitled to claim.

The chapter on Dalton may correct some perennial errors, e.g. that he was an inaccurate worker, and did nothing after his proposal of the atomic theory. His early work on the physical properties of gases was recognised by his election to the Paris Institut, and if he had done nothing else it would give him a claim to be an outstanding figure of his times. His later work on the combustion of hydrocarbons is important. His explanation of the constancy of composition of the atmosphere, and of the aurora borealis, were both proposed by others (the second by Faraday) who were unaware of Dalton's publications.

This volume covers a period of exceptional interest both to chemists and to historians mainly concerned with other aspects of the times. The latter now have available a study taking account of recent research in the field.

CAMBRIDGE, *October 1961*

CONTENTS

CONTENTS

LIST OF ILLUSTRATIONS

ABBREVIATIONS IN REFERENCES

In footnotes references are given to periodical publications in the order: year of publication, volume number in small roman numerals, page (see below, (a)). In some cases the title of a book or periodical is given in full. In other cases abbreviated titles are given, as in (a) below, or simply a name, with or without a number, as in (b). The full titles (or references to pages on which they occur) will be found in the list of authors and publications beginning on p. xv. Again, in separate chapters or sections dealing with one person, a list of his publications in which they are denoted by numbers (or sometimes letters) is given towards the beginning of the section, and these abbreviations (c) are used throughout that part only. Examples of the types of abbreviation are shown below:

(a) Triewald, KAH, 1742, iii, 112, 211. See list of publications for KAH.

(b) J. C. Fischer, viii, 91. See list of authors under J. C. Fischer.

(c) Bergman, ch. V, p. 188, footnote 1 reads: XXX (1779); A, ii, 36. Items I–XLIX of Bergman's dissertations are given on p. 182 (the fourth page in the section on Bergman), and A is the book referred to in the list on p. 183. In other chapters the reference is given to the *Opuscula* of Bergman, i.e. item A. In the chapter on Priestley, Hartog (5) refers to the numbered item in the list on p. 239, and so on.

Titles given in full are not reproduced in the lists of authors and abbreviations. Places of publication, unless otherwise given, are London, Paris, and Berlin for works in English, French, and German. The size of a book is usually octavo (8°) unless otherwise stated. Biographical details are given in a standard form with the places and dates of birth and decease, e.g. Baumé (Senlis, 26 February 1728–Paris, 15 October 1804).

The spelling of French names varied in the period of the Revolution. One form is used in the text but the alternatives are given in the Index.

LIST OF AUTHORS

BECKMAN, J. (1) A History of Inventions, Discoveries, and Origins, tr. W. Johnson, revised W. Francis and J. W. Griffith, 2 vols., 1846.

Biogr. Univ. Biographie Universelle, 85 vols., 1811–62.

BIRCH, T. (1) History of the Royal Society, 4 vols. 4°, 1756–7.

BLACK, J. *Lectures* — see p. 132.

BM. British Museum (Library), London.

BN. Bibliothèque Nationale, Paris.

BOERHAAVE, H. (2) Elementa Chemiae, 2 vols. 4°, Leyden, 1732. (4) A New Method of Chemistry, 2 ed. by P. Shaw, 2 vols. 4°, 1741.

BOLTON, H. C. (1) A Select Bibliography of Chemistry 1492–1892 (Smithsonian Miscell. Collection), Washington, 1893.

BRANDE, W. T. A Manual of Chemistry, 6 ed., 2 vols., 1848.

BROUGHAM, LORD. (1) Lives of Philosophers of the Time of George III. (In *Works*, London and Glasgow, 1855, repr. 1872.)

BROWN, HARCOURT. Scientific Organizations in Seventeenth Century France, Baltimore, 1934.

CAP, P. A. Études Biographiques pour servir à l'Histoire des Sciences, 2 vols., 1857–64.

Cat. Catalogue.

Cat. of Sci. Papers. Catalogue of Scientific Papers, 4 series, The Royal Society of London.

CHAPTAL, J. A. C. (1) Elements of Chemistry, tr. W. Nicholson, 3 vols., 1791.

CUVIER, G. (1) Recueil des Éloges Scientifiques lus dans les Séances Publiques de l'Institut Royal de France, 3 vols., 1819–19–27. (2) Rapport Historique sur les Progrès des Sciences Naturelles, 1828. (3) Histoire des Progrès des Sciences Naturelles, depuis 1789 jusqu'à ce jour, 2 vols., Brussels, 1837–8.

DAREMBERG, C. V. (1) Histoire des Sciences Médicales, 2 vols., 1871.

DELACRE, M. (1) Histoire de la Chimie, 1920.

DIERGART, P. Beiträge aus der Geschichte der Chemie dem Gedächtniss von Georg W. A. Kahlbaum, Leipzig and Vienna, 1909.

DNB. Dictionary of National Biography.

DUMAS, J. B. (1) Leçons sur la Philosophie Chimique professées au Collège de France en 1836, ed. Binau (*sic*), 1837. (2) *ib.*, 2 ed. by Bineau, 1878.

DUVEEN, D. Bibliotheca Alchemica et Chemica, 1949.

DUVEEN, D., and KLICKSTEIN, H. S. A Bibliography of the Works of A. L. Lavoisier, 1954.

EB. Encyclopædia Britannica (ed. quoted).

Ency. Brit. Suppl. — see p. 719.

Ency. Méthod. Chimie. Encyclopédie Méthodique, department Chimie (Chymie).

E & O (Black) — see p. 136; (Priestley) — see p. 244, IV or VI.

E & O *Nat. Phil.* — see p. 244, V.

FAUJAS DE SAINT-FOND, B. Voyage en Angleterre, en Écosse et aux Îles Hébrides, 2 vols., 1797.

FELDHAUS, F. M. (1) Die Technik der Vorzeit, Leipzig and Berlin, 1914.

FERGUSON, J. Bibliotheca Chemica: Catalogue of the Alchemical, Chemical and Pharmaceutical Books in the Collection of the late James Young, 2 vols., Glasgow, 1906 (repr. London, 1954).

FISCHER, J. C. Geschichte der Physik, 8 vols., Göttingen, 1801–8.

FOSTER, SIR MICHAEL. Lectures on the History of Physiology during the Sixteenth, Seventeenth and Eighteenth Centuries (Cambridge Natural Science Manuals. Biological Series), Cambridge, 1901.

FOURCROY, A. F. DE. (1) Système des Connaissances Chimiques et de leurs applications aux phénomènes de la nature et de l'art, 11 vols. 8°, 1801–2; (2) article in Ency.Méthod.(see above), Chimie, 1796, iii, 303–781 (ib., 1793, ii, also quoted); (3) Elements of Natural History and Chemistry, tr. W. Nicholson, 3 ed., 3 vols., 1790; (4) Élémens d'histoire naturelle et de chimie, 5 ed., 5 vols., 1793.

GIBSON, R. J. HARVEY. Outlines of the History of Botany, 1919.

GMELIN, J. F. (1) Geschichte der Chemie seit dem Wiederaufleben der Wissenschaften bis an das Ende der achtzehnten Jahrhunderts, 3 vols., Göttingen, 1797–8–9.

GMELIN, L. Handbook of Chemistry, tr. H. Watts, 19 vols., 1848–72.

GOBET, N. — see p. 65.

GREN, F. A. C. Systematisches Handbuch der gesammten Chemie, 2 ed., 4 vols., Halle, 1794–4–5–6.

HELLER, A. Geschichte der Physik, 2 vols., Stuttgart, 1882–4.

HOEFER, F. (1) Histoire de la Chimie, 2 ed., 2 vols., 1866–9.

JAGNAUX, R. Histoire de la Chimie, 2 vols., 1891.

JÖCHER, C. G. Allgemeines Gelehrten-Lexicon, 4 vols. 4°, Leipzig, 1750–1.

KAHLBAUM, G. W. A. (ed.). Monographien aus der Geschichte der Chemie, 8 vols., Leipzig, 1897–1904.

KOPP, H. (1) Geschichte der Chemie, 4 vols., Brunswick, 1843–4–5–7 (repr. in one vol., Leipzig, 1931). (2) Beiträge zur Geschichte der Chemie, 3 pts., Brunswick, 1869–75. (3) Die Entwickelung der Chemie in der neuern Zeit, Munich, 1873. (4) Die Alchemie in älterer und neurer Zeit. Ein Beitrag zur Culturgeschichte, 2 pts., Heidelberg, 1886.

LADENBURG, A. Lectures on the History of the Development of Chemistry since the Time of Lavoisier, tr. by L. Dobbin, Edinburgh, 1905.

LASSWITZ, K. (1) Geschichte der Atomistik vom Mittelalter bis Newton, 2 vols., Hamburg and Leipzig, 1890 (repr. 1926).

LAVOISIER, A. L. (1) Opuscules Physiques et Chimiques, 2 ed., 1801.

LENGLET DU FRESNOY. Histoire de la Philosophie Hermetique. Accompagnée d'un Catalogue raisonné des Ecrivains de cette Science [Anon.], 3 vols. 12°, 1742.

LIPPMANN, E. O. VON. (1) Abhandlungen und Vorträge zur Geschichte der Naturwissenschaften, 2 vols., Leipzig, 1906–13. (2) Entstehung und Ausbreitung der Alchemie, 3 vols. (i, ii, Berlin, 1919–31; iii, Weinheim, 1954). (3) Beiträge zur Geschichte der Naturwissenschaften und der Technik, 2 vols. (i, Berlin, 1923; ii, Weinheim, 1953). (4) Geschichte des Zuckers, 2 ed., 1929. (5) Geschichte der Rübe als Kulturpflanze, 1925. (6) Urzeugung und Lebenskraft, 1933. (7) Zeittafeln zur Geschichte der organischen Chemie, 1921. (8) Die Geschichte des Wismuts, 1930.

MACQUER, P. J. (1) Dictionnaire de Chymie [anon.], 2 vols., 1766. (2) ib., 2 ed., 4 vols. 8°, 1778. (3) Chymisches Wörterbuch, tr. J. G. Leonhardi — see p. 81.

MANGET, J. J. Bibliotheca Chemica Curiosa, seu Rerum ad Alchemiam pertinentium Thesaurus instructissimus, 2 vols. f°, Geneva, 1702.

MARSH, J. E. The Origins and Growth of Chemical Science, 1929.

MELLOR, J. W. (1) A Comprehensive Treatise on Inorganic and Theoretical Chemistry, 16 vols., 1922–37.

METZGER, H. (1) Doctrines Chimiques en France, 1923.

MURRAY, J. A System of Chemistry, 4 vols., Edinburgh, 1806–7.

NBG. Nouvelle Biographie Générale, ed. F. Hoefer, 46 vols., 1852–66 (vols. i–ix with title Nouvelle Biographie Universelle, NBU).

NICHOLSON, W. A Dictionary of Chemistry, 2 vols. 4°, 1795.

OSTWALD, W. (1) Lehrbuch der allgemeinen Chemie, 2 ed., 3 vols. (I, II i, II ii with incomplete part), Leipzig, 1910–11. (2) Elektrochemie, ihre Geschichte und Lehre, Leipzig, 1896. Ostwald's *Klassiker*. Klassiker der exacten Naturwissenschaften. Founded by W. Ostwald, sev. vols., Leipzig.

PARKES, S. (1) Chemical Essays, 2 ed., 2 vols., 1823. (2) The Chemical Catechism, 5 ed., 1812.

PARTINGTON, J. R. (1) Origins and Development of Applied Chemistry, 1935. (2) The Composition of Water, 1928. (3) A Short History of Chemistry, 1937, 3 ed., 1960. (4) A History of Greek Fire and Gunpowder, Cambridge, 1960. (5) A Text-Book of Inorganic Chemistry, 1921, 6 ed., 1961. (6) Advanced Treatise on Physical Chemistry, 5 vols., 1949–54.

POGGENDORFF, J. C. (1) Biographisch-literarisches Handwörterbuch zur Geschichte der exacten Naturwissenschaften, sev. vols., Leipzig and Berlin, 1863–. (2) Histoire de la Physique, tr. E Bibart and G. de la Quesnerie, 1883.

PRIESTLEY, J. E & O — see p. 244.

PRINGLE, J. — see p. 249.

RAMSAY, W. (1) The Gases of the Atmosphere, 4 ed., 1915. (2) Essays Biographical and Chemical, 1909.

READ, J. (1) Prelude to Chemistry, 1936. (2) Humour and Humanism in Chemistry, 1947.

ROSCOE, H. E., and SCHORLEMMER, C. Treatise on Chemistry; q. by date and vol.

ROSENBERGER, F. Die Geschichte der Physik in Grundzügen, 3 pts. in 4 vols., Brunswick, 1882–90.

SACHS, J. VON. Geschichte der Botanik, Munich, 1875.

SAVERIEN, A. Histoire des Philosophes Modernes avec leurs Portraits, 8 pts. 12°, 1760–73.

SCHELENZ, H. Geschichte der Pharmacie, 1904.

SMILES, S. Lives of the Engineers. Boulton and Watt, 1874 or 1904.

SOTHERAN, H. Annotated Catalogues of Works [for sale], q. by number of cat., date, number of item (or page).

SPIELMANN, J. R. Instituts de Chymie, tr. Cadet, 2 vols. 12°, 1770.

SPRENGEL, K. (1) Histoire de la Médecine, tr. A. J. L. Jourdain, revised E. F. M. Bosquillon, 9 vols., 1815 (i–vii)–1832 (viii–ix). (2) Versuch einer pragmatischen Geschichte der Arzneykunde, 6 ed., 6 vols. in 7, Halle, 1821–40.

THOMSON, T. (1) History of Chemistry, 2 vols., 1830 (reprint, n.d.). (2) A System of Chemistry, 4 vols., 1817 (other eds. q. by year and vol., see p. 719). (3) History of the Royal Society from its Institution to the end of the Eighteenth Century, 4°, 1812. (4) A System of Chemistry of Inorganic Bodies, 1831. (5) Travels in Sweden, 1813. (6) Chemistry of Animal Bodies, Edinburgh, 1843. (7) Chemistry of Organic Bodies. Vegetables, 1838. (8) An Outline of the

Sciences of Heat and Electricity, London and Edinburgh, 1830; 2 ed., London, 1840.

THORNDIKE, L. A History of Magic and Experimental Science, 8 vols., London (i–ii) and New York (iii–viii), 1923–58.

TROMMSDORFF — see J. der Pharmacie.

VICQ-D'AZYR, F. Éloges Historiques, publ. with notes by J. L. Moreau (de la Sarthe), 3 vols., 1805.

VOIGT — see Magazin.

WALKER, W. Memoirs of the Distinguished Men of Science of Great Britain living in the Years 1807–8, 1862.

WATTS, H. Dictionary of Chemistry, 5 vols. and 3 Supplements, 1874–81. (New ed. by H. F. Morley and M. M. Pattison Muir, 4 vols., 1890–94.)

WEEKS, M. E. Discovery of the Elements, 6 ed., Easton, Pa., 1956.

WHEWELL, W. (1) History of the Inductive Sciences, 3 ed., 3 vols., 1857.

WIEGLEB, J. C. Geschichte des Wachsthums und der Erfindungen in der Chemie, 3 vols., Berlin and Stettin. (1) in der ältesten und mittlern Zeit, 1792. (2) in der neuern Zeit, 3 pts. (I, i, I, ii and II), 1790–1.

LIST OF PERIODICAL PUBLICATIONS

Abhl. Bayerischen Akad. Wiss. Abhandlungen der Königlich Bayerischen Akademie der Wissenschaften, Munich.

Abhl. K. Akad. Wiss. Berlin. Abhandlungen der Königlich Preussischen Akademie der Wissenschaften, Berlin.

Abhl. Sächs. Akad. Wiss. Phil. hist. Kl. Abhandlungen der Königlich Sächsischen Akademie der Wissenschaften. Philologisch-historische Klasse.

Abhl. d. Schwed. Akad. Wiss. — see p. 159.

ACR. Alembic Club Reprints, Edinburgh.

Acta Acad. Mogunt. — see p. 568.

Acta Acad. Nat. Curios. Acta Academiae Germanicæ Naturæ Curiosorum (see Vol. II, p. 317), Nürnberg.

Acta Lit. Svec. — see p. 159.

AdS, h, m; AdS (C); AdS *Mém. div. Sav.* — see p. 10.

Allgem. J. Chem. Allgemeines Journal der Chemie, ed. N. Scherer, 10 vols., Leipzig, 1798–1803 (contd. as *N. allgem. J. Chem.*).

Amer. J. Pharm. American Journal of Pharmacy, Philadelphia.

Amer. J. Sci. American Journal of Science, New Haven.

An. Fis. Quim. Anales de la Real Sociedad Española de Física y Química, Madrid.

Angew. Chem. Angewandte Chemie.

Ann. Annalen der Chemie (Liebig's).

Ann. Chim. — see p. 495.

Ann. Chim. Anal. Annales de Chimie Analytique (also with title Chimie Analytique).

Ann. des Mines. Annales des Mines.

Ann. Gén. Sci. Phys. Annales générales des Sciences Physiques, Brussels, 1819–21.

Ann. Med. Hist. Annals of Medical History, New York.

Ann. Mus. d'Hist. Nat. Annales du Muséum d'Histoire Naturelle.

Ann. Phil. Annals of Philosophy, 1813–26.

Ann. Phys. Annalen der Physik — see p. 576.

Ann. Sci. Annals of Science, 1936–.

Archeion. See *Archiv*.

Arch. Pharm. Archiv der Pharmazie.

Arch. Sci. Phys. Nat. Archives des Sciences Physiques et Naturelles, Geneva (contin. of *Bibl. Univ.* and earlier vols. bound with this).

Archives. Archives internationale d'histoire des sciences, 1947– (contin. of Archeion).

Atti R. Accad. Torino. Atti della Reale Accademia delle Scienze di Torino, Turin.

B.A. Rep. British Association for the Advancement of Science. Reports of Meetings, 1832–.

Ber. Berichte der Deutschen chemischen Gesellschaft.

Beschäft. Berlin. Ges. naturforsch. Freunde — see p. 213.

Bibl. Brit. Bibliothèque Britannique, Geneva.

Bibl. Univ. Bibliothèque Universelle, Geneva.

Brit. Med. J. British Medical Journal.

Brit. Quart. Rev. British Quarterly Review.

Bull. Acad. Bruxelles. Bulletin de l'Académie Royale des Sciences et Belles Lettres de Bruxelles, Brussels.

Bull. Acad. Sci. U.R.S.S. Bulletin de l'Académie des Sciences de Russie.

Bull. British Soc. Hist. Sci. Bulletin of the British Society for the History of Science.

Bull. Soc. Chim. Bulletin de la Société Chimique de Paris (from 1906, de France).

Bull. Soc. Franç. Hist. Méd. Bulletin de la Société Française d'Histoire de la Médecine.

Bull. Soc. Philomath. Bulletin des Sciences par la Société Philomathique.

Chem. Age. Chemical Age.

Chem. and Ind. Chemistry and Industry (Society of Chemical Industry).

Chem. News. Chemical News (1860–1932).

Chem. Weekbl. Chemisch Weekblad (Amsterdam).

Chem. Ztg. Chemiker Zeitung, Cöthen.

Comment. Petropol. — *see* p. 202.

Compt. Rend. Comptes Rendus hebdomadaires des Séances de l'Académie des Sciences (Paris).

Crell — *see* p. 598.

Dansk. Vidensk. Selskab. Skriv. — *see* p. 160.

Denkschr. Akad. Wiss. Munich. Denkschriften Bayerische Akademie der Wissenschaften, Munich.

Dingl. J. Dingler's Polytechnisches Journal.

Edin. N. Phil. J. Edinburgh New Philosophical Journal, Edinburgh.

Edin. Phil. J. Edinburgh Philosophical Journal, Edinburgh.

Gaz. Méd. Paris. Gazette Médicale de Paris.

Glasgow Med. J. The Glasgow and West of Scotland Medical Journal.

Gött. Nachr. Nachrichten der Akademie der Wissenschaften zu Göttingen.

HAB; *Hist. Acad. Berlin.* Histoire de l'Académie Royale des Sciences et des Belles Lettres de Berlin (includes Mémoires).

Ind. Eng. Chem. Industrial and Engineering Chemistry, Easton, Pa.

Introd. Obs. Phys. — *see* p. 494.

J. Amer. Chem. Soc. Journal of the American Chemical Society, Easton, Pa.

J. Chem., J. Chem. Phys., J. f. Chem. (a) Journal für die Chemie und Physik, ed. Gehlen, 9 vols., Berlin, 1806–10. (b) Journal für Chemie und Physik, ed. Schweigger, 69 vols., Nürnberg, 1811–33 (three series with alternative titles, see Bolton, (1), 1071); contd. as *J. prakt. Chem.*

J. Chem. Educ. Journal of Chemical Education, Easton, Pa.

J. Chem. Soc. Journal of the Chemical Society (London).

J. Chim. Méd. Journal de Chimie Médicale.

J. de l'École Polytechnique. Journal de l'École Polytechnique.

J. de Médecine — *see* p. 76.

J. de Pharm. Journal de Pharmacie et des Sciences Accessoires (1815–41).

J. der Pharmacie. Journal der Pharmacie, ed. J. B. Trommsdorff, Leipzig.

J. de Phys. — *see* p. 494.

J. der Phys. Journal der Physik, ed. Gren, 8 vols., Halle and Leipzig, 1790–94 (contd. as Neues Journal der Physik, 4 vols., 1794–8, then as Annalen der Physik).

J. des Mines. Journal des Mines.

J. des Savants (des Sçav.). Journal des Savants (Sçavans).

J. Franklin Inst. Journal of the Franklin Institute, Philadelphia.

J. Iron and Steel Inst. Journal of the Iron and Steel Institute.

J. Pharm. Chim. Journal de Pharmacie et de Chimie.

J. Phys. Chem. Journal of Physical Chemistry, Easton, Pa. (formerly, Ithaca, New York).

J. prakt. Chem. Journal für praktische Chemie, Leipzig.

J. Roy. Inst. Journal of the Royal Institution of Great Britain.

J. Roy. Inst. Chem. Journal of the Royal Institute of Chemistry.

J. Soc. Chem. Ind. Journal of the Society of Chemical Industry.

Jahres-Ber. Jahres-Bericht uber die Fortschritte der physischen Wissenschaften, later Jahres-Bericht über die Fortschritte der Chemie und Mineralogie, by J. J. Berzelius, tr. by C. G. Gmelin (i–iii) and F. Wöhler (iv–xxvii), Tübingen.

KAH — *see* p. 159.

Magazin für d. neus. Zustand der Naturkunde. Magazin für den neuesten Zustand der Naturkunde, ed. Voigt.

Manchester Mem. (Proc.). Memoirs (or Proceedings) of the Manchester Literary and Philosophical Society.

Med. Chirurg. Trans. Medico-Chirurgical Transactions.

Meddel. K. Vetensk. Nobelinst. Meddelanden från K. Vetenskapsakademiens Nobelinstitut, Stockholm.

Medical Communications — *see* p. 656.

Med. Trans. Coll. Physicians. Medical Transactions published by the College of Physicians in London.

Mém. Acad. Berlin — *see* Hist. Acad. Berlin.

Mém. Acad. Dijon. Mémoires de l'Académie des Sciences, Arts et Belles Lettres de Dijon.

Mém. Acad. Sci. — *see* p. 10.

Mém. Acad. Toulouse. Mémoires des Sciences etc. de l'Académie Royale de Toulouse.

Mém. Acad. [Roy.] Turin. Mémoires de l'Académie Royale des Sciences à Turin, Turin.

Mém. de l'Inst. — *see* AdS, p. 10.

Mem. Mat. Fis. Soc. Ital. Memorie di Mathematica e di Fisica della Società Italiana delle Scienza, residente in Modena, Modena.

Mém. Muséum d'Hist. Nat. Mémoires du Muséum d'Histoire Naturelle.

Mem. Soc. Arcueil. Mémoires de Physique et de Chimie de la Société d'Arcueil, 3 vols., 1807–9–17.

Mem. Soc. Ital. Memorie de Matematica e di Fisica della Società Italiana delle Scienze, Rome.

Mém. Soc. Roy. de Méd. See p. 447.

Mém. Soc. Roy. Sci. Lille. Mémoires de la Société Royale des Sciences de l'Agriculture et des Arts de Lille.

Mém. Soc. Roy. Sci. Montpellier. Mémoires de la Société Royale des Sciences de Montpellier.

Mem. Wernerian Soc. Memoirs of the Wernerian Natural History Society.

Miscell. Acad. Nat. Curios. Miscellanea curiosa sive Ephemerides Medico-Physicæ Germanicæ Academiæ Naturæ Curiosorum, Nürnberg (see Vol. II, p. 317).

Miscell. Berolin. Miscellanea Berolinensia.

Miscell. Taurin. — *see* pp. 87, 127.

Monit. Scient. Moniteur Scientifique.

N. Acta Acad. Nat. Curios. — see *Nova Acta*.

N. allgem. J. Chem. Neues allgemeines Journal der Chemie, ed. A. F. Gehlen, 8 vols., Leipzig, 1803–6.

N. J. der Phys. (Gren) — *see* p. 576.

Neue Abhl. Acad. Erfurt. Neue Abhandlungen der Kurfürstlich-Mainzischen Akademie nützlicher Wissenschaften zu Erfurt.

Nicholson's J. Journal of Natural Philosophy, Chemistry, and the Arts, ed. W. Nicholson.

Nouv. Mém. Acad. Dijon. Nouveaux Mémoires de l'Académie des Sciences, Arts et Belles Lettres de Dijon.

Nouvelles Archives du Muséum d'Hist. Nat. Nouvelles Archives du Muséum d'Histoire Naturelle.

Nova Acta Acad. Nat. Curios. — *see Acta Acad. Nat. Curios.*

Nova Acta Reg. Soc. Sci. Upsal. — *see* p. 159.

Nova Actorum Upsal. — *see* above.

Novi Comment. Soc. Gott. Novi Commentarii Societatis Regiae Scientiarum Gottingensis (1769–77).

Nye Saml. Kgl. Danske Videns. Selsk. Skrift. — *see* p. 160.

Obs. Phys. — *see* p. 494.

Pharm. J. Pharmaceutical Journal.

Pharm. Monatshefte. Pharmazeutische Monatshefte, Vienna.

Pharm. Rundschau. Pharmazeutische Rundschau, New York.

Pharm. Ztg. Pharmazeutische Zeitung.

Phil. Coll. Philosophical Collections (publ. for the Royal Society, 1681–2, 7 pts.).

Phil. Mag. Philosophical Magazine.

Phil. Trans. Philosophical Transactions of the Royal Society of London. (Abridged ed., 18 vols., 1809.)

Proc. Amer. Phil. Soc. Proceedings of the American Philosophical Society, Philadelphia.

Proc. Belfast Nat. Hist. Phil. Soc. Proceedings of the Belfast Natural History and Philosophical Society.

Proc. Chem. Soc. Proceedings of the Chemical Society, London.

Proc. Leeds Phil. Soc. Proceedings of the Philosophical and Literary Society of Leeds.

Proc. Roy. Inst. Proceedings of the Royal Institution, London.

Proc. Roy. Inst. Chem. Proceedings of the Royal Institute of Chemistry, London.

Proc. Roy. Irish Acad. Proceedings of the Royal Irish Academy, Dublin.

Proc. Roy. Phil. Soc. Glasgow. Proceedings of the Royal Philosophical Society of Glasgow.

Proc. Roy. Soc. Proceedings of the Royal Society of London.

Proc. Roy. Soc. Edin. Proceedings of the Royal Society of Edinburgh, Edinburgh.

Proc. Roy. Soc. Med. Proceedings of the Royal Society of Medicine, London.

Proc. Soc. Antiq. Scotland. Proceedings of the Royal Society of Antiquaries of Scotland.

QS. Quellen und Studien zur Geschichte der Naturwissenschaften und der Medizin, Leipzig.

Quart. J. Sci. [*Arts*]. Quarterly Journal of Literature, Science and the Arts (Royal Institution, London).

Quart. Rev. Quarterly Review.

Recueil — *see* p. 159.

Rev. gén. Sci. Revue générale des Sciences Pure et Appliquées.

Rev[*ue*] *Scient.* Revue Scientifique.

Samml. chem. und chem.-techn. Vorträge. Sammlung chemischer und chemisch-technischer Vorträge, Stuttgart.

Schriften Berlin. Ges. Naturforsch. Freunde. Schriften der Berlinischen Gesellschaft der Naturforschender Freunde.

Schweiz. Apotheker Ztg. Schweizerische Apothekerzeitung, Zürich.

Sci. Proc. Roy. Dublin Soc. Scientific Proceedings of the Royal Dublin Society, Dublin.

Sci. Progr. Science Progress.

Skrifter Videns. Selsk. — *see* pp. 159–60.

Smithsonian Misc. Coll. Smithsonian Miscellaneous Collections, Washington.

Times Lit. Suppl. The Times Literary Supplement.

Trans. Amer. Phil. Soc. Transactions of the American Philosophical Society, Philadelphia.

Trans. Geol. Soc. Transactions of the Geological Society, London; *ib.* of Cornwall, Penzance.

Trans. Hist. Soc. Lancashire and Cheshire. Transactions of the Historic Society of Lancashire and Cheshire.

Trans. Newcomen Soc. Transactions of the Newcomen Society for the Study of the History of Engineering and Technology.

Trans. Roy. Irish Acad. Transactions of the Royal Irish Academy, Dublin.

Trans. Roy. Soc. Edin. Transactions of the Royal Society of Edinburgh, Edinburgh.

Trans. Soc. Arts. Transactions of the Society for the Encouragement of Arts, Manufactures and Commerce (later Royal Society of Arts).

Virchow's Archiv. Archiv für pathologische Anatomie und Physiologie und für klinische Medizin, ed. R. L. K. Virchow.

Voigt — *see Magazin.*

Wien Ber. Sitzungsberichte der mathematisch-naturwissenschaftliche Klasse der K. Akademie der Wissenschaft zu Wien, Vienna.

Z. angew. Chem. Zeitschrift für angewandte Chemie, Leipzig.

Z. anorg. Chem. Zeitschrift für anorganische Chemie, Leipzig.

Z. Instr. Zeitschrift für Instrumentenkunde.

Z. phys. Chem. Zeitschrift für physikalische Chemie, Leipzig.

Z. physiol. Chem. Zeitschrift für physiologische Chemie (Hoppe-Seyler), Strassburg.

ERRATA — VOLUME II

The first figure in the list denotes the page of the book, the second the line of text from the top of the page or, if asterisked, the foot of the page not counting footnotes; these are indicated by an obelisk (†). The faulty word is not repeated but the place of the correct reading will be obvious.

CHAPTER I

CHEMISTRY IN FRANCE. I. 1600 TO 1700

CHEMISTRY IN MEDICINE

Paracelsan medicine and chemistry were made known in France by Roch le Baillif, Sieur de la Rivière (Falaise, ?–Paris, 5 November 1605), a Calvinist who became first physician to King Henri IV in 1594,[1] and was also an astrologer. He encouraged and protected Beguin and invited Davisson to France:

Le Demosterion De Roch Le Baillif Edelphe Medecin Spagiric. Auquel sont contenuz Trois cens Aphorismes Latins & François. Sommaire veritable de la Medecine Paracelsique, extraicte de luy en la plus part, par ledict Baillif, 4°, Rennes, Pierre le Bret. Avec priuilege du Roy, 1578 (viii ll., 190 pp., 2 fold. tables), Duveen, 343; in Latin, 8°, Paris, 1578; P. L. Jacob, Curiosités des Sciences Occultes, 1862, 17 (3 principles), 75 (reality of transmutation), 111 (astrological medicine).

Lazarus Rivière (Montpellier; 1589–1655) was a different person, whose medical writings contain many excerpts from Sennert: Opera Medica Universa, f°, Lyons, 1663, and later eds., last in 1738; NBG, 1863, xlii, 344.

The lawyer Pierre Le Loyer (1550–1634) of Angers reported in 1586 that he saw a Paracelsan in Paris who was refuted in Parliament and prohibited, his ignorance being disclosed by those appointed to examine him. Le Loyer also declaimed against 'Raimond Lulle . . . with his fifth essence', with power to chase away devils.[2]

Jacques Bongars (1546–1612), the Calvinist historian of the Crusades, in a Berne MS. refers favourably to Paracelsus, who replaced Plato's god, examplar, and matter, and Aristotle's matter, form, and privation, by three principles, salt, sulphur, and mercury, although he also recognised four elements in two spheres, fire and air in the upper and water and earth in the lower.[3] The latter idea was attributed by Barchusen[4] to Severinus (see Vol. II, p. 163):

hæcque in duos globos esse distributa: unumquemque vero globum complexu suo continere bina elementa: superiorem globum, cœlum vel ignem & aërem: inferiorem autem, terram & aquam complecti. . . . Triplici generis esse hæc corporum principia, & nomine Salis, Sulphuris & Mercurii innotuisse. Neque vero horum unumquodque esse simplex, sed suum cuique esse Sal, suum Sulphur, suum Mercurium.

Gui Patin, an influential member of the medical faculty of the University of Paris (which defended classical medicine and Galen and opposed Arabic and chemical medicine), advised a young physician in 1646: 'Above all, shun books of chemistry.'[5] One of his colleagues, an otherwise unknown Jacques

---

[1] Gobet, 1779, ii, 699 (Jean Ribit); Hoefer, (1), ii, 24; NBG, xlii, 343 (other works).
[2] Thorndike, vi, 533. [3] Thorndike, vii, 157.
[4] *Historia Medicinæ*, Amsterdam, 1710, 442–3. [5] Thorndike, vii, 526.

Perreau (d. 1660), published 'A wet-blanket on triumphant antimony'.[1] Opposition to the use of chemistry in medicine was a great help to a Paris physician in getting on in Patin's time, but in 1637 antimony was admitted as a purgative by order of the medical faculty, confirmed in 1666 by a vote of 92 out of 102.[2] Claude Germain, one of the faculty, was nearly poisoned by antimony and wrote a large book against it.[3] An alchemical book was attributed to him.[4]

Galenical medicine continued to flourish. In 1685, de Rouviere, apothecary in ordinary to the King, exhibited the preparation of theriac, from 58 dozen vipers and a number of other constituents, to meetings of the Faculty of Medicine in Paris in a series of lectures and demonstrations, the operation being finally finished 'with approbation and applause'.[5]

BEGUIN

Jean Beguin, a native of Lorraine, studied medicine and pharmacy at Sedan (?), visited Italy, Germany and Hungary to study mining, and opened a school and laboratory of chemistry and pharmacy in Paris, where he was Almoner to King Louis XIII.[6] In 1608 he published an edition of the *Novum Lumen Chymicum* of Sendivogius (see Vol. II) with a preface, which most authors have confused with the first edition of Beguin's own book, which was published in 1610:

Tyrocinium Chymicum e Naturæ fonte et manali [corrected in later eds. to manuali] experientia depromptum, 8°, *s.l.*, 1610 (70 pp., BM 1033. e. 7); 12°, Cologne, 1611 (90 pp., BM 8907. a. 21, a pirated ed.); 12°, Paris, 1612 (133 pp.; in Bodleian Lib.), revised and enlarged by Beguin; 12°, Cologne, 1612 (viii ll., one blank, 195 pp., the ed. used; pirated), repr. 1614 (195 pp., BM 1035. a. 6); ed. by Jeremias Barth, of Sprottau, Silesia, pupil of Beguin, who sent him a French version: Secreta Spagyrica revelata sive Tyrocinium Chymicum, 8°, *s.l.*, 1618 (382 pp., BM 1034. e. 9; the *Cat.* gives Guben as place of publ. but Pelshofer in the 1634 ed. gives Frankfurt on the Oder); ed. Hartmann [Glückradt], Tyrocinium Chymicum . . . Hac quarta editione . . . studio et opere Christophori Glückradts, 8°, Königsberg, 1618 (BM 1034. g. 6, 537 pp.; BN *Cat.* gives xlviii, 542 pp.); Novum Lumen ad Tyrocinium Chymicum, Ex autographo Joannis Beguini denuo recognitum, 12°, Cologne, 1625 (contains Sendivogius's Novum Lumen followed by Beguin's Tyrocinium with some pp., not in 1618 ed., added); ed. by Johann Georg Pelshofer of Graz, from 1627 prof. med. in Wittenberg: Tyrocinium Chymicum . . . Christophoro Glückradt et . . . Jeremias Barthio notis . . . nunc vero a Johanne Georgio Pelshofero . . . in unum systema redactis, 8°, Wittenberg, 1640 (lxxx, 480 pp., index, BN 28052), 1650; Venice, 1643 (BM 8906. a. 3), all with 480 small pp. text; ed. Pelshofer with epistles of 'Gluctradt', Barth's notes, and Beguin's letters, 12°, Wittenberg, 1656 (engr. t.p., lxxviii, 480, xliv pp.); 8°, Geneva, 1659; ed. Gerhard Blasius, professor of medicine in Amsterdam, 12°, Amsterdam,

---

[1] *Rabbat-Joye de l'Antimoine triomphant, ou examen de l'Antimoine justifié de M. Renaudot*, 4°, Paris, 1654 (BN 4° Te[151]. 87; Gmelin, (1), i, 662; for Renaudot, see Vol. II, p. 173).

[2] Thorndike, vii, 530.

[3] *Orthodoxe, ou de l'Abus de l'Antimoine, dialogue . . . pour détromper ceux qui donnent ou prennent le vin et pouldre émétique*, 4°, Paris, 1652 (BM 1033. k. 12); Gmelin, (1), i, 663.

[4] *Icon Philosophiæ Occultæ, sive vera Methodus componendi magnum antiquorum philosophorum lapidem*, 8°, Paris, 1672 (26 ff., 99 pp.; BN R 37163); 12°, Rotterdam, 1678 (BM); Manget, 1702, ii, 845–56; Kopp, (4), ii, 344, calls him physician to Queen Marie Louise of Poland; the work is dedicated to John Casimir, King of Poland, and mentions Sendivogius; Ferguson, i, 313; Thorndike, vii, 528, 530.

[5] Thorndike, viii, 100.

[6] Bolton, (1), 295; Ferguson, i, 94; Gmelin, (1), i, 603; Holmyard, *J. Soc. Chem. Ind.*, 1924, xlii, 655; Kopp, (1), ii, 12; Metzger, (1), 1923, 36; Patterson, *Ann. Sci.*, 1937, ii, 243; Read, (2), 1947, 81; Rodwell, *Phil. Mag.*, 1868, xxxv, 1 (6); Thorndike, viii, 106.

1669 (engr. t.p., xxiv, 314, viii pp.); ed. Pelshofer, Notis & medicamentorum formulis in unam systema redactis . . . , sm. 8°, Venice (Ballonium), 1669 (xl, 360, xxiv pp., fold. table). Some Latin eds. were publ. with Philip Müller's Miracula & Mysteria Chymico-Medica, 12°, Wittenberg, 1614 (2 ed.), 1616, 1623; Rouen, 1651; Amsterdam, 1659 (Duveen, 416–17).

French tr.: Les Élémens de Chymie, 12°, Paris, 1615 (290 pp.; Read); the following, ed. Lucas de Roy, are in the BN, which does not possess the 1st and 2nd (1620, augmentez par I.L.D.R.B.I.C.E.M, viii ll., 398 pp., xxv ll.; Gurney Cat. 26 (1960) no. 70) eds., all 8°: 3 ed. Paris, 1624 (482 pp.), 1626; 4 ed. Rouen, 1626, 1627, 1637 (all pp. xvi, 432, xlviii index); Lyon, 1645 (xvi, 384 pp.), 1646 (xvi, 445 pp.); Rouen, 1660 (xii, 469 pp.); the BN Cat. does not seem to give the index pp.

English tr. by Richard Russell: Tyrocinivm Chymicvm: or, Chymical Essays, Acquired from the Fountain of Nature, And Manual Experience, 8°, London, Passenger, 1669 (engr. t.p., x, 136, v pp.; apparently from 1612 Latin ed. and hence incomplete). Ferguson mentions two German trs. but gives no dates.

This 'Chemistry for Beginners', beginning with a slim volume of 70 pp. but kept up to date until it swelled to nearly 500 pages in some later editions, was obviously a 'best seller' and was also pirated. It gave way in the end to another immensely popular book by another Frenchman, the *Cours de Chymie* of Nicolas Lemery (see p. 29). Beguin's book was compiled for his students at the instigation of Jeremias Barth, to serve in lieu of notes. It consists mainly of pharmaceutical preparations, and describes some substances for the first time. It adopts the three principles of Paracelsus, salt, sulphur and mercury (bk. i, c. 2). It mentions an *oleum sulphuris*, obtained by distilling sulphur, quicklime and sal ammoniac (bk. ii, c. 6; already in Libavius), afterwards called *spiritus sulphuris volatilis Beguinii* (it is ammonium polysulphide), and a spirit of sulphur *per campanam* (sulphuric acid) made by burning sulphur under a glass bell (bk. ii, c. 4). It gives a clear description of the preparation of mercurous chloride, called *sublimatus dulcis*, by distilling an intimate mixture of 8 oz. of corrosive sublimate and 6 oz. of mercury (bk. ii, c. 18); also by dissolving mercury in aqua fortis and precipitating with common salt (*præcipitatus albus, manna mercurii*) (bk. ii, cs. 13, 18); this preparation had been obscurely mentioned by Croll in 1609 (see Vol. II, p. 165). The corrosive sublimate was made by subliming a mixture of mercury, green vitriol (ferrous sulphate), salt, and saltpetre.

What is called *ceraunocryson diaphoreticum*, made by dissolving gold in aqua regia (aqua philosophica) and precipitating with oil of tartar (potassium carbonate) (bk. ii, c. 16), may have been fulminating gold if the aqua regia was made with sal ammoniac, or else gold oxide; what is called *bezoardicum metallicum* was apparently gold oxide (bk. ii, c. 16),[1] not antimonic acid (so named by Hartmann and Quercitanus). Beguin prepared finely-divided gold by covering six grains of fulminating gold in a silver dish with rectified spirit and covering with a glass bell-jar after lighting the spirit. The fulminating gold exploded (officium suum faciet) and gold powder or calx (pars quædam terrea) settled on the glass, from which it was washed off with spirit and dried. This saved a good deal of gold powder otherwise lost (bk. ii, c. 16).

Benzoic acid or flowers of benzoin (*flores benzoini*) was made by subliming gum benzoin from a dish into a paper cone (bk. ii, c. 18). An 'oil of benzoin'

[1] Wiegleb, (1), 1792, 219.

obtained by distillation is vaguely described by Alexis of Piedmont (1555).[1] The distillation of a fragrant spirit and two oils (red and yellow) from sugar of lead (lead acetate) (Beguin, bk. ii, c. 4) would give acetone; this was given by Libavius.

The preparations are arranged according to properties, flowers of sulphur and flowers of benzoin, etc., being treated together. The short third book deals with the quintessences of human blood, wine, corals, and pearls, a quintessence being defined as an ethereal, celestial, and very subtle substance composed of the three principles of the original body, deprived of their gross, corruptible, and mortal qualities, and obtained by distillation.

Beguin[2] gives a diagram showing the reaction in the distillation of corrosive sublimate (mercuric chloride) and stibnite (antimony sulphide), when butter of antimony (antimony trichloride) and cinnabar (mercuric sulphide) are formed:

Mercure sublimé

Mercure   ⌄   Esprit vitriolic
          Antimoine
Regule   ⌃   Soulphre

ie dis que l'esprit vitriolic a une extreme sympathie avec les metaux . . . destillant le mercure sublimé avec l'antimoine, l'esprit vitriolic du sublimé quitte le mercure, & se ioinct & attache au regule de l'antimoine . . . & calcine le regule & passe en liqueur gommeuse ou huileuse par le bec de la cornuë . . . apres que toute la liqueur gommeuse est destillee, ne reste plus dans la cornuë que le mercure du sublimé, & le soulphre de l'antimoine: & parce qu'ils ont une extréme sympathie par ensemble . . . ils se subliment par ensemble au col de la cornuë en cinabre.

This is a clear description of a reaction of double decomposition in terms of affinity (sympathie).

DAVISSON

The Jardin du Roi in Paris was on a site where the botanist, historian, poet, and alchemist Jacques Gohory (or Gohorri) (Paris; beginning of 16 cent.–13 March 1576), a follower of Paracelsus,[3] had a garden in 1572. The formation of a botanic garden in Paris, on the lines of that in Montpellier, was mooted by Henri IV and Sully. The foundation took place in 1626 by Jean Héroard and Guy de la Brosse, physicians of Louis XIII, and la Brosse was the first Superintendant of the Jardin Royale des Plantes Medicinales, the definitive organisation under his control being in 1634 or 1635. The nephew of la Brosse was Fagon, who became physician to Louis XIV about 1680. Buffon was for a long time (1739–88) Superintendant, and enlarged its scope; he was assisted by Daubenton, 'garde et démonstrateur du cabinet du Roi' attached to the institution, then known as the Jardin du Roi. In 1793 the Convention, on the advice of Lakanal, continued it with the title of Muséum National d'Histoire Naturelle, which name it still bears.[4]

[1] *Les Secrets*, Rouen, 1661, i, 116, 125; see Vol. II, p. 28.
[2] *Les Elemens de Chymie*, Bk. ii, c. 12; Rouen, 1627, 243–5 (not in the 1612 Latin ed.).
[3] See Vol. II, p. 162; Lacour, NBG, 1857, xxi, 83.
[4] Blanchard, in Diergart, 1909, 343; P. A. Cap, *Le Muséum d'Histoire Naturelle, histoire de la fondation et des developpments*, 4°, Paris, 1854 (239 pp., frontispiece, 5 plans, 16 portrs.;

The first professor of chemistry in the Jardin du Roi, appointed in July 1648, was William Davisson (Davison, or Davidson), born in Aberdeenshire about 1593, M.A. of Marischal College, Aberdeen, who migrated to Paris and gave private instruction in chemistry and pharmacy. He is said to have been M.D. of Montpellier. In 1644 he became councillor and physician to King Louis XIII. In 1651 he went to Warsaw as physician to John Casimir, King of Poland. He is said to have died in Paris about 1669. His descendants became French with the name d'Avisson.[1] On 21 October 1649 Evelyn[2] 'went to heare Dr. D'Avinson's lecture in the physical garden, and see his laboratorie, he being Prefect of that excellent Garden and Professor Botanicus,' evidently taking him for a Frenchman.

Davisson's textbook 'Philosophy of the Art of Fire, or Course of Chemistry' was issued in four parts at various dates between 1633 and 1635, some copies in old bindings having two or more parts:

Philosophia Pyrotechnica seu Curriculus Chymiatricus, 8°, Paris, Parts III–IV, 1633 and 1640; Parts I–II, 1635 and 1642; in four parts, 1635 (Nourry-Thiébaud *Cat.* 67 (1939), No. 883), 1641, 1657 (*ib.*, 66 (1938), No. 870); my copy is made up as follows (in old binding): blank leaf, t.p. Philosophia Pyrotechnica, Willielmi D'Avissoni Scoti Doctoris Medici. Sev Cvrricvlvs Chymiatricvs nobilissima illa & ex optatissima Medicinæ parte pyrotechnica instructus . . . (16 lines of text), Parisiis. Apud Ioannem Bessin, propè Collegium Remense. M·DC·XXXV. Cum Priuilegio Regio, & Approbatione, *v* blank, ix ll. (3 blank) with engr. emblem on last *v*, pp. 1–208, xiv unpaginated ll. incl. second dedication, pp. 209–393 (Finis Secundæ Partis), *v* blank, i l. blank; t.p. Pars Tertia Cvrricvli Chymici de Vocabvlis Chymicæ Operationi inseruientibus. Ex curriculo W. D. Doctoris Med. in vsum auditorum suarum excerpta. Parisiis. M·DC·XXXIII (no printer's name), *v* blank, ii ll. dedic., 3–42 pp., i l. blank; t.p. Pars Quarta Cvrricvli Chymici Operationes Chymicas Mvlto faciliore Methodo, . . . Parisiis. M.DC.XXXIII (no printer's name), *v* blank, xi ll. (last *v* blank), 3–178 pp. (Finis), i l. errata. (There is no sep. t.p. for Pt. II.) This is the ed. quoted below.

Parts III and IV were published in 1633 (the BM lists them separately but they are bound together in 1034. g. 9. (1–2.)), parts I and II in 1635. Glasgow University Library has parts III and IV bound together with single t.p.: Cvrricvlvs Chymiatricvs . . . Parisiis. Svmtibvs Avthoris, M.DC.XXXIII (probably published privately). The BM copy (1034. g. 10) of the 1635 ed. has a portrait of Davisson, perhaps inserted.

Hamy, *op. cit.*, 26, and Thorndike wrongly said there was no ed. of 1635, the first they saw being the second ed. of 1640, which has the title *Cursvs Chymiatricvm*; Hoefer mentions a copy of this autographed 'd'Avissone' (as the name is printed on the t.p.) in Baudrimont's library. The BN copy has Part II (487 pp.) and Part III (272 pp.), 1640; the BM copy has: Philosophia Pyrotechnica . . . seu Cursus Chymiatricus, Paris, Bessin, 1641 (Parts I and II), and Curriculi Chymici (Parts III and IV, pagination continuous), Paris, Bessin, 1640 (1034. g. 10. (1.–3.)).

II. French tr.: the t.p. of my copy reads (Duveen and Thorndike add accents not in my copy, except those given):

Les Elemens de la Philosophie de l'Art du Feu ou Chemie. Contenans les plus belles obseruations qui se rencontrent dans la resolution, preparation, & exhibition des Vegetaux, Animaux, & Mineraux, & les remedes contre toutes les maladies du corps

4 plain and 15 hand-coloured plates; Wheldon and Wesley, *Cat.* 83 (1955–6), no. 143; BN S 7097); *Guide Bleu de Paris*, Paris, Hatchette, 1948, 143; de Milt, *J. Chem. Educ.*, 1941, xviii, 503.

[1] Comrie, *History of Scottish Medicine*, 1932, i, 377 (portr); E. T. Hamy, *Nouvelles Archives du Muséum d'Hist. Nat.*, 1898, x, 1–38 (portr.); Ferguson, i, 201; Hoefer, (1), ii, 234; J. Small, *Proc. Soc. Antiq. Scotland*, 1875, x, 265 (portr.); Henderson, DNB, 1884, xiv, 182; Metzger, (1), 45; de Milt, *J. Chem. Educ.*, 1941, xviii, 503; Read, (2), 1947, 88 (portr.); *id.*, *Archives d'Hist. Sci.*, 1951, xxx, 660; *id.*, *William Davidson of Aberdeen* (*Aberdeen University Studies*, cxxix), Aberdeen, 1951 (32 pp.); Thorndike, viii, 123.

[2] *Diary*, ed. Bray, 1870, 202.

humain, comme aussi la Metallique, appliquée à la Theorie, par vne verité fondée sur vne necessité Geometrique, & demonstrée à la maniere d'Euclide. Oeuure nouueau, & tres-necessaire à tous ceux qui se proposent ietter de bons fondemens pour apprendre la Philosophie, Medecine, Chirurgie, & Pharmacie. Traduit du Latin du sieur Dauissone . . . par Iean Hellot, Maistre Chirurgien à Paris, 8°, Paris, F. Piot, 1651, pp. xviii, 1–54, 1–6, viii unnumb., 55–677 (2 blank, Duveen gives 3, there are two pages numbered 80), 4 plates (Duveen gives 5) and folding table at end of second part. The spelling 'Chemie' (also used in the text) is noteworthy.

The same sheets were issued with a new t.p., same contents as above. 'Seconde Edition', Piot (with different address), 1657, and a slight alteration at the beginning (the dedication to John Casimir, King of Poland, is omitted). Lenglet Dufresnoy, 1742, iii, 3, mentions an ed. of 1675, the tr. being by Davisson himself, as 'peu connue' but preferable to those of 1651 and 1657, but Read, 1951, 15, says there is no ground for this statement.

There is no translation into any other language but French and the book (which has no table of contents or index) could not compete with the more systematic ones of Beguin, Le Févre, Glaser, and Lemery. The French versions differ considerably from the Latin; the theoretical part is much abbreviated and the practical part extended and rearranged, and it is a much better book. How much of the alteration is due to the translator Jean Hellot (grandfather of the famous chemist Jean Hellot) is not clear; the book makes use of very recent works, e.g. of Glauber.

The second Latin edition[1] and the French translation[2] include a discussion and a plate of crystal shapes as related to the five solids (figura hexagonali, cubica, pentagonali, octaedrica, rhombica), 'opus novum et a nullo ante me, quod sciam, elaboratum' — the beginning of chemical crystallography.

Parts I–III of the Latin version consist of rambling dissertations on almost every subject except chemistry, with copious quotations from old Greek and Latin authors, the Old Testament, the *Qabbalah*, Neopythagorean and Neoplatonic authors, Paracelsus, and 'the brothers of the Rosy Cross';[3] as Thorndike says they are 'very pretentious and tiresome'. Part IV, 'ex curriculo in vsum auditorum suorum tantum excerpta', begins with 25 pages of an exhortation to curious and studious youths in the form of dialogue between a Peripatetic and a Spagyric (anticipating the style of Boyle's *Sceptical Chymist*, 1661). Only now does Davisson get down to any practical chemistry. He divides the material into vegetable, mineral, and animal, in this order, for which classification he quotes 'Rasis in libro Diuinitatis'[4] or in the French translation[5] 'Rhases Arabe au liure de la triplicité' (with a long extract). This division was followed by Le Févre, Glaser, Lemery, and Boerhaave. Davisson includes amber among vegetables. Then comes a long section on mineral acids, salts, and metallic remedies, including preparations of mercury and antimony, showing a competent knowledge of recent publications. It adopts[6] the three 'hypostatic' principles, salt, sulphur, and mercury, and refers to Paracelsus with respect. Read says the book contains no new theoretical idea or practical preparation of any real importance. Other works by Davisson are:

[1] 1641, Pars IV, pp. 184–209: Doctrine de symbolo & mutationem elementorum; plate between pp. 216–17 in BM copy but MS. note says it should follow p. 185; p. 76 has a description and plate of a furnace.
[2] 1651, 614 f.: La doctrine du symbole, proportion & mutation entre les Elemens.
[3] 1635, i, 57.   [4] 1635, i, 302.   [5] 1651, i, 80–3.   [6] 1635, i, 336.

1. Commentariorum in . . . Petri Severini Dani Ideam Medicinæ Philosophicæ . . . Prodromus, 4°, The Hague, 1660 (708 pp.; BM 543. c. 7. (1.); BN Rés. T⁵. 9 (1)) and 1663. A commentary on Severinus giving some details of Davisson's own life.

2. Oblatio Salis sive Gallia Lege Salis Condita. Tractatvs Salis naturam . . . , 8°, Paris, Jean Promé, 1641, xii (one blank), 130 pp.; BM 1034. g. 10.

3. Theophrasti Verdici Scoti Doctoris medici Plicomastix seu Plicæ numero morborum Α'πόσπασμα Typis Universitatis Abredoniensis in Scotia impressus Nunc veró Dantisci cum amplissimo Ser. Sac. Reg. Majestatis Privilegio venditur per Jacobum Pufflerum, 4°, Dantzig (printed in Aberdeen), 1668 (BN Td.¹³⁵. 4); on the disease of the hair, plica Polonica.

4. Collectanea Chimica Medico-Philosophica Polonica, 4°, Antwerp, 1698 (ment. by Ferguson).

5. Observations sur l'Antimoine, 8°, Paris, 1651 (Lenglet Dufresnoy, iii, 145; perhaps a reissue of the section with that title in the Elemens, pp. 549–602).

BASSO

The five elements, spirit (or mercury), oil (or sulphur), salt, earth (fæces or caput mortuum) and phlegm, were apparently first proposed by the French physician Sebastian Basso, whom de Launay[1] calls: vir acerrimi judicii et scientiæ maximæ (see on him Vol. II). Basso says:

Vix ulla res est ex qua non eliciant tres naturas valde inter se differentes; quarum quæ subtilior est & volatilior, spiritum vocant, seu etiam mercurium, Quæ vero crassior & pinguior, oleum & sulphur apellant, Quæ vero omnium maxime fixa ex intimis veluti partis cujusque penetralibus ultima educitur, sal illia nuncupatur. Praeter has tres naturas valde utiles, superest quædam materia terrestris & inutilis quam fæces vocant & caput mortuum. Est insuper aqueus quidam & insipidis liquor quem phlegma dicunt. . . . Iam si videat ex re qualibet spiritum, oleum, salem, phlegma, fæces.[2]

DE CLAVE

Estienne de Clave (dates unknown) followed Davisson at the Jardin du Roi.[3] In 1641 he attacked the Aristotelian four elements and replaced them by Basso's five elements: water or phlegm, earth, mercury or spirit, sulphur or oil, and salt.[4] In his Paradoxes he attacks the opinions of Aristotle, Theophrastos, Avicenna, Cardan, Fallopius, Agricola, etc., on the formation of stones and metals; in the preface he says he proposed to write forty treatises giving the fruits of his researches of over thirty years.[5]

In his Cours de Chimie (1646) he defines chemistry as 'un art qui enseigne la

[1] Da Varia Aristotelis in Academia Parisiensi fortvna; in Opera omnia, f°, Cologne, 1732, IV, i, 224 (end of c. xvi) — the passage is not in the separate issue of the work, Paris, 1653.

[2] Basso, Philosophia naturalis adversus Aristotelem libri XII. In quibus abstrusa Veterum Physiologia restauratur, & Aristotelis errores solidis rationibus refelluntur, 8°, Geneva, 1621 (xxxviii, 701, ii blank, xxviii, i errata), 35–6; 2 ed., 8°, Amsterdam, Elzevir, 1649, 31–2; Lasswitz, (1), i, 339, 470.

[3] Jöcher, i, 1943; Bayle, Dictionnaire Historique et Critique, Paris, 1820, v, 129; Ferguson, i, 162; Thorndike, vii, 192; viii, 121.

[4] Novvelle Lvmière Philosophiqve des vrais principes et elémens de la Nature, et qualité d'iceus, contre l'opinion commune, 8°, Paris, 1641, 4 f., 26 f., 39 f., 255 f., 316 f.; Le Cours de Chimie d'Estienne de Clave, qui est le second Livre des principes de Nature, 8°, Paris, 1646 (188 pp.), 4 f., 23 f., etc. (the Principes de Nature is said to have been published in 1635); Paradoxes ov Traittez philosophiqves des pierres et pierreries contre l'opinion vulgaire, par Estienne de Clave, 8°, Paris, 1635 (pp. xxiv, 492, 1 l. errata).

[5] Thorndike, viii, 121, mentions chemical works by de Clave of 1630 in a Rennes MS., and in the same year he lectured on chemistry in Paris.

façon de couvertir les mixtes en suc et liqueur' (p. 1), gives an account of chemical apparatus, describes the heating of white arsenic and saltpetre in a crucible to form a mass (potassium arsenate) which deliquesces to 'huile d'arsenic fixé' (p. 100), mentions butter of antimony (p. 119), calomel (sublimé doux) (p. 133), mercuric acetate (vitriol de mercure) (p. 133), 'bisemut ou estain de glace' (bismuth) (p. 134), ferrous nitrate in green crystals (vitriol de Mars par eau forte) (p. 142), cupric nitrate (vitriol de Venus avec eau forte) (p. 147), silver chloride (lune cornée) (p. 155; from Croll), and fulminating gold (or petant) (p. 157).

In August 1624 Jean Bitault, Antoine Villon, and de Clave proposed to hold a public disputation in Paris on theses connected with Aristotle and Paracelsus,[1] in which it was asserted that mixts consisted not of four but of five elements: earth, water, salt, sulphur (or oil) and mercury (or spiritus acidus), and that Aristotle from ignorance or malice had ridiculed the true views of the ancients that all is contained in all and that all is composed of atoms (omnia esse in omnibus et omnia componi ex atomis seu indivisibilibus). These theses they were prepared tenaciously to defend and intrepidly to sustain (mordicus defendimus, et intrepidi sustinemus). The Theological Faculty, however, thought otherwise; it pronounced them 'falsa, temeraria et in fide erronea'. De Clave was arrested and in September the Parliament of Paris forbade the discussion of the theses under penalty of death, not only in Paris but in any other country, an absurd threat which was not taken very seriously outside Paris.[2]

SAUVAGEON. DE ROCHAS. ARNAUD

G. Sauvageon revised in 1630 the *Pharmacopœia* of Brice Bauderon (1540–1623) first printed in 1588, wrote on the powder of sympathy, and compiled a text-book:

Traicte Chymique contenant les preparations, usages, facultez et doses des plus celebres et usitez medicamens chymiques. Reueu et augmenté en cette derniere edition, Paris, 1643; repr. 1644, 1648, 1650, 1654, and 1681; Gmelin, (1), i, 664; Thorndike, viii, 126; reprod. in La Pharmacopée of Bauderon, 1681, BM 546. k. 12.

It defends chemical remedies, saying (with some truth) that these go back beyond Paracelsus to Lull, Arnald of Villanova, and Mesuë, but are more difficult to prepare than the Galenical. It refers to the 'learned public lectures in chemistry at the Jardin Royal' for fuller details, and deals with antimony, mercury, etc., ending with potable gold.

Henri de Rochas, physician and royal councillor, son of a general of the mines in Provence, wrote on mineral waters, on intermittent fevers, and books on 'demonstrative' and on 'reformed' physics, which are alchemical.[3] The

---

[1] De Launoy, *De Varia Aristotelis* etc., in *Opera*, IV, i, 220 f.; Lasswitz, (1), i, 482 f.; Thorndike, vii, 185 (q. orig. docs.).

[2] A letter from Schelhamer from Paris in April 1642 to Joachim Jungius refers to de Clave's publication of 1624: tota Parisiensis schola ipsi se opposuit . . . et publico Parlamenti edicto Dno de Clave injunctum est a scribendo in posterum abstineret et civitate excederet: Guhrauer, *Joachim Jungius und sein Zeitalter*, Stuttgart and Tübingen, 1850, 259.

[3] *La Physique Demonstratif*, 8°, Paris, 1644 (BM 774. e. 8); *La Physique Reformée contenant la refutation des erreurs populaires et le triomph des verites philosophiques*, 4°, Paris, 1648 (BM 537. b. 6); Ferguson, ii, 281; Thorndike, viii, 274.

first work has a long first book on sulphurous, vitriolic, aluminous, nitrous, and ferruginous mineral waters, a second book on the universal spirit, the origin of nature, the Hermetic philosophy, the chemical principles, and 'the cabinet of the curious'; the third book is on 'the triumph of spagyric medicine'. The second work follows Van Helmont in identifying water with the first matter of all mixed bodies, although air is important for all life, animal, vegetable, or mineral. It follows Paracelsus in adopting the three principles, salt, sulphur, and mercury, as special causes of diseases as well as cures for them, on the doctrine that like cures like.

E. R. Arnaud (Christian names unknown) wrote a small introduction to chemistry or 'true physics':

Introdvction à la Chymie, ov la vraye Physiqve ov le lectevr trevvera la definition de toutes les operations de la Chymie; La façon de les faire, & des Exemples en suitte tres rares sur chaque Operation; & le tout dans vn tres-bel ordre, sm. 8°, Lyon, Clavde Prost, 1650 (xl, 112 pp.; BN R 26957); 2 ed., 8°, Lyon, 1655 (112 pp.; BM 1033. d. 10. 13.); Gmelin, (1), i, 744; Ferguson, i, 47; Thorndike, viii, 105, 128; Sotheran, *Cat.* 85 (1937), no. 1064.

It discusses the definition and antiquity of the name 'Chymie', deals with furnaces, vessels, and fire, and in the second book with processes: calcination, dissolution, sublimation, rectification, descension, exaltation, circulation, ablution, digestion, putrefaction, fermentation, extraction of essences, tinctures, etc., liquefaction, coagulation, and fixation. Arnaud recommends chemical remedies, saying that 'in the most obscure, difficult and dangerous maladies it is better to hazard a doubtful remedy than give nothing at all'.[1]

J. B. Duhamel

Jean-Baptiste Duhamel (Vire, Normandy, 1624–Paris, 6 August 1706), besides being a mathematician, philosopher, and theologian, was much interested in chemistry and physics.[2] He wrote several books:

A. De meteoribus et fossilibus libri duo. In priore libro mixta imperfecta, quaeque in sublimi aere vel gignuntur, vel apparent, fuse pertractantur. Posterior liber mixta perfecta complectitur; ubi salium, bituminum, lapidum, gemmarum, & metallorum naturae, causae, & usus inquiruntur, 4°, Paris, Lamy, 1660 (xiv ll., 310 pp., iii ll.). The first part is on geology etc., the second is a compendium of chemistry and alchemy. NBG gives: De Meteoris et Fossilibus, per dialogos, 4°, Paris, 1659.

B. De consensu veteris et novæ philosophiæ libri duo, 4°, Paris, 1663 (280 pp. BN R 3761); Oxford, 1669 (431 pp.); De consensu veteris et novæ philosophiæ libri quatuor, seu Promotæ per experimenta philosophiæ pars prima . . . Editio nova, 12°, Rouen, 1675 (574 pp.; BN R 13549).

C. De corporum affectionionibus cum manifestis, tum occultis, libri duo, seu Promotae per experimenta philosophiae specimen, 12°, Paris, 1670 (xii, 556 pp., index; BN R 13536).

D. Philosophia vetus et nova, ad usum scholæ accommodata, 4 vols. 12°, 1678; 2 ed. 6 vols. 12°, Paris, 1681 (BM; anonymous, composed by order of Colbert); 3 ed. 2 vols. 4°, 1684 (BN), 4 ed. 1687 (BM).

E. Regiæ Scientiarum Academiæ Historia, 4°, Paris, 1698 (BM 482. f. 16); a history of the Paris Académie des Sciences.

---

[1] 1650, p. xviii, sign. c̄ 3v.   [2] NBG, 1856, xv, 99; Thorndike, vii, 498; viii, 204.

Book iv of B is on chemical principles. In 1668 Duhamel met Boyle in England and two chapters in the second edition (1669) of B contain experiments on the elasticity of air and refer to Boyle's work on it. C refers to many modern authors, including Boyle, Bacon, Gilbert, Willis, Hooke, Gassendi, Descartes, Pascal, Galileo, Torricelli, Guericke, Tachenius, and Erasmus Bartholinus. Boyle[1] quotes Du Hamel's praise in C of his own *Experiments and Observations touching Cold*, 1665. Duhamel was the first Secretary of the Académie Royale des Sciences (1666–97).

The Académie Royale des Sciences was founded by Colbert in 1666, members being Huygens, Roberval, Picard, Perrault, and the chemists Duclos and Bourdelin, Duhamel being secretary. It was renewed in 1699 by the Abbé Bignon, with a new constitution and under the protection of the Duc d'Orleans. Like the Royal Society, it was at first strongly influenced by Bacon (through Huygens), the members compiling 'histories' of natural phenomena, arts and crafts, producing a natural history of animals and plants, and later a catalogue of machines and inventions. As with the Royal Society, the influence of Bacon soon declined, and the views of Descartes became prominent. This movement began under Fontenelle, who was secretary for forty years from 1699.[2]

The bibliography of the publications of the Académie des Sciences is difficult, since some were reprinted.[3]

B. Mémoires de Mathématique et de Physique tirez des Registres de l'Académie Royale des Sciences, 2 vols. 4°, Paris, 1692 (the BN has only one vol., 1692); repr. in C.

C. Histoire de l'Académie Royale des Sciences Depuis 1666. jusqu'à son Renouvellement en 1699; 2 vols. 4° (i, ii), Paris, 1733. The set continues with: Memoires de l'Academie Royale des Sciences, Depuis 1666. jusqu'à 1699, in the volumes III, i, 1733; III, ii, 1733; III, iii, 1734; IV, 1731; V, 1729; VI, 1730; VII, i, 1729; VII, ii, 1729; VIII, 1730; IX, 1733 (a mathematical treatise); X, 1730. Two index vols. were publ. separately. This publication is denoted by AdS (C) in the references.

D. Histoire de l'Academie Royale des Sciences. Année M.DC.XCIX [etc.] Avec des Mémoires de Mathématique & de Physique, pour la même Année. Tirés des Registres de cette Academie, 4°, Paris, 1702–97. The volumes consist of two parts, separately paginated, *Histoires* (consisting of summaries of papers nominally prepared by the Secretary) and *Mémoires* (consisting of the papers in full, if they were so published). These are denoted by AdS h and m, respectively, without qualifying letter. Some references to an Amsterdam reprint are denoted by (A). The index volumes: Table Alphabetique des Matieres contenues dans l'Histoire & les Memoires de l'Academie Roïale des Sciences, for the earlier vols. are very useful, since they contain chronological lists of memoirs under authors; they were compiled by Louis Godin (1704–60), who edited C.

In 1789 (1791) the word Royale was dropped in a new vol. i. In 1798 the publication started as Mémoires de l'Institut National des Sciences et Arts in a new vol. i. In 1806 two vols. had the titles: Mémoires de l'Institut des Sciences, Lettres et Arts, and Mémoires de l'Institut; classe des Sciences Mathématiques et Physiques, respectively. In 1816 it became Mémoires de l'Académie Royale de l'Institut de France (vol. i), but the word Royale was dropped in 1850 (vol. xxi). In 1860 it became Mémoires de l'Institut Impérial de France (vol. xxv), but in 1872 (vol. xxxviii) the publication became Mémoires de l'Académie des Sciences de l'Institut de France.

Some other publications by the Academy which have been used are:

E. Pièces qui ont remporté les prix de l'Académie Royale des Sciences (1720–72), 9 vols., 1721–77 (continuation in *Mém. div. Sav.*, 1750–86, vii–xi).

F. Mémoires de Mathématiques et de Physique, presentés à l'Académie Royale des Sciences par divers Sçavans et lus dans ses Assemblées, earlier section 11 vols. 4°,

---

[1] *Works*, 1744, ii, 130.

[2] J. L. F. Bertrand, *L'Académie des Sciences et les Academiciens de 1666 à 1793*, Paris, 1869 (BM 8308. cc. 3); Harcourt Brown, 1934; George, *Ann. Sci.*, 1938, ii, 372; E. Maindron, *L'Académie des Sciences*, Paris, 1888.

[3] Gmelin, (1), ii, 204, 430–4 (contradictory titles); no one seems to have troubled to give a recent complete bibliography.

1750–86; new series from 1827, with the title: Mémoires présentés par divers Savants à l'Académie des Sciences de l'Institut de France. This publication is uniformly denoted by AdS Mém. div. Sav.

Abridged English trs. of earlier vols. of publications of the Académie des Sciences appeared (see Gmelin, (1), ii, 432, who does not mention: Memoirs of the Royal Academy of Sciences in Paris, epitomized with the Lives of the late Members of that Society . . . , tr. by John Chamberlayne, 8°, 1721).

G. Descriptions des Arts et Métiers faites ou approuvées par messieurs de l'Academie Royale des Sciences, in a number of luxurious folio vols. The number of treatises in the work is differently given, but is said to be about 73, with 13,500 pp. of text and over 1800 plates; Guerlac, Chymia, 1959, v, 73 (98); Maindron, 1888, 314, lists 84 titles (with one more not issued with the approbation of the Academy but usually included) in 27 vols. f°, 1761–83 (as in CUL set XXVII, 49. 1—).

H. Machines et Inventions approuvées par l'Académie Royale des Sciences, depuis 1666 jusqu'en 1754. Avec leur description, 7 vols. 4°, Paris, 1735–77, with about 500 folding plates; compiled by Gallon.

It is hoped that the above list will enable a reader to find the publications given in the references without difficulty. They have all been seen by the author.

MARIOTTE

The work of Edme Mariotte (d. 1684) on the compressibility of air and his restatement of Boyle's law (1679) has been mentioned in Vol. II. His *Essai de la Vegetation des Plantes* (1676)[1] in three parts deals fully with the 'chemical principles' of plants, regarding these as composed of 'principes grossiers et visibles', viz. water, sulphur or oil, common salt, saltpetre, volatile salt (ammonia), earths, etc., but these, according to the chemists, are themselves composed of 'trois ou quatre principes plus simples', e.g. saltpetre of its phlegm or insipid water, its spirit, its fixed salt, etc.; and these simpler principles are again composed of parts differing among themselves which cannot be perceived by any artifice. The salts, earths, oils, etc., furnished by different plants on distillation are all the same, and the differences found proceed only from the more or less perfect union of some of these gross principles and of their simplest parts, or on their separations.

Any kind of plant can be grown in a pot of earth by the action of rain water and the principles of the different plants are therefore the same. Fire is not an element of plants, since it is composed of the same principles as inflamed bodies; the fire of burning charcoal results from the strong agitation of parts of its sulphur, saltpetre, etc., and the flame of a candle is only ignited smoke, and this smoke is composed of the same elements as the wax. Hence fire cannot be taken as a principle. As for air, it is always in water and consequently in the juices of plants, as is easily recognised by the effervescences of distilled liquors. Since the substances separated by the distillation of different kinds of plants are the same, chemistry can give no explanation of the differences.

DUCLOS

Samuel Cottereau Duclos, the king's physician and one of the first members of the Academy, retired in 1685 to a Capuchin convent, where he died in 1715.[2]

---

[1] *Oeuvres*, 1717, i, 121–47 (Lettre écrit à M. Lantin . . . sur le Sujet des Plantes); J. von Sachs, *Geschichte der Botanik*, Munich, 1875, 499; Thorndike, viii, 75.

[2] Condorcet, *Oeuvres*, Paris, 1847, ii, 33–9; Hoefer, (1), ii, 294.

He opposed Boyle's corpuscular theory in 1669.[1] He investigated over sixty French mineral waters, finding in them common salt, a nitrous or gypsum-like substance, and other salts, but no alum, vitriol, sulphur, or bitumen.[2] He also investigated drinking water, using various reagents (1670).[3] He detected a bitter salt (Epsom salt) in some mineral spring waters and sea water (1667–8, 1670–1, 1684).[4] Contrary to some statements, Duclos did not examine microscopically the product of evaporation of mineral waters.[5] Duclos discussed coagulation (1669),[6] and obtained crystals (salt of sorrel; acid potassium oxalate) from sorrel juice (1668).[7]

Perrault and Duclos found that on calcining chalk or limestone there was a loss of weight of a quarter or a third, which they put down to escape of moisture (1668).[8] Duclos found that metallic antimony increases by one-tenth of its weight when calcined by a burning mirror and thought this was due to a combination of the calx with sulphureous or earthy particles in the air; he mentions that Boulduc had found a *loss* in weight on calcining antimony in earthen vessels (1667).[9]

Duclos attempted to analyse plants by dry distillation (1668–9, 1670–1, 1673),[10] and these experiments were continued by other academicians, including Bourdelin (1678, 1680, 1683–4, 1686–7, 1689, 1693),[11] Borel (1688),[12] Dodart (1688),[13] and Boulduc. Homberg (1692, 1695)[14] said the fourteen hundred distillations gave worthless results, since cabbage and hemlock gave the same products.

Fourcroy[15] says early minutes of the Academy in several large folio volumes contain details of the analysis of plants by dry distillation made by Duclos, Perrault, Dodart, Boulduc, Bourdelin, Geoffroy, etc., which are of no value, since all the different vegetable matters gave the same products. Later, the method of extraction by solvents was used by La Garaye (see p. 88), Boulduc, Geoffroy, Neumann, Boerhaave, Rouelle and Gaubius.

Duclos[16] asserted that bodies can act upon one another without physical contact by means of a universal spirit which surrounds and penetrates them, and through which Nature impressed on them their specific characters as type ideas, the originals of which (as Plato said) existed in the mind of the First Cause — a sort of theological ether of space. The universal spirit had been invoked earlier by Le Févre (p. 19).

[1] AdS (C), 1733, i, 79.
[2] Observations sur les eaux minérales de plusieurs provinces de France, faites en l'Académie royale des Sciences en l'année 1670 & 1671; AdS (C), 1731, iv, 41–119; sep. with same title, 12°, Paris, 1675, 203 pp. and plate (BN S 19861; Nourry-Thiébaud *Cat.* 66 (1938), 382); Thorndike, viii, 374–6; Latin: *Observationes super aquis mineralibus diversarum provinciarum Galliæ in Academia Scientiarum Regia in Annis 1670 et 1671 factæ,* 12°, Leyden, 1685 (BN); English tr. *Observations on the Mineral Waters of France,* 12°, London, 1684; Gmelin, (1), ii, 272.
[3] AdS (C), 1733, i, 123.   [4] AdS (C), 1733, i, 27, 50, 123, 387; 1731, iv, 41 f.
[5] G. Rath, *A. Med.,* 1957, xli, 1.   [6] AdS (C), 1733, i, 87.   [7] AdS (C), 1733, i, 57.
[8] AdS (C), 1733, i, 47.   [9] AdS (C), 1733, i, 21.
[10] AdS (C), 1733, i, 50, 121, 161.
[11] AdS (C), 1733, i, 252, 307, 373 (also milk, and vipers), 405; 1733, ii, 9, 26, 68, 182; AdS, 1734, h 47.
[12] AdS (C), 1733, ii, 49.   [13] AdS (C), 1733, ii, 52.   [14] AdS (C), 1733, ii, 148, 246.
[15] (2), iii, 338; see also Delépine, *La Synthèse totale en Chimie Organique, Classiques de la Découverte Scientifique,* Paris, 1937, 1 f., giving Bourdelin's results from a MS. of 1681.
[16] Dissertation sur les Principes des Mixtes Naturels (1677), AdS (C), 1731, iv, 1; publ. sep., 12°, Amsterdam, 1680 (103 pp.; BN R 13581).

A different person is the Paris physician Dominique Du Clos (1597–1684) who spent his life in alchemical pursuits, finally burning his manuscripts so that they could not mislead others.[1] Jean-Baptiste Besard (Besançon, c. 1576– ?), a lawyer and physician, published a work on alchemy with recipes for medicines and cosmetics.[2]

C. BOURDELIN

Claude Bourdelin (Lyon, 1621–Paris, 15 October 1699)[3] in 1683[4] found that 13 oz. of iron filings increased in weight by 6 oz. 7 scruples on rusting. On distilling the rust, the last part of the liquid distillate effervesced with acid [due to the ammonium carbonate formed in the rust], which Duclos told him was due to the water separating the volatile salt of the iron. Bourdelin also tried to find the greatest dilution in which sal volatile would effervesce with acid: he mixed a solution of 1 scruple in $1\frac{1}{2}$ scruples of water with 16 grains of spirit of salt mixed with 24 grains of water, and got a strong effervescence; when 7 times as much water was added, and then 9 grains of spirit of salt added to 24 grains of the solution, there was still a considerable effervescence (1682).[5] He examined mineral waters (1683)[6] and the distillation of plants (see p. 12).

Pierre Borel (Castres, Languedoc, 1620–Paris, 1689), besides his bibliography,[7] published an analysis of urine (1688),[8] described the distillation of sal ammoniac with iron (1688),[9] and showed that oil of vitriol dissolves marble best when it is diluted (1687).[10]

BARLET

Annibal Barlet, who had a laboratory in Paris in which he gave instruction by demonstrations, compiled a course of chemistry and an abridgement of it for the use of students:[11]

A. Le vray et methodiqve Covrs de la Physiqve resolvtive, vvlgairement dite Chymie. Representé par Figures generales & particulieres. Povr connoistre la Theotechnie Ergocosmiqve, C'est à dire, l'art de Diev, en l'ovvrage de l'vnivers, 4°, Paris, N. Charles, 1653, woodcut frontispiece, 5 ll., 626 pp., 5 ll., 36 full-page woodcuts, large folding plate, and two large folding tables (BM 1034. h. 2), the ed. quoted; Seconde édition. Avec l'indice des matières, & quelques additions, 4°, Paris, 1657 (BM 1034. h. 3) with two folding tables more.
B. Abregé des choses plvs necessaires. Dv Vray et Methodiqve covrs de la Physiqve resolvtive Uulgairement dicte Chymie. Extraict de la Theotechnie Ergocosmiqve, 12°, s.l.e. a,[12] BM 1032. b. 13.

The first part of A is mystical and unintelligible and is illustrated by obscure plates. There is no alchemy proper in it. The second part is practical, the preparation of medicines, their supposed compositions and their uses being

[1] Gmelin, (1), ii, 19; Kopp, (4), i, 235 (in (1), ii, 61, he confuses him with S. C. Duclos).
[2] *Antrum Philosophicum, In Quo Pleraque arcana physica . . . ad experimenti legem breviter, &*
sincerem reuelantur, 4°, Augsburg, 1617 (xii, 248 pp.); BM 776. d. 4; Duveen, 76; Hoefer, (1), ii, 323; Thorndike, vii, 173.
[3] Fontenelle, AdS, 1699, h 122; *Oeuvres*, 1790, vi, 96.
[4] AdS (C), 1733, i, 371.   [5] AdS (C), 1733, i, 345.   [6] AdS (C), 1733, i, 367.
[7] *Bibliotheca Chimica sev Catalogvs Librorvm Philosophicorvm Hermeticorvm*, 12°, Paris, 1654 (pp. xii, 276).
[8] AdS (C), 1733, ii, 51.   [9] *Ib.*, 52.   [10] *Ib.*, 28.
[11] Ferguson, i, 72; Gmelin, (1), i, 744; F. S. Taylor, *Ann. Sci.*, 1952, viii, 285; Thorndike, viii, 129.
[12] Paris, 1653 ?

clearly explained. This part is illustrated by many plates (see Fig. 1) showing a
laboratory, all very much alike with a chemist called Hermes (no doubt Barlet
himself), assistants, and auditors (who often have their backs to the demonstrations). The subjects come from the animal, vegetable, and mineral kingdoms
in this order; the animal part is much fuller than in the early edition of
Lemery's text-book (1675) and perhaps suggested the additions to the later
ones. Stress is laid on the design of furnaces.

Des Vegetaux.   4. Figure.

FIG. 1. BARLET. A LECTURE DEMONSTRATION.

The elements are fire, sal ammoniac, water, mercury, sulphur, air, and salt,
and they have both internal and external qualities.[1] Barlet speaks of 'parties
indivisibles, dites Atomes'.[2] The red fumes of nitric acid are 'esprits rouges
vray fleuue de Phlegeton'.[3] The alchemical symbols of the metals, with their
supposed meanings, are given.[4] There are descriptions of the preparation of
'alcool de vin, c'est à dire tres subtile', with oiled parchment over the neck of
the alembic,[5] a definition of flame,[6] the precipitation of milk of sulphur (lait de
souphre),[7] and the sublimation of flowers of amber.[8] 'Bismuth ou estain de
glace' is used to make a white cosmetic by dissolving it in nitric acid and pre-

[1] A, 51, 69.   [2] A, 115.   [3] A, 422, 444.   [4] A, 180 f.; Beckmann, (1), ii, 23.
[5] A, 366.   [6] A, 368.   [7] A, 464.   [8] A, 481.

cipitating with salt water, but although the title of this section includes 'zinch et autres Marcassites', nothing is said about zinc.[1] Corrosive sublimate (sublimé corrosif) and calomel (sublimé doux ou dulcifié) are made as usual by sublimation.[2] Butter of antimony (gomme d'antimoine, antimony trichloride) is made by distilling corrosive sublimate with stibnite (antimony sulphide) or metallic antimony, and it is emphasised that when the metal is used no cinnabar (mercuric sulphide) is formed.[3] Potassium arsenate (crystaux d'arsenic) is made by dropping a mixture of white arsenic and saltpetre into a red-hot crucible, dissolving the product in water, filtering, and evaporating, when the liquid deposits 'crystaux qui se formeront table sur table en diamants contigus'[4] — this is long before Macquer's preparation (see p. 87). Fourcroy[5] mentions Barlet's use of litmus paper in testing mineral waters.

Barlet was the teacher of the Aberdeen physician Dr. Matthew Mackaile, known for his books on the Moffat well and on salts and spirits:

Moffet-Well: Or, a Topographico-Spagyricall description of the Mineral Wells, at Moffet in Annandale of Scotland . . . As also, The Oily-Well . . . at St. Catherines Chappel in the Paroch of Libberton. To these is subjoyned, A Character of Mr. Culpeper and his Writings, 8°, Edinburgh, 1664, Duveen, 375.

The Diversitie of Salts and Spirits Maintained. Or, The Imaginary Volatility of some Salts and Non-entity of the Alcali, before Cremation and Identity of all Alcalies . . . by an onely Lamp-Furnace resolved into real Improbability . . . As Also, Scurvie Alchymie discovered. By Matt. MacKaile Apoth. and Chirurg. Alias, Chirurgo-Medicine, 12° in 4's, Aberdeen, 1683.

John Evelyn also attended Barlet's course and there is a MS. of his notes of the lectures in Christ Church, Oxford. On 22 January 1649 Evelyn 'went thro' a course of Chymistrie' at Sayes Court (his house near London).[6]

In December 1650 Evelyn[7] met in the lodging of Mt. Ratcliffe in Paris 'an impostor that had like to have impos'd upon us a pretended secret of multiplying gold; 'tis certain he had liv'd some time in Paris in extraordinarie splendour, but I found him to be an egregious cheate'. In June 1651 Evelyn recorded that the Abesse of Boucharvant 'but for me had been abus'd by that chymist Du Menie'.[8] In January 1652 an enameller Antonio told Evelyn of a Genoese jeweller whom he met in Cyprus who had 'a great Arcanum, and had made projection before him severall times'; also a person in a goldsmith's shop in Amsterdam who converted a pound of lead into 4 oz. of gold by a projection powder and then vanished;[9] all this, says Evelyn, Antonio 'asserted with greate obtestation', but he had been a great rover and spoke ten languages and 'there are so many impostors and people who love to tell strange stories'. There were plenty of alchemists in Paris about 1650 as well as genuine chemists like Barlet.

BLAISE DE VIGENÈRE

Blaise de Vigenère (Saint-Pourçain, Bourbonnais, 5 April 1523–Paris, 19 February 1596) a classical scholar and literary man, secretary to the Duc de Nevers and King Henri III, wrote a theological-alchemical treatise on fire and salt, quoting the Zohar, Hermes, Geber, Rhases, Avicenna, etc., which was published posthumously:

[1] A, 505. [2] A, 549. [3] A, 557, misnumbered 547.
[4] A, 471–2. [5] (1), iv, 291. [6] Diary, ed. Bray, 1870, 198.
[7] Diary, ed. Bray, 1870, 209. [8] Ib., 211. [9] Ib., 217.

Traicté dv Fev et dv Sel. Excellent et Rare Opuscule du sieur Blaise de Vigenaire Bourbonnois, trovvé parmy ses papiers apres son decés, 4°, Paris, 1618, engr. t.p., 267 pp.; Paris, 1622, same t.p. and 267 pp. but extra leaf a ii after t.p.

Kopp, (1), iv, 359, dates this 1608, as does Ferguson, ii, 511, who adds eds. of 1642 and 1651 (Rouen), none of which he had seen; M. Offenbacher, Paris, in 1937, offered me the one of 1618 as 'edition originale'. Duveen, 603, gives 4°, Paris, 1622, and English tr., A Discourse of Fire and Salt, Discovering Many secret Mysteries, As well Philosophicall, As Theologicall, 4°, London, 1649, and another issue of 1649 is described by Patterson, *Ann. Sci.*, 1939, iv, 61, who says the first French ed. was of 1618, not 1608; Lenglet du Fresnoy, i, 319; Jöcher, iv, 1595; NBG, 1866, xlvi, 140; D. Métral, Blaise de Vigenère, Paris, 1939.

In this he describes the preparation of oil of vitriol by the bell process (1618, 94), but the most interesting passage is that describing crystalline benzoic acid, obtained by the sublimation of gum benzoin (*ib.*, 91): 'puis augmentant le feu par ses degrez, apparoistront infinies petites aiguilles & filamens, telles qu'ès dissolutions de plomb & de l'argent vif.' With further rise of temperature, these melt and form 'vne moüielle' (marrow).

Benzoic acid is mentioned by Michel de Nostredame (Nostredamus) (Saint-Remi, Provence, 14 December 1503–Salon, 2 July 1566), who qualified in medicine at Montpellier but is better known as an astrologer:

Excellent & / movlt vtile opvscv- / le a Tovts Necessaire, qui desirent auoir cognoissance / de plusieurs exquisites Rece- / ptes, diuisé en deux / parties . . . composé par Maistre Michel de Nostredame docteur en Medecine de la ville de Salon de Craux en Prouence, & de nouueau mis en lumiere, sm. 8°, Paris, Oliuier de Harsy, 1556 (214 pp., v ll.; BM 1037. a. 21); sm. 8°, Lyon, A. Volant, M.D.LVI (1556) (228 pp., vi ll.; BM 1038. a. 6); German tr.: Michaelis No- Stradami. Dess Weitberü / mbten / Hocherfarnen / Philo- / sophi . . . zwey Bücher . . . , 8°, Augsburg, 1589 (viii ll., 206 pp., v ll.; BM 717. e. 37).

The first book deals with cosmetics, beginning with the preparation of corrosive sublimate, which is used to whiten the skin, and describing a toothpowder composed of powdered flint, marble, glass, and salt (1589, 42), and aqua fortis (nitric acid) for turning the hair golden-yellow (1589, 67) — all of which would have disastrous results. The second book deals with sweetmeats and confectionaries made from sugar, such as marzipan. Nostredame describes the preparation of oil of benzoin by distilling gum benzoin and mentions the snow-like sublimate.[1] Benzoic acid is also described by Alexis of Piedmont (1557) (Vol. II, p. 28), Libavius (1597, Vol. II, p. 267), and Turquet de Mayerne (1608) (Vol. II, p. 174), so that de Viginère's mention of it is late, but he describes very clearly the crystalline form. Since Libavius calls the product 'instar mannæ', he seems to have used Nostredame's account.

The name benzene is derived from that of benzoic acid and this in turn from gum benzoin. 'Benzui' appears in documents of 1461 as a gift from the Sultan of Egypt to the Doge of Venice, and in 1476 to the Queen of Cyprus, and repeatedly later; it was known in India very much earlier and Ibn Battūta (*c.* 1340) calls it lubān Jāwi ('incense of Java', i.e. Sumatra), corrupted by Portuguese and Spanish merchants into benjawi, benjoim (beijoim in Vasco da Gama, 1497), benzoin, etc.; English benzoin, benjamin, etc.[2]

[1] *Opuscvle*, Paris, 1556, 37, 40; Lyon, 1556, 42, 45: La façon vraye pour faire l'huylle de benioin . . . prendres la neige qui est comme vne chandelle . . . receuoir la neige, que plusieurs appellent mannes ou ros cyriacus; Augsburg, 1589, 23 f. (ein Schnee).

[2] Roscoe and Schorlemmer, *Treatise*, 1888, III, iv, 151; Schaer, in Diergart, 1909, 285. The name has nothing to do with bezoar (see Vol. II, p. 97).

LE FÉVRE

Nicolas Le Févre (as he signed his name; other spellings are Le Fèvre, Lefévre, Le Febure, Lefebvre, etc.) (Sedan (?), *c.* 1615–London, in the Spring of 1669) was the son of an apothecary. He was first instructed by his father, then at Sedan (where there was a Protestant Academy) by Dr. Duhan, doctor of medicine and professor of philosophy. He then moved to Paris, where he conversed with Du Clos, to whom, he says, he was indebted for the well-being he acquired in his profession. He was then called by Antoine Vallot (Rheims, or Montpellier, 1594–Paris, 9 August 1671), who favoured the use of chemical remedies, the first physician to King Louis XIV and Superintendant of the Jardin du Roi, to fill the place of demonstrator in chemistry at the Jardin du Roi. This was vacated by Davisson in 1651 (see p. 5) but Evelyn[1] recorded on 18 January 1647: 'I frequented a course of Chemistrie, the famous Mr. Le Febure operating upon most of the nobler processes.' In 1660 Le Févre left for England and on 15 November 1660 he was created by warrant 'chymist' to King Charles II, becoming on 31 December 1660 professor of chemistry and Apothecary in Ordinary to the King. He worked in a laboratory in St. James's Palace.[2] Pepys recorded a visit on 15 January 1669 to 'the King's little elaboratory, under his closet, a pretty place; and there saw a great many chymical glasses and things, but understood none of them'.[3] Le Févre became F.R.S. on 20 May 1663.[4] Boerhaave[5] says Le Févre is accurate in describing his experiments and careful in pointing out which are dangerous, 'but he has this defect, that in his reasonings he has too much of the chemical spirit'; this would seem to us unobjectionable in a chemist. Boyle (1663) mentions him as 'Monsieur L. F. who was the French King's chymist' and his *ens primum* of balm,[6] which rejuvenated an old hen. In 1660, when he left for England, Le Févre's text-book was published in Paris:

A. Traicté de la Chymie. Tome Premier. Qui servira d'instruction & d'introduction tant pour l'intelligence des Autheurs qui ont traité de la Theorie de cette Science en general: Que pour faciliter les moyens de faire artistement & methodiquement les operations qu'enseigne la pratique de cét Art, sur les Animaux sur les vegetaux, & sur les mineraux, sans la perte d'aucune des vertus essentielles qu'ils contiennent. — Tome Second. Qui contient la suite de la preparation des sucs qui se tirent des Vegetaux, comme aussi celle de leurs autres parties, & celle des Mineraux. A Paris, Chez Thomas Jolly, Libraire Iuré, ruë S. Iacques, aux Armes d'Hollande. 1660. Auec Priuilege du Roy. (xiv ll., 510 pp.; t.p., pp. 510–1092, ix ll.; engr. f.p. to i and 8 double plates); Duveen, 345; Sotheran *Cat.* 795 (1925), no. 11364 (has not servira in line 1 and some caps.); not in BM or BN.

B. (*a*) Second Edition, revuë, corrigée & de beaucoup augmentée de bon nombre d'excellens remedes, par l'Autheur, 2 vols. 8°, Paris, Chez Tho. Jolly and J. d'Houry, 1669 (BN); (*b*) Nouvelle Édition, corrigée de plusieurs Fautes, suivant la Copie imprimé

---

[1] *Diary*, ed. Bray, 1870, 195.

[2] Dumas, (2), 56; Ferguson, ii, 17; Goodwin, DNB, 1892, xxxii, 399; Hoefer, (1), ii, 276; Kopp, (2), iii, 185; Metzger, (1), 62; Read, (2), 101 (portr.); Saverien, 1769, vii, 37, 49–70 (analysis of the *Traité*); Thorndike, viii, 130; L.T. in NBG, 1859, xxx, 342; Thomson does not mention Le Févre.

[3] *Diary*, ed. Braybrook, 1858, iv, 81.

[4] Sprat, *History of the Royal Society*, 1667, 432; his name is not in Thomson's *History of the Royal Society*.

[5] (4), 1741, i, 47.   [6] *Usefulness of Experimental Natural Philosophy*; *Works* 1744, i, 518.

(*sic*) à Paris, 2 vols. 12°, 2 engr. t.ps., 8 double copperplates, Leyden, Chez Doude, 1669. (*c*) 2 vols. sm. 8°, Paris, J. d'Houry, 1674 (vol. I, vii ll. incl. engr. t.p., t.p., plate of English royal arms; dedic. to King Charles II signed N. Le Févre; Avx Lectevrs, dated Du Laboratoire Royal au Palais de S. Iames, Londres le 1669 (*sic*); Privilege du Roy (Louis XIV) dated 5 December 1668; 389 pp., vii pp. index; 6 fold. plates; vol. II, pp. 441, x index, 2 fold. plates). The t.ps. of the 2 ed. the same as those of the first, except 'Traité' instead of 'Traicté' and the words 'des sucs que se tirent' omitted on t.p. of vol. ii; other eds.: (*d*) Cours de Chymie, 2 vols. 12°, Leyden, 1696 (Ferguson); (*e*) 5 ed. ed. and enlarged by Du Monstier, Apoticaire de la Marine & des Vaisseaux du Roi; Membre de la Société Royale de Londres & de celle de Berlin, 5 vols. 12°, Paris, 1751 (BN R 41326–30, Ferguson). 'Du Monstier' was the Abbé Lenglet du Fresnoy (BN *Cat.* 1911, xliv, 435); he was not F.R.S.

C. English tr. 'by P.D.C. Esq; one of the Gentlemen of His Majesties Privy-Chamber':

(*a*) A / Compendious Body / of / Chymistry, / which will serve / As a Guide and Introduction both for understanding / the Authors which have treated of / The Theory of this Science in general: / And for making the way Plain and Easie to perform / according to Art and Method, all Operations, which / teach the Practise of this Art, upon / Animals, Vegetables, and Minerals, / without losing any of The Essential Vertues contained in them / By N. le Febvre . . . 4°, London, Tho. Davies and Theo. Sadler . . . , 1662, with sep. t.ps. to each part. A Compleat Body of Chymistry . . . , dated 1664; Liverpool and Glasgow Univ. Libraries; Bradley, *Times Lit. Suppl.*, 1926, 496 (22 July); Murray, *ib.*, 525 (3 August).

(*b*) A / Compleat Body / of / Chymistry: / Wherein is contained whatsoever is necessary for the attaining to the curious knowledge of this Art; Com- / prehending in general the whole practice thereof: / and teaching the most exact preparation of Ani- / mals, Vegetables and Minerals, so as to reserve their / essential Vertues. / Laid open in two Books, and dedicated to the use of all Apo- / thecaries &c. / Part I / 4°, London, Printed by Tho. Ratcliffe for Octavian Pulleyn Junior, 1664 (pp. xii, 312, vi; sep. t.p., 364, viii): dedicated to King Charles II and (sep.) 'to the Apothecaries of England'. CUL L.5.9; Sotheran *Cat.* 795 (1925), no. 11366; BM 43. d. 22 has the t.p.: A Compendious Body of Chymistry: teaching the whole practice thereof by the most exact preparation of Animals, Vegetables, and Minerals, preserving their essential vertues (with variations of punctuation this is the t.p. of the second part of (*c*), with 'Compleat' instead of 'Compendious').

(*c*) A / Compleat Body / of / Chymistry [title on pages: A Compendious Body of Chymistry]: / wherein is contained whatsoever is necessary for / the attaining to the Curious Knowledge of this Art; / Comprehending in General the whole Practice thereof: / and Teaching the most exact Preparation of Animals, Ve- / getables and Minerals, so as to preserve their Essential / Vertues. / Laid open in two Books, and Dedicated to the Use / of all Apothecaries, &c. / By Nicasius le Febure [*sic*], Royal Professor in Chymistry to His / Majesty of England, and Apothecary in Ordinary to His / Honourable Household.

Rendred (*sic*) into English, by P.D.C. Esq; one of the Gentlemen of His Majesties Privy-Chamber. Part I. With Additions, 4°, London, O. Pulleyn Junior, 1670 (pp. xvi; 286, vi), sep. t.p. A / Compleat Body / of / Chymistry: / Teaching the whole Practice thereof, by the most / exact Preparation of Animals, Vegetables and / Mi- / nerals, preserving their essential Vertues. / By Nicasius le Febure; Royal Professor in Chymistry to his Ma- / jesty of England, and Apothecary in Ordinary to His Ho- / norable Household, and Fellow of the Royal Society . . . The Second Part. 4°, London, John Wright, 1670 (pp. 1–320, viii index). Page heading of both parts: A Compendious Body of Chymistry. (My copy, q. in text.) Sotheran *Cat.* 839 (1934), no. 565, has the above title as far as 'Privy-Chamber' but continues: 'corrected and amended; with the Additions of the late French copy', 8 copperplates, mostly folding.

D. German tr.: Chymischer Handleiter, und Guldnes Kleinod, 8°, Nürnberg, 1672 (Hoefer); 1675 (Ferguson), 12°, 1676 (Bolton, (1), 610), 8°, 1685, ed. Cardilucio (Ferguson; xxxiv, 867, lv pp.), 12°, 1688 (Bolton; lii, 1149, xix pp.); I have not seen any of these.

E. Latin, 2 vols. 4°, Besançon, 1737 (Ferguson). Le Févre also published on Sir

Walter Raleigh's 'great cordial', composed of viper's flesh, bezoar, hartshorn, coral, pearls, etc.:

F. A Discourse upon Sir Walter Rawleigh's Great Cordial . . . rendered into English by Peter Belon, sm. 8°, London, 1664 (xviii, 110 pp.); Ferguson mentions a later French version (1665) which he had not seen. Le Févre is said to have translated into French (from the Dutch) Sir Thomas Browne's Religio Medici: La Religion du Medecin, 12°, s.l.e.a. (Keynes, A Bibliography of Sir Thomas Browne, Cambridge, 1924, 45; Ferguson gives s.l., 1668; O. Leroy, A French Bibliography of Sir Thomas Browne, London, 1931, 33, gives from a Paris bookseller's catalogue (Vrin): Traduit par Nicolas Le Febvre, 12°, La Haye, 1668 (not seen).

Le Févre says the book was the fruit of the work of 30 years[1] and in his preface that he had made use of the works of Basil Valentine, Paracelsus, Van Helmont and Glauber, and wrote in French since the famous German chemists had written in their mother tongue. He complains that the French chemists are often impatient and careless.[2] Le Févre's treatise has perhaps not received the attention it deserves: it is important in the transmission into French and English circles of German chemistry in a systematic form. Lemery's much more popular work often merely reproduces the practical part of Le Févre's with the mystical and theoretical elements expurgated or partially replaced by atomic speculations. Hoefer thought Le Févre was less a practical than a philosophical chemist, 'qui aime mieux discuter la valeur des théories que descendre dans le detail des faits,' but if allowance is made for the mystical and astrological material taken over from his German authorities his book is really very practical. It begins with a preliminary discourse on the nature of chemistry, which is 'a practical and operative science of natural things', divided into three branches, philosophical or wholly scientific, medical or Iatrochemistry, and pharmaceutical. The text proper begins with a discussion of the principles and elements of natural things, which are a 'universal spirit' which forms material things by its specific ferments acting on appropriate matrices under the influence of the stars, and five principles: two passive (water or phlegm, and earth), and three active (mercury or spirit, sulphur or oil, and salt), which had been introduced by de Clave.[3] These principles are separated from vegetable matters by fire. The elements are still fire, air, water and earth (the first two rejected by de Clave)[4] and in addition to all these are the arcanas or magisteries of Paracelsus.[5]

Chemists deny that air participates in the composition of mixed bodies. The function of air in combustion is to remove the smoky matter from the flame, which otherwise would be extinguished.[6] Le Févre gives a long description, with a plate, of the calcination of powdered metallic antimony by means of a burning glass, and says[7] that 12 grains of metal increase to 15 grains in spite of the vapours exhaled, and this 'wonder' is due to the fixation of sunlight by 'a miraculous fire which constitutes the principle of antimony'.

The text[8] says the burning glass was 3 or 4 ft. in diameter, made by cementing two concave pieces of glass by fish-glue and filling with water through a hole (the plate shows a small glass); and the operator wore green glass spectacles to protect his eyes

[1] C (c),ii, 320.   [2] C (c), ii, 197.   [3] Novvelle Lvmiere Philosophiqve, 1641, 39 f.
[4] Op. cit., 4 f., 26 f.   [5] Le Févre, C (c), i, 7 f., 13 f., 17 f., 30 f., 52.
[6] C (c), i, 37, 75.   [7] C (c), i, 78; ii, 215.   [8] C (c), ii, 216.

FIG. 2. LE FÉVRE. CALCINATION OF ANTIMONY.

from the glare. The operator is shown left-handed so that the engraving was probably executed in reverse from a right-handed drawing; in the reproduction in Valentini's *Museum Museorum*, Frankfurt, 1704, the operator is right-handed and in modern attire.

The increase in weight of antimony on calcination by solar light was first mentioned by Hamerus Poppius (1618):

Basilica Antimonii, in qva Antimonii Natvra Exponitvr et Nobilissimæ Remediorum formulæ, quam pyrotechnica arte ex eo elaborantur, quam accurate traduntur: Manvali Experientia Comprobata & conscripta ab Hamero Poppio Thallino, 4°, Frankfurt, Apvd Antonivm Hvmmivm, 1618 (50 pp., 1 blank), 21–2; also in Hartmann, *Praxis Chymiatrica*, 8°, Geneva, 1648, 608:

De Calcinatione Antimonii per ignem cœlestem, seu radios solares. Sit ad manus speculum incensorium siue lenticulare, siue metallicum concauum, quod nempe radios Solares refringendo vel reflectendo concentret, vt obiecta combustibilia inflammet: id Soli opponatur, ita vt pyramidis luminosæ apex ante Antimonij puluerisati & iuxta in marmore in modum metæ vel coni in acumen fastigiati summitatem feriat, & breui fastigium metæ Antimonij, cum multi fumi profusione ad niuis albedinem calcinabitur, qua parte calcinata à corpore nigro cultello remota, vlterius relinquatur, donec ita per vices totus Antimonij conus ad albedinem sit redactus: & (quod mirabile) licet copiosus fumus multum de Antimonio dissipari arguat, tamen Antimonij pondus post calcinationem auctum potius quam diminutum deprehenditur.

Sir Thomas Browne[1] mentions the experiment, saying that 'mistake may be made in this way of trial, whether the Antimony is not weighed immediately

[1] *Pseudodoxia Epidemica*, bk. iv, c. 7; *Works*, ed. Sayle, 1927, ii, 141; ed. Keynes, 1928, iii, 36.

upon the calcination; but permitted the air; it imbibeth the humidity thereof, and so repaireth its gravity'. Goddard in 1664 reported on 'calcining antimony in the sun with a burning-glass', and 'found it so far from increasing in weight, that the weight was decreased from twelve grains to between three or four. Mr. Boyle affirmed, that he had the like success in such an experiment, but that Monsieur Le Febure, who asserted the increase of antimony calcined by the sun, hearing the want of success with him, answered, that it had not been calcined enough to reduce it to a fixed salt fit for the imbibing of air.'[1]

Le Févre describes and figures chemical furnaces and apparatus, including an air-thermometer with two bulbs and a water-index, for measuring temperatures; and also shows a lamp furnace with an oil lamp (which could have one or more wicks of different sizes) adjustable by a screw.[2]

'Mixts' are divided into the 'three families of Nature, animals, vegetables, and minerals'.[3] Minerals are divided into metals (fusible and malleable), stones (infusible) and marcasites or middle minerals (fusible but not malleable), including salts and glass.[4] Metals and minerals are of different sexes; gold, lead and antimony are male, the other metals female.[5] Le Févre warns his readers against the frauds of alchemy.[6] The first volume deals with honey, wax, manna, mummy, blood, urine, vipers and their distillation, and (also in the first part of the second volume) with preparations of vegetables, such as distilled waters, syrups, and salts, and fermentation. The second volume treats of the distillation of spirit of wine and its dehydration with salt of tartar to *alkool*,[7] which should ignite gunpowder on burning; the distillation of vinegar (when phlegm comes over first),[8] tartar and cream of tartar (cremor tartari),[9] opium (of which it gives a good account, including tests for adulteration), oils, resins, benzoin and its 'flowers' or 'volatile sulphurous salt' (benzoic acid),[10] and camphor. Then follow mineral substances, 'the proper part of chemistry, as some think',[11] divided into earths, gems (for which it refers to Boetius de Boot), stones (including quicklime), metals and marcasites or middle minerals, which are zinck (not mentioned again), bismuth, cobolt, and cadmia, as natural, and litharge, pompholix and tutty, as artificial; he does not describe the last in detail. Then follow salts, and sulphureous mixts (sulphur, arsenic, orpiment, realgar, ambergris, karabe or amber, spermaceti, asphaltum, naphtha, petrole or natural rock oil, coal and jet).

Metals are generated in the earth from mercury and sulphur under the influence of the planets.[12] Crocus of gold is the precipitated oxide.[13] Iron vitriol (vitriol de Mars) is made by dissolving steel filings in dilute oil of vitriol and crystallising,[14] iron salt (sel de Mars, ferrous acetate) by dissolving steel filings in vinegar and crystallising,[15] red crystals of iron (ferric acetate) by dissolving iron in aqua fortis and digesting with vinegar;[16] red spirit of mercury (really anhydrous ferric chloride) is made by subliming a mixture of iron filings and corrosive sublimate.[17] The butter or corrosive icy oil (beurre ou huile glaciale

[1] Birch, (1), 1756, i, 452.   [2] C (c), i, 87 and plate.
[3] C (c), i, 103; see Lemery, p. 32.   [4] C (c), i, 59 f.   [5] C (c), i, 62.
[6] C (c), ii, 74.   [7] C (c), ii, 8.   [8] C (c), ii, 14.   [9] C (c), ii, 19.
[10] C (c), ii, 59.   [11] C (c), ii, 72.   [12] C (c), ii, 117.   [13] C (c), ii, 130.
[14] C (c), ii, 144.   [15] C (c), ii, 147.   [16] C (c), ii, 150.   [17] C (c), ii, 190.

corrosive) of tin, made by distilling a mixture of tin filings and corrosive sublimate, is stannic chloride;[1] in the process mercury is also formed, as it is 'no
longer coagulated by the spirits of salts which have forsaken it to act on the
body of the tin'. Cassini in 1683[2] showed the academicians a small phial of a
liquid which fumed strongly when the stopper was removed, and Borel said it
had been made from corrosive sublimate, tin, and mercury.

The semi-metals (demy-metaux et moyens mineraux) are later said to be
mercury or quicksilver (vif-argent), antimony (antimoine), and bismuth (bis-
mut, antimoine blanc, antimoine femelle, étain de glace).[3] Le Févre gives a
good description of the preparation of mercury compounds, including the distillation of mercury from vermilion or artificial cinnabar (sublimed from mercury and sulphur) with iron filings, when the sulphur of the cinnabar joins to
the iron (s'est joint au fer); two forms of mercuric oxide are red precipitate
(precipité du mercure sans addition) made by heating the metal in a flat-
bottomed flask called a 'hell' (enfer), and arcanum corallinum made by heating
the nitrate; corrosive sublimate is made by subliming the nitrate with calcined
green vitriol and common salt; calomel (sublimé doux), made by subliming an
intimate mixture of this with mercury, is also called sweet and mitigated
eagle, tamed dragon, and panchymagog of Quercetanus: the acrimonious
spirits of the corrosive sublimate are enervated by working upon the extra
mercury.[4]

The description of antimony preparations, mostly from 'Basil Valentine'
and Zwelffer, is also very full.[5] Antimony is 'a marcasite destined by nature to
be a metal which has fainted on the way': it has been called the wolf, Proteus,
root of metals, sacred lead, philosophical lead, eastern lion, red lion, first being
of gold, etc. Glass of antimony is best made by fusing calcined and crude
antimony together (Sb_2O_3 with Sb_2S_3),[6] and diaphoretic antimony (the oxide)
by deflagrating stibnite (the sulphide) with saltpetre and washing with boiling
water.[7] Regulus of antimony (the metal) is made by strongly heating stibnite
with iron horse-shoe nails or iron or steel filings, then throwing in some saltpetre and pouring into a conical iron mould. It is purified by repeatedly fusing
and throwing saltpetre on it until the metal on solidifying exhibits a star.
Perpetual cups (pocula perpetua) or pills (pillulæ perpetua) of antimony are
said to act merely by emanation of inward virtue. Wine is allowed to stand in
the cups, and the pills are washed and used again after evacuation.[8] Boyle[9]
says: 't'would have seem'd incredible, a few years ago, . . . that a cup, made of
a substance, insoluble by the stomach, shou'd, without any sensible diminution of its weight, communicate a strong cathartic, and emetic, quality to any
liquor pour'd therein.' Bergman[10] knew that the metal must oxidise to dissolve;
in a closed bottle, Rhine wine in contact with metallic antimony, after filtra-

[1] C (c), ii, 172; see Libavius, Vol. II, p. 256.   [2] AdS (C), 1733, i, 374.
[3] B (c), ii, 246, 277, 333; C (c), ii, 174 f.   [4] C (c), ii, 177–85.
[5] C (c), ii, 197 f.   [6] C (c), ii, 202.   [7] C (c), ii, 208.
[8] C (c), ii, 212; for actual specimens of antimonial cups, pocula vomitoria (antimonii), calices
vomitorii, see St. Cl. Thomson, Proc. Roy. Soc. Med., 1926, xix, Hist. Med., 123; Schelenz,
1904, 480, says they go back to the time of 'Basil Valentine'; see Lemery, Cours de Chymie,
1756, 261, Pomet, General History of Drugs, 1737, 360.
[9] Works, ed. Shaw, 1725, i, 102.   [10] Essays, 1788, i, 406.

tion, 'did not show the slightest token of an emetic virtue.' James Primerose, of Scottish ancestry but born in Bordeaux (as, later, was Joseph Black), M.D. Montpellier 1617, who practised in Hull, was opposed to Harvey's theory of the circulation of the blood, and published many medical works as well as a treatise on the antimonial cup.[1]

Butter of antimony (antimony trichloride) distilled from stibnite or regulus of antimony and corrosive sublimate contains no mercury, but is antimony dissolved by the saline spirits which had coagulated the mercury into sublimate,[2] and it may be made without mercury by distilling vitriol, salt and antimony.[3] By precipitating it with water, an emetic powder of Algarot, named after the Italian Algarotti of Verona (who called it *pulvis angelicus*) is obtained.[4] Bezoar mineral or Jovial bezoar (antimonic acid) is made from butter of antimony and nitric acid,[5] and tartar emetic (tartre emetique purgatif) by boiling the oxide (deflagrated glass of antimony and saltpetre) with tartar and water.[6] Magistery of bismuth (magistere de l'étain de glace) is made for outward application as a cosmetic by dissolving bismuth in aqua regia, precipitating with tartarised spirit of wine or oil of vitriol, and washing.[7]

Salts, which are minerals soluble in water, are fixed or alkaline, volatile, and essential, the latter separating by crystallisation from vegetable juices.[8] If 4 oz. of common salt are agitated and boiled with 8 oz. of water, only 3 oz. are dissolved and the remaining ounce of salt is left: 'the weight of Nature cannot be transgressed.'[9] Sel gemme (rock salt) is the same as common salt.[10] Vitriolated tartar (tartre vitriolé)[11] is potassium sulphate, made by neutralising salt of tartar (potassium carbonate) with oil of vitriol and evaporating: 'the acid and alkali change one another into a neutral substance (se changeoient l'un l'autre en un estre neutre)'; it is also made by heating tartar and green vitriol (ferrous sulphate) and extracting with water,[12] or from the residue from the preparation of nitric acid (vitriolated nitre).[13] Soluble or purging tartar (neutral potassium tartrate) is made from tartar and salt of tartar,[14] and is soluble in cold water. 'Fixed salt' (calcium chloride) is made by fusing quicklime with common salt or sal ammoniac (when spirit, i.e. ammonia, is also obtained).[15] *Terra foliata* (potassium acetate; terre feuillé dissoluble du nitre fixe) is made by neutralising distilled vinegar with salt of tartar, evaporating to dryness and crystallising from alcohol.[16]

The preparation of green vitriol (ferrous sulphate) from roasted pyrites is described:[17] there are three kinds of vitriol, blue (from Cyprus or Hungary, copper sulphate), green (from Spa, etc., ferrous sulphate), and white, 'sold in small cakes and called in France white copperas' (couperose blanche) and used as an eye-lotion (zinc vitriol or zinc sulphate): the best is green vitriol, the blue,

[1] *The Antimoniall Cup twice Cast; or, A Treatise concerning the Antimoniall Cup, shewing the abuse thereof. First written in Latine by James Primerose, Dr. of Physicke, in consideration of a small Pamphlet set forth by the Founder of the Cup, Translated into English by Robert Wittie, M.A. Philiatr.*, 12°, London, 1640 (BM 1036. a. 13. (3.); NBG, 1862, xli, 45).

[2] Le Févre, C (c), ii, 188.   [3] C (c), ii, 224.   [4] C (c), ii, 226.
[5] C (c), ii, 228.   [6] C (c), ii, 238.   [7] C (c), ii, 241.
[8] C (c), i, 96 f.; ii, 243 f.; see Lemery, p. 39.   [9] C (c), i, 193.
[10] C (c), ii, 244.   [11] B (c), ii, 34; C (c), ii, 25.   [12] C (c), ii, 31.
[13] C (c), ii, 261.   [14] C (c), ii, 32.   [15] C (c), ii, 245, 270.
[16] C (c), ii, 257; this is mentioned by Lull (Vol. I).   [17] C (c), ii, 274.

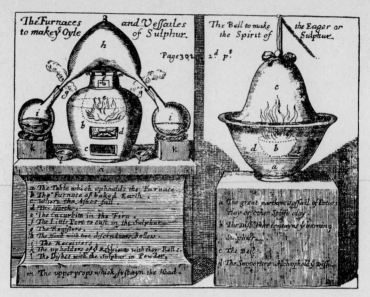

FIG. 3. PREPARATION OF SULPHURIC ACID (OIL OR SPIRIT
OF SULPHUR) ACCORDING TO LE FÉVRE (1660).

which contains silver or copper, has too little acid spirit. Spirit of sulphur
(esprit de soulfre) is made by burning sulphur under a glass bell or alembic
(Fig. 3).[1] This preparation, usually ascribed to Le Févre, was known long
before to Biringuccio (1540), Gesner, Porta, and Beguin.

A 'philosophical spirit of wine' prepared by repeatedly distilling alcohol
with oil of vitriol[2] must have contained ether. Volatile vitriol of Venus (copper
acetate), obtained in blue crystals from a solution of verdigris in distilled
vinegar, yields on distillation and rectification a colourless spirit of Venus
(esprit de Venus), i.e. concentrated acetic acid.[3] Spirit of Saturn is distilled
from sugar of lead (sucre ou sel de Saturne).[4] The distillation of amber yields a
spirit, an oil, and 'volatile salt' (succinic acid) of acid taste, soluble in water,
which can be sublimed in white crystals.[5] One of Le Févre's special preparations was a volatile salt of vipers obtained by distillation,[6] and he extols the
virtues of tobacco.[7]

GLASER

The successor of Le Févre at the Jardin du Roi was Christopher or Chris-
tofle Glaser, said to have been born in Basel, where he graduated in medicine.
He was demonstrator to Vallot at the Jardin du Roi, then professor, and
Apothecary to the King and the Duke of Orleans. He was involved in the

[1] C (c), ii, 301.   [2] C (c), ii, 29.
[3] C (c), ii, 153 f.: from Johann Zwelfer, *Appendix ad Animadversiones in Pharmacopœiam
Augustanum*, printed (sep. pag.) at the end of his *Animadversiones in Pharmacopœiam Augustanum*, 4°, Nürnberg, 1667, 52 (*spiritus Veneris*): the dedication is dated 1656.
[4] Le Févre, C (c), ii, 169.   [5] C (c), ii, 315.   [6] C (c), i, 144.   [7] C (c), i, 234.

poisoning case of the Marchioness de Brinvilliers, having probably supplied the poison (arsenic) to Sainte-Croix, and was imprisoned in the Bastille, but was afterwards liberated. He is said to have died in 1670–73 or in Basel in 1678.[1] Glaser was the teacher of Lemery, whose unfavourable opinion of him (see p. 28) was, Ferguson said, exaggerated and unjustified. Hoefer said of Glaser: 'On ne sait rien de particulier sur la vie de ce chimiste pharmacien, dans le laboratoire duquel Nicolas Lemery avait appris la plupart de ses procédes'; de Milt[2] showed in detail that parts of Lemery's *Cours de Chymie* (1675) closely resemble parts of Glaser's book (which is not surprising), but this in turn was largely based on Le Févre's. The preparation of pearl white (bismuth oxynitrate), the sale of which is said to have made a fortune for Lemery, is described by Glaser. Glaser was the author of a text-book, dedicated to Vallot, the titular professor at the Jardin du Roi. It is severely practical (which displeased Dumas) and reversed Le Févre's order of treatment into mineral, vegetable, and animal products, an order later copied by Lemery. Glaser says in the preface: Je ne donne aucune preparation, que je n'aye faite.

Traité de la Chymie, enseignant par vne brieve & facile Methode toutes ses plus necessaires preparations, 8°, Paris, l'Author, 1663 (381 pp.; engr. t.p. and t.p., CUL L.6.3); 2 ed., reueuë & augmentée par l'Autheur, 8°, Paris 1668 (xviii, 394, iv pp.; engr. t.p. dated 1667; BN); 3 ed. 12°, 1672 (449 pp.; BN; Read reproduces the t.p. of what he calls the '3 ed., Paris, 1673'), 1674 (450 pp., BN); 8°, Lyon, 1670 (397 pp.; BN), 1673; 12°, Brussels, 1676 (BM 1035. a. 22); Read says there were 13 or 14 eds. between 1663 and 1710.

English tr. 'by a Fellow of the Royal Society', The Compleat Chymist, or, A New Treatise of Chymistry, 8°, London, 1677 (t.p., xiv, 288, ii pp.; CUL).

German tr., Chimischer Wegweiser, das ist, sichere Anweisung zur Chimischen Kunst . . . übersetzet von einem Philochimico [Jean Menudier, a Frenchman], . . . , 12°, Nürnberg, 1677, BM 1035. b. 12. (1.); Jena, 1710 (both 528 pp.); Novum Laboratorium Medico-Chymicum. Das ist: Neu-eröffnete Chymische Artzney und Werck-Schul, in drey Bücher abgetheilet . . . übersetzet von Johann Marschalck Austriaco, sm. 8°, Nürnberg, 1677, engr. title and 6 plates of apparatus.

The earlier French editions are well-printed and have very good plates, and the book was evidently very carefully compiled and was expensive to produce. It gives definitions of chemical operations in alphabetical order, from 'alkooliser' (powering finely) to 'vitrifier' (1668, pp. 13–26), describes and illustrates vessels and furnaces (pp. 26–56) and lutes (pp. 57–61), and the seven degrees of fire (pp. 61–4). The second book deals with preparations, minerals (including metals, coral and amber) occupying a large part of the whole (pp. 76–287). Vegetables (pp. 288–372) take less space and the short section on animals (pp. 372–94) deals with the distillation of human skull and blood, vipers, urine, wax, manna, honey, and May dew. In describing diaphoretic gold, made by burning linen rags soaked in a solution of gold in aqua regia mixed with saltpetre, Glaser says that a silver vessel rubbed with the moistened powder is gilded (pp. 93–5). He describes the casting of fused silver nitrate

[1] Beckmann, (1), i, 47; Dumas, (2), 69; Ferguson, i, 320; Gmelin, (1), ii, 227; Hoefer, (1), ii, 281; NBG, 1857, xx, 794; Read, (2), 114; Thorndike, viii, 135.
[2] *J. Chem. Educ.*, 1942, xix, 53–60.

(pierre infernale, caustique perpetuel) in iron moulds (p. 103); its corrosive effects are due to the nitric acid. He says 1 lb. of lead increases in weight by more than 2 oz. on calcination 'à cause des corpuscles du feu qui s'incorporent auec luy', and tin and other imperfect metals similarly increase in weight (p. 109).

In his description of salts Glaser mentions sel prunel made by throwing sulphur on fused saltpetre (p. 213), and sel antifebrile (afterwards called *sal polychrestum Glaseri*, from πολύχρηστος, very useful; native potassium sulphate is now called *glaserite*) by heating saltpetre and sulphur and crystallising the potassium sulphate from water (p. 215; Beguin had, apparently, used this method before Glaser). Oil of arsenic (arsenic trichloride) is made by distilling regulus of arsenic (the element) with corrosive sublimate, the residual mercury passing over at a higher temperature (p. 270); magistery of bismuth (the oxynitrate) by pouring a solution of 'bismuth ou estain de glace' in nitric acid into water (p. 203, before Lemery). He mentions 'zinck', which 'approaches very close to the nature of bismuth but contains a purer sulphur' (p. 203); although the metal was known to Le Févre (see p. 21) and Glaser, they knew very little about it.

DE LOCQUES

Baudrimont[1] says of zinc: 'Sous le règne de Louis XIV, il a été l'objet de recherches chimiques très étendues, qui sont demeurées manuscrites.' This probably refers to a MS. by Nicolas de Locques, 'spagyric physician of his Majesty', who published a course of chemistry.[2] De Locques defines a magistery as the extraction of the most formal and radical substance from the composite in the form 'd'humide blanchastre, de sperme ou de chyle'. His 'practical' recipes are unintelligible and his descriptions of substances mystical. He says saltpetre is composed of the most subtle part of common salt and grease of sea-water on the one hand, and of light on the other. It is everywhere but is not vulgar nitre; it is volatile, a congealed air found in the air, the sea, and on the surface of the earth, a 'sweet sulphur' — perhaps he has a vague idea of oxygen.

THIBAUT

Pierre Thibaut dit le Lorrain published a course of chemistry[3] which is quite practical and includes an abridgement of 25 pages at the end. The materials are not grouped under the three kingdoms.

[1] *Traité de Chimie Générale et Expérimentale*, 1846, ii, 143.
[2] *Les Rudimens de la Philosophie Naturelle touchant le Systeme du Corps Mixte. Cours Theorique, ou sont clairement expliquez les Preceptes & les Principes de la Chymie*, 8°, Paris, 1665, BM 1034. i. 3. (1-3.); bound up with a *Cours Pratique. Où il est traité des operations suivant la Doctrine de Paracelse*; *Les Rudimens . . . De la Fermentation*; *Les Vertus Magnetiques du Sang* (1664); *Propositions touchant la Physique Resolutive* (1665); and *Elemens Philosophiques des Arcanes et du Dissolvant General* (1668). Ferguson, ii, 42; Thorndike, viii, 138-41.
[3] *Cours de Chymie*, 8°, Paris, 1667, BM 1035. f. 20, 285 pp. and index; 1674; Leyden, 1672; Eng. tr. by William Aglionby, M.D., *The Art of Chymistry as it is now practised. Now translated into English by a Fellow of the Royal Society*, 16°, 1668 (BM 8906. de. 43), 1675 (pp. xxx, 279); Ferguson, *A. Nat.*, 1913, vi, 83-96; Bolton, (1), 869; Thorndike, viii, 141.

CHARAS

Moyse Charas (Uzès, 2 April 1619–Paris, 17 January 1698), whose speciality was the medicinal use of vipers,[1] conducted for nine years a course of chemistry at the Jardin du Roi. On the revocation of the Edict of Nantes in 1685 he left for England and became pharmacist to Charles II. He went to Holland in 1685; the Spanish Ambassador there persuaded him to go to Spain to treat the King, but he was imprisoned by the Inquisition. He became a Catholic, returned to Paris, and was a member of the Academy.[2] Charas is best known for his *Pharmacopœia*.[3] Cap says Charas 'paraît faire peu de cas de Glaser, sous le nom duquel pourtant il avait publié années auparavant un traité de chimie', and Dorveaux suggested that Charas and Glaser were the same person. Charas also published on the great heat evolved on mixing oil of vitriol and water, explosively if water is added to the fuming acid, which he says explains the source of heat in hot-springs (1692),[4] and on the nature of salts, which he divided into three classes, volatile, fixed, and acid (i.e. the acids) (1695).[5]

An Italian, Carlo Lancilotti, published some chemical works covering the usual ground but paying special attention to animals (man, viper, toad, flying animals, fish, ants, millepedes and scorpions).[6]

LA FAVEUR

Sebastian Matte La Faveur was distiller and demonstrator in ordinary in the medical faculty of the university of Montpellier, and also simultaneously gave a course in Paris till 1684, when Lemery succeeded him. In his text-book[7] he claimed to have given some improved processes. The four parts are on elements, operations, and apparatus; minerals; vegetables; and animals; a supplementary *Advis* concerns the qualitative analysis of mineral waters. He

[1] *Thériaque d'Andromachus*, 12°, Paris, 1668 (BN), 1685 (BN); *Nouvelles expériences sur la vipère*, 8°, Paris, l'Auteur, 1669 (BN); *ib., avec une suite de nouvelles expériences*, 1672 (BN); 2 edit. 1694 (BN); *New Experiments upon Vipers*, 8°, London, 1670 (BN).

[2] Cap, 1857, i, 117; Condorcet, *Éloges des Académiciens*, Paris, 1773, 134; *id., Oeuvres*, 1847, ii, 72–6; Dorveaux, *Isis*, 1930, xiv, 492; Ferguson, i, 151; Hoefer, (1), ii, 241; NBG, 1854, ix, 712; Thorndike, viii, 31.

[3] *Pharmacopée Royale Galenique et Chymique*, 2 vols. 8°, Paris, 1672 (BN); 4°, Paris, 1676 (vii ll., 1060 pp., xvii ll., 5 plates of apparatus, 1 plate symbols; BM 43. h. 13; CUL L.3.6; Ferguson ments. eds. of Paris, 1681, 1682, 1692; Lyon, 1693, 1753; Latin, *Pharmacopœa Regia*, 4°, Geneva, 1683); *The Royal Pharmacopœa, Galenical and Chymical, according to the Practice of the most eminent and learned Physitians of France. Faithfully Englished*, f°, London, J. Sharkey, 1678 (viii, 272, 245, iii, 12 index, 6 plates); 4°, 1687.

[4] AdS (C), 1733, ii, 153; 1730, x, m 183.   [5] AdS (C), 1733, ii, 252.

[6] *Guida alla Chimica*, 12°, Modena, 1672 (BN 8° Te¹⁵¹. 97 (1); 12°, Venice, 1697 (3 pts. in 1 vol.; BN R 40580–2); *Nuova Guida alla Chimica*, 8°, Venice, 1677; 12°, Venice, 1681 (BM 1034. c. 22. (1.)); *Vaglia Chimico*, 12°, Venice, 1682 (BM 1034. c. 22. (2.)); *Farmaceutica Antimoniale, overo Trionfo dell' Antimonio*, 12°, Modena, 1683 (BM 1035. a. 30. (2.); BN); *Farmaceutica Mercuriale, overo Trionfo del Mercurio*, 12°, Modena, 1683 (BM 1035. a. 30. (1.); BN); Ferguson, ii, 6; Gmelin, (1), ii, 21, 227, 286; Kopp, (4), ii, 380; Thorndike, viii, 144 (ed. of 3 vols. 12°, Venice, 1697); Dutch: *Het brendende Salamander*, 8°, Amsterdam, 1680 (BM 1033. a. 17); German (from the Dutch): *Der Brennende Salamander*, 8°, Frankfurt, 1681 (BM 1033. a. 18); Ferguson also has a German ed., 8°, Lübeck, 1697, and *Opuscoli Diversi*, 12°, Modena, 1677, containing other tracts. The bibliography of Lancilotti needs sorting out.

[7] *Pratique de Chymie divisée en quatre parties*, 12°, Montpellier, 1671 (360 pp., fold. plates); J. V. in NBG, 1861, xxxiv, 274 (wrongly says the demonstratorship at Montpellier dated from 1675, since La Faveur has this title on the t.p. of his book in 1671); Thorndike, viii, 141.

discovered a styptic water. The book is practical, chemistry being defined as the art of separating the parts of natural bodies, purifying them, and then putting them together for medical purposes. He recommends fulminating gold (crocus solis) for medical use. Theorising in physics before learning mechanics and chemistry is deprecated. Sebastian was succeeded at Montpellier by his son Jean Matte La Faveur (Montpellier; 1 February 1660–7 August 1742), who became a corresponding member of the Paris Academy in 1699. He described the experiment of mixing concentrated solutions of calcium chloride and alkali carbonate, which form a precipitate of calcium carbonate.[1] He also published a chemical analysis of a coral (lithophyton), until then believed to be a plant,[2] and a process for obtaining mercury from red precipitate.[3]

TRESFEL

Malbec de Tresfel[4] praised metallic remedies, animal and vegetable preparations being neglected. His theoretical work deals with the three kingdoms, the five constituents (phlegm, terre damné, mercury, sulphur, salt), fire (a fourth invisible element), and the two principles mercury and sulphur. It praises antimony and the great elixir of Paracelsus, and deals with vitriol, sulphur, saltpetre, pearls, corals, bezoar, ambergris, tartar, wine, and the seven metals. The second book has more on antimony preparations, and deals with gold, reserving, however, the subject of potable gold for special treatment. A book of secrets and perfumes by Tresfel was published several times.[5]

N. LEMERY

Nicolas Lemery (Rouen, 17 (or 19) November 1645 (or 1644)–Paris, 19 June 1715), the son of a Protestant attorney (procureur) of the Parliament of Normandy, studied with an apothecary Bourdot, a relative at Rouen, but left in 1666 for Paris, where he worked in Glaser's laboratory in the Jardin du Roi. He soon left Glaser (who, he found, was secretive and unpleasant, as Fontenelle says, 'un vrai chimiste') and went to Montpellier, where he worked with a pharmacist Verchant, and gave lessons in chemistry which attracted even the professors of the University. He also practised medicine. In 1672 he moved to Paris, where he at first worked in the laboratory of a friend who was apothecary to the Prince de Condé, but he later set up a manufacturing laboratory of his own in a basement in the Rue Galand. Here he gave experimental lectures which made him famous, being attended by all classes, including ladies, and also by foreign students, e.g. from Scotland.

In 1681 Lemery, a Protestant, fell into disfavour: he declined an offer to go

---

[1] Sur une coagulation chimique, *Mém. Soc. Roy. Sci. Montpellier*, 1766, i, 177; see Lana, Vol. II, p. 333.
[2] *Ib.*, 1766, i, 20.
[3] *Ib.*, 181–2; H.F. in NBG, 1861, xxxviii, 274; Gmelin, (1), ii, 527; iii, 27.
[4] *Abrégé de la Théorie et des véritables principes de l'Art appellé Chymie*, 12°, Paris, 1671 (84 pp.); *Abrégé des Operations vulgaires et sophistiques de la fausse Chymie*, 12°, Paris, 1671 (116 pp.; BN R. 52803); Thorndike, viii, 367.
[5] Gmelin, (1), i, 659.

as professor of chemistry to Berlin (perhaps because he was not allowed to go), but in 1683 he visited England, where he was received by Charles II, to whom he presented the fifth edition of his text-book. He returned to France in 1684, when he became M.D. of Caen and practised in Paris, but this was stopped on the revocation of the Edict of Nantes in 1685. His laboratory was dispersed but he gave some lessons to Lord Salisbury; in 1686 he became a Catholic — as Haag says, 'il avait vu la Bastille de près', and after some opposition was received back into the medical faculty, and resumed his lectures and laboratory work. In 1699 he became a member of the Paris Academy.[1]

FIG. 4. N. LEMERY, 1645–1715.

Lemery's very popular text-book, first published in 1675, went through very many editions ('se vendit comme un Ouvrage de Galanterie ou de Satyre' Fontenelle says), including pirated ones, and was translated into Latin, English, German, Dutch, Italian, and Spanish:

A. Cours de Chymie, contenant la maniere de faire les operations qui sont en usage dans la Medecine, par une methode facile, avec des raisonnements sur chaque opera-tion, pour l'instruction de ceux qui veulent s'appliquer à cette science, 12°, Paris, L'Auteur, 1675 (534 pp., plates); 2 ed. 1677 (584 pp.); 3 ed. 1679 (London Chem. Soc.; also descr. as 2 ed.); 4 ed. 8°, 1681 (780 pp.), 1682 (BN), 5 ed. 1683 (used by

[1] Bouvet, Isis, 1928, x, 166; Cap, 1857, i, 180–226; Dumas, (2), 70; Ferguson, ii, 20; Fonte-nelle, AdS, 1715, h 73; id., Oeuvres, 1790, vi, 369; 1825, i, 296; Gmelin, (1), ii, 129; E. and E. Haag, La France Protestante, 1856, vi, 538–44 (list of works); Hoefer, (1), ii, 283; Kopp, (1), i, 183; (2), iii, 186; Leroux, Isis, 1925, vii, 430; Louvet, NBG, 1859, xxx, 598; Metzger, (1), 27, 281; Miall, Chem. and Ind., 1935, liv, 347; J. M. Quérard, La France Littéraire, Paris, 1833, v, 141; Read, (2), 116; Saverien, 1796, vii, 129; Shaw, in Boerhaave, (4), i, 48; Thomson, (1), i, 235; Thorndike, viii, 146; J. Tonnet, Notice sur N. Lemery . . . presenté à l'Acad. Royale de Rouen pour le concours de l'an 1838, Niort, 1840.

Kopp, 3 plates), 6 ed. 1687; 7 ed. (2 issues), 1690 (xvi, 768 pp., 7 plates of apparatus, plate of symbols, which appeared first in this ed., portr.; this is the ed. mostly quoted in the text below); 8 ed. 1696 (xvi, 836 pp., pls., portr., CUL), 1697 (xiv, 792 pp.; BM), 9 ed. 1701 (xvi, 836 pp., portr., CUL), 10 ed. 1713 (xxiv, 938 pp., portr.), 11 ed., the last revised by the author, 1730 (xxiv, 938 pp., portr.); new ed. by Théodore Baron, 4°, Paris, d'Houry, 1756 (xxiv, 945 pp.; another ed., 4°, Paris, d'Herrisant, 1756; Nourry, *Cat.* 42 (1931), nos. 780–1; Duveen, 349) and 1757, d'Houry (xxiv, 782 pp.; London Chem. Soc.); other eds. in French mentioned are: Amsterdam, 1682, and (2 vols.) 1698; Leyden, 1697, 1716, 1730; Lyon, 1703, 1713, 1716, 1724 (two issues); Brussels, 1744, 1747; 4°, Avignon, 1751.

B. Latin tr. by A. I. C. de Rebecque, M.D., Cvrsvs Chymicvs Continens Modum parandi Medicamenta Chymica Usitatoria . . . , 12° (not 16°), Geneva, 1681 (x, 664, xiv pp.; Eloy, Dictionnaire Historique de la Médecine, 1775, ii, 115, gives an ed. of 1691).

C. English trs.:

(*a*) A / Course / of / Chymistry. / Containing / The Easiest Manner of per- / forming those Operations that are in / Use in Physick. . . . Translated by Walter Harris, / Doctor of Physick, sm. 8°, London, Kettilby, 1677 (xxxii, 324 last blank, xx pp., tr. from the first French ed., 1675); An / Appendix / To A / Course / of / Chymistry . . . , Translated by Walter Harris, sm. 8°, London, 1680 (xvi, 140, xii pp., tr. from additions to the 2 and 3 French eds.; in my copy bound with the Course, 1677, but some eds. apparently have the Course dated 1680).

(*b*) A Course of Chymistry . . . The Second Edition very much Inlarged, tr. by Harris from the 5 French ed., 8°, London, Kettilby, 1686 (xxviii one blank, 548, xiv, ii list of books printed for Kettilby, incl. Mayow Tractat. quinq. è med. de sal. nitro).

(*c*) A Course of Chymistry . . . , tr. by Jas. Keill from the 8 French ed., 8°, London, 1698 (814 pp., 7 plates, table of symbols).

(*d*) A Course of Chymistry . . . , tr. by Jas. Keill from the 11 French ed., 8°, London, 1720 (engr. t.p., xvi, 543 pp., 7 plates, table of symbols).

Harris and Keill attended Lemery's lectures; Keill says they occupied 3 or 4 days a week for 8 weeks and he gives a programme extending over 34 days.

D. German tr.: Cours de Chymie, oder der Vollkommene Chymist . . . aus der 9 Frantzöischen (*sic*) Edition ins Teutsche übersetzet, 12°, Dresden, 1698 (Sotheran *Cat.* 839 (1934), no. 577); 4 ed., 8°, Dresden and Leipzig, 1734 (2 pts. 652, 390 pp.; Ferguson); Cursus Chymicus, oder Vollkommener Chymist . . . Aus dem Frantzö-sischen übersetzt und bey dieser fünfften Auflage aufs neue durchgesehen . . . von Johann Christian Zimmermann, 8°, Dresden, 1754 (portr., pp. viii, 978, xlvi index, 46 Anhang); an ed. of Dresden, 1713 (pt. i 652 pp., pts. ii–iii 386 pp.) is ment.

E. Dutch tr.: Het philosoophische Laboratorium of der Chymisten Stook-Huis, 8°, Amsterdam, 1683 (vi, 551 pp., engr. f.p.); an ed. of 2 vols., 1698, is ment.

F. Italian tr.: Corso di Chimica, 8°, Venice, 1700 (Gmelin); Corso Chimico, che contiene il Modo di fare l'Operationi, che sono in Uso nella Medicina . . . colle Aggiunzioni de Signor Andrea Matone, 12°, Naples, 1705 (Sotheran *Cat.* 795 (1925), no. 11386, 'first Italian ed.'); 2 vols., Venice, 1732; 3 vols., Venice, 1763 (I have not seen any of these). Ferguson, ii, 228, has Mantissa Chymica Spagyrica è Gallico in Italicum traductum as pt. ii of Prospectus Pharmaceuticus Galenico-Chymicus, f°, Milan, 1698.

G. Spanish tr.: Corso Chymico, 4°, Madrid, 1703 (492 pp.); Saragossa, 1710 (Duveen).

Lemery also wrote a *Pharmacopoeia* which went through several editions and translations:

H. (*a*) Pharmacopée Universelle, 4°, Paris, 1698 (xvi, 1050, xxxviii pp.); also 1705 (1092 pp.; Ferguson), 1706, 1715, 1763; (*b*) Traité Universelle des Drogues Simples, mises en ordre alphabetique . . . Ouvrage dépendant de la Pharmacopée Universelle, 4°, Paris, 1698 (vii ll., 838 pp. xxxi ll. index; Spielmann-Cadet, ii, 384, 'plutôt 99'), 1714, 1732, 1733, 1759; Amsterdam, 1716; Rotterdam, 1727 (590 pp.; Ferguson); enlarged and rewritten by Samuel Morelot; (*c*) Nouveau Dictionnaire général des Drogues simples et composées, Paris, 1807 (Sotheran *Cat.* 917 (1957), 78); (*d*) Pharmacopoeia Lemeriana contracta: Lemerey's Universal Pharmacopœia abridged, 12°, London, 1700.

In my opinion it is inferior to that of Pierre Pomet (Paris; 2 April 1658–18 November 1699), chief druggist to Louis XIV.[1]

Lemery's monograph on antimony, read in sections to the Academy in 1699 and dedicated to the President, the Abbé Bignon, is a tedious collection of experiments, showing little advance over 'Basil Valentine's' *Triumphal Chariot*:

J. (*a*) Traité de l'Antimoine, contenant l'Analyse Chymique de ce Mineral, & un recueil d'un grand nombre d'operations rapportées à l'Academie Royale des sciences, avec les raisonnemens qu'on a crus necessaires . . . , 12°, Paris, J. Boudot, 1707 (xxviii 1 blank, 620, xxiv pp.); (*b*) Neue chymische Geheimnüsze des Antimonii . . . übersetzt von J. A. Mahler, 8°, Dresden, 1709; (*c*) Trattato dell'Antimonio, che contiene l'Analisi e una Raccolta di gran Numero di Operazioni, traduzione di Selvaggio Canturani, 8°, Bologna, 1717; 12°, Venice, 1732 (Sotheran *Cat.* 839 (1934), no. 582).

A work incorrectly attributed to Lemery[2] is a collection of recipes:

K. (*a*) Recueil de Curiositez rares et nouvelles des plus admirables effets de la nature et de l'art. Avec des beaux secrets gallans . . . recherchées par le Sieur d'Emery [or d'Hemery], sm. 8°, Paris, L. Vendosme, 1676 (v ll., 358 pp., i l., 136 pp., iii ll.; the last part with sep. t.p. Méthode pour jetter en sable liquide . . . toutes sortes d'animaux après le naturel, et géneralement mouler en plastre, is probably an additional work); 2 vols. 12°, Leyden, 1684 (BN); (*b*) Modern Curiosities of Art & Nature, 12°, London, 1685 (CUL); New Curiosities in Art and Nature: or, A Collection Of the most Valuable Secrets in all Arts and Sciences . . . Composed by the Sieur Lemery, Apothecary to the French King. Translated into English from the Seventh Edition (1710). with Supplement, 8°, London, 1711 (CUL; Ferguson).

Lemery's text-book, reasonably concise and clearly written, superseded those of Beguin, Le Févre, Glaser, and Ettmuller.[3] Its chief rival was Barner's *Chymia philosophica* (Nürnberg, 1689), based on iatrochemical ideas but attempting to deal with the subject as a science rather than an art. It was also written in a modern language and could be used by an increasing number of readers not familiar with Latin. Hoefer says: 'Lemery avait le talent de décrire les choses les plus obscures et les plus arides avec une simplicité et une précision remarquables. Ce talent est la pierre de touche d'un esprit qui sait apprécier l'importance des détails.' The processes described in the book had been carried out by its author. Lemery's book owes a good deal to Le Févre's (much of what Kopp attributes to Lemery is in Le Févre), and this in turn made use of German sources going back to Paracelsus through the chemists of the Jardin du Roi (see p. 4). These included metallic remedies, particularly antimony, popularised by Lemery, and the development of French chemistry from his time is really a continuation of German. This link has mostly been overlooked. When the new theory of phlogiston, which also originated in Germany, began to make headway Lemery's book gave way to Macquer's (1749), based on this theory.

---

[1] *Histoire Générale des Drogues*, f°, Paris, 1694; 2 vols. 4° 1735;'*A Compleat History of Druggs* . . . *To which is added what is further observable on the same Subject, from Messrs Lemery and Tournefort* . . . , 4°, 1712, 3 ed. 1737 (419 pp., index).

[2] Gibbs, *Ann. Sci.*, 1953, ix, 88.

[3] *Chemia experimentalis atque rationalis*, Leyden, 1684.

Lemery opposed alchemy and exposes many of its tricks;[1] he calls it 'Ars sine arte, cujus principium mentiri, medium laborare et finis mendicare'. He reports[2] that astrologers taught that infinite numbers of small particles pass between the planets and the corresponding metals, passing easily through the pores of the metal and its planet but not through other bodies, and hence the planets and metals nourish and perfect one another. He thinks this is a reasonable theory but not necessary in chemistry, and he rejected the idea of astrologers and some chemists that the moon had an influence on the brain.[3]

Lemery professed to deal only with pharmaceutical chemistry and to describe everything simply and plainly:

Je tasche de m'y rendre intelligible et d'éviter les expressions obscures dont se sont servis les autheurs qui en ont ecrit avant moy[4] . . . la chymie est une science demonstrative[5] . . . mon dessein est simplement de faciliter les moyens pour travailler en Chymie, et de depoüiller autant que je pourray de ce qui la rend mysterieuse et cachée.[6]

He inserted fairly long dissertations on theory which happened to interest him, and even included some geological speculations on the formation of minerals,[7] rather after the style of Palissy (Vol. II, p. 69). He defines chemistry as 'an art which teaches how to separate the different substances which are found in a compound body (qui se rencontre dans un mixte)'; 'mixts' are 'things that naturally grow and increase, such as minerals, vegetables and animals'. A universal spirit which produces different things according to the different matrices or pores of the earth in which it is contained (as was assumed by Le Févre), he thinks is too metaphysical. He recognises five principles separated by analysis from mixts, three active (spirit or mercury, oil or sulphur, and salt), and two passive (water or phlegm, and earth or *teste morte*).[8] These principles are separated from vegetable and animal materials by destructive distillation but are not easily recognised in minerals, and no separation can be made of gold and silver. Earth has been called *terra damnata*, but 'on pouvait être plus charitable envers cette pauvre terre, et ne la damner si facilement'.[9]

After a short account of salts (enabling him to introduce his theory of points and pores), Lemery gives a description, illustrated by plates, of furnaces and vessels,[10] lutes[11] and the degrees of fire,[12] of which he had four; Glaser[13] had seven but thought four sufficient for all practical purposes. Lemery then gives a list of technical terms (the 9th and later eds. had a plate of symbols), and then proceeds to the main work, divided into three parts dealing, respectively, with minerals (in which he includes amber), vegetables, and animals (in the first edition including only vipers, urine, honey and wax). This classification[14] was foreshadowed by Le Févre and even by Dioskourides, Galen and Aëtios.[15] There are often 'objections' to statements in the text, each followed by a 'réponse', perhaps the result of discussions in the lectures.

Lemery's favourite and almost his only theory ('a new opinion of mine')[16] is

[1] A, 1690, 81 f.   [2] A, 1690, 79.   [3] A, 1690, 105.   [4] A, Preface.
[5] A, 1690, 6.   [6] A, 1690, 538.   [7] A, 1690, 74.   [8] A, 1690, 2–5.
[9] A, 1690, 32.   [10] A, 1690, 32–66.   [11] *Ib.*, 67–8.   [12] *Ib.*, 68.
[13] *Traité de la Chymie*, 1668, 61.
[14] Schorlemmer, *Rise and Development of Organic Chemistry*, 1894, 12.
[15] Sprengel, (1), ii, 205.   [16] C (*a*), 1720, 12.

based on the development of the atomic theory by Descartes and Gassendi, which endowed the particles of bodies with pores and spicules of varying sizes and shapes. Lemery[1] mentions the abridgment of Gassendi by Bernier.[2] He says that acids have pointed particles which prick the tongue. When a metal dissolves in an acid the points of the acid enter the pores of the metal, tear the mass apart, and suspend the particles in the liquid. When a metal solution is precipitated (e.g. a lead solution by hydrochloric or sulphuric acids) the acid points enter the metal pores and are carried down with the precipitate:[3] 'la partie la plus aiguë de ces pointes est demeurée dedans.' Lemery's atomic theory was criticised by Stahl.[4] Lemery discussed the difficult question why aqua regia dissolves gold but not silver, and nitric acid silver but not gold, and answered it at great length.[5] The points of the nitric acid are blunted by the spirit of salt in aqua regia so that they cannot enter the pores of the silver but they can enter the larger pores of gold (which is more malleable than silver): the fine points of the nitric acid do enter the pores of the gold but are too flexible to break up the mass of the metal.

The same conclusion was reached by Nicolas Hartsoeker[6] on the ground that the pores of gold are so large that a particle of spirit of salt and one of spirit of nitre joined together fill the pores more exactly than when separate; the pores of silver are too small to admit these particles joined but admit single particles of spirit of nitre, and the spirit of salt particles are always joined in pairs. This sort of description has quite a modern ring. Exactly the opposite conclusion to Lemery's was reached by Homberg[7] by the same type of reasoning, and atomic hypotheses are peculiarly adapted to 'prove' diametrically opposite suppositions. Newton[8] suggested that the two acids were 'subtil' enough to 'penetrate' either metal, and if they did not it was due to lack of 'attractive Force'. Boerhaave[9] pointed out that copper dissolves both in aqua fortis and aqua regia, and remarked that good chemistry refrains from generalities which are not based on observations (bona chemia abstinentia utitur in his, horret universalia, nisi solis observationibus collecta).

The shapes of crystals depend on the shapes and sizes of the *acid* spicules contained in them.[10] Effervescence when an acid and an alkali come together is caused by the points of the acid, which are in violent motion, entering the pores of the alkali, which is composed of stiff and brittle parts. The acid spicules, not having freedom of movement, split and break the parts of the alkali in attempting to escape. The effervescence with coral is less violent than with silver, since there is less resistance to be overcome. Neutrality results when all the points are broken off and all the pores are stopped.[11] This skilful linking of dull facts with attractive theory must have endeared Lemery's book to students.

Among the alkalis (he usually writes the name with a capital K) Lemery describes soda (soude), and he thinks the alkali of plant ash is not pre-existent

[1] A, 1690, 272; not in 1675 ed.
[2] *Abrégé de la Philosophie de Gassendi*, 8 vols. 12°, Lyon, 1678; NBU, 1853, v, 626.
[3] A, 1690, 9, 20, 24, 98, 100, 109, 236, 240, etc.
[4] *Specimen Beccherianum*, 1703; 1738, 18.   [5] A, 1690, 381 f.
[6] *Conjectures physiques*, 4°, Amsterdam, 1706, livre ii, disc. 8, art. 20 (BM 536. k. 7); *Eclaircissemens sur les Conjectures physiques*, 4°, Amsterdam, 1710, 137, criticising Homberg; Gmelin, (1), ii, 236, 242, quotes F. André, *Entretiens sur l'Acide et sur l'Alkali*, Paris, 1677 (who thought fire and light are acids and gold is almost entirely composed of sulphur), and Bertrand, *Reflexions nouvelles sur l'Acide et sur l'Alcali*, Lyon, 1683, as dealing with the theory of spikes and pores.
[7] AdS, 1706, m 260; (A) m 336.   [8] *Opticks*, Qu. 31, 1730, 357–8.
[9] (2), ii, 477.   [10] A, 1690, 236.   [11] A, 1690, 22, 25.

in the plant but formed by the fire.[1] He recognises three species of salts: fixed, volatile and essential, the last crystallising from vegetable juices (acid tartrates and oxalates).[2]

Lemery had very accurate views on the functions of manures. He says the salts of plants are taken up from the soil: dung and other matters which are said to fatten and fructify lands do so only by their salts. Every salt is not fit to fertilise soil but only a volatile salt (salt of ammonia) or one approaching to the nature of saltpetre.[3] Earths which neutralise acids do not contain a concealed alkali.[4] The caustification of alkali by quicklime is due to the igneous particles (matter of fire) of the quicklime combining with the alkali.[5] Lime is a stone the moisture of which has been all dried up by fire and replaced by igneous matter, the fiery particles rendering the lime caustic.[6]

The primary salt, contained in all other salts, is *sel fossile* or *sel gemme* (common salt), formed in the earth by the circulation of acid liquors which soak into stones and dilate them by a coction during several years. This curious theory is supported by analogy: du mélange des acides avec quelque matiere alkali, nous retirons tous les jours par la Chymie, une substance semblable à du sel; or la pierre est un alkali [since some stones effervesce with acids].[7] A saline salt (sel salé) is 'un mélange d'acide et d'alkali, ou plutôt un alkali soulé et rempli d'acide'.[8] Lemery recognised that borax is a sel salé,[9] and he obtained boric acid ('sel volatil narcotique de vitriol') by decomposing borax with oil of vitriol.[10]

'Saltpetre is formed in stones and earths by the acid of the air' and it differs from common salt 'solely in that it has more spirit'.[11] When spirit of nitre (nitric acid) is mixed with alkali salt (potash) it makes a good saltpetre.[12] Saltpetre is not inflammable of itself and does not contain any sulphur; it does not burn when thrown into a red-hot crucible. It is true that a great flame is produced when saltpetre is thrown on ignited charcoal, but this is because of the sulphur in the charcoal;[13] 'the sulphurous fuliginosities or oily parts of the carbon, which are rarefied and elevated with violence by the volatile part of the nitre.' The mixture of alcohol and spirit of nitre (nitric acid) inflames, as it is like a very exalted saltpetre and sulphur; the corpuscles of fire are small igneous bodies or a subtle matter in very rapid motion, which can set other particles in motion, and the motion of the igneous corpuscles can be retained when they form part of gross matter.[14]

Sal ammoniac (sel armoniac) is found naturally near volcanoes; an artificial kind is made in Venice etc. by evaporating 5 pts. of urine, 1 pt. of sea salt and ½ pt. of chimney soot and subliming. It is sublimed in flowers in a cucurbit: then 'lift your head gently and collect the flowers with a feather'.[15]

---

[1] A, 1690, 23 f.; Kopp, (1), iii, 44.   [2] A, 1690, 1 f.
[3] A, 1690, 16; C (d), 1720, 9; cf. Digby, Vol. II, p. 425.   [4] A, 1690, 23, 319.
[5] A, 1690, 322; cf. L. Lemery AdS, 1709; m 400 f.; (A) m 520 f.: matter of fire and light.
[6] A, 1675; 1690, 317 (with additions); C (a), 1677, 140.   [7] A, 1690, 15.
[8] A, 1756, 22; not in 1690 ed.   [9] AdS, 1703, h 49; (A), h 60.   [10] C (d), 305.
[11] A, 1690, 15.   [12] C (d), 1720, 10.   [13] A, 1675; 1690, 376; C (a), 171, 184.
[14] A, 1690, 370-1; this idea is borrowed from Descartes and there is some reminiscence of Mayow's views.
[15] A, 1690, 378 f.

Lemery also described the volcanic sal ammoniac found near Vesuvius.[1] When sal ammoniac is heated with lime, 'volatile spirit of sal ammoniac' (ammonia) is formed, since 'quicklime, which is alkali, destroys the power of the acid of sea salt (sel marine acide) by which the volatile salt is in a manner enchained in the sal ammoniac'. Water must be added otherwise the retort would burst, and when pouring out, 'turn your head to one side to avoid the very subtle vapour.'[2] The spirit is also made by distilling sal ammoniac with salt of tartar (potassium carbonate), when sel febrifuge (potassium chloride) is also formed, since this 'n'est autre chose qu'un melange de sel de tartre et de la partie fixe et acide du sel armoniac'.[3]

A vitriol is 'a mineral composed of an acid salt and a sulphurous earth' and there are four kinds: blue (from copper mines of Hungary and Cyprus), white (le plus dépuré de substance métallique — Lemery does not know that it contains zinc), green (German, English and Roman: it must not change the colour of a piece of iron rubbed with it — absence of copper), and yellow (German 'natural colcothar').[4] Lemery uses the name 'vitriols' for metallic salts in general. Silver nitrate is 'vitriol de Lune'[5] and copper nitrate is 'vitriol de Venus'.[6] Oil of vitriol is made by distilling English green vitriol: it is full of particles of fire and becomes hot when mixed with water. That from German blue vitriol (containing copper sulphate) is less pure and has a suffocating odour (due to sulphur dioxide). Lemery must have obtained sulphur trioxide, since he once got a solid 'salt' which fumed strongly, hissed in water, and after six months deliquesced to oil of vitriol.[7] He mentions the reactions of acids and alkalis with several vegetable indicators.[8]

Lemery describes the method of making sulphuric acid (esprit de soulfre) by burning sulphur under a glass bell (campane de verre) or in an improved 'machine' using a large inverted funnel; air must be allowed to enter.[9] He later burnt a mixture of 4 lb. of sulphur powder and 4 oz. of saltpetre, inflamed in a pottery dish by a red-hot horse shoe, in a large round earthen pot containing some water and with a cover, but he preferred the first method on account of impurities introduced from the saltpetre (il mesle son acide avec le sien et le rend moins pur qu'il ne seroit s'il avoit esté fait avec le soulfre seul). The acid is concentrated to a brown very acid liquid by heating.[10] Sulphur is a compound of an oil and an acid.[11] Milk (magistery) of sulphur is precipitated by acid from a solution of liver of sulphur: the vapour evolved (hydrogen sulphide gas) blackens silver.[12] Sympathetic ink is made from sugar of lead solution,[13] or the filtrate from 'magistery' of bismuth,[14] and the black letters developed by sponging with a solution of alkali sulphide: a chemical explanation is given, since 'sympathy and antipathy are general terms which explain nothing'.[15]

A full description is given in later editions of the preparation and properties of the Bolognian stone (phosphorescent barium sulphide; see Vol. II, p. 334).[16]

[1] AdS, 1705, h 66; (A), h 83.   [2] A, 1675; 1690, 385.   [3] A, 1675; 1690, 391.
[4] A, 1690, 400.   [5] A, 1690, 111.   [6] A, 1690, 159.   [7] A, 1690, 410 f.
[8] A, 1690, 414; not in 1675 ed.   [9] A, 1675; 1690, 418; C (a), 214.
[10] A, 1690, 431.   [11] A, 1690, 12.   [12] A, 1690, 425.   [13] A, 1690, 324.
[14] A, 1756, 110.   [15] A, 1690, 326.
[16] A, 1690, 657, giving some observations made by Homberg (see p. 44).

Lemery noticed that iron is prejudicial to the phosphorescence. He explained the phosphorescence as due to the fire of the solar rays acting on the 'very exalted sulphur' in the stone and setting it on fire (en allume le soulfre superficiel & la fait paroistre ardente, de la mesme maniere que le feu allume un charbon).[1]

Lemery explained subterranean fires, earthquakes, and thunder and lightning as due to the explosion of hydrogen gas.[2] The hydrogen was prepared from iron filings and diluted spirit of vitriol (sulphuric acid). He obtained green vitriol by evaporation of the solution. The inflammable gas was also obtained with spirit of salt (hydrochloric acid), but not with spirit of nitre (nitric acid) or aqua regia, and it is necessary to dilute the sulphuric acid. Lemery noticed that the gas burnt quietly at the mouth of the vessel when the action was vigorous, otherwise it exploded: he did not realise that the explosibility was due to admixture with air. He calls the inflammable gas a 'sulphur' (nous ne connoissons rien d'inflammable ni de plus en mouvement que le soulfre), and thought it must come from the iron; in some ways he leans towards the phlogiston theory but he never uses the name phlogiston for the inflammable principle.

The inflammability of the 'fetid vapour' evolved in the solution of iron in hydrochloric acid is described by Boyle (Vol. II, p. 526), that from iron and dilute oil of vitriol is mentioned by Cramer,[3] who says a flask with a narrow neck is destroyed by the explosion. Von Wasserberg mentions an accident on igniting the 'suffocating elastic vapours' which terrified Jacquin's demonstrator in Vienna: a flask with a long neck exploded, leaving the man holding the neck only.[4]

Volcanic action was imitated by burying 50 lb. of a moist mixture of iron filings and sulphur in the ground, when it became red hot and emitted sulphurous fumes.[5] Such 'expériences curieuses et extraordinaires' formed one of the six reproaches brought against chemists by Malebranche,[6] who also smugly charged them with greater interest in 'experiments which relate to profit and neglect of those which serve to illuminate the mind'.

Gold is best purified by melting with antimony (sulphide), although cupellation, cementation, and 'départ' with aqua fortis are used.[7] Lemery is sceptical as to the value of 'the pretended potable gold'.[8] Fulminating gold (safran d'or) is made by precipitating a solution of gold in aqua regia (a solution of sal ammoniac in aqua fortis) with ammonia or oil of tartar (potassium carbonate solution). It excites sweat, expels noxious humours, and moderates

[1] A, 1690, 673–4.
[2] Explication Physique et Chimique des Feux souterrains, des Tremblemens de terre, des Ouragans, des Éclairs et du Tonnerre; AdS, 1700, m 101 (107); (A), m 131; C (d), 1720, 118; A, 1756, 154; Kopp, (1), iii, 261, 263, 273.
[3] Elementa Artis Docimasticae, Leyden, 1739, i, 45: cum exhalatione fœtidissimi vaporis, si solutio fit in vase angusti colli; accenditur enim, & violentissime disjicit vasa.
[4] Wasserberg, Institutiones Chemicae, Regnum minerale, Vienna, 1778, i, 184: vas ipsum impetu maximo, horrendo fragore in millena frustra disjecerunt . . . terrore vix non mortuus, pallidus, infelix experimenti imitatur.
[5] A, 1690, 176 (first in this ed.); C (d), 1720, 115; Roscoe and Schorlemmer, 1923, ii, 1283; Fourcroy, (1), vi, 171, says Bucquet could not repeat the experiment.
[6] De la Recherce de la Verité, 1674; 4°, Paris, 1678, 137.
[7] A, 1690, 92.
[8] A, 1690, 85, 89.

the strong action of mercury. The explosion is due to the escape of enclosed spirits.[1]

Arsenic (orpiment) is 'a mineral composed of much sulphur and a caustic salt': regulus of arsenic (elementary arsenic) is made by heating white arsenic with salt of tartar and soap, and a 'corrosive oil of arsenic' (the chloride) by distilling 'arsenic' (sulphide ?) with corrosive sublimate.[2] 'Caustic arsenic' (potassium arsenate) is made by deflagrating a mixture of arsenic (sulphide), sulphur, and saltpetre in an iron mortar by touching it with a red-hot iron, then calcining in a crucible.[3]

Antimony (stibnite, antimony sulphide) is 'a mineral composed of a sulphur similar to the common and a substance very like a metal (fort approchante au metal), or an acid salt enveloped in much sulphur; the fanciful alchemical names of antimony are given (Proteus, Plomb Sacré, Plomb des Philosophes, Plomb des Sages, Lion rouge, le Loup, parce qu'ils ont cru qu'il avoit du rapport qui devoroit ses enfans comme il devore les métaux).[4] A regulus (metal) can be made from stibnite heated with iron nails and purified by heating with saltpetre: the iron is reduced to scoria by union with the sulphur and the regulus, being the heaviest part, sinks to the bottom.[5] The 'star' (crystalline form of pure antimony, see Vol. II, p. 682), which appears on the metal has nothing to do with Mars (owing to the iron remaining in the metal attracting effluvia from Mars), as many chemists think, but 'comes from the antimony itself'; Lemery thought at first a little iron remained in it, which made the metal harder,[6] but in his treatise on antimony[7] he says the stellate regulus is most easily made without iron and is pure antimony. Butter or glacial oil of antimony (antimony trichloride) is made by distilling a mixture of corrosive sublimate with regulus of antimony or with stibnite (when cinnabar is also formed), or a solution of stibnite in spirit of salt.[8] Numerous preparations of antimony are described, including tartar emetic, which 'est une crème de tartre chargée des parties sulphureuses du foye d'Antimoine'.[9] The 'perpetual pills' of metallic antimony (see p. 22) really lose weight slowly.[10]

The material which is apparently first described by Glauber as *panacea antimonialis* (Vol. II, p. 357) was made known under the name of *mineral kermes* by Simon, a Carthusian friar, who obtained the method of preparation through a surgeon Ligerie, who made it known for a consideration in 1720 at the instigation of Dodart, the physician to the King of France. Ligerie obtained it from Chastenai, the King's Lieutenant at Landau, who received it from an apothecary who had been a pupil of Glauber.[11] The preparation had actually been given by Lemery, who called it 'souffre doré d'antimoine',[12] viz. by boiling the scoria from the preparation of antimony from a mixture of stibnite, tartar and saltpetre, with water and precipitating with vinegar. The material was investigated by Geoffroy (1734–5),[13] Baumé, Fourcroy, and other chemists, and was formerly much used in medicine. It is antimony tetrasulphide Sb_2S_4 or pentasulphide Sb_2S_5.

---

[1] A, 1690, 97.　　[2] A, 1690, 311 f., 316.　　[3] A, 1690, 315.
[4] A, 1690, 258.　　[5] A, 1690, 270 f.　　[6] A, 1690, 272 f.
[7] *Traité de l'Antimoine*, 12°, Paris, 1707, 504.
[8] A, 1690, 294, 305.　　[9] A, 1690, 555; C (d), 411.　　[10] A, 1690, 263.
[11] Lemery, AdS 1720, h 50, m 417; Model, *Chymische Nebenstunden*, St. Petersburg, 1762, 171; Fourcroy, (3), 1790, ii, 270.
[12] A, 1690, 268.　　[13] AdS, 1734, m 417; 1735, m 54.

Lemery made use of the balance and very often gives the weights of the preparations: 1 oz. of silver gives 1 oz. 3 drachms of precipitate (silver chloride)
with salt, the increase being due to the points of the acid broken off in the
pores of the metal.[1] When 1 lb. of cinnabar is reduced with 3 lb. of quicklime,
3 lb. $\frac{1}{2}$ oz. of lime is left in the retort; when 16 oz. of cinnabar are reduced with
16 oz. of iron, 13 oz. of mercury come over and 19 oz. less 2 scruples of residue
is left; 1 lb. of mercury gives 1 lb. 3 oz. of corrosive sublimate; and 16 oz. of
corrosive sublimate with 12 oz. of mercury give $26\frac{1}{2}$ oz. of calomel.[2] One
drachm of gold gave four scruples of aurum fulminans,[3] 1 oz. of silver, 1 oz.
5 drachms of lapis infernalis (silver nitrate).[4] The 'surprising' increase in
weight of antimony, tin, or lead on calcination is due to the fixation of the
matter of fire or of light; 4 oz. of antimony increased by $2\frac{1}{2}$ drachms, 32 oz. of
tin gave 34 oz. of calx:[5]

les pores du plomb sont disposez en sorte que les corpuscles du feu s'y estant insinuez
ils demeurent liez et aglutinez dans les parties pliantes et embrassantes du métal sans
en pouvoir sortir et ils en augmente les poids.

Glaser[6] held the same theory, which is Boyle's (Vol. II, p. 530).

A method of powdering tin by shaking the fused metal in a round wooden
box coated inside with chalk is first given in the fifth edition (1683).[7] Bismuth
or 'étain de glace' is a sulphurous marcasite found in tin mines; another species
is zinck.[8] Bismuth is made in England and France by melting impure tin with
tartar and saltpetre.[9] Magistery of bismuth or Spanish white, used as a cosmetic, is precipitated by pouring a solution of bismuth in aqua fortis (which
crystallises on cooling) into water or salt water: this was the basic nitrate or oxychloride, respectively;[10] it is said its persistent use makes the skin brown and
rough;[11] it was safer than corrosive sublimate formerly used (Vol. II, p. 21.)

Steel is made by heating iron with animal matters, the alkaline salt of which
'kills the acids of iron which hold its pores open, and thus renders it more
compact'; hence the humidity of the air enters less easily, and steel rusts more
slowly than iron. Although iron (Mars) contains an acid vitriolic salt, it contains much earth and salt and hence is of an alkaline nature, fermenting
(effervescing) with acids, and is also of an astringent nature. Iron is preferable
to steel in medicine.[12]

A long account is given of mercury or quicksilver (vif-argent) and its compounds. Lemery claims that he was the first to give in his lectures a correct
explanation of its medicinal effects, although others had published it later. In
the earlier editions he referred to the work on the venereal disease by Nicolas
de Blegny (1653–1722), the royal surgeon (1687), but omitted this mention in
later editions.[13] Corrosive sublimate (mercuric chloride), 'un mercure penetré

[1] A, 1690, 119.   [2] C (d), 1720, 134, 143, 149.   [3] A, 1690, 97.   [4] A, 1690, 114.
[5] A, 1690, 141, 265; Gmelin, (1), ii, 130; Kopp, (1), iii, 123.
[6] Traité de la Chymie, 1668, 109: à cause des corpuscles du feu qui s'incorporent avec lui
[i.e. lead].
[7] C (b), 1686, 92.   [8] A, 1690, 135, from Glaser, see p. 26.
[9] Lemery, H (a), 1698, 105.   [10] A, 1690, 137; C (d), 93.
[11] A, 1756, 110; cf. K (b), 1711, 42.   [12] A, 1690, 165–6.
[13] B, 1681, 210; A, 1690, 192–258; this ed. included a 'mercurial panacea', corrosive sublimate dulcified by many sublimations and infused for a fortnight in spirit of wine.

d'acides et élévé par le feu au haut du vaisseau', is made by subliming the white salt (mercuric nitrate) made by evaporating a solution of mercury in nitric acid (16 oz. of mercury giving 22 oz. of salt, the augmentation coming from the acid) with common salt and calcined green vitriol.[1] He later[2] claimed to have obtained it from mercury and salt alone. Mercurous chloride (sublimé doux de mercure, appellé Aquila alba) is made by subliming corrosive sublimate with mercury, when some of the acid points are broken;[3] or by precipitating a solution of mercury in dilute aqua fortis with common salt or spirit of salt.[4] The common salt or its spirit is composed of points coarser than those of spirit of nitre and they knock out the latter from the pores of the mercury, whence it happens that the mercury precipitates by its own weight. Mercurous chloride is turned black by ammonia.[5]

Lemery[6] though corrosive sublimate was adulterated with arsenic, which could be detected by its blackening with salt of tartar (potassium carbonate): s'il noircit il y a infailliblement de l'arsenic, au contraire s'il jaunit, il est bon. This was disproved by Barchusen,[7] who showed that alkali did not discolour arsenic, and by Louis Lemery,[8] who showed that the black colour is due to mercurous chloride. The name calomel used later for mercurous chloride, is supposed to be derived from καλομέλας, beautiful black.[9]

A poison is 'anything which can break and destroy the union and economy of the humours of the body by corroding the parts or interfering with the natural course of the spirits'. Poisons act in two ways, either by coagulating the blood (poisonous plants and animals) or by corroding the intestines (corrosive sublimate and arsenic).[10]

Amber (karabé) is included among the mineral substances, but Lemery says of its volatile salt (succinic acid): 'I have recognised that this salt is an acid similar to that of plants' (oxalic acid).[11] Benzoic acid (fleurs de benjoin) 'has a very agreeable acidity'.[12] Lemery speaks of the 'sucs tartareux du raisin et des limons' and does not distinguish tartaric and citric acids;[13] distilled vinegar is also described as a 'sel acide essentiel ou tartareux';[14] 'being heavier than phlegm it rises last on distillation.'[14] Spirit of turpentine (esprit de therebentine) is properly an ethereal oil (un huile ætherée).[15] In the section on vegetables Lemery deals with jalap, rhubarb, guaiacum, cinnamon, cloves, and nutmeg, and in the later editions with paper, quinquina, and juniper berries.[16] He describes a quantitative experiment on the distillation of guaiacum wood.[17]

Fermentation is due to the presence of much 'essential salt' in the must of grapes which, in detaching itself from the oily parts to which it is bound, penetrates and divides them by its subtle cutting points until it has rarefied them into spirit. This effort causes the ebullition. The grosser parts separate as scum and tartar.[18] Fermentation is slower than the effervescence of acid and alkali, since in it the points of the acid press against oily particles which are soft and pliable like wool.[19] Spirit of wine is, thus, 'the oily part of the wine

[1] A, 1690, 210.   [2] AdS, 1709, h 34, m 42; (A), m 50.
[3] A, 1690, 222.   [4] A, 1690, 235.   [5] C (d), 1720, 153.   [6] A, 1690, 216.
[7] Pyrosophia, Leyden, 1698, 194.   [8] AdS, 1734, h 49, m 259.
[9] Kopp, (1), iv, 192.   [10] A, 1690, 217.   [11] A, 1675; 1690, 442.   [12] A, 1690, 611.
[13] A, 1690, 189.   [14] A, 1675; 1690, 546.   [15] A, 1690, 609.
[16] A, 1690, 447 f.   [17] A, 1690, 458.   [18] A, 1675; 1690, 527.   [19] A, 1690, 27.

rarefied by the acid salts',[1] or 'un soulfre fort exalté et fort susceptible du mouvement',[2] and the residue after distillation is 'un vin dépouillé de ses esprits sulphureux'.[3] The distillation of brandy (eau de vie) from wine, and of spirit of wine from brandy, is described. A tall machine called a 'serpentin' is used by the artists for this, but is not really necessary, a long-necked matras, heated on a water bath, being just as good, the joints being well luted with wet bladder.[4]

Sweet spirit of nitre (esprit de nitre dulcifié) is made from alcohol and spirit of nitre (nitric acid), the heat generated coming from the friction between the sulphurous particles and the spirit of nitre.[5] The 'esprit de sel dulcifié de Bazil Valentine' is made from equal parts of alcohol and spirit of salt digested at a gentle heat for three or four days; the sulphurous spirit of the wine breaks the acid points and takes away part of their movement.[6]

Wine becomes acid (forming vinegar) because the tartar deposited in the alcoholic fermentation dissolves again in a second fermentation, with some dissipation of volatile spirit, the rest of the spirit remaining fixed.[7] In distilling tartar only one spirit, not two, is obtained, with some oil.[8] On distilling crystaux de Vénus (copper acetate) a 'Spirit of Venus' (esprit de Vénus) is obtained:[9] the 'esprit ardent de Saturne' obtained by distilling sugar of lead is inflammable, Lemery thought because of some alcohol remaining in the vinegar used to make the sugar of lead.[10] Destructive distillation does not disclose the true principles of vegetables.[11]

Lemery describes the preparations of opium in detail. He thought from his experiments that it contained a spirituous part soluble in water and a resinous, gummous, or earthy insoluble part, the particles of which, carried to the small vessels of the brain, condensed the spirits and moderated their motion, thus causing sleep; the objections to his theory were, as usual, answered; the tincture is called 'laudanum'. Since some think opium is cold to the fourth degree they toast it, and add to laudanum corals, pearls, theriac, extract of saffron, etc., but experience teaches that if given in a dose of $\frac{1}{2}$ to 3 grains of evaporated laudanum it is not in the least dangerous.[12]

In the early editions the section on animals described only, in a few pages, vipers and their distillation, the distillation of urine and its volatile salt (ammonia), honey and its distillation, and the distillation of wax. In later editions (from the fifth, 1683), this section was enlarged to contain a good account of phosphorus,[13] in which Lemery tells an amusing story of a small piece of phosphorus left by an oversight on his bedroom table, which got into the sheets when the bed was made and took fire in the night on being warmed, burning a large hole in the coverlet. There are also sections on the distillation of human skulls, of the moss (usnée) growing on skulls in Ireland (where bodies are left on gibbets till they fall to pieces), and the preparation of 'English

[1] A, 1675; 1690, 528, 530.   [2] A, 1690, 370.   [3] A, 1690, 530, 534.
[4] A, 1675; 1690, 531, 535.   [5] A, 1690, 368.   [6] A, 1690, 351, 357.
[7] A, 1675; 1690, 543.   [8] A, 1675; 1690, 560.
[9] A, 1675; 1690, 162: concentrated acetic acid; see Le Févre, p. 24.
[10] A, 1675; 1690, 149.
[11] A, 1690, 20.   [12] A, 1675; 1690, 585 f.   [13] A, 1690, 642; C (d), 476.

drops' by the distillation of human brains and skulls and adding tincture of opium.[1]

Pliny[2] quotes Demokritos (i.e. Bolos, see Vol. I) as saying the skull of a malefactor was a powerful remedy. 'English drops' were a speciality of Dr. Jonathan Goddard (Greenwich, 1617–London, 24 March 1675), professor of physic at Gresham College, F.R.S., M.D. Oxford, chief physician of the army under Cromwell; and they are said to have been given to King Charles II on his deathbed. The King is said to have paid Goddard £5000 for the recipe.[3] Goddard prepared his secret remedies himself, but Tournefort[4] says Lister gave him the secret of Goddard's drops. Goddard's secrets were published by an apothecary J. Shipton as an appendix in the second edition of the pharmacopœia of George Bate (d. 1669).[5] Goddard's quantitative 'Experiments of Refining Gold with Antimony' were published posthumously.[6] The medicinal use of vipers is a legacy of the old 'theriac', the use of which persisted till the end of the 18 cent.[7]

Tincture and extract of Peruvian bark (quinquina) appear in the fifth edition (1683),[8] with oil and spirit of paper (a remedy for deafness) made by distilling pellets of paper in a retort and separating by filtering through a cone of 'papier gris' in a funnel (in which the thick black oil remains).[9] This edition also describes sugar and a spirit made by distilling it with sal ammoniac.[10] The ash of honey contains iron, since it is attracted by a magnetised knife-blade.[11] The later editions of the book contain a list of remedies with doses, including four cosmetics, one being his 'magistère de bismuth',[12] and several remedies 'contre les Vapeurs'.[13]

Besides the memoirs mentioned above, Lemery read some unimportant communications to the Academy of Science: on mineral waters, camphor,[14] honey,[15] the analysis of cow's urine by distilling to dryness, igniting the residue, and weighing,[16] on hydromel,[17] wax and manna,[18] the analysis of woodlice by dry distillation,[19] coral,[20] and on the odour of rosemary developed when a solution of gold in aqua regia is precipitated by ammonia or oil of tartar (potassium carbonate solution).[21]

L. LEMERY

Louis Lemery (Paris; 25 January 1677–9 June 1743), son of Nicolas, was a physician, M.D. Paris 1698. He gave a course of lectures on chemistry at the Jardin du Roi in 1708 and became demonstrator in 1731. He published a treatise on foods[22] and a large number of papers in the memoirs of the Academy,[23] e.g. on iron,[24] essential oils,[25] an iron precipitate or 'tree',[26] chemical

---

[1] C (d), 1720, 506 f.; A, 1756, 867 f.   [2] Hist. Nat., xxviii, 1 (2).
[3] Creighton, DNB, 1890, xxii, 24.   [4] AdS, 1700, m 71.
[5] Pharmacopoeia Bateana, cura J. Shipton, 8°, 1688; 2 ed., 12°, 1691, accesserunt Arcana Goddardiana; later eds. were edited by W. Salmon.
[6] Phil. Trans., 1678, xii, 953 (no. 137).   [7] Thorndike, v, 470; see Charas, p. 27.
[8] C (b), 1686, 393.   [9] C (b), 387.   [10] C (b), 409.   [11] A, 1756, 882.
[12] A, 1690, 730.   [13] A, 1690, 759.   [14] AdS, 1705, h 59, m 38; (A), h 74, m 47.
[15] AdS, 1706, h 36, m 272; (A), h 45, m 352.   [16] AdS, 1707, m 33; (A), m 41.
[17] AdS, 1707, h 35; (A), h 44.   [18] AdS, 1708, h 53; (A), h 64, 67.
[19] AdS, 1709, h 38; (A), h 48; woodlice were an old medicine, Pliny, Hist. Nat., xxx, 5 (12).
[20] AdS, 1710, h 48; (A), h 63.   [21] AdS, 1712, h 46; (A), h 60.
[22] Traité des Alimens, 1702, 1705, 1709, 2 vols. 1755; A Treatise of all Sorts of Foods . . . also of Drinkables, tr. D. Hay, 12°, 3 ed., 1745.
[23] De Mairan, AdS, 1743, h 195–208; Gmelin, (1), ii, 546–8; Hoefer, (1), ii, 374.
[24] AdS, 1706, h 32, m 119.   [25] AdS, 1707, h 37, m 5, 517.   [26] AdS, 1707, h 32, m 299.

precipitations,[1] the different colours of mercury precipitates,[2] the contraction on the solution of salts in water,[3] sal ammoniac,[4] the origin of nitre,[5] borax,[6] corrosive sublimate,[7] and alum and vitriols (especially white).[8] He proved that iron is present in plants and is not generated by their combustion,[9] as Geoffroy thought (see p. 50). He followed his father's theory of the presence of points on acid particles.[10] In his lectures he mentioned a case of rapid poisoning by a dose of turpeth mineral (basic mercuric sulphate) given by a surgeon to a woman against his advice.[11] He[12] differed from his father's explanation of phosphorescence (see p. 36) and suggested that phosphorescent bodies act like sponges towards light, absorbing it, but retaining it with such feeble power that very trivial causes suffice for its extrication.

HOMBERG

Wilhelm Homberg (Batavia, Java, 8 January 1652–Paris, 24 September 1715) was the son of Johann Homberg, a German from Saxony in the service of the Dutch East India Company, and commander of the Arsenal in Batavia. The family moved to Europe when Wilhelm was still young and he was educated at Amsterdam, Jena, Leipzig, and Prague for the profession of law, which he began to practise at Magdeburg in 1674. He had a great interest in science and taught himself botany and astronomy. In Magdeburg he became acquainted with the famous Otto von Guericke (Vol. II, p. 514) and made experiments with him. Homberg now decided to abandon law and studied science and medicine at Padua, Bologna (where he experimented on the Bolognian stone, phosphorescent barium sulphide, see Vol. II, p. 334), and Rome (where he worked with the astronomer Cellio, who published a work on the Bolognian stone).[13] In Italy Homberg also studied music and art. He passed through France, where he studied with Lemery, to London to work in Boyle's laboratory. He then pursued his medical studies at Amsterdam (under de Graaf) and then Wittenberg, where he took the M.D. and became acquainted with Kunckel and interested in phosphorus (see Vol. II, p. 371), of which he published an account in 1692. After a tour through Saxony and Hungary, where he studied mining, he worked in Hiärne's laboratory in Stockholm. He then returned to Paris. When he was on the point of leaving for Holland he was induced to stay by Colbert, and he worked with the French chemists, especially with Lemery, to whom he was greatly attached. He became a Catholic in 1682.

Colbert died in 1683, and Homberg's father, now very understandably weary of his wanderings, abandoned him to his own resources. An alchemist who worked for his friend the Abbé Chalucet (afterwards bishop of Toulon) gave

[1] AdS, 1711, h 31, m 56.   [2] AdS, 1712, h 42, m 51.
[3] AdS, 1716, m 154.   [4] AdS, 1716, h 28.
[5] AdS, 1717, h 29, m 31, 122.   [6] AdS, 1728, m 273; 1729, m 282.
[7] AdS, 1734, h 49, m 259.   [8] AdS, 1735, h 26, m 262, 385.
[9] AdS, 1707, h 43, m 5, 176.   [10] AdS, 1708, h 61, m 376.
[11] N. Lemery, Cours de Chymie, ed. Baron, 4°, 1756, 229.
[12] Sur la matiere du feu ou de la lumière, AdS, 1709, h 6, m 400.
[13] Il Fosforo, ovvero le pietra Bolognese preparata per far rilucere fra l'ombre, 8°, Rome, 1680.

Homberg a bar of gold made by art, for which he realised 400 francs, and in 1685 he returned to Rome, where he practised medicine. The Abbé Bignon recalled him to Paris in 1691 and nominated him a member of the Academy. Homberg soon after began to give lessons in chemistry to the Duke of Orleans (Regent in 1715), who had a splendid laboratory and had purchased the large 3 ft. concave polished copper burning mirror of Tschirnhaus, with which Homberg made experiments.

There were two well-known glass burning mirrors. One made for Villette at Lyon, 30 in. diam., was purchased by Louis XIV for the Jardin du Roi. A second larger one of Villette was purchased by the Landgrave of Hesse-Cassel.[1] The copper mirror made for Tschirnhaus in 1687 was purchased by the Duke of Orleans for the Paris Academy.[2]

In 1704 Homberg became first physician to the Duke of Orleans. In 1708 he married Marguerite-Angélique, the daughter of the king's physician Denis Dodart (1634–1707), and his wife assisted him in his chemical experiments. In 1712 he was suspected of being involved with the Duke of Orleans in a series of cases of poisoning in high quarters, but no evidence was brought against him.[3] His friend Fontenelle says Homberg was a man of the highest character, peaceful and gentle in manner, and fond of good company.[4]

In 1683 Mariotte and Homberg found the ratio of the densities of air and water to be 1 : 630.[5] In 1687 Homberg found that a globe 13 in. diam. lost 1 oz. in weight when pumped out to a vacuum in which phosphorus does not glow.[6] In 1698 he pointed out that the density of air depends on the temperature, pressure, and dryness of the atmosphere.[7]

Homberg, who was more successful in experiment than theory, published over 60 memoirs on chemical subjects.[8] He believed in the possibility of the transmutation of metals and some experiments in 1684 on this led him to the discovery of 'Homberg's pyrophorus', a powder spontaneously inflammable in air and obtained by strongly heating a mixture of human excrement and alum out of contact with air.[9] In the course of this work he obtained a water with only a faint smell, which he gave to his lady friends for use as a cosmetic, and also a colourless oil without evil smell, which failed to convert mercury into silver, as was expected.[10] In 1693–6[11] he showed that fused calcium chloride, obtained by heating slaked lime with sal ammoniac, is phosphorescent ('Homberg's phosphorus'). In 1702[12] he obtained a volatile sublimate (sel volatil

[1] Phil. Trans., 1665, i, 95; abgd. ed. 1809, i, 34.
[2] Phil. Trans., 1687, xvi, 352; abgd. ed., 1809, iii, 385; Thomson, (3), 373; Winderlich, Chymia, 1949, ii, 37.
[3] Saint-Simon, Mémoires, ed. Chéruel, 1857, x, 150: 'Humbert.'
[4] Cap, 1857, i, 185; 1864, ii, 214; Figuier, L'Alchimie et les Alchimistes, Paris, 1860, 64; Fontenelle, AdS, 1715, h 82; id., Oeuvres, 1790, vi, 383–98; 1825, i, 307; Gmelin, (1), ii, 125 (list of papers); Hoefer, (1), ii, 298; F. M. Jaeger, Chem. Weekblad, 1918, xv, 316, 602; id., Historische Studien, Groningen, 1919, 171–97; Kopp, (1), i, 181; iv, 65; id., (4), i, 56; Quérard, La France Littéraire, Paris, 1830, iv, 122; Saverien, 1769, vii, 173; Thomson, (1), i, 238.
[5] AdS (C), 1733, i, h 361.   [6] AdS (C),1733, ii, h 19.   [7] AdS (C), 1733, ii, h 333.
[8] List in Table Alphabetique des Matieres, AdS, 1729, ii, 321–2.
[9] AdS, 1711, m 39, 234; (A), m 49, 307.
[10] Macquer, Elements of the Theory and Practice of Chymistry, tr. Reid, London, 1764, ii, 369.
[11] AdS (C), 1733, ii, 281; 1730, x, 445; AdS, 1712, h 40.
[12] AdS, 1702, m 33 (52); (A), m 66.

narcotique du vitriol) by heating borax with green vitriol: this was really boric acid.

If it were true that Homberg in 1695 showed that calamine is the ore of metallic zinc this would be important. Hommel[1] says (without a reference): 'Homberg stellte durch eine Reihe von Untersuchungen (1695) endgültig fest, dass Galmei das Erz des Zinks sei.'[2] This seems to be taken from Kopp's statement:[3] 'Homberg, welcher 1695 über die Verwandlung des Kupfers in Messing durch Zink oder Galmei Untersuchungen anstellte, sagte bestimmt, der Galmei sei das Erz des Zinks.' All I have been able to find on the matter is Homberg's laconic statement (1695):[4] 'de faire du laiton sans zinc & sans calamine', but I may have overlooked the source.

Homberg's publications on 'Kunckel's phosphorus' (1692–6)[5] have been mentioned previously (Vol. II, p. 373). His minor researches (some reported in title only) are on the breaking of Rupert's drops in a vacuum (with emission of light) and the recognition that the glass was in a state of strain (1692),[6] on the silver tree (arbre de Diane), an improvement of Lemery's experiment (1692),[7] the evaporation and freezing of water under the receiver of an air-pump (1693),[8] the phosphorescence of the Bolognian stone (1694),[9] on acid spirits (1695),[10] dyeing with logwood, carthamus, and cochineal (1695–6),[11] Chinese ink (1695),[12] the extraction of cacao butter (1695),[13] the imitation of gems by coloured pastes (1696, 1712),[14] sympathetic inks (1698),[15] the prevention of rusting of iron by a paste of lard, camphor, and graphite (1699, the first black-lead paste for stoves, etc.),[16] the preparation of a very fusible alloy (for anatomical injections) from equal weights of lead, tin, and bismuth (1699),[17] the extraction of essential oils from plants by distilling with dilute sulphuric acid (1700),[18] the solution of mercury in acids (1700),[19] the suggestion that the shapes of salt crystals depend on the nature of the base,[20] the supposed conversion of silver into gold by repeated cupellation (when the 'silver particles surround themselves with the matter of light and become gold particles') or by fusion with stibnite (containing traces of gold),[21] the efflorescence of salt solutions (1710),[22] the distillation of acids from blood, flesh, milk, vipers, flies, and ants (1712),[23] and the separation of gold and silver by fusing with a mixture of salt and nitre, when gold is removed, leaving silver (1713).[24] These varied interests remind us of Boyle.

Homberg's quantitative experiments on the neutralisation of acids and bases are the first determinations of equivalent weights. Simon Boulduc (d. Paris, 1729; demonstrator in the Jardin du Roi) tried in 1698[25] to find the

[1] *Chem. Ztg.*, 1912, xxxvi, 918 (920).
[2] Roscoe and Schorlemmer, 1923, II, i, 663, give 'Galmei', calamine, as 'blende'.
[3] (1), iv, 119.   [4] AdS (C), 1733, ii, 257.
[5] AdS (C), 1733, ii, 135, 181, 281; 1730, x, 84–90, 110–14, 445.
[6] AdS (C), 1733, ii, 138; 1730, x, 215.
[7] AdS (C), 1733, ii, 150; 1730, x, 171, and plate; AdS, 1704, h 40.
[8] AdS (C), 1733, ii, 170; 1730, x, 255.   [9] AdS (C), 1733, ii, 214; 1730, x, 33.
[10] AdS (C), 1733, ii, 250.   [11] AdS (C), 1733, ii, 236, 277.
[12] AdS (C), 1733, ii, 236.   [13] AdS (C), 1733, ii, 248.
[14] AdS (C), 1733, ii, 277; AdS, 1712, h 47, m 187.
[15] AdS (C), 1733, ii, 334.   [16] AdS, 1699, h 58.   [17] AdS, 1699, m 165.
[18] AdS, 1700, h 56, m 206.   [19] AdS, 1700, h 55, m 190.
[20] AdS, 1702, m 33; (A), m 43 (58); cf. Lemery, p. 33.
[21] AdS, 1709, m 106; (A) m 133.   [22] AdS, 1710, m 426.
[23] AdS, 1712, h 45, m 8, 267.   [24] AdS, 1713, m 65.   [25] AdS (C), 1733, ii, 335.

amount of acid in distilled vinegar by neutralising with salt of tartar (potassium carbonate), evaporating, and weighing the solid salt.

Boulduc also published analyses of ipecacuanha,[1] gamboge, jalap, colocynth, and black hellebore,[2] scammony,[3] hyssop,[4] Indian catechu,[5] rhubarb,[6] bryony[7] and agaric.[8] These crude experiments were the beginning of vegetable chemistry.

In 1699[9] Homberg tried to determine the concentrations of several acids by this method of neutralisation with salt of tartar, evaporation, and weighing the residue. The increase over the weight of the salt of tartar gave the weight of acid in the salt. Homberg neglected the loss of weight due to the escape of carbon dioxide (of which he was not aware). To neutralise (*souler*) 1 oz. of salt of tartar required the weights of the acids given below. 1 oz ($℥$) = 8 drachms; 1 drachm ($ʒ$) = 60 grains (gr.):

	Wt. of acid used	Incr. in wt. of dry residue	Wt. of dry acid in 1 oz. of acid
Distilled vinegar	14 ℥	3 ʒ 36 gr.	
Spirit of salt	2 ℥ 5 ʒ	3 ʒ 14 gr.	1 ʒ 15 gr.
Spirit of nitre	1 ℥ 2 ʒ 36 gr.	3 ʒ 10 gr.	2 ʒ 28 gr.
Eau forte	1 ℥ 2 ʒ 30 gr.	3 ʒ 6 gr.	
Oil of vitriol	5 ʒ	3 ʒ 5 gr.	60 ʒ 5 gr.

From Homberg's figures the percentages of base (K_2O) and acid anhydride in the salts may be calculated as follows.[10] For the acetate:

$$1 \, ℥ = 8 \, ʒ \, K_2CO_3 = 8 \times (94/138) = 5{\cdot}45 \, ʒ \, K_2O, \text{ and } 2{\cdot}55 \, ʒ \, CO_2.$$
$$3 \, ʒ \, 36 \text{ gr.} = 3 + (36/60) = 3{\cdot}60 \, ʒ.$$

Acid radical = $3{\cdot}60 + 2{\cdot}55 = 6{\cdot}15$; alkali = $5{\cdot}45$, sum $11{\cdot}60$;
$\therefore$ per cent. acid = $(6{\cdot}15/11{\cdot}6) \times 100 = 53$, and per cent. alkali = 47.

Thus the following table is found (modern values in brackets):

	Acetate	Nitrate	Sulphate	Chloride*
Base	47 (48)	49 (46·5)	49·2 (54·1)	48·5 (63)
Acid	53 (52)	51 (53·5)	50·8 (45·9)	51·5 (37)

* In the chloride an equivalent of fictitious oxygen has been transferred from the chlorine to the metal.

Homberg concluded that all acids differ only in water content, and that the dry acids combine in equal proportions with alkali. In 1700[11] he prepared spirit of salt (hydrochloric acid) and spirit of nitre (nitric acid) both having specific gravities of 1·2 (as measured by a new specific gravity bottle), and assumed that they were of equal strength: cette cinquième partie que les esprits pesoient au delà, venoit des sels, et qu'ainsi les sels qui font toute la force des

[1] AdS, 1700, h 46, m 1, 76.   [2] AdS, 1701, h 58, m 106, 131.
[3] AdS, 1702, m 187.   [4] AdS, 1705, m 186.   [5] AdS, 1709, m 227.
[6] AdS, 1710, m 163.   [7] AdS, 1712, h 41.   [8] AdS, 1714, h 27.
[9] AdS, 1699, h 52, m 44; (A), h 62, m 69; *Phil. Trans.*, 1700, xxii, 530.
[10] Marsh, 1929, 45, gives different figures from Homberg's results.
[11] Observations sur la quantité d'acides absorbez par les alcalis terreux; AdS, 1700, h 55, m 64; (A), h 61, m 81.

Esprits, avoient de part et d'autre un poids égal. He found (incorrectly) that equal weights of quicklime and slaked lime (chaux éteinte) were required for the neutralisation of identical weights of acid, hence he concluded that the causticity of quicklime is not due to an alkali but 'des particules ignés que la calcination avoit fait entrer dans la Chaux,' which particles are 'fort agissantes' and escape on slaking. This view, which 'revoltent un peu l'Esprit', is made probable by the experiment with antimony described by Le Févre (p. 19). Homberg says:

The different quantities of each alkali necessary to absorb the same quantity of an acid . . . are the measure of the passive force of each alkali, and to render this measure more precise it is necessary to add further the greater or less time required by each alkali to absorb the acids (et pour rendre cette mesure tout à fait précise, il y faut joindre encore le plus ou le moins de temps qu'il a fallu à chaque Alkali pour absorber les Acides).

There is a glimmer here of the law of mass action. The 'alkalis' are crabs' eyes (Vol. II, p. 230), coral, pearls, mother of pearl, bezoars, human calculus, oyster shells, calcined hartshorn, quicklime and slaked lime, bole, Tripoli earth and terra sigillata — a curious set. What Homberg calls the 'passive force' of an alkali is measured by the quantity of acid it neutralises: 'si la force des acides consist à pouvoir dissoudre, celle des Alkali consiste, pour ainsi dire, à être dissoluble, et plus ils le sont, plus ils sont parfait dans leur genre.' The weights of the same alkali which neutralise identical weights of different acids measure the 'active force' of each acid, whilst the weights of the same acid which neutralise identical weights of different alkalis measure the 'passive force' of each alkali.

Homberg left the incomplete manuscript of a systematic work on chemistry, fragments of which were published in 1702–9.[1] He defines chemistry as the art of reducing compound bodies into their principles by means of fire, and composing new bodies in the fire by the mixture of different matters.[2] He recognises as the principles of vegetables and animals (which he thinks form only one class) salt, sulphur, water and earth. Minerals may contain these, but metals also contain mercury, with sulphureous, earthy, and sometimes saline matter. Fossil salts, simple stones and earths contain no mercury. Sulphur is active, earth passive, and salt, water and mercury are neutral (moyens). Vegetables contain acid, urinous, and lixivial salts, animals only the last two. Acids have pointed, alkalis spongy particles. Acids distilled from plants and woods, and spirit of nitre (nitric acid made from nitre, found in the soil) contain vegetable sulphur; acids of vitriol, sulphur and alum contain a bituminous sulphur; spirit of salt contains a mineral sulphur.

Homberg later explained that there are four species of sulphur: 'souffre végetal, animal, bitumineux et metallique', the first two being practically the same and the last very difficult to demonstrate,[3] although it is probably

[1] (a) Essais de chimie, AdS, 1702, h 45, m 33; (A), h 59, m 43; (b) Suite des essais de chimie, article 3, du souphre principe, AdS, 1705, m 88; (A) m 117; (c) Suite de l'article trois des essais de chimie, AdS, 1706, m 260; (A) m 336; (d) Suite des essais de chimie: Art. IV, du mercure, AdS, 1709, m 106; (A) m 133.
[2] AdS, 1702, m 33; (A) m 43.
[3] Suite de l'article trois des essais de chimie, AdS, 1706, m 260; (A) m 336.

identical with the matter of light (j'appelle soufre metallique la matiere de la lumiere).[1] Common sulphur is not the same as the sulphur principle but contains it: by distilling common sulphur with oil of turpentine[2] he concluded that it contained the inflammable or fatty principle (sulphur) combined with a salt (i.e. acid) and an earth in about equal amounts, together with a negligible quantity of a metal.[3] The acids from sulphur and vitriol are identical.[4]

In 1710[5] Homberg referred to Lemery's experiment on the action of oil of vitriol on iron (see p. 36) and said the inflammable matter (i.e. hydrogen) must have come from the metal. He also obtained it by the action of oil of vitriol and spirit of salt on zinc, which metal he thought was a mixture of iron and tin.

Homberg regarded the *sel principe* as a constituent of acids and alkalis and thought he had proved by experiment that these were interconvertible.[6] If a metal is put into a solution of another metal in an acid, the solvent quits 'the metal which it dissolves with more difficulty':[7] thus iron precipitates copper from vitriolic waters. Homberg's views on the pointed structure of acid particles and his mechanical theory of solution and neutralisation[8] are very similar to Lemery's (p. 33).

His theory of the calcination of metals is similar to Boyle's (Vol. II, p. 530). In 1700[9] he refers to the increase in weight of metallic antimony calcined by a burning glass and says one is: 'obligé d'admettre ici une introduction des particules du feu, qui restent dans le corps du regule, et qui le rendent plus pesant, qu'ils n'était avant la calcination.' He describes[10] experiments by Duclos (p. 12) and himself on the calcination of metallic antimony by a burning glass in which 4 oz. increased in weight by one-tenth; 'on ne saurait douter qu'il ne soit produit par la matiere de la lumiere.' Mercury on calcination also increases in weight: the matter of light hacks and breaks the smooth globular particles of mercury, so roughening them and producing points: 'et comme ces pointes qui rendent chaque grain du mercure herissé sont une matiere sensible et pesante, le mercure dans cet état augmente de volume et pese plus.'

In explaining combustion, Homberg says a flame is 'a liquid composed of the matter of light and the oil of wood or of charcoal, much lighter than air'.[11] Inflammability is not so much due to sulphur as to a mixture of oil and acid: nous comprendrons qu l'inflammabilité n'est pas le caractere du souffre, mais du mêlange d'une matiere huileuse quelconque avec un sel acide.[12]

[1] AdS, 1709, m 106; (A) m 133.
[2] Cf. Ettmüller, *Nouvelle Chymie raisonnée*, Lyon, 1693, 159.
[3] Essai d'analyse du soufre commun, AdS, 1703, m 31; (A) m 36.
[4] *Ib.*, (A) m 47.
[5] Observations sur les matieres sulfureuses et sur la facilité de les changer d'une espece de soufre en une autre, AdS, 1710, m 225; (A), m 302.
[6] Du sel principe Chymique, AdS, 1702, m 33; (A) m 47; 1708, m 312; (A) m 403; 1714, m 186; (A) m 240.
[7] AdS, 1702, m 44; (A) m 57.
[8] AdS, 1702, m 33; (A) m 54 f.; 1709, m 354; (A) m 463.
[9] AdS, 1700, h 57, m 64; (A) h 61, m 88.
[10] Observations faites par le moyen du verre ardent, AdS, 1702, h 34, m 141; (A) h 45, m 186; cf. 1705, m 88; (A) m 117; 1706, m 260; (A) m 336; 1709, m 106; (A) m 133.
[11] AdS, 1702, m 141 (145); (A) m 192.   [12] AdS, 1706, m 260 (270); (A) m 349.

SEIGNETTE

Elie Seignette (La Rochelle; 1632–1698) in making soluble tartar (potassium tartrate) from tartar (potassium hydrogen tartrate) substituted soda (sodium carbonate) for potash (potassium carbonate) and obtained a new salt, potassium sodium tartrate, now called Rochelle salt or (on the Continent) Seignette's salt. This he called sel polychreste and after its discovery in 1648–1660 (probably 1655) he and his brother Jehan (Rochelle; 1623–1663), who kept the process secret, made large sums from its sale.[1] The father of Jehan and Elie Seignette was Jehan Seignette, an apothecary of La Rochelle. Elie's discovery is usually incorrectly attributed to his son Pierre Seignette (d. La Rochelle, 11 March 1719). What the brothers call 'le faux polychreste' was potassium sulphate, described by Glaser (p. 26). Lemery[2] says there was a different one used by Seignette, who alone knew its composition; he left some of it with Lemery to distribute in Paris. The preparation was first published by Boulduc in 1731.

[1] Van Klooster, *J. Chem. Educ.*, 1959, xxxvi, 314; Gmelin, (1), ii, 252, gives the following publications on it: *Les Principales Utilités et l'Usage le plus familier du véritable Sel Polychreste de M. Seignette*, 4°, La Rochelle, n.d.; *La Nature, les Effets et l'Usage du Sel Alcali Nitreux de M. Seignette*, 4°, n.d.; *Le faux Sel Polychreste, les Utilités de la Poudre Polychreste du dit, et Apologie de son Sel Polychreste par un Medecin*, 8°, La Rochelle, 1675; van Klooster gives the title as *Traité du faux Polychreste*.

[2] *A Course of Chymistry*, tr. Harris, 1686, 298; *Cours de Chymie*, 1690, 366.

CHAPTER II

CHEMISTRY IN FRANCE. II. 1700 TO 1750

G. F. BOULDUC

Gilles François Boulduc (Paris, 20 February 1675–Versailles, 17 January 1742),[1] son of Simon Boulduc (see p. 44), was demonstrator in the Jardin du Roi. He published on Glauber's salt,[2] native Glauber's salt,[3] and Epsom salt,[4] which he thought could be made from alum and potash, confusing it with potassium sulphate. He prepared corrosive sublimate by heating mercuric sulphate with common salt,[5] a process used on the large scale in Holland. He used alcohol to separate the salts in mineral waters.[6] He followed a suggestion made to him by Grosse and prepared Seignette's salt from cream of tartar and soda crystals (which he remarks have an alkaline reaction).[7] Boulduc was perhaps the first to give the composition of gypsum (selenite) as sulphate of lime, since he obtained it by precipitating calcium chloride solution (oil of lime) with Glauber's salt:[8]

Quand je verse sur l'Huile de Chaux une dissolution de Sel de Glauber, l'acide vitriolique de ce Sel quitte sa base, s'unit avec la Chaux contenuë dans ladite Huile, & forme avec elle de la Selenite.

Benjamin Allen[9] had said he 'understood it to be form'd of a Loamy Clay; in conjunction of a Vitriolic Juice', since it is produced near Harwich from chalky stones and 'coperas' stones (i.e. pyrites).

E. F. GEOFFROY

Étienne François Geoffroy (aîné, the elder) (Paris; 13 February 1672–6 January 1731), the son of a wealthy apothecary, studied botany, chemistry, and anatomy in Paris. In 1692 he went to Montpellier to study pharmacy with an apothecary, whose son went to Paris to study with Geoffroy's father. He qualified as a pharmacist in 1693. He had been interested in chemistry by Homberg, a friend of his father. He visited London in 1698 as physician to Count Tallard, the Ambassador Extraordinary, and became F.R.S.; he was a member of the Academy in 1699. After travels in Holland and Italy, where he went in 1700 as physician to M. de Louvois, he took over his father's business

---

[1] Poggendorff, (1), i, 257; Hoefer, (1), ii, 377, says d. 17 February.   [2] AdS, 1724, m 118.
[3] AdS, 1727, h 29, m 375.   [4] AdS, 1731, h 34, m 347.   [5] AdS, 1730, m 357.
[6] AdS, 1726, h 30, m 306; 1729, m 258; in a concise history of mineral waters, Fourcroy, (1), iv, 290, says Boulduc used lime water as a test.
[7] AdS, 1731, m 124.   [8] AdS, 1735, m 443 (450).
[9] *The Natural History of the Chalybeat and Purging Waters of England*, 8°, London, 1699, 106.

in Paris, but he had the ambition to become a physician and studied in secret. He became M.B. of Paris in 1702 and M.D. in 1704. In 1707 he took charge of the lectures in chemistry at the Jardin du Roi, where Fagon was nominally professor, and succeeded the latter in 1712; in 1709 he followed Tournefort as professor of medicine at the Collège Royal. In 1726 he was dean of the medical faculty in Paris.[1] Geoffroy's pharmaceutical lectures were posthumously published, first in English.[2]

FIG. 5. ÉTIENNE FRANÇOIS GEOFFROY (1672–1731).

He was an opponent of alchemy and exposed several alchemical tricks.[3] He investigated cold solutions and fermentations (effervescences) (1700).[4] He thought[5] that the iron contained in vegetable ashes was not present in the plants but had been produced by the action of fire, and concluded that other

[1] De Fère, NBG, 1857, xx, 30; Fontenelle, Oeuvres, 1792, vii, 390–400; 1825, ii, 281; Gmelin, (1), ii, 540 (list of papers); Hoefer, (1), ii, 370; Kopp, (1), i, 213; Phil. Trans. abdg., 1809, iv, 336; Quérard, La France Littéraire, 1829, iii, 317 (says d. 5 Jan. 1731); Thomson, (1), i, 242.
[2] A Treatise of the Fossil, Vegetable and Animal Substances that are made use of in Physick . . . Translated from a Manuscript Copy of the Author's Lectures, read at Paris, by G. Douglas, M.D., 8°, London, 1736; Tractatus de materia medica, 3 vols. 8°, Paris, 1741 (BN); tr. A. Bergier, Traité de la matière medicale, 7 vols. 12°, Paris, 1743 (BN), 1756; J. and W. Thomson and D. Craigie, Life of Cullen, 1859, ii, 560, say the work shows a lack of critical discrimination.
[3] Des supercheries concernant la pierre philosophale, AdS, 1722, h 37, m 61; (A) h 52, m 81.
[4] AdS, 1700, h 53, m 110 (Observations sur les dissolutions et sur les fermentations que l'on peut appeler froides, parcequ'elles sont accompagnées du refroidissement des liquides dans lesquels elles se passent); Phil. Trans., 1701, xxii, 951.
[5] AdS, 1705, h 64, m 362; 1707, h 43, m 176; (A), 1705, m 478; 1707, m 224.

metals could be composed from suitable constituents. This was disproved by L. Lemery.[1]

In 1704 Geoffroy[2] confirmed Homberg's 'analysis' of sulphur (p. 47) by 'composing' it by heating a sulphate with charcoal, obtaining liver of sulphur, hence concluding that sulphuric acid and combustible matters form sulphur. He mentions experiments of Boyle, Glauber and Becher and speculated on the constituents of metals. He showed[3] that the calces obtained from iron, copper, tin, and lead with a burning mirror were different, and he supposed that the other constituent of the metals, which he calls 'principe huileux' or 'soufre principe', was the same. This is practically the phlogiston theory. Geoffroy was influenced by Boyle and was also acquainted with Stahl's writings, quoting Stahl's edition of Becher's *Physica Subterranea* and his *Specimen Beccherianum* (1703),[4] and saying that calces are 'the dead bodies of the metals, from which the soul has been removed by fire'; the metal combines with fire, which increases its weight by one-tenth (Boyle's theory of the fixation of ponderable igneous corpuscles). Homberg's and Geoffroy's memoirs were criticised by Hartsoeker.[5]

Geoffroy described the white fumes produced with ammonia and volatile acids (hydrochloric and nitric) mentioned by Kunckel (1677), and Boyle (1684).[6] In 1717[7] he described experiments with saltpetre in which it lost half its weight on strong heating (he missed the evolution of oxygen), and concluded that this was water. He regarded saltpetre as a compound of $\frac{1}{2}$ water $+ \frac{1}{4}$ absorbent or alkaline earth $+ \frac{1}{4}$ acid. He considered that acids could be converted into alkalis, e.g. by calcining tartar or by deflagrating nitre with charcoal. He thought[8] an alkali is formed in a metallic calx by incineration, since the calces of lead, tin, and antimony, as well as quicklime, which is not a simple absorbent earth but contains an alkali, all disengage ammonia from sal ammoniac. He showed that infusion of roses is coloured red by acids and green by alkalis,[9] and determined the densities of solutions of acids by weighing in a specific gravity bottle with a narrow neck.[10] He noticed the solidification of olive oil on absorption of nitrous fumes.[11]

Prussian blue was accidentally obtained by Diesbach, a colour manufacturer of Berlin, in 1704, by precipitating an iron solution with an alkali obtained from the alchemist Johann Conrad Dippel which had been used in making 'Dippel's animal oil' (see Vol. II, p. 378). It was first described anonymously in 1710[12] as a non-poisonous pigment suitable for oil colours,

[1] AdS, 1707, h 43, m 5, 176.   [2] AdS, 1704, h 37, m 278; (A) h 46, m 374.
[3] AdS, 1709, h 34, m 162; 1718, m 202; (A), 1709, h 45, m 205; 1718, m 256; *Phil. Trans.*, 1709, xxvi, 374.
[4] AdS, 1720, m 20; (A), m 24.
[5] *Eclaircissemens sur les Conjectures physiques*, 4°, Amsterdam, 1710, 62 ff., 137 ff.
[6] AdS, 1713, h 39; (A), h 53.
[7] AdS, 1717, h 34, m 226; (A), m 291: Du changement des sels acides en sels alcalins volatils urineux.
[8] AdS, 1720, m 20; (A), m 24.   [9] *Phil. Trans.*, 1699, xxi, 43.
[10] *Phil. Trans.*, 1700, xxii, 530, and table.
[11] AdS, 1719, m 71; (A), m 93; cf. Boyle, *Physiological Essays*, 1661, *Works*, 1744, i, 270; see Vol. II, p. 546.
[12] *Miscell. Berolinensia*, 1710, i, 377: notitia cœruli Berolinensis nuper inventi.

but the method of preparation was kept secret. This was described by John Woodward,[1] viz. calcining potash (potassium carbonate) with bullock's blood, precipitating a solution of the product with a solution of green vitriol and alum, and treating the green precipitate with spirit of salt. John Brown[2] showed that the alum was unnecessary, but no other metal except iron (as green vitriol) produced the colour; hence he concluded that 'iron is the metal that is the subject of this beautiful colour'.

In two papers on Prussian blue[3] Geoffroy showed that it could be made from a variety of animal substances such as blood, wool, burnt horn, hoofs, etc., and thought that any animal material would serve. At first he thought that the blue colour was due to a bituminous constituent of the iron which, when rarefied by the heat of the fire, appears on the blue surface of tempered steel; but in the second paper he abandoned this idea and concluded that the blue colour is due to the inflammable principle, 'c'est à dire le bitume penetré de la matière subtile, ou feu élémentaire.'

Geoffroy was one of the first French chemists to adopt the phlogiston theory: his affinity table[4] contains phlogiston as the 'principe huileux ou Soufre Principe', with its special symbol. His researches on alum[5] led him to conclude that its base is the earth of clay (alumina), combined with sulphuric acid, but he thought he had converted the earth of clay into silica (perhaps crystalline alumina) by strong ignition.[6]

Tables of Affinity

The first affinity tables were published by Geoffroy.[7] The summary of the memoir by Fontenelle, the Secretary of the Academy, says the transfer of a body such as an acid from one body, such as a metal, with which it is united, to a third body 'is a thing of which the possibility had never been guessed by the most subtle philosophers, and of which the explanation even now is not easy'. This was written in ignorance of prior publications by Boyle (see Vol. II, p. 502), Mayow (Vol. II, p. 606), and Glauber (Vol. II, p. 355).

The physical authors who attempted to explain the nature of affinity usually invoked obscure forces,[8] but the dislike of Newtonian ideas by the French Academy caused it to forbid the use of the word *attraction*, under the influence of Descartes (Newton himself also disbelieved in forces acting at a distance), and Geoffroy uses the neutral word 'rapport' as the translation of the old meaning of *affinis*. After 1730 the name *affinity* (*affinité*) was in common use,

---

[1] *Phil. Trans.*, 1724, xxxiii, 15 (in Latin); tr. in Abdg. ed. 1809, vii, 4.

[2] *Phil. Trans.*, 1724, xxxiii, 17; Abdg. ed. 1809, vii, 6.

[3] AdS, 1725 (1727), m 153, 220.   [4] AdS, 1718, m 202.

[5] AdS, 1724, m 380; 1744, m 69.   [6] AdS, 1746, h 65, m 284.

[7] Table des differens Rapports observés en Chimie entre differentes substances, AdS, 1718, h 35–7, m 202–12; Eclaircissements sur la table inserée dans les Memoires de 1718 concernant les Rapports observés entre differentes Substances, AdS, 1720, h 32, m 20–34; the table is reproduced in Macquer, *Elemens de Chimie theorique*, 1749, plate, and explanation, 256–73; tr. Reid, *Elements of . . . Chemistry*, London, 1764, i, 159, plate vi; *A Table of the Affinities between Several Substances: by Mr. Geoffroy* (4 pp.) *A Table of the Solubilities of Bodies: with Substances not Soluble by these Bodies: by Mr. Gellert* (7 pp.), 12°, London [1780 ?, BM 8907. a. 10]; Ostwald, *Lehrbuch*, 1911, II, ii, 20.

[8] Rohault, *Physica*, Pars I, cs. 20–2; London, 1697, 65 f.

and Bergman's (1775) use of the Newtonian name *attraction* was not generally followed.

Newton in 1699 had been admitted one of the very few foreign associates of the Academy, but his ideas were first made popularly known by Voltaire on his return from England in 1728.[1] Before this they were explained to French chemists in extracts from Freind's book (see Vol. II, p. 479) in the *Nouveau Cours de Chymie* (1723, see p. 58). A few backward authors continued to oppose them: the Abbé Para du Phanjas (1724–97) thought 'the reasoning and calculation of those who pretend to establish the influence of weight in chemical phenomena rest on ruinous principles'.[2] The Encyclopaedists fully accepted the Newtonian picture of the universe, but this is of little or no help in chemistry.

Geoffroy says:

On observe en Chimie certains rapports entre differens corps, qui font qu'ils s'unissent aisément les uns aux autres. Ces Rapports ont leurs degrés et leurs loix . . . parmi plusieurs matieres confonduës et qui ont quelque disposition à s'unir ensemble, on s'aperçoit qu'une de ces substances s'unit toujours constamment avec une certaine autre préferablement à toutes.

When two substances which have this disposition unite together and a third is added, it may join with one of them by making it let go the other. The following general proposition may be stated:[3]

Toutes les fois que deux substances qui ont quelque disposition à se joindre l'une avec l'autre, se trouvent unies ensemble; s'il en survient une troisième qui ait plus de rapport avec l'une des deux, elle s'y unit en faisant lâcher prise à l'autre.

Geoffroy's table[4] is based on his own observations and those of others. The top line contains the symbols for the acid spirits, acid of common salt, nitrous (nitric) acid, vitriolic acid, absorbent earth (alumina), fixed alkali, volatile alkali, metallic substances, sulphur, mercury, lead, copper, silver, iron, regulus of antimony, and water. In each vertical column are the symbols of the substances (including the 'principe huileux ou soufre principe', i.e. phlogiston) in decreasing order of affinity (rapport) from above, with the one at the head. The table was intended to apply both to dry reactions and wet reactions. Any substance in a column will displace all those below it from combination with the substance standing at the top. Geoffroy gives a detailed explanation of the table, pointing out that the affinities of different acids for metals, e.g., are different. In two cases, where the affinities are not very well known, there are three symbols in one place. In many experiments the separation 'n'est pas toujours parfaitment exacte et précise', on account of the viscosity of the liquid, its movement, the figure of the precipitating and precipitated parts, 'et autres choses semblables.' Fontenelle in his summary[5] says:

cette Table devient en quelque sorte prophetique, car que l'on mêle ensemble des substances, elle fera prévoir l'effet et le resultat, . . . un spectacle agréable à l'Esprit . . . plus la Chymie se perfectionnaira, plus la Table de M. Geoffroy se perfectionnaira aussi . . . si la Phisique ne sçauroit arriver à la certitude des Mathématiques, du moins ne peut-elle mieux faire que d'en imiter l'ordre.

[1] Freund, *Study of Chemical Composition*, Cambridge, 1904, 283.
[2] *Théorie des Nouvelles Découvertes en genre de Physique et de Chymie*, 8°, Paris, 1786, 44 f., 49.
[3] AdS, 1718, m 202 (203); (A), m 257.   [4] *Ib.*, m 212.   [5] AdS, 1718, h 35–7.

In his second memoir,[1] Geoffroy answers certain objections to his table, e.g. by Neumann, who also sent him a problem proposed by Stahl: 'to separate vitriolic acid from salt of tartar (potash) in an instant and in the palm of the hand.' These two substances, according to the table, should have very great

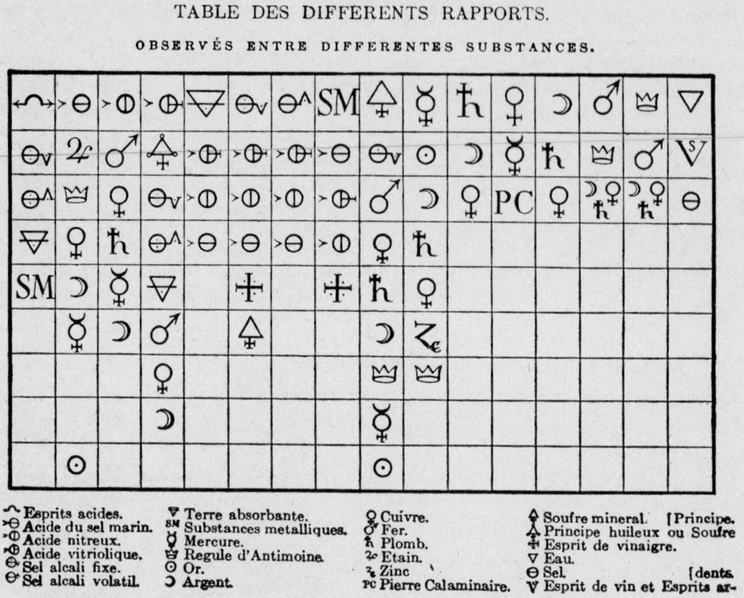

TABLE DES DIFFERENTS RAPPORTS.

OBSERVÉS ENTRE DIFFERENTES SUBSTANCES.

Esprits acides.
Acide du sel marin.
Acide nitreux.
Acide vitriolique.
Sel alcali fixe.
Sel alcali volatil.
Terre absorbante.
SM Substances metalliques.
Mercure.
Regule d'Antimoine.
Or.
Argent.
Cuivre.
Fer.
Plomb.
Etain.
Zinc
PC Pierre Calaminaire.
Soufre mineral. [Principe.
Principe huileux ou Soufre
Esprit de vinaigre.
Eau.
Sel.
Esprit de vin et Esprits ardents.

FIG. 6. GEOFFROY'S AFFINITY TABLE.

affinity. Neither of the two solutions proposed by Geoffroy fulfilled the conditions. Stahl's son in 1724 made the method known to Boulduc, viz. adding silver nitrate to the potassium sulphate, when silver sulphate is precipitated, and in 1737 Pott used calcium nitrate, when calcium sulphate is precipitated.[2]

Since quicklime and the calces of some metals (e.g. of lead) set free ammonia from sal ammoniac, Geoffroy thought they contained an alkali. He quotes Stahl's works in the original. Calcination is explained as due to escape of the 'oily principle' (phlogiston), which leaves the metal as the soul leaves the body, being elevated by fire, and the calx remains as the cadaver of the metal, e.g. of lead. Calcination is a sort of fermentation among the particles of the metal. Modern authors who begin the phlogiston theory in France with Macquer (see p. 83) overlook Geoffroy.

Geoffroy's affinity table was criticised by Baron.[3] Affinity tables were published by many chemists. Guyton de Morveau,[4] who distinguished between

---

[1] AdS, 1720, h 35–7, m 20–34.   [2] Pott, *Dissertations Chymiques*, 1759, iii, 223 f.

[3] Ed. of Lemery, *Cours de Chymie*, 4°, 1756, 214, 230, 233–4 (je pense que toutes ces affinités & ces rapports tant vantés n'ont rien d'absolu & de réel), 353; Jagnaux, 1891, i, 308, is wrong in saying that the expression 'faiseurs de tables', to which Macquer, (2), 1778, i, 67, objected, is to be found in Baron's notes; Macquer says it is in 'a work printed in 1775', probably Monnet, *Traité de la Dissolution des Métaux*, Amsterdam and Paris, 1775; q. by J. C. Fischer, 1805, vi, 294, which said the whole theory of affinity was a chimera, which could give nothing useful to true science; but Macquer refuted this at length.

[4] *Ency. Méthod.*, *Chymie*, 1786 (7), i, 535–613: art. 'Affinité'; J. C. Fischer, 1803, iv, 78–81.

affinity and attraction and defined the former as 'the force with which bodies of different nature tend to unite', refers to extensions of Geoffroy's tables by Grosse (1730), Gellert (1750), Rüdiger (1756), Limbourg (1758), Marherr (1762), de Fourcy (1773),[1] Demachy (1774), Bergman (1775), Erxleben (1775), Weigel (1775), Wenzel (1777), and Wiegleb (1781).

Grosse's table with 19 columns is in a collection of dissertations[2] which mentions a larger table in Clausier's translation of Quincy's *Pharmacopœia*. C. E. Gellert[3] gives a table in 28 columns of symbols in which the substances having *least* affinity with the substance at the head are placed first in the column, i.e. the opposite to Geoffroy's order. At the foot of each column are substances insoluble in the substance at the head. Gellert uses letter symbols: cobalt = K, bismuth = W, zinc = X, and denotes a calx by C, e.g. calx of zinc = C.X, calx of bismuth = C.W. Bergman also added a symbol for calx to that of the metal, but he used special symbols. Anton Rüdiger[4] gives a table in 15 columns and indicates in a special table substances which do not combine with one another. Jean Phillipe de Limbourg (Theux, nr. Spa; 1726–1 February 1811), M.D. Leyden, who studied under Rouelle, F.R.S. 1771, physician in Spa, criticised Geoffroy's table and gave an extended one in 33 columns of symbols.[5] Philipp Ambrosius Marherr (Vienna, 1738–Prague, 1771)[6] also criticised Geoffroy's table.

C. J. GEOFFROY

E. F. Geoffroy's younger brother (Geoffroy cadet) Claude Joseph Geoffroy (Paris; 2 August 1685–9 March 1752) was a pharmacist. He published a large number of papers in the *Mémoires* of the Academy,[7] the most interesting being on sal ammoniac and borax. In the 17 cent. dried animal dung, including but not exclusively camel's dung and never camel's urine, was used as fuel in Egypt and on burning evolved a thick smoke, the soot from which was collected and taken to factories, where it was carefully heated in fifty large glass globes set in a gallery furnace, when cakes of crude sal ammoniac sublimed on the upper parts of the globes as a dull-greyish mass. The process was described by several travellers who visited Egypt and saw it in operation in the Delta.[8]

[1] *Obs. Phys.*, 1774, i, 197.

[2] Demachy, *Recueil de dissertations physico-chimiques*, Amsterdam, 1774; de Morveau, *op. cit.*, 537.

[3] *Anfangsgründe zur metallurgischen Chemie*, 2 vols., Leipzig, 1751–5; 2 ed., 1776, i, 172 (opposite), 231.

[4] *Systematische Anleitung zur reinen und überhaupt applicirten oder allgemeinen Chemie*, Leipzig, 1756, §§ 246–65, table on p. 266.

[5] *Dissertation sur les Affinités chymiques, qui a remporté le prix de Physique de l'an 1758, quant à la partie Chymique, au Jugement de l'Académie Royale des Sciences, belles Lettres & Arts, de Rouen*, v. sm. 4°, Liège, 1761, 87 pp. and folding table.

[6] *Dissertatio chemica de affinitate corporum*, 12°, Vienna, 1762 (xvi, 99 pp.); German tr. by E. G. Baldinger, *Chemische Abhandlung von der Verwandtschaft der Körper*, 12°, Leipzig, 1764 (144 pp.) q. by Bolton, 1893, (1), 654; and Bischof, *Lehrbuch der Stöchiometrie*, Erlangen, 1819, 5 (who gives a difft. title for the first, says it is in 4°, and the second in 8°).

[7] Gmelin, (1), ii, 543; Hoefer, (1), ii, 372; NBG, 1857, xx, 33; Quérard, *La France Littéraire*, 1829, iii, 317 (says b. 8 August 1685); Thomson, (1), i, 244.

[8] Sicard, *Nouveaux Mémoires des Missions de la Compagnie de Jesus*, Paris, 1717, ii; Thomas Shaw, *Travels, or Observations relating to several parts of Barbary and the Levant*, f°, Oxford, 1738, Appendix, 55; 2 ed., 4°, London, 1757, 480; R. Pococke, *Description of the East and Some other Countries*, 2 vols. f°, London, 1743, i (Observations on Egypt), 259–60, plate LXXI

Joseph Pitton de Tournefort (Aix, Provence, 5 June 1656–Paris, 28 December 1708), professor of botany in the Jardin du Roi (1683), said that sal ammoniac is a compound of ammonia and an acid, which he did not name.[1] Tournefort's book on materia medica was first published posthumously in English.[2]

The composition of sal ammoniac was explained by Homberg.[3] Following the note on sal ammoniac by L. Lemery in 1716,[4] C. J. Geoffroy published an account of the process of manufacture, and he was the first to make sal ammoniac in France, the process used in Egypt having been described in a letter from the Jesuit Sicard.[5] Further papers on the subject were published by Du Hamel.[6]

In 1718[7] C. J. Geoffroy confirmed the production of water by the combustion of spirit of wine noticed by Van Helmont (Vol. II, p. 224); he tried to determine the amount of water in spirit by burning it in a small silver cylinder (2 in. high and 2 in. diam.) and measuring the residual water. From 8 oz. of alcohol he obtained 5 oz. 7 dr. 36 gr. of pure water. He tried to prepare white vitriol from calamine and sulphuric acid, which he regarded as its constituents, but obtained a green salt (due to impurity).[8] He recognised that the vitriols are metallic salts of sulphuric acid.[9] He prepared brass of varying composition by alloying copper and zinc in different proportions,[10] and by examining the fracture under a lens observed yellow, reddish, and white constituents (the α-, β-, and γ-brass phases). He says zinc (sic) came from Germany or the Indies.

He showed,[11] after Boulduc (see p. 49), that Seignette's or Rochelle salt (potassium sodium tartrate) is a compound of tartar and Alicante alkali (soda) and[12] that the base of common salt is a constituent of borax, Glauber's salt and boric acid being formed by the action of sulphuric acid on borax; and he described the green flame of a solution of boric acid in alcohol.

Borax, supplied by Dutch and Venetian trade from Tibet, was then thought

(preparation in Cairo); Lucus, *Voyage du Sieur Paul Lucas dans la Turquie, L'Asie, Sourie, Palestine, Haute & Basse Egypte, &c.*, 2 vols. Amsterdam, 1744, ii, 6 (in the Delta from camel's urine, etc.); C. Lyell, KAH, 1750 (1751), xii, 241–58; Hasselquist, *ib.*, 258–64; Scheffer, *ib.*, 265–6; Rodenschöld, *ib.*, 267–8; German tr., C. Leyell, *Abhl. d. Schwed. Akad. der Wiss.*, 1755, xiii, 251–65; Hasselquist, *ib.*, 266–71; Scheffer, *ib.*, 272–3; Rudenskiöld, *ib.*, 274; French trs., Leyel, Hasselqvist, and Scheffer, in *Recueil des Mémoires . . . contenus dans les Actes de l'Acad. d'Upsal et dans les Mémoires de l'Acad. Roy. des Sciences de Stockholm*, Paris, 1764, i, 127 f.; Hasselqvist, *Voyages and Travels in the Levant*, London, 1766, 55, 67, 304 f.

[1] AdS, 1700, m 71: Comparaison des analyses du sel ammoniac, de la soie et de la corne de cerf.

[2] *Materia Medica, or a Description of Simple Medicines generally used in Physick . . . also their operating and acting upon Human Bodies . . . with Appendix, shewing the Nature and Use of Mineral Waters*, 8°, London, 1708; tr. (by John Martyn ?) from a French MS.; the French ed. appeared first in 1717.

[3] AdS, 1702, m 33 (41); (A), m 62.   [4] AdS, 1716, h 28–30; 1721, h 35–6.

[5] Geoffroy, AdS, 1716, h 28; (A), h 34; 1720, h 46–50, m 189–207; 1723, h 38–40, m 210–22 (with figure of cakes of Egyptian sal ammoniac evidently taken from the tops of flasks in which it was sublimed).

[6] AdS, 1735, h 23–6, m 106–16, 414–34, 483–504.

[7] AdS, 1718, m 37; (A) m 46; cf. Boerhaave, Vol. II, p. 749.

[8] AdS, 1713, h 35, m 168.   [9] AdS, 1728, h 34, m 301.

[10] AdS, 1725, m 57–66.   [11] *Phil. Trans.*, 1735, xxxix, 37, no. 436.

[12] Nouvelles expériences sur le borax, AdS, 1732, h 52, m 398.

to be an artificial product (see Vol. II, p. 262), since its origin was kept secret.[1] That it was Tibetan *tinkal* purified by recrystallisation was explained by Johann Georg Model.[2] John Hill, in his translation of Theophrastos[3], asserted that borax 'is a . . . Salt, made by the Evaporation of an ill-tasted and foul Water, of which there are Springs in Persia, Muscovy, and Tartary', and the source of borax in the lakes of Tibet was described by William Blane and by Joseph de Rovato.[4] The composition of borax was finally cleared up by Baron (p. 71).

C. J. Geoffroy[5] mentioned as a 'volatile salt' the crystals deposited from essential oils. He published on antimony, tartar emetic, and kermes mineral.[6] He showed[7] that soap is readily soluble in hot alcohol, the liquid on cooling setting to a clear jelly, and that the oil set free from the soap (really oleic acid) by the action of acids is more soluble in alcohol than the original oil. In his paper on Prussian blue[8] he argued that the 'soufre animal' of the organic material sets free iron in a fine state of division which, when mixed with the sulphurous principle and absorbent earth, exhibits a blue colour. (Until recently, the blue colour of ultramarine was ascribed to finely-divided sulphur.) He translated the work on assaying of Christian Carl Schindler.[9]

N. Geoffroy

C. J. Geoffroy's son N. Geoffroy[10] showed that lead and bismuth increase in weight on calcination.[11] He heated 4 ounces of lead in an earthen pot, applying wind from a bellows. In three-quarters of an hour half the lead had disappeared as smoke and the rest was changed to litharge, which was reduced to metal and re-heated as before, and so on, until all the lead had disappeared except a small amount of litharge too minute to be easily reduced. The increase in weight of bismuth was the same whether the metal was heated in glass, earthenware, or iron vessels, and Geoffroy says that this disproves the theory of Boerhaave that the increase is due to some material taken up from the vessel,[12] but Boerhaave[13] had suggested that the increase in weight of lead might be due to absorption of an acid from the combustible of the fire (as Tachenius thought, see Vol. II, p. 296), or of fire itself (referring to Boyle).

[1] Pott, *Dissertations Chymiques*, tr. Demachy, 1759, ii, 337.
[2] *Chymische Nebenstunden*, St. Petersburg, 1762, 192.
[3] *Theophrastus's History of Stones*, 2 edit., London, 1774, 119.
[4] *Phil. Trans.*, 1787, lxxvii, 297, 301; Abdg. ed., 1809, xvi, 282, 284.
[5] AdS, 1727, m 114.
[6] AdS, 1734, h 52–5, m 417–34; 1735, m 54–70, 311–26; 1736, m 414–34 (on a new detonating phosphorus).
[7] AdS, 1741, h 78, m 11; *Phil. Trans.*, 1742, xlii, 71. [8] AdS, 1743, m 33.
[9] *L'Art d'Essayer les Mines et les Métaux, publié en Allemand par M. Schindlers et traduit en françois par feu M. Geoffroy, le fils . . .* , 12°, Paris, 1759 (BN).
[10] NBG, 1857, xx, 35; Weeks, *J. Chem. Educ.*, 1934, xi, 428; *id.*, *Discovery of the Elements*, 1956, 108, calls him Claude François Geoffroy.
[11] AdS, 1753, m 296.
[12] Cf. Guyton de Morveau, *Digressions Académiques*, Dijon, 1772, 99 f.
[13] (2), ii, 453: An hoc ab acido materiae combustibilis in plumbum rapto, an ab igne?

Astruc

E. F. Geoffroy was succeeded at the Collège Royale by Jean Astruc (Sauve, Languedoc, 19 March 1684–Paris, 5 May 1766), formerly professor of medicine in Montpellier. He published on fermentation,[1] muscular motion,[2] and on the cause of digestion,[3] some medical, botanical, and geological works, and a famous history of the Montpellier medical school.[4] He opposed the Iatromathematical theory of digestion by trituration and supposed that it was due to a ferment (par le moyen d'un levain). He discussed the production of woad (pastel) and recognised that it was the same as indigo.[5]

D'arquier[6] reports that Deidier, apothecary in Montpellier, 'dans sa Chymie'[7] says he had drawn from 60 or 80 pots of well water 3 'onces d'un esprit salé, acide, qui dissolvoit l'or dans la main, sans qu'elle fût endommagé'.

The Phlogiston Theory in France

The earlier development of chemistry in France, as represented by Beguin, Le Févre, and Lemery, was based on German sources such as Paracelsus, transmitted through the Jardin du Roi (see p. 4). A new phase began with the introduction of the phlogiston theory by E. F. Geoffroy, which made headway after the publication of an anonymous book:

Nouveau Cours de Chymie, suivant les Principes de Newton & de Sthall [*sic*]. Avec un Discours Historique sur l'Origine & les progrez de la Chymie, 2 vols. sm. 8°, Paris, 1723; vol. i, pp. lxvij, Approbation (3 pp.), 246 pp.; vol. ii, fly-leaf: Suite du Nouveau Cours de Chymie, marked 247 (*v.* blank), pp. 247–796 (references are to this ed.).

Nouvelle Edition Revûe & corrigée, 2 vols. 8°, Paris, 1737; vol. i, pp. c, 253, Approbation, Autre Approbation, 1 leaf; vol. ii, fly-leaf, Nouveau Cours de Chymie. Seconde Partie, 1–540 pp.

Venel[8] says the book: 'nous apportât le stahlianisme, & fît la même révolution dans notre chimie, que les réflexions sur l'attraction que publia M. Maupertuis . . . ont opérée dans notre physique, en nous faisant recevoir le newtonianisme.' It is attributed to Jean Baptiste Senac (1693–1770), physician to Louis XV, by Fourcroy,[9] Gmelin,[10] and Kopp,[11] but Baron,[12] who criticises it with undue severity, said it was compiled by students in the Jardin du Roi from lectures by Geoffroy and Boulduc. The first person singular is often used, as in lectures.

The book (i, 3) says Keill first tried to reduce chemical operations to the

---

[1] *Tractatus de motus fermentativa causa, novam et mechanicam hypothesin continens*, 8°, Montpellier, 1702.

[2] *Dissertatio physica de motu musculari*, Montpellier, 1710.

[3] *Traité de la Cause de la Digestion, où l'on refute le nouveau systême de la trituration et du broïetement*, 8°, Toulouse, 1714.

[4] *Mémoires pour servir d'Histoire de la Faculté de Médecine de Montpellier*, ed. Lorry, Paris, 1767; NBU, 1852, iii, 486; Gmelin, (1), ii, 418; iii, 32.

[5] *Mémoires pour l'Histoire Naturelle de la Province de Languedoc*, 4°, Paris, 1737, 327–33.

[6] *Mém. Acad. Toulouse*, 1782, i, 15–34.

[7] Presumably Antoine Deidier, *Chymie Raisonnée*, Lyon, 1715; Bolton, (1), 394.

[8] *Ency. Méthod., Chimie*, 1796, iii, 302.   [9] (2), 1796, iii, 740; *id.*, (1), 1802, i, 26.

[10] (1), ii, 682.   [11] (1), iv, 179.   [12] Ed. of Lemery, *Cours de Chymie*, 1756, pref. iii.

laws of mechanics, using the principles of Newton,[1] but the book by Freind
(see Vol. II, p. 479) seems to have served as a source for this part. As for
Stahl, the preliminary discourse (I, liv) says 'M. Alberti son disciple nous a
donné un ouvrage merveilleux intitulé *Fundamenta Chymiæ*', which perfectly
confirms the principles of Newton. Descartes' theory of matter is criticised,
but although matter is defined as 'an extended, impenetrable and divisible
substance, indifferent towards rest or motion' (i, 7), nothing is said of its
having weight.

After a good historical introduction (pp. iii–lxvii), the first volume deals
with matter (p. 4), the principles of bodies (p. 8), saying that 'Bécher est le
seul qui ait éclairci la Théorie Chymique' (p. 15), sulphur or oil (p. 35) or
'phlogistique' (p. 37), le melange des Elemens (p. 44), le Magnétisme des
Corps (p. 74) and the cause of the magnetism of bodies (p. 118), i.e. affinity,
les Dissolvans (p. 126), the 'alkaest' (p. 148), and the operations of chemistry
in general (p. 151), which include calcination (p. 154), distillation (p. 168),
sublimation (p. 180), fermentation (p. 188), digestion (p. 215), extraction
(p. 224), precipitation (p. 230) and crystallisation (p. 241). The second volume,
on the operations of chemistry in particular, deals with gold, silver, tin, lead,
copper, iron, mercury and antimony, and their compounds (pp. 248–503);
vitriol, 'colkothar' and alum (pp. 506–26), arsenic, stones, sulphur (pp. 526–
563), amber, salt, and nitre (pp. 563–83); then follow vegetables and their
salts, oils, etc. (pp. 607–71), wine and spirit of wine, vinegar, tinctures,
elixirs, etc. (pp. 671–98), tartar, soluble tartar and soap (pp. 698–730), putrefaction (p. 730) and opium (p. 732); and finally animals and their products,
including milk, urine, sal ammoniac, white of egg, blood, salt of vipers and
English drops (pp. 742–96). The descriptions of the increase in weight of a
metal on calcination as due to the entry of igneous corpuscles, which by
lodging between the pores decrease the specific gravity (i, 115, 160; ii, 314 f.,
328 f.), are taken from Freind (see Vol. II, p. 479).

FIZES

An anonymous publication of the lectures on chemistry given in Montpellier[2] is said to have been compiled by J. A. Gontard from lectures by
Antoine Fizes (Montpellier; 1690–14 August 1765), professor of mathematics
(1718) and medicine (1732) at Montpellier, whose medical theories were a
mixture of mathematics, mechanics, hydraulics, and chemistry, and who published several medical works.[3] The compiler (Gontard) says in the preface that
he gathered the material during the seven years he 'assisted at the courses of
one of the most enlightened physicians of the century'. The lecturer says
(p. 178) that he was deputed to examine the manufacture of tartar in Agnane

[1] Keill, *Phil. Trans.*, 1708, xxvi, 97; see Vol. II, p. 478.
[2] *Cours de Chymie de Montpellier. Par J.A.G.D.M.*, 8°, s.l., 1749; the same as the *Leçons de
Chymie de l'Université de Montpellier*, 8°, Paris, 1750; 191 pp. with a list of 'Operations du
Cours Public de Chymie de Montpellier', lecture experiments.
[3] Fisquet, NBG, 1856, xvii, 786; a MS. of 1736, 'Recüeuil de Leçons de Chimie faite par
Monsieur Tizes [sic] Proffesseur en Medecine à Montper' (123 pp.) was advertised, Sotheran
Cat. 832 (1932), 388.

and published on it in the *Memoires* of the Paris Academy for 1727. This note of eleven lines[1] was sent from the Royal Society of Science of Montpellier by Fizes, and a MS. note in my copy of the book says 'Fizes par Gontard'. The text is mostly a collection of practical operations and descriptions of the medical uses of the products, and very little theory, although phlogiston is mentioned several times and a brief explanation of it is given (p. 96). The Cartesian and Newtonian hypotheses are said to be equally useless in chemistry (p. 22), and affinity and attraction explain nothing (p. 113). In the preparation of butter of antimony (antimony trichloride) by heating antimony sulphide with mercuric chloride ($Sb_2S_3 + 3HgCl_2 = 2SbCl_3 + 3HgS$):

Le soufre qui a quitté l'antimoine pour se joindre au mercure, reste avec lui . . . mais vouloit entrer dans la maniere dont tout cela se fait, d'ou vient que l'esprit de sel quitte le mercure pour se joindre au régule et en chasser le soufre, c'est vouloir expliquer ce qu'on n'expliquera jamais: c'est l'affinité, c'est attraction, tout cela ne dit rien.

DU PETIT

François Pourfour du Petit (Paris; 24 June 1664–18 June 1741), army doctor, then a physician in Paris, made experiments on efflorescence (la végétation des sels).[2] He gave a correct explanation of the purification of saltpetre by crystallisation, viz. that the solubility of saltpetre increases rapidly with rise of temperature whilst that of common salt does not:[3] le sel marin ne peut se dissoudre dans l'eau très-chaude en plus grand quantité que cette même eau n'en peut tenir en dissolution, lorsqu'elle est tout-à-fait froid. He made experiments on the adherence of the particles of air to one another and to bodies they touch,[4] including the adhesion of air and gas bubbles in liquids adhering to solids. Petit made observations on the eye, describing an ophthalmometer (1728).

REAUMUR

René Antoine Ferchault, Sieur de Reaumur (not Réaumur) (Rochelle, 1683–Bermondière, Maine, 17 October 1757) was educated in law, but having an ample fortune he removed in 1703 to Paris, where he became a pupil of Varignon and devoted himself to scientific and technical investigations. He became a member of the Academy in 1708 and F.R.S. in 1738. He was a man of wide knowledge, an able mathematician and natural historian as well as a chemist. His most important work was in entomology, and his book on insects[5] was epoch-making. On his death he left to the Academy his large natural history and mineral collections, and 138 note-books dealing with the useful arts.[6] Some time between 1716 and 1727 he participated in a memorial

[1] AdS, 1725 (1727), m 346: Manière de préparer, de dépurer et de blanchir le cristal de tartre·
[2] AdS, 1722, h 31–7, m 95–116, 331–48.
[3] De la precipitation du sel marin dans la fabrique du salpêtre, AdS, 1729 (1731), h 19–22, m 225–34.
[4] AdS, 1731, h 1–6, m 56–68.
[5] *Memoire pour servir à l'histoire des insectes*, 6 vols., 4°, Paris, 1734–42.
[6] Anon., *Endeavour*, 1957, xvi, 183; Hoefer, NBG, 1862, xli, 794; McKie, *Sci. Progr.*, 1957, xlv, 619; Quérard, *La France Littéraire*, 1835, vii, 481; Saverien, 1773, viii, 205; Thomson, (1), i,

to the Academy, stressing the importance of chemistry to the useful arts.[1]

After the publication of some mathematical papers, he turned to applied science and natural history. In an investigation of the strength of ropes he showed that this is less than the combined strength of the cords composing the rope.[2] His first paper on natural history was on shells, which he showed are produced by the successive addition of new parts to the exterior.[3] Bohn had shown that spiders could spin a silk which, it was suggested, might be used in textiles, but Reaumur[4] found that spiders could not be fed together without attacking and destroying one another. He investigated the way in which sea-animals attach themselves to solids, finding that some do this by various threads or pinnæ, others use a kind of cement or adhesive, and others by suction, and he discovered an insect which lives inside snails.[5] His investigations on the purple dye[6] are interesting. William Cole, of Bristol,[7] had found that a shell fish (Purpura lapillus) used in Ireland for marking linen a purple colour yielded a juice which turned purple on exposure to light, which he thought was similar to the ancient Tyrian dye. Reaumur found on the coast of Poitou large numbers of buccinæ and in places where they collected there were rounded grains, white or yellowish, the liquor from which squeezed on linen developed a purple colour when exposed to light. A solution in a closed bottle did not become purple but did so, in light, when air was admitted.[8]

Reaumur found that the popular belief that when crabs, lobsters, etc., lose their claws they are soon replaced by new ones is correct;[9] his explanation of the shock of the torpedo fish as due to a series of very rapid impacts delivered by muscles of peculiar structure[10] is incorrect; the true explanation, that it is electric, was given later by Walsh and by Cavendish (see p. 306). Reaumur,[11] having found that fossil bones from Languedoc acquire the colour of turquoise on heating, thought incorrectly that the turquoise may have a similar origin, but his investigation of the formation of pearls[12] led him to suspect, correctly, that they are a pathological formation in the oyster. He showed that false pearls were made from a small fish called 'able' or 'ablete' in France, and used mixed with glue as a varnish for wax or plaster spheres. Other papers are on the sands of rivers containing gold and the method of extraction,[13] on banks of fossil shells in Touraine which can be used as a fertiliser,[14] on the shape of a cast lead bell which rings,[15] on a copper ore like verdigris,[16] and an inflammable gas evolved from shore mud.[17]

In 1752[18] Reaumur described some important experiments on the digestive

273; J. Torlais, *Un esprit encyclopédique en dehors de l'Encyclopédie: Réaumur; d'après des documents inédits*, Paris, 1936.

[1] E. Maindron, *L'Académie des Sciences*, 1888, 103–10: the document is anonymous but has corrections by Reaumur, 'et qui nous paraît devoir lui être attribué.'

[2] AdS, 1711, h 82, m 6.   [3] AdS, 1715, m 303.

[4] Examen de la soie des araignées, AdS, 1710, m 386; it is said that this memoir was translated into Chinese.

[5] AdS, 1710, h 10, m 305, 439; 1711, h 12, m 115.

[6] AdS, 1711, h 11, 166, m 370.   [7] *Phil. Trans.*, 1685, xv, 1278, no. 178.

[8] See De Francheville, *Hist. Acad. Berlin*, 1767, 41.

[9] AdS, 1712, m 223.   [10] AdS, 1714, m 344.   [11] AdS, 1715, m 174.

[12] AdS, 1716, m 229; 1717, m 177.   [13] AdS, 1718, m 68.

[14] AdS, 1720, m 400.   [15] AdS, 1726, m 243.   [16] AdS, 1723, m 12.

[17] AdS, 1741 (1744), h 36.   [18] Sur la digestion des oiseaux, AdS, 1752, h 49, m 266.

process in birds of prey. He demonstrated the solvent power of gastric juice by letting a kite, which rejected 'casts', swallow food in a small metal tube covered with wire gauze at the ends. A swallowed sponge when squeezed out gave an opalescent acid liquid which turned blue paper red. Birds feeding on seeds have a powerful gizzard and swallow small stones to assist the trituration in the gizzard.

Since Van Helmont had shown that gastric juice is acid (see Vol. II, p. 236) this had been disputed and nearly all physiologists thought it was neutral or even alkaline; Sylvius de le Boë and Stahl minimised its importance. Haller[1] concluded that it was neutral and did not act as a ferment; it is a macerating liquid which softens and dissolves food, digestion imparting a 'wholesome animal nature' to food, giving it the beginning of vitality. The pancreatic juice served, at least partly, to soften and dilute the cystic juice so that it mixes better with the food, and 'there may be other functions of the liquid not as yet well known to us' (Claude Bernard, 1846, was the first to make these known).

Edward Stevens[2] from experiments similar to Reaumur's on man and animals concluded that digestion 'is not the effect of heat, trituration, putrefaction, or fermentation alone, but of a powerful solvent secreted by the coat of the stomach . . . it is probable that every species of animal has its peculiar gastric juice capable of dissolving certain substances only'.

Lazaro Spallanzani (Scandiano, nr. Reggio, 12 January 1729–Pavia, 11 February 1799), professor of logic, metaphysics, and Greek at Reggio (1754) and of natural history at Modena (1760) and Pavia (1769), showed that the gastric juice could digest food outside the stomach, but he thought it was not acid, and that digestion is not a fermentation, of which he recognised three kinds: vinous, acetous and putrefactive.[3] Spallanzani gives an analysis of gastric juice made by his colleague the chemist Scopoli, who found that it contained water, a saponaceous and gelatinous animal substance, sal ammoniac, and an earthy matter like that existing in all animal fluids. It precipitated silver chloride from silver nitrate. 'This phenomenon might induce us to suppose that common salt exists in the gastric juice, but the salt contained in this fluid is not common salt but sal ammoniac.'[4]

John Hunter[5] attacked Reaumur's work as 'a piece of anatomical ignorance' and Spallanzani's as like that of 'all mere experiment makers'. He distinguished digestion from fermentation (which is a spontaneous process, including putrefaction) in its effects, and says it is also different from chemical solution 'which is only the union of bodies by elective attraction', whilst digestion 'is a species

[1] *Elementa Physiologiæ*, 4°, Leyden, 1764, vi, 227–39.
[2] *Dissertatio physiologica, inauguralis, de Alimentorum concoctione*, 8°, Edinburgh, 1777 (BM T. 335. (6.)); *Thesaurus Medicus*, 1785, iii; also (with Hunter's essay) in the Appendix to the tr. of Spallanzani's *Dissertations* by Beddoes (see below); Thomson, *Animal Chemistry*, 1843, 593.
[3] Spallanzani, *Dissertazione di fisica animali e vegetabili*, 8°, Modena, 1780; tr. J. Senebier, *Expériences sur la digestion*, 8°, Geneva, 1783, and *Opuscules de Physique, Animale et Végetale*, 2 vols., Pavia, 1787, ii, 394–730; *Dissertations relative to the Natural History of Animals and Vegetables*, tr. [by T. Beddoes], 2 vols. 8°, London, 1784, 2 ed. 1789 (all vol. i consists of six dissertations on digestion).
[4] Foster, 1901, 218; Thomson, (2), 1817, iv, 605.
[5] *Phil. Trans.*, 1772, lxii, 447; *Observations on Certain Parts of the Animal Oeconomy*, 4°, London, 1786, 147–88 (Observations on Digestion).

of generation, two substances making a third . . . converting both vegetable and animal matter into the same kind of substance or compound' (chyle) which no chemical process can effect; it is an assimilating process, 'in this respect somewhat similar in its action to that excited by morbid poisons.' In 1772 he says of gastric juice: 'in all the animals, whether carnivorous or not . . . I constantly found that there was an acid, though not a strong one', but in 1782 the acid 'is only formed occasionally' and is perhaps due to 'a sugar which afterwards becomes acid'.

Bassiano Carminati (1750–1830), professor of pathology and materia medica in Pavia, found that the gastric juice of carnivora is neutral when fasting (a state used by Spallanzani), but becomes strongly acid after the animal has been fed.[1] The presence of free hydrochloric acid in gastric juice was confirmed by Prout (see p. 714); it was disputed during the nineteenth century but is now established. The first, more abundant, portion removed from the stomach is only weakly acid, being diluted by the slightly alkaline mucus contained in the fasting stomach, but the last portion removed is strongly acid.

Reaumur showed that eggs can be preserved by dipping them into melted grease.[2] He contrived a method of hatching chickens by exposing the eggs to artificial heat,[3] as had long been practised in Egypt and (unknown to him) had been invented by Drebbel (see Vol. II, p. 324).

Reaumur investigated porcelain and imitated it in devitrified glass ('Reaumur's porcelain').[4] Specimens of true porcelain from China and Japan, he found, did not change at the highest temperatures he could produce, whilst European imitations melted at quite moderate temperatures. He concluded that the imitations were glass frits, whilst true porcelain consists of two bodies, one infusible and the other fusible to a glass which makes the ware translucent. This opinion was confirmed by the account of the Chinese process of making porcelain sent from China by the Jesuit missionary Father d'Entrecolles (1664–1741).[5] Reaumur's imitation porcelain was made by heating a glass vessel embedded in sand to redness, and then allowing it to cool very slowly, when crystallisation occurs. The material is then translucent and more refractory than glass. True porcelain was made in France at Sèvres as a result of experiments by Count de Lauraguais, D'Arcet, and Legay, and Macquer, then director of Sèvres, recommended to the government that a prize should be offered for the discovery of a suitable clay. A pharmacist Villaris described a white clay of Saint-Yrieux-la-Perche in Haute Vienne, which Macquer found to be suitable.

Reaumur's investigations on the changes of volume on fusion and solidification[6] are some of the earliest in this field. He examined (i) whether solid

[1] *Ricerche sulla natura e sugli usi del succo gastrico in medicina ed in chirurgia*, 4°, Milan, 1785; NBU, 1854, viii, 770; Foster, 1901, 222.
[2] AdS, 1735, m 465.
[3] *Sur l'art de faire éclore et d'élever en toute saison des oiseaux . . . soit par le moyen de la chaleur de fumier, soit par le moyen de celle du feu ordinaire*, Paris, 1749; English and German trs.
[4] AdS, 1727, m 185; 1729, m 325.
[5] Du Halde, *Description . . . de la Chine*, 1735, ii, 177; Hoefer, (1), i, 14.
[6] AdS, 1726, h 7, m 273.

floated or sank in fused metal, (ii) whether a piece of solid floats if fused metal is poured on it, (iii) the concavity or convexity of the surface on solidification (a method which had been used by Hooke).[1] He found that water, bismuth, and iron expand on solidification. He had previously studied the crystallisation of fused metals and minerals.[2]

Reaumur's thermometer, containing alcohol, had really only one fixed point (the freezing point), and although described in 1730–1[3] was inferior to Fahrenheit's of 1724, which contained mercury and had three fixed points; Reaumur does not seem to have known of Fahrenheit's prior publication.[4] Reaumur determined the specific gravities of spirits of wine and the contractions on mixing alcohol and water.[5] He described freezing mixtures of ice and salts[6] and investigated the sparks struck from steel by flint.[7]

Reaumur's most useful publication is on 'the art of converting iron into steel and of softening cast iron',[8] which laid the foundations of the steel industry in France. In this he describes seven types of fracture of iron and steel,[9] and the cementation process, previously a secret; he showed that iron bars are converted into steel when heated embedded in a mixture of 2 pts. of soot, 1 pt. of charcoal powder, 1 pt. of wood ashes and $\frac{3}{4}$ pt. or less of common salt,[10] and concluded[11] that steel is iron impregnated with sulphureous (combustible, i.e. carbon) particles and saline particles which accompany them: les parties sulfureuses n'entrent pas seuls dans le fer, elles sont accompagnée de parties salines . . . il est donc visible que des soufres, et des sels s'introduisent dans le fer qui est en place pour être converti en acier. He refers to books of 'secret' recipes, containing mostly useless material:[12] le nombre de ces prétendus secrets est si grand que quand le véritable secret en seroit un, on auroit aussi-tôt fair de le chercher de nouveau.

Reaumur, who mentions that Perrault (1613–88) had noticed that a steel wire becomes thicker when heated and quenched, proved that steel increases in volume by $\frac{1}{48}$ in this treatment.[13] His process for converting cast iron into steel is really that described in 1540 by Biringuccio (Vol. II, p. 34), viz. immersing a piece of solid wrought iron in molten cast iron: le fer avide des soufres boit une partie de ceux de la font qui en a plus de lui.[14] He also found that cast iron is converted into malleable iron when it is heated embedded in what he calls 'safran de Mars', an oxide of iron.[15]

The cementation process described by Reaumur seems to have originated in the 17 cent., Rhys Jenkins[16] thought in England by William Ellyott and Matthias Mersey,

---

[1] *Micrographia*, 1665, 39.　　　　　[2] AdS, 1724, m 307.

[3] AdS, 1730, m 452; 1731, m 250; von Oettingen, Ostwald's *Klassiker*, 1894, No. 57, with Fahrenheit's and Celsius's papers and notes; J. N. Friend, *Nature*, 1937, cxxxix, 395, 585; Cohen and Cohen-de Meester, *Nature*, 1936, cxxxviii, 428.

[4] *Phil. Trans.*, 1724, xxxiii, 140; Celsius's scale (1742) has f.p. 100°, b.p. 0°.

[5] AdS, 1733, m 165.　　　　　　　　[6] AdS, 1734, m 167.

[7] AdS, 1736, m 391; see Hooke, Vol. II.

[8] *L'Art de convertir le fer forgé en acier et l'art d'adoucir le fer fondu et de faire des ouvrages de fer fondu aussi fines qu'en fer forgé*, 4°, Paris, 1722, 17 plates; also in *Descriptions des Arts et Métiers*, 1762; tr. Sisco and Smith, *Reaumur's Memoir on Iron and Steel*, Chicago, 1956; Percy, *Metallurgy of Iron and Steel*, 1864, 768, 804 f., 848.

[9] *L'Art*, 1722, 153 f.　　　[10] *Ib.*, 31.　　　[11] *Ib.*, 203 f., 207.

[12] *Ib.*, 9.　　　[13] *Ib.*, 314.　　　[14] *Ib.*, 250 f.　　　[15] *Ib.*, 472.

[16] *Trans. Newcomen Soc.*, 1922–3, iii, 16–27; discussion, 27–32, *Isis*, 1927, ix, 134.

patents being taken out in 1614; D. Brownlie and de Laveleye[1] thought in Liége; the usual idea that it originated somewhere, at some time, in Germany has not been substantiated.

On the publication of his work on steel in 1722 Reaumur was given a pension of 12,000 livres by the Duke of Orleans, but he made it over to the Academy for the perfection of the arts. He also introduced the manufacture of tinplate into France, showing that the iron sheets must be very clean and free from oxide before they are dipped in the bath of melted tin covered with tallow.[2] The nature of steel continued to be obscure till the work of Berthollet and Guyton de Morveau (see p. 530). In 1779 Jean Demeste, a Liége surgeon who made chemistry a hobby, thought that ordinary iron contains zinc, which is removed when it is converted into steel.[3]

DE GENSSANE

De Genssane (d. 1780, nothing seems to be known of his birth or Christian name), a director of mines in Languedoc, concessionaire of mines in Franch-Comté, member of the Société des Sciences of Montpellier and 'correspondant' of the Paris Academy, wrote on mining engineering, on the Alsatian mines,[4] and on smelting with mineral coal in a book[5] containing descriptions and illustrations of furnaces, and dealing with lead, copper, zinc, bismuth, cobalt, mercury, antimony, arsenic, brass, etc.

GOBET

Nicolas Gobet (c. 1735–c. 1781), of a family from Auvergne, studied mineralogy, travelled with Jars in 1762 to visit metal works (see p. 101), and later became librarian to the Count of Provence and secretary of the council of the Count of Artois. He composed several works and issued an edition of the *Essays* of Jean Rey in 1777 (see Vol. II, p. 631).[6] His book on the history of mineralogy[7] reprints some earlier works which are now often unobtainable:

(1) Pierre Belon, Description des Mines de Siderocapsa, 1546–9; Gobet, i, 53.

(2) Jean de Malus (père), La Recherche et Descouverte des Mines de Montagnes Pyrenées (written in 1600, revised by Jean Dupuy); Gobet, i, 75.

(3) César d'Arcons, Sur les Mines Metalliques en France, 4°, Bordeaux, 1667; Gobet, 461, text 477.

(4) Charles Hautin de Villars, Mémoire concernant les Mines de France, 1712–30, and Traité de l'art métallique, 1730 (extract from Barba); Gobet, i, 176.

[1] *J. Iron and Steel Inst.*, 1930, cxxi, 455–76 (with discussion).
[2] AdS, 1725, h 29, m 102; Principes de l'art de faire le fer blanc.
[3] *Lettres du Docteur Demeste . . . Sur la Chymie, la Docimasie, la Cristallographie, la Lithologie, la Minéralogie & la Physique en général*, 2 vols. 12°, Paris, 1779; tr., *Briefe über die Chemie, Probierkunst, Kristallographie, Lithologie, Mineralogie und Physik*, 8°, St. Petersburg, 1784; Gmelin, (1), iii, 620; Kopp, (1), iv, 141.
[4] AdS, *Mém. div. Sav.*, 1763, iv, 141; Gobet, 1779, ii, 743–94.
[5] *Traité de la fonte des mines par le feu du charbon de terre, ou Traité de la construction et usage des fourneaux propres à la fonte et affinage des métaux et des minéraux par le feu du charbon de terre*, 2 vols. 4°, Paris, 1770, 1776 (ii ll. 68, 326 pp.; 8, 22, 504 pp.; 76 folding plates).
[6] NBG, 1857, xx, 866.
[7] *Les anciens Minéralogistes du Royaume de France; Avec des Notes*, 2 vols., Paris, 1779 (pagin. cont.).

(5) Jean Astruc, Mine de plomb pris de Durfort, Alais, 1737; Gobet, i, 505.

(6) Other items in Gobet are Reaumur on iron mines (i, 197), mines in Baigorri (Navarre) (i, 202), Gascony (i, 232), Roussillon (i, 249), Auvergne (ii, 515), Limosin (ii, 530), Limoges (ii, 540), Glanges (ii, 554), Berry (ii, 565), Lyon (ii, 581), and Alix (ii, 706). Gobet quotes works by the Abbé de Sauvages (on mercury and vitriol) (ii, 510), Yves de Michel (1651) (ii, 636), Chambon (1714) (ii, 644), Nicolas le Ragois (1682) (ii, 671), Courtepée (1760) (ii, 678), Sebastian Munster (1550) (ii, 702), Jean Vic (1636) (ii, 720), and Dunod [1737] (ii, 724), and has a note on *vasa murrhina* (ii, 708, see Vol. I).

Du Fay

Charles François de Cisternay Du Fay (Paris; 14 September 1698–16 July 1739) was first a captain in the French army (1723), then became associate chemist of the Academy and (1732) superintendent of the Botanic Garden in Paris.[1] He published on a 'sel de chaux' obtained by evaporating lime water,[2] on the solubility of glass,[3] on the manufacture of potash in the Rhine provinces,[4] and on colour and solution of stones (changes of colour of gems on heating).[5] In a memoir on phosphorescent bodies (including barium sulphide and phosphorus)[6] he reverted to N. Lemery's old theory (see p. 36) that the phosphorescence arises from an actual combustion taking place in the 'sulphureous part' of the body. He experimented on the phosphorescence of diamonds: four hundred yellow diamonds were all phosphorescent; some white, rose-coloured, blue, or green, were not. He recognised that the diamond must first be exposed to the sun, but when it ceases to shine it phosphoresces again when heated in the dark. Yellow diamonds, he thought, contained sulphur.[7] He described experiments on the bleaching of crimson silk in sunlight and introduced test-liquors giving in a few minutes results which would require several days exposure to sunlight.[8]

In six memoirs on electricity[9] he distinguished two kinds of electricity, vitreous and resinous 'électricité' or 'matière électrique'; I. B. Cohen[10] thinks not completely with the meaning of two 'electric fluids' in the sense understood by Robert Symmer[11] (who mentions Du Fay), although Priestley[12] puts Du Fay's 'discovery of two electricities' or two kinds of 'electric matter', alongside Franklin's theory that 'the vitreous electricity is positive, or a redundancy of electric matter; and the resinous, negative, or a want of it'.

L. C. Bourdelin

Louis Claude Bourdelin (Paris; 18 October 1696–13 September 1777), the nephew of Claude Bourdelin (see p. 13), entered the Academy in 1725 and

[1] Fontenelle, AdS, 1739, h 73; *Oeuvres*, 1792, vii, 522–38.
[2] AdS, 1724, h 39, m 88.   [3] AdS, 1727, h 25, m 32.
[4] AdS, 1727, h 34.   [5] AdS, 1728, m 50.
[6] AdS, 1730, h 48–52, m 524–35.   [7] AdS, 1735, h 1–4, m 347–72.
[8] AdS, 1737, h 56–62, m 253–68; Hellot, *The Art of Dyeing*, London, 1789.
[9] AdS, 1733, h 4, m 233, 457; 1734, m 341, 503; 1737, m 86; *Phil. Trans.*, 1734, xxxviii, 258; abdg. ed., 1809, vii, 629; *Versuche und Abhandlung von der Electricitaet der Coerper*, 8°, Erfurt, 1745 (7 ll., xxiv, 311 pp., 1 folding plate, 1 engraving in text).
[10] *Franklin and Newton*, Philadelphia, 1956, 372 f.
[11] *Phil. Trans.*, 1759, li, 371.   [12] *History of Electricity*, 1769, 43.

soon after became professor of chemistry in the Jardin du Roi (where in 1770–1 he was followed by Macquer).[1] His health was poor and his publications unimportant. In memoirs on lixivial salts (1728)[2] and lixivial salt of guaiacum (1730)[3] he tries to show that alkali is present in plants before combustion. Other publications are on amber (1742),[4] in which he thought he had shown that succinic acid contains hydrochloric acid (he burnt it with saltpetre containing chloride), and on boracic acid (sel sédatif), which he thought contained sulphuric acid.[5] He found that copper salts (blue vitriol) as well as boric acid colour an alcohol flame green.[6]

HELLOT

Jean Hellot (Paris; 20 November 1685–15 February 1766) was intended for the church but an uncle interested him in chemistry. He was a pupil of E. F. Geoffroy. He visited England (he became F.R.S. in 1740). After his return to France he was elected to the Academy in 1735 and was a member of various commissions. He was made inspector general of dyeing in 1740 and his interests were mainly technical.[7] In 1737[8] he described a salt crystallising in prisms from a solution of the heated residue from evaporated urine, but he thought it was a kind of gypsum. It was recognised as a definite salt (microcosmic salt) by F. G. Haupt in 1740.[9] In 1737 a stranger in Paris offered to communicate a process for making phosphorus, and Hellot, Du Fay, Geoffroy, and Duhamel were commissioned to try it in the laboratory of the Jardin du Roi. The process succeeded, a reward was given the stranger, and Hellot published in great detail the method of preparation of phosphorus by distilling the residue of evaporated urine with sand,[10] but thought it was a compound of 'acide du sel commun uni à une matière grasse' (hydrochloric acid and fatty matter). He gives the date of Brand's discovery as 1677 and says Hanckewitz had the complete monopoly of the manufacture of solid phosphorus in Europe, no one else being able to make it. He thought some experimenters had not really obtained solid phosphorus, stopping the process when they observed phosphorescence in the receiver and not persisting with the application of a very high temperature.

Hellot's publications on dyeing and the theory of dyes[11] are important. He

[1] Condorcet, AdS, 1777, h 118; Oeuvres, 1847, ii, 270–82; Dorveaux, Isis, 1930, xiv, 492; for another Claude Louis Bourdelin, 1667–1711, see AdS, 1711, h 108.
[2] AdS, 1728 (1730), m 384.   [3] AdS, 1730 (1732), m 33.   [4] AdS, 1742, m 143–75.
[5] AdS, 1753, h 178, m 201; 1755, h 67, m 397; cf. La Sône, AdS, 1755, h 61, m 119.
[6] AdS, 1755, h 67, m 397.
[7] AdS, 1766 (1769), h 167; Hoefer, (1), ii, 375; Quérard, La France Littéraire, 1830, iv, 56; Thomson, (1), i, 284.
[8] AdS, 1737, m 342.
[9] Diatribe Chemica de sale urinæ perlato mirabile, 4°, Königsberg, 1740; Gmelin, (1), ii, 368, 710.
[10] AdS, 1737, m 342.
[11] AdS, 1740, h 59, m 126; 1741, h 79, m 38; L'Art de la teinture des laines et des étoffes de laine en grand et petit teint. Avec une instruction sur les deboüillis, 12°, Paris, 1750; new ed. 1786; The Art of Dyeing Wool, Silk and Cotton. Translated from the French of M. Hellot, M. Macquer and M. Le Pileur d'Apligny, London, Baldwin, 1789; repr. 1901 (Macquer in silk, 233 f., d'Alpigny on cotton, 341 f.); tr. A. G. Kästner, Färbekunst, oder Unterricht Wolle und wollene Zeuge zu farben, 8°, Altenburg, 1751, 2 ed. 1764, 3 ed. by C. A. Hoffmann, 1790 (Gmelin, (1),

assumed a purely physical explanation that the dye entered the pores of the wool (which must first be dilated), and the pores are then closed by its astringent action. Mordants such as alum act by forming lakes and also close the pores of the fabric. Dyes deposited on the surface are easily washed off. Hellot says the colouring particles are encased and cemented in the pores in the same manner, as Chaptal said, as a diamond is set in the bezel (collet) of a ring.[1] He clearly appreciated the action of mordants, and said 'the salts and metallic solutions unite with the particles of the colouring ingredient'.[2]

In 1745 Hellot went to Lyon to study the refining of the precious metals and on his return to Paris was commissioned to examine the processes of mining and assaying.[3] He showed in 1763 that the cupellation process often gives too little silver.[4] He published a translation of Schlüter's *Unterricht von Hütten-Werken* (see Vol. II, p. 715)[5] in which the arrangement is improved and new matter added. Hellot also improved the manufacture of porcelain at Sèvres, and was the first important French industrial chemist. Oil of vitriol was then imported from Holland; Hellot described in detail the preparation of fuming sulphuric acid by distilling green vitriol, obtaining an 'icy oil of vitriol' which must have been sulphur trioxide.[6] He showed that strongly ignited alumina is insoluble in acids.[6]

In 1763 he was associated with Montigny and Duhamel on an Academy committee in the investigation of a fire-damp explosion in a coal mine in Briançon, apparently the first recorded event of this kind in France. The report[7] gives an account of fire-damp (les vapeurs inflammable) and choke-damp, and recommends thorough ventilation of mines as a preventive of explosions.

Hellot showed that white vitriol is formed by dissolving zinc in dilute oil of vitriol, and butter of zinc (zinc chloride) by distilling zinc oxide with sal ammoniac. He thought zinc was a compound and tried to decompose it.[8] He called sulphuric, hydrochloric and nitric acids 'acides minéraux'. The red nitrous fumes he thought were due to the presence of iron in nitre.[9] He investigated sympathetic ink, which he showed was prepared from a cobalt mineral. He also says writing on paper with dilute silver nitrate becomes visible only after three or four months if the paper is kept closed up, but after an hour if it is exposed to sunlight, 'parce qu'on accélére l'évaporation de l'acide.'[10] He investigated ether.[11]

iii, 29; Bolton, (1), 521). The 'teinturiers de grand teint' dyed in fast colours for a luxury market, the 'teinturiers de petit teint' used cheaper and more fugitive but brilliant colours for cheaper kinds of cloth; Guerlac, *Chymia*, 1959, v, 73–112.

[1] Hellot, *The Art of Dyeing*, 1901, 72, 80; Chaptal, *Chemistry applied to Arts and Manufactures*, 1807, iv, 418; J. J. Beer, *Isis*, 1960, li, 21–30, says this physical theory was revived by W. Crum about 1843.

[2] *The Art of Dyeing*, 1901, 119–20, 137.
[3] Sur l'exploitation des mines, AdS, 1756, m 134.
[4] Hellot, Tillet, and Macquer, AdS, 1763, m 1.
[5] *De la Font, des Mines, des Fonderies*, etc., 2 vols. 4°, Paris, 1750–3, 55 plates.
[6] AdS, 1738, m 288.   [7] AdS, 1763, m 235.
[8] AdS, 1735, m 12, 221.   [9] AdS, 1736, m 23.
[10] AdS, 1737, m 101, 228; see Hoffmann, Vol. II, p. 699; Beckmann, (1), i, 109.
[11] AdS, 1739, m 62.

DUHAMEL DU MONCEAU

Henri Louis Duhamel du Monceau (Paris; 1700–22 July 1781 or 23 August 1782), said to be of Dutch descent, the family having settled in France in the 15 cent., was a pupil in the Collège d'Harcourt, where he made little progress, but he attended the lectures of Du Fay, Bernard de Jussieu, Geoffroy and Lemery. He became F.R.S. in 1734 and a member of the Paris Academy in 1740. A man of considerable wealth, he was able to devote his life to the service of his country in a variety of ways, e.g. as inspector general of the navy, in which capacity he made many experiments. His work in physiology, botany, agriculture, meteorology, and applied chemistry was mostly done in collaboration with his brother on his large estate at Denainvilliers, where he was the first to cultivate the potato in France.[1] In his first book on trees[2] he describes the manufacture of maple sugar in Canada, in his second book on trees[3] the manufacture of soap in Marseilles. He wrote a number of the treatises on industrial arts published in the *Descriptions des Arts et Métiers* (see p. 11):

L'art du charbonnier, 1761; Additions et corrections relatives à l'art du charbonnier, n.d.; L'art du cirier, 1762; L'art du tuilier et du briquetier, 1763 (with Fourcroy and Gallon); L'art du raffiner le sucre, 1764, new ed. by J. E. Bertrand, 4°, Paris, 1812; L'art du chandelier, 1764; L'art de faire des pipes à fumer le tabac, 1771; L'art de faire differentes sortes de colles, 1771; L'art du potier de terre, 1773; L'art du savonnier, 1774; L'art de fabriquer l'amidon, 1775; the volume on L'art du convertir le cuivre rouge en laiton, 1764, sometimes attributed to Duhamel, is by Gallon. Of the 73 treatises in the collection, 19 are by Duhamel, 3 by Reaumur (2 with additions by Duhamel; Reaumur's treatises were published after his death in 1757) and one by Duhamel, Fourcroy and Gallon.

Duhamel's treatises are written in a non-technical style and were intended for persons of good general education rather than specialists. Most of his chemical work was in collaboration with Grosse, a young chemist and a member of the Academy (see p. 49). Duhamel and Grosse showed that tartar contains potash, but they regarded it as a true acid.[4] They obtained pure ether[5] by adding water to the distillate from alcohol and sulphuric acid and then distilling at a gentle heat. Grosse found that on saturating nitric acid with lead a black powder deposited, which he said contained mercury.[6]

Important memoirs by Duhamel are on the purple dye (extending Reaumur's observations of 1711),[7] on the preparation of sal ammoniac,[8] and especially those in which the alkalis potash and soda are differentiated.[9] Duhamel proved that the salts of the two alkalis with mineral acids (acides

---

[1] Condorcet, *Oeuvres*, 1847, ii, 610–43 (Dumonceau); Hoefer, (1), ii, 366, 387; Kopp, (1), i, 218; iv, 31; Thomson, (1), i, 289; Vicq d'Azyr, i, 121 (says d. 13 August 1782).

[2] *Traité des Arbres et Arbustes qui se cultivent en France en pleine terre*, 2 vols. 4°, 1755, i, 32.

[3] *De la Physique des Arbres*, 2 vols. 4°, 1758, ii, 83.

[4] AdS, 1732, h 47, m 323; 1733, h 39, m 260.

[5] Recherches chimiques sur la composition d'une liqueur très-volatile connue sous le nom d'éther, AdS, 1734, m 41.

[6] AdS, 1733, h 41, m 313–28.

[7] Quelques expériences sur la liqueur colorante qui fournit la pourpre, espéce de coquille qu'on trouve abondamment sur les côtes de Provence; AdS, 1736, m 49.

[8] AdS, 1735, h 23, m 106, 414, 483.

[9] Sur la base du sel marin, AdS, 1736, h 65, m 215–32; Kopp, (1), iii, 69, says Duhamel first used the name 'base' for a substance forming salts with acids.

mineraux) differ in crystalline form, solubility, etc., and that the base of
common salt is identical with the alkali (soda) of the kali plant, of Egyptian
natrum, and of borax (la plus grande partie du Borax est encore de ce genre).
He converted common salt into Glauber's salt by heating it with oil of vitriol,
and converted the sodium sulphate into sulphide (hepar sulphuris) by heating
with charcoal, whereby he had 'rompu en partie l'union de l'acide vitriolique
avec la base du sel marin, parce que dans cet état la force de l'acide vitriolique
se trouva partagée entre la matière inflammable et le Sel alkali'. By the action
of vinegar he converted the sodium sulphide into acetate, the solution of which
he evaporated to dryness without isolating the salt. On strongly heating the
sodium acetate a fetid oil came over, and on breaking the retort the gaseous
contents (acetone vapour) ignited like spirit of wine. The residue was the 'sel
alkali fixe' (soda), 'car en effet que pourroit il m'être resté autre chose.'[1] The
reactions used by Duhamel were:

$$2NaCl + H_2SO_4 = Na_2SO_4 + 2HCl$$
$$Na_2SO_4 + 2C = Na_2S + 2CO_2$$
$$Na_2S + 2CH_3COOH = 2CH_3COONa + H_2S$$
$$2CH_3COONa = Na_2CO_3 + (CH_3)_2CO.$$

A more direct method was to evaporate common salt two or three times with
nitric acid (esprit de nitre), when cubic nitre (nitre quadrangulaire; sodium
nitrate) was formed. This was deflagrated with charcoal in a crucible and the
alkali extracted from the residue with water:

$$3NaCl + 4HNO_3 = 3NaNO_3 + NOCl + Cl_2 + 2H_2O$$
$$4NaNO_3 + 5C = 2Na_2CO_3 + 2N_2 + 3CO_2.$$

It is curious that Duhamel[2] says nitre is not decomposed by a 'feu le plus
violent'. He did not reach a high enough temperature and his mistake was
corrected by Pott.[3]

Duhamel showed[4] that when plants growing on the sea shore, the ash of
which is mainly soda, are grown inland, the soda is gradually replaced by
potash, and this was confirmed by Louis Claude Cadet,[5] who analysed the
ashes of kali plants on Duhamel's estate at Denainvilliers. John Mitchell[6] had
completely confused the two kinds of alkali. Guyton de Morveau[7] said that
Marggraf and Duhamel had 'in a way exhausted the resources of chemistry
without reaching success' in attempts to find an economical process for
making soda from common salt, which is 'much to be desired'. Success was
first achieved by Leblanc (see p. 563).

The name potash (potasse), from the German Pottasche (pot ash), was first approved
by the Académie française in 1762:[8] its origin is probably, as Bergman[9] suggested, the

[1] Ib., m 224.   [2] AdS, 1736, m 215 (218).
[3] Miscell. Berolin., 1743, vii, 285; Dissertations Chymiques, 1759, ii, 297.
[4] AdS, 1767, h 51, m 233, 239.
[5] Sur le soude de Varech, AdS, 1767, h 53, m 487; 1774, h 22, m 42.
[6] On the Preparation and Uses of the various kinds of Potash, Phil. Trans., 1748, xlv, 541.
[7] Élémens de Chymie, Dijon, 1778, iii, 197.   [8] Lippmann, (1), ii, 321.
[9] Ed. of Scheffers Chemiske Föreläsningar, Uppsala, 1775, § 34, n. 2; tr. Weigel, 1779, 67.

method of boiling the extract of wood ashes in iron pots. Scheffer[1] says the French pearl-ash (Perl-Asche or cendre gravelée) was made by burning wine yeast (Hefe) or impure tartar. The name 'potassa' was proposed by Murray.[2]

Duhamel[3] showed that trees could be grown in filtered and in distilled water, thus repeating Van Helmont's experiment. In a memoir on lime[4] he showed that lime water is precipitated by a solution of mild alkali (potassium carbonate), which he attributed to the union of an acid in the lime with an earth in the alkali. He obtained crystals of potassium bicarbonate (cf. Cavendish, p. 317). He found that limestone lost nearly half its weight on burning to quicklime, but regained part on slaking by exposure to air, but a loss of $5\frac{1}{2}$ oz. per lb. remained. This memoir was specially noticed by Lavoisier.[5]

Duhamel[6] confirmed that the bones of birds fed on madder are coloured red by its dye. Belchier[7] had found the same with animals and birds. Duhamel had been informed by Sir Hans Sloane that the bones of young animals fed on madder were tinged red. By feeding them alternately with food mixed with madder and with ordinary food, Duhamel found that the bones developed alternate layers of red and white, and concluded that bones increase by the addition of successive layers and not by addition of earthy matter in the meshes of the organised network which forms their tissues. The question was discussed from both points of view by later physiologists, but Duhamel's method of experiment was certainly ingenious. Experiments on the subject were made by Berzelius.[8] Duhamel gave the results of experiments on the spontaneous combustion of large pieces of cloth soaked in oil and compressed.[9] Thomson says two accidental combustions in Russia twenty years after were suspected to be due to sabotage, but the empress Catharine II suspected the true cause and had experiments made which confirmed Duhamel's.

BARON

The composition of borax, after its investigation by Geoffroy (p. 56), was finally settled by Théodore Baron.[10] There were three physicians called Baron: Hyacinthe Théodore Baron the father (Paris; April 1686–28 July 1758) and his two sons, Hyacinthe Théodore Baron (Paris; 12 August 1707–27 March 1787) and Théodore Baron d'Hénouville (Paris; 17 June 1715–10 March 1768), a pupil of Rouelle, whom he succeeded as demonstrator in the Jardin du Roi. According to Hoefer[11] the last is the one concerned here. The author of the papers calls himself 'M. Baron' and in his edition of Lemery's *Cours de Chymie* simply 'Baron'. He showed that borax is formed by the combination of soda with the substance (boric acid) previously called *sel sédatif*, etc.: 'on

[1] *Op. cit.*, § 35; 1779, 71.   [2] *System of Chemistry*, Edinburgh, 1806, ii, 76.
[3] AdS, 1748, h 71, m 272.   [4] AdS, 1747, m 59; begun in 1733.
[5] *Opuscules Physiques et Chimiques*, 1801, 153–6.
[6] *Phil. Trans.*, 1740, xli, 390.   [7] *Phil. Trans.*, 1736, xxxix, 287, 299.
[8] *N. allgem. J. Chem.*, 1805, iv, 119.   [9] AdS, 1757, m 150.
[10] Expériences pour servir à l'analyse du borax, AdS *Mém. div. Sav.*, 1750, i, 295–328 (read January 1747), 447–77 (read July 1748); D'un Sel apporté de Perse sous le nom de Borech, *ib.*, 1755, ii, 412–34 (read June 1752, mentions Model, see p. 57); Baron, ed. of Lemery's *Cours de Chymie*, 1756, 539.
[11] (1), 1869, ii, 383; NBG, 1852, iv, 544.

peut régénerer le borax en unissant le sel sédatif avec le sel du soude.' Scheele proved this independently in 1768.[1] R. A. Vogel[2] later concluded that borax is a compound of an acid like vitriolic acid with a peculiar alkali, different from soda, but Baron's result was generally accepted.

In his notes to his edition of Lemery's *Cours de Chymie* (1756) Baron makes constant use of the phlogiston theory and often quotes Stahl. He says[3] that in the formation of red precipitate *per se*, saline particles from the air unite with the mercury (he does not mention the increase in weight).

Sodium acetate was apparently first obtained by Duhamel (1736, see p. 70) but he did not isolate it. Crystalline sodium acetate is mentioned by J. F. Meyer[4] as *terra foliata tartari crystallisabilis*, but Thomson[5] says it 'seems to have been first examined by Baron', who in his memoir on borax (1747)[6] describes it as 'un sel neutre singulier qui n'a été jusqu'ici connu de personne' and as containing 'l'acide du vinaigre uni à l'alkali fixe minéral'. He gives its preparation and properties, but does not name it.

MALOUIN

Paul Jacques Malouin (Caen, 1701–Versailles, 31 December 1777) succeeded Astruc at the Collège Royal, was pensionnaire chimiste of the Academy and professor of chemistry at the Jardin du Roi (1745), F.R.S. 1753.[7] He wrote on milling and baking in the *Descriptions des Arts et Métiers* (see p. 69), 1767, xxii (Description et Détails des Arts du Meunier, de Vermicellier et du Boulanger). It is said that when Parmentier had read a paper on baking to the Academy in which he criticised Malouin he dared not look at him, whereupon the old man said: 'Recevez mes compliments; vous avez vu mieux que moi.' Malouin also wrote some of the chemical articles in the first *Encyclopédie*, some medical works, and books on pharmaceutical chemistry.[8] His chemical papers are on the analogies between tin and zinc,[9] on salt of lime,[10] and an analysis of the 'eaux savonneuses' of Plombières,[11] which he thought contained fixed alkali and fatty matter. He confirmed that zinc is a peculiar metal but was unable to combine it with sulphur. He plated iron and copper with zinc to prevent corrosion. The memoir on salt of lime dealt with Du Fay's preparation (see p. 66) and Malouin showed that it was merely the 'cream' (calcium carbonate) collecting on lime water exposed to air.

---

[1] Nordenskiöld, *Scheele, Nachgelassene Briefe*, 1892, 23.
[2] *De sale sedativo Hombergii*, Göttingen, 1759 (not in BM); in *Opuscula medica selecta*, 4°, Göttingen, 1768, 215–40.
[3] Lemery, *Cours de Chymie*, 1756, 245.
[4] *Alchemistische Briefe*, Hannover, 1767; q. by Kopp, (1), iv, 341.   [5] (2), 1807, iii, 61.
[6] AdS, *Mém. div. Sav.*, 1750, i, 295 (326–8).   [7] Condorcet, *Oeuvres*, 1847, ii, 320–33.
[8] *Traité de Chimie, contenant la manière de préparer les remèdes qui sont le plus en usage dans la pratique de la médecine*, 12°, Paris, 1734, 2 vols. 1755; *Lettre en réponse à la critique du Traité de Chimie*, 12°, Paris, 1735; *Pharmacopée Chimique ou Chimie Médicinale*, 2 vols. 12°, 1750, 1755–6; the first tr. by G. H. Königsdörfer, *Die medicinische Chemie*, 2 vols. 8°, Altenburg, 1763–4; Gmelin, (1), ii, 378; Hoefer, (1), ii, 393.
[9] AdS, 1742, h 44, m 76; 1743, m 70.
[10] AdS, 1745, h 38–43, m 93–106.   [11] AdS, 1746, h 49, m 109.

G. F. ROUELLE

Guillaume François Rouelle (Mathieu, nr. Caen, Normandy, 16 September 1703–Passy, nr. Paris, 3 August 1770) came from a family of agriculturists and throughout his life retained some characteristics of his origin. He studied at the College of Blois and the University of Caen, and in Paris, where he became an apothecary in 1725. He was demonstrator in chemistry from 1742 to 1768 at the Jardin du Roi, where Bourdelin and later Macquer were professors, resigning on account of ill-health.[1]

Many famous French chemists (including Lavoisier in 1763–4) were his pupils and Hoefer says: 'il faut revendiquer pour lui une part glorieuse dans cette grande révolution scientifique dont Lavoisier est le chef'; what Lavoisier would have thought of this may be imagined. Rouelle was eccentric in habits and blunt in speech, although well liked by his contemporaries. On entering the laboratory for his lecture he was correctly dressed in velvet and with a powdered wig, holding his three-cornered hat under his arm. As he warmed to his subject he dispensed with hat, wig, coat, and waistcoat in turn. His lectures (many manuscript copies of which are extant) announced some original discoveries, often first made known by his pupils, whom he accused of plagiarism, which he considered the worst human vice.[2] Some of his lectures, including a history of chemistry, were published from notes taken by Diderot (the editor of the *Encyclopédie*) by Henry.[3] The Bibliothèque Nationale has the following publications attributed to him:

1. Cours d'Expériences Chimiques: les plantes, les animaux et les minéreaux sont l'objet de ces expériences, 4°, *c.* 1759, 4 pp., stating that G. F. Rouelle commencera ses expériences [le 17] novembre 176[6] (BN 8° Te^{163}. 1244); presumably a syllabus of his course.
2. Expériences faites par MM. Rouelle et D'Arcet d'après celles de M. Sage sur la quantité d'or qu'on retire de la terre végétale, et les cendres des végétaux, 12°, *s.l.e.a.*, 19 pp. (BN S. 21941).
3. Exposé des principes et de vertus de l'eau d'une source découverte à Vaugirard, 4°, *s.a.*, 8 pp.
4. Analyses chimiques des nouvelles eaux minérales, vitrioliques, ferrugineuse, découvertes à Passy, 12°, Paris, 1757 (viii, 133 pp.; reprint of analyses by Venel, Bayen, Rouelle, and Cadet de Gassicourt; BN 8° Te^{163}. 1244).

Although he taught the phlogiston theory Rouelle was not the first to introduce this into France (as is often said), since it had been used by Geoffroy and was fully explained in the *Nouveau Cours de Chymie, suivant les Principes de Newton & de Sthall* (see p. 58) in 1723, at a time when Rouelle was still a student.[4] Lavoisier (1772)[5] says Stahl's phlogiston theory was not known in France until this book was published. Rouelle firmly supported the theory.[6]

[1] Cap, 1857, i, 231–63; Hoefer, NBG, 1863, xlii, 710; *id.*, (1), ii, 378; McKie, *Endeavour*, 1953, xii, 130 (portr.); Schofield, *Pharm. J.*, 1948, clxi, 199; Venel, *Ency. Méthod., Chimie*, 1796, iii, 302; I have not seen: J.-P. Constant, *L'Enseignement de la Chimie au Jardin Royal des Plantes de Paris*, Cahors, 1952; P. Dorveaux, *Revue d'histoire de la Pharmacie*, 1933, xxi, 169–86.
[2] F. M. Grimm, *Correspondance littéraire, philosophique et critique*, 16 vols., Paris, 1879, ix, 106.
[3] *Revue Scient.*, 1884, viii, 97; 1885, ix, 801; for a manuscript at Clifton College, see Holmyard, *Makers of Chemistry*, Oxford, 1931, 189.
[4] Anon. (J.R.P.), *Nature*, 1954, clxxiii, 429.
[5] *Oeuvres*, 1865, iii, 261–73.   [6] Fourcroy, (2), iii, 455.

D

In 1744 Rouelle entered the Academy and published a memoir on salts.[1] At that time the definition of a salt given by Tachenius (Vol. II, p. 293) had been much confused by Stahl (Vol. II, p. 678), but in the definition and classification of salts into acid, neutral (and basic), Rouelle had long been anticipated in the book by Rothe (1717), which he could have read in the French translation (1741) (Vol. II, p. 687). Rouelle says:

je donne à la famille des sels neutres toute l'extension qu'elle peut avoir; j'apelle sel neutre moyen ou *salé*, tout sel formé par l'union de quelqu'acide que ce soit, ou minéral ou végétal, avec un alkali fixe, un alkali volatil, une terre absorbante, une substance métallique, ou une huile.

He placed salts in six classes according to their crystalline form and ease of crystallisation and gives a table of salts arranged under the acid for the genus and the bases (he uses the name 'base') for the species, and says:

je me suis servi d'une petite croix pour exprimer l'union d'une acide à une substance quelconque afin d'exprimer brièvement les sels neutres que n'ont point en Chymie de caractère propre ou simple.

He regarded a metallic salt as a compound of the acid and the metal, not the calx. He characterised the water of crystallisation of a salt: j'appelle cette eau qui entre ainsi dans la formation des crystaux, l'eau *de la crystallisation*, afin de la distinguer de l'eau qui se dissipe par l'evaporation, à laquelle je donne le nom d'*eau surabondante à la crystallisation*, ou d'eau de la dissolution. In 1745[2] Rouelle described the various forms of the crystals of common salt (including 'hopper' crystals) deposited in various circumstances. He was much interested in crystallography.

In 1754[3] Rouelle speaks of a 'point de saturation' and says a neutral salt is: 'formé par l'union d'un acide avec une substance quelconque qui lui sert de base, et lui donne une forme concrète ou solide.' He distinguished between (1) neutral salts (sels neutres, parfaits ou salés) and (2) acid salts (sels neutres avec excès ou surabondance d'acide).

In acid salts: il ne faut pas que l'acide soit simplement mêlé avec le sel neutre, il faut qu'il y ait cohérence de cet acide avec les autres parties, qu'il fasse combinaison, et qu'il y en ait une just quantité: l'excès d'acide a aussi son point de saturation. As an example he quoted corrosive sublimate (mercuric chloride) which he thought (as many did later) was the neutral salt calomel (mercurous chloride) combined with an excess of acid.

Rouelle's class (3), sels neutres qui ont une très petite quantité d'acide, did not include what we call basic salts, since he gave as an example silver chloride, which is insoluble because of the small quantity of acid it contains, although it is quite neutral to vegetable colours. He did point out that turpeth mineral (basic mercuric sulphate) and the salt which remains in solution when turpeth is precipitated from a solution of mercuric sulphate by water, contain different proportions of acid.

[1] Sur les sels neutres; AdS, 1744, m 353–64.
[2] AdS, 1745, h 32, m 57–79: Sur la crystallisation du sel marin.
[3] AdS, 1754, h 79–86, m 572–88: Sur la surabondance d'acide qu'on observe en quelques Sels neutres.

Rouelle showed that in addition to neutral *arcanum duplicatum* (sulphate of potash), a compound of acid and alkaline 'salts' (i.e. acid and alkali; Rothe did not call these 'salts'), an acid sulphate (potassium hydrogen sulphate, $KHSO_4$) can be obtained by heating the neutral sulphate with sulphuric acid, and he instanced other cases. He emphasised that there is true combination (combinaison) between the parts of acid salts, and although Baumé[1] maintained that they were only mixtures, Rouelle's point of view was defended by Bayen (1774-5) in the case of basic salts of mercury,[2] and by Bergman (1775)[3] in the case of acid salts.

Most of the material in Rouelle's memoirs was well known to German chemists but their publication was probably useful in instructing the members of the Paris Academy. Double salts seem to have been first recognised by Fourcroy (1790)[4] in the case of magnesium ammonium sulphate: he calls them 'triple salts', the 'double salts' (as in the old nomenclature) being compounds of an acid and a base.

In 1747 Rouelle described the inflammation of turpentine and other essential and fatty oils by concentrated nitric acid,[5] an experiment he showed in his lectures, challenging his young auditors to find out how it was done. Borrichius (1673)[6] had described it with insufficient detail and other chemists (e.g. Dippel) could not succeed without adding some concentrated sulphuric acid.[7] Rouelle first added a small quantity of very concentrated nitric acid, which produced a 'mushroom' of finely divided carbon, and, after some decomposition had occurred, poured on a fresh portion of acid, when ignition occurred. He recognised[8] that the success of the experiment depended on the use of very concentrated nitric acid. Some oils inflamed only when concentrated sulphuric acid was used as well, and Rouelle knew that it acted by withdrawing water from the nitric acid: l'acide vitriolique concentré se charge du phlegme de l'acide nitreux, il le concentre, & le met par conséquent en état d'agir avec beaucoup plus de force sur les huiles.[9] This correct interpretation preceded by exactly a century the use of the 'mixed acid' in nitrating aromatic hydrocarbons such as benzene, patented by Mansfield in 1847.[10] Rouelle also noticed that nitric acid renders olive oil white and solid.

Rouelle obtained monoclinic sulphur by allowing fused sulphur to solidify until about half was still liquid and pouring off the liquid.[11] His memoir on mummies[12] describes the examination of actual specimens. His extensive researches on vegetables were not published. He attempted to determine their proximate principles (principes immédiates) by analysis and divided them

[1] *Chymie expérimentale et raisonnée*, Paris, 1773, i, 390; ii, 189 f.
[2] *Opuscules Chimiques*, Paris, An VI, i, 315 f.
[3] De attractionibus electivis, § ix; in *Nova Acta Reg. Soc. Sci. Upsal.*, 1775, iii, 159-248; *Opuscula physica et chemica*, Upsaliæ, 1783, iii, 318.
[4] (4), 1793, ii, 182: une espèce de sel triple, ou composé d'un acide et de deux bases.
[5] AdS, 1747, h 59-65, m 34-56: Sur l'inflammation des huiles par l'esprit de nitre.
[6] *Thom. Bartholini Acta medica et philosophica Hafniensia*, Copenhagen, 1673, i, 133.
[7] Gren, 1794, § 698; i, 432.
[8] *Op. cit.*, m 40.   [9] *Op. cit.*, m 51.
[10] Romocki, *Geschichte der Explosivstoffe*, 1895, i, 217.
[11] Fourcroy, (3), 1790, ii, 128; Murray, 1806, ii, 401; see Baumé, p. 93.
[12] AdS, 1750, h 53-62, m 123-50: Sur les embaumements des Égyptiens; Partington, (1), 1935, 173.

into five (Fourcroy says three) classes; he also examined the salts contained in vegetables.[1]

Rouelle was a very expert manipulator; Fourcroy[2] says the process for making phosphorus described by Hellot (see p. 67) was so difficult that no chemist repeated it 'but Rouelle, the elder, who, in his courses of chemistry, went through it several times with success'. Fourcroy[3] says Rouelle between 1750 and 1770 devised a modification of Hales's apparatus consisting of a retort and a receiver having a delivery tube carrying the gaseous products to a jar filled with and inverted over water in a trough. This apparatus was improved by Lavoisier[4] who refers it to Hales 'corrigé par feu M. Rouelle'.

H. M. ROUELLE

G. F. Rouelle's younger brother, Hilaire Martin Rouelle (Mathieu, nr. Caen, February 1718–Paris, 7 April 1779) lived with and assisted him and in 1768 succeeded him as demonstrator in the Jardin du Roi.[5]

The following publications are attributed to H. M. Rouelle:

1. Procédés du cours de chimie de M. Rouelle, 4°, s.l.e.a., 64 pp. (BN R. 8443).
2. Prospectus d'un cours de chymie expérimentale et théorique . . . ouvrira le 12 novembre 1770, 4°, Paris, 1770, 15 pp. (BN S. 6435).
3. Notice de la doctrine de Rouelle, relative à plusieurs points importans de l'histoire naturelle de la terre. (Extrait du Dictionnaire de géographie-physique), Paris, 1790 ? (BM 970. e. 7. (5.)).
4. Tableau de l'Analyse Chimique, ou Procédés du Cours de Chimie de M. Rouelle, 8°, 1774 (xxii, 184 pp. BN R. 49565), said to be based on a publication of G. F. Rouelle of 1760.
5. Recherches Chimiques sur l'Étain, publiées par ordre du Gouvernement, 8°, 1781 (Bolton, (1), 788).
6. Observations sur l'urine de chameau fraîche et putrefiée, par M. Rouelle, . . . du 16 avril 1777, s.l.e.a., 7 pp. (BN S. 33929).

In November 1773 it was announced:[6]

M. Rouelle commencera son Cours de chimie, le lundi 15 Novembre 1773, à trois heures & demi de l'après-midi, & continuera les lundi, mardi, jeudi & vendredi de chaque semaine, à la même heure, dans son laboratoire, rue Jacob, au coin de la rue des deux Anges.

Rouelle published an account of fixed air and artificial mineral waters[7] in which he says that he and his brother found in 1754 that the 'vapeur' (i.e. hydrogen

---

[1] Fourcroy, (2), iii, 338; Cap, op. cit.; there is perhaps a confusion here with H. M. Rouelle; see p. 77.
[2] (3), 1790, iii, 235.   [3] (2), iii, 409.
[4] Opuscules Physiques et Chimiques, 1774; 1801, 267.
[5] D'Arcet, J. de Phys., 1780, xvi, 168–74; Gmelin, (1), ii, 521; Hoefer, (1), ii, 382; NBG, 1863, xlii, 711; Thomson, (1), i, 301. Thomson barely mentions G. F. Rouelle and attributes all his papers to H. M. Rouelle, who, he says, was too open and honest to become a member of the Academy or acquire honours. Gmelin either attributes the papers of H.M. to G.F. or does not distinguish them. Hoefer says H.M. published several researches of his brother and attributes those we shall mention to G. F. Rouelle.
[6] Journal de Médecine, Chirurgie, Pharmacie, &c. . . . Par M. H. Roux, Paris, 1773, xl, 479 (November).
[7] J. de Médecine, 1773, xxxix, 449 (May): Sur l'Air fixe & sur ses Effets dans certaines eaux minérales (mentioning 'Prietzly'); Crell's Beyträge, 1785, I, iii, 86; reprod. in full in Lavoisier, Opuscules, 1801, 157–74, by 'M. Rouelle'.

sulphide) evolved from liver of sulphur by acids is inflammable, and describes how he was nearly poisoned by inhaling it: 'je . . . me trouvait subitement dans l'impossibilité d'inspirer, et surtout d'expirer.'

H. M. Rouelle and D'Arcet[1] made experiments on heating diamonds in closed vessels, their results being summarised by Lavoisier.[2] H. M. Rouelle obtained transparent glacial phosphoric acid by decomposing bone-ash with nitric acid, precipitating calcium sulphate with sulphuric acid, evaporating, and then adding alcohol (which precipitated acid calcium phosphate); he mentions that Proust was interested in this modification of Scheele's process and had published the secret which Rouelle gave him.[3]

Crude grey sea-salt he found contained metallic mercury.[4] Becher[5] said he would show in the second book of his *Physica Subterranea* (which was never published) that common salt contains something mercurial.[6] The presence of mercury in sea-water was disproved by Marcet.[7]

Rouelle and D'Arcet examined the purple solid formed by exploding gold wire with the electrical machine of M. Comus, and thought it was similar to purple of Cassius.[8] In making stannic chloride by distilling tin and corrosive sublimate Rouelle obtained a residue which he thought contained tin and lead.[9] H. M. Rouelle[10] showed independently of Retzius (see p. 200) that the acid of tartar can be transferred to lime or magnesia to form insoluble compounds from which it can be liberated, and independently of Marggraf (see Vol. II, p. 728) that the base of soluble tartar, prepared by the action of lime on tartar, is potash. He mentions the inflammable distillate from sugar of lead,[11] previously described by Boerhaave (see Vol. II, p. 757). Macquer[12] reported that Bucquet, by this process, obtained 'un acide du vinaigre' which 'a une odeur fétide, & dont l'acidité est tres foible'. Rouelle showed that human and animal blood and dropsical fluid contain soda,[13] and that vegetables contain pre-formed soda;[14] he says he had communicated the result to Venel in 1748 and had read it to the Académie in 1769.

[1] *Introd. Obs. Phys.*, 1773 (1777), i, 480; *Obs. Phys.*, 1773, i, 17 (Sur la destruction du Diamant dans les vaisseaux fermés); *J. de Médecine*, 1773, xxxix, 50–86 (January) (Expériences nouvelles Sur la destruction du Diamant dans les vaisseaux fermés); Crell's *Beyträge*, 1785, I, ii, 114.
[2] AdS, 1772 (1776), m 564; *Oeuvres*, ii, 38 (58 f.).
[3] *J. de Médecine*, 1777, xlviii, 299–322: Sur l'acide phosphorique retiré des os des animaux (October); Proust, *Obs. Phys.*, 1777, x, 377 (November, mentioning Sage and Rouelle).
[4] *J. de Médecine*, 1777, xlviii, 322–5: Sur le sel marine Gris, ou sel de Gabelle (October).
[5] *Physica Subterranea*, 1738, 142.
[6] Kopp, (1), iv, 179, says: 'Becher sagt in seiner Physica subterranea, er habe Quecksilber aus Kochsalz und Thon erhalten; ebenso erwähnt Senac in seinem Nouveau Cours de Chymie (1723) des Quecksilber im Kochsalz'; I have not found either statement; see Proust, *J. de Phys.*, 1799, xlix, 153.
[7] *Phil. Trans.*, 1822, cxii, 448.   [8] *J. de Médecine*, 1773, xl, 163–8.
[9] *J. de Médecine*, 1777, xlviii, 445–8: Observations chymiques sur la liqueur fumante de Libavius (read to the Académie in 1770).
[10] *J. de Médecine*, 1773, xxxix, 369–73 (April): Sur quelques combinaisons de l'Acide du Tartre avec la Craie & plusieurs Chaux métalliques (of calcium, lead, antimony, and iron); Crell's *Beyträge*, 1785, I, i, 125; Kopp, (1), iv, 349–50, credits this work to G. F. Rouelle.
[11] *Tableau d'Analyse Chimique*, 1774, q. by Kopp, (1), iv, 346.
[12] *Dictionnaire*, 1778, iii, 208.
[13] *J. de Médecine*, 1773, xl, 68–76 (July); Crell's *Beyträge*, 1785, I, iii, 92.
[14] *Obs. Phys.*, 1773, i, 13–16; *J. de Médecine*, 1773, xxxix, 86–90 (January): Sur la présence de l'alcali minéral tout formé dans les végétaux; Crell's *Beyträge*, 1775, I, 124.

Rouelle investigated milk sugar (sel ou sucre de lait),[1] starch (amidon),[2] and gluten (matière glutineuse, que j'appelle aussi végéto-animale),[3] made analyses of flies and ants (which gave a little essential oil)[4] and investigated chlorophyll, which he calls 'fécule' or colouring principle.[5]

Rouelle was an independent discoverer (see Boerhaave, Vol. II, p. 758) of urea in urine. He called it soapy matter (matière savonneuse), since it is soluble in alcohol, the extractive matter (matière extractive) being insoluble. It is crystallisable and of a saline nature.[6] The residue from the evaporation of urine contains: 'deux substances, l'une savonneuse & l'autre extractive . . . très soluble dans l'eau.' The first is soluble in 'grand quantité dans l'esprit de vin & l'autre ne s'y dissout point'. The first 'je la nomme savonneuse, à cause de cette solubilité'. It was found also in cow's and horse's urine but this kind is rather different. The extractive matter was more abundant in them than in human urine, brown in cow's and black in horse's urine. Rouelle regarded the soapy matter as the nutritive principle of vegetables taken as food which had changed its nature by digestion and circulation. He did not obtain it pure; it was difficult to dry, was dark brown and unctuous, and could be taken for 'un miel fortement cuit'. On distillation it gave more than half its weight of volatile alkali (ammonia), a little oil and some sal ammoniac. He says he had found Glauber's salt in urine 'depuis 1770, tant aux cours particuliers que je fais chez moi qu'à celui du Jardin du roi'. In observations on camel's urine (no. 6, p. 76) he found that it contains a volatile 'salt' which he thought was benzoic acid (camel's urine is very rich in hippuric acid). He published a preparation of nitrous ether.[7]

VENEL

Gabriel François Venel (Combes, nr. Béziers (or Tourbes), 22 August 1723–Montpellier, 29 June 1775) was a pupil of Rouelle and from 1759 professor of chemistry in Montpellier. His article 'Chymie' in the *Encyclopédie* (1753, iii), which was reprinted by Fourcroy,[8] gives an uncritical sketch of the history, criticising Boyle very adversely and lauding Stahl immoderately.[9] He attributed negative weight to phlogiston (see p. 614). In two memoirs presented to the Academy in 1750[10] he attempted to prove that effervescent mineral waters contain a quantity of common air (he says this) in solution. He separated the 'air surabondante' (really carbon dioxide) by agitation and collected and measured it in a moist bladder. He often mentions Hales. He prepared an artificial mineral water by mixing soda (sodium carbonate) and muriatic acid

[1] *J. de Médecine*, 1773, xxxix, 250: Analyse du Petit-Lait préparé sans Crême de Tartre; Crell's *Beyträge*, 1785, I, iii, 77–86 (with following papers).
[2] *Ib.*, 258: ment. work of 1770–1.   [3] *Ib.*, 262.   [4] *Ib.*, 263.
[5] *Ib.*, 264; *ib.*, 1773, xl, 59–67 (July); Crell's *Beyträge*, 1785, I, iii, 87.
[6] Sur l'urine humain, & sur celles de vache & de cheval, comparées ensemble; par M. Rouelle, démonstrateur en chimie au Jardin royal des Plantes, &c.; *Journal de Médecine*, 1773, xl, 451–468; Crell's *Beyträge*, 1785, I, iii, 92.
[7] *Obs. Phys.*, 1773, ii, 144–5; Mitouard, *ib.*, 323–4.
[8] *Ency. Méthod.*, *Chimie*, 1796, iii, 262 f.
[9] On Venel, see *Obs. Phys.*, 1777, x, 3; Partington and McKie, *Ann. Sci.*, 1937, ii, 380.
[10] AdS, *Mém div. Sav.*, 1755, ii, 53, 80; abstr. in *Obs. Phys.*, 1777, ii, 33; Lavoisier, *Opuscules Physiques et Chimiques*, 1801, 32 f.; Fourcroy, (2), 1796, iii, 363; cf. Brouzet, AdS, *Mém. div. Sav.*, 1755, ii, 337.

in water in a closed bottle. Venel was less correct than Van Helmont and F. Hoffmann, both of whom distinguished carbon dioxide from common air. His name *eau aërée* (aërated water), however, is still in use. Lavoisier says Venel first impregnated water with fixed air (carbon dioxide), but, as Thomas Henry[1] pointed out, this had been done before by Brownrigg (see p. 124). Du Tour[2] also made experiments on the 'air' dissolved in water, describing the apparatus, and found that water freed from air does not act on iron.[3]

[1] Tr. of Lavoisier, *Essays Physical and Chemical*, 1776, 183.
[2] AdS, *Mém. div. Sav.*, 1755, ii, 477–500.   [3] *Ib.*, 496.

CHAPTER III

CHEMISTRY IN FRANCE. III. 1750 TO 1800

In this chapter some French chemists publishing in the period 1750–1800 are considered, Lavoisier, Fourcroy, Berthollet, Vauquelin, and Chaptal being dealt with in separate chapters later.

MACQUER

Pierre Joseph Macquer (Paris; 9 October 1718–15 February 1784), M.D. Paris 1742, professor of chemistry in the Jardin du Roi (1771), had from 1757 collaborated with Baumé in giving courses in a private laboratory. He entered the Académie in 1745 at the age of 27 and was later a member of the Academies of Stockholm, Turin, and Philadelphia (he was not F.R.S.).[1] Condorcet's idea that he was descended from an old Scots family of Ker, who left the country with the Stuarts, was dismissed by Thomson; another suggestion is that his ancestors were an Irish family of Maguire who went to France with James II in 1689.[2]

Macquer was an excellent teacher and the author of a text-book and of a dictionary of chemistry which were deservedly very popular, the first replacing Lemery's *Cours de Chymie* which had then become old-fashioned.

I. Elemens de Chymie Theorique, sm. 8°, Paris, 1749 (xxii pp., i leaf, 336 pp., xii ll., 4 folding plates), 1751, 1753, 1756. The date 1741 in Ferguson is an error.

II. Élemens de Chymie Pratique, contenant la description des opérations fondamentales de la Chymie, 2 vols. 12°, Paris, 1751 (half-title, xvi pp., iv ll. index, 517 pp.; viii ll., 574 pp.; BM 1035. f. 25); 1754–6 (Chem. Soc. Library), 1756 (BM 46. b. 7; Sotheran *Cat.* 832 (1932), p. 387).

III. Élémens de la théorie et de la pratique de la Chimie, 2 vols. 1775 (with the new discoveries).

IV. Elements of the Theory and Practice of Chymistry, tr. by Andrew Reid, 2 vols. 8°, London, 1758 (London Chem. Soc. Libr.); 2 ed., 1764; 3 ed., 3 vols., Edinburgh, 1768; repr. of 3 ed., 2 vols., London ('The Third Edition'), 1775; 5 (last) ed., one vol., Edinburgh, 1777 (Sotheran *Cat.* 800 (1926), 724: *ib.*, 832 (1932), 387).

These are based on his lectures, which were read from written notes and were more concerned with facts than theories: after explaining the facts he added the most plausible explanations, but in a doubting tone, and as a concession to young people, 'who always wish to believe something', as his pupil Condorcet

[1] L. J. M. Coleby, *The Chemical Studies of P. J. Macquer*, 1938; Condorcet, AdS, 1784, h 20; *id.*, *Oeuvres*, 1847, iii, 125–38; Ferguson, ii, 60; Gmelin, (1), ii, 548; Kopp, (1), i, 220; Thomson, (1), i, 295; Vicq d'Azyr, 1805, i, 277.
[2] McKie, *Nature*, 1949, clxiii, 627; *Endeavour*, 1957, xvi, 133.

FIG. 7. PIERRE JOSEPH MACQUER (1718–1784).

says, adding that in Macquer's books chemistry appears as 'une science simple, fondée sur les faites'. The two works are clearly written and were popular university text-books; Thomson says Black recommended them for many years in his courses. There are said to have been German, Dutch, Italian, Spanish and Russian translations.

Macquer was the author of the first dictionary of chemistry in the modern sense:

V. Dictionnaire de Chymie, contenant La Théorie & la Pratique de cette Science, son application à la Physique, à l'Histoire Naturelle, à la Medecine & à l'Economie animale; . . . , 2 vols. 8°, Paris, 1766 (anonymous), xxvj, 1 l. Additions et Changemens, 616; 686, 1 l.

VI. Do., Seconde Edition, revue & considérablement augmentée; same title as V but 'aux Arts dépendans de la Chymie' instead of 'à l'Economie animale' and with author's name; 4 vols. 8°, Paris, 1778 (the ed. quoted; I, xxxvij, i l., 568 pp.; II, ii ll., 655 pp., i l. errata; III, ii ll., 520 pp., i l. errata; IV, ii ll. (one errata), 776 pp., incl. Avertissement *335–*336, Table des Matières, 335–754, Table des Auteurs, 755–76; 305–33 (334 blank), Ordre dans lequel on peut lire les principaux articles de ce Dictionnaire, comme si c'étoit un Traité suivi); also 2 vols. 4°, Paris, 1778 (I, lii pp., i l., 687 pp., vignette on t.p. and engr. at beginning of text showing a laboratory; II, ii ll., 856 pp., vignette and engr. as in I). Swiss eds.: 4 vols. 8°, Yverdun (ed. Struve), 1779; 5 vols. 8°, Neuchatel, 1789; 'en Suisse', 4 vols. 8°, 1779–80 (Ferguson, ii, 60; Duveen, 578; Sotheran Cat. 832 (1932), 387).

VII. A Dictionary of Chemistry. Containing the Theory and Practice of that Science; its application to Natural Philosophy, Natural History, Medicine, and Animal Economy . . . [tr. by James Keir], 2 vols. 4°, London, 1771; 2 ed. with Appendix, A Treatise on the Various Kinds of Elastic Fluids or Gases, 3 vols. 8°, 1777 (Sotheran Cat. 832 (1932), 387). A copy annotated by Keir shows that he was preparing a new ed., which never appeared (Gurney, Cat. 20 (1958), no. 387).

VIII. Allgemeine Begriffe der Chemie in alphabetischer Ordnung aus dem franzö-

sischen übersetzt und mit Anmerkungen vermehrt von Carl Wilhelm Pörner, 3 vols. 8°
Leipzig, 1768–9 (Bolton, (1), 68).

IX. Herrn Peter Joseph Macquers ... Chymisches Wörterbuch oder Allgemeine
Begriffe der Chymie nach alphabetischer Ordnung. Aus dem Französischen nach der
zweyten Ausgabe übersetzt und mit Anmerkungen und Zusätzen vermehrt von D.
Johann Gottfried Leonhardi, 6 vols. 8°, Leipzig, 1781–3 (engraved frontisp. to vol. i);
[same title] Zweyte verbesserte und vermehrte Ausgabe, 7 vols. 8° (6 only in BM),
Leipzig, 1788–8–9–9–90–90[–91].

X. Neue Zusätze und Anmerkungen zu Macquer's Chymischem Wörterbuch erster
Ausgabe, 2 vols. 8°, Leipzig, 1792 (Bolton, 68).

XI. Chymisches Wörterbuch .. Dritte ganz umgearbeitete Ausgabe mit Hinweg-
lassung der blossen Vermuthungen und mit Ergänzungen durch die neuern Erfahrungen veranstaltet von Jer. Benj. Richter, 3 vols. 8°, Leipzig, 1806–9 (Bolton, 69).

XII. Dizionario di Chimica di Pietro Giuseppe Macquer; tradotto del Francese, e
corredato di note e di nuovi articoli da Giovanni Antonio Scopoli (with sev. articles by
Volta), 11 vols. 8°, Pavia, 1783–4 (BM 1034. l. 13–22); 10 vols. 8°, Venice, 1784–5
(BN R 42467–76).

XIII. Chymisk Dictionnaire ... med tilføjede Anmerkninger. Af det Franske
oversat of Hans von Aphelen, 3 vols., Copenhagen, 1771–2 (Bolton, 69).

Macquer and Baumé (see p. 80) collaborated from 1757 in giving a course
of chemistry in a private laboratory, an account of which they published:

XIV. Plan d'un Cours de Chymie expérimentale et raisonnée, avec un discours
historique sur la Chymie, 8°, Paris, 1757 (lxiij, 80 pp.; approbation by Malouin 19
November 1757; BN R 16933 and 42459).

In the historical introduction of XIV the authors reject the early fables of
the origins of chemistry, which originated among Egyptian priests though the
books of Hermes are not chemical (p. i f.). Stahl is praised; an author had
accused him of obscurity 'qu'on ne trouvera jamais dans cet auteur, à moins
qu'on ne soit encore bien novice en Chymie' (p. lvi). The course begins with
the 'principles' fire, air, water and earth, combined fire being phlogiston (p. 12).
Then come salts and acids (p. 22 f.), the base of borax being the same as that
of common salt (p. 34). In the section on metals (p. 34 f.) there is nothing on
the increase in weight on calcination. Burning zinc 'makes the principle of
metals [phlogiston] sensible to the eyes' (p. 52). The section on docimacy
(p. 55 f.) includes water analysis and the analysis of vegetable matter (p. 59 f.),
oil being more complex than phlogiston (p. 62). Fermentation (p. 69 f.), ether
and 'ethers' [esters], tartar (an 'acide concrete & huileux') (p. 72), and putrid
fermentation follow, closing with the analysis of animal matters (p. 76 f.). The
section on salts includes a rational nomenclature, vitriols (metallic sulphates
forming glassy crystals) e.g., being grouped together.

Macquer attempted to replace the old names by more systematic ones; he
calls the ammonium salts *sel ammoniac, sel ammoniac vitriolique, sel ammoniac
nitreux, sel ammoniac végétal* (acetate),[1] and in his long article 'sels' he classifies
salts into sels vitrioliques (sulphates), sels nitreux (nitrates), sels marins ou
simplement sels (chlorides, e.g. with the bases soda, potash, ammonia, lime,
alumina, silver, copper, iron, tin, and other metals), sels tartareux, sels acéteux,
sels phosphoriques (phosphates), borax ou sels de borax (borates, mostly
unknown), etc.[2]

In 1749[3] Macquer says there is reason to think the four elements are perhaps

---

[1] VI, 1778, i, 156.   [2] VI, iii, 399 f.   [3] I, 2.

not the most simple elements of matter, but 'since experience has taught us that we cannot by our senses discover the principles of which they are composed, we may most reasonably consider them as simple homogeneous bodies, and the principles of the rest'; and he maintained this in 1778.[1] In 1749 he regarded the element of fire as 'a substance composed of infinitely small particles, continually agitated by a most rapid motion, and in consequence essentially fluid', and the same as the phlogiston principle and sulphur.[2] Macquer was a steadfast supporter of the phlogiston theory, which he explains in his earliest text-book.[3] He called it 'the surest guide which can be taken in chemical researches, and the numerous experiments which are made every day, far from destroying it, become on the contrary so many new proofs which confirm it'.[4] He never adopted Lavoisier's views, but gave a full account of them as known in the second edition of his *Dictionary*, along with the experiments and conclusions of Bayen (see p. 394),[5] but always speaking in terms of the highest respect of Stahl.

Macquer was not interested in quantitative investigation, and in 1778 when he had previously been told by Lavoisier of experiments 'qu'il reservoit *in petto*' which would destroy the theory of phlogiston he was at first greatly perturbed ('son air de confiance me faisoit mourir de peur'), but on being told that they placed the matter of fire in the air and not in the combustible he informed Guyton de Morveau that he was completely relieved.[6] In private conversations, however, Macquer admitted that he feared the phlogiston theory was doomed (dont il prévoyait la perte totale).[7] In 1783[8] he said that Lavoisier, by 'a large number of very beautiful experiments', had given 'considerable probability' to his new views.

Macquer considered that the calces of all metals were utlimately the same earthy element and differed only by incomplete expulsion of phlogiston;[9] at first he regarded phlogiston (which is identical in all bodies) as 'elementary fire, combined and become one of the principles of combustible bodies', or 'essentially no other thing than pure fire, but deprived of its activity by the union which it has contracted with any given substance',[10] which is perhaps present in a nearly pure state in the exhalation from glowing charcoal.[11] Addition of phlogiston increases the absolute weight and sometimes the specific gravity of a body.[12]

It is doubtful if Macquer at first regarded mercuric oxide (precipité per se) as a true calx; he says[13] the process of calcination serves 'to give mercury, by the action of fire, the appearance of a metallic calx'; it has the appearance 'but no more', since on strong heating 'it sublimes and is wholly reduced to running mercury, without the addition of any other inflammable matter, which proves that during this long calcination [three months] it lost none of its

[1] VI, ii, 4.   [2] I, 12.   [3] I, 1749, 14.
[4] Macquer and Baumé, XIV, lvij; Macquer, VI, 1778, I, xxxiv.   [5] VI, i, 344 f.; ii, 353 f.
[6] Guyton de Morveau, *Ency. Méthod.*, *Chymie*, 1789, i, 628.   [7] Fourcroy, (2), iii, 454.
[8] *Journal des Sçavans*, 1783, 867.   [9] V, i, 258 f.
[10] V, ii, 202, 203, 219.
[11] V, i, 246; ii, 220; VI, i, 339.   [12] V, ii, 204; VI, iii, 105.
[13] II, 1751; IV, 1764, i, 400; Lavoisier later proved that it is a true calx; see p. 390.

phlogiston'. He also[1] remarks that 100 lb. of lead give 110 lb. of minium on calcination, 'a prodigious and almost incredible augmentation, if it be considered that, far from adding any thing to the lead, we have on the contrary dissipated part of it.' None of the several ingenious hypotheses to account for this fact is entirely satisfactory, and hence Macquer, having 'no established theory to proceed upon', leaves it unexplained. Macquer later adopted the theory that phlogiston is the matter of light (see p. 85).

Macquer adopted Van Helmont's name gas: un nom barbare qui ne désigne rien dans notre langage, ni, je crois, dans aucune autre.[2] He calls Priestley's dephlogisticated air 'gas ou air dephlogistiqué'[3] or gas aërien (cet air beaucoup plus pure de celui de l'athmosphere que je nomme gas aërien).[4] He calls fixed air (air fixe) gas méphytique,[5] gas inflammable includes hydrogen (which he thought came from metals), methane (feu brisou) and carbon monoxide;[6] gas nitreux is nitric oxide,[7] gas acide marin is hydrogen chloride,[8] gas acide sulfureux volatil is sulphur dioxide,[9] gas alkali volatil is ammonia,[10] gas acide spathique is either hydrogen fluoride or silicon fluoride.[11] He gives an excellent account of the then very recent work on these gases.

Macquer sometimes confuses nitrogen and carbon dioxide under the names gas méphytique, air fixe, air gaseux, acide aërien, or simply gas,[12] and regarded them as compounds of phlogiston and dephlogisticated air, although he sometimes correctly differentiates nitrogen (air phlogistiqué) as insoluble in water,[13] and he also suggests that it is a compound of dephlogisticated air with less phlogiston than fixed air: 'l'état de . . . l'air phlogistiqué . . . paroît être moyen entre celui d'air pur et celui de gas méphytique parfait.'[14]

He noticed in 1776–7 that when a cold saucer is held in a hydrogen flame (sous-coupe que léchoit la flamme) it becomes wetted with droplets of a liquid which was apparently pure water (qui ne nous a paru en effet n'être que de l'eau pure).[15] He mentions that de Lassone[16] had obtained an inflammable air (carbon monoxide) by heating zinc oxide and charcoal, or Prussian blue (cyanogen ?), and also mentions the inflammable gas from liver of sulphur (hydrogen sulphide) which 'M. Rouelle l'enflamme tous les ans dans notre cours du Jardin du Roi' (see p. 77), but he thought they were all more or less pure inflammable air: je persiste à penser qu'il n'y a qu'une seule espece de gas inflammable.[17]

Macquer's observation in 1771[18] that a strongly heated diamond burns in air with a small flame (je vis distinctement qu'il étoit tout enveloppé d'une petite flamme légere et comme phosphorique) showed, as was recognised later,[19] that the primary product of the combustion of carbon is carbon monoxide.

As a consequence of the new work on gases,[20] Macquer modified the theory

[1] IV, i, 388.   [2] V, i, 550; VI, ii, 240 (241).   [3] VI, ii, 256.   [4] VI, ii, 271.
[5] VI, ii, 272.   [6] VI, ii, 305.   [7] VI, ii, 321.   [8] VI, ii, 361.
[9] VI, ii, 371.   [10] VI, ii, 379.   [11] VI, ii, 384.
[12] VI, i, 395 (Combustion); ii, 240 f., 263, 272 f., 289, 296 f., 328 f. (Gas).
[13] VI, i, 83 (Air); ii, 276 (Gas méphytique).   [14] VI, ii, 297.
[15] VI, ii, 314–15; Macquer says this and the following article were revised in October 1776.
[16] AdS, 1776, h 29, m 686: De plusieurs espèces d'air ou émanations aëriformes extraites par divers voies.
[17] VI, ii, 318.   [18] VI, i, 494.   [19] Dixon, J. Chem. Soc., 1899, lxxv, 630.   [20] VI, ii, 240–407.

of phlogiston by making the following two assumptions: (1) phlogiston 'is nothing but the proper substance of light, immediately or mediately fixed in bodies';[1] (2) air is the precipitant of light and *vice versa*:[2]

Is it not manifest by the essential circumstances of combustion that the phlogiston or fixed fire in the combustible body is separated only by the action of the air which takes its place in the measure that this phlogiston is disengaged, and becomes free fire, and that in consequence the air is here the decomposing intermediary, the true precipitant of the matter of fire?

He admitted that Lavoisier's experiments proved that pure air or dephlogisticated air (oxygen) is fixed in combustions and in calcination of metals, but he supposed also that phlogiston, which is the matter of light, is at the same time emitted.[3] The reason why calx of mercury (red precipitate) is reduced at a red heat without the addition of phlogistic material such as charcoal is that phlogiston is:

nothing but the combined matter of light, and all bodies being permeable to light when they are heated to visible redness, the matter of fire passing through the vessels in which the reduction without addition is made, can combine with the mercury calx (chaux de mercure) in sufficiently great quantity to give it its metallic form because of the great disposition of this calx to unite with the principle of inflammability.[4]

Light is the only material form of fire; heat is not a substance but 'a particular state, a form of existence, of which all material substances are susceptible'; it is quite different from light. The particles of light falling on a body can set up a violent agitation of its parts and so produce heat.[5] Combustible bodies such as oils, fats, resins, spirits, ethers, etc., are all ultimately of vegetable origin,[6] and there are circumstances which lead us to think that the phlogiston they contain was derived from the absorption and fixation of light.[7] Bernard Christopher Meese, a physician of Frankener (Friesland) who died aged 21, proved that light is necessary for the growth of plants and that much less oil is obtained from etiolated than from green plants on distillation;[8] and Opoix[9] showed from many facts that light is the material principle of colours, and that from its fixation as phlogiston in bodies it produces every species of colour according to its mode of combination. Macquer said:[10]

phlogiston is nothing but the pure matter of light fixed immediately in bodies without the concourse of any intermediate (especially of air). Its primitive source is in vegetables, and by the action of the vital force (l'action vitale organique) which produces this fixation, resulting in the production (la composition) of all oily substances. The matter of light, once fixed and become phlogiston, in vegetable oils . . . is the primary source of all known phlogistic compounds and combustibles,

and animals obtain all their nourishment from plants. As Coleby[11] said: 'We have only to substitute the comparatively modern conception of the "energy of light" for Macquer's "matter of light" to realize the essential truth underlying his ideas.' The energy evolution and absorption in oxidation and reduction are parallel to his phlogistic processes. In his criticism of Macquer's

[1] VI, iii, 123.
[2] VI, iii, 133; Fourcroy, (2), iii, 454.
[3] VI, i, 395; ii, 260.
[4] VI, ii, 261.
[5] VI, ii, 171–4, 179, 186.
[6] VI, iii, 136, 142.
[7] Ib., 143.
[8] Obs. Phys., 1775, vi, 445–59.
[9] Ib., 1776, viii, 100, 189.
[10] VI, iii, 144.
[11] 1938, 37.

theory[1] Lavoisier ignored (as he usually did) the distinction between heat and light, regarding heat as material, and it was Berthollet in his observations on the effect of sunlight on chlorine water[2] who showed that the chemical effects of heat and light can be completely different. In criticising Macquer for believing that light is material but without weight, Lavoisier passed over the same objection to his own 'matter of heat' which is also the 'matter of light'.

In 1749,[3] Macquer explained Geoffroy's affinity table (see p. 54) in detail, and reproduced it in its original form; although the progress of chemistry had introduced some corrections and added new affinities, the latter were not sufficiently well founded by experiments and were also subject to exceptions, and the original table contained all the fundamental facts. He would, however, point out the exceptions and add a very small number of new ones. In 1766[4] he followed Buffon[5] in supposing that, although the volumes, masses, forms and distances of the integrant and constituent parts (molecules) of bodies are unknown, it can hardly be denied that their actions are due to the same force, the reciprocal gravitation of the small bodies, modified by size, density, figure, intimacy of contact, distance, etc., and the law of force might be determined indirectly. Macquer classified[6] affinities into (i) simple and (ii) complex. Simple affinity is exerted either (a) between the integrant parts of the same body, producing aggregation, or (b) between the parts of different bodies, producing a body of different nature (e.g. green vitriol from iron and vitriolic acid), when it is called affinity of composition. Complex affinity (affinité compliquée) comes into play when more than two bodies act on one another, when the forces involved are affinities of composition. In such cases (a) the three bodies may unite to form one; (β) a product is formed from three bodies although one (e.g. water) may have no affinity with one of the other two separately (e.g. sulphur in liver of sulphur, i.e. sulphur + potash): this is called affinity of the intermediary (in this case potash); Henckel[7] had called this affinitas appropriata, the third body (e.g. potash) being the corpus approprians. A third case (γ) is when the third body combines with one of those of a compound and sets the other free (e.g. alkali + metal salt = alkali salt + precipitate); and a fourth (δ) is reciprocal affinity (affinité réciproque),[8] which is involved when a principle which has been separated with another is in turn made to leave that which has separated it; this arises when the two principles have nearly equal affinities with the third principle, and their separation is produced by peculiar circumstances of the operation. When four principles are involved (ε), double affinity (affinité double) arises (e.g. when two salts exchange radicals), in which case decomposition ensues when the sum of the affinities of each of the principles of the two compounds formed exceeds the sum of those between the principles of the original substances.

[1] AdS, 1783 (1786), m 505; Oeuvres, ii, 623.   [2] Obs. Phys., 1786, xxix, 81–5.
[3] I, 1749, 256–73.   [4] V, ii, 195.   [5] Histoire Naturelle, 1765, XIII, xii–xx.
[6] V, i, 47 f.; VI, i, 57 f. (Affinité).
[7] De mediorum chymicorum appropriatione, Dresden, 1727; in Pyritologie, 4°, Paris, 1760, ii, 285, 352.
[8] Fourcroy, (3), 1790, i, 68, says Baumé first introduced the name affinité réciproque; see p. 92.

A summary will now be given of some of the experimental researches of Macquer. In 1745 he examined the solubility of oils in alcohol.[1] Even as late as 1778[2] he thought the fatty acids liberated by mineral acids from soaps, although freely soluble in alcohol, were practically identical with the original oils. In an investigation of the solubilities of dried salts in alcohol[3] he found that chlorides and nitrates are more soluble than sulphates; salts in which 'the acid is less strongly united with the base' are more soluble. He continued to call acids and bases 'salts'.[4] In 1747[5] he recognised that gypsum is a compound of vitriolic acid with a calcareous earth, which he thought was somewhat different from lime. He thought in 1751 that in the caustification of alkalis by lime, saline and acrid particles of the lime combine with the alkaline salt (the alkali carbonate), but the origin of causticity 'is one of the most subtle, and the most difficult to answer, in all chemistry'.[6] In 1778[7] he gave a long discussion of Meyer's and Black's theories of caustification and recognised that Black's, based on 'one of those capital discoveries which make an epoch in the history of science',[8] cannot be controverted: par la même raison qu'il étoit inutile d'en faire aux épicycles et tous les cieux de crystal qu'imaginoient les défenseurs du système de Ptolémée.[9] It is noteworthy, however, that the heat evolved with acids is greater with quicklime or caustic alkalis than with limestone or mild alkalis, which might seem to indicate that fire is the immediate cause of causticity; probably the difference is due to the heat carried away in the effervescence of the mild kinds with acids.[10] Macquer thought that limestone loses both water and gas on calcination and the heat evolved in slaking quicklime is the result of great affinity.[11]

Macquer's theory of acids and alkalis is practically the same as that of Stahl (Vol. II, p. 678): he regarded all acids as derived from an 'acide primitif' (vitriolic acid) and divided them into mineral, vegetable, and animal.[12] He speaks of earth as one of the four elements, and of a primitive earth, the 'terre vitrifiable' of Becher (see Vol. II, p. 644), which he identified with rock crystal.[13] He thought that although some fixed alkali pre-exists in vegetable matter, it is partly generated by the action of fire.[14] Ammonia (alkali volatil) is a true alkali of smaller 'force' than the fixed alkalis potash and soda.[15]

He thought phosphorus was a kind of sulphur formed by the combination of marine (hydrochloric) acid and phlogiston.[16] In his researches on arsenic (1746–8)[17] he calls the compounds of white arsenic with alkalis [arsenites] 'livers of arsenic' (foies d'arsenic) by analogy with liver of sulphur, the old idea (Geber, Vol. I) that arsenic is a combustible principle similar to sulphur still persisting. In 1746 he discovered potassium arsenate (nouveau sel neutre

[1] AdS, 1745, h 35–8, m 9–25.   [2] VI, ii, 440; Gren, 1794, ii, 177.
[3] Miscellanea Taurinensia; Mélanges de philosophie et de Mathematiques de la Société Royale de Turin, 1762–65 (1766), iii, 1; 1770–3, v, 137; Intr. Obs. Phys., 1771 (1777), i, 461.
[4] VI, iii, 383.   [5] Observations sur la chaux et sur la plâtre, AdS, 1747, h 65, m 678.
[6] II; IV, 1764, ii, 190.   [7] VI, i, 290–333.   [8] Ib., 298.   [9] Ib., 302.   [10] Ib., 306 f.
[11] V, i, 251 (Chaux); VI, i, 356, 363 (Chaux terreuse).
[12] V, 1766, ii, 417, 428; VI, i, 3, 16; iii, 386, 397.
[13] V, ii, 563 f.; VI, iv, 53 f.   [14] V, i, 79; VI, i, 103 f.   [15] V, i, 96; VI, i, 121.
[16] I, 1749, 34; IV, 1764, i, 34; in VI, iii, 151, it is a compound of 'a particular acid' and phlogiston.
[17] AdS, 1746, h 59, m 223; 1748, h 63, m 35.

arsenicale)[1] by fusing white arsenic with nitre and crystallising from water: he describes its crystalline form. Sodium arsenate was discovered in 1748 by using cubic nitre (sodium nitrate).[2] Arsenic acid was first prepared by Cavendish (p. 310) and Scheele (p. 218), although de la Metherie[3] mentions that its existence had been suspected by Barlet (see p. 15) and Macquer.

Macquer in his memoirs on Prussian blue (1749–52)[4] says he knew only Geoffroy senr.[5] and the Abbé Ménon[6] as previously having formed definite views on the nature of Prussian blue, the former regarding the colour as the bitumen of iron separated by the saponaceous alkali and precipitated on the white earth of alum (which Macquer says is really an opinion borrowed from Brown);[7] and the latter as that of the iron itself precipitated in its natural colour by the organic lye and deposited on the earth of alum. Macquer tried to show that both these apparently contradictory views were in part correct. He concluded that the colour is due to phlogiston: cette matière colorante du bleu de Prusse est une matière inflammable dans un état singulier, & que je crois très-peu connu.[8] By digesting Prussian blue with a solution of caustic potash he obtained a yellow neutral solution of a salt (potassium ferrocyanide) which he thought was a compound of alkali and phlogiston (alkali phlogistiqué).[9] He evaporated the solution to dryness and obtained a neutral solid but not crystals. Crystalline potassium ferrocyanide (alkali prussien crystallisé) was obtained by spontaneous evaporation by Guyton de Morveau as:[10] très-beaux crystaux poliedres nets & transparens, les uns figurés en prismes courts, terminé par une pyramide, les autres composés de deux pyramides unies base à base.

Macquer's investigations on platinum[11] resulted, it is said,[12] in the closing of the mines by the Spanish government for fear the metal would be mixed fraudulently with gold.

Baumé and Macquer[13] disproved experiments reported by Juncker, Wallerius, and Teichmeyer[14] in which other metals were supposed to be converted into mercury (see Vol. II, p. 317). Macquer in 1773 investigated the manufacture of 'flint glass' (sic),[15] and in 1777 he prepared glacial phosphoric acid with Pouilletier de la Salle,[16] who had assisted him in composing his Dictionary.

In 1750 Macquer was charged by the court to investigate an offer by the Comte de La Garaye, a philanthropist and fanatic who converted his castle in Brittany into a hospital, to reveal the secret of the remedies which he used, in exchange for funds to run this institution. La Garaye prepared these medicines from minerals by long maceration with neutral salt solutions, and used a mercurial tincture made by a process lasting several months. Macquer found that this tincture was merely a solution of corrosive sublimate in spirit of

[1] Ib., see I, 1749, 167.   [2] I, 171.   [3] Obs. Phys., 1786, xxv, 3 (23).
[4] AdS, 1749, h 111, m 255–65; 1752, h 79–85, m 60–77; Coleby, 1938, 52.
[5] AdS, 1725, m 153–72.   [6] AdS, Mém. div. Sav., 1750, i, 563, 573.
[7] Phil. Trans., 1724, xxiii, 17.   [8] AdS, 1752, m 60 (69).
[9] V, i, 222; VI, i, 267.   [10] Elémens de Chymie, Dijon, 1778, iii, 159.
[11] Sur un nouveau metal connu sous le nom d'Or blanc ou de Platine, AdS, 1758, h 51, m 119; V, ii, 148; VI, iii, 178.
[12] Saverien, 1769, VII, p. xxxiv.   [13] VI, ii, 588 f.
[14] Institutiones Chemiae Dogmaticae et Experimentalis, 4°, Jena, 1729.
[15] AdS, 1773, h 27, m 502.   [16] Sage, AdS, 1777, m 32.

wine,[1] but he reported favourably[2] and the King bought the secret for a high price.

Macquer defined fermentation as an intestine motion among the insensible parts of a body, producing a new disposition and different combination of them. He recognised three kinds: vinous, acetous, and putrefactive.[3] He thought spirit of wine consisted of oil or phlogiston united to water by the aid of an acid.[4] Acetous and putrefactive fermentation follow vinous fermentation in stages. Putrefaction produces volatile alkali (ammonia).[5] The preparation of ether is 'one of the most beautiful and instructive phenomena of chemistry'. Spirit of wine is an oil intimately combined with a large amount of water; when part of this combined water (eau principe) is removed from alcohol by the hot oil of vitriol, the alcohol becomes more like an oil and less miscible with water; the resulting ether is 'l'ésprit de vin, auquel l'acide vitriolique a enlevé une partie de son eau principe: c'est par conséquent un esprit de vin altéré dans son essence, et qui se rapproche de la nature huileuse'.[6] This is essentially correct. The product of the later stages of distillation is the sweet oil of vitriol (huile douce de vitriol), alcohol from which still more water has been removed. This product was later investigated by Magnus (see Vol. IV). Macquer still supposed, with Boerhaave (Vol. II, p. 757), that the smell of essential oils is due to a *spiritus rector*, a kind of gas which escapes from them:[7] principe volatil odorant, c'est à dire, de l'esprit recteur de la substance dont elles sont tirées . . . et qu'elles perdent toutes ces propriétés, à mesure qu'il s'évapore.

In 1768 Macquer investigated the solubility of india rubber in ether,[8] and showed that it was precipitated from the solution by water. According to Murray,[9] Cavallo[10] first showed that the ether must be washed with water before it will dissolve rubber, Grossart[11] having found that ordinary ether does not dissolve it. Coal-tar naphtha was used as a solvent for rubber by J. Syme,[12] and the solution was used for making waterproof fabrics ('macintoshes') by Charles Macintosh in 1823 (Brit. Pat. 4804/1823).[13]

Macquer wrote on silk dyeing (1763).[14] His method of dyeing scarlet,[15]

[1] La Garaye, *Chymie hydraulique, pour extraire les sels essentiels des végétaux, animaux et minéraux, avec l'eau pure, par M. C[laude]. C.D.L.G.*, 18°, Paris, 1745; enlarged ed. with notes by Parmentier, 1775 (BN R. 40353-4); Vicq d'Azyr, 1805, i, 289 (il est permis de croire que le commissaire du roi n'apporta pas une grande rigeur dans l'examen des remèdes); Thomson, (1), i, 297; NBG, 1859, xxviii, 814.

[2] AdS, 1755 (1761), h 51-61, m 25-35; Coleby, 1938, 59.   [3] I, 1749, 190; VI, ii, 159.
[4] AdS, 1745; I, 1749, 197.   [5] I, 1749, 223; VI, ii, 159.
[6] V, i, 458, 461; VI, ii, 85 f.   [7] IV, ii, 126; VI, ii, 451.
[8] AdS, 1768, h 58, m 209: Sur un Moyen de Dissoudre la Résine Caoutchouc.
[9] 1807, iv, 187.   [10] *Phil. Trans.*, 1781, lxxi, 509.
[11] *Ann. Chim.*, 1791, xi, 143; a ref. to Berniard, *Obs. Phys.*, 1789, xvi, as having found this is incorrect; two papers by him there deal only with the extraction of phosphoric acid from egg-shells (p. 150) and the Wieliczka salt mines (p. 459).
[12] *Ann. Phil.*, 1818, xii, 112.
[13] Roscoe and Schorlemmer, *Treatise*, 1889, III, v, 493; H. Schurer, *Trans. Newcomen Soc.*, 1951-3 (1956), xxviii, 77-87.
[14] *L'Art de la Teinture en Soie*, in *Descriptions des Arts et Métiers* (see p. 69), 1763, I (ix, 86 pp., incl., 71 f., a previously unpubl. work by Hellot); an Arabic tr. was publ., Bulāq, 1823 (BN).
[15] *Méthode pour tiendre en soie en plusieurs nuances de rouge vif de cochineaille, et autres couleurs*, 4°, Paris, 1769, 8 pp. (BM).

according to Bancroft,[1] did not give good results. Macquer proposed Prussian blue as a fast dye. His book is more original than Hellot's (see p. 67) but the first really modern work was Berthollet's (see p. 514). Macquer at first adopted Hellot's physical theory of dyeing (see p. 68) but later[2] proposed a chemical theory:

ce n'est point ici un simple enchassement des atomes colorés dans les pores . . . il y a de plus une adhérence réelle de contact, et même une combinaison chymique . . . en vertu de l'affinité plus ou moins grande.

Mordants are earthy or metallic salts: they are decomposed by soluble dyes, which precipitate their base; this combines with the coloured parts of the dye, and the coloured precipitates adhere to the textile. The mordant often changes the colour of the dye.

Macquer worked on the production of true porcelain at Sèvres, the first successful results with kaolin from St. Yrieix being obtained in 1765, and in 1769 the production of the first true French porcelain was begun.[3]

BAUMÉ

Antoine Baumé (not Beaumé) (Senlis, 26 February 1728–Paris, 15 October 1804), the son of an inn-keeper, was a pupil of E. F. Geoffroy's, in 1752 entered the Collège de Pharmacie in Paris, soon becoming master apothecary and demonstrator in chemistry, and at the same time carried on the business of pharmacist until 1780, and again after the Revolution had deprived him of his means. He became a member of the Institut in 1796. He says[4] that he was lecture demonstrator to Macquer for 25 years, when they gave 16 courses, each with over 2000 experiments, and that he himself made over 10,000 experiments in addition: 'j'ai plus opéré que lu, et je m'en sais bon gré.' Besides some communications to the Academy[5] Baumé wrote several books:

I.   Dissertation sur l'aether, dans laquelle on examine les différents produits du mélange de l'esprit de vin avec les acides minéraux, 12°, Paris, 1757 (xii, 332 pp.; BN).
II. Plan d'un cours de chimie expérimentale et raisonnée, avec un discours historique sur la chymie, 8°, Paris, 1757, in collaboration with Macquer (pp. lxiij, 80; see p. 80).
III. Manuel de Chymie, ou Exposé des opérations de la Chymie et de leurs produits. Ouvrage utile aux personnes qui veulent prendre une idée de cette science, ou qui ont le dessein de se former un Cabinet de Chymie, 12°, Paris, 1763 (xii, 495 pp.); 2 ed. 1765 (xvj, 501 pp., 1 l.); Bishop Watson when appointed professor in Cambridge learnt his chemistry from an 'operator' from Paris and Baumé's *Manuel*, which he greatly esteemed.
IIIA. Tr. [by John Aikin] A Manual of Chemistry; or a brief account of the Operations of Chemistry, and their Products, 12°, printed Warrington publ. London, 1778; 2 ed. with additions, 12°, Warrington and London, 1786.
IIIB. Handbuch der Scheidekunst, 8°, tr. Wasserberg, Vienna, 1774.

[1] *Philosophy of Permanent Colours*, London, 1794, i, 311.   [2] VI, iv, 27.
[3] Macquer, VI, iii, 211–33; Guerlac, *Chymia*, 1959, v, 73 (84 f.); the laboratory notes are still at Sèvres.
[4] *Chymie expér. et raisonn.*, 1773, I, pref. ii.
[5] AdS, *Mém. div. Sav.*, 1760, iii, 209 (read 1755) on vitriolic (i.e. common) ether; 1768, v, 405, 425 (presented 1757) on the cooling of liquids by evaporation; 1774, vi, several papers.

IV. Chymie expérimentale et raisonnée, 3 vols. 8°, Paris, 1773, with portrait (two issues). Trs. (not seen): IVA. Erläuterte Experimental-Chemie, tr. J. C. Gehlen, 3 vols. 8°, Leipzig, 1775; IVB. Chimica sperimentale e ragionata del Sig. Bome (*sic*), 3 vols. 8°, Venice, 1781.

IV contains a long preface (I, i–xl) summarising its contents, an elaborate table of contents (I, xli–lxxiv), 'prolegomena' (I, lxxv–cxlvi) containing descriptions of furnaces and apparatus, a glossary of terms (I, cxlvii–clx), and the text proper is on theory, lime, vitriolic acid and sulphur, gypsum, nitric, hydrochloric and acetic acids, fixed alkali, alum, clay, liver of sulphur, saltpetre. Vol. ii is on mineral alkali (soda), animal alkali (ammonia) and their salts, borax and boric acid (sel sedatif), arsenic, cobalt, nickel, antimony, zinc, bismuth, mercury, tin, lead, iron, and copper; vol. iii is on silver, gold, platinum, ceramics, glass, ores and assaying (essai ou docimasie), pyrites, mineral waters, salines, and 'reflexions on the philosophers' stone'. Vegetable and animal chemistry are missing, being treated in VI. The treatment is clear, detailed, and practical.

V. Opuscules Chimiques, faisant suite à la Chimie expérimentale et raisonné, 8°, Paris, An VI (1798), 452 pp. (BN).

VI. Éléments de Pharmacie, Théorique et Pratique, Contenant toutes les Opérations fondamentales de cet Art, avec leur définition, et une Explication de ces opérations par les principes de la Chimie . . . , 8°, Paris, 1762, and later eds., e.g. 8 ed., 2 vols. 8°, 1797 (pagin. cont., 877 pp.; the pref. says: La première édition de ces Éléments a essuyé des censures très-vives. C'est le sort de tous les écrits sur les Sciences. In consequence he had removed polemical matter).

VII. Mémoire sur les Argilles ou Recherches et Expériences chymiques et physiques sur la nature des terres les plus propres à l'Agriculture, & sur les moyens de fertiliser celles qui sont stériles, 8°, Paris, 1770 (pp. xiv, 87; Duveen, 52). The preface says Baumé twice unsuccessfully submitted the essay for a prize of the Academy of Bordeaux but, since the chemical point of view was 'absolutely new', he now printed it.

Baumé had a large manufacturing laboratory, making sal ammoniac (from 1770), red precipitate, tin and mercury chlorides, sugar of lead, etc.[1] He also invented processes for gilding clocks, dyeing in two colours, bleaching silk 'sans s'écruer', purifying saltpetre, and removing the bitter principle from horsechestnut starch.[2] He published a long account of the distillation of spirit of wine, describing a still,[3] and determined the alcohol content by a hydrometer,[4] which was modified by Guyton de Morveau[5] and by Charles Macintosh,[6] whose form was made and sold by Twaddell, the Glasgow instrument-maker;[7] a set in a box, 9 in. by 11 in., cost £2 12s. 6d. in Glasgow. The Baumé and Twaddell scales are still used in technology.

Baumé[8] uses the name 'combination' or 'chemical composition' for what Becher and Stahl called 'mixtion' (see Vol. II, p. 664). In combination the

---

[1] Scheffer, *Chemiske Föreläsningar*, Uppsala, 1775, § 60; tr. Weigel, 1779, 133; says Egyptian sal ammoniac was sold in Venice, but it was a mistake to say that it was prepared there from soot, salt, and urine; Bergman in a note says it was reputed to be made by Gravenhorst in Brunswick and by Baumé in Paris, but he had seen no specimens of the salt they made.

[2] Anon., *Chemist and Druggist*, 1928, cviii, 198; Gmelin, (1), ii, 550; Hoefer, NBG, iv, 819; Kopp, (1), ii, 115; Poggendorff, (1), i, 116.

[3] *Obs. Phys.*, 1778, xii, 1–37.

[4] *Éléments de Pharmacie*, 5 ed., 1784; 8 ed., 1797, 343; *Nicholson's J.*, 1797, i, 37; Poggendorff says the hydrometer was descr. in the *Avant Coureur*, 1768–9.

[5] *Ann. Chim.*, 1797, xxi, 3.

[6] Hardie, *Chem. and Ind.*, 1952, 606.

[7] Parkes, *Chemical Essays*, 1823, i, 211, 215.

[8] III, 1765, 3, 18; IV, i, 11 f.

'integrant molecules' come into juxtaposition and remain adherent. The bodies forming a compound are 'corps hétérogène, principes, ou parties constituantes' (e.g. acid and alkali of a salt). 'Corps (ou parties) homogènes' are molecules detached from the same body, e.g. water, oil or metal. The 'parties intégrantes' are the smallest molecules separated from a body which still conserve its properties, and if further divided the body is decomposed: les plus petites molécules séparées d'un corps, mais qui conservent les propriétés du corps d'où elles ont été séparées. On peut supposer cette division portée à un tel excès, qu'il n'est plus possible de diviser davantage ces corps, sans les décomposer.

Baumé devoted special attention to affinity.[1] He pointed out that two sets of tables would be necessary, one for reactions in solution ('wet way', voie humide) and one for reactions in fusion ('dry way', voie seche).[2] Stahl[3] had clearly pointed out this distinction (so kehret sich das gantze Blat um), and[4] also that nitric acid decomposes potassium or sodium chloride on heating, leaving potassium nitrate (nitrum regeneratum). Baumé[5] found that when vitriolated tartar (potassium sulphate) is dissolved in hot nitric acid, potassium nitrate crystallises on cooling, although sulphuric acid is shown in Geoffroy's table above nitric acid. He calls this *affinité réciproque* (see p. 86):

I took four drachms (gros) of vitriolated tartar reduced to a fine powder, mixed it with three drachms of very pure fuming spirit of nitre. A considerable effervescence was at once excited, accompanied by heat and very red vapours of nitrous acid. The mixture became pasty. I diluted it with a sufficient quantity of water to dissolve the saline mass and I set the liquid to crystallise. The salt which I obtained proved to be very pure nitre, crystallised partly in needles and partly in small cubic crystals.

In 1763 Baumé explained the reaction.[6] The fixed alkali contains phlogiston. When it is combined with vitriolic acid the phlogiston is shared between the alkali and acid. Nitric acid contains much phlogiston. Nevertheless it is very avid of that presented to it. It combines by this principle with the alkali of the vitriolated tartar and sets free the vitriolic acid, which has less affinity for the inflammable principle than nitric acid has.

Baumé[7] recognised seven kinds of affinity: (i) of aggregation (cohesion), (ii) simple, (iii) compound (e.g. mercury added to an alloy of lead and tin), (iv) intermediate (e.g. acid added to marble and water), (v) of decomposition, (vi) reciprocal, (vii) double (of four bodies).

Baumé never gave up the old views, regarding phlogiston as a compound of vitrefiable earth and fire in very varying proportions:[8] il y a nécessairement beaucoup de variété dans cette combinaison du feu pur avec la terre. He defended Meyer's theory of *acidum pingue* but rejected this name, calling it 'feu pur'. He found[9] that mercury is converted by a solution of liver of sulphur or 'volatile liver of sulphur' (ammonium polysulphide) into black sulphide which, slowly in the first case but in three days in the second, was converted

---

[1] IV, i, 19–39.   [2] *Ib.*, i, 22.   [3] *Beweiss von den Saltzen* 1723, 425 (ch. 46).
[4] *Ib.*, 224 (ch. 23); *Fundamenta Chemiae*, 1747, iii, 257.
[5] AdS, *Mém. div. Sav.*, 1774, vi, 231–6 (read 23 December 1760): Expériences sur la décomposition du tartre vitriolé par l'acide nitreux seul; IV, i, 436.
[6] IV, i, 438–9.   [7] III, 1765, 8; IV, i, 23.   [8] IV, i, 143 f.   [9] IV, ii, 465.

into red vermilion. This had been discovered previously by Hoffmann (see Vol. II, p. 698).

Baumé thought the loss in weight of marble on heating was mostly water. The action of fire was to combine the phlogiston and water not dissipated, with part of the calcareous earth, forming an alkaline matter. Caustic alkalis contain 'a certain quantity of pure, or nearly pure fire'.[1] The newly discovered fixed air and other gases he regarded, with Hales, as air containing various impurities.[2] Baumé thought he had obtained borax by a process said to be used in China, in which a mixture of grease, clay and dung was watered in a trench for some years.[3] He considered that some fixed alkali is formed by the combustion of plants but most of it was formed in nature 'by the humid way'.[4] His opposition to Rouelle's views on salts has been mentioned (p. 75). He regarded liver of sulphur as very rich in phlogiston, hence the vapour escaping when it is heated in air, when it is converted into vitriolated tartar, is poisonous.[5] He noticed the phosphorescence of warm sulphur vapour, rising from heated gunpowder, in air:[6] si on la porte dans un lieu obscur, on verra que cette vapeur qui paroissoit au jour une fumée blanche, est une vraie flamme, mais bleuâtre et légere.

Baumé quite clearly describes the preparation of plastic sulphur (soufre mou) and prismatic sulphur:[7]

On met du soufre dans un creuset: on le place entre quelques charbons ardents: il ne tarde pas à entrer en fusion. Cette premiere fusion est liquide; mais, en tenant le soufre un instant de plus sur le feu, il acquiert une consistance beaucoup plus épaisse. Lorsqu'il est dans cet état, on le coule dans une terrine pleine d'eau; on trouve qu'il a acquis une couleur rouge, et qu'il est mou comme de la cire.

If poured before becoming thick, the product is brittle. The plastic sulphur is used to make copies of seals. Baumé thought it contained more phlogiston than ordinary sulphur.

Si au lieu de prendre le soufre dans cet état d'épaissement, on le retire du feu immédiatement après qu'il est fondu, et qu'on le laisse refroidir tranquillement, les parties prennent entre elles un arrangement symmétrique disposé en aiguilles, qui forment une crystallisation du soufre.

Plastic sulphur was carefully described by William Irvine junr.[8]

Baumé thought that tartar (potassium hydrogen tartrate) on heating in closed vessels is partly converted into soda owing to combination of phlogiston with the potash,[9] and in 1770 that silica is converted into alumina by fusing with alkali in a crucible.[10] Scheele (see p. 230) proved that the alumina came from the clay crucible. Fulminating gold, which is not formed unless ammonia is present, does not evolve ammonia with alkali and contains no ammoniacal nitre (ammonium nitrate); its explosive properties are due to a nitrous sulphur (soufre nitreux) insoluble in water, formed by the combination of phlogiston with nitric acid.

Baumé describes a terrible accident in his laboratory with fulminating gold

[1] IV, i, 181, 319.
[2] IV, i, 62 f.; iii, 493, 693; the 'fear that he would be accused of partiality' led Lavoisier, Opuscules Physiques et Chimiques, 1774; 1801, 180–7, to transcribe the last portion.
[3] IV, ii, 132.   [4] IV, ii, 203, 318.   [5] IV, i, 395.
[6] Macquer, Dict. Chymie, 1766, ii, 494.   [7] IV, i, 239–40.
[8] Chemical Essays, 1805, 475.   [9] IV, ii, 23.   [10] IV, i, 330.

by turning a stopper in a phial containing it, when a few grains only in the neck of the phial exploded and blinded the operator.[1] He thought that Macquer's phlogisticated alkali (potassium ferrocyanide), which he calls alkali prussien saturé,[2] gave a blue precipitate with mineral acids because they contain iron; it also gave a blue precipitate with distilled vinegar but the filtrate could be neutralised again with alkali to give a solution which could be used as a test for iron. (The precipitate with mineral acids was hydroferrocyanic acid, which oxidised in air.)

The 'esprit de saturne' which he obtained by distilling lead acetate was impure acetone.[3] Although the author of a special work on ethers (I), Baumé had difficulty in obtaining ethyl chloride (see Glauber, Vol. II, p. 360), which is readily made by the action of gaseous hydrogen chloride on alcohol.[4] Rouelle obtained it by distilling alcohol with stannic chloride,[5] a process described[6] by the Marquis de Courtanvaux (François César de Tellier, Paris; 1718–7 July 1781),[7] who also[8] found that the concentrated acetic acid obtained by distilling copper acetate solidified on cooling; this had been noticed previously by Lauraguais (Louis Léon Felicité, Comte de Lauraguais, later Duc de Brancas, Versailles, 3 July 1733 (or 1735)–Paris, 9 (or 8) October 1824), who discovered ethyl acetate (éther aceteux) by the action of this concentrated acetic acid on alcohol.[9] Baron de Bormes[10] obtained ethyl chloride by distilling alcohol with zinc chloride. Lauraguais[11] found that ether dissolves completely in about ten volumes of water, which is correct for room temperature. H. N. Draper[12] found that it is much more soluble in hydrochloric acid. The preparation of ethyl chloride and acetate was investigated by Thenard.[13]

Priestley[14] says he did not know him very well but Baumé, 'although an opponent of the whole of pneumatic chemistry, was a good operator in the old way' and his 'fires were as hot as any raised by later chemists'. Baumé opposed the new theory in V (1798), reproaching his friend Macquer for having abandoned *acidum pingue* and adopted the 'new system of the cause of the causticity of lime'.[15] He attacked Lavoisier's views (he avoids mentioning his name whenever he can), e.g. the 'pretended decomposition and recomposition of water'.[16] The 'modern doctors' had: embrouillé par mille obscurités ce que l'on savait de mieux depuis Jean Rey et d'après ce que j'ai dit dans ma *Chimie*: ils pretendent aujourd'hui que les chaux métalliques doivent leur forme à la

[1] IV, iii, 76 f.   [2] IV, ii, 605.   [3] IV, ii, 530.
[4] Woulfe, *Phil. Trans.*, 1767, lvii, 51.
[5] Lauraguais, *J. des Sçav.*, Amsterdam, 1759, xliv, 318–29; Gren, 1794, ii, 549.
[6] AdS, *Mém. div. Sav.*, 1768, v, 19 (read 1762).
[7] Condorcet, *Oeuvres*, 1847, ii, 456–66.   [8] AdS, *Mém. div. Sav.*, 1768, v, 72.
[9] *J. des Sçav.*, Amsterdam, 1759, xliv, 318–29 (July); AdS, 1759, h 100; Pelletier, *Obs. Phys.*, 1786, xxviii, 138; Gren, 1794, ii, 600.
[10] AdS, *Mém. div. Sav.*, 1774, vi, 613.
[11] Expériences sur les mélanges qui donnent l'éther, sur l'éther lui-même, et sur sa miscibilité dans l'eau, AdS, 1758, h 49, m 29–33.
[12] *Chem. News*, 1877, xxxv, 87.
[13] *Ann. Chim.*, 1807, lxi, 291, 303; *Mém. Soc. Arcueil*, 1807, i, 74, 115, 140; 1809, ii, 5, 23, 492.
[14] *The Doctrine of Phlogiston Established*, Northumberland, U.S.A., 1800, 32; 1803, 44.
[15] V, 4, 26, etc.
[16] *Ib.*, 5; an appendix to VI, 1797, 875–7, 'Nouvelles Observations sur la Decomposition et sur la Recomposition de l'Eau,' concluded 'avec la plus grande assurance, que jusqu'ici, l'eau n'a pas encore été ni décomposée, ni recomposée'.

présence de l'oxygène.[1] The assumption that vitriolated tartar (potassium sulphate) contains sulphur is absurd: 'Quelle doctrine, bon dieu! veut-on enseigner à des commençants.' He could not pass such injurious doctrines in silence.[2]

LASSONE

Joseph Marie François de Lassone (Carpentras, 3 July 1717–Paris, 8 December 1788) at first followed a medical career and was first physician to Louis XVI.[3] He showed that cream of tartar dissolves in a solution of boric acid[4] and investigated tartar emetic.[5] In five memoirs on zinc[6] he tried to show (1772) that this contains phosphorus, from the colour of the flame and the phosphorescence of flowers of zinc (zinc oxide), but he recognised correctly (1775) that the solubility of zinc in alkalis shows that its calx has acidic properties, like that of arsenic. He investigated the sandstone of Fontainebleau,[7] Vichy water,[8] phosphorus and its acid[9] and the preparation of mineral acids by distillation.[10] He described several inflammable gases obtained by the action of heat on substances.[11] He found that zinc dissolves in a solution of caustic alkali (volatile or fixed) with evolution of inflammable air (hydrogen), and that an inflammable air evolved on heating flowers of zinc (zinc oxide) with charcoal burns with a blue flame and does not detonate when its mixture with air is kindled: he thus obtained carbon monoxide, but did not analyse it. He also obtained inflammable gases by heating Prussian blue (cyanogen), verdigris (methane, etc.), etc. He distinguished two species of inflammable air, one detonating and the other not, and Rozier[12] proposed the problem as to whether there were several or only one species of inflammable air, the latter being mixed with impurities. Volta had also obtained inflammable air from zinc and alkali.[13]

CHAUSSIER

François Chaussier (Dijon, 1746–Paris, 9 June 1828) was professor in the Faculty of Medicine in Paris, First Physician in the Maternity Hospital, and for a time professor of chemistry in the École Polytechnique.[14] Most of his writings are medical or medico-legal. He described a number of experiments with hydrogen, including its ignition by an electric spark, to the Dijon Academy in 1777.[15] He discovered sodium thiosulphate (hydrosulfure sulfurè

[1] Ib., 60.   [2] Ib., 311.
[3] Condorcet, AdS, 1788, h 23; id., Oeuvres, 1847, iii, 294–305; LZE in NBG, 1859, xxix, 771.
[4] AdS, 1755, h 61, m 119: de la Sône.
[5] AdS, 1768, h 61, m 520 (de Lassone); Mém. Soc. Roy. de Méd., 1776 (1779), 371.
[6] AdS, 1772, h 31, m 380; 1775, h 10, m 1, 8; 1776, h 26, m 563; 1777, h 35, m 1.
[7] AdS, 1775, m 371; 1775, m 68; 1777, h 18, m 43.   [8] AdS, 1771, h 41, m 1.
[9] AdS, 1780, h 33, m 508: with Cornette.   [10] AdS, 1781, h 29, m 645: with Cornette.
[11] Notices d'une suite d'expériences nouvelles, qui font connoître la nature et les propriétés de plusieurs espèces d'airs ou émanations aëriformes, extraites par diverses voies d'un grand nombre de substances; AdS, 1776, h 29 (Sur les Gas aëriens), m 686–96; Crell, Neueste Entdeckungen, 1781, ii, 138–50; Macquer, (2), ii, 315; Fourcroy, (2), iii, 489.
[12] Obs. Phys., 1777, ix, 321 (May, 1777).
[13] Scopoli, in Macquer's Chym. Wörterbuch, ed. Leonhardi, 1788, ii, 813.
[14] Poggendorff, (1), i, 426; NBG, 1854, x, 147–50.
[15] Obs. Phys., 1777, x, 309; Fourcroy, (1), iii, 492.

de soude) by the action of sulphur dioxide on sodium sulphide solution and in other ways.[1]

Cadet-Gassicourt

Louis Claude Cadet-Gassicourt (or de Gassicourt) (Paris; 24 July 1731–17 October 1799), was at first an apothecary, then director of the Sèvres porcelain factory.[2] He entered the Academy in 1766. He discovered an impure cacodyl compound ('Cadet's fuming liquor') by distilling arsenious oxide with potassium acetate.[3] He concluded that borax contained copper, arsenic and a vitrifiable earth,[4] but not boric acid (sedative salt), the acidity of which he thought was due to hydrochloric acid. He gave improved methods for making potassium acetate (terre foliée du tartre)[5] and of ether,[6] showing that fresh alcohol could be added to the distillation residue. He thought fixed alkali (potash) was converted into volatile alkali (ammonia) by distilling with alcohol and nitrate of mercury (probably by reduction of the nitrate),[7] and investigated the 'volatility' of diamond when heated in open or [imperfectly] closed vessels.[8]

In September 1774 he had a dispute with Baumé on the effect of heat on red precipitate *per se* (mercuric oxide), which he found was reduced to mercury, whilst Baumé[9] said that it merely sublimed. A commission consisting of Sage, Brisson, and Lavoisier, appointed in 1774 by the Academy, reported in favour of Cadet;[10] they all missed the evolution of oxygen, discovered about the same time by Priestley.

His son Charles Louis Cadet-Gassicourt (Paris; 23 January 1769–21 November 1821) was a barrister but published some chemical works[11] and many books on pharmacy and general subjects.[12] He translated Spielmann's book (see Vol. II, p. 689), in which he mentions that 'le sieur Lombard' in Paris was making cooking vessels of glass, 'qui souffrent un feu de charbon très-vif', thus anticipating 'modern' glass oven-ware.[13]

Quatremère-Disjonval

Denis Bernard Quatremère-Disjonval (Paris, 4 August 1754–Bordeaux, 1829–30) in a memoir on indigo[14] described the preparation of picric acid (discovered by Woulfe)[15] by the action of nitric acid on indigo and mentioned that

[1] *Bull. Soc. Philomath.*, 1799, no. 33, 70 (Vauquelin, *ib.*, 71).
[2] Gmelin, (1), ii, 529; Hoefer, (1), ii, 390; NBU, 1854, viii, 67; Scherer, *Allgem. J. Chem.*, 1801, vii, 488.
[3] AdS, *Mém. div. Sav.*, 1760, iii, 623.
[4] AdS, *Mém. div. Sav.*, 1768, v, 105, 117; AdS, 1766, h 64, m 365.
[5] AdS, *Mém. div. Sav.*, 1763, iv, 518; AdS, 1780, m 583.
[6] AdS, 1774, h 23, m 524.   [7] AdS, 1769, h 66.
[8] *Obs. Phys.*, 1772, ii, 401.   [9] *Chymie expér. et raisonn.*, 1773, ii, 390.
[10] Cadet, *Obs. Phys.*, 1775, vi, 55; Lavoisier, *Oeuvres*, 1868, iv, 188; Partington and McKie, *Ann. Sci.*, 1938, iii, 1 (53).
[11] *Dictionnaire de Chimie*, 4 vols. 8°, Paris, 1803 (BN).
[12] NBU, 1854, viii, 70; E. Pariset, *Histoire des Membres de l'Académie Royale de Médecine*, Paris, 1845, i, 130; Poggendorff, (1), i, 357.
[13] Spielmann, *Instituts de Chymie*, tr. Cadet, 1770, i, 49, long note.
[14] Mémoire sur l'Indigo, AdS, *Mém. div. Sav.*, 1780, ix, 1–164.
[15] *Phil. Trans.*, 1771, lxi, 114.

it stains the skin a saffron-yellow colour. He was first a manager of a dye-works in Sedan, then adopted a political career and was banished from Paris by Napoleon. He published a collection of memoirs.[1] Beddoes[2] speaks of the 'excessive ignorance' which he 'betrays of the most common observations in chemistry'.

SAGE

Balthazar Georges Sage (Paris; 7 May 1740–9 September 1824), at first apothecary at the Invalides, was from 1778 professor of assaying at the Paris Mint, where he established a museum of minerals. He was instrumental in the foundation of the École des Mines in 1783 and became its Director. After the Revolution he lost this place but was reinstated at the Mint, where he lectured. In 1801 he became a member of the Institut. He remained a phlogistian till his death, published pamphlets against the new nomenclature and theory in 1810, and opposed it in his autobiography in 1818. He became blind in 1805. His later lectures, e.g. in 1802, were quite out of date and poorly attended.[3]

Sage discovered hypophosphoric acid ($H_4P_2O_6$), which is formed along with phosphorous acid when sticks of phosphorus are exposed in a funnel to moist air.[4] He showed that phosphorus reduces solutions of metallic salts to the metals (1781).[5] He obtained crystals from a solution of a copper salt in ammonia[6] and observed crystals of red oxide of copper on a copper statue which had lain for some time under water.[7] He showed that silver chloride is reduced by iron (1776).

Sage[8] seems to have discovered solid potassium ferrocyanide independently of Guyton de Morveau (see p. 88). He published on litharge,[9] the specific gravities of acids,[10] and many analyses of minerals.[11] He noticed that realgar (As_2S_2) is converted into orpiment (As_2S_3) on exposure to light;[12] many specimens in modern museums are spoiled from ignorance of this. He showed that alcohol is oxidised by nitric acid to oxalic acid.[13]

Sage had some peculiar ideas. He supposed that a universal acid (*acide igné*) forms oxygen when combined with phlogiston and water, hydrogen when combined with excess of phlogiston, and produces other acids (phosphoric,

[1] *Collection de Mémoires Chymiques et Physiques*, 4°, Paris, 1784 (312 pp.).
[2] Tr. of Bergman, *A Dissertation on Elective Attractions*, London, 1785, 322.
[3] Ferguson, ii, 312; Gmelin, (1), ii, 537; Poggendorff, (1), ii, 732, who says many of Sage's works 'sind zwar gedruckt, nicht aber in den Buchhandel gekommen'. Kahlbaum and Hoffmann, *Monographien*, i, 43, 129–30; a letter from Paris in 1787, q. by Speter, *Samml. chem. u. chem.-techn. Vorträge*, 1910, xv, 197, says: 'Sage lehnet sich wider die Lavoisiersche Sekte auf, die er Antiphlogistiker nennt . . . er lacht gewaltig über die Oxygenisten.' Sage. published: *Exposé sommaire des principales découvertes faites dans l'espace de 54 années par B. G. Sage*, 1813, *Enumération des découvertes minéralogiques faites pendant l'espace de 60 années par B. G. Sage*, 1819, and *Analyse du lait de vache, suivie de la liste chronologique des ouvrages publié dans l'espace de 54 ans*, 1820.
[4] AdS, 1777, m 435.
[5] Fourcroy, (3), iii, 242, says the Marquis de Bullion discovered this, and also mentions Sage.
[6] AdS, 1766, h 74.　　　　　　　[7] AdS, 1778, m 210.
[8] *Acta Acad. Mogunt.*, 1778–9, iii, 64: animal salt, or Geoffroy's alkali phlogistique.
[9] *Ib.*, 61.　　　　[10] *Ib.*, 67.
[11] AdS, 1782, m 307 (bismuth sulphide), 310 (arsenic and antimony), 314 (beryl), 315 (iron clay), 316 (native mercuric oxide from Idria).
[12] *Phil. Mag.*, 1802, xiii, 42.　　　　[13] AdS, 1785, m 233.

sulphuric, nitric, muriatic) when mixed with other materials.[1] He thought sea water contained a peculiar alkaline gas (gaz neptunien) which prevented its purification by distillation.[2]

Becher, and Henckel, claimed to have found gold in vegetables. Philip Jacob Sachs[3] and Joh. Paterson Hain[4] also wrote on 'aurum vegetabile'. Lucas Schröck junr.[5] reported on grains of gold found in the viscera in dissections (de auro anatomo) and said Camerarius in 1713 had been concerned with gold found in the stomach of a goose. Paterson Hain said the grape stones in a Hungarian vineyard were of gold but Born a century later showed that they were the golden-yellow eggs of an insect.[6] Sage[7] found gold in rotted manure, earth, garden mould, etc., and obtained 300 grains from 1 cwt. of vine ashes. Berthollet found $40\frac{8}{25}$ grains in 1 cwt. of ashes, and Rouelle and D'Arcet, and Deyeux, also claimed to have obtained it.[8]

Some of the many other publications by Sage can only be mentioned:

Essais sur le Vin, les Pierres, les Bézoards, & d'autres parties d'Histoire Naturelle & de Chimie; Traduction d'une Lettre de Monsieur Lehmann, sur la Mine de Plomb Rouge, 12°, Paris, 1769 (xii, 251 pp., 3 ll., Duveen, 523), tr. Beckmann, Chemische Untersuchungen verschiedener Mineralien, Göttingen, 1775; Élémens de Minéralogie Docimastique, 8°, Paris, 1772, 2 ed. 2 vols. 1777; Mémoires de Chimie, 8°, Paris, 1773 (pp. vii, 262, xxxviii, 1 folding plate); Expériences propres à faire connoître que L'Alkali Volatil Fluor est le remède le plus efficace dans les Asphyxies, 8°, Paris, 1778; Observations Nouvelles sur les Propriétés de l'Alkali Fluor Ammoniacal; D'après quelques Expériences faites par M.B** ... Servant d'addition à celles qu'on a déjà publiées sur le même objet, dont on donne ici le résumé, 8°, Paris, 1778; L'Art d'Essayer l'Or et l'Argent, Tableau comparé de la coupellation des substances métalliques par le moyen du plomb ou du Bismuth, Procédé pour obtenir l'Or plus pur que par la voie du Départ, 8°, 1780; Observations sur l'emploi du zinc. Preuves de l'innocuité de ce métal, Paris, 1809; Exposé des Effets de la Contagion Nomenclative et Refutation des Paradoxes qui dénaturent la Physique, 8°, Paris, 1810 (56 pp.).

NAVIER

Pierre Toussaint Navier (St. Dizier (Champagne), 1 November 1712–Paris, 16 July 1779) was a physician in Châlons-sur-Marne.[9] He studied under Geoffroy. He described the preparation of ethyl nitrite by the action of nitric acid on alcohol,[10] and ten methods of amalgamating iron and dissolving mercury in vegetable acids.[11] He is said to have found that chlorauric acid ($HAuCl_4$) is soluble in ether, but the reference given for this is incorrect.[12] Navier's method of preparing ethyl nitrite by mixing alcohol and nitric acid in equal volumes in a closed bottle, when after ten days an ethereal liquid

[1] Analyse Chimique et Concordance des Trois Règnes, 3 vols. 8°, Paris, 1786.
[2] Analyse de l'eau de mer, 1817; Cuvier, (1), i, 240.
[3] Miscell. Acad. Nat. Curios., 1670, i, 225 (no. cxxxi).
[4] Ib., 1671 (1688), ii, 187 (no. cxiii).   [5] Ib., 1719, Cent. VIII, 330, Obs. xlix.
[6] Kopp, (1), ii, 232; perhaps Born, Brief über mineralogische Gegenstände, 1774 ?
[7] AdS, 1778, h 25.
[8] Chaptal, Elements of Chemistry, 1791, ii, 441–2; Expériences faites par MM. Rouelle et d'Arcet d'après celles de M. Sage sur la quantité d'or qu'on retire de la terre végétale et des cendres des végétaux, 12°, s.l.e.a.,19 pp. (BN S 21941).
[9] Vicq D'Azyr, 1805, iii, 140, 160.   [10] Letter to Duhamel, AdS, 1742, 379.
[11] AdS, Mém. div. Sav., 1774, vi, 325–50.
[12] Découverte d'un éther d'or, AdS, Mém. div. Sav., 1771, q. in Poggendorff, (1), ii, 260; it is not in any vol. of this publication; Vicq D'Azyr, iii, 161.

swam to the top, was also described by G. H. Sebastiani,[1] according to R. A. Vogel[2] without knowledge of Navier's work. Black[3] published a safer process (see p. 133). Fourcroy[4] describes a violent explosion of an apparatus for making nitrous ether modified from one of Woulfe, which occurred in the lecture room of the École de Médecine in 1773. The head of the alembic was hurled into the dome of the theatre and fell in a thousand pieces.

Navier published a book on antidotes to mineral poisons[5] which Fourcroy[6] says aroused the anger of the empirical physicians by its scientific spirit.

BRISSON

Mathurin Jacques Brisson (Fontenay-le-Comte, 30 April 1723– Broissi, nr. Versailles, 23 June 1806) was professor of physics in the Collège de Navarre, the École Centrale, and the Lycée Bonaparte, Paris. He compiled a table of specific gravities.[7] A very long table of specific gravities, with a history of the subject, had been given by Richard Davies in 1748.[8] It is to such works that we must still turn for information on the specific gravities of turnips, maize, or treacle. Brisson, although a physicist, also tried his hand on two chemical books.[9] He collaborated with Macquer, Cadet, Baumé, and Lavoisier in experiments on the combustibility of diamond (1773; see p. 383), and with Sage and Lavoisier on the reduction of mercuric oxide (1774, see p. 96).

DEMACHY

Jacques François Demachy (Paris; 30 August 1728–7 July 1803), pharmacist at the Hôtel-Dieu, then Chief Apothecary in the Military Hospital at St. Denis, was a pupil of Rouelle, and besides translating Pott's, Spielmann's, Marggraf's and Juncker's books from Latin and German, published a number of works on technical and pharmaceutical chemistry:[10]

I. Instituts de Chymie, ou Principes Élémentaires de cette Science, présentés sous un nouveau jour, 2 vols. 12°, Paris, 1766.
II. Procédés Chimiques Rangés Méthodiquement et Définies. On y joint le Précis d'une Nouvelle Table des Combinaisons ou Rapports, 12°, Paris, 1769 (the Précis, giving affinity tables, was issued separately, n.d. (c. 1770)).
III. Recueil des Dissertations Physico-Chimiques, Présentées à Différentes Académies, Amsterdam and Paris, 1774 (BM 233. g. 31): contains affinity tables of Geoffroy

[1] Dissertatio inauguralis de nitro, ejus relationibus et modo cum ejus acido oleum naphthæ parandi, Erfurt, 1746; BM 7306. g. 4. (3.).
[2] Institutiones Chemicæ, Göttingen, 1755; tr. Wiegleb, Lehrsätze der Chemie, Weimar, 1775; Kopp, (1), iv, 308.
[3] Crell, Neueste Entdeckungen, 1783, xi, 97.   [4] (2), iii, 411.
[5] Contrepoisons de l'arsenic, du sublimé corrosif, du vert-de-gris, et du plomb, etc., 2 vols. 12°, Paris, 1777.
[6] (3), 1790, i, 16.   [7] Pésanteur Spécifique des Corps, 1787.   [8] Phil. Trans., 1748, xlv, 416.
[9] (1) Principes Élémentaires de l'Histoire Naturelle et Chimique des Substances Minérales, 1797, tr. Elements of Natural History and Chymical Analysis of Mineral Substances, 1800; (2) Éléments ou Principes Physico-Chymiques, 4 vols., 1800, tr. The Physical Principles of Chemistry, Translated from the French, to which is added a short Appendix by the Translator, 1801 (ix, 424, xxiv pp.).
[10] Gmelin, (1), ii, 534; Poggendorff, (1), i, 547; Querard, La France Littéraire, 1830, ii, 467; L. G. Toraude, J. F. Demachy . . . Histoire et Contes, précédes d'une Étude . . . sur sa vie et ses Oeuvres, la. 8°, Paris, 1907 (BN 4° Ye. 291).

(1718), Grosse (1730), Gellert (1750), Rüdiger (1756), the Encyclopédie (1763), and Limbourg (1758), in 7 folding tables.

IV. L'Art du Distillateur d'Eaux-Fortes, &c., in Descriptions des Arts et Métiers (see p. 11), f°, Paris, 1773.

V. L'Art du Distilleur Liquoriste; Contenant Le Bruleur d'Eaux de Vie, etc., in the same Descriptions, etc., f°, 1775. The last two works were translated and extended by Hahnemann as:

VA. Herrn Demachy's Laborant im Grosse, oder Kunst die chemischen Produkte fabrikmässig zu verfertigen, in drei Theilen, mit Herrn Doktor Struves Anmerkungen und eine Anhang einiger Abhandlungen H^{rn} Apotheker Wieglebs, als der vierte Theil, aus dem Französischen übersetzt und mit Zusätzen versehen, von Samuel Hahnemann, 2 vols. 8°, Leipzig, L. Crusius, 1784 (BN V. 36357-8; not in BM), reprinted 1801.

VB. Der Liquerfabrikant, 2 vols., Leipzig, 1785 (v. rare).

VI. Manuel du Pharmacien, 2 vols., Paris, 1788.

VII. Demachy also added several sections to his translation of Juncker's Conspectus Chemiae; Élémens de Chymie . . . traduits du Latin sur la IIe Edition de M. Juncker, avec des Notes, 6 vols. 12°, Paris, 1757.

He believed in the possibility of the conversion of water into earth and air.[1] De Luc[2] thought water was transformed into air by the action of electricity. Demachy discovered the crystalline hydrate of stannic chloride[3] and observed the rise in temperature on the formation of tin amalgam or on mixing lead and bismuth amalgams. He opposed the antiphlogistic theory.

CORNETTE

Claude Melchior Cornette (Besançon, 1 March 1744–Rome, 11 May 1794)[4] worked particularly on salts, the action of fuming nitric acid on charcoal powder,[5] mercurous sulphate,[6] phosphorus (with Lassone),[7] the action of nitric acid on oils,[8] and ammonium nitrate.[9] His *Mémoire sur la Formation du Salpetre*, 8°, Paris, 1779 (xii, 84 pp.) was included in the *Recueil des Mémoires sur la Formation & la Fabrication du Salpêtre* (1786).[10] He extended Baumé's observation on reversible reactions (see p. 92) by showing that hydrochloric acid decomposes potassium sulphate.[11]

OPOIX

Christophe Opoix (Provins; 28 February 1745–12 August 1840), an apothecary, regarded phlogiston as the principle of colours, its successive rarefactions causing a corresponding change in the prismatic scale of colours.[12] Opoix also published several works on common and mineral waters.[13]

[1] *Obs. Phys.*, 1774, iii, 408; 1775 (1778), iv, 37.
[2] *Idées sur la Météorologie*, 1786, 543, Appendix, 491.
[3] *Nova Acta Acad. Nat. Curios.*, 1770, iv, 60.   [4] Gmelin, (1), iii, 443; Poggendorff, (1), i, 480.
[5] AdS, 1779, m 479.   [6] AdS, 1779, m 485.   [7] AdS, 1780, m 508.
[8] AdS, 1780, m 567.   [9] AdS, 1783, m 745.
[10] AdS, *Mém. div. Sav.*, 1786, xi, 1 f.   [11] AdS, 1778, h 17, m 44, 333; 1779, h 20, m 487.
[12] *Obs. Phys.*, 1776, viii, 100, 189 (read to the Academy by Macquer); *Observations physico-chimiques sur les Couleurs*, Paris, 1784; *Théorie des Couleurs et des Corps Inflammables*, Paris, 1808.
[13] Poggendorff, (1), ii, 328; NBG, 1863, xxxviii, 709.

DUHAMEL

Jean Pierre François Guillot Duhamel (Nicorps, nr. Coutances, Dép. La Manche, 31 August 1730–Paris, 19 (or 20) February 1816) was in 1775 Commissar of the Conseil pour l'inspection des forges et des fourneaux, and later professor of metallurgy in the École des Mines and inspector of mines; he became a member of the Academy in 1786.[1] He travelled in Germany, Great Britain, and Scandinavia to inspect metallurgical processes, in which he was accompanied by Gabriel Jars. Chaptal[2] says Gellert (see Vol. II, p. 709) made brass with calcined blende but it was brittle and of poor colour; Duhamel and Jars made good brass from calcined blende, and Chaptal found that it was necessary to expel all the sulphur of the blende by roasting.

JARS

Gabriel Jars (Lyon, 26 or 29 January 1732–Clermont, 20 or 26 August 1769) published on mining engineering and metallurgy.[3] His best-known work was published posthumously by his brother G. Jars, also a metallurgist (d. 1796):

Voyages Métallurgiques ou Recherches et Observations Sur les Mines & Forges de fer, la Fabrication de l'acier, celle du fer-blanc, & plusieurs mines de charbon de terre, faites depuis l'année 1757 jusques & compris 1769, en Allemagne, Suéde, Norvege, Angleterre & Écosse, 4°, vol. i, Lyon, 1774, vols. i–iii, Paris, 1774–80–81 (vols. ii and iii have different later parts of the title); German tr. by Gerhard, 4 vols. 8°, Berlin, 1777–85.

This deals with mines of all kinds of metals, the manufacture of azure, white lead, minium, brass, alum, sulphur, vitriol, salt, bricks, tiles, pottery, coinage, etc. Baron Dietrich (see p. 211) also published a work on mines and metallurgy etc., in France in six parts in four volumes:

Description des Gîtes de Minerai, des Forges et des Salines des Pyrénées, 2 vols. 4°, Paris, 1786; do. de Haute et Basse-Alsace (pts. 3–4), 4°, Paris, 1789; do. de la Lorraine Méridionale (pts. 5–6), 4°, Paris, An VIII (1799–1800).

MONNET

Antoine Grimoald Monnet (Champeix, Auvergne, 1734–Paris, 23 May 1817), was an apothecary in Paris and gave private lectures on chemistry. In 1774 he became inspector-general of mines in France; he lost this post on the Revolution but became an inspector again in 1794.[4] His publications are mostly

[1] NBG, 1856, xv, 103; Poggendorff, (1), i, 616; Thomson, *Ann. Phil.*, 1818, xi, 161.
[2] *Chemistry applied to Arts and Manufactures*, 1805, iii, 289.
[3] Une espèce de siphon à élever de l'eau, AdS, 1760, h 160; Observation sur la circulation de l'air dans les mines, AdS, 1768, h 18, m 218, 229; Description d'une nouvelle machine executée aux Mines de Schemnitz, AdS, *Mém. div Sav.*, 1768, v, 67; D'un grand Fourneau à raffiner le cuivre, AdS, 1769, m 589; Procédé des Anglais pour convertir le plomb en minium, AdS, 1770 (1773), m 68–72; Observations métallurgiques sur la séparation des métaux, AdS, 1770, h 59, m 514, describing the methods for smelting ores containing silver and copper, or silver, lead, and copper, and the separation of gold from argentiferous copper by a dry process.
[4] Poggendorff, (1), ii, 187; Thomson, *Ency. Brit. Suppl.*, 1801, i, 277, 304, 319.

on mineralogy and technology. His theoretical views were mostly erroneous and he was a bitter opponent of Lavoisier's theory.[1] He wrote on mineral waters[2] but his best work is on the manufacture of vitriols and alum.[3] In a dissertation on arsenic, crowned by the Berlin Academy,[4] he confirmed Brandt's proof that white arsenic is the calx of metallic arsenic and denied that arsenic is a constituent of metals. He obtained crystals of corrosive sublimate by mixing a solution of mercury in nitric acid with common salt or hydrochloric acid.[5] Many of Monnet's papers appeared in the *Miscellanea Taurinensia*.[6] His proof that when nitre is heated with clay, etc., the silica displaces the nitric acid from the alkali[7] was confirmed by le Veillard (1772).[8]

Monnet in his treatise on the dissolution of metals[9] said the whole theory of affinity was a chimera which could give nothing useful to science, but Macquer[10] refuted this. He also maintained that cobalt and nickel are modifications of the same metal. He found that the purple precipitate formed by tannin with a solution of a gold salt dissolves in nitric acid to a blue solution.

PARMENTIER

Antoine Augustin Parmentier (Montdidier, 17 April (August) 1737–Paris, 17 December 1813)[11] was a pharmacist with the French army in Germany, where he was five times taken prisoner, and on one of these occasions lived entirely on potatoes, the cultivation of which he introduced into France. He made the new vegetable popular by presenting a bouquet of the flowers to Louis XVI, who wore some as a button-hole. Parmentier, who became chief pharmacist in the Hôtel des Invalides and inspector general of health, published a large number of works on applied organic chemistry (bread-making, fermentation, vinegar, etc.); with Deyeux he attempted the analysis of milk and of blood. He was an indefatigable worker, often beginning at three in the morning so as to find time for research in the midst of his innumerable public duties. His publications on beet sugar,[12] extractive matter,[13] chocolate,[14] and the history of sugar[15] may be mentioned. He wrote several books on potatoes,

---

[1] Dissertationes et expériences relatives à la théorie des chimistes pneumatistes (read May, 1789), *Mém. Acad. Turin*, 1788–89 (1790), v, 123–205; *Demonstration de la fausseté des principes des nouveau chimistes*, Paris, 1798.

[2] *Traité des eaux minérales*, 12°, Paris, 1768.

[3] *Traité de la vitriolisation et d'alunation, ou l'Art de fabriquer les vitriols et l'Alun*, 12°, Amsterdam and Paris, 1769 (xxiv, 288, errata, 2 plates), with supplement: *Dissertation sur la minéralisation et sur l'état du Soufre dans les Mines et les Métaux* (pp. 154–66).

[4] *Dissertation sur l'arsenic*, 4°, Berlin, 1774.   [5] KAH, 1770, xxxi, 102.

[6] 1766–9, iv, 47 (decomp. of nitre by salts and earths), 71 (minium), 75 (rectification of volatile alkali), 93 (combination of mercury with tartar); *Mém. Acad. Turin*, 1778–9 (1790), v, 123 (pneumatic app.; arsenic and manganese).

[7] *Miscell. Taurin.*, 1766–9, iv, 47.

[8] Cadet and Lavoisier, in Lavoisier, *Oeuvres*, 1868, iv, 126.

[9] *Traité de la Dissolution des Métaux*, Amsterdam and Paris, 1775, q. by J. C. Fischer, 1805, vi, 294.

[10] *Dict. de Chymie*, 1778, i, 67.

[11] Cuvier, (1), 1819, ii, 164–90; Hoefer, (1), ii, 534; *J. de Médecine*, 1777, xlvii, 195; La Wall, *Four Thousand Years of Pharmacy*, New York, 1927, 367; NBG, 1862, xxxix, 232; Poggendorff, (1), ii, 362; A. F. de Silvestre, *Notice biographique sur Parmentier*, Paris, 1815 (22 pp.).

[12] *Ann. Chim.*, 1802, xlii, 289.   [13] *Ib.*, 1802, xliii, 19.

[14] *Ib.*, 1803, xlv, 139.   [15] *Ib.*, 1811, lxxx, 89, 293.

including their use in making bread without flour, and was devoted to the vegetable.

CLOUET

Louis Clouet (Singly, nr. Mézières, 11 November 1751–Cayenne, 4 June 1801) collaborated with Lavoisier in work on saltpetre earths[1] but is best known for his work on steel, which he showed is formed by heating wrought iron with diamond powder,[2] an observation confirmed by Pepys, who used a notched electrically heated iron wire.[3] Clouet also worked on the composition of enamels,[4] and confirmed[5] Scheele's observation (see p. 234) that prussic acid is formed by passing ammonia gas over strongly heated charcoal. Clouet was a pupil of Monge at Mézières and worked with him on the liquefaction of sulphur dioxide by cooling.[6]

BUCQUET

Jean Baptiste Michel Bucquet (Paris; 18 February 1746–24 January 1780) was educated for the bar but studied medicine and chemistry. In 1776 he succeeded Roux as professor of chemistry and natural history, giving a single course (as Fourcroy did later), in the Paris École de Médecine. He also assisted Lavoisier in some researches. Bucquet was an excellent teacher but died very young after a painful illness.[7] His lectures were published.[8] In a memoir on arsenic (1772)[9] he described the preparation of crystalline arsenic acid (nitre d'arsenic) from a solution made by boiling arsenious oxide with nitric acid, and showed that it formed with potash the same salt (potassium arsenate) as Macquer had obtained by heating arsenious oxide with nitre. In a memoir on carbon dioxide (air fixé) (1773), referring to Hales, Black, Macbride, Priestley, etc.,[10] he claimed to have improved the generating apparatus of Black and Macbride. He showed that fixed air obeys Boyle's law. It had no acidic reaction towards syrup of violets. In 1778 Bucquet and Fourcroy called fixed air 'acide crayeux' (chalky acid) and its salts with alkalis or alkaline earths 'craies' (chalks).[11] In a research on sal ammoniac (1773)[12] Bucquet, who criticised Black's experiments, found that dry carbon dioxide is not absorbed by quicklime, and concluded that fixed air and lime do not combine without an intermediate, which is water. This is an early recognition of the effect of moisture on

[1] AdS, *Mém. div. Sav.*, 1786, xi, 503.
[2] Sur la combinaison du diamant avec le fer, *J. des Mines*, 1799, ix, 3; *Nicholson's J.*, 1800, iii, 131.
[3] In Children, *Phil. Trans.*, 1815, cv, 363 (371).
[4] *Ann. Chim.*, 1800, xxxiv, 200.   [5] *Ann. Chim.*, 1791, xi, 30.
[6] Hatchette, *Ann. Chim.*, 1803, xlvi, 97; Lavoisier, *Traité de Chimie*, 1789, 244 (Clouet); Nicholson, *Dict. of Chemistry*, 1795, ii, 925; Fourcroy, (1), 1801, ii, 74 (Monge).
[7] Condorcet, *Oeuvres*, 1847, ii, 410–33; Fourcroy, (2), iii, 339, 411, 756; Vicq d'Azyr, i, 249.
[8] *Introduction à l'étude des corps naturels tirés du règne minéral*, 2 vols. 12°, Paris, 1771 (BN 19980–1; Fourcroy, *op. cit.*, 756, says 1772); *Introduction à l'étude des corps naturels tirés du règne végetale*, 2 vols. sm. 8°, Paris, 1773, highly praised by Fourcroy.
[9] AdS, *Mém. div. Sav.*, 1780, ix, 643, 659.
[10] Sur l'air qui se dégage des corps dans les temps de leur decomposition, AdS, *Mém. div. Sav.*, 1776, vii, m 1; report by Desmarets and Lavoisier in Lavoisier, *Oeuvres*, 1868, iv, 155.
[11] Fourcroy, (1), iv, 5.
[12] AdS, *Mém. div. Sav.*, 1780, ix, 563; report by Jussieu and Macquer, in Lavoisier, *Oeuvres*, 1868, iv, 263; Macquer and Lavoisier, *ib.*, 276, 279.

chemical reactions. Bucquet's work on gases overlaps Lavoisier's early re-searches (1774) (see p. 388) and probably provided him with much information.

Bucquet also worked on the mineral zeolite (1773).[1] His memoirs on blood and on ethers were not printed.[2] Macquer[3] mentions that Bucquet obtained a fetid acid by distilling sugar of lead, much weaker than that from verdigris: this would contain acetone. Bucquet's memoir on the effects of gases on animals[4] contains a short history of discoveries on gases.

D'ARCET

Jean D'Arcet (or Darcet) (St. Sever, Dép. Landes, 7 September 1725–Paris, 13 February 1801)[5] became director of the Sèvres porcelain works and was the first to make true porcelain in France. He constructed a high-temperature furnace (feu de charbon)[6] and carried out experiments on the effects of high temperatures on various materials.[7] He found at first that a diamond dis-appeared when strongly heated even in a closed crucible.[8] The Academy asked for a repetition of the experiment, when it was found that the diamond remained when strongly heated in a perfectly closed crucible.[9] D'Arcet made a fusible alloy of lead, bismuth, and tin.[10] He gives the composition of Newton's fusible metal[11] as 8 pts. Bi, 4 pts. Sn, 4 pts. Pb, or 5Bi, 3Sn, 5Pb, and Bianchy's (sic) as 5Bi, 4Sn, 1Pb; D'Arcet tested many of these ternary alloys and found that 8Bi, 2Sn, 6Pb becomes liquid in boiling water. Marggraf[12] found that 2Bi, 1Sn, 1Pb melts in boiling water. D'Arcet[13] published researches showing how church bells could be melted down to cast cannon.

Jean Pierre Joseph D'Arcet (Paris; 31 August 1777–2 August 1844), son of Jean D'Arcet, published on applied chemistry and metallurgy,[14] including the decomposition of barium salts by potash and soda,[15] potash and soda puri-fied by alcohol,[16] alkali carbonates,[17] a proposal to use sodium instead of

[1] AdS, *Mém. div. Sav.*, 1780, ix, 576.   [2] Summaries in Vicq d'Azyr.
[3] *Dictionnaire*, 1778, iii, 208.
[4] *Mémoire sur la Manière dont les Animaux sont affectés par differens Fluides Aériformes Méphitiques; & sur les moyens de remedier aux effets de ces Fluides. Précédé d'une Histoire abrégée des différens Fluides Aériformes ou Gas*, 8°, Paris, 1778 (xv, 93 pp., with laudation by Lavoisier, 87–90).
[5] Cuvier, AdS, An XI, iv, 74–88; Dizé, *Précis historique sur la vie et les travaux de Jean d'Arcet*, Paris, An X (1802), says he was b. at Douazit, Landes, and d. 24 Pluviôse, An IX; Hoefer, (1), ii, 530; Matignon, *Chem. Ztg.*, 1909, xxxiii, 553.
[6] AdS, 1767, h 57, m 298.
[7] Mémoire sur l'action d'un feu égal, violent et continué sur un grand nombre de terres, de pierres et chaux métalliques, AdS, 1766, h 75.
[8] *Intr. Obs. Phys.*, 1771 (1777), i, 108.
[9] D'Arcet and Rouelle, *Intr. Obs. Phys.*, 1772 (1777), i, 484.
[10] D'Arcet, *J. de Médecine*, 1775, xliii, 552–61 (Expériences: Sur quelques alliages métal-liques qui ont la propriété de se ramollir, et même de fondre et de couler dans l'eau bouil-lante); *Obs. Phys.*, 1777, ix, 217–21.
[11] Bolley, *Dingl. J.*, 1853, cxxix, 438, gives Newton's alloy as 8Bi, 3Sn, 5Pb.
[12] *Obs. Phys.*, 1777, ix, 60.
[13] *Supplément à l'Instruction sur l'Art de séparer le Cuivre du Métal des Cloches*, 4°, Paris, 1791; and with Pelletier, *Instruction sur l'Art de séparer le Cuivre du Métal des Cloches. Publié par ordre du Comité de Salut Public*, 4°, Paris, 1794 (18 pp., ii ll., 9 pp., i l., 3 plates).
[14] NBG, 1855, xiii, 104; Poggendorff, (1), i, 521.
[15] *Ann. Chim.*, 1804, xlix, 95 (with Anfrye); 1807, lxi, 247.
[16] *Ann. Chim.*, 1808, lxviii, 175.   [17] *Ann. Chim.*, 1809, lxxi, 200.

potassium nitrate in the arts,[1] and on the composition of Chinese gongs and cymbals.[2]

COLLET-DESCOTILS

Hippolyte Victor Collet-Descotils (Caen, 21 November 1773–Paris, 6 December 1815),[3] mostly called simply 'Descotils', was engineer-in-chief and professor of chemistry in the Royal Corps of Mines. He accompanied Napoleon to Egypt and was a member of the Institut in Cairo, later of the Société d'Arcueil. He analysed several minerals and reported on the manufacture of indigo in St. Domingo and Egypt,[4] and on henna.[5] He suggested that the colours of some salts of crude platinum are due to a new metal[6] which he did not isolate; this was iridium. In this research he examined the metal found with native platinum which has 'une grande résistance à l'action des acides' (now called osmiridium). Vauquelin[7] and Fourcroy and Vauquelin[8] also confounded iridium and osmium, ascribing both to a single metal which they called *ptene*, and iridium and osmium were first characterised by Smithson Tennant.[9] Collet-Descotils examined a lead ore from Mexico in which del Río claimed to have discovered a new metal 'érithrone',[10] which was really vanadium (see Vol. IV), but Collet-Descotils[11] reported that it was only basic lead chromate. He reported on Mushet's process for converting iron into steel.[12]

SIGAUD DE LA FOND

Joseph Aignan Sigaud de la Fond (Bourges; 5 January 1730–26 January 1810), graduated master in medicine in Paris in 1770; he became demonstrator in experimental physics in the Collège Royale, professor there in 1760, in Bourges in 1786, and professor of physics and chemistry in the École Centrale in 1795. Fourcroy was his pupil.[13] He assisted Macquer in 1776 in experiments showing that water is formed in the combustion of inflammable air[14] and published books on gases and on physics.[15] He improved the nitric oxide eudiometer and found only slight differences in the goodness of different specimens

[1] *Ann. Chim.*, 1817, vi, 206.   [2] *Ann. Chim.*, 1833, liv, 331.
[3] Thomson, *Ann. Phil.*, 1817, ix, 417; Poggendorff, (1), i, 464.
[4] *Ann. Chim.*, 1800, xxxiii, 87–8.   [5] Berthollet and Descotils, *ib.*, 95.
[6] *Ann. Chim.*, 1804, xlviii, 153.   [7] *Ann. Chim.*, 1803, xlvi, 333.
[8] *Ann. Chim.*, 1804, xlviii, 177; 1804, xlix, 188, 219; 1804, l, 5.
[9] *Phil. Trans.*, 1804, xciv, 411.   [10] Humboldt, *Ann. Phys.*, 1804, xviii, 118 (122).
[11] *Ann. Chim.*, 1805, liii, 268.   [12] *J. des Mines*, 1802–3, xiii, 421–3.
[13] Boyer, NBG, 1864, xliii, 966; Poggendorff, (1), ii, 927, calls him 'Jean René' and says he was born in Dijon in 1740.
[14] Macquer, *Dictionnaire*, 1778, ii, 313–14; see p. 436.
[15] *Essai sur différentes espèces d'air qu'on désigne sous le nom d'air fixe*, 8°, Paris, 1779 (iv ll.; pp. xvi, 400, 5 fold. plates); *Essai sur différentes espèces d'Air Fixe ou de Gas, pour servir de suite et de supplément aux Élémens de Physique du meme Auteur. Nouvelle edition, revue et augmentée*, par M. Rouland, 8°, Paris, 1785 (xiv ll., 499 pp., 8 plates, one showing the apparatus used by Rouland to carry out the experiment of Macquer and Sigaud de la Fond (1776); account of balloon ascents of Montgolfier, Charles, and Robert); *Leçons de Physique Expérimentale*, 2 vols. 8°, Paris, 1767; *Traité de l'Électricité*, 12°, Paris, 1771; *Description & Usage d'un Cabinet de Physique Expérimentale*, 2 vols. 8°, Paris, 1775 (Sotheran *Cat.* 800 (1926), nos. 11999–12001; 908 (1955), 84); *Éléments de Physique*, 4 vols. 8°, Paris, 1787; other works in Poggendorff.

E

of air, even in crowded rooms and hospitals.[1] A similar result was found by the same method by Priestley (1779; see p. 254).

SEGUIN

Armand Seguin (Paris; c. 1765–24 January 1835), an army contractor who amassed a fortune, worked with Lavoisier on respiration (1789) (see p. 473), and with Fourcroy and Vauquelin on the composition of water (1790) (see p. 452). His papers are published in the *Annales de Chimie*, of which he was one of the editors, many after long delay.

He used burning phosphorus in eudiometry.[2] He gave an extract from de Morveau's article 'Air' in the *Encyclopédie*[3] and a summary of Lavoisier's *Traité*,[4] and also published papers on vegetation (1792),[5] on the theory of heat,[6] on the salubrity of air (1792),[7] on cinnabar (1802)[8] and on quinquina,[9] in which he found that an extract of cinchona bark is precipitated by tannin and hence erroneously supposed that the active principle is gelatin. Seguin's best work is on tannin.

Guyton de Morveau, Maret and Durande[10] found that an infusion of galls is feebly acid; gallic acid was obtained by Scheele (see p. 233). Berthollet[11] showed that gallic acid is not the true astringent principle; it has only a sour taste. Deyeux[12] showed that galls contain some peculiar extractive principle which he thought was combined with gallic acid to produce the astringent property.

Nicolas Deyeux (Paris; March 1745–25 April 1837), professor of pharmacy in the medical faculty and of chemistry and pharmacy at the École Centrale, pharmacist to Napoleon, an editor of the *Annales de Chimie*, also published on formic acid,[13] the preparation of carbon monoxide[14] by passing carbon dioxide over heated charcoal, and the extraction of beet sugar.[15]

Seguin,[16] in a set of experiments on quick tanning, first recognised tannin (*tanin*) as a peculiar substance which precipitates glue from a solution in water and combines with animal skin. Proust[17] and Davy[18] made further investigations on tannin, on the methods for its preparation, its properties, and the amount of it present in different tanning materials. Wuttig[19] still thought tannin and gallic acid were the same.[20] A report on Seguin's quick tanning process was presented by Lelièvre and Pelletier.[21]

[1] *Essai*, 1779, 87, 180 f., 309; on Jean Rey, *ib.*, 315.
[2] *Ann. Chim.*, 1791, ix, 293.   [3] *Ann. Chim.*, 1790, vii, 46.
[4] *Ann. Chim.*, 1789, ii, 226.   [5] *Ann. Chim.*, 1814, lxxxix, 54.
[6] *Ann. Chim.*, 1789, iii, 148; 1790, v, 191.   [7] *Ann. Chim.*, 1814, lxxxix, 251.
[8] *Ann. Chim.*, 1814, xc, 252, 268.   [9] *Ann. Chim.*, 1814, xci, 273, 304; 1814, xcii, 121.
[10] *Élémens de Chymie*, Dijon, 1778, iii, 403 f.
[11] *Elements of the Art of Dyeing*, 1791; 1824, i, 86 f.   [12] *Ann. Chim.*, 1793, xvii, 3.
[13] *Obs. Phys.*, 1778, xii, 352.   [14] *Ann. Chim.*, 1805, liii, 76.
[15] *Ann. Chim.*, 1811, lxxvii, 42.   [16] *Ann. Chim.*, 1797, xx, 15.
[17] *Ann. Chim.*, 1798, xxv, 225; 1799, xxxv, 32; 1802, xlii, 89; AdS, *Mém. div. Sav.*, 1805, i, 184.
[18] *Phil. Trans.*, 1803, xciii, 233; *Elements of Agricultural Chemistry*, 1813, 77.
[19] *N. allgem. J. Chem.*, 1806, vi, 194.
[20] See M. Nierenstein, *Incunabula of Tannin Chemistry*, 1932; *The Natural Organic Tannins*, 1934.
[21] *Ann. Chim.*, 1797, xx, 15–77; Claude Hugues Lelièvre (Paris, 28 June 1752–Neuilly, 18 October 1835) was a mining engineer who published on mineralogy, and reported on the

In 1804 (published in 1814) Seguin, Lelièvre, and Pelletier,[1] in a memoir on opium, showed that the aqueous extract is precipitated by alkalis and the precipitate is soluble in acids. It could be crystallised from alcohol, the solution turning syrup of violets green. Seguin called the alkaline substance (morphine, etc.) 'une nouvelle matière végéto-animale et crystalline.' From the filtrate from the alkali precipitate he obtained with baryta a precipitate from which a peculiar acid (une acide toute particulière) could be set free by sulphuric acid. Its solution gave a red colour with ferrous sulphate. Seguin was not sure whether it was a definite acid or a mixture of malic and acetic acids contaminated with vegetable matter. It was meconic acid.

ADET

Pierre August Adet (Nevers; 18 May 1763–c. 1832), Commissar in Domingo and physician to the Ministry of Marine, later serving under Napoleon, was an editor of the *Annales de Chimie*. He published on stannic chloride,[2] a reply[3] to Priestley's *Considerations on Phlogiston* (see p. 244), and was the author of *Leçons Élémentaires de Chimie*, 1804. He collaborated with Lavoisier's assistant Hassenfratz.

HASSENFRATZ

Jean Henri Hassenfratz (Paris; 20 December 1755–26 February 1827), from 1795 professor of mineralogy in the École des Mines and from 1797 professor of physics in the École Polytechnique, published on respiration,[4] affinity,[5] metallic acids (tin and iron),[6] the calcination of metals in pure air (oxygen),[7] the distinction between inflammation and combustion,[8] the amounts of light produced by different combustibles,[9] hydrometry,[10] the oxides of iron,[11] and papers on mineralogy, etc. He put forward the humus theory of vegetation,[12] and published a large work on iron and steel.[13] He and Adet devised a system of symbols in which, e.g., the metals are denoted by capital letters (C cuprum, P plumbum, S stannum, Fe ferrum, Sb stibium) enclosed in circles.[14]

LAGRANGE

Edme Jean Baptiste Bouillon la Grange (or Lagrange) (Paris; 12 July 1764– 24 August 1844) was Fourcroy's assistant from 1788, later professor in the

extraction of soda from common salt, *J. de Phys.*, 1794, xlv, 118, 191; *Ann. Chim.*, 1797, xix, 58.

[1] *Ann. Chim.*, 1814, xcii, 225: a second memoir is promised.
[2] *Ann. Chim.*, 1789, i, 5.   [3] *Ann. Chim.*, 1798, xxvi, 302.
[4] *Ann. Chim.*, 1791, ix, 261.   [5] *Ann. Chim.*, 1792, xiii, 3, 25.
[6] *Obs. Phys.*, 1786, xxviii, 281.   [7] *Obs. Phys.*, 1786, xxix, 305.
[8] *Obs. Phys.*, 1788, xxxiii, 384.   [9] *Ann. Chim.*, 1797, xxiv, 78.
[10] *Ib.*, 1798, xxvi, 7, 132; 1798, xxvii, 116; 1798, xxviii, 282.
[11] *Ib.*, 1808, lxvii, 309; 1809, lxix, 113.
[12] *Ib.*, 1792, xiii, 178, 318; 1792, xiv, 55; Wiesner, *Jan Ingen-Housz*, Vienna, 1905, 131; see Vol. IV.
[13] *La Sidérotechnie, ou l'Art de traiter les minérales de Fer pour en obtenir de la Fonte, du Fer ou de l'Acier*, 4 vols. 4°, Paris, 1812, with 65 large plates.
[14] Guyton de Morveau, etc., *Méthode de Nomenclature Chimique*, 1787, 311, and plates.

École de Pharmacie. He supposed that lactic,[1] gallic,[2] and malic[3] acids are impure acetic acid, although he had shown[4] that camphoric acid, discovered by Kosegarten,[5] is a peculiar acid different from benzoic acid; Lagrange discovered camphoric anhydride. He also studied the compounds of suberic acid,[6] discovered in 1786 by Brugnatelli[7] by oxidising cork with nitric acid, and[8] described the preparation of nitrous ether (ethyl nitrite) by distilling alcohol, nitric acid, and copper turnings. He investigated the viscous matter (glu) of the mistletoe[9] which had been studied by Vauquelin.[10] It was named bird-lime by Thomson.[11] Lagrange published his course as a popular treatise.[12]

Lagrange[13] clearly distinguished tannin and gallic acid; he recognised that the sublimate from gallic acid (pyrogallic acid) is different from the original acid (1806), and this was confirmed by Berzelius.[14] Lagrange[15] concluded that ambergris contained a resin, adipocire (see p. 547), and benzoic acid.

[1] *Ann. Chim.*, 1804, l, 272.   [2] *Ann. Chim.*, 1806, lx, 156.
[3] Lagrange and Vogel, Gehlen's *J. der Chem.*, 1807, iii, 615.
[4] *Ann. Chim.*, 1797, xxiii, 153; 1798, xxvii, 19.
[5] *De Camphora et partibus quæ constituunt*, Göttingen, 1785; reported by Crell, *Obs. Phys.*, 1785, xxvii, 297.
[6] *Ann. Chim.*, 1797, xxiii, 42, 153.   [7] Crell's *Ann.*, 1787, I, 145.
[8] *Ann. Chim.*, 1819, xii, 109.
[9] *Ann. Chim.*, 1806, lvi, 24–36; *Nicholson's J.*, 1806, xiii, 144.
[10] *Ann. Chim.*, 1799, xxviii, 223.
[11] (2), 1807, v, 141; the name is used in the tr. of Lagrange's paper, 1806. See Vol. II, p. 546.
[12] *Manuel d'un Cours de Chimie, ou Principes élémentaires théoriques et pratiques de cette Science*, 2 vols. 8°, Paris, 1799 (BM 958. d. 11); 3 ed., 3 vols. 1802; 5 ed., 3 vols., 1812 (includes an historical sketch, not mentioning Boyle); *Manual of a Course of Chemistry; or, a series of Experiments and Illustrations necessary to form a complete course of that Science. With an Appendix*, 2 vols., London, 1800.
[13] *Ann. Chim.*, 1805, lv, 32 (list of astringents); 1805, lvi, 172; 1806, lx, 156.
[14] *Ann. Chim.*, 1815, xciv, 296 (303); Gerhardt, *Traité de Chimie Organique*, iii, 876, says gallic and pyrogallic acids were first distinguished by L. Gmelin.
[15] *Ann. Chim.*, 1803, xlvii, 68.

CHAPTER IV

HALES AND BLACK

The collection of gases in bladders and over water or other liquids had been carried out at early meetings of the Royal Society and by Boyle. Mayow transferred a gas from one vessel to another. The existence of gases different from common air was recognised clearly by Mayow; other contemporary English workers mostly called them 'factitious air' or 'air generated *de novo*'. The inflammable gas from mines and the asphyxiating gas in wells or caves were recognised in the 17 cent.[1] Boyle[2] sent some 'Articles of Inquiry touching Mines' in which questions were asked on conditions in mining, including the 'damps' and the atmosphere of mines. Thomas Shirley[3] described an inflammable gas from a ditch and from the earth near Wigan. This is mentioned by Boyle in 1685.[4] Moslyn[5] and Beaumont[6] mentioned fiery damps in mines. Lister[7] and Jessop[8] distinguished four kinds of 'damps' in Yorkshire mines: (i) the common, extinguishing a flame and suffocating; (ii) pease-bloom damp, smelling like this, not mortal; (iii) pestilential, visible, hanging on the roof, and if broken is suffocating; (iv) inflammable and explosive, viz. fire-damp (methane, previously described by 'Basil Valentine', Vol. II, p. 196). Sir James Lowther[9] collected fire-damp at Whitehaven in bladders and found that it remained inflammable for some days. John Maud[10] imitated Lowther's gas by hydrogen from iron filings and dilute oil of vitriol; the air was 'generated de novo out of the mixture, or else recovered from being locked up in the body of the metal in an unelastic state', and the mixture of it with air exploded when kindled.

CLAYTON

John Clayton (Lancashire, 1657–Dublin, 23 September 1725), descended from the Claytons of Fulwood in Lancashire, B.A. Merton College, Oxford, 1677, went out soon after ordination (probably in 1683) to Virginia. In 1687 he became Rector of Crofton, near Wakefield, F.R.S. 1688; he was Rector of St. Michan's, Dublin, 1698–1725, and Dean of Kildare, 1708–25.[11]

---

[1] Refs. in Gmelin, (1), ii, 110–14, and Hoefer, (1), ii, 251.
[2] *Phil. Trans.*, 1666, i, 330, no. 19.   [3] *Phil. Trans.*, 1667, ii, 482, no. 26.
[4] *Works*, ed. Birch, 1744, iv, 283.   [5] *Phil. Trans.*, 1677, xii, 895, no. 136.
[6] *Phil. Collect.*, 1681, x, 6, no. 1.   [7] *Phil. Trans.*, 1675, x, 391, no. 117.
[8] *Ib.*, 1675, x, 450, no. 119.   [9] *Ib.*, 1733, xxxviii, 109.   [10] *Ib.*, 1736, xxxix, 282.
[11] Westley-Gibson, DNB, 1887, xi, 19, and Hunt, *ib.*, 1887, xi, 13, confused him with Robert Clayton (who also appears in Royal Society records) and John Clayton, 1693–1773; W. T. Layton, *The Discoverer of Gas Lighting. Notes on the Life and Works of the Rev. John Clayton, D.D., 1657–1725*, London, 1926 (BM 8716. d. 11); Browne, *J. Chem. Educ.*, 1940, xvii, 53; Read, (2), 196, says the discovery of coal gas was made in 1687, not 1684 as Layton suggested,

Clayton first made coal gas. In a letter of 12 May 1688 published in 1693[1] he refers the cause of thunder to:

'some Sulphureous Spirits which I have drawn from Coals, that I could no way condense, yet were inflammable; nay, would burn after they had pass'd through Water, and that seemingly fiercer, if they were not overpower'd therewith. I have kept of this Spirit a considerable time in Bladders; and tho' it appeared as if it were blown with Air, yet if I let it forth, and fired it with a Match or Candle, it would continue burning till all were spent.'

A copy of an undated letter from Clayton to Boyle (who died in 1691) was sent to the Royal Society in 1740 by his eldest son, Dr. John Clayton, then Bishop of Cork, and was published in 1744.[2] In this he mentions a ditch two miles from Wigan the water of which 'would seemingly burn like Brandy, the Flame of which was so fierce, that several Strangers have boiled Eggs over it'. Coal was found beneath by digging, and if a candle was put in the hole 'the Air catched Fire, and continued burning'. Clayton then put some coal from a neighbouring pit into a retort and distilled it in an open fire.

'At first there came over only *Phlegme*, afterwards a black *Oil*, and then likewise a *Spirit* arose, which I could noways condense, but it forced my Lute, or broke my Glasses. Once, when it had forced the Lute, coming close thereto, in order to try to repair it, I observed that the Spirit which issued out caught Fire at the Flame of the Candle. . . . I then had a mind to try if I could save any of this Spirit, in order to which I took a turbinated Receiver, and putting a Candle to the Pipe of the Receiver whilst the Spirit arose, I observed that it catched Flame, and continued burning at the End of the Pipe, though you could not discern what fed the Flame.' He filled bladders with the 'spirit' by attaching them to the pipe of the receiver. 'I kept this Spirit in the Bladders a considerable time, and endeavour'd several ways to condense it, but in vain. And when I had a Mind to divert Strangers or Friends, I have frequently taken one of these Bladders, and pricking a Hole therein with a Pin, and compressing gently the Bladder near the Flame of a Candle till it once took Fire, it would then continue flaming till all the Spirit was compressed out of the Bladder; which was the more surprising, because no one could discern any Difference in the Appearance between these Bladders and those which are filled with common Air.'

In thin bladders, he found, the 'spirit' would lose its inflammability in 24 hours, 'though the bladder became not relax at all.'

HAUKSBEE

Francis Hauksbee (Hawksbee), Curator of Experiments of the Royal Society, F.R.S. 1705, died about 1713,[3] published mostly on electricity.[4] He found the densities of air and water to be in the ratio 1 : 885.[5] He published on: (i) firing gunpowder on a red-hot iron *in vacuo Boyliano* and on air produced

since Clayton was then in Virginia, returning in May, 1686, and sending his first letter to the Royal Society in May, 1688.

  [1] *Phil. Trans.*, 1693, xvii, 781 (788) no. 201.
  [2] *Phil. Trans.*, 1739, xli, 59 (publ. in 1744 according to Read): An Experiment concerning the Spirit of Coals, by the Rev. John Clayton, D.D.
  [3] Anderson, DNB, 1891, xxv, 171.
  [4] *Physico-Mechanical Experiments on Various Subjects, containing an Account of several surprizing Phenomena touching Light and Electricity*, 8°, 1709; 2 ed., 1719; and two posthumous works, *Proposal for a Course of Chemical Experiments*, 1731, and *An Essay for introducing a Portable Laboratory*, 1731.
  [5] *Phil. Trans.*, 1706, xxv, 2221, no. 305.

from gunpowder,[1] (ii) the production and propagation of light from phosphorus in vacuo,[2] (iii) the freezing of common water and water freed of air,[3] in which he found little difference but perhaps that free from air freezes more easily, (iv) specific gravities of metals,[4] (v) capillarity.[5] In (i) he says the space after the gunpowder was dropped on a red-hot iron in vacuum contained an air which he found by warming was 'actuated like common air'; but in later experiments[6] in which 'air' from burning gunpowder drove water from a vessel, he says:

'whether the space deserted by the water is possessed by a body of the same weight and density, or is of the same quality as common air, I dare not affirm; since an experiment I have lately made, to try how much the heat produced by the explosion of gunpowder might contribute to the size of the space dispossessed by the water, seems to conclude it otherwise; . . . the whole space at first deserted by the water on firing the gunpowder was not supplied with real air.'

He could not account for the 'odd phenomenon' of a loss or absorption of air when it reached its former temperature, but could only suggest that:

'the springs or constituent parts of the ambient air, as well as those contained in the body of the gunpowder, may, on firing, be capable of being broken, or at least so distended, as to possess so large a space, and require so long a time to recover their natural state again.'

This was the result of the (unobserved) absorption of the gas by water; the theory is based on Boyle's (Vol. II, p. 523). Experiments similar to Hauksbee's on the volume of gas generated in the combustion of gunpowder were made by Benjamin Robins,[7] who found that an ounce of powder produced 572 cu. in. of 'elastic fluid', the nature of which he did not investigate.

Hauksbee allowed air to pass through a red-hot brass tube, and through red-hot charcoal, into an exhausted receiver, and found that the 'factitious air' in the receiver, although he thought it had the same density as ordinary air, extinguished flame and would not support the life of animals or birds. Air passed through a red-hot glass tube was unchanged. He says:

'As to the elasticity and specific gravity of the said medium, I have made several accurate trials, but find it nowise differing from common air, in respect to those properties.' He asked 'whether air itself may so suffer in its own nature, by any sort of fire, as to be divested of the power of subsisting life or flame, or whether the effluvia or steams proceeding from the red-hot metals . . . do not very much contribute, if not wholly occasion the effects'.[8]

In his experiments on the light from phosphorus 'in vacuo' Hauksbee confirmed the observation of Slare[9] and Lemery (see p. 40) that the glow is brighter in air under reduced pressure.

[1] Ib., 1705, xxiv, 1806, 1807; 1707, xxv, 2409.   [2] Ib., 1705, xxiv, 1865.
[3] Ib., 1709, xxvi, 302.   [4] Ib., 1712, xxvii, 511.
[5] Ib., 1709, xxvi, 258; 1713, xxviii, 153; Physico-Mechanical Experiments, 1709, 139; 1719, 98, 179, 314, 329.
[6] Phil. Trans., 1707, xxv, 2409, no. 311.
[7] New Principles of Gunnery, 1742; in Mathematical Tracts, ed. J. Wilson, 2 vols. 8°, 1761, i, 59 f., 67.
[8] Phil. Trans., 1710, xxvii, 199: on the effects of air passed through red-hot metals, etc.
[9] Phil. Collect., 1681, 84, no. 4.

Hauksbee's nephew, also named Francis Hauksbee, described[1] an electrical machine consisting of 'a sphere of glass with the air exhausted' and pointed out that the electric light in the (partially) exhausted globe has a purple tint.

MOITREL D'ELEMENT

Some interesting experiments on the manipulation of air over water were shown in private lectures by Moitrel d'Element, who described himself as an engineer and demonstrator in physics, but was a physician then living in Paris, who died in America:

La manière de rendre l'air visible, et assez sensible pour le mesurer par pintes, ou par telle autre mesure qu'on voudra, pour faire des jets d'air, qui sont aussi visibles que des jets d'eau; et quelques autres expériences de physique sur la nature de l'air . . . dédiées aux dames, privately printed in Paris, 1719, and sold for 3 sous; repr. in Gobet's ed. of the *Essays* of Jean Rey, 1777, 183–212 (mentioning other works now lost); Fourcroy, (2), iii, 404; Hoefer, (1), ii, 333 (his attribution of poverty to Moitrel seems to be imaginary). The tract was made known to Gobet by Baumé; it was in the collection of Falconet, and fetched 28 sous when this was sold. It is not in the Bibliothèque Nationale, according to Gobet.

Moitrel dedicated his small work to 'the ladies' since, he says, they showed an interest in his experiments — which the Academicians treated with disdain — and asked sensible questions about them. He describes, e.g., the transference of air from an inverted vessel into another vessel filled with and inverted in water. He added some experiments of de Polinière[2] to his own.

HALES

Stephen Hales (Bekesbourne, Kent, 17 (or 7) September 1677–Teddington, 4 January 1761) entered Corpus Christi College, Cambridge (then called Bene't College — it is still in Bene't Lane) in 1696, becoming a Fellow in 1702–3, M.A. in 1703, and B.D. in 1711; in 1733 he became D.D. of Oxford. In August 1709 Hales became 'Perpetual Curate' or (as he calls himself) Minister of Teddington, Middlesex, where he was a friend of Alexander Pope. He also had a living at Farringdon, Hampshire. He became F.R.S. in 1718, received the Copley medal in 1739, and in 1753 was elected to the Paris Academy. He was one of the founders of the Society of Arts, and was Vice-President in 1755.

Hales was a busy inventive man like Priestley, but was below Priestley in originality, and rather commonplace. He was an active parish priest but declined a canonry of Windsor in order to have time for his scientific researches. He was buried under the tower (now the porch) of Teddington Church. Horace Walpole calls him 'a poor, good, primitive creature'; Peter Collinson says Hales treated his enemies calmly, 'not from want of discern-

---

[1] *Course of Mechanical, Optical, Hydrostatical, and Pneumatical Experiments . . . with the Explanatory Lectures read by William Whiston*, 4°, [c. 1735], 20 copperplates; Sotheran *Cat.* 773 (1919), 141, no. 1768.
[2] *Expériences de Physique*, 2 vols., Paris, 1709; 4 ed., 1734.

ment' but 'like those experiments which, upon trial, he found could never be applied to any useful purpose.'[1]

Hales was a student of theology in Cambridge, but he was a friend of William Stukeley (Holbeach, Lincs., 7 November 1687–London, 3 March 1765), who interested Hales in chemistry, botany, and dissections of animals,[2] and they made experiments on chemistry in the 'elabatory' in Trinity College,

FIG. 8. STEPHEN HALES, 1677–1761.

built by Richard Bentley and supervised from 1703 by Jean François Vigani (see Vol. II, p. 686). Hales published two famous books and some minor works:

I. Vegetable Staticks: Or, An Account of some Statical Experiments on the Sap in Vegetables: Being an Essay towards a Natural History of Vegetation. Also, a Specimen of An Attempt to Analyse the Air, By a great Variety of Chymio-Statical Experiments; Which were read at several Meetings before the Royal Society, 8°, London, 1727, xvi ll., 376 pp., 19 plates (imprim. dated 16 Feb. 1727), the ed. quoted; 2 ed. 1733, 3 ed. with Amendments, as Vol. I of Statical Essays (see No. II), 4 ed. Statical Essays, containing Vegetable Staticks; or an account of Statical Experiments on the Sap in Vegetables, being an Essay towards

[1] Anon., *Brit. Quart. Rev.*, 1845, ii, 229–33; AdS, 1762 (1764), h 213–30; Brande, 1848, I, xlviii; A. E. Clark-Kennedy, *Stephen Hales D.D., F.R.S.*, Cambridge, 1929 (*Isis*, 1930, xiii, 370); F. Darwin, DNB, 1890, xxiv, 32; Fourcroy, (2), iii, 352–60; Gmelin, (1), ii, 724–30; W. Vernon Harcourt, *Phil. Mag.*, 1846, xxviii, 478; Ramsay, (1), 28–38; Saverien, 1773, viii, 179; C. Singer, *A History of Biology*, Oxford, 1931, 363 f.; C. M. Taylor, *The Discovery of the Nature of the Air*, London, 1923, 33; T. Thomson. *Ann. Phil.*, 1820, xv, 161; Z. in NBG, 1858, xxiii, 135.

[2] Clark-Kennedy, 14 f.

a Natural History of Vegetation: of use to those who are curious in the Culture and Improvement of Gardening . . . , 1769 (Bolton, (1), 509; Ramsay, (1), 29).

French tr. by J. L. L. Buffon: La Statique des Végétaux et l'Analyse de l'Air, 4°, Paris, 1735, with pref. and analytical table of contents; German tr. by C. Wolff, 4°, 1747 (Gmelin, (1), ii, 725, who also gives Dutch tr., 8°, 1750); Italian tr., 8°, Naples, 1759 (with II), 3 ed. 1776; the French tr. includes the long 'Appendix' published at the end of II (1733); long summary of I by Desaguliers, *Phil. Trans.*, 1727 (1728), xxxiv, 264–91; 1728 (1729), xxxv, 323–31.

II. Statical Essays: containing Hæmastaticks; Or, An Account of some Hydraulick and Hydrostatical Experiments made on the Blood and Blood-Vessels of Animals. Also An Account of some Experiments on Stones in the Kidneys and Bladder; with an Enquiry into the Nature of those anomalous Concretions. To which is added, An Appendix, Containing Observations and Experiments relating to several Subjects in the first Volume. The greatest Part of which were read at several Meetings before the Royal Society. With an Index to both Volumes. Vol. II (first ed.), 8°, London, 1733 (imprim. dated 28 Feb. 1733), xxiv ll., 361 pp., xi ll. (the ed. quoted); 2 ed. 1740, 3 ed. 1769.

French tr. by F. B. de Sauvages: Haemastatique, ou la Statique des Animaux: expériences hydrauliques faites sur des Animaux vivans . . . Traduit de l'Anglais, et augmenté de plusieurs Remarques et de deux Dissertations de Médecine, sur la Théorie de l'Inflammation, et sur la Cause de la Fièvre; par Mr. de Sauvages, 4°, Geneva, 1744 (xxii, 348 pp.). The tr. of I by Buffon and of II by de Sauvages were publ. together by Sigaud de la Fond, 2 pts. in 1 vol., 8°, Paris, 1779–80 (Wheldon and Wesley, *Cat.* 83 (1955–6), no. 44).

III. Philosophical Experiments . . . Shewing how Sea-Water may be made Fresh and Wholesome . . . To which is added, An Account of several Experiments and Observations on Chalybeate or Steel-waters . . . , 8°, London, 1739 (imprim. dated 29 March), xviii ll., 163 pp., iv ll; on the preservation of flesh and corn, making sea-water potable by distillation, treatment of water reservoirs, hygiene of harbours, etc.; Clark-Kennedy, 147: 'dull reading and calls for little comment'; the only important suggestion is that acid should be added to fresh water or distilled sea water to prevent putrefaction.

IV. An Account of some Experiments and Observations on Mrs Stephens's Medicines for dissolving the Stone, with Supplement, London, n.d. (1740); French tr., Paris, 1742 (1743, Gmelin, (1), ii, 461, who gives a Portuguese tr., 8°, London, 1742).

V. An Account of some Experiments and Observations on Tar Water, London, 1745 (Clark-Kennedy, 146 f.).

The primitive state of chemistry in Hales's university about the same time is shown in the lectures of Prof. John Hadley, F.R.S. (d. 5 November 1764).[1] Hales's work on 'airs' was carried out in the period 1710–27;[2] his first paper, on the rise of sap, was read to the Royal Society in 1718.[3] He often quotes 'the illustrious Sir Isaac Newton', Mr. Boyle, and Hauksbee, but mentions Mayow (whom he had read) only twice in passing, and Geoffroy in 'the French Memoirs'. Hales's work, as Pringle said,[4] was inspired by Newton's hint[5] that: 'Dense Bodies by Fermentation rarify into several sorts of Air, and this Air by Fermentation, and sometimes without it, returns into dense Bodies'; and his uncritical guess that the particles of air 'Shaken off from Bodies by Heat or Fermentation' may occupy 'above a Million of Times more space than they

---

[1] *Plan of a Course of Chemical Lectures*, Cambridge, 1758 (45 pp.); Sotheran *Cat.* 800, nos. 10969–70; Hadley also examined a mummy, *Phil. Trans.*, 1764, liv, 1; he was succeeded by Richard Watson (Vol. II, p. 765).

[2] Clark-Kennedy, 93 f.   [3] *Ib.*, 59 f.

[4] A Discourse on the Different Kinds of Air, 1773; in *Six Discourses delivered by Sir John Pringle, Bart. when President of the Royal Society; on occasion of Six Annual Assignments of Sir Godfrey Copley's Medal*, London, 1783, 12.

[5] *Opticks*, Quer. 30–1; 1730, 349 f., 371.

did before in the form of a dense Body'. Hales's apparatus was crude.[1] He heated all kinds of materials in a bent iron gun-barrel in a fire, collecting the 'air' in a large glass bell (such as was used to cover plants) filled with and suspended by a rope in water in a bucket (Fig. 9), also a glass or iron retort luted

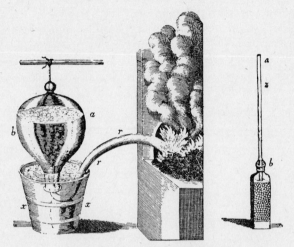

FIG. 9. APPARATUS USED BY HALES.

ON THE LEFT IS THE GUN BARREL (r) HEATED IN A FIRE. THE GAS IS COLLECTED IN THE GLOBE (ab) OVER WATER IN THE TUB (xx). ON THE RIGHT IS A BOTTLE FILLED WITH FERMENTING PEAS OVER MERCURY. THE PRESSURE OF THE GAS EVOLVED DRIVES THE MERCURY INTO THE VERTICAL TUBE (ab), WHICH IS FIRMLY FIXED INTO THE BOTTLE AND DIPS INTO THE MERCURY ON WHICH THE PEAS FLOAT.

to a long-necked flask pierced at the bottom to admit a siphon for withdrawing air from the flask (Fig. 10). He thus separated the generator from the receiver, an important step. The 'force' of air from fermenting peas was

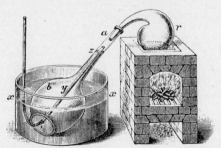

FIG. 10. HALES'S APPARATUS FOR MEASURING THE VOLUME OF GAS EVOLVED BY HEATING A SUBSTANCE IN A RETORT.

The water in the receiver was first raised by withdrawing air through the siphon yz.

measured by the rise of mercury, over which they were placed in a closed bottle, in a vertical tube (Fig. 9). Air from fermenting peas, distilled oyster shell, amber, peas, and beeswax, when brought in contact with a lighted candle 'immediately flashed' because of the 'sulphureous spirit' in it.[2] Hales found that a burning candle 'absorbed' only two-thirds of the quantity of air in a

[1] Fourcroy, (2), iii, 401.   [2] I, 171: Expt. LVII.

receiver if rags soaked in a lixivium of sal tartar and dried were wrapped round the inside walls, as compared with the absorption without them, because, he says, there was less air available.[1] Two grains of phosphorus burnt in air in a retort absorbed 3 cu. in. of air; in a large receiver the same quantity of phosphorus absorbed 28 cu. in. of air; 3 grains of phosphorus weighed soon after it was burnt had lost $\frac{1}{2}$ grain, but 2 grains weighed some hours after it was burnt, 'having run more *per deliquium* by absorbing the moisture of the Air', increased 1 grain in weight.[2] 'Flaming brimstone . . . absorbs much air.'[3]

Hales's quantitative experiments[4] were tabulated by Lavoisier,[5] but the figures he gives do not agree with those in Hales's book, from which the following table is compiled:

Substance distilled	Quantity distilled		Air generated		wt. of air ÷ wt. of substance
	vol. cu. in.	wt. grains	vol. cu. in.	wt. grains	
Hog's blood	1	—	33	—	—
Tallow	< 1	—	18	—	—
Horn	$\frac{1}{2}$	241	117	33	1 : 7
Oyster shell	$\frac{1}{2}$	266	162	46	1 : 6
Oak wood	$\frac{1}{2}$	135	108	30	1 : 4
Wheat	—	388	270	77	1 : 4
Peas	1	318	396	113	1 : 3
Mustard seed	1 oz.	437	270	77	1 : 6
Amber	$\frac{1}{2}$	135	135	38	1 : 3·55
Tobacco	—	142	153	[44]	1 : 3
Honey + calx of bones	1	359	144	41	1 : 9
Beeswax	1	243	54	15	1 : 16
Sugar	1	373	126	36	1 : 10
Coal	$\frac{1}{2}$	158	180	51	1 : 3
Fresh earth	1		43		
Antimony	$\frac{1}{4}$		28		
Pyrites	1		83		
Seasalt + calx of bones	$\frac{1}{2}$		16		
Nitre + calx of bones	$\frac{1}{2}$	211	90		1 : 8
Oil of aniseed	1		22		
Olive oil	1		88		
Tartar	1	443	504	144	1 : 3
Bladder stone	$\frac{3}{4}$	230	516	[148]	1 : 2
Gall stone	$\frac{1}{6}$	52	108	[30]	1 : 2

			Air absorbed cu. in.		
Sal ammoniac	1 drachm	—	$2\frac{1}{2}$	—	—
Phosphorus	—	2	28	—	—
Sal ammoniac + oil of vitriol	$\frac{1}{2}$		15		

Hales's main weakness was his failure to appreciate the *qualitative* differences of the 'airs' he measured and then threw away. His conclusions are vague: 'air abounds in animal, vegetable and mineral substances', and by its

[1] I, 271; a completely incorrect account of the experiment is given by Harcourt, 1846, 510.
[2] I, 169.   [3] I, 183.
[4] A Specimen of an attempt to analyse the Air by a great variety of chymio-statical Experiments, I, chapt. vi, pp. 155–317.
[5] *Opuscules*, 1774; 2 ed. 1801, 12 f.; Fourcroy, (2), iii, 356; see Clark-Kennedy, 59 f., 98.

presence somehow 'leavens' them; it 'is very instrumental in the production and growth of animals and vegetables, both by invigorating their several juices, while in an elastick active state, and also by greatly contributing in a fix'd state to the union and firm connection of the several constituent parts of those bodies, *viz*. their water, salt, sulphur and earth'.[1]

Hales thought (with Boyle) that 'our atmosphere is a *Chaos*, consisting not only of elastick, but also of unelastick air particles . . . as well as sulphureous, saline, watry and earthy particles'. He emphasised that: 'elasticity is not an essential immutable property of air particles; but they are, we see, easily changed from an elastick to a fixt state, by the strong attraction of the acid, sulphureous and saline particles which abound in the air', and are also capable of once more resuming the elastic state. He regarded air as an element. He speaks of air as 'this now fixt, now volatile, Proteus among the chymical principles . . . this much neglected volatile Hermes, who has so often escaped thro' . . . burst receivers, in the disguise of a subtile spirit, a meer flatulent explosive matter'.[2]

Thomson[3] said 'Dr. Hales had demonstrated (as had previously been done by Van Helmont and Glauber) that *air* is given out by a vast number of bodies in peculiar circumstances. But he never suspected that any of the *airs* which he obtained differed from common air.' If they were inflammable they were air loaded with inflammable particles, and if they did not support life they were air loaded with noxious particles. Harcourt[4] quoted Hales[5] to show that he thought there were *different* kinds of airs, but Wilson[6] pointed out that the experiments 'went no further than to show that a permanent gas was frequently developed during chemical changes'; that it was different from atmospheric air 'was but an opinion'. Hales spoke vaguely of *the* air being 'tainted' or 'infected' with 'fumes', 'vapours', or 'acid and sulphureous spirits'.

Hales supposed that 'air' can exist in an unelastic form in many substances, from which it can be set free again (as Van Helmont had said of gas). His views seem to have had little influence abroad. Stahl in 1731 said that air cannot be condensed by itself or with other mixtures to a solid.[7] Fourcroy[8] was surprised that Boerhaave did not go further than Hales and that Stahl neglects Hales. D'Alembert[9] said, after the time of Boerhaave and Stahl, that: 'l'air élémentaire, ou l'air proprement dit' is homogeneous and is 'l'ingrédient fondamental de tout l'air de l'atmosphère'. Other substances or exhalations mix with it to form common air, but are impurities. Only air is permanently elastic, all other vapours being, like steam, only temporarily aëriform. He mentions Boyle, Hooke, Hales, and Newton.

Hales separated the 'air' (carbon dioxide) from mineral waters in bottles filled with them and inverted in a small glass cistern set 'in a boyler'; from Pyrmont water he obtained nearly twice as much air as from rain or common water, 'which air contributes to the briskness of that and many other mineral waters.'[10]

[1] I, 313 f.   [2] I, 315–16.   [3] (1), i, 339.
[4] 1846, 478 (510 f.).   [5] I, 247, 312.   [6] *Life of Cavendish*, 1851, 192–3.
[7] *Experimenta, Observationes, Animadversiones*, CCC, *Numero Chymicae et Physicae*, 1731, 312, § 247.
[8] (2), iii, 361.   [9] Art. Air, *Encyclopédie*, 1751, i, 225.
[10] I, 175; see III, 95 f. (Experiments and Observations on Chalybeate Waters); see Brownrigg, p. 123.

He mentions[1] that lead increases in weight $\frac{1}{20}$ 'by the action of the fire' in forming minium (oxide), and he obtained 34 cu. in. of air by heating 1 cu. in. or 1922 grains of minium. It was this air, he says, that burst the vessel in Boyle's experiment (see Vol. II, p. 537), although Nieuwentyt had attributed the effect 'wholly to the expansion of the fire particles lodged in the minium', he supposing fire to be 'a particular fluid matter, which maintains its own essence, and figure, remaining always fire, tho' not always burning'. It 'adheres to many bodies and adds something to their composition'; lead ash becomes heavier on conversion into minium 'by the operation of the Flame, and therefore is impregnated with a great many Fire-Particles that join themselves to it . . . these Fire-Particles being excited and put into motion by the Fire of the Burning-Glass dilated themselves, and thereby burst the Glass'. Only part of the air is proper for supplying flame or fire.[2] Hales thought that the increase in weight of metals on calcination is due to the circumstance that 'the sulphureous and aereal particles of the fire are lodged in many of those bodies which it acts upon, and thereby considerably augments their weight'; the sulphur produces the colour of red lead.[3] He knew that red lead gives 'air' on heating.

Hales says[4] 'From 211 grains, or half a cubick inch of *Nitre*, mixed with calx of bones, there arose 90 cubick inches of air, *i.e.* a quantity equal to 180 times its bulk; so that the weight of air in any quantity of nitre is about $\frac{1}{8}$ part'. This must have been oxygen. Jörgensen[5] calculated from the equation $2KNO_3 = 2KNO_2 + O_2$ that Hales had obtained about 95 per cent. of the theoretical yield of oxygen. Ellis[6] thought Hales 'without realising what he had done, first actually collected oxygen'.

Hales's theory of combustion and respiration is the same as Mayow's but is stated more superficially: he seems partly to reject the idea of a *vivifying spirit* in the air, saying that air is made unfit for respiration by loss of elasticity and the presence of gross vapours; and fire is due to the action and re-action of the air and sulphur of the fuel:[7] 'the action and re-action of the aereal and sulphureous particles is in many fermenting mixtures so great, as to excite a burning heat, and in others a sudden flame.'[8] He found that in equal receivers the air suffered a larger diminution by burning large candles, and with equal candles the diminution was proportionally greater in small than in large receivers. He[9] mentions Mayow twice, as having found a contraction of $\frac{1}{30}$ of air by the burning of a candle without giving the size of the vessel (which Hales found had an influence on the result), and as having found a contraction of $\frac{1}{14}$ by the respiration of a mouse. Hales says nothing of Mayow's apparatus or his other experiments or conclusions, all superior to his own.

---

[1] I, 286.

[2] Nieuwentyt, *The Religious Philosopher: Or, The Right Use of Contemplating the Works of the Creator . . . Designed for the Conviction of Atheists and Infidels*, tr. from Dutch by John Chamberlayne, 3 edit., 2 vols., London, 1724, ii, 310 f., 314; experiments on phosphorus and its preparation, *ib.*, 325 f.

[3] I, 286.   [4] I, 178; Expt. LXXII.

[5] Die Entdeckung des Sauerstoffes, *Samml. chem. u. chem.-techn. Vorträge*, 1909, xiv, 123.

[6] *A History of Fire and Flame*, 1932, 238 f.

[7] I, 250, 273 f., 276, 283.   [8] I, 314.   [9] I, 230, 232.

Hales supposed that 'a considerable part of the elasticity of the air is . . . constantly destroyed' in respiration in the lungs, 'where it is charged with much vapour',[1] 'whence probably some of it, together with the acid spirits, with which the air abounds, are conveyed to the blood', the air particles 'continually changing from an elastick to a strongly attracting state', the lungs being adapted to 'seize, and bind that volatile *Hermes*' by its 'sulphureous particles, which abound in the blood'. This idea, and the name 'Hermes', were taken from Mayow, and so was the following experiment with nitric oxide, which had been prepared by Boyle and Mayow.

Priestley[2] says: '*nitrous air* obtruded itself upon Dr. Hales;[3] but even he had no idea of there being more than *one kind of air*, loaded with different vapours; and was very far from imagining that they differed from one another so very essentially as they are now known to do.' The reference is to Hales's experiment[4] in which 1 cu. in. each of Walton pyrites (Mayow used iron) and compound aqua fortis 'expanded with great heat and fume into a space equal to 200 cubick inches, and in a little time it condensed into its former space, and then absorbed 85 cubick inches of air'.

He seems to refer to Mayow (whom he does not name) when he says[5] that the extinction of burning candles and matches in a small quantity of air 'seems not to be due to their having rendred that air effete, by having consumed its *vivifying spirit*; but should rather be owing to the great quantity of acid fuliginous vapours, with which that air is charged, which destroy a good deal of its elasticity, and very much clog and retard the elastick motion of the remainder'. In respiration also[6] the fatal effect of 'noxious vapours, has hitherto been supposed to be wholly owing to the loss and waste of the *vivifying spirit of air*, but may not unreasonably be also attributed to the loss of a considerable part of the air's elasticity, and the grossness and density of the vapours, which the air is charged with'. Hales thus prepared the way for Priestley's erroneous views on combustion and respiration.

Hales never doubted that *the whole* of the air could be absorbed, although he never observed this: 'I made some attempts both by fire, and also by fermenting and absorbing mixtures, to try if I could deprive all the particles of any quantity of elastick air of their elasticity, but I could not effect it: There is therefore no direct proof from any of these Experiments, that all the elastick Air may be absorbed, tho' it is very probable it may.'[7] In this he was far behind Mayow, whom he had read.

Hales[8] devised an apparatus with valves for breathing repeatedly the same quantity of air, which could be passed through rags which had been wetted with a lixivium of salt of tartar (potassium carbonate, which would absorb carbon dioxide) and then dried. He found that he could breathe 3 mins. as compared with $1\frac{1}{2}$ mins. without the salt. This was because the salt is 'a strong imbiber of sulphureous steams'. When the four 'diaphragms' were dipped in

[1] I, 240, 243 f., 250, 316 (Hermes).
[2] *Experiments and Observations on Air*, 1777, iii, 325.
[3] Gren, 1794, i, 434, also wrongly said Hales discovered nitrous air.
[4] I, 220.   [5] I, 273.   [6] I, 247.   [7] I, 311.   [8] I, 262-70.

strong solutions of salt of tartar, sea salt, and white wine vinegar he could breathe 3 mins.; with salt of tartar and the diaphragm well dried, 5 mins., and once with well calcined (and hence somewhat causticised) salt of tartar, $8\frac{1}{2}$ mins. Hales did not care to repeat the experiments, 'fearing I might thereby some way injure my lungs, by frequently breathing in such gross vapours.' He thought salt of tartar 'should be the best preservative against noxious vapours, as being a very strong imbiber of sulphureous, acid and watry vapours, as is sea salt also'. He made quantitative experiments on the increases in weight of the diaphragms, and the whole description is, from the experimental side, very good. Hales recommended impregnated 'mufflers' for use in laboratories, homes on fire, when 'stink pots' were thrown in ships or military mines, but 'in the case of the damps of mines . . . they are not a sufficient screen from so very noxious vapours'.

Desaguliers[1] reported that Hales had told him he had been able to breathe through one of his 'diaphragms' for $8\frac{1}{2}$ minutes. Hales may have got his idea from a remark by Hooke[2] that if: 'expir'd air might be forc'd to pass through a wet or oyly sponge before it were again inspir'd, it might much cleanse, and strain away from the air divers fuliginous and other noisome steams, and the dipping of it in certain liquors might, perhaps, so renew that property in the air which it loses in the lungs . . . that one square foot of air might last a man for respiration much longer, perhaps, then ten will now serve him of common air.'
By breathing through weighed wood ashes (which absorb moisture and some carbon dioxide) Hales found that 20·4 oz. Troy of water is carried off by respiration in 24 hours.[3] R. Foregger[4] notes that Hales had two types of respiratory apparatus: (i) closed circuit (*Vegetable Staticks*, 1727), (ii) open circuit (*A Description of Ventilators*, 1743, 'respirator').

D'arquier[5] reported some observations on foul air in a well, made in 1747, mentioning Boyle, Hauksbee, and Hales. It was found that a pistol would not fire in it. Its properties were attributed to its lack of elasticity. De Mengaud[6] reported some experiments in which salt of tartar was exposed to the mephitic air (missing the formation of bicarbonate). He concluded that the asphyxiating property was not due to moisture.

Hales introduced artificial ventilation, his ventilators being fitted in ships, in the French prisons by Duhamel, and later in the London prisons at Savoy and Newgate.[7] Ventilation was one of Hales's obsessions.

Hales's ventilators were double bellows worked manually or by a windmill. Similar apparatus was simultaneously devised by Triewald in Sweden,[8] which was fitted to ships in the spring of 1741, and Samuel Sutton devised a much more practical apparatus depending on the rise of heated air, fresh air taking its place, which was brought to the notice of the Royal Society by Dr. Mead, a model being shown.[9] Both Hales and Sutton had great difficulty in getting their ideas tried on ships. Sutton complained, justly, that Hales had seen the experiment with his apparatus and heard Dr. Mead's account of it, 'which account was published in the Philosophical Transactions some time before the book of Ventilators was printed.' Hales does not mention Sutton in his

[1] *Phil. Trans.*, 1728 (1729), xxxv, 331.   [2] *Micrographia*, 1665, 140.
[3] II, 327–9.   [4] *Anesthesiology*, 1956, xi, 235.
[5] *Mém. Acad. Toulouse*, 1782, i, 15–34: Mémoire sur un Méphitis.
[6] *Ib.*, 35; Sur le Sel de Tartre, dans le même Méphitis.
[7] Hales, *A Description of Ventilators*, 1743; *A Treatise on Ventilation*, 1755; Clark-Kennedy, 151–69.
[8] KAH, 1742, iii, 112, 211.   [9] *Phil. Trans.*, 1742, xlii, 42.

book, and although he may have thought his own invention was better, 'to ignore Sutton, in the way he did, was quite unfair.'[1] Bigot de Morogues[2] investigated the accumulation of bad air in ships and the method of ventilation, and Marcorelle (of Toulouse) the bad air in a well.[3]

A Mrs Stephens had cured the Postmaster-General, Lord Carteret, of the stone (calculus) and a public subscription to collect £5000 was started to purchase her remedy. The sum was not reached and Parliament was asked to make it up. A commission was appointed, including Hales, and when it reported an Act of Parliament was passed in May, 1739, to provide the money. For £5000 this lady revealed to the Archbishop of Canterbury, on behalf of Parliament, that her remedy consisted of a powder, a decoction, and pills. The powder was of egg-shells and garden snails 'well calcined until the snails had done smoaking'; the decoction was of herbs and soap, etc.; and the pills of burnt snails, herbs, soap, and honey.[4] Burnt snails were reported by Pliny[5] as a remedy for urinary calculi, and this lingered on in popular medicine.

The Stephens recipe was published in the official London Gazette of 16 June 1739[6] and Hales published on it (IV) in 1740 or 1741. He recommended the use of lime water. In an appendix to his *Haemastaticks* (1738),[7] describing the distillation of human calculi, their solution in alkaline and acid solutions (salt of tartar, oil of vitriol, nitric acid), etc., Hales suggests that the liquids acted as solvents by communicating vibrations in tune with vibrations in the parts of the calculus. He made cruel and useless experiments with live dogs. He also tried distillation experiments with marbles, stones, etc., and (mentioning Van Helmont) suggested that a cause of the calculus is a 'tartarine' quality in hard waters, which deposit a fur on boiling in kettles,[8] and he concluded that 'the hardness of many waters, and their curdling and coagulating of soap may be in a good measure owing to the tartarine quality with which they are impregnated',[9] which is near the truth, established by Cavendish (p. 319).

Nathaniel Henshaw[10] in the preface to his book refers to air in plants (Hales's idea); he deals with respiration,[11] saying that air cools the lungs and deprives them of fuliginous exhalations by a purely mechanical effect;[12] it causes the blood to froth, or acquire a tendency to froth, in the lungs, 'like bottled beer',[13] and life is a continued fermentation of the blood.[14] The book describes an air-chamber for people to live in.

Hales also concluded that air can be condensed in the substance of plants. He connected the assimilative function of the leaves with the action of light, but (misled by Newton's corpuscular theory of light) he thought light may 'by freely entring the expanded surfaces of leaves and flowers, contribute much to

[1] Clark-Kennedy, 158.
[2] AdS, *Mém. div. Sav.*, 1750, i, 394–410.
[3] *Ib.*, 1755, ii, 609 (614).
[4] Clark-Kennedy, 124 f.
[5] *Hist. Nat.*, xxx, 21.
[6] Guerlac, *Isis*, 1957, xlviii, 124 (140).
[7] An Account of some Experiments on Stones in the Kidnies and Bladder. With an Inquiry Into the Nature of those anomalous Concretions; II, 187–252.
[8] II, 236.   [9] II, 241.
[10] *Aero-Chalinos: or, A Register for the Air; In Five Chapters*, . . . 8°, Dublin, 1664 (98 pp.); 2 ed., 12°, London, 1677 (166 pp.).
[11] 1677, 60 f.   [12] *Ib.*, 77.   [13] *Ib.*, 86–9.   [14] *Ib.*, 94.

the ennobling the principles of vegetables'.[1] He thought[2] plants probably draw through their leaves 'some part of the nourishment from the air', which Priestley[3] afterwards said was his opinion also. It had been suggested before by Malpighi (see Vol. II, p. 568).

Sachs[4] regarded Hales's theoretical views, which had generally been overlooked, as important. Hales taught that air plays an important part in the formation of plants; it can pass in through the leaves and bark, and move in the spaces of the wood. The condensed air can be set free again by fermentation and dry distillation. In its condensed form, air is highly attractive, in its free form highly repulsive, and the interaction of the attractive and repulsive forces produces all the activities in animal and vegetable bodies. In nutrition the sum of the attractive forces is greater than the sum of the repulsive, and at first slimy and then hard parts are formed. The hard parts can absorb water and (as in the fermentation of vegetables) the repulsive forces predominate and new vegetables can be formed from the products. The mechanism of the nutrition of animals and plants is the same and is capable, by small changes of texture, of supplying the needs of both. A great quantity of air is incorporated in vegetable and animal bodies, and by its elasticity prevents the agglomeration of attracting particles by opposing its repulsive force to the attractive force, causing motion and supplying invigoration in its free state, so that there is a constant cycle of growth and decay. Hales's experiments on the loss of water from plants by evaporation from the leaves and its replacement by the roots belong to the history of botany.

Hales's *Hæmastaticks* is a gruesome book. The dedication to the King says: 'The study of Nature will ever yield us fresh Matter of Entertainment, and we have great reason to bless God for the . . . strong Desire he has implanted in our Minds to search into and contemplate his Works.' In this search 'Man's original Grant of Dominion over the Creatures' is likely to be 'inlarged'. The book opens with the sentence: 'In December I caused a Mare to be tied down alive on her Back', and goes on to describe the stages leading to the death of the animal after 14 to 15 quarts of blood were 'evacuated'. Hales repeated the experiment with the dog which Hooke had refused to repeat (Vol. II, p. 564). The skin was 'flead off the belly of a live frog and the abdomen opened on each side' so that the muscles could be examined under a microscope, a 'most agreeable scene'. The experiments with large animals were made in the vicarage garden with the assistance of Hales's parishioners, and Alexander Pope was 'sorry he has his hands so much imbued in blood'.[5]

How much further Hales got than Borelli (see Vol. II, p. 443) is a matter for physiologists to decide. Sir Michael Foster[6] said: 'We may almost say, even not forgetting Hales, that Borelli brought our knowledge of the subject nearly to the point at which after the lapse of more than a century, indeed of nearly two centuries, Poiseuille and Weber took it up again.' Clark-Kennedy[7] says Hales was the first to measure the blood pressure directly and his experiments

---

[1] I, 327.   [2] I, 325.   [3] Rutt, *Memoirs of Priestley*, 1832, i, 299.
[4] *Geschichte der Botanik*, Munich, 1875, 515 f., 583.
[5] Clark-Kennedy, 55.   [6] 1901, 80.   [7] 1929, 23, 31.

'brought out certain facts that are now regarded as fundamental in the comparative physiology of the circulation in different animals'. In other fields, e.g. in the physiology of respiration, 'on the whole he followed Mayow, with whose work he was familiar, but not as closely as he should.'[1]

Hales got no further than supposing that the blood particles in the lungs, 'by the extraordinary Frictions that they there undergo, . . . are much heated and dilated,' but 'are at the same time refrigerated and contracted by the fresh Air that is continually taken into the Lungs';[2] 'it is very probable that one considerable use of the Lungs, is to refrigerate the Blood', although ''tis probable also that the Blood may in the Lungs receive some other important Influences from the Air . . . yet it must be confessed that we are still much in the dark about it'.[3] These are Harvey's ideas and Mayow in 1674 had got much further than this. Some glimmering ideas on osmosis which have been read into some of Hales's statements[4] can be found in Borelli (Vol. II).

Hales was mentioned by Joannes Baptista Abati.[5] In addition to his books and pamphlets, Hales published some unimportant papers in the *Philosophical Transactions*, some on medical subjects, of which he had little knowledge,[6] also a plan of a new thermometer,[7] checking fires by damp earth,[8] electrifying an egg,[9] the strengths of purging waters,[10] the cause of earthquakes,[11] the antiseptic properties of lime water,[12] blowing fresh air through distilling liquors,[13] the ventilation of ships,[14] and blowing air through ill-tasting milk.[15] His apparatus for 'blowing showers of fresh air' through the liquid in a still[16] was modified by Brownrigg;[17] Hales mentions previous experiments by Littlewood and Baily. The purification of sea water by distillation with alkali (wood-ash, etc.) was described by Appleby,[18] Chapman,[19] and Newland.[20]

We take leave of Hales with disappointment. If he had paid less attention to Newtonian 'staticks' and more to Mayow, he might have gone much further. His really important contribution to chemistry was his separation of the apparatus for generating a gas from the apparatus for collecting it, and his work inspired Priestley.

BROWNRIGG

Interest in mineral waters continued in the eighteenth century. Van Helmont (*c.* 1620) had recognised that the water of Spa contains dissolved gas sylvestre (carbon dioxide), which is developed in the gaseous form in the Grotto del Cane in Naples (see Vol. II, pp. 228–9). Johann Philipp Seip

[1] *Ib.*, 101 f., 108.   [2] II, 1733, 97.   [3] *Ib.*, 105–6.   [4] II, 48, 74, 114, 126.
[5] *De præcipua aëris atmosphærici tam in perficiendis, quam in dissolvendis organicis corporibus potestate. Dissertatio habita in magno Pisani Athenæi Auditoris*, 4°, Pisa, J. P. Giovannelli, 1764, 24 pp., referring also to 17-cent. work.
[6] *Phil. Trans.*, 1744–5, xliii, 20, 502.
[7] *Phil. Trans.*, 1747, xliv, 693; expansion of a lead rod.
[8] *Phil. Trans.*, 1748, xlv, 277.   [9] *Phil. Trans.*, 1748, xlv, 409.
[10] *Phil. Trans.*, 1750, xlvi, 446: weights of solids on evaporation.
[11] *Phil. Trans.*, 1750, xlvi, 669: kindling of sulphureous vapours by lightning.
[12] *Phil. Trans.*, 1754, xlviii, 826.   [13] *Phil. Trans.*, 1755, xlix, 312.
[14] *Phil. Trans.*, 1755, xlix, 332.   [15] *Phil. Trans.*, 1755, xlix, 339.
[16] *Phil. Trans.*, 1755, xlix, 312.   [17] *Phil. Trans.*, 1756, xlix, 534.
[18] *Phil. Trans.*, 1753, xlviii, 69; mentioning the addition of silver nitrate by Clark.
[19] *Phil. Trans.*, 1758, l, 635.   [20] *Phil. Trans.*, 1772, lxii, 90.

(Pyrmont, 28 November 1686– ? Waldeck ?) recognised that the gas collecting in the Grotto del Cane is probably the same as that dissolved in Pyrmont water.[1] Shaw[2] collected 'air' from Scarborough water and Francis Home[3] from the chalybeate water of Dunse (Scotland), but they seem to have thought it was common air. Dr. J. Wall[4] wrote on the 'mineral spirit' of Malvern water.

The presence of 'sulphur' (really hydrogen sulphide) in Harrowgate water was recognised by Simpson (see Vol. II, p. 607). John Rutty,[5] who noticed that sulphureous waters blacken silver, attributed their 'fetor' to sulphur, quoting a letter of 1750 from Hales saying that they contain a 'subtle volatile sulphur'. Donald Monro[6] also investigated 'sulphureous waters'.

Other papers on mineral waters are by C. H. Senckenberg,[7] J. Martyn,[8] J. Rutty,[9] J. Walker,[10] J. Milles,[11] J. Rutty,[12] D. P. Layard,[13] M. Morris,[14] T. Percival,[15] M. Dobson,[16] and on waters containing copper by W. Henry[17] and J. Rutty.[18] Some careful experiments on mineral waters containing dissolved carbon dioxide were made by Brownrigg.

William Brownrigg (High Close Hall, Cumberland, 24 March 1711–Ormanthwaite, nr. Keswick, Cumberland, 6 January 1800),[19] M.D. Leyden 1737, F.R.S. 1742, and a physician in Whitehaven, published a book on salt manufacture,[20] and some remarks on Hales's method of purifying sea water[21] in which he describes superheating steam for use in engines, and a safety-valve. His papers on platinum[22] are interesting, but his most valuable publications are two papers on mineral waters in which he describes a 'mineral elastic spirit' or (1774) 'mephitic air', i.e. carbon dioxide.[23]

Brownrigg says his first paper was communicated to Hales, Pringle[24] that, at

[1] *Phil. Trans.*, 1737–8, xl, 266, no. 448: Relatio de Caverna vaporifera sulphurea in Lapicidina Pyrmontana, quæ similis est Foveæ Neapolitanæ Grotta del Cane dicta, à Dno Misson & aliis descriptæ . . . communicata à Johanne Philippo Seip M.D.; Gmelin, (1), ii, 784, quotes *Diss. de spiritu et sale aquarum mineralium præsertim Pyrmontanarum*, 4°, Göttingen, 1748.

[2] *An Enquiry into the Contents, Virtues and Uses of the Scarborough Spaw Waters*, London, 1734; see Vol. II, p. 759.

[3] *An Essay on the Contents and Virtues of Dunse-Spaw*, Edinburgh, 1751.

[4] *Phil. Trans.*, 1756, xlix, 459.

[5] *A Methodical Synopsis of Mineral Waters. . . . Interspersed with Tables . . .* , 4°, London, 1757 (660 pp.; Duveen, 522); *Phil. Trans.*, 1759, li, 275.

[6] *Treatise on Mineral Waters*, 2 vols. 8°, London, 1770; *Phil. Trans.*, 1772, lxii, 15.

[7] *Phil. Trans.*, 1741, xli, 830: Cheltenham.   [8] *Ib.*, 1741, xli, 835: Epsom.

[9] *Ib.*, 1756 (7), xlix, 648: Pennsylvania.

[10] *Ib.*, 1757, l, 117: Moffat, chalybeate, alkaline to syrup of violets.

[11] *Ib.*, 1757, l, 25: Carlsbad.   [12] *Ib.*, 1760, li, 470; chalybeate, Amlwych, Anglesey.

[13] *Ib.*, 1766, lvi, 10: Somersham (contains alum and vitriol).

[14] *Ib.*, 1766, lvi, 22: Somersham (alum and vitriol).

[15] *Ib.*, 1772, lxii, 455: Buxton and Matlock.   [16] *Ib.*, 1774, lxiv, 124: Matlock, petrifying.

[17] *Ib.*, 1752, xlvii, 500: Wicklow.   [18] *Ib.*, 1756 (7), xlix, 648: Pennsylvania.

[19] J. Dixon, *The Literary Life of William Brownrigg, to which are added an Account of the Coal Mines near Whitehaven, etc.*, Whitehaven, 1801, 239 pp.; reprinted in *Ann. Phil.*, 1817, x, 321, 401; Bettany, DNB, 1886, vii, 85; Russell-Wood, *Ann. Sci.*, 1950, vi, 436; 1951, vii, 199.

[20] *The Art of Making Common Salt*, London, 1748.

[21] *Phil. Trans.*, 1756, xlix, 534, see p. 123.

[22] *Phil. Trans.*, 1750, xliv, 584 (590), 594: communicated by W. Watson, to whom they are sometimes ascribed.

[23] An Experimental Enquiry into the Mineral Elastic Spirit, or Air, contained in Spa Water, *Phil. Trans.*, 1765, lv, 218 (the paper had been read 24 years before); Continuation of an Experimental Inquiry concerning the Nature of the Mineral Elastic Spirit, or Air, contained in the Pouhon Water, *Phil. Trans.*, 1774, lxiv, 357.

[24] *Six Discourses*, 1783, 15.

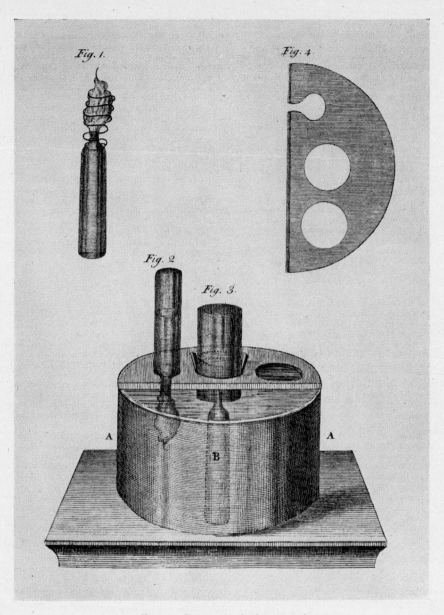

FIG. 11. BROWNRIGG'S APPARATUS.

Brownrigg's request, it was not published until he had made it 'more worthy of that honour'. In it he describes the collection of the 'very subtle, light, and permanently elastic fluid' or 'true mineral air' from the water in bladders or in bottles filled with water and with the necks inverted in water by passing through a hole in a wooden shelf *above* the water level in a trough, the bottle being kept in place by wooden wedges (Fig. 11). This is a form of pneumatic trough; Priestley's trough (see p. 250) had the shelf *below* water level in the trough. Bergman[1] in work begun in 1770 but published in 1774, had also used a trough with a shelf above water level with a hole for the neck of an inverted bottle filled with water (Fig. 12). Hales, and later Cavendish, and Bergman, suspended the inverted vessel filled with water by means of strings, which was hardly, as G. Wilson[2] claimed, more convenient than Brownrigg's apparatus.

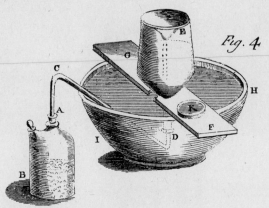

FIG. 12. BERGMAN'S APPARATUS FOR COLLECTING A GAS OVER WATER.

Brownrigg says the mineral spirit of Spa water is apparently identical with that 'most subtle and active exhalation, which, in many places perspires from springs and lakes, and other openings of the earth; or arises in pits and mines, where it is discovered by extinguishing flame; and from its pernicious effects, in killing all animals that breathe therein, [and] is known to our miners by the name of choak damp'. He passed a mouse on a piece of cork under water into a bottle of air, in which it lived comfortably 24 hours, but when passed into a bottle of air from spa water it died in a few seconds, first holding up its head very high. It did not struggle. The name choke-damp was mentioned (from some English source) by Leonhardi.[3] Brownrigg knew that 'in proportion as this mineral air is separated by heat in the same proportion the more gross earthy parts of the water seem also to separate from it', but the correct explanation was first given by Cavendish in 1767 (p. 319).

Brownrigg had fire-damp (methane) from coal mines conveyed to his laboratory in Whitehaven, and Spedding of Whitehaven (who invented the method of removing it from mines in pipes from the 'blowers' in the coal) had the idea that it might be conveyed in pipes and used to light the streets of the town at night.[4] A description of the Whitehaven coal mine, probably written by Brownrigg, is given by W. Hutchinson.[5] Brownrigg also published notes on

[1] De acido aereo; Of the Aerial Acid, *Essays*, 1788, i, Plate II, fig. 4.
[2] *Life of Cavendish*, 1851, 196.
[3] *Macquers Chymisches Wörterbuch*, 1788, ii, 831.
[4] G. Jars, *Voyages Métallurgiques*, 4°, Paris, 1774, i, 248; R. L. Galloway, *Annals of Coal Mining*, 1898, i, 348–9, 407, 488.
[5] *The History of the County of Cumberland*, 1794, ii, 54, mentioning the 'fulminating damp'.

stilling waves by oil[1] and on a natural salt found in coal mines,[2] and there are some unpublished papers in the archives of the Royal Society.

SALUZZO

Giuseppe Angelo, Count of Saluzzo (Comte de Saluces) (Saluzzo, Piedmont, 2 October 1734–Turin, 16 June 1810), in memoirs on the elastic fluid ('fixed air') evolved by gunpowder, quotes Bernoulli (see Vol. II, p. 628) and describes further experiments.[3] He thought this was atmospheric air, although he pointed out that it would not support combustion or respiration. He found that the gas occupied 200 times the volume of the powder. It again supported combustion and life when purified by passing through rags impregnated with alkali or by exposure to ice-cold for twelve hours. Gunpowder burnt in air in which charcoal, candles and sulphur had burnt out. The air so produced, he found, was like that evolved in the effervescence of an acid and an alkali.

Saluzzo also published on the action of quicklime on various bodies (e.g. sulphur and sal ammoniac),[4] the change of colour of juice of violets,[5] Boyle's *ens veneris*, the bleaching and dyeing of silk, vegetable and animal oils,[6] comparative chemistry (by analogy with botanical classification),[7] dephlogisticated air (gas déphlogistique) and causticity,[8] the reduction of some metallic calces (chaux métalliques),[9] the adsorption of gases and vapours on charcoal (de la prétendue absorption du charbon dans les vases clos),[10] fluorspar,[11] the improvement of pneumatic chemical apparatus,[12] and artificial mineral waters.[13]

PLUMMER

Andrew Plummer held the chairs of medicine and chemistry in Edinburgh. He had been a pupil of Boerhaave and began to lecture on chemistry about 1726, apparently only on the preparation and chemical properties of medicines.[14] He became paralysed in 1755 and Cullen and Black were candidates for the chair of chemistry, Cullen being elected.[15] Plummer revived, however, and it was arranged that Cullen and he should hold the chair conjointly, but Plummer died on 16 April 1756. He published two chemical papers, in the first of which[16] he mentions that oil of vitriol dissolves iron only when it is diluted, and that the 'steams' evolved kindle at the flame of a candle. This had

[1] *Phil. Trans.*, 1774, lxiv, 445; mentioned by Aristotle, Pliny, and Plutarch.
[2] *Phil. Trans.*, 1774, lxiv, 481.
[3] *Miscellanea Taurinensis; Mélanges de Philosophie et de Mathématique de la Société Royale de Turin*, Turin, 1759, i, Mém. 3, 115; 1760–1, ii, 94, 216; tr. in *Collection Académique . . . concernant l'Hist. Nat. . . . de la partie étrangère*, Paris, 1789, xiii; Fourcroy, (2), iii, 367.
[4] *Miscell. Taurin.*, 1762–5 (1766), iii, 73.   [5] *Ib.*, 1762–5, iii, 153.
[6] *Ib.*, 1766–9, iv, 169 f. (174, 193).   [7] *Ib.*, 1770–3, v, 191.
[8] *Mém. Acad. Roy. Turin*, 1784–5 (1786), i, 1, 51; 1784–5 (1786), ii, 148, 180; mentioning Morozzo and Lavoisier.
[9] *Ib.*, 1786–7 (1788), iii, 149; showing in plate IV bottles with three tubes fixed in a cover-plate and not with necks, and in plate VI a globular receiver with three tubes — *not* 'Woulfe's bottles'.
[10] *Ib.*, 1786–7, iii, 180.   [11] *Ib.*, 1786–7, iii, 327.
[12] *Ib.*, 1788–9 (1790), iv, 83: mentioning on p. 91 'fioles à double col' used with a vertical tube as a *manometer* — no figure.
[13] *Ib.*, 1788–9, iv, 241.   [14] J. Thomson, *Life of Cullen*, 1859, i, 39.
[15] Thomson, *op. cit.*, 1859, i, 86 f., 93 f.
[16] Remarks on Chemical Solutions and Precipitations, *Essays and Observations Physical and Literary read before a Society in Edinburgh*, Edinburgh, 1754, i, 284.

been published by N. Lemery in 1700 (see p. 36). In the second paper Plummer[1] recorded experiments similar to those published by Homberg in 1700 (see p. 44) on the composition of salts. Plummer found that 960 grains of fixed alkali (potassium carbonate) when 'satiated' (neutralised) with vitriolic, nitric and muriatic acids, gave on evaporation to dryness 982 grains of vitriolated tartar (K_2SO_4), 1200 grains of nitre (KNO_3), and 1080 grains of digestive salt of Sylvius (KCl). Thus the weights of the three acids for 100 of alkali are calculated as 2·29, 25 and 12·25. This quantitative work must have been known to Black when he began his own about the same time.

CULLEN

William Cullen (Hamilton, Lanarkshire, 15 April 1710–Kirknewton, nr. Edinburgh, 5 February 1790) was at first an apothecary in London and Scotland, M.D. Glasgow 1740, lecturer in chemistry in Glasgow (1746), then professor of medicine (1751); lecturer in chemistry (1755), professor of chemistry (1756) and theory of physic (1766), and finally professor of medicine (1773), in Edinburgh; F.R.S. 1777. Cullen is shown in the portrait by Cochrane with a large wig, a large nose, and a protruding lower lip.[2] At Glasgow, Cullen did some work in a small laboratory (Wightman says it was available to students on a voluntary basis, but only a few used it). A letter on the alkalis to Dr. John Clerk of Edinburgh was sent to the Edinburgh Philosophical Society in 1753 but was not published.[3] Cullen and Black had a research laboratory in Edinburgh, also used for lecture preparations but not for teaching undergraduates.[4] Cullen's Edinburgh lectures on history of chemistry[5] were based on Borrichius's *Conspectus* (see p. 160) in the earlier part and on Boerhaave's *Chemistry* tr. by Shaw (see Vol. II, p. 743) in the later. His Edinburgh lectures on chemistry are in MSS. 42 and 49 of the London Medical Society Library. The lectures were divided into (i) general doctrines, on the laws of combination and separation, and the sources and modes of communication of heat and its effects on bodies, and (ii) particular doctrines, dealing with the five classes of bodies: salts, inflammables, waters, earths, and metals, with the properties

[1] Experiments on Neutral Salts compounded of different acid Liquors and alcaline Salts, fixt and volatile; *Essays and Obs.*, 1754, i, 315; Guyton de Morveau, *Ency. Méthod., Chymie*, 1787, i, 594.

[2] Bettany, DNB, 1888, xiii, 279; Comrie, *Isis*, 1926, viii, 558; *id., History of Scottish Medicine*, 1932, i, 311 (portr.); Faujas Saint-Fond, *Voyage en Angleterre, etc.*, Paris, 1797, ii, 274; Guthrie, in *An Eighteenth Century Lectureship in Chemistry*, ed. Kent, Glasgow, 1950, 49; Sir W. Hamilton, *Discussions on Philosophy and Literature*, London, 1852, 238; Mackenzie, *Isis*, 1936, xxv, 283; Stirling, *Some Apostles of Physiology*, 1902 (portr.); J. Thomson, *An Account of the Life, Lectures and Writings of William Cullen, M.D.*, Edinburgh, 1832; 2 ed. with second vol. completed by J. and W. Thomson and D. Craigie, Edinburgh and London, 1859, i, 25, 29, 38 f. (chemical lectures), 54 (expts. on cold); ii, 687–90 (bibl.); T. Thomson, *Ency. Brit. Suppl.*, Edinburgh, 1801, I, ii, 463–8; *id.*, (1), ii, 303 (says b. 11 December 1712); Wightman, *Ann. Sci.*, 1955, xi, 154; 1956 (1957), xii, 192; Crosland, *ib.*, 1959 (1961), xv, 75; on Cullen's medicine, Allbutt, *Greek Medicine in Rome*, 1921, 529; Daremberg, 1870, ii, 1102.

[3] J. Thomson, 1859, i, 57; Dobbin, *Ann. Sci.*, 1936, i, 138.

[4] J. Coutts, *A History of the University of Glasgow*, Glasgow, 1909, 533; Speakman, *Chem. and Ind.*, 1947, 219.

[5] Kent, *An Eighteenth Century Lectureship in Chemistry*, Glasgow, 1950, 15; I saw this MS. in 1932 in the possession of Prof. J. M. Thomson; it is now in Paisley Public Library.

of vegetable and animal substances, and concluding with the applications of chemistry in some of the practical arts.[1] Angus Smith[2] says 'a manuscript copy of Dr. Cullen's lectures in 1762–3 in the laboratory of Owens College, Manchester, from the late Dr. Henry's library, mentions four elements, which, by simple combination, could be formed into seven, but any proportionate combination to account for the number in nature, is not given'.

About 1750–2, in Glasgow, Cullen wrote essays on bleaching and on the manufacture of common salt, proposing improvements in the processes,[3] and T. Thomson[4] says he paid attention to the utility of chemistry in medicine, arts, and manufactures.

In his lectures from 1758 Cullen used affinity diagrams, which were also used in 1759 by Fordyce.[5] He included lectures on heat, referring to the well-known experiment (mentioned by Francis Bacon, see Vol. II, p. 397) for proving that the sense of touch is untrustworthy in comparing temperatures, in which the hands are placed one in hot and one in cold water, and then both in tepid water.[6] After 1766 Cullen devoted himself mostly to medicine and materia medica.

In 1755 Cullen read to the Edinburgh Philosophical Society an essay 'Of the Cold produced by evaporating Fluids, and of some other means of producing Cold'.[7] In this he describes the lowering of temperature produced by the evaporation of a volatile liquid under the receiver of an air pump, and by the sudden (adiabatic) expansion of air. He froze water in a vessel in which was immersed another vessel containing nitrous ether evaporating rapidly in an exhausted receiver, using an air thermometer in these experiments. In this work, Cullen was assisted by Matthew Dobson of Liverpool and afterwards of Bath.[8]

T. Thomson says Cullen in Edinburgh taught a mixture of the medical theories of Hoffmann and Stahl, and these, 'so far as medical theories have any influence on practice, still continue [in 1830] in some measure prevalent.'

Daremberg says Cullen contested the current humoral pathology, adopted Hoffmann's view (see Vol. II, p. 692) that the seat of disease is in the solid parts of the body, and regarded life as a function of the nervous system. Cullen issued an edition of Haller's elementary work on physiology with an analytical table of contents.[9] In this it is taught that digestion is a particular kind of fermentation, digestion by the gastric juice outside the stomach being doubtful. Air is present in the animal fluids but respiration is not the source of animal heat, which depends on the motion of the blood, the fibrin of which is called 'gluten'.

Cullen's book on materia medica is based on lectures begun in 1761 (a pirated edition appeared in 1771).[10]

[1] J. Thomson, i, 44.   [2] *Manchester Mem.*, 1856, xiii, 144.   [3] J. Thomson, i, 74–9.
[4] (1), i, 304, 315.   [5] J. Thomson, 1859, i, 44, 123, 570 f.; on Fordyce, see p. 692.
[6] Cleghorn, *Disputatio Physica Inauguralis, Theoriam Ignis complectans*, Edinburgh, 1779, 12.
[7] *Essays and Observations*, etc., Edinburgh, 1756, ii 145; repr. with Black's *Experiments upon Magnesia Alba*, etc., Edinburgh, 1782, 117 f.
[8] J. Thomson, 1859, i, 460; Black, *Elements of Chemistry*, 1803, ii, 97.
[9] Alberti v. Haller *Primæ Lineæ Physiologiæ*, Edinburgh, 1767; *First Lines of Physiology*, 1779, 1801.
[10] *A Treatise on the Materia Medica*, 2 vols. 4°, Edinburgh, 1789; J. Thomson, 1859, i, 141, 611; ii, 523–64; it was tr. into French, German (by Samuel Hahnemann) and Italian. Cullen's works were collected and published, 2 vols., Edinburgh, 1827.

A pupil, later a rival, of Cullen was John Brown (Lintlaws, or Preston, Berwickshire, 1735 or 1736–London, 7 October 1788), whose theory of 'excitability'[1] was adopted by Broussais and by Girtanner.[2]

Another pupil of Cullen, later of Black, was Benjamin Rush (1745–1813), who in 1799 became, at Philadelphia, the first professor of chemistry in America.[3] He published an account of maple-sugar[4] in which he commends the nutritive value of sugar, and rejects the idea that sugar is damaging to the teeth.

BLACK

Joseph Black (Bordeaux, 16 April 1728–Edinburgh, 6 December 1799) was born in Bordeaux where his father, who was born in Belfast but was ultimately of Scottish descent, had a wine business. His mother was Margaret Gordon of Houghhead, Aberdeenshire. Black's father had become very French and wrote English with some difficulty. Joseph was sent to school in Belfast in 1740, and in 1744 (Guerlac; or 1746) entered Glasgow University, where he studied languages and natural philosophy (he was the favourite pupil of Dr. Robert Dick), then, about 1748, anatomy and medicine under Cullen. Black says he studied chemistry in the publications of Marggraf and Reaumur.[5]

---

[1] *Elementa Medicinæ*, 8°, Edinburgh, 1794, 1805; Engl. tr. by T. Beddoes, 2 vols. 8°, London, 1795; German tr. *J. Browns Biographie nebst einer Prüfung seines Systems ... und einer Erklärung der Brownschen Grundsätze* (by Beddoes), 1797; J. Brown, *Works*, 3 vols., London, 1804.

[2] Daremberg, (1), ii, 1120.

[3] *The Letters of Benjamin Rush*, ed. L. H. Butterfield, 2 vols. Princeton, 1951 (incl. Priestley); G. W. Corner, *The Autobiography of Benjamin Rush*, Princeton, 1948; Miles, *Chymia*, 1953, iv, 37; M. B. Savin and H. J. Abrahams, *J. Franklin Inst.*, 1956, cclxii, 425; E. F. Smith, *Chemistry in America*, New York, 1914 (BM 360 c. 91. 155); *id.*, *Early Science in Philadelphia*, *Isis*, 1928, x, 177.

[4] An Account of the Sugar Maple-Tree of the United States, and of the Methods of obtaining Sugar from it, together with observations upon the advantages both public and private of this sugar, in a Letter to Thomas Jefferson, Esq. Philadelphia printed, London reprinted, 1792 (1 leaf, 24 pp.).

[5] T. Andrews, *B.A. Rep.* 1871, i, 189 (three letters of Lavoisier to Black; reprinted in Riddell, *Proc. Belfast Nat. Hist. Phil. Soc.*, 1921, 135); *Ann. Chim.*, 1791, viii, 225–9 (letter of Black to Lavoisier); Anon., *Brit. Quart. Rev.*, 1845, ii, 233–42; *Bibl. Brit.*, 1805, xxviii, *Sci. Arts*, 133–46, 324–42; A. Crum Brown, 'The Development of the Idea of Chemical Composition', Inaug. Lect., Edinburgh, 1869, 19 f.; Lord Brougham, *Lives of Philosophers of the Time of George III*, in *Works*, London, 1855 (or Edinburgh, 1872), i, 1 f., 477 (Brougham attended Black's lectures; crit. by Anon., *Brit. Quart. Rev.*, 1845, ii, 197); Lord H. Cockburn, *Memorials of his Time*, Edinburgh, 1856, 50; A. M. Clerke, DNB, 1908, ii, 571; E. Cohen, *Chem. Weekbl.*, 1919, xvi, 168; J. D. Comrie, *History of Scottish Medicine*, 1932, i, 315; L. Crell, *Ann.*, 1785, I, 346 and plate, Fig. VI (Black's symbols); Faujas Saint-Fond, *Voyage en Angleterre, en Écosse et aux Iles Hébrides*, Paris, 1797, ii, 267; A. Ferguson, *Trans. Roy. Soc. Edinb.*, 1805, V, ii, 101 (dated 23 April, 1801: life of Black; incorrectly says Black d. 26 November, which is followed by Robison); R. Foregger, *Anesthesiology*, 1957, xviii, 257 (identification of CO_2); Hjelt, *Chem. Ztg.*, 1913, xxxvii, 277 (letters of Black on Scheele); Hutton, Shaw, and Pearson, *Philosophical Transactions Abridged*, 1809, xiii, 610; H. Guerlac, *Isis*, 1957, xlviii, 124–51, 433–56 (with portr. of youthful Black); W. P. Jorissen, *Chem. Weekbl.*, 1919, xvi, 1579 (Black's res. on magnesia); J. E. Mackenzie, The Chair of Chemistry in the University of Edinburgh in the 18 and 19 Centuries, *J. Chem. Educ.*, 1935, xii, 503–11; D. McKie, *Ann. Sci.*, 1936, i, 101; 1959 (1961), xv, 65 (MS. of Black's lectures); *id.* and Heathcote, *The Discovery of Specific and Latent Heats*, London, 1935 (summary in *Isis*, 1936, xxv, 227); M. M. Pattison Muir, *Heroes of Science. Chemists*, 1883, 30–52; J. P. Muirhead, *Correspondence of James Watt*, 1846, p. xxii; E. W. J. Neave, *Isis*, 1936, xxv, 372 (summary of Lectures); Z. Neufville, *Tentamen Medicum Inaugurale, De Natura Aeris Fixi ...*, Edinburgh 1778; J. R. Partington, *College Course of Inorganic Chemistry*, 1948, 45 (experiments); *id.*, *Chymia*, 1960, vi, 27; W. Ramsay, (1) *Joseph Black, M.D. A Discourse delivered in the Universit*

Black worked for three years in Cullen's laboratory.[1] In 1750 or 1751 (Guerlac says 1752) he moved to Edinburgh and on 11 June 1754 presented his M.D. dissertation 'on the acid humour originating from food, and on magnesia alba'.[2] This deals mainly with the acidity of the stomach and the superiority of magnesia alba (carbonate of magnesia) as an antacid, but has an appendix of chemical experiments and a full explanation and proof of Black's doctrine of the relation between mild and caustic alkalis, which was afterwards perfected and read in English on 5 June 1755 to the Philosophical Society at Edinburgh, and published in 1756 (see p. 136).

Black succeeded Cullen as professor of anatomy and lecturer on chemistry in Glasgow in 1756, but exchanged the chair of anatomy with the professor of medicine. He succeeded Cullen as professor of chemistry in Edinburgh on 1 November 1766, and occupied that position, at the same time practising medicine, until his peaceful death, seated in his chair, in 1799. From 1791 he had an assistant in his lectures and Hope was appointed adjunct professor, succeeding Black on his death. Black's last course of lectures was given in 1796–7. He was very popular as a lecturer, taking great pains both with his courses and with his lecture experiments. The lectures were intended for students having no previous knowledge of chemistry and were revised as time went on. He also did a good deal of consulting work.

Black was tall, very pale, with large dark eyes, and a feeble and slender appearance. He dressed carefully in black with silver-buckled shoes and silk stockings, and carried a cane or green silk umbrella.[3] On account of his poor health he did hardly any research in later life. Robison says: 'many were induced, by the report of his students, to attend his courses, without having any particular relish for chemical knowledge.' His lectures were taken down by students and manuscript copies are extant.[4] Some of the lectures were

of Glasgow on Commemoration Day, 19th April, 1904, Glasgow, 1904 (26 pp.; repr. in Diergart, 1909, 431); id., (2) The Gases of the Atmosphere, 1915, 48 (portr.); id., (3) Life and Letters of Joseph Black, M.D., London, 1918 (with intr. and life of Ramsay, by F. G. Donnan), including rather inaccurate quotations from Black's letters; J. Read, (2), 158–76; H. Riddell, Proc. Belfast Nat. Hist. Phil. Soc., 1919, xx, pt. 3, 49–88 (Black's connexion with Belfast; see Thorpe; Riddell showed, from a note in the Matriculation Album of Glasgow University, that Black died on 6 December 1799; see also Dobbin, Occasional Fragments of Chemical History, Printed for Private Circulation, Edinburgh, 1942, 1, from Chemist and Druggist, 1899); J. Robison, Lectures on the Elements of Chemistry, delivered in the University of Edinburgh; by the late Joseph Black, M.D., now published from his Manuscripts, 2 vols. 4°, Edinburgh, 1803; biography in vol. I, xvii f. largely from Ferguson; N. Scherer, Allgemeine J. der Chemie, 1801, vi, 59 (portr.), 98, 108, 346; M. Speter, Chem. Ztg., 1928, lii, 913; id., Z.f. Instrumentenkde., 1930, l, 204 (Black's simple balance, from Ramsay, 1918, 130, letter from Black to J. Smithson, 18 September 1790; Smithson, Ann. Phil., 1825, x, 52–4 (figure); Faraday, Chemical Manipulation, 1842, 62–4); J. and W. Thomson, An Account of the Life, Lectures, and Writings of William Cullen, Edinburgh, 1859, i, 46 f., 573; T. Thomson, Ann. Phil., 1815, v, 321; id., (1), i, 313 (largely from Robison; incorrectly says Black d. 10 November); T. E. Thorpe, Nature, 1920, cvi, 165 (from Riddell); A. W. Tilden, Famous Chemists, 1921, 22 f.; J. C. Wiegleb, (2), 1791, ii, 139 f. (Meyer and Black).

[1] Guerlac, 127–8.

[2] Dissertatio Medica Inauguralis, de Humore acido a cibis orto, et Magnesia alba, Edinburgh, 1754, 8°, 46 pp.; repr. in 1785 in Thesaurus Medicus Edinburgensis novus, 4 vols. Edinburgh and London; tr. by A. Crum Brown, J. Chem. Educ., 1935, xii, 225, 268; the t.p. describes him as 'Josephus Black, Gallus', i.e. as French.

[3] Cockburn, 50 (about 1793).

[4] There are two copies in the Chemical Society Library, London, and copies in University College, and the Patent Office, London.

published anonymously;[1] a more complete account was published by Robison.[2]

John Robison (Boghall, nr. Glasgow, 1739–Edinburgh, 30 January 1805),[3] professor of natural philosophy in Edinburgh and a friend of Watt from his youth, added some polemical notes criticising the French chemists, who, he thought, had not given Black sufficient credit for work on chemistry and heat.

FIG. 13. JOSEPH BLACK, 1728–1799.

Apart from his work on alkalis (1756) Black published only two substantial papers, in the transactions of the Royal Societies of London (he was never F.R.S.) and Edinburgh. In the first[4] he says he found that water which has recently been boiled freezes when exposed to cold air as soon as it reaches the freezing-point, whilst unboiled water, containing dissolved air, freezes only if constantly stirred. Black suggested that the boiled water is constantly absorbing air, which disturbs it, whereas the other water remains in a state of rest. The second reports analyses of the waters of hot-springs in Iceland,[5]

[1] An Enquiry into the General Effects of Heat; with Observations on the Theory of Mixture, London, 1770 (119 pp.).
[2] Lectures on the Elements of Chemistry, delivered in the University of Edinburgh; by the late Joseph Black, M.D., now published from his Manuscripts, 2 vols. 4°, Edinburgh, 1803; American ed., Philadelphia, 3 vols. 8°, 1806–7 (Weil, Cat. 16 (1950), no. 40).
[3] Playfair, Trans. Roy. Soc. Edin., 1812, vii, 495; Smiles, Lives of the Engineers. Boulton and Watt, 1904, 39, 79, 427 (portr.); Stronach, DNB, 1897, xlix, 57.
[4] The supposed effect of boiling on water in disposing it to freeze more readily, ascertained by experiments; Phil. Trans., 1775, lxv, 124–9.
[5] An Analysis of the Waters of Some Hot Springs in Iceland, Trans. Roy. Soc. Edin., 1794, iii, 95–126 (read 4 July 1791) (at the end are two letters from J. T. Stanley); Ann. Chim., 1793, xvi, 40; 1793, xvii, 113.

which showed that they contain silica held in solution by caustic soda. An extract from this paper, on a method of collecting small amounts of precipitates, was published in German.[1] Some minor chemical discoveries of Black were published in German by his pupil Crell.[2] These are incorporated in Black's *Lectures* (1803). They include[3] a method of preparation of ethyl nitrite which he described in a letter to Cullen in 1753[4] on 'ethers'; it consisted in stratifying alcohol over concentrated nitric acid, separated by a layer of water, in a phial, and allowing to stand so that the liquids mixed by diffusion, oxides of nitrogen being evolved. He used quicklime instead of chalk in Scheele's process of making tartaric acid from tartar.[5] He still believed that common ether is a compound of alcohol and sulphuric acid.[6] Black[7] gave an essentially correct explanation of the eutectic point in the freezing of a salt solution. Although he included water gas (a mixture of carbon monoxide and hydrogen), marsh gas, fire-damp, etc., as 'inflammable air', he doubted if they 'have anything in common with hydrogen besides their inflammability'.[8] William Higgins[9] correctly said: 'I think, neglecting to discriminate between the light and heavy inflammable airs, has been the chief cause of all the errors and confusion that at present prevail in the science of chemistry.'

Black[10] about 1767–8 showed his friends a balloon filled with hydrogen rising to the ceiling, which they at first suspected was raised by a black thread. In his lectures, Black argued at some length that hydrogen balloons would never be of any use for aerial voyages. The first hydrogen balloon of taffeta proofed with a solution of rubber in turpentine was made in Paris in August 1783 by Jacques Alexandre César Charles, who made an ascent to 3467 m. in Paris on 1 December 1783. Blanchard crossed from Dover to Calais in a gas balloon on 7 January 1785. Military balloons were used by the French at least as early as 1796.[11]

Black's analyses of salts were very good; he found that 100 parts of soda crystals (washing soda) contain 20 of soda (Na_2O), 16 of carbonic acid (CO_2) and 64·0 of water; that 100 of dry Glauber's salt (Na_2SO_4) contain 15 of soda, 27 of sulphuric acid (SO_3) and 58 of water; and that 100 of common salt ($NaCl$) gave 235 of silver chloride.[12] Black's balance is said to be in the Royal Scottish Museum.

The familiar 'Black's blowpipe' was described and illustrated by Jacquin.[13] Ross[14] quotes J. J. Griffin[15] as saying that the blowpipe was invented by a

[1] Gren's *N. J. der Physik*, 1796, iii, 114.
[2] *Neueste Entdeckungen*, 1783, xi, 97–9; 1783, x, 140–1 (phosphoric acid and preparation of phosphorus).
[3] *Lectures*, ii, 324. [4] J. Thomson, *Life of Cullen*, 1859, i, 578.
[5] *Lectures*, i, 482. [6] *Lectures*, ii, 331.
[7] *Ib.*, i, 132. [8] *Ib.*, ii, 222, 247.
[9] *A Comparative View of the Phlogistic and Antiphlogistic Theories*, 1789, 251.
[10] *Ib.*, ii, 228; Lord Brougham, *Works*, 1872, i, 12; Thomson, (1), ii, 329; Clerke, DNB, 1908, ii, 574; Ramsay, (3), 1918, 78.
[11] Feldhaus, (1), 646; Rosenberger, 1887, iii, 74.
[12] *Lectures*, 1803, i, 364, 376; ii, 662; Kopp, (1), ii, 74.
[13] Scherer's *Allgem. J. Chem.*, 1802, viii, 575, and plate V, fig. 3.
[14] *Pyrology*, 1875, 19.
[15] *Chemical Recreations*, 'Pt. I, p. 111'; it is not in the part on blowpipes in the 6 ed., Glasgow, 1826, 87.

German workman in Glasgow.[1] Black's laboratory furnace with a carbon lining was very efficient.[2] Hope was able to convert barium carbonate to oxide in such a furnace.

Black[3] once obtained amethyst-coloured crystals (ferric nitrate) from a solution of iron in nitric acid. According to Robison,[4] Black as early as 1762 ascribed the increase in weight of metals on calcination to absorption and fixation of 'air'. He explained the alkalinity of borax by 'the weakness of the acid'.[5] He used the name 'alkaline earths' for 'calcareous earth' (quicklime), magnesia, barytes, and 'strontites',[6] these with alumina and silica being 'elementary earths';[7] he does not distinguish the acidic silica from the basic alumina. He mentions that Hutton found alkali in zeolites.[8] He proposed the names (which were never used) 'lixiva' and 'trona' for potash and soda, 'argilla' for alumina, and called the volatile alkali 'ammonia', but he objected to the 'barbarous' name 'silica' for 'siliceous earth'.[9] He simplified Bergman's symbols.[10]

Affinity diagrams were used by Black in his lectures.[11] Thomson[12] says Robison told him that Black, who used the diagrams from the beginning of his professorship, informed him that he had learnt them from Cullen. Klaproth and Wolff[13] say that Cullen used numbers to represent affinities (see Fig. 14) and that Black later abandoned this method, as it used only mechanical, not chemical, conceptions. William Keir[14] used algebraic symbols for the attractions. The statements on mass action[15] must have been added by Robison from

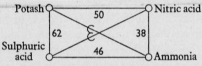

FIG. 14. AFFINITY DIAGRAM.

Berthollet (1801), mentioned in a footnote. Black[16] criticised the 'corpuscular theory of chemistry' used by Lemery (see p. 33) as an unwarrantable extension of the views of Bacon and Boyle; he approved of Newton's views on chemical attraction, but passes over his atomic speculations.

Sal ammoniac was manufactured in Edinburgh from the soot of bituminous coal from about 1756 by James Davie and James Hutton, and since Hutton was an intimate friend, Black was probably interested in the process. About the same time the Earl of Dundonald was making sal ammoniac as a by-product in the manufacture of coke.[17]

[1] Accounts of blowpipes in Obs. Phys., 1781, xviii, 207, 253, 467 (Bergman's); 1785, xxvi, 492 (Saussure's); 1786, xxviii, 345 (Hassenfratz's; oxygen blowpipe of Fourcroy).
[2] Black, Lectures, i, 317, 322, 334; Faujas Saint-Fond, ii, 270; Beschreibung eines neuen chemischen Ofens, nebst drey Kupfertafeln, 8°, Leipzig, 1782, q. by Gmelin, (1), iii, 478.
[3] Lectures, ii, 466.   [4] Ib., ii, 398.   [5] Ib., i, 483.
[6] Ib., ii, 22.   [7] Ib., ii, 154.   [8] Ib., ii, 162.
[9] Ib., i, 493; ii, 150 f.; Thomson, Ency. Brit. Suppl., 1801, I, i, 302.
[10] Crell in Chem. Ann., 1785, I, 346 and plate, Fig. vi.
[11] Lectures, i, 258 f., 465; Crosland, Ann. Sci., 1959 (1961), xv, 75.
[12] Ann. Phil., 1814, iii, 334; R. Angus Smith, Manchester Mem., 1856, xiii, 145 f.; J. Thomson, Life of Cullen, 1859, i, 44, 570 f. (letters of G. Fordyce and Cullen).
[13] Chymisches Wörterbuch, Berlin, 1810, v, 297–334 (302).
[14] Disputatio Physica Inauguralis de Attractione Chemica, Edinburgh, 1778; Black, Lectures, i, 466.
[15] Lectures, i, 277.   [16] Ib., i, 260 f.
[17] Beckmann, (1), 1846, ii, 407; Parkes, (1), 1823, ii, 437–68; Muspratt, Chemistry, n.d., i, 183; A. and N. Clow, Nature, 1947, clix, 425; id., The Chemical Revolution, London, 1952, 419.

John Evelyn, a smoke-abatement fanatic,[1] saw at Greenwich in July 1656 a process of Sir John Winster for charring sea-coal in large earthen crucibles like glass-pots 'using a barr of yron in each crucible or pot' with a hook at the end, so that 'the coales being mealted in a furnace with other crude sea-coales under them, may be drawn out of the potts sticking to the yron, whence they are beaten off in greate halfe-exhausted cinders, which being rekindl'd make a cleare pleasant chamber fire, depriv'd of their sulphur and arsenic malignity'.[2]

In an introductory lecture (about 1775) Black recommended Macquer's *Elements of the Theory and Practice of Chymistry* (London, 1758) and Lewis's *New Dispensatory* for the average students; for further reading he referred to 'Dr. Boerhaave's treatise on fire', Martin's 'Essay on Heat & Thermometers', Neumann's 'Chemical Works', abridged by Lewis (1759), and the 'Diction. Chemie' in which 'McQuer' is said to have had 'the principal hand', particularly the translation (by Keir, 1771), containing 'many new observations which were not known to McQuer'.[3]

Robison[4] reports Black as saying: 'Chemistry is not yet a science. We are very far from the knowledge of first principles. We should avoid anything that has the pretentions of a full system.' After criticising Stahl's, Macquer's, Boerhaave's, and Fourcroy's definitions of chemistry, Black proposed that it is the study of 'the effects produced by heat and by mixture, in all bodies, or mixtures of bodies, natural or artificial . . . with a view to the improvement of arts and the knowledge of nature'.[5] The 'chemical substances' are treated in the order: salts (still including acids and alkalis), earths, inflammable substances, metals, and waters, no distinction being made between inorganic and organic substances, and it was not thought necessary 'to constitute a class of airs or gases'.[6] The order is rather chaotic; because nitric oxide is evolved from mercury in nitric acid, an account of the use of this gas in eudiometry is given in the section on mercury.[7] Lavoisier's 'opinions' are introduced rather late in the course[8] in the section on combustion, and the older theories are given fully. Robison[9] says Black 'never would allow Stahl's doctrine to be spoken of in a slighting manner'. Scheele 'was the first person who, from a number of ingeniously contrived experiments, concluded by very fair reasoning, that atmospheric air is a mixed fluid, composed of about two parts of azotic gas, and one part of vital air or oxygen gas, along with a very small admixture of carbonic acid'. Black greatly admired Scheele, who is quoted oftener than any other chemist (142 times, Lavoisier 84, Priestley 68, Cavendish 45, Boerhaave 45, and Stahl 24).

Experiments on Magnesia and Alkalis

Black in his lectures said his experiments on lime and the alkalis were made as a result of trying to find a solvent which would dissolve the stone in the bladder without, like the caustic alkalis, destroying the substance of the bladder.[10] Hales had been interested in this (see p. 121). There was a dispute

---

[1] *Fumifugium; or, The inconvenience of the aer, and smoake of London dissipated*, 4°, London, 1661 (BM 1170. h. 4. (1.)).
[2] Evelyn, *Diary*, ed. Bray, 1870, 249.　　[3] Read, 166.　　[4] Black, *Lectures*, i, 547.
[5] *Ib.*, i, 11–12.　　[6] *Ib.*, i, 345.　　[7] *Ib.*, ii, 522.　　[8] *Ib.*, ii, 209.
[9] *Ib.*, ii, 750.　　[10] *Ib.*, ii, 50 f.; Brougham, 1872, 4; Guerlac (1957), 138.

between two Edinburgh professors. Robert Whytt (1714–66) said lime water made from quicklime prepared by calcining oyster-shells was best,[1] whilst Charles Alston (1683–1760) preferred lime made from limestone.[2] Whytt supposed that limestone on burning took up 'particles of fire'. Alston found that successive quantities of equally strong lime water were formed by water standing over lime. Both noticed the crust formed on exposure to air. Alston did not believe that particles of fire were introduced but that the change of limestone into quicklime was 'a necessary Consequence of the Change made in its Parts from the Fire'; he found that the crust was much heavier than the lime in the water (more than double), which he attributed to 'the Air, or something attracted from it'; but some inconclusive experiments gave no definite results. They might have given a hint to Black, and were quantitative.

Black's first experiments were with quicklime. An entry in his memoranda just before one dated November 1752 hints of a way of catching the caustic principle escaping from quicklime on slaking, but says: 'Nothing escapes — the cup rises considerably by absorbing air.' A few pages further on he compares the loss of weight from an ounce of chalk on calcination with that from the same weight dissolved in hydrochloric acid. Further experiments in 1752 led to the main results.[3] In another memorandum (probably before mid-January 1754) he says: 'when I precipitate lime by a common alkali, there is no effervescence. The air quits the alkali for the lime, but it is lime no longer, but C.C.C. [chalk]: it now effervesces, which good lime will not.' Robison[4] says Black 'had discovered that a cubic inch of marble consisted of about half its weight of pure lime, and as much air as would fill a vessel holding six wine gallons' — perhaps in the last months of 1753.[5]

In his *Inaugural Dissertation* Black asks what is the cause of the loss in weight when magnesia is calcined, and says it is probably mostly air:

Aërem forte: experimenti enim vigesimi consideratione, verisimile admodum videtur, ponderis, ustione amissi, partem maximam aëre evanido constare: et hoc quidem coroboratur, quod aërem nullam, post ustionem, in acido injecta emittat. Nonne etiam verisimile, aërem iterum magnesiae ab alkali restitui, quo tempore illam hoc de acido depellebat: alkali fixum aëre certe abundare, ex ingeniosi Hales experimentis constat.[6]

The dissertation contains no experiments on chalk or limestone, or on fixed air, which is curious if the researches did begin with lime.

Black's publication in 1756 (read 5 June 1755)[7] is in two parts, the first on

---

[1] *An Essay on the Virtues of Lime-Water in the Cure of the Stone*, Edinburgh, 1752; enlarged ed. 1755; *Phil. Trans.*, 1757, l, 209, 383, 386.

[2] *Phil. Trans.*, 1751, xlvii, 265; *A Dissertation on Quick-Lime and Lime-Water*, Edinburgh, 1752; 2 ed. 'with additions', 1754 (mentioning 'Mr. Joseph Black, now very deservedly promoted Doctor of Medicine, and whose inaugural Dissertation De magnesia alba demonstrates an extraordinary progress in chemistry'); *A Second Dissertation on Quick-Lime and Lime-Water*, Edinburgh, 1755; *A Third Dissertation on Quick-Lime and Lime-Water*, Edinburgh, 1757; Sprengel, (1), v, 502; Comrie, *History of Scottish Medicine*, 1932, i, 307; Alston was a student of Boerhaave.

[3] Black, *Lectures*, 1803, i, xxiii, xxvi.   [4] In Black, *Lectures*, i, xxvi.   [5] Guerlac, 437.

[6] *Dissert.*, 1754, 37; q. by Paul, in Watts, *Dict. of Chem.*, 1872, ii, 777.

[7] Experiments upon Magnesia alba, Quicklime, and some other Alcaline Substances, in *Essays and Observations, Physical and Literary, read before a Society in Edinburgh, and Published by them*, Edinburgh, 1756, ii, 157–225 (art. 8); q. as 'E & O'; repr. with Cullen's *Memoir*

magnesia and the second on lime and the alkalis. In the first part, after mentioning Hoffmann's publication (see Vol. II), he describes the preparation of magnesia alba (basic magnesium carbonate) from solutions of Epsom salt and pearl ashes (potassium carbonate), showing that the filtrate contains vitriolated tartar (potassium sulphate), and the preparation from magnesia alba of magnesium sulphate, nitrate, chloride, and acetate. From the properties of the salts he showed that magnesia is 'a substance very different from those of the calcarious class' (lime)[1] and that it precipitates chalk from lime water.[2] He then showed that 3 oz. of magnesia alba heated in a glass retort lost $\frac{7}{12}$ of its weight and was converted into calcined magnesia (magnesium oxide). The loss of weight he attributed to loss of 'air' or 'fixed air'; in the receiver there was only 5 drachms of whitish alkaline water:

of the volatile parts contained in that powder, a small proportion only is water; the rest cannot, it seems, be retained in vessels, under a visible form[3] . . . the volatile matter, lost in the calcination of magnesia, is mostly air; and hence the calcined magnesia does not emit air, or make an effervescence, when mixed with acids.[4]

$$\text{magnesia alba} = \text{calcined magnesia} + \text{water} + \text{fixed air}$$
$$\text{magnesia alba} + \text{acid} = \text{magnesia salt} + \text{fixed air}$$
$$\text{calcined magnesia} + \text{acid} = \text{magnesia salt.}$$

Black mentions that Hales had 'proved that alkaline salts contain a large quantity of fixed air, which they emit in great abundance when joined to a pure acid'. Black made experiments on the loss in weight when magnesia alba or 'fixed alkaline salt' (potassium carbonate) was treated with dilute sulphuric acid in a flask. Two drachms of alkali lost 1 scruple 8 grains, two drachms of magnesia 1 scruple 16 grains. Two drachms of magnesia were reduced 'by the action of a violent fire' to 2 scruples and 12 grains and then dissolved in acid without loss of weight:

I chose a Florentine flask, on account of its lightness, capacity, and shape, which is peculiarly adapted to the experiment; for the vapours raised by the ebullition circulated for a short time, thro' the wide cavity of the vial, but were soon collected upon its sides, like dew, and none of them seemed to reach the neck, which continued perfectly dry to the end of the experiment.[5]

In the second part of the paper Black says[6] that limestone effervesces with acids, giving off fixed air. On heating it forms quicklime and (in contrast to magnesia alba) only a trace of water: the considerable loss in weight must be due to the escape of fixed air:

$$\text{limestone} = \text{quicklime} + \text{fixed air.} \tag{1}$$

There were three alkalis recognised in Black's time: vegetable (potash),

on the Cold Produced by Evaporation, Edinburgh, 1777, 1782, 1796; repr. in ACR, ii; complete French tr. in Obs. Phys., 1774, i, 210, 261; German tr., Altenburg, 1757; see Guerlac (1957); an excellent almost contemporary summary is given by Lewis in his tr. of Neumann, The Chemical Works, 1759, 473.

[1] E & O, 1756, ii, 165; ACR, i, 10.   [2] E & O, 170; ACR, 13.
[3] Black's definition of fixed air is identical with Van Helmont's of gas sylvestre; see Vol. II, p. 227.
[4] E & O, 174; ACR, 16.
[5] E & O, 179; ACR, 19; Black did not use any drying-tube for the escaping gas.
[6] E & O, 185; ACR, 22.

marine (soda) and volatile (ammonia), and a mild and caustic form of each. The mild form (carbonate) was converted into the caustic (hydroxide) by treatment with slaked lime. In 1751 Macquer[1] said:

the design of this operation is to combine with the fixed alkali all the saline acrid parts of the quicklime . . . We shall not attempt to explain here why an alkali combined with quicklime acquires such a great causticity. This question seems to be one of the most subtle and the most difficult to answer in the whole of chemistry. It depends on the cause of the alkaline properties of quicklime.

In 1747 Duhamel du Monceau (see p. 71) found that lime water is precipitated by a solution of mild alkali (potassium carbonate), but he thought that this results from the union of an acid in the lime with an earth in the alkali. He also found that limestone loses nearly half its weight (the correct loss is 0·44) on burning to quicklime but regained part on slaking by exposure to air (hydration and partial conversion to carbonate). Black found that if a given weight of limestone is converted into quicklime according to equation (1), the quicklime slaked with water, and the slaked lime boiled with a solution of mild alkali (potassium carbonate), the alkali becomes caustic and the original weight of limestone is recovered:

$$\text{quicklime} + \text{mild alkali} = \text{limestone} + \text{caustic alkali}. \tag{2}$$

Equations (1) and (2) show that:

$$\text{mild alkali} = \text{caustic alkali} + \text{fixed air}. \tag{3}$$

If quick-lime is mixed with a dissolved alkali it shows an attraction for fixed air superior to that of the alkali. It robs this salt of its air, and thereby becomes mild itself, while the alkali is consequently rendered more corrosive, or discovers its natural degree of acrimony or strong attraction for water; which attraction was less perceivable as long as it was saturated with air. And the volatile alkali [ammonium carbonate] when deprived of its air, besides this attraction for various bodies, discovers likewise its natural degree of volatility, which was formerly somewhat repressed by the air adhering to it, in the same manner as it is repressed by the addition of an acid[2] . . . as the calcarious earths and alkalis attract acids strongly and can be saturated with them, so they also attract fixed air, and are in their ordinary state saturated with it: and when we mix an acid with an alkali or earth, the air is set at liberty . . . because the alkaline body attracts it more weakly than it does the acid, and because the acid and air cannot both be joined to the same body at the same time.[3]

In the first part of his paper[4] Black investigated 'the peculiar degree of attraction for acids' of magnesia, 'or what was the place due to it in Mr. Geoffroy's table of attractions' (see p. 52), and at the end[5] he says 'a new column may be added to that table . . . where the alkaline substances are all considered as in their pure state and free of fixed air':

Acids	*Fixed Air*
fixed alkali	calcarious earth
calcarious earth	fixed alkali
{ volatile alkali and magnesia	magnesia
	volatile alkali

[1] *Élémens de Chimie Pratique*, 1751; tr. *Elements of Chymistry*, 1764, ii, 190.
[2] E & O, 190; ACR, 25.   [3] E & O, 185; ACR, 22.
[4] E & O, 168; ACR, 12.   [5] E & O, 224–5; ACR, 46.

When limestone is dissolved in acid, fixed air is evolved with effervescence and a salt is formed. On addition of mild alkali to the solution, the original weight of limestone is reprecipitated and there is no effervescence because the fixed air of the mild alkali joins to the lime to produce limestone. Slaked lime does not contain any parts more caustic than the rest, and 'as any part of it can be dissolved in water, the whole of it is also capable of being dissolved'. Caustic alkali contains no lime or a mere trace which had been dissolved by the water.

Quick-lime does not attract air when in its most ordinary form, but is capable of being joined to one particular species only . . . to this I have given the name of fixed air, and perhaps very improperly; but I thought it better to use a word already familiar in philosophy, than to invent a new name, before we be more fully acquainted with the nature and properties of this substance.

On exposing lime water to the open air:

the particles of quick-lime which are nearest the surface gradually attract the particles of fixed air which float in the atmosphere. But at the same time that a particle of lime is thus saturated with air, it is also restored to its native state of mildness and insolubility; and as the whole of this change must happen at the surface, the whole of the lime is successively collected there under its original form of an insipid calcarious earth, called the cream or crusts of lime-water.[1]

Black says fixed air 'is different from common elastic air' and that it 'is dispersed thro' the atmosphere, either in the shape of an exceedingly subtile powder, or more probably in that of an elastic fluid',[2] thus leaving it in the class of what Cavallo[3] called 'bodies of which it is difficult to say, whether they are really combined with the aereal particles, or are merely suspended in that fluid, in consequence of their being of the same specific gravity'. When Black speaks of 'particles', as the quotation above shows, he means particles in solution or in a gas. This is as near as he then allowed himself to approach the atomic theory (see p. 154).

Black used 'a small silver dish over a lamp' for evaporating solutions of caustic potash to dryness and fusing the alkali; for:

'having once evaporated a part of the same ley in a bowl of English earthen or stone ware, and melted the caustic with a gentle heat, it corroded and dissolved a part of the bowl, and left the inside of it pitted with small holes.'[4]

Black obtained crystals of potassium bicarbonate by exposing a solution of potassium carbonate to the air in an open dish for two months. They had a milder taste than salt of tartar (potassium carbonate) 'and yet they seemed to be composed only of the alkali, and of a larger quantity of air than is usually contained in that salt'.[5]

Fourcroy[6] says Black's discoveries were unknown in France until about 1770;[7] they were: (1) the elastic fluid fixed air, previously confounded (especially by Hales) with atmospheric air, is quite different from this; (2) it is contained in alkalis, calcarious earths, and magnesia in their natural states, and is the cause of their effervescence with acids; (3) it is driven out by fire and by acids, and in the first case the earths become caustic;

[1] E & O, 189; ACR, 24, 30.   [2] E & O, 198–9; ACR, 30.   [3] A Treatise on Air, 1781, 369.
[4] E & O, 203; ACR, 33.   [5] E & O, 218; ACR, 42.   [6] (2), iii, 365.
[7] The paper of 1756 was tr. in Obs. Phys., 1774, i, 210, 261.

(4) its presence in lime and alkalis renders them mild; (5) lime takes it from alkalis, which then become caustic; (6) fixed air is contained in the atmosphere and is absorbed from it by alkaline substances. This is an admirable summary.

In a letter to Cullen of 3 January 1754, Black says:[1]

'I had mixed together some chalk and vitriolic acid at the bottom of a large cylindrical glass; the strong effervescence produced an air or vapour, which, flowing out at the top of the glass, extinguished a candle that stood close to it, and a piece of burning paper, immersed in it, was put out as effectually as if it had been dipped in water; yet the smell of it was not disagreeable.'

In his 1756 paper he refers to the formation of a film on lime water exposed to the atmosphere by fixed air,[2] and the milkiness produced in lime water by fixed air in a carbonate,[3] but the lime water test for the gas is first mentioned in his lectures[4] as discovered in 1756 (1757 in text, probably in error).

Black did not then publish any experiments on fixed air, saying[5] that although he intended to 'make this air, and some other elastic fluids which frequently occur, the subject of serious study', his move from Glasgow to Edinburgh laid 'a load of new official duties' on him. In 1757 (1756) he had made a number of observations on fixed air, which were followed by those of Macbride (see p. 143). In his publication in 1756, Black did not mention the taste of fixed air or its action on coloured indicators, but he says:[6] 'These considerations led me to conclude, that the relations between fixed air and alkaline substances was somewhat similar to the relation between these and acids.' Keir[7] suggested in 1771 that fixed air is acidic. Priestley in 1772[8] said: 'It is not improbable but that fixed air may be of the nature of an acid, though of a weak and peculiar sort. Mr. Bergman of Upsal, who honoured me with a letter upon the subject . . . says that it changes the blue juice of tournsole into red'. Bergman's memoir on 'the aerial acid' was published in 1774.[9] Cavendish[10] had given a minute description of the properties of fixed air, but does not mention its acidity.

Felice Fontana[11] and Marsiglio Landriani[12] thought that fixed air extricated by acids owed its acidity to the latter, but Bewley[13] showed that the gas separated from mild magnesia and from the volatile alkali by heat alone showed the same acid properties, and he called it 'mephitic acid'.

Black, without making the experiment, incorrectly supposed that the gas evolved in the explosion of fulminating gold is fixed air,[14] but later[15] he accepted Berthollet's proof[16] that it is nitrogen.

[1] J. Thomson, *Life of Cullen*, 1859, i, 50.   [2] E & O, 189; ACR, 24.
[3] *Ib.*, 202; ACR, 32.   [4] *Lectures*, ii, 88.
[5] *Ib.*, ii, 86 f.   [6] E & O, 185; ACR, 22.
[7] Tr. of Macquer's *Dictionary of Chemistry*, 1771, i, 36; ii, 838; *A Treatise on the Various Kinds of . . . Gases*, 1779, 110.
[8] *Phil. Trans.*, 1772, lxii, 153.
[9] KAH, 1774, xxxiv, 170; see p. 189.   [10] *Phil. Trans.*, 1766, lvi, 141 f.
[11] *Ricerche Fisiche sopra l'Aria fissa*, unknown to bibliographers but perhaps contained in his *Opuscoli Scientifici*, 8°, Florence, 1783 (BM 716. f. 7).
[12] *Ricerche Fisiche intorno allo Salubrità dell' Aria*, 8°, Milan, 1775 (BN R12797); German tr., 8°, Basel, 1778.
[13] In Priestley, E & O (see p. 244), 1775, ii, Appendix, 337 f.
[14] E & O, 180; ACR, 19.   [15] *Lectures*, ii, 668, 682.   [16] AdS, 1785, m 316.

Black in his lectures[1] showed the experiment of decanting fixed air from a jar over a burning candle, which was extinguished. In 1757 (1756) he showed that fixed air is evolved in fermentation by partly emptying a phial filled with lime water in a brewer's vat and shaking, when the lime water became milky. On the same day he fixed a piece of charcoal in the broad end of a bellows nozzle, put it in a fire, inserted the other end in a vessel of lime water and blew air over the charcoal, when the lime water became milky. He proved that fixed air is evolved in respiration by breathing out through lime water in a U-tube, when the lime water became milky. In the winter of 1764–5, Robison says, Black rendered a considerable quantity of caustic soda 'mild and crystalline, by causing it to filtre slowly by rags, in an apparatus which was placed above one of the spiracles in the ceiling of a church, in which a congregation of more than 1500 persons had continued near ten hours'.[2] Thus, in 1756, Black had ascertained the effects of fixed air on animals, its production by respiration and fermentation, and by the burning of charcoal, and inferred its presence in small quantities in the atmosphere.[3] Pringle in 1773[4] said Black had taught these properties of fixed air 'for several years', and had distinguished fixed air from 'air arising from the solution of metals by acids', i.e. hydrogen.

The use of lime in bleaching was forbidden by law, although Francis Home in 1756 said it was used in Manchester and in Scotland. John Williamson of Lambeg obtained permission to experiment on its use without incurring the penalties laid down by an act of Queen Anne, but although the results were very good the Linen Board refused to sanction the use of lime. In 1770 it awarded James Ferguson of Belfast £300 for the application of lime in bleaching, but no use of the experiments was made and the act still remained in force. As late as 1815 a bleacher was prosecuted for using lime, which was then constantly in use. The Scottish Board of Manufacturers paid Home £100 for his experiments and his proposal to use sulphuric acid instead of buttermilk as a sour.[5]

Francis Home, professor of materia medica in Edinburgh, wrote some medical works, and works on agriculture[6] and on bleaching;[7] the very scarce second edition of the last contains in an appendix a section by Black:

Francis Home, Experiments on Bleaching. To which are Added, I. An Experimental Essay on the Use of Leys and Sours in Bleaching. By James Ferguson, M.D. II. An Explanation of the Effect of Lime upon Alkaline Salts; and a Method pointed out whereby it may be used with Safety and Advantage in Bleaching, by Joseph Black, M.D. (pp. 265–82). III. An Abstract of the foregoing Essays, containing, Practical Rules and Plain Directions for the Preparation and Use of the Sours made of Oil of Vitriol, and of the Leys made of Bleaching-ashes with the addition of Quick-lime, 12°, Dublin, 1771, ii ll. 295 pp.

[1] Black, in F. Home, Experiments on Bleaching, 2 ed., Dublin, 1771, 265 f.; Lectures, i, 92.
[2] Lectures, ii, 87.   [3] Ib., ii, 87 f.
[4] Six Discourses delivered when President of the Royal Society; on Occasion of Six Annual Assignments of Sir Godfrey Copley's Medal, 1783, 19.
[5] S. H. Higgins, History of Bleaching, 1924, 14 f., 17.
[6] The Principles of Agriculture and Vegetation, 8°, Edinburgh, 1758.
[7] Experiments on Bleaching, 8°, Edinburgh, 1756 (dealing with the causes of hardness in water, 257 f.); German tr., Versuche im Bleichen, 8°, Leipzig, 1777.

On 20 September 1763 Black wrote to his father[1] saying:

'I have at last wrote a paper upon the use of lime in bleaching which I transmitted some posts ago to Mr. Ferguson, & shall do anything further that is in my power. I see at the foot of your letter to James Burnet you mention a memorial from the Linnen Manufacturers which at their desire you had sent me. I received the letter you enclosed to me from Mr. Ferguson in April last, but I have not seen anything else upon the subject . . . You likewise mention a considerable grateful reward promised by the Commissioners of the Linnen Board; I should be glad "entre nous" to know the particulars of this for I never heard of any reward before, nor ever expected it.'

Ramsay[2] refers to and quotes from the correspondence with Ferguson on the subject of bleaching, and extracts from this correspondence are also quoted in Ferguson's essay in this volume. The last (anonymous) section is by Macbride; it is purely practical. Ferguson quotes from Black's 1756 paper, from Macbride's book (with a crude sketch of his apparatus) and other publications, and describes several experiments on caustification, etc. Black's section consists of a summary of his 1756 paper with a few additions, and descriptions of commercial alkalis and their caustification. He says of 'fixed or Mephitic air':

'more or less of it is naturally and commonly attached to all the alkaline or bleaching salts; that while thus attached to them, it has the appearance and properties of a fixed and saline salt, and remains united to the particles of the salt, when this last is dissolved in water. But when separated from the salt, and exhibited pure by itself, it always appears under the form of a subtile, light, transparent fluid, like air, only a little heavier than air.'[3]

Black describes the experiment of decanting fixed air from a cylinder in which it was generated over a burning candle, and the method (given in more detail by Ferguson)[4] of determining the content of fixed air in an alkali by counterpoising a solution of it in a flask along with a phial of sulphuric acid on a balance pan, adding the acid to the alkali solution, and finding the loss in weight.[5] Half an ounce of pearl ashes (K_2CO_3) contained 66 grains of fixed air, other alkalis less, Muscovy alkali being quite free from it. Common kelp contains much common salt but could be mostly freed from it by crystallisation and could then be causticised by lime (the only known method of removing fixed air) for use in bleaching. Black points out the advantage of using caustic alkali. To find if an alkali contains lime, a pearl ash solution is added to a solution of it, which becomes milky.

Robison[6] found in a bundle marked 'old notes, excerpts &c' a description which he says dates 'previous to 1766' in which Black says he heated nitrous ammoniac (ammonium nitrate) and obtained incoercible vapours which made lighted paper 'burn with prodigious violence'. They did not precipitate lime water, and when they filled the air of the laboratory 'the effect on his breathing and sensation was very far from being unpleasant'. He 'wonders at the quantity of water obtained' in the receiver. Robison says Black must have obtained 'nitrous oxyd'.

In a letter to John Williams, a mining engineer, dated Edinburgh 18 April

[1] Ramsay, (3), 1918, 36–7.   [2] Ib., 52 f.   [3] Home, 1771, 268–9.   [4] Ib., 243.
[5] E & O, 179; ACR, 19; Lectures, ii, 120.   [6] Lectures, i, 554.

1777, Black says:[1] 'There are, in most parts of Scotland, different kinds of stone, which can, without much difficulty, be melted or softened by fire, to such a degree, as to make them cohere together', and he names several.

MACBRIDE

David Macbride (Ballymoney (Antrim), 26 April 1726–Dublin, 18 or 28 December 1778),[2] who had studied in Glasgow, became a naval surgeon, then studied with Hunter, and settled in Dublin in 1749, where he succeeded as a surgeon only after many years. He published five essays on chemical and medical researches:

Experimental Essays on the following Subjects: I. On the Fermentation of Alimentary Mixtures. II. On the Nature and Properties of Fixed Air (pp. 23–105). III. On the respective Powers, and Manner of Acting, of the different Kinds of Antiseptics. IV. On the Scurvy; with a Proposal for trying new Methods to prevent or cure the same, at Sea. V. On the Dissolvent Power of Quicklime, 8°, London, 1764; 2 enl. and corr. edit., Experimental Essays on Medical and Philosophical Subjects: particularly, I. On the Fermentation . . . (as above), 8°, London, 1767.

He refers in the preface to Hales, Black, and Pringle. In the essay on fermentation he describes experiments showing that 'the Subtile Gas, as it was termed by the old chemists', i.e. fixed air or carbon dioxide, is 'the grand preserver of animal fluids from putrefaction; attempers acrimony; is a principal agent in nutrition; and, perhaps contributes somewhat to animal heat'.[3] In the section on fixed air[4] he describes an apparatus (Fig. 15) of two bottles connected by a curved tube for leading the fixed air generated in one bottle into lime water, alkali solution etc., in the other. This apparatus, he says, was devised by Black, who communicated it to Hutcheson, lecturer in chemistry at Trinity College, Dublin.

With this apparatus, Macbride showed that putrefying animal matters generate fixed air, although fixed air arrests their putrefaction and appears to make them fresh again. Foods also give out fixed air, which thus seems to be formed in digestion and absorbed by the blood, to be evacuated with the urine or by transpiration. Blood, sweat, and urine precipitate lime water (really due to the phosphates).[5]

Macbride thought that the cohesion of the solid parts of the body depends on fixed air and that the resolution of bodies into their first principles is due to a loss or separation of it;[6] but as Black[7] said, this 'was not well founded and was . . . in some measure refuted afterwards, by the experiments and discoveries of others', which showed that only part of the gas evolved was fixed air, 'by much the greater part being an inflammable vapour, and other kinds.'

Macbride thought scurvy was due to lack of fixed air, and vegetables, rich in

[1] John Williams, *An Account of some Remarkable Ancient Ruins, lately discovered in the Highlands and Northern Parts of Scotland*, 4°, Edinburgh, 1777, 81–3.
[2] Archbold, DNB, 1893, xxiv, 424; *Dublin Quart. J. Medical Sci.*, 1847, iii, 281; Poggendorff, (1), ii, 2, 1425; Reilly, *J. Chem. Educ.*, 1950, xxvii, 237 (portr.); see also Lavoisier, *Opuscules Physiques et Chimiques*, 2 ed., Paris, 1801, 47–56; Fourcroy, (2), iii, 368 f.
[3] 1764, 10–12.   [4] 1764, plate opp. p. 52.
[5] Fourcroy, (2), iii, 368.   [6] 1767, 61, 71.   [7] *Lectures*, ii, 89.

fixed air, could effect a cure, for which he recommended an infusion of malt. Quicklime accelerates the decomposition of animal matters by absorption of fixed air. Macbride showed that oil does not unite with mild but only with caustic alkali to form soap, and that when a solution of soap is exposed to fixed air, the alkali is separated and the oil slowly collects on the surface of the liquid. He also showed that fixed air is soluble in alcohol. He concluded that

Fig. 2.

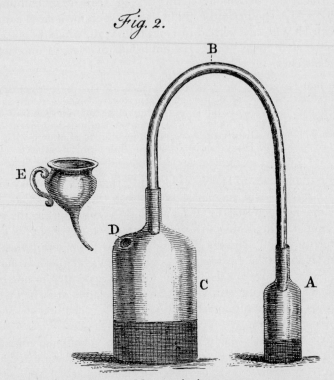

FIG. 15. MACBRIDE'S APPARATUS.

the volatile alkali formed in putrefaction is sometimes caustic and sometimes combined with fixed air. Fixed air is contained in the atmosphere, since quicklime and caustic alkalis exposed to the air become effervescent.

Macbride's theories made a great impression in France and Germany. Cavendish afterwards showed (see p. 317) that much of the air generated in putrefaction is inflammable, although it does contain some fixed air. Macbride also published on tanning,[1] describing the extraction of oak bark with lime water, and a *Methodical Introduction to the Theory and Practice of Medicine* (4°, London, 1772; 2 ed. 2 vols. 8°, Dublin, 1776), which was translated into Latin, French, German, and Dutch.

[1] *Some Account of a New Method of Tanning . . . invented by D. Macbride,* Dublin, 1769; *Phil. Trans.,* 1778, lxviii, 111.

J. F. Meyer

Black's theory was opposed by Johann Friedrich Meyer (Osnabrück; 24 October 1705–10 November 1765), an apothecary in Osnabrück, in a book with a characteristic title:

I. Chymischen Versuche zur näheren Erkenntniss des ungelöschten Kalchs, der elastischen und elektrischen Materie, der allerreinsten Feuerwesens, und der ursprünglichen allgemeinen Säure, Hanover and Leipzig, 1764 (BM). French: Essais de Chymie sur la Chaux Vive, tr. Dreux, Paris, 1765. See M. F. Boehm, Examen Acidi Pinguis, 4°, Strasbourg, 1769 (with biographical notice of Meyer); de Fourcy, Obs. Phys., 1774, i, 197.

Some 'alchemical letters' by Meyer, published posthumously by Andreæ, record Meyer's experiments on transmutation, made in consequence of results found by his friend Dr. Constantini in Hanover:

II. Alchymistische Briefe. Von dem Verfasser der Chymischen Versuche zur nähern Erkäntnis des ungelöschten Kalchs, &c. an den Herausgeber gegenwärtiger Briefe, 4°, Hanover, 1767 (Sotheran Cat. 832 (1932), 389); Lettres Alchymiques de M. Meyer à M. André, Apothicaire à Hanovure: Mises en François par le Traducteur des Essais de Chymie sur la Chaux vive, etc. [F. F. Dreux], 12°, Paris, 1767 (BN R 43767); Ferguson, ii, 93; Duveen, 402. An 'essay' by Meyer is said to be included in the Sammlung vermischter Abhandlungen itzlebender Scheidekuenstler, 8°, Hamburg, 1782, 296 pp.

Meyer[1] mentions Black only very briefly, from a German translation. He says limestone on burning takes up an oily acid (*acidum pingue*) from the fire (not pure fire, as Lemery taught), and this is transferred to the mild alkali when it becomes caustic. Since limestone and alkali always effervesce with acids, it follows that quicklime and caustic alkali, which do not effervesce with acids, are already saturated with *acidum pingue*. Caustic alkalis feel slippery to the fingers because they contain the 'oily' *acidum pingue*. Meyer thought that metals increase in weight on calcination because they absorb *acidum pingue* (their calces are precipitated from solutions of their salts by caustic alkalis). Meyer's theory had been proposed long before by Tachenius:[2] calcinatis coralijs si addatur alcali vegetabile, hoc ab eis elicit acidum ex flamma hausta, & coralia cadunt in puluerem album insipidum; calcined coral does not effervesce with vinegar because it is saturated with acid of flame.

Lord Brougham[3] says Black:

'seemed to have felt hurt at the objection urged by ... Meyer to his doctrine of causticity. ... The unsparing severity of the lecture in which Black exposed the ignorance and dogmatism of this foolish reasoner cannot well be forgotten by his hearers, who ... observed how well fitted he was, should occasion be offered, for a kind of exertion exceedingly different from all the efforts that at other times he was wont to make.'

Robison[4] says Meyer's publication:

gave Dr. Black considerable uneasiness; and, for several years, he was at the pains to refute all his arguments ... but without adding a single experiment to those by which

---

[1] I, 15.   [2] *Clavis*, c. viii; 1697, 127; see Vol. II, p. 292.   [3] 1872, 19 f.
[4] Black, *Lectures*, 1803, I, xxxii–xxxiii; the lectures as published do not mention Meyer.

he had already established it. Yet the obvious and simple experiment, of making the matter expelled from marble by a calcining heat pass into a solution of caustic alkali, and render it effervescent and mild, would have ended all disputes. This was done by Jaquin, in Vienna, in 1767, and at once silenced all the German chemists, as the experiments of Well, in which he calcined marble by a burning glass, put an end to Meyer's theory.

Guyton de Morveau[1] and Fourcroy[2] say *acidum pingue* is very like phlogiston: 'on y voit perpétuellement des matières augmenter de poids et en perdant un principe.' Black's researches, with their substitution of addition of fixed air in place of loss of *acidum pingue*, formed an exact parallel with Lavoisier's (later) theory, with its substitution of addition of oxygen in combustion instead of loss of phlogiston.[3] Fourcroy[4] gave ten benefits bestowed by Black's researches, which[5] 'have rendered Chemistry quite a new science'; also:[6]

'on peut même regarder ce premier travail de Black comme une des plus brillant époques de la chimie, comme la source de toutes les decouvertes qui se sont bientôt succédées avec rapidité.' Yet:[7] 'Peu de livres offroient plus de génie & un ensemble mieux ordonné que celui de Meyer', who contrived to cover the truth 'd'une espèce de voile, & c'est ce qu'il a fait avec tout l'addresse & tout le talent imaginable.'

Lavoisier's opinions of Black and Meyer are considered later (p. 389). Thomson[8] thought Meyer himself recognised the truth and importance of Black's theory, 'though he did not at first, on that account, give up his own theory.'

Black's and Meyer's theories were taken up and one or other defended by a number of chemists.[9]

JACQUIN

Nicolaas Jozeph Edler von Jacquin (Leyden, 16 February 1727–Vienna, 24 October 1817) was descended from a French family which emigrated to Holland. He travelled in America (1755–9), became professor of chemistry, mining, and metallurgy in Schemnitz, then until 1797 professor of chemistry and botany in Vienna, being made a baron in 1806.[10] He was the author of a good text-book.[11] He defended Black's theory:

Examen chemicum Doctrinæ Meyerianæ de Acido Pingui, et Blackianæ de aere fixo, respectu calcis, 8°, Vienna, 1769 (96 pp. BM B. 672. (3.)); German tr.: Chymische Untersuchung der Meyerischen Lehre von der Fetten Säure und der Blackischen Meynung von der Fixen Luft, 12°, Vienna, 1790 (Sotheran *Cat.* 800 (1926), no. 11154); *Obs. Phys.*, 1774, i, 123; an ed. of 1771 is mentioned by Poggendorff, (1), i, 1185, and Fischer; summary in Fourcroy, (2), iii, 373 (who says it was translated into French and English).

Jacquin gives the arguments for and against each theory, but supports Black's; he seems to have regarded fixed air as little different from atmospheric

---

[1] *Obs. Phys.*, 1774, iii, 418. [2] (2), iii, 373. [3] Kopp, (1), iii, 35.
[4] (3), 1790, i, 350. [5] *Ib.*, 473. [6] (2), iii, 367.
[7] *Ib.*, 371–3. [8] *Ency. Brit. Suppl.*, 1801, I, i, 301.
[9] Summary in J. C. Fischer, 1804, v, 191–220; Fourcroy, (2), iii, 373 f.; Gren, 1794, i, § 437, 288 f.; Hoefer, (1), 1869, ii, 354; Kopp, (1), iii, 34 f.; Lavoisier, (1), 1801, 60–88.
[10] Lindau, NBG, 1858, xxvi, 273.
[11] *Anfangsgründe der medicinisch-practischen Chymie; zum Gebrauch seiner Vorlesungen*, 8°, Vienna, 1783, 2 ed. 1785 (BM 45. e. 9); Ferguson, i, 431.

air; the first is fixed in limestone with loss of elasticity, the second is condensed in its pores and is removed by an air-pump. The loss of nearly half its weight when limestone is converted into quicklime made Jacquin suspect Meyer's theory. He heated limestone in an earthenware retort with a tubulated receiver. It gave a little water, then six or seven times its volume of an elastic fluid, and lost $\frac{13}{32}$ of its weight. If the heating is discontinued before the air is evolved, but the water is expelled, quicklime is not formed, and if only part of the air is expelled, only the surface becomes quicklime. Lime is not converted into limestone by water, and may be kept under water not exposed to air. The crust forming on lime water is chalk and on heating behaves exactly like limestone. The air evolved on heating limestone is the same as that formed by the action of acids on it, or on alkalis, all precipitating lime water. Jacquin repeated Black's and Macbride's experiments and confirmed their results, which he made widely known in Germany.

Joseph Franz Edler von Jacquin (Schemnitz, 7 February 1766–Vienna, 4 December 1839), son of the above and nephew of Ingen Housz, professor of chemistry and botany in Vienna, was the author of a text-book[1] with a folding plate showing a Woulfe's bottle, and a description of it.

WIEGLEB

Meyer's theory of the *acidum pingue* found a warm supporter in Wiegleb (see p. 567):

(a) Kleine chymische Abhandlungen von dem grossen Nutzen der Erkentniss des Acidi pinguis bey der Erklärung vieler chymischen Erscheinungen. . . . Nebst einer Vorrede worinnen Herrn Meyers Leben erzählt und von dessen Verdiensten gehandelt wird von E. G. Baldinger, sm. 8°, Langensalza, 1767 (112 pp., BM 1032. a. 30); 2 ed., 1771 (182 pp.; Duveen, 619); (b) Fortgesetzte kleine Abhandlungen, Langensalza, 1770; (c) Vertheydigung der Meyerischen Lehre vom Acido Pingui, gegen verschiedene darwider gemachte Einwürfe, 8°, Altenburg, 1770 (115 pp., i l., BM 1034. i. 6; Duveen, 619).

Wiegleb relied on the supposed fact that chalk cannot be converted into lime by the heat of a burning glass.[2] Johan Jacob Well[3] and W. H. S. Bucholz[4] showed that caustic lime can be so produced. Wiegleb[5] then modified his view, and assumed that chalk on burning loses fixed air but also takes up the matter of fire (equivalent to acidum pingue). Well was criticised by C. E.

---

[1] *Lehrbuch der allgemeinen und medicinischen Chemie zum Gebrauch seiner Vorlesungen*, 2 vols. 8°, Vienna, 1793 (BM 1034. k. 17); 4 ed., 1810; tr. by H. Stutzer, *Elements of Chemistry*, London, 1799, 3 ed., 1803 (vi ll., 415 pp.; Gurney *Cat.* 26 (1960), no. 352; Sotheran *Cat.* 800 (1926), no. 11155); portrs. of the two Jacquins in *Allgemeines Journal der Chemie*, (Scherer), 1802, ix.

[2] (c); Kopp, (1), iii, 38–9.

[3] *Rechtfertigung der blackschen Lehre von der figirten Luft gegen die vom Herrn Wiegleb Apotheker in Langensalza darwider gemachten Einwürfe*, 8°, Vienna, 1771 (viii ll., 164 pp., Duveen, 616); *Supplementum in I. I. de Well defensionem doctrinæ Blackianæ et Epicrisin super calcis incalescentia . . .*, ed. I. J. Langmajer, 8°, Vienna, 1778 (BM 958. b. 17).

[4] *Chymische Versuche über das Meyersche Acidum pingue*, Weimar, 1771.

[5] Tr. from Latin of R. A. Vogel, *Lehrsätze der Chemie*, 8°, Weimar, 1775, § 137 (BM 1035. l. 5).

Weigel[1] but replied,[2] and Weigel dealt his reply in 1772.[3] Michael Friedrich Boehm, a pupil of Spielmann, rejected[4] both Black's and Meyer's theories and said limestone became caustic by loss of water; causticity was capacity for combining with water. C. F. Wenzel[5] accepted Black's theory but (since he did not distinguish between fixed air and oxygen) could not understand why metallic calces displace ammonia from sal ammoniac like quicklime but do not effervesce with acids. Limestone loses weight on solution in acids, metallic calces do not, and this will never be explained.

CRANZ

Heinrich Johann Nepomuk von Cranz, according to Lavoisier[6] and Fourcroy,[7] 'physician to the King of Prussia', but correctly according to Kopp[8] a medical professor in Vienna, published an attack on Black's theory which included personal abuse of Jacquin.[9] He said that limestone loses only water on calcination, and quicklime effervesces with acids and can absorb from the atmosphere all it had lost on calcination. Black did not explain the heat evolved on slaking quicklime, the swelling, and the acrid vapour evolved. An explanation of this had been given but not published by Black,[10] viz. that owing to chemical attraction the water becomes solid and its latent heat is set free. Nor, said Cranz, does Black's theory explain the great heat evolved when quicklime dissolves in nitric acid, whilst limestone dissolves without heat, but Meyer's theory explains this by the presence of *acidum pingue* in the quicklime. The film on lime water can form under the surface and on the walls of the vessel and hence cannot come from fixed air absorbed from the atmosphere, but (as Meyer had said) is lime which has lost acidum pingue. The whole of a piece of quicklime is not convertible into milk of lime or soluble in water (Black had proved the contrary).

Lime water dissolves sulphur, camphor, and resins like spirit of wine, yet the latter is not said to remove fixed air from these substances. Effervescence of limestone or lime in acids is only slight when they are weak, whilst there is strong effervescence of strong caustic lyes with acids. If loss of fixed air is the cause of causticity, why are the neutral salts formed with effervescence by the action of acids not caustic? Limestone is precipitated from its solution in nitric acid by a caustic alkali as well as a mild alkali, the precipitate effervescing with acids in the first case, although it is somewhat soluble in water and is alkaline. If the caustic alkali solution is poured in carefully, it collects at the bottom of

[1] *Observationes chemicæ et mineralogicæ*, 2 pts. 4°, Göttingen and Greifswald, 1771–3 (BM 457. c. 32); tr. J. T. Pyl, *Chemisch-mineralogische Beobachtungen*, 2 pts. 8°, 1779 (BM 970. i. 5).
[2] *Forschung in die Ursache der Erhitzung des ungelöschten Kalckes, nebst einigen freimüthigen Gedanken über dessen Erhitzung bewirken sollende Feuermaterie*, Vienna, 1772.
[3] *Observationes*, etc., 1772, ii.   [4] *Examen Acidi Pinguis*, Dissert., 4°, Strasbourg, 1769.
[5] *Lehre von der Verwandtschaft der Körper*, 1777; 1782, 253–90.
[6] *Opuscules Physiques et Chimiques*, 1801, 73–87.   [7] (2), iii, 38, 374.   [8] (1), iii, 38.
[9] *Examinis Chemici Doctrinæ Meyerianæ de Acido Pingui et Blackianæ de Aere Fixo respectu calcis rectificatio*, 8°, Leipzig, 1770 (212 pp.; BM 1034. i. 1); summary in *Obs. Phys.*, 1773, ii, 123; Fischer, v, 195–204; Cranz also published a medical work, *Solutiones difficultatum circa Cordis Irritabilitatem*, 8°, Vienna, 1761 (76 pp.; vignette portr. of author).
[10] *Lectures*, 1803, ii, 73.

the solution of the lime salt, but on shaking there is effervescence and limestone is precipitated. Quicklime dissolved in nitric acid is precipitated with effervescence by caustic alkali. Precipitation of lime water by the air evolved in effervescences is not due to combination with air but because it renders the water lighter. Why does the same principle dissolve iron but render quicklime insoluble?

Cranz found very variable decreases in weight when both limestone and quicklime were dissolved in nitric acid, and the loss with quicklime was sometimes greater. (Lavoisier says Cranz used too small weights and too shallow vessels.) When ammonia is set free from mild volatile alkali by lime, the residue is still lime and not chalk. If causticity is due to loss of air, then animals should be cauterised under an air-pump receiver.

Experiments with Macbride's apparatus (see p. 144), although apparently supporting Black's views, were explained in terms of the evaporation of *acidum pingue*. It is true that the bottle containing the effervescing material loses weight, and the bottle containing the caustic alkali gains weight, which it does by absorbing air, but this is not the reason why the caustic alkali becomes mild; it is not a real combination but only a solution as in water of ordinary air, and the separation of *acidum pingue* is the true cause. Some results of Cranz were simply false and his experiments badly done; even when he got correct results, as with Macbride's apparatus, he was so obsessed by his preconceived theory that he would not give the true explanations. His attack on Black is one of the most stupid and incorrect of all, yet Lavoisier, who calls him 'Crans', after 7 pages on Black devotes 15 pages to him.

SMETH

Diderik van Smeth[1] argued that common air is known only by its physical properties and its true nature is unknown. To say that a substance is air because it has properties apparently in common with air is unphilosophical; it is an error to say that an elastic fluid is disengaged by effervescence or fermentation if only its subtilty, elasticity, and weight are considered, since one should on the same grounds call the electric fluid, a crowd of incoercible vapours, and even water, an air. Air is a solvent, dissolving water and different vapours as water dissolves salts, and many bodies augment in weight in air; 272 grains of Homberg's pyrophorus exposed to air on a sensitive balance gained 20 grains in half an hour, 21 grains next day, and 15 grains during the next seven days, a total of about a fifth of its weight. This pyrophorus inflamed; another, which did not, gained three-tenths of its weight in three days. Quicklime increased in weight during the first month of exposure to air and after three months its weight had increased by a quarter, and it had fallen to a fine powder. It liberated solid volatile alkali from sal ammoniac. On exposure to intense fire it

---

[1] Didericus de Smeth, *Dissertatio Philosophica Inauguralis de Aëre Fixo*, 4°, Utrecht, 1772 (103 pp.) (BN Rz 943; Sotheran *Cat.* 800 (1926), no. 12005); summary in Lavoisier, (1), 1801, 88; Fourcroy, (2), iii, 376; Fischer, 1804, v, 204–18.

did not lose all the weight gained (as Duhamel had also found in 1747) and did not give all the fixed air to be expected from Black's experiments.

Smeth concluded from these quantitative experiments that the increase in weight of quicklime on exposure to air is due mostly to absorption of moisture and air plays only a very minor part; the increase in weight of Homberg's pyrophorus (see p. 43) on exposure to air, he thought, is also due to absorption of moisture. Lavoisier,[1] who reported this work, afterwards[2] proved that the increase in weight of the pyrophorus is due to absorption of part of the air. Smeth completely confused fixed air and common air, e.g. when he noticed that more 'air' is evolved from caustic lye than from mild alkali solution under the receiver of an air pump, and that caustic lye does not become mild when exposed to compressed air.

Smeth repeated Macbride's experiment in the form as modified by De-machy, attaching to the beak of a retort a phial containing caustic volatile alkali (ammonia) which crystallised. The vapour of the volatile alkali formed a cloud where it met the fixed air, and the crystals when exposed to air lost nearly all their penetrating smell. The gas from putrefying flesh had the same action on alkalis as that disengaged in effervescence. Smeth distinguished between the elastic emanations in effervescence and fermentation, and common air, speaking of *gas vinificationis, gas acetificationis, gas septicum, gas salinum seu effervescentiarum*, and *gas aquæ et terræ seu subterraneum*, but not clearly distinguishing them except by odour, effect on life, etc.

After showing that atmospheric air does not render caustic alkalis mild and effervescent, Smeth said it remained to prove that it was different from the fluid causing effervescence, a point recognised by Black and Macbride but not sufficiently specified, since their name 'fixed air' might mean common air. Smeth pointed out that: (i) common air does not render caustic alkalis mild and effervescent, whilst the gas from effervescences and fermentations does, (ii) common air supports and is necessary for combustion, whilst the emanation extinguishes flame, (iii) common air is necessary for the life of animals, whilst the emanation is a poison, as is seen by the accidents in fermentation vats, (iv) atmospheric air promotes putrefaction whilst the gas from effervescences and fermentations retards it, (v) the emanation varies considerably in elasticity, like water vapour, which is sometimes extremely dilated and sometimes almost liquid (under (v), Smeth seems to understand the fixation of the gas in solids), and (vi) the emanation of effervescences is more subtle and tenuous than common air, passing into bodies into which common air cannot penetrate (it is, actually, denser than common air, as Black and Cavendish had shown).

Smeth objected (with reason) to the name 'fixed air', since it has no true relation to common air. It is the *æstus* of the ancients, Van Helmont's gas sylvestre, and Boyle's factitious air, which occurs in the Grotto del Cane and other caves. It varies with the body from which it is disengaged and does not exist ready formed in bodies; it is a miasma composed of the detritus from the collision of the particles of solids and liquids, being formed only by the violent

[1] (1), 1801, 88 f.   [2] AdS, 1777 (1780), m 363.

intestine motion of the particles, as in effervescences, fermentations, and combustions, which break and tear up the particles of the bodies. Smeth did not examine the various gases carefully and he did not realise that four of the gases he names are the same (carbon dioxide), the septic gas he does not describe adequately.

Smeth disagreed with Hales's opinion that the solidity of bodies is due to fixed air. To be antiseptic it is not necessary that it shall exist in the bodies from which it is disengaged nor that it shall contribute to the cohesion and salubrity of flesh. Antiseptic properties belong to a crowd of other bodies, particularly the products of vinous fermentation, and it could equally well be said that spirit of wine is a cement of bodies. Smeth also disbelieved Macbride's theory of astringents as bodies closing the pores and blocking the disengagement of fixed air; we are too far from knowing the true mode of action of astringents to allow us to accept such a theory so lightly.

At the end of his work Smeth mentions the air in the wells of Utrecht, covered with a vault and 8–20 ft. deep, in which a suffocating air collects which must be allowed to escape by leaving them open for twelve hours before going down. This air resembles the fixed air disengaged in fermentation and effervescence in extinguishing candles, rendering lime water milky, and changing quicklime into chalk. The water of these wells is salubrious. He also passed air over glowing charcoal, collected it in a vacuous receiver, and showed that it produced a fume with ammonia. In the year in which Smeth's theories appeared, Priestley was reading his first paper on airs to the Royal Society. Cavendish had firmly established the nature of fixed air some years before Smeth wrote, proving that distinct gases exist, and from that time the views of Black could hardly be traversed with plausibility. Nevertheless, they were.

DEMACHY

Demachy[1] described many experiments, all of which (except a few which gave uncertain or even erroneous results) support Black's theory. This did not restrain him from drawing conclusions unfavourable to Black's, and giving quite incorrect explanations of them. Macbride's results were said to be due to acid vapours carried over with the air in the apparatus. The precipitation of lime water by solutions of mild alkalis, although it had been correctly explained by Black and Macbride, did not seem to Demachy to be an effect of fixed air. In one experiment he shook caustic ammonia solution in a flask which had been filled with the vapours from oil of tartar and spirit of vitriol (carbon dioxide), and found that the ammonia acquired the property of effervescing with acids and precipitating lime water (as, of course, it should on Black's theory), but he explained this as due to the vapour of spirit of vitriol carried over by the air. The absorption of air in the combustion of sulphur, he thought, was due to the formation of water from air, and the gases evolved on distillation were supposed to come from water which they contained (as he tried to

[1] *Obs. Phys.*, 1774 (1785), iii, 408–12.

prove by experiments with an aeolipile). The French chemists of this period were evidently behind even Hales.

Guyton de Morveau at first asserted that Black's separation of magnesia from Epsom salt was incorrect, since these salts are 'entièrement Seidlitiens'.[1] He had probably been using Glauber's salt supplied by a French pharmacist as Epsom salt. But in 1777[2] he believed that fixed air 'en forment réellement un nouvel être'. Krenger in a paper on spathic iron ore[3] opposed Meyer's theory. J. B. M. Bucquet[4] described many experiments which he thought unfavourable to Black's views, saying: un grand nombre de faits que le Docteur Black a avancés sur l'air fixé, ne sont rein moins que prouvés. He found correctly that dry fixed air is not absorbed by quicklime and concluded that: il ne suffit pas de rendre à la chaux de l'air fixé pour la convertir en craie, qu'il faut un intermède pour que cette union se fasse, & que cet intermède est l'eau.[5]

Duc de Chaulnes

In a long memoir[6] the Duc de Chaulnes showed that the gas evolved in the fermentation of beer is fixed air. He showed that it has an acid reaction and forms a crystalline salt (potassium bicarbonate) with vegetable alkali (potassium carbonate). He found that a glass globe of $737\frac{1}{2}$ cu. in. capacity, weighing vacuous 7 lb. 1 oz. 7 gros, weighed 3 gros 66 grains more when filled with air and 3 gros 42 grains more (i.e. 7 gros 36 grains in total) when filled with fixed air, which therefore has nearly twice the density of air (correct, $1\frac{1}{2}$).

Weber

Jacob Andreas Weber[7] described many experiments with quicklime and alkalis, concluding that Black's and Meyer's theories are both false. The sun is a great electrified sphere, its electric matter sets the earth's atmosphere in motion, this gives heat to other bodies. Boyle's experiments showed that heat is a ponderable body, quicklime heats with water, and causticity is caused by electric matter in the form of phlogiston being removed from mild alkali by lime, etc.[8]

A curiosity in the literature is the section 'Remarques sur l'Acidum Pingue' in a book[9] of 'Phylantropos, Citoyen du Monde', which contains a recipe for the ambrosia served at the table of the gods 'translated' from an Anglo-Saxon manuscript in the

[1] *Encyclopédie*, ed. Diderot, Paris, 1765, ix, 858.
[2] *Suppl.* to *Encyclopédie*, 1777, ii, 275.
[3] *Obs. Phys.*, 1775, vi, 225; Crell's *Ann.*, 1784, II, 161; Parmentier, in his tr. of Model, *Récréations Physiques*, 1774, ii, 250, said Krenger was 'un François déguisé en étranger'.
[4] AdS, *Mém. div. Sav.*, 1780, ix, 563; presented 1 August 1773.   [5] *Ib.*, 568.
[6] Memoire et Expériences Sur l'Air Fixe qui se dégage de la Bière en fermentation, AdS, *Mém. div. Sav.*, 1780, ix, 521–50, 551–62; *Obs. Phys.*, 1777, ix, 287–91; Fourcroy, (2), iii, 479–81; the experiments were made in Sept. 1771, the memoir was read on 3 Dec. 1775.
[7] *Neuentdeckte Natur und Eigenschaften des Kalkes und der äzenden Körper, nebst einer öconomisch-chemischen Untersuchung des Kochsalzes und dessen Mutterlauge*, 8°, Berlin, 1778.
[8] See *ib.*, 150–4.
[9] *Le Diadème des Sages, ou Démonstration de la Nature Inférieure*, 12°, Paris, 1781; tr. *Der Schmuck der Weisen, oder gründlicher Darstellung der physischen Unterwelt*, 8°, Vienna, 1782.

library of an Anglo-Saxon prince! The author is said to be O. de Loos, an alchemist (Sedan, 1725–Paris, 1785).[1] He declared that Meyer's theory is false.

Black's Researches on Heat[2]

There is a legend that Black's work was instrumental in leading James Watt to his invention of the steam engine with the condenser. Although Robison[3] says Watt heard two courses of Black's lectures and thus became acquainted with the theory of latent heat, which was of assistance to him in the invention of the condensing steam engine, Watt himself, while expressing gratitude to Black, said that he never attended his lectures.[4] It was said that Watt was befriended by Professor Dick in Glasgow, but Dick had been dead for many years before Watt's attention was directed to steam carriages by Robison and to the Newcomen engine by Professor Anderson. For about 16 years (1757–73) Watt had his workshop in Glasgow College while Anderson (whose brother was a schoolfellow of Watt) was Professor of Natural Philosophy, and for nine of these years Black was Professor of Medicine and Lecturer on Chemistry. James Muir,[5] in reporting this, adds 'there is no evidence that Watt sought or received any direct help from Anderson or from anyone else when making his inventions'.

Jean Jacques Dortous de Mairan (Béziers, 26 November 1678–Paris, 20 February 1771)[6] had emphasised the slowness with which ice melts, and showed that ice melts faster in contact with salts in freezing mixtures.[7] Black says he began in 1756 to meditate on the slowness with which ice melts, that he divined the cause in 1757, and that he explained it in his lectures in 1757–8 or 1758–9. He made some decisive experiments on latent heat of fusion in December 1761, being assisted in the work by his pupil William Irvine, and gave an account of the work in his lectures from 1761, and to the literary society in Glasgow on 23 April 1762.

Thomson[8] says Black had some vague notion that the heat so received by the ice during its conversion into water was not lost, but was contained in the water. This opinion was founded on a curious observation of Fahrenheit, recorded by Boerhaave,[9] that water might in some cases be made considerably colder than melting snow, without freezing. In such cases, when disturbed it would freeze in a moment, and in the act of freezing always gave out a quantity of heat.

[1] Poggendorff, (1), i, 1496; Thiebaud, Paris, Cat. 64 (1938), no. 925; Duveen, 366.
[2] Landriani, Dissertation de la chaleur latent, in Obs. Phys., 1785, xxvi, 88–100, 197–207 (histor.); Black, Lectures, 1803, I, xxxviii, 116, 125, 137, 157; Black, letter to Watt, in Muirhead, Correspondence of James Watt, 1846, xxiii; Robison, in Black, Lectures, I, xlii, xlv, 503; Thomson, (2), 1817, i, 107; Harcourt, B.A. Rep., 1839, 46; Lord Brougham, Works, 1872, i 12; Clerke, DNB, 1908, ii, 572; Knott, in Edinburgh's Place in Scientific Progress (Brit. Assoc.), 1921, 9; McKie and Heathcote, The Discovery of Specific and Latent Heats, 1935, 11, 31.
[3] Black, Lectures, I, Pref., and xliii.
[4] J. Robison, A System of Natural Philosophy. With Notes by D. Brewster, Edinburgh, 1822, pp. ii–x, 113–21 (account of his invention of the engine); D. Fleming, Isis, 1952, xliii, 3.
[5] John Anderson. An Address to the Andersonian Chemical Society, Glasgow, 1930, 20.
[6] Dissertation sur la Glace, 12°, Bordeaux, 1716, Béziers, 1717, Paris, 1729, 1749 (all in BN); J. C. Fischer, iii, 297, gives Paris 1737; the 1749 ed. is corrected and enlarged to nearly double the original size; engr. fp., pp. xxix, (x), 384, xx, 5 plates.
[7] Ib., 1749, 323, 353–67.   [8] (1), i, 320–4.   [9] (2), 1732, i, 162.

According to Thomson, Black was so convinced of the truth of the latent heat of steam, by analogy with the latent heat of fusion, that 'he taught the doctrine in his lectures in 1761, before he had made a single experiment on the subject'. Black[1] says he made three experiments on 4 October 1762, finding 810, 830, and 750° F. per lb. for the latent heat of steam. In experiments on 9 October 1764, with the assistance of Irvine, he found 739 and 750, and a few weeks later James Watt, 'with a smaller still, better fitted for trials of this question' obtained a more accurate result of 825, and still later fixed it between 900 and 950. (The correct figure is 970.) These results were required by Watt in his invention of the improved condensing steam engine in 1765.

Black[2] says: 'as the ostensible effect of the heat . . . consists, not in warming the surrounding bodies, but in rendering the ice fluid; so, in the case of boiling, the heat absorbed does not warm surrounding bodies, but converts the water into vapour. In both cases, considered as the cause of warmth, we do not perceive its presence: it is concealed, or latent, and I gave it the name of *latent heat*.' Again:[3] 'I suppose a cause . . . namely, that it is a special combination of the substance of bodies with the material cause of heat, which, while it continues in this state of combination, I call *latent heat*'; and[4] 'I consider fluidity as depending, immediately and inseparably, on a certain quantity of the matter of heat, which is combined with the fluid body, in a particular manner, so as not to be communicable to a thermometer, or to other bodies, but capable of being extricated again by other methods, and of re-assuming the form of moveable or communicable heat'. In evaporation:[5] 'a particle of water, in the instant of its becoming a particle of vapour, attracts and unites with itself one or more atoms of this cause of heat . . . and retains them as parts or ingredients of its vaporous form . . . when a particle of vapour again becomes water, these atoms of heat are set at liberty by the fixed laws of chemical affinity', for example, when the vapour is condensed to liquid by contact with a cold metal, as in the cooling-worm of a still, when the particles of heat 'unite with the cold substance of the pipe'.

Black[6] correctly says that Lavoisier's theory that gases contain heat in combination 'is founded on the doctrine of latent heat, and is, indeed, an extension of it'. Lavoisier's theory of combustion in oxygen is that: 'the burning body collects, and condenses this sort of air, depriving it at once of its vaporous and elastic aerial form; or, if it does not absolutely condense it to a solid matter, it diminishes, to a great degree, its capacity for heat.'

William Irvine (Glasgow; 1743–9 July 1787) was lecturer on materia medica and chemistry in the University of Glasgow.[7] His papers were edited by his son and published in 1805.[8] He did not accept Black's doctrine of latent heat but supposed that the heat absorbed in melting was due to the greater capacity

[1] *Lectures*, 1803, i, 157, 171.   [2] *Lectures*, 1803, i, 157.
[3] *Ib.*, i, 141.   [4] *Ib.*, i, 144.
[5] *Ib.*, i, 165.
[6] *Ib.*, i, 239–40.
[7] Kent, *An Eighteenth Century Lectureship in Chemistry*, Glasgow, 1950, 140.
[8] *Essays, Chiefly on Chemical Subjects*, London, 1805.

for heat of water as compared with ice.[1] These alternative theories were subjects of discussion for some time.

Black's discovery of specific heat arose as follows. Boerhaave[2] said that in an experiment made for him by Fahrenheit on mixing mercury and water at different temperatures, the mercury produced the same heating or cooling effect as a quantity of water two-thirds the volume of the mercury. Boerhaave concluded that the heat is distributed between different bodies in proportion to the space occupied by each, and the final temperature is half the difference of heat in each (nascetur temporatio respondens dimidiatae differentiae caloris in utroque, ut prius in aqua, si aequales permiscerentur portiones). Black[3] quotes Boerhaave as saying expressly that:

'the quicksilver, whether it was applied hot to cold water, or cold to hot water, never produced more effect in heating or cooling an equal measure of the water than would have been produced by water equally hot or cold with the quicksilver, and only two-thirds of its bulk . . . The inference which Dr. Boerhaave drew from this experiment is very surprising. Observing that heat is not distributed among different bodies in proportion to the quantity of matter in each, he concludes that it is distributed in proportion to the space occupied by each body; a conclusion contradicted by this very experiment.

. . . 'very soon after I began to think on this subject, (anno 1760) I perceived that . . . the quantities of heat which different kinds of matter must receive . . . to raise their temperature by an equal number of degrees, are not [only] in proportion to the quantity of matter in each, but in proportions widely different from this. Quicksilver has less *capacity* for the matter of heat than water (if I may be allowed to use this expression) has; it requires a smaller quantity of it to raise its temperature by the same number of degrees.'

Robison[4] infers that Black used what is called the 'method of mixtures' in determining specific heats. Hopson[5] says that Fahrenheit complained to Gaubius (who took over Boerhaave's lectures on chemistry) that Boerhaave had not understood the meaning of his experiment. Thomson[6] says Black satisfied himself, by mixing known amounts of hot and cold water and finding the temperature of the mixture, that the mercury thermometer is an accurate measure of temperature, and he read this work to the Literary Society of Glasgow on 28 March 1760, not knowing then that he had been anticipated by Brook Taylor,[7] who used a linseed oil thermometer and found that the rise from the mark in cold water was 'accurately proportional to the quantity of hot water in the mixture, that is, to the degree of heat'.

Black published no account of his experiments on latent and specific heats, but they are referred to in the anonymous work of 1770, based on his lectures,[8] and this establishes Black's priority on specific heats over Wilcke (1781),[9] who

[1] Crawford, *Experiments and Observations on Animal Heat*, 1788, 84, 92; Irvine, *Essays*, 115, 128; Black, *Lectures*, 1803, i, 505; Partington, *Advanced Treatise on Physical Chemistry*, 1952, iii, 467.

[2] (2), 1732, i, 269–70.   [3] *Lectures*, i, 79–81.

[4] *Ib.*, i, 506.   [5] *An Essay on Fire*, London, 1781, 21.

[6] (1), i, 323.   [7] *Phil. Trans.*, 1723, xxxii, 291.

[8] *An Enquiry into the General Effects of Heat; with Observations on the Effect of Heat and Mixture*, 1770, 22, 39, 48.

[9] Om Eldens specifica myckenhet uti fastra kroppar, och des afmätanda: KAH, 1781, ii, 49–78; *Obs. Phys.*, 1785, xxvi, 256–68, 381–8 (Sur la chaleur spécifique des Corps); for Gadolin see p. 234.

used the name 'specific heat (specific-varme)'; the name specific heat (chaleur spécifique) seems to have been used first by J. H. de Magellan,[1] who also gave a table of 43 specific heats determined by Kirwan,[2] the first published table of specific heats. William Cleghorn (Granton, Midlothian, 30 October 1754– Dublin, 20 April 1783),[3] a pupil of Cullen and Black, considered that there is a repulsive force in the particles of fire, making them recede from one another, and a variable attractive force between the particles of fire and material bodies.[4] Black says this theory is 'the most probable I know', but 'altogether a supposition'.[5]

CRAWFORD

Adair Crawford (Ireland?, 1748–9–Lymington, 29 July 1795), F.R.S. 1786, was a physician in St. Thomas's Hospital, London, then professor of chemistry at Woolwich Arsenal, where he was assisted by Cruickshank in the discovery of strontium (see p. 656). Crawford visited Scotland in 1776 and became acquainted with Black's and Irvine's researches on heat. He began researches on animal heat and combustion in Glasgow in 1777 and communicated them in the autumn of that year to Dr. Reid, Mr. Wilson, and Dr. Irvine. In the session 1777–8 they were made known to many of the professors and students in Edinburgh and in the winter they were explained by Crawford to the Royal Medical Society in Edinburgh.[6] They were published in 1779.[7]

Crawford called the quantity of heat in a body the *absolute heat*; the *relative heat* is the same 'power' considered as having a relation to the effects by which it is known and measured. Bodies of equal weight and temperature contain unequal quantities of absolute heat, and this is called *comparative heat* (Wilcke's *specific heat*). The capacities of bodies for receiving heat are proportional to the quantities of absolute heat they contain, the masses and temperatures being the same; if T is the temperature, c the capacity, and A the absolute heat, then $A = T \times c$. Absolute heat is the same as the element of fire.[8] He denied that bodies contain *chemically* combined heat[9] and adopted Irvine's theory.[10] In the first edition of his book Crawford uses the phlogiston theory but in the second edition he adapts his theories to the new antiphlogistic theory of oxygen.

Crawford was the first to determine specific heats of gases, in 1779 using bladders as containers and in 1788 two thin sheet brass cylinders, one vacuous and the other filled with the gas, which were heated in boiling water and then immersed in two identical water calorimeters.[11] The specific heats at constant volume found in this way were much too high; but his determination of the

---

[1] *Essai sur la Nouvelle Théorie du Feu Élémentaire, et de la Chaleur des Corps*, London, 1780, 167.
[2] *Ib.*, 177 (see p. 662).   [3] McKie and Heathcote, *Ann. Sci.*, 1958 (1960), xiv, 1.
[4] *Disputatio Physica inauguralis, Theoriam Ignis complectens*, Edinburgh, 1779, 16.
[5] *Lectures*, 1803, i, 33–4.   [6] Hunt, DNB, 1888, xiii, 49.
[7] *Experiments and Observations on Animal Heat, and the Inflammation of Combustible Bodies. Being an Attempt to Resolve these Phænomena into a General Law of Nature*, 8°, London, 1779 (120 pp.); 2 ed. 'with very large additions', 1788 (viii ll., 491 pp., 4 plates); dedicated to Kirwan; Partington and McKie, *Ann. Sci.*, 1938, iii, 347.
[8] *Animal Heat*, 1788, 1–17.   [9] *Ib.*, 57.
[10] *Ib.*, 88.   [11] *Ib.*, 1779, 34 f.; 1778, 157 f., 177.

heat of combustion of hydrogen, by exploding a mixture of hydrogen and oxygen in a metal calorimeter,[1] is very good, and more accurate than the result of Lavoisier and Laplace (see p. 433).

Crawford concluded that the specific heat ('capacity for containing heat') of dephlogisticated air (oxygen) is 4·6 times that of common air.[2] He also concluded[3] that 'the capacities of bodies for containing heat are diminished by the addition of phlogiston, and increased by the separation of this principle'. The ratios of the specific heats of the calces (oxides) of metals to those of the metals were found to be (calx : metal) tin, 14·7 : 10·4, iron 8 : 3·1, lead 19·9 : 14·7, antimony 11·6 : 4·5.

The capacities of arterial to venous blood were[4] in the ratio 11½ : 10 and 'the blood in its progress thro' the system gives out the heat which it had received from the air in the lungs'.[5] In respiration the absolute heat in the pure air (oxygen) is also decreased.[6] In combustion 'no part of the heat can be derived from the combustible body . . . [but] depends upon the separation of absolute heat from the air by the action of phlogiston'.[7]

Crawford's experiments and conclusions were criticised by William Morgan.[8] He criticised Crawford's calculation of the cooling correction in the calorimetric experiments by the 'rule of fourth proportional', finding different values for the specific heat of mercury when different masses of mercury and water were used. In experiments with bladders or thin glass flasks, 'though I have repeated those Experiments in all the variety of methods I could think of, I have never yet been able to distinguish the least difference between any kinds of air' (common air, carbon dioxide, hydrogen, nitrogen, and oxygen) and 'all the airs contain the same quantity of absolute heat'.[9] He criticised Crawford's theories of animal heat[10] and combustion,[11] and concluded[12] that they were 'rather more brilliant than solid'.

Crawford's theory of combustion was also disproved by measurements of specific heats of gases by Delaroche and Bérard,[13] who found that the specific heat of oxygen (0·9765) is lower than that of carbonic acid gas (1·2583) for equal volumes, and hence on Crawford's theory cold should be produced by the combustion of charcoal.

DE LA RIVE

Charles Gaspard De la Rive (Geneva; 14 March 1770–18 March 1834) studied medicine in Edinburgh and became president of the Royal Society of Edinburgh. His inaugural dissertation for the M.D. was on animal heat.[14] He returned to Geneva in 1799, and took an active part in the production of the journal *Bibliothèque Britannique*, later called *Bibliothèque Universelle*. He

---

[1] *Ib.*, 1788, 254.   [2] 1779, 53.   [3] 1779, 58–68; 1788, 279, 304.
[4] 1779, 54, 69; 1788, 273.   [5] 1779, 75.   [6] 1788, 144.   [7] 1779, 77–8.
[8] *An Examination of Dr. Crawford's Theory of Heat and Combustion*, London, 1781, 77 pp., 1 plate, i l. errata (BM 8755. b. 34).
[9] *Ib.*, 31, 34, 37.   [10] *Ib.*, 44.   [11] *Ib.*, 51.   [12] *Ib.*, 55.
[13] *Ann. Chim.*, 1813, xxxv, 72; *Ann. Phil.*, 1813, ii, 134, 211, 369, 426; Regnault, AdS, 1862, xxvi, 3.
[14] *Tentamen Physiologicum Inaugurale, De Calore Animale*, Edinburgh, 1797 (iv ll., 60 pp.; Duveen, 165).

published on the sound produced by a jet of hydrogen burning in a tube (see
B. Higgins, p. 730),[1] on Dalton's atomic theory,[2] and on animal heat,[3] in which
he developed Crawford's theory. His son Auguste Arthur De la Rive (Geneva,
9 October 1801–Marseilles, 27 November 1873) was the distinguished elec-
trician and friend of Faraday (see Vol. IV).

[1] *J. de Phys.*, 1806, lv, 165; *Bibl. Univ.*, 1818, ix, 111.
[2] *Bibl. Brit.*, 1811, xlvi, 38–56.
[3] *Bibl. Univ.*, 1820, xv, 37; *Ann. Chim.*, 1820, xv, 103.

CHAPTER V

CHEMISTRY IN SCANDINAVIA. I.
BORRICHIUS TO BERGMAN

The present chapter deals with the countries Denmark, Sweden, and Finland, and also with Lomonosov in Russia. In all these countries during the eighteenth century there was considerable activity in science, and academies were founded.

The Uppsala Academy issued publications from 1720:

Acta Literaria Sveciæ Upsaliæ publicata, Volumen primum Continens Annos 1720. 1721. 1722. 1723. & 1724, Uppsala and Stockholm, n.d., pp. 608; then with new pagination, 1725 (pp. 1–114), 1726 (115–232), 1727 (233–360), 1728 (361–486), 1729 (487–614): published by a Society of Savants.

Acta Regiæ Societatis Scientiarum Upsaliensis, 1740 f.; *Nova Acta*, 1773 f.; French tr. of parts: *Recueil des Mémoires les plus intéressants de chymie, et d'histoire naturelle, contenus dans les Actes de l'Académie d'Upsal et dans les Mémoires de l'Académie des Sciences de Stockholm*, tr. by Auguste Roux and Baron d'Holbach, 2 vols. 12° (pagin. continuous), Paris, 1764 (covers the period 1720–60): this is referred to as 'Recueil, 1764'.

The Stockholm Academy of Sciences, founded in 1739, issued memoirs from 1741:

Kongl. Swenska Wetenskaps Academiens Handlingar, 1739 (publ. 1741)–1746 (vols. i–vii); 1747–79 (vols. viii–xl), with title *Kongl. Svenska Vetenskaps Academiens Handlingar*. The 40 vols. 1741–79 form the first series. A new series began in 1780 (vol. i) and continued to 1812 (vol. xxxiii) as *Kongl. Vetenskaps Academiens nya Handlingar*. From 1813 to 1854 a new series *Kongl. Vetenskaps Academiens Handlingar* appeared without vol. nos. All the volumes in these series were in 8°. A new series in 4° began in 1855. All these series are denoted in refs. by KAH.

A German tr. of earlier vols. appeared as: *Der Königl. Schwedischen Akademie der Wissenschaften Abhandlungen*, 41 vols.; 1749–53 (i–x), Hamburg; 1754–65 (xi–xxiv), Hamburg and Leipzig; 1766–79 (xxv–xli), and Index, 1783, Leipzig; tr. by A. G. Kästner; *Neue Abhandlungen*, 12 vols., Leipzig, 1784–92, and Index, 1794; tr. 1786–91 by Kästner and Brandis, 1792 by Kästner and Link.

The vowels *a* and *o* with superscript *e* in older publications are denoted by *ä* and *ö* as in modern Swedish. The vowel *å*, pronounced *o*, is retained.

One of the five founders of the Royal Swedish Academy of Sciences was Mårten Trievald (Triewald) (1691–1747), who visited England in 1716–26, when he was overseer of a coal-mine in Newcastle-on-Tyne. He attended lectures by Desaguliers, and was acquainted with Newton. His publications are mostly on practical topics.[1]

The Academy of Science (Royal from 1781) in Copenhagen published:

Skrifter, som udi det Kiøbenhavnske Selskab af Lærdoms og Videnskabers Elstere, 1743(5)–1777, which in 1777, xi, became *Skrifter, som udi det Kongelige Videnskabers*

---

[1] Poggendorff, (1), ii, 1135; Ferguson, ii, 467.

Selskab; five parts (1781–99) were entitled *Nye Samling Skrifter.* From 1801(1800)–18(1809–12) it appeared as *Det Kongelige Danske Videnskabers Selskabs Skrivter; Afhandlinger* in 1824–46, *Skrifter* from 1849; from 1824 an additional *Oversigt over det Kongelige Danske Videnskabernes Selskabs Forhandlinger* appeared.

BORRICHIUS

Oluf (or Ole) Borch (Olaus Borrichius) (Synder Borch, Ripen, Jutland, 7 April 1626–Copenhagen, 13 October 1690) was professor of poetry, botany and chemistry in the university of Copenhagen, and royal surgeon. He bequeathed his large library and his laboratory for the benefit of poor medical students. He was a man of great learning who travelled extensively in Europe. He was a very copious author and some of his publications are of great interest in the history of alchemy (see Vol. I).[1] He published a pamphlet on assaying,[2] a pharmaceutical dictionary,[3] on symbols,[4] on stones in nature and in the human body,[5] on medical botany,[6] on the antiquity of alchemy (which he traced back to Tubal Cain),[7] and a short history of chemistry, published posthumously.[8] He contributed many papers on various subjects[9] to Thomas Bartholin's *Acta Medica et Philosophica Hafniensia* (5 vols., Copenhagen, 1673–80).

Thomas Bartholin (Bartholinus) (Copenhagen, 20 October 1616–Hagested, 4 December 1680) was professor of mathematics (1647) then anatomy (1648–61) in the University of Copenhagen, and King's physician (1670);[10] he wrote *De luce animalium*, Leyden, 1647 (see Vol. II, p. 549). His brother Erasmus Bartholinus discovered the double refraction of light in Iceland spar.[11]

BM MS. Sloane 1235 (35–60) contains chemical processes by Borrichius in two books, (i) on chemical principles and operations, (ii) the effects of chemical operations, metals, semi-metals, coral, amber, and the vegetable kingdom; and letters from him are in the Boyle papers in the Royal Society.

[1] Short bibl. by Torbern Geill in Erik Warburg, *Subacute and Chronic Pericardian and Myocardial Lesions,* tr. A. Andersen and G. Seidelin, 1938; for alchemy in Denmark, see Fjelstrup, *A. Nat.,* 1910–11, iii, 141, 196.
[2] *Docimasticae metallica clarè, & compendiaro tradita,* 4°, Hafniæ, [1660], 1677 (46 pp.), tr. as *Metallische Probier-Kunst, deutlich und kurtz beschrieben, verteutscht durch Georg Kus,* 8°, Kopenhaven, 1680 (74 pp.).
[3] *Lingua Pharmacopoeorum, sive de accuratâ Vocabulorum in Pharmacopoliis usitatorum pronunciatione,* 4°, Hafniæ, 1670; adapted by Richard Brown as: *Prosodia Pharmacopoeorum: or, The Apothecary's Prosody. Shewing the exact Quantities in the Pronunciation of the Names of Animals, Vegetables, Minerals and Medicines, and of all other Words made use of in Pharmacy, many of which have been hitherto pronounced false,* 8°, London, 1685 (xxiv ll., 237 pp.).
[4] *De Cabala characterali dissertatio,* 12°, Hafniæ, 1649.
[5] *Dissertatio de Lapidum Generatione in Macro & Microcosmo. Cui accessit additio Exc: D. Doct. Joseph Langoni,* 12°, Ferrariæ, 1687 (76 pp. and index), also 4°.
[6] *De usu plantarum indigenarum in medicina, et sub finem, de clysso plantarum, & thee specifice, enchiridion,* 4°, Hafniæ, 1690 (101 pp.).
[7] *De Ortu, et Progressu Chemiæ Dissertatio,* sm. 4°, Hafniæ, P. Haubold, 1668; *Hermetis Ægyptiorum, Et Chemicorum Sapientia,* 4°, Hafniæ, P. Haubold, 1674 (vii ll., 448 pp., iv ll.), dedicated to Colbert.
[8] *Conspectus Scriptorum Chemicorum Illustriorum,* sm. 4°, Havniæ, S. Garman, 1696, and 1697.
[9] List in Gmelin, (1), ii, 119.
[10] Maar *et al., Janus,* 1916, xxi, 273–377.
[11] *Experimenta Crystalli Islandici Disdiaclastici Quibus mira & insolita Refractio detegetur,* Copenhagen, 1670.

Borrichius discovered the inflammation of spirit of turpentine by nitric acid:[1]

intra horæ mediæ spatium, remoto operculo, spiritus terebinthinæ ab acidis aquae fortis particulis irritatus effervescere incipit, & inter crassi fumi volumina flamma conspicuam emittens, supraq; oras vitri strenuè erumpens conflagrabit.

Slare[2] was at first unable to repeat the experiment but he later succeeded by using very concentrated nitric acid.[3] Borrichius showed that solutions of silver are not blue,[4] found that a mixture of sulphur and nitre burned with a flame when heated in a closed retort,[5] but nitre alone is not combustible,[6] investigated fixed and volatile alkalis,[7] opium,[8] and Norwegian talc;[9] he obtained alcohol from sugar, honey, etc.,[10] and showed that antimony increases in weight on calcination.[11] He refers to the increase in weight of lead heated on a cupel, although fumes are evolved, as puzzling to metallurgists (stupent ferè Metallurgi), and said the cause must be, in part, that the air previously included in the mass cannot enter because of the impervious cupel, partly because some particles of fire, or rather smoke, have penetrated the pores of the hot cupel and, when their points are broken off, become earth and so add to the weight:[12]

quod partim aër, qui ante inclusus moderabatur pondus, nunc propter soliditatem cupellæ ingredi eandem amplius nequeat, partim quod igneæ quædam particulæ, sive mavis fuliginis, insinuantes sese in poros cupellae adhuc celentis, tandem ibi fractis cuspidibus terrae evadant, atque ita pondus aggravent.

He mentions that lead will not dissolve in concentrated nitric acid,[13] and refers to the bending of long crystals of sal ammoniac.[14] He found[15] that water distilled ten times still left a white earth on evaporation in a glass retort, and reports that Edmund Dickinson at Oxford (see Vol. II) had obtained the same result after a hundred distillations.[16] His most remarkable discovery, long overlooked,[17] is that of oxygen. In his paper on nitre[18] he says it is a salt full of windy particles (particulis flabelliferis prægnantem), which cause charcoal to burn as if it were blown by bellows. Nitre heated alone in a glass retort on a sand-bath does not burn, but if mixed with sulphur it deflagrates like turpentine with nitric acid:

sive flamma in carbone luculentior, quàm ante, non qvia nitrum accenditur, sed qvia follis vicem sustinet (p. 213). . . . Ego ergo nitrum contemplor, ut salem infinitis particulis flabelliferis prægnantem, avt ut salinorum laterum follem clavsum distentumq́; qui motu ignis reciprocante luculentur apertus qvaqvaversum spargit flatus suos, & magno impetu obstantia elidet (p. 214). . . . Hinc particulæ ignis in nitrum

[1] Acta, 1673, i, 133.　　　　　　　　[2] Phil. Trans., 1683, xiii, 289–302.
[3] Phil. Trans., 1694, xviii, 200, no. 213.
[4] Acta, i, 128; the blue colour developed when silver dissolves in dilute nitric acid is due to nitrogen trioxide, N_2O_3.
[5] Ib., i, 135.　　　　　[6] Ib., 1680, v, 213.　　　　　[7] Ib., 1675, ii, 169 f.
[8] Ib., 1680, v, 351.　　　[9] Ib., 1680, v, 208.　　　　[10] Ib., 1677, iv, 177.
[11] Ib., 1675, ii, 189.　　　[12] Docimasticæ, 1677, § 26, p. 13; Probier Kunst, 1680, § 26, p. 36.
[13] Docimasticæ, 1677, 11.
[14] De Ortu, 1668, 114.　　　[15] Hermetis Ægyptiorum, 1674, 397.
[16] Dickinson, Physica vetus et vera, 4°, London, 1702, 240, 247.
[17] Jörgensen, Die Entdeckung des Sauerstoffes, Samml. chem.-u. chem.-techn. Vorträge, Stuttgart, 1909, xiv, 122.
[18] Acta, 1680, v, 213–16.

retorto vitro contentum ab arenâ validè calente impulsæ nihil accendunt, sed si nitro illi aliqvid sulphuris miscueris, accendunt & qvidem alacriter, de qvo videantur experimenta in Actes nostris Medicis Anni 1671, & 1672. Si qvis adhuc suspicetur nitrum inflammari, admoveat frustulum ejus accensæ candelæ, & satis diu ibi contineat, nihil flammæ concipi evidentissime spectabit (pp. 215–16).

He says the silversmiths, in refining silver, put thin plates of it together with nitre in a crucible, lute another crucible with a hole in the bottom over the first one, and heat in a fire. A rush of gas, often reaching several feet, issues from the hole (ad aliquot pedes in altum assurgit), more like a violent wind than a flame (in hâc operatione multo plus flatuum violentissimorum qvam flamma erumpit). It sometimes burns, but if nitre alone is in the crucible there is no flame (in flammam non abeat, solo nitro ibi præsente). He will not decide whether the wind is air or another kind of corpuscles:

utrum autem partes illæ flatuum generatrices constant ex intercepto inter laminulas aëre, an ex aliter atque aliter figuratis corpusculis, ii ulterius despiciant, qvibus otium et volupte.

Oxygen gas, which had eluded Mayow in 1674, was now calling loudly on Borrichius, but without effect. In 1772 Priestley obtained it by the same method, but there was to be a weary interregnum of the phlogiston theory between the two events, which some acute mind, long before Lavoisier, could have prevented.

Hjärne

Urban Hjärne (Haierne, Hierne) (Sqvoritz, Ingermanland, 20 December 1641–Stockholm, 22 March 1724), who had travelled in Holland, England, France and Germany, was assessor (1675) in and later president of the mining academy in Stockholm, and director of the public chemical laboratory established for him there in 1683 by Charles XI.[1] He published analyses of mineral waters[2] in which he observed the evolution of bubbles of 'mineral spirit' (carbon dioxide), noted the smell, taste, appearance, and source, and used chemical tests: tincture of galls, syrup of violets, 'Lackmuss oder Tornisol' (litmus), corrosive sublimate, copper and iron vitriols, sugar of lead, liver of sulphur, solution of sulphur in milk of lime, etc.[3] He mentions the ore kupfernickel.[4] Hjärne was convinced of the possibility of the transmutation of lead into gold by General Paykull in 1706:[5] a coin was struck with the legend *Hoc aurum arte chemica conflavit Holmiae 1706 O. A. v. Paykull.* Hjärne's papers were collected[6] and published in one volume in 1712:

[1] *Recueil,* 1764, I, iv; *Biographiskt Lexicon öfver Namnkunnige Svenska Män,* Uppsala, 1840, vi, 158–67; Ferguson, i, 407; Strandberg, *Lychnos,* 1936, i, 208 (portr.); Åkerström, *ib.,* 1937, ii, 187; Lindroth, *ib.,* 1941, vi, 191; Åberg, *J. Chem. Educ.,* 1950, xxvii, 334.
[2] *Tractatus de acidulis Medeviensibus,* 12°, Linköping, 1679; *Een kort Anladning till Atstillige Malm-och Bergarters, Mineraliers Wäxters, och Jordeflags sampt flere sältsame Tings,* 4°, Stockholm, 1694 (unpaged); *Kurtze Anleitung, wie man Gesund-oder Heyl-Brunnen und Mineral-Wasser auffsuchen, prüfen, und gebrauchen kan . . . ,* 12°, Stockholm, (1708 ?, pref. dated 1707); cf. Bergman, *Essays,* i, 98.
[3] *Kurtze Anleitung,* 43 f.
[4] *Kort Anladning . . . ,* 1694, sect. xi. Om halfwas metallen, fol. c 3 r.
[5] Berzelius, *Lehrbuch der Chemie,* 1841, x, 23 f.
[6] *Actorum laboratorii Stockholmiensis parasceve eller förberedelste,* 4°, Stockholm, 1706, according to Poggendorff, (1), i, 1113.

Urban Hierne . . . Archiatri et Consiliarii Metall. Acta et Tentamina Chymica in Regio Laboratorio Stockholmiensi, elaborata et demonstrata, in decades redacta atque divisa una cum praemissa parasceve seu praevia manuductione ad experimenta rite perficienda, 4°, Holmiae, 1712 (engr. frontisp.); sec. t.p., Actorum Chymicorum Holmiensium Parasceve id est Praeparatio ad Tentamina in Regio Laboratorio Holmiensi peracta, ut et compendiosa Manuductio . . . , Holmiæ, 1712; dedic. to Roy. Soc. London, portr. of 'Hiaern', aged 71, A.D .1712 .ix ll., 204 pp., i l. errata, 2 plates.

The contents of the British Museum copy are:

p. 1: Preface, description of origin of laboratory, mentioning several other royal laboratories, and saying Queen Christina of Sweden was devoted to chemistry.
Sect. I. (i) De Elementis in genere (p. 13); (ii) de terra (p. 16); (iii) de aqua (p. 18); (iv) de aere (p. 22) — mentioning Mariotte; (v) de igne (p. 29) — fixed in various materials, e.g. sulphur, pyrites, gems, soft metals; (vi) de influentis coelestibus & quomodo ex iis principia Chemica primum formentur (p. 45: astrological); (vii) de principiis chymicis (salt, sulphur, mercury) (p. 52); (viii) de sale & primum de sale acido (p. 54): sal completum dividitur in acidum & alcali; (ix) de alcalibus & primo de sale urinoso (p. 57); (x) de alcali fixo seu lixivioso (p. 60); (xi) de sale communi (p. 62); (xii) de sale nitroso seu petroso (p. 67) — est sal compositum ubique parabile, laxè conjunctum cum multo urinoso sale & plurimo acido, pauciore sale fixo, multo aëre, multaque aqua & paucissima denique terra; (xiii) de nitro antiquorum seu natro & sale calcario (p. 71); (xiv) de sale armeniacoso (p. 73); (xv) de sale essentiali (p. 75); (xvi) de sulphure (p. 84); (xvii) de mercurio (p. 94); (xviii) de principiis putavis, spiritu, phlegmate, et capite mortuo (p. 98).
Sect. II. (i) de solutione (p. 100); (ii) de praecipitatione (p. 103); (iii) de praecipitationum speciebus (p. 109); (iv) de materiis ad praecipitationis probationem necessariis in specie (p. 112); (v) diagnosis salium et sulphurum, per dicta praecipitantia (p. 124); (vi) adversariorum objectiones diluuntur (p. 130); Appendix in coloribus in praecipitatione rite observandis (p. 140); Index characterum chymico . . . (pp. 148–50). Parasceues capiti quinti Appendix de calore & ignibus (pp. 151–204): de calore (p. 151), de combustione seu de igni culinari (p. 161), de igne humido centrali (p. 175), de ignibus subterraneis ardentibus et montibus ignivomis (pp. 189–204), p. 205 errata.

The work was reissued in 1753[1] by Wallerius, who added a second volume:

Urbani Hierne Actorum Chemicorum Holmiensum, Tomus primus, hoc est, Parasceve sive Præparatio ad Tentamina, in Reg. Laboratorio Holmiensi peracta, . . . , Stockholm, 8°, 1753 (frontisp., pp. xviii, [ii], 283, [viii]); Tentaminum Chemicorum in Reg. Laboratorio Holmiensi peractorum, Tomus secundus. Nunc primum in lucem editorum . . . , Stockholm, 8°, 1753 (pp. xi, [i], 194, [x]); both vols. ed. by J. G. Wallerius.
Vol. II is divided into eight 'tentamina' (essays): (i) de sale ac pingue terrarum (p. 1); (ii) de duplici formicarum sale, tum acido tum volatile (p. 40), in which Hjärne describes the production of formic acid by distilling ants on a sand bath, and the preparation of a lead salt; (iii) de volatile sale urinoso plantarum, sive praevia putrefactione (p. 52); (iv) de sale volatile urinoso in regno mineralem (p. 73); (v) de aucto pondere quorundam corporum, post ustionem vel calcinationem (p. 112); (vi) de alkali fixi præexistentia in corporibus, antequam comburuntur (p. 125); (vii) de acido universali sulphureo, & a quo subjecto purum obtinere potest (p. 157); (viii) de defectu eorum supplendo, quæ in patria deficiunt (p. 177) — common salt, wine; index.
Another part was published in 1744: KAH, 1744, v, 170: utdrag utur . . . Hiærnes Actis Laboratorii Chymici Tentam. VI. om Hedegräset (a mossy plant).

Hjärne complains of the negligence, idleness, luxury, dissolute morals, ignorance, and occasional ill-health of his assistants, which impeded the work in the laboratory. His most important essays are on formic acid (II, ii), in

---

[1] Gmelin, (1), ii, 118, says 1750, Poggendorff, (1), i, 1113, says 1752, but both appear to be wrong.

which he describes the distillation of ants on a sand-bath and the preparation of the lead salt of the acid; and the increase in weight of metals on calcination (II, v), which he thought was due to the absorption of a 'fatty and sulphurous acid' (acidum pingue ac sulphureum) from the charcoal and wood, although he recognised that metals could be calcined without the latter. In his essay on the volatile alkaline salt in the mineral kingdom (II, iv) he describes the distillation of Scotch coal and the separation of ammonia from the liquid distillate by distilling with quicklime.

SWEDENBORG

Emanuel Swedenborg (Svedborg) (Stockholm, 29 January 1688–London, 29 March 1772) came of a family of miners of Stora Kopparberg (the famous copper mine near Fahlun). His father, a bishop, had travelled a good deal, set up a printing press and published many works; he had no theosophic or mystical views. Emanuel had a religious education and was destined for the church, and to religion he returned later in life. He studied mathematics, science, and ancient languages at Uppsala, where in 1709 he became doctor with a thesis on a classical subject. He then travelled for four years in England, Holland, and France. In 1716 he was appointed Assessor-Extraordinary of the Council of Mines in Sweden, on the basis of his knowledge of mechanics and military engineering, and Director of the Jern-Kontoret (Iron Bureau) in Stockholm, which was established by Gustavus Adolphus and still publishes *Jern-Kontorets Annaler*.

In 1719, after the death of King Charles XII, he received a patent of nobility from Queen Ulrica, taking the name Svedenborg (German and English Swedenborg, as it is pronounced), the Swedish *en* corresponding with the German *von*. In 1719 he published a work on decimal coinage. In this period he was a keen student of science, including chemistry, and throughout his life he was sober, industrious, and free from ambition. The only honour he received or sought was the addition of 'en' to his name. In 1721–2 he explored the mines of Sweden, Holland, England, and Germany at the expense of Duke Ludwig Rudolph of Brunswick. In 1724 he became Ordinary Assessor to the Board of Mines and in 1729 was admitted to the Academy of Sciences of Uppsala. In 1733 he was again inspecting mines in Saxony.

After the publication of his *Regnum Subterraneum* (1734) Swedenborg began the second epoch of his life. In 1736–9 he travelled in Holland, France, and Italy, and for a time relaxed his austere mode of life. He was now interested in biology and psychology, but his published works on these subjects are not original. In 1745, at the age of 57, he had a vision in London, and began the third phase of his life, the foundation of a new religious or theosophical body, the Swedenborgians, who are now fairly numerous in Great Britain and America. His many theological works are out of our province. Swedenborg died in London; his remains were moved to Stockholm in 1908.[1]

[1] Dingle, *Endeavour*, 1958, xvii, 127; Dumas, (1), 1837, 252; *id.*, (2), 1878, 274; Gmelin, (1), ii, 570; Grieve, EB[14], xxi, 653; Hoefer, (1), ii, 427; J. Hyde, *A Bibliography of the Works of*

Kopp does not mention Swedenborg; Hoefer says he 'did not add much to the domain of science'; Dumas notices favourably his attempts to explain affinity in terms of the forms and forces of the particles, and his studies in crystallography. Grieve says Swedenborg's scientific work has only been properly appreciated in fairly recent times; his palæontology is important, and he suggested a nebular hypothesis and the formation of planets and the sun long before Kant and Laplace (he thought the 'natural' motion was spiral rather than circular or rectilinear).[1] He gave a lucid explanation of phosphorescence. His work on the magnet[2] describes experiments on the solution in acids, etc., of the magnet, of no particular value, but the general treatise on magnetism[3] is not without interest, and proposes an alignment or molecular theory of magnetisation rather like the modern one. In physiology he gave a correct account of the motions of the brain and suggested the functions of the ductless glands.[4]

In 1721 Swedenborg published anonymously a 'geometrical explanation of chemistry and physics', a work on the nature of fire and inventions on iron and fire and a new furnace, and a new method of finding longitude:

A. Prodromus Principiorum Rerum Naturalium Sive Novorum Tentaminum Chymiam & Physicam Experimentalem Geometrice explicandi, 8°, Amsterdam, 1721 (199, i pp.; the BM copy has his autograph letter of presentation to Boerhaave); reissued with new t.p. 1727, and Hildburghausen 1754.
B. Observata et Inventa circa Ferrum et Ignem Nova et Præcipue circa Naturam Ignis Elementarem, una cum Nova Camini Inventione, 8°, Amsterdam, 1721 (56 pp.).
C. Methodus Nova Inveniendi Longitudines Locorum, 8°, Amsterdam, 1721.
D. Some Specimens of a Work on the Principles of Chemistry, with Other Treatises, tr. C. E. Strutt, 8°, London, 1847 (253 pp., 20 plates).
E. Miscellanea observata circa res naturales, praesertim mineralia, ignem et montium strata, 8°, Pts. i–iii, Leipzig, 1722; Pt. iv, Hamburg, 1722. Tr. C. E. Strutt.
F. Miscellaneous Observations connected with the Physical Sciences, 8°, London, 1847 (pp. xvi, 168).
G. Miscellanea Physica et Mineralogica ex Annis 1715 ad 1722, publ. in photolithographed facsimile by R. L. Tafel, Stockholm, 1869, from MSS. in Linköping Cathedral.

Whilst he was in Leipzig in 1733 Swedenborg completed his most important scientific work, which was published at the expense of the Duke of Brunswick-Lüneburg:

Emanuel Swedenborg, London, 1906; M. Lamm, *Swedenborg; en studie öfver hans utveckling till mystiker och anderskådore*, Stockholm, 1915; tr. by Ilse Meyer-Lune, *Swedenborg, eine Studie über seine Entwicklung zum Mystiker und Geisteslehrer*, Leipzig, 1922 (see Very, *Isis*, 1935, xxiii, 520; Tafel, *ib.*, 459); Louisy, NBG, 1865, xliv, 690; A. J. Matter, *Emmanuel de Swedenborg, sa vie ses écrits et sa doctrine*, Paris, 1863; G. Trobridge, *A Life of Emanuel Swedenborg, with a popular exposition of his philosophical and theological teachings*, London, 1912 (on science, 256 f.).
[1] *Suns and Worlds of the Universe*, ed. Bowers, London, 1899 (tr. of *De chao universali solis et planetarum: deque separatione ejus in planetas et satellites; Principia Rerum Naturalium*, 1734, 387 f.; *Opera*, Stockholm, 1908, ii, ed. Arrhenius and Stroh); Dingle, 1958.
[2] *De Modis magnetem destruendi; deque chymicis tentaminibus* (or *De Chymicis Experimentis circa Magnetem*), in *Principia Rerum Naturalium*, 1734, 194 f (see J 1, p. 166).
[3] *Ib.*, 125–372.
[4] Swedenborg, *The Brain*, ed. Tafel, Lund, 1822; *The Animal Kingdom*, tr. Wilkinson, London, 1843; *Regnum Animale*, ed. Tafel, Tübingen, 1848.

J (1). Opera philosophica et mineralia, 3 vols., f°, Dresden and Leipzig, Frederick Hekel, 1734, in three parts.

Part I: Principia Rerum Naturalium sive novorum Tentaminum Phænomena Mundi Elementaris Philosophice explicandi, with portr., 452 pp., and 28 copper-plates. Tr. by Rev. A. Clissold as: The Principia; or, the First Principles of Natural Things, being New Attempts toward a Philosophical Explanation of the Elementary World, 2 vols. 8°, London, 1845–6 (incl. the Prefaces only of Part II, on Iron, and Part III, on copper). It contains disquisitions on philosophical principles, magnetism, and the universe. The sections on air, fire, water, and vapour (1734, pp. 413 f.) are of no chemical interest.

J (2). Part II: Regnum Subterraneum sive Minerale de Ferro deque Modis Liqua-tionum Ferri per Europam passim in Usum receptis: deque de Conversione Ferri crudi in Chalybem: de Vena Ferri et Probatione ejus: pariter de Chymicis Præ-paratis et cum Ferro et Victriolo ejus factis Experimentis &c. &c., with 35 copper-plates and folding map of the Siberian iron-field.

Tr. by Bouchu: Traité de fer, in the Descriptions des Arts et Métiers, faites ou approuvées par meisseurs de l'Académie Royale des Sciences (see p. 11), f°, Paris, 1762 (vol. II of the series); Modern Swedish tr.: Opera Philosophica et Mineralia. . . . Svensk upplaga. Del 1. Om järnet, ed. S. Arrhenius (the famous chemist), V. Carlheim-Gyllensköld, and H. Sjögren, f°, Stockholm, 1923.

An earlier work on Swedish iron is the Uppsala thesis of Petrus Saxholm: Dis-sertatio Historico-Politico De Ferro Suecano Osmond, sm. 4°, Upsaliæ, Werner, 1725 (iv ll., 31 pp., i l.; 1 copperplate, 2 woodcuts in text) which deals with the manufacture and trade. On the Osmond furnace, see Vol. II, p. 61; Johannsen, Geschichte des Eisens, Düsseldorf, 1925, 100.

J (3). Part III: Regnum Subterraneum sive Minerale de Cupro et Orichalco deque Modis Liquationum Cupri per Europam passim in Usum receptis: de Secretione ejus ab Argento: de Conversione in Orichalcum: inque Metalla diversi Generes: de Lapide Calaminari: de Zinco: de Vena Cupri et Probatione ejus: pariter de Chy-micis Præparatis, et cum Cupro factis Experimentis &c. &c., with 89 copperplates.

Tr. in 1901 by A. H. Searle, whose MS. (deposited with the Swedenborg Society in London) was reproduced in mimeograph in three parts (without plates): Swedenborg's Treatise on Copper, 3 pts. f°, London, 1938, British Non-Ferrous Metals Research Association, Misc. Publ. 333.

The Treatise on Copper and Brass, J (3), is in three parts. The first deals with: (i) the methods of smelting and refining copper in use at the time in Sweden, England, Germany (including Eisleben and Mansfeld), Russia, the Pyrenees, Venice, Innsbrück, Hungary, and Bohemia; (ii) the separation of silver from copper; (iii) the manufacture of brass in various countries; and (iv) casting bell-metal, statuary, cannon, printing type, and shot. The second part describes the assaying of copper ore, including the silver content. The third part deals with the density of copper, the preparation of compounds of copper, and various chemical experiments (copied from books) on copper and brass. The short and disappointing section on zinc[1] gives the process used at Goslar (see Vol. II, p. 108), mentions that in England the zinc ore (blende ?) is like lead ore and is 'smelted on a sloping slab with a moderate fire', says (from the Dictionnaire universel de Commerce) that the zinc sold in Paris is in large square and thick loaves, and gives some observations on zinc made by Brandt in Stockholm (see p. 168). It mentions a 'special treatise' on zinc which was apparently planned. The works on iron and copper display an immense amount of study and observation, and contain long extracts from other works, but they do not present much original material.

[1] 1734, iii, 382–4.

Some of the above treatises were reprinted in the *Works* of Swedenborg, begun in 1907:

Emanuel Swedenborg Opera quædam aut inedita aut obsoleta de rebus naturalibus, Holmiae:
K. I. Geologica et Epistolae (Retzius, Nathorst and Stroh), 1907 (portr.).
II. Cosmologica (Arrhenius, Stroh), 1908 (contains Principia Rerum Naturalium).
III. Miscellanea de Rebus Naturalibus (Stroh), 1911 (contains A and B).

The *Principles of Chemistry* (D) consists of attempts to explain the properties of substances in terms of the supposed forms of their particles, which are shown in the figures in great detail. Various modes of stacking of spherical particles are discussed, with calculations of space-filling, not without interest from the point of view of modern lattice theory (p. 8 f.). Acids have wedge-shaped particles which divide metals, etc. (p. 79 f.). Deposits of salt on land are from a primeval ocean (p. 3 f.). Common salt is generated at the bottom of the sea by the disintegration of particles of water, the salt particles having the shape of the voids between the water particles (p. 33 f.). Nitre is generated in many ways when acid particles, water particles, and subtle (igneous) matter are suitably mixed (p. 86 f.). There is a 'theory' of lead (p. 133 f.); the increase in weight on calcination (p. 159) is due to the fire only, 4 oz. increasing by 16 grains (p. 164); and 'experiments' on silver (p. 171 f.) and mercury (p. 175 f.); 8 parts of mercury give 9 parts of red precipitate (p. 176); all this is taken from books by Boyle, Hjärne, Boerhaave, and Lemery (mentioned on p. 2).

The *Observations on Iron and Fire* (B; in D, 181 f.) contain descriptions of smelting furnaces (with plates) and a description of the smelting of iron ore with charcoal. The treatise on iron contains nothing of special interest, but gives brief notes of the chemical and other properties of iron. The treatise on fire (p. 199 f.) postulates that its particles are hollow bubbles, identical with the solar rays, and there are some remarks on the variations of temperature in rooms, all stated mathematically as if they were ascertainable facts, e.g. 'volumes of heat are carried upwards in the duplicate ratio of the times'. It includes a description of a kind of wind-furnace based on the idea that 'fire' will remain in charcoal without consuming it if only air is excluded, so that when it has got hot, the apertures are to be closed. This is poor chemistry.

Some treatises, e.g. *On Salt* and *On Sulphur*, mentioned by Swedenborg in his other works, form parts of a treatise on *The Genuine Treatment of Metals* to be in 19 parts, projected in 1722, but not published; the treatise on salt was published in 1910:

L. De Sale communi, hoc est de sale fossili vel gemmeo marino et fontano, ed. A. Acton, Philadelphia, 1910; hydrometer, p. 5; hydrostatic balance, p. 9; tests; description of Wieliczka mine, p. 16 f.; Cardona, Cheshire, etc.; salt meadows, p. 26; 'graduation', p. 70 f.; spirit of salt, p. 93 f.; mineral waters; saltpetre, p. 126; curved salt crystals, and 'Egyptian' salt, p. 133; this treatise is very practical and well illustrated.
Other treatises exist in manuscript; see J (3), 1938, iii, 400.

BRANDT

Georg Brandt (Riddarhytta, Westmanland, 26 June 1694–Stockholm, 29 April 1768) was Warden of the Stockholm Mint and later professor of chemistry in the University of Uppsala, founded in 1477.[1]

He showed (1733)[2] that white arsenic (arsenious oxide) is the calx of a metal (arsenic) which he obtained as a regulus by heating to redness a paste of white arsenic, pure fixed alkali (potash), volatile alkali, and sal ammoniac. Bergman[3] mentions that Schroeder in his *Pharmacopoeia Medico Chymica*, 1649, had referred to regulus of arsenic (which was known to Albertus Magnus, see Vol. I).

Brandt[4] classed mercury, antimony, bismuth, cobalt, arsenic and zinc as semi-metals, rejecting cinnabar, vitriols, etc., from this class. He considered that true metals solidify from fusion with a convex surface. The semi-metals have a metallic appearance but are brittle under the hammer. He describes metallic zinc (*spiauter, conterfeth*) from the East Indies, Rammelsberg, and Dalecarlia and Rattwick in Sweden, as a semi-metal. Blende is an ore of zinc and white vitriol is a compound of zinc, since it can be prepared by dissolving zinc in sulphuric acid, and if the solution of white vitriol is precipitated with alkali and the precipitate (zinc carbonate) heated with copper and charcoal, brass is produced.

In a further investigation of cobalt[5] he obtained the impure metal (cobalt regulus). By roasting a Swedish pyrites (linnaeite, Co_3S_4) used to make smalt and free from arsenic he obtained a black powder, which he reduced with charcoal powder and fluxes in the intense heat of a smith's forge with bellows. He obtained the metal (containing iron) as reddish-grey grains or as a fibrous compact mass with a reddish tinge, malleable under a hammer, of high melting point, attracted by a magnet, and forming an alloy with iron or steel (cobalt steel) which was also malleable and as magnetic as pure iron (3 partes reguli cobalti cum una parte ferri in unam massam conflati, compositum evadere, quod â magnete trahitur, ferri instar puri). It did not alloy with bismuth. He proved that the blue colour of smalt is due to cobalt and not to bismuth or arsenic, or to iron as had been assumed by Henckel (1744; see Vol. II, p. 708).

J. G. Lehmann,[6] who does not mention Brandt,[7] later denied that bismuth or arsenic is the cause of the blue colour of smalt, but he was not clear that this was due to a particular metal. Brandt's results were confirmed in 1780 by Bergman (see p. 190), who first obtained fairly pure cobalt. Even in 1783 it was reported from Vienna that cobalt was an alloy of iron and arsenic.[8]

Brandt also published on the attraction between gold and mercury (1731),[9]

[1] Gmelin, (1), ii, 568–70; iii, 61; Hoefer, (1), ii, 423; Lindberg, *Lychnos*, 1936, i, 308.
[2] *Acta Lit. Svec.*, 1733, iii, 39; *Recueil*, 1764, i, 1 f.
[3] *Opuscula*, 1780, ii, 274.   [4] *Acta Lit. Svec.*, 1735, iv; *Recueil*, i, 8.
[5] Cobalti nova species examinata et descripta, *Acta Reg. Soc. Sci. Upsal*, 1742 (1748), 33–41; *Recueil*, 1764, i, 38; KAH, 1746, vii, 119 (Färgcobolt).
[6] *Cadmiologia, oder Geschichte des Farben-Kobolts*, 4°, Berlin, 1760; see Vol. II, p. 712.
[7] As Bergman noted: *Scheffers Föreläsningar*, Uppsala, 1775, § 320; tr. Weigel, 1779, 595.
[8] Kopp, (1), iv, 154.   [9] *Acta Lit. Svec.*, 1731, iii, 1; *Recueil*, i, 26.

on green vitriol (he points out that concentrated sulphuric acid does not act on iron),[1] the distillation of nitric acid, affinities in solution, etc.,[2] a test for the purity of tin,[3] ore deposits,[4] the difference between potash and soda,[5] the volatile alkali,[6] the solution of gold in aqua fortis (it dissolves when 3 pts. of gold are alloyed with 16 pts. of silver),[7] and lime, which has alkaline properties and contains an acrid volatile part separated by distillation with urine — really from the urine (1749).[8] In his memoir on iron (1751) he supposed cold-shortness to be due to alloy with arsenic, bismuth or antimony, and red-shortness to an acid of sulphur insufficiently expelled on roasting the ore; steel contains more combustible matter (really carbon) than iron, and when this is increased by heating with substances containing fire-resisting fatty matter, such as horn or bird's claws (carbonised on heating in closed vessels) it forms steel.[9]

Brandt also described the precipitation and separation of gold (from solution) by green vitriol (1752),[10] common salt and its acid,[11] alkalis and the (supposed) earth contained in them (including experiments on Prussian blue and borax),[12] and the separation of iron and copper from their ores.[13]

WALLERIUS

Johan Gotschalk Wallerius (Nerike, 11 July 1709–Uppsala, 16 November 1785) was professor of chemistry in Uppsala (1750–67) and a very copious author.[14] The following works are of interest to us:

I. Mineralogia, eller Mineral-Riket, 8°, Stockholm, 1747 (BM 990. a. 19).

IA. Mineralogie, oder Mineralreich, tr. by J. D. Denso, 2 ed., Berlin, 1763 (long pref., 600 pp., index; BM 953 b. 21).

IB. Mineralogie, ou description générale des substances du regne mineral, traduit de l'Allemand, 2 vols. 8°, Paris, 1753 (BM 987. h. 9–10; with 4 plates).

II. Systema Mineralogicum, quo corpora mineralis in classes, ordines, genera et species . . . , 2 vols. (portr. in vol. i), Holmiæ, 1772–75 (BM 233. k. 26–27) and Vienna, 1778 (Chem. Soc. London).

IIA. Mineralsystem, worinnen die Fossilien nach Klassen, Abtheilungen, Gattungen, Arten und Spielarten angeordnet . . . , 2 pts., Berlin, I (1781) tr. N. G. Leske, II (1783) tr. E. B. G. Hebenstreit (BM 726. g. 5–6).

III. Lucubrationum Academicarum specimen . . . de Systematibus Mineralogicis et systemate mineralogico rite condendo, 8°, Stockholm, 1768 (158 pp.).

IV. Chemia Physica, in Swedish, 3 pts. 1759–83; in Latin, 2 pts. 1760–65; German tr.:

IVA. Der Physischen Chemie, 5 pts. in 3 vols., I Gotha, 1761 (tr. by Mangold), II, i, ii, and II, iii–iv, Leipzig, 1776 (tr. by Weigel, the ed. quoted) (BM 1034. a. 22–24); other eds. ment. by Bolton and Poggendorff.

V. A work on agricultural chemistry appeared as a dissertation by Count Gustavus Adolphus Gyllenborg: Åkerbrukets chemiska Grunder, Stockholm, 1761, 1778;

---

[1] KAH, 1741, ii, 49; Recueil, i, 68.   [2] KAH, 1743, iv, 89.
[3] KAH, 1744, v, 215.
[4] Reglor angånde malmstreck grufors brytning, KAH, 1745, vi, 29.
[5] KAH, 1746, vii, 289; Recueil, ii, 515.   [6] KAH, 1747, viii, 300; Recueil, i, 149.
[7] KAH, 1748, ix, 45; Recueil, i, 304.   [8] KAH, 1749, x, 133; Recueil, i, 179.
[9] KAH, 1751, xii, 205; Recueil, i, 256.   [10] KAH, 1752, xiii, 128; Recueil, i, 316.
[11] KAH, 1753, xiv, 295; 1754, xv, 53; Recueil, ii, 346.
[12] KAH, 1756, xvii, 46; Recueil, ii, 459.
[13] KAH, 1764, xxv, 228; German tr. 1767, xxvi, 235.
[14] Bolton, (1), 901; Ferguson, ii, 528; Gmelin, (1), ii, 383, 566–8, 702, 704, 745; iii, 56; Hoefer, (1), ii, 426; Poggendorff, (1), ii, 1252.

Agriculturae fundamenta chemica, Stockholm, 1761; Chemische Grundsätze des Feldbaus, Berlin, 1764, Berne, 1765; Élémens d'Agriculture physique et chymique, traduits du Latin, Yverdun, 1766 (BM 987. c. 18); L'Agriculture reduit à ses vrais principes, Paris, 1773; The Natural and Chemical Elements of Agriculture, tr. from the Latin by John Mills, 12°, London, 1770; Kopp, (1), ii, 132, says the experiments of Wallerius on this subject go back to 1730.

VI. Elementa Metallurgiæ speciatim Chemicæ conscripta, Stockholm, 1768. Tr. as: VIA. Anfangsgründe der Metallurgie besonders der chymischen, Leipzig, 1770 (Gmelin says 1769 in error).

VII. Meditationes physico-chemicae de origine mundi, imprimis Geocosme ejusdemque metamorphosi, Stockholm and Leipzig, 1779 (BM 990. e. 11); De l'origine du monde et de la terre en particulier, transl. by J. B. D. Varsovie, Paris, 1780 (BM 7107. a. 50), on cosmology.

VIII. Dissertations partly collected in 1780-81: Disputationum Academicarum Fasciculus Primus continens Physico Chemicas et Chemico Pharmaceuticas emendatas et correctas nec non necessariis observationibus et annotationibus illustratas, Holmiae et Lipsiae, 1780, introd. + 422 pp.; Disputationum Academicarum Fasciculus Secundus, continens Chemico Mineralogicas et Metallurgicas, emendatas et . . . illustratas, Holmiae et Lipsiae, 1781, prelim. + 367 pp. (BM 956. i. 2). Contents: I (1780): i De Principiis Corporum, p. 1; ii De Salibus Alkalinis eorumque usu medico, p. 21; iii De Origine Salium Alkalinorum, p. 57; iv De Natura et Origine Nitri, p. 77; v De Origine Oleorum in Vegetabilibus, p. 117; vi De Differentia et Examine Oleorum, p. 134; vii De Dulcificatione Acidorum, p. 157 (in this, publ. in 1763, he questioned the real existence of true 'salt naphtha' (ethyl chloride), which had been noticed by G. F. Rouelle (see p. 73); Kopp, (1), iv, 310); viii De Materiali differentia Luminis et Ignis, p. 177; ix An Calor à Sole ?, p. 212; x Animadversiones Chemicae ad ictum Fulminis in Arce Regia Upsaliensi d. xxiv. Aug. 1760, p. 236; xi De Lapide Tonitruali, p. 264; xii De Indole Aquae mutabili, p. 276; xiii Qua Dubia quaedam, contra Transmutationem Aquarum mota, refelluntur, p. 302; xiv Continuatio Dissertationis, qua dubia quaedam, contra transmutationem Aquarum mota, refelluntur, p. 319. Sect. II. xv Censurae circa Praeparationem Medicamentorum Chemicorum, p. 335; xvi De incongrua Medicamentorum mixtura, p. 364; xvii De Cinnabaris in Corpus Humanum Effectu, p. 384; xviii Analysis et Synthesis Pulveris laxantis d'Ailhaud, p. 403.

II (1781) sectio I chemico-mineralogicas continet: i De Vegetatione mineralium, p. 3; ii De Palingenesia, p. 16; iii De diversitate Montium extrinseca, p. 38; iv De natura et indole Montium diversa, p. 53; v De origine Montium, p. 64; vi De incrementiis Montium dubiis, p. 75; vii De Montibus ignivomis, p. 86; viii De collibus ad Uddevalliam conchaceis, p. 107; ix De Gigantum reliquiis, p. 133; x Observationes mineralogicae ad plagam occidentalem sinus Bothnici, p. 150; xi De Tellure olim per ignem non fluida, p. 165. Sectio II continet Chemico-metallurgicas; xii De fatiscentia Corporum mineralium in aëre, p.187; xiii De Metallorum calcinatione in igne, p. 217; xiv De utilitate Tostionis minerarum metallicarum, p. 246; xv De ustulatione minerae ferreae, p. 258; xvi De fusionibus Minerarum metallicarum, p. 277; xvii De calcarei lapidis usu in fusionibus minerarum ferri, p. 292; xviii De nobilitate ferri, imprimis sueogothici, p. 305; xix De Patroni officinarum ferri necessaria inspectione in operationes metallurgicas, in officinas fusoriis et malleatoriis ferri, p. 324; xx De experimentis, pro facilitanda praecipitatione fusoria cupri e minera Magni Cuprimontii, frustra tentatis, p. 349.

IX. Hydrologia eller Wattu-Riket, indelt och beskrifvet, jämte Anledning til Vattuprofvers anställande, 8°, Stockholm, 1748 (BM 957. f. 25); German tr. by J. D. Denso: Hydrologie, oder Wasserreich . . . nebst einer Anleitung zur Herstellung der Wasserproben, 12°, Berlin, 1751 (BM 1171. d. 22).

Gmelin mentions also: Bref om Chemiens rätta Beskaffenhet, nytta och waerde, Stockholm and Uppsala, 1751; and Censuras circa præparationem medicamentorum chemicam, Uppsala, 1755.

In his *Mineralogy* Wallerius classed graphite as a kind of talc (see Imperato, Vol. II, p. 95) and proposed to restrict the name marcasite to a variety of pyrites (it had previously been used for bismuth, zinc, etc.). He considered heavy spar (barium sulphate) to be a kind of gypsum, calling it *gypsum lamel-*

losum or *marmor metallicum*,[1] or *gypsum spathosum* or *tung spat.*[2] He regarded wolfram (ferrous tungstate $FeWO_4$) as an ore of iron (*vulfram, spuma lupi, ferrum arsenico mineralisatum*).[3] Thomson[4] remarks that Wallerius, J. L. Woltersdorf,[5] F. A. Cartheuser[6] and J. H. L. von Justi[7] had followed Linnæus[8] in dividing minerals into *petræ, mineræ*, and *fossilia*. Cronstedt (1758, see p. 174) reverted to Avicenna's four classes (see Vol. I).

In the treatise on metallurgy (VI) Wallerius mentions the hydrogen from iron or zinc and vitriolic acid as a 'metallic vapour',[9] and gives the theories of formation of metallic veins.[10] He says the increase in weight of metals on calcination is certain, and gives as a possible explanation the separation of combustible parts lighter than air (particularum inflammabilium, aëre leviorum, separatione).[11] He mentions the distillation of zinc in Sweden in stone or iron retorts, from the calcined ore and charcoal,[12] gives the theories of the formation of steel,[13] and describes the manufacture of brass[14] and smalt.[15] Wallerius's pupil Carl Petersen had investigated the calcination of metals.[16]

The first volume of Wallerius's *Physical Chemistry* (IV) contains a brief and poor history of chemistry,[17] saying that he proposed to write a separate work on this.[18] It mentions the blowpipe (a brass Cementir-rohr or Löthrörgen)[19] without describing its use, deals with symbols,[20] furnaces, vessels, and operations, the transmutation of metals,[21] fermentation, etc. Vol. II, i, treats of salts and their products, acids and alkalis, with a long section on borax and its acid.[22] Vol. II, ii, deals with sulphur and bitumens and their products, Vol. II, iii, with semi-metals, viz. mercury, arsenic (including the regulus),[23] cobalt, etc. (Kobold, Saflor (*sic*) and Schmalte), including metallic cobalt;[24] nickel and speise[25] (he thought kupfer-nickel was composed of cobalt, iron, and arsenic), bismuth,[26] antimony,[27] and zinc (zink oder Tuttanego).[28] Vol. II, iv (paged continuously with iii), deals with complete metals (ganzen Metallen), viz. iron (including cold- and red-short), copper, lead (which increases in weight but decreases in density in the ratio 5 : 2 on calcination, with reference to *N. Hamburg. Mag.*, Bd. II, St. 10, pp. 375–8), tin, silver (the nitrate, from its bitter taste is called *fel metallorum*), gold and platinum.[29]

In his *Agricultural Chemistry* (V) Wallerius compared the chemical constituents of soils and plants. The belief in palingenesia (see Vol. II, index)

[1] I, 1747, 55, 58.   [2] II, 1777, i, 161.
[3] I, 1747, 268; II, 1772, i, 326 (where it is confused with pyrolusite); II, 1775, ii, 254 (Weisser Eisenstein).
[4] (2), 1817, iii, 251.
[5] *Systema Minerale dass ist Mineralsystem . . .*, 4°, Berlin, 1748; Ulm, 1755.
[6] *Elementa Mineralogiæ systematice disposita*, 8°, Frankfurt on the Oder, 1755.
[7] *Grundriss des gesamten Mineralogie*, 8°, Göttingen, 1757, 2 ed. 1765.
[8] *Systema Naturæ*, f°, Leyden, 1735.   [9] VI, Sect. I, c. ii, § iv.
[10] VI, Sect. I, c. iii, § xxv f.   [11] VI, Sect. I, c. iv, § v.   [12] VI, Sect. III, c. viii, § iv.
[13] VI, Sect. IV, c. i, § iii.   [14] VI, Sect. IV, c. ii, § v.   [15] VI, Sect. IV, c. iii, § viii.
[16] Dissertation, *Om metallernes calcinationer i Eld*, 4°, Uppsala, 1761, q. by Gmelin, (1), ii, 568, 702; Hoefer, (1), ii, 427.
[17] IVA, I, 1 f.
[18] Gmelin, (1), ii, 712, gives *Bref om Chemiens rätta beskaffenhet, nytta och waerde*, 8°, Stockholm and Uppsala, 1751.
[19] IVA, I, 66.   [20] *Ib.*, 46 f.   [21] *Ib.*, c. xxvi, 319 f.
[22] IV, II, i, 180–209: mentioning the green flame coloration, 200.   [23] IV, II, iii, 128.
[24] *Ib.*, 139 f.   [25] *Ib.*, 155.   [26] *Ib.*, 168.   [27] *Ib.*, 187.   [28] *Ib.*, 256 f.   [29] *Ib.*, 525.

persisted in this time; A. F. Pezold (1719), Bauer (1724), and the famous physician G. F. Franck of Franckenau[1] having supported it. A dissertation of G. R. Hoyer presented under Wallerius[2] again disproved the belief. Macquer[3] reported from Wallerius some processes in which mercury is artificially produced. A story of the supposed demonstration of transmutation by Wallerius before the King of Sweden in 1767 seems to be based on the experiments of Brandt on the solution of gold, when alloyed with silver, in aqua fortis (see p. 169).[4]

Wallerius published on copper smelting (1743),[5] saltpetre,[6] and the 'vegetation' of mercury (1754)[7] by allowing mercury to stand in a solution of mercury in aqua fortis evaporated until most of the mercury salt separated as a white powder. In papers on the earth obtained from water, plants, and animals (1760),[8] he supported the theory that water is convertible into earth, e.g. in Eller's experiments (see Vol. II, p. 716) in which water was triturated in a glass mortar. Wallerius published on platinum,[9] the star of antimony (de stella reguli antimonii),[10] and on cedar-water and tar.[11] In one of seventeen dissertations on the difference between the matters of light and fire[12] Wallerius says fire (ignis) is a kind of motion which causes decomposition of combustible matter by heat (calor), by which the indestructible matter of light (lux), which is different from the matter of heat, becomes free and visible. The matter producing heat is a very fluid, mobile, volatile and elastic substance which is combined with the matter of light and obtains its activity from this. Combustible matter or phlogiston is a matter producing heat, combined with a subtle earth:

His observationibus patet, quum ignis non alia aggredi possit corpora, quam quæ in se quidpiam de materia phlogistica, vel materiam caloris continent, eundem consistere in motu et decompositione materiæ calorificæ et phlogisticæ, unde lucis materia indestructibilis fit libera et conspicua. Nullus itaque ignis vulgaris sine alimento atque sine effluviis existere potest, à decompositione particularum ortis (§ 5, p. 194).

Haec materia lucis, cum subtilissima materia combinata, constituit in corporibus principiatum, materiam calorificam, cui si accesserit aliud terrestre, producitur phlogiston (§ 10, p. 211).

His theory of the cause of the increase in weight of metals on calcination (the separation of combustible parts lighter than air) has been mentioned above (p. 171).

---

[1] *De Palingenesia sive resuscitatione artificiali Plantarum, Hominum et Animalium à suis cineribus*, Halle, 1717; German tr. by J. C. Nehringer, Leipzig, 1716, q. by Gmelin, (1), ii, 332.
[2] *De palingenesia*, Uppsala, 1764, q. by Gmelin.   [3] *Dictionnaire*, 1778, ii, 588.
[4] Oseen, *Lychnos*, 1940, v, 73.   [5] *Recueil*, 1764, i, 93.   [6] KAH, 1749, x, 270.
[7] KAH, 1754, xv, 254; *Recueil*, ii, 389: a general account of metal 'trees'.
[8] KAH, 1760, xxi, 39, 142, 191, 252; *Recueil*, ii, 542.   [9] KAH, 1765, xxvi, 161.
[10] *Acta Acad. Nat. Curios.*, 1752, ix, 253, dated Uppsala, 1749.
[11] *Ib.*, 1752, ix, 244.
[12] VIII; I, viii, p. 177 (De materiali differentia Luminis et Ignis); § 5, p. 194; § 10, p. 211; cf. Leonhardi, Macquer's *Chymisches Wörterbuch*, Leipzig, 1788–91, i, 657 f.; Berzelius, *Lehrbuch der Chemie*, 1833, ii, 259.

SWAB

Anton Swab (or Svab) (Fahlun, 9 August 1703–Stockholm, 28 January 1768) was assessor to the Mining Academy of Stockholm, and ennobled as von Swab in 1751. He discovered native antimony (alloyed with some arsenic) in Salberg in Vastmanland, and examined it on charcoal before the blow-pipe.[1] He noticed the formation of gelatinous silica ('mineral gelatin') formed by the action of acids on some zeolite minerals, finding that some soft kinds of glass are similarly acted upon by the three mineral acids; a sediment in some bottles of Rhine wine was found to be similarly formed by the action of acid in the wine on the glass.[2]

Bergman[3] says zinc was extracted by distillation from its ores in 1742 by Swab in Westervik in Dalecarlia, but the process was soon given up. It was afterwards effected in larger quantity in Sweden by Cronstedt and Rinman. In another place[4] he says 'about 40 years before' (1734) von Swab distilled zinc in Tuna Socken (Tina Kirchspiel) but soon gave up. This work was unknown to Marggraf (see Vol. II, p. 726). W. A. Ross[5] supposed that von Swab first made extensive use of the blowpipe (known to the ancient Egyptians) in chemical experiments; von Engeström first used the charcoal block, Gahn the platinum wire loop (platinum foil being first used by Wollaston), and cobalt solution (see p. 201).

CRONSTEDT

Axel Frederic Cronstedt (Södermanland, 23 December 1702 (or 1722)–Stockholm, 19 August 1765) occupied no academic position. He was a Bergrath and a member of the Stockholm Academy of Sciences.[6] He investigated the copper-coloured mineral called Kupfer-nickel by Hjärne (see p. 162), who wrongly thought it contained copper. Johann Heinrich Link (Linck, or Lincke) (Leipzig; 17 December 1674–29 October 1734), an apothecary in Leipzig, supposed[7] that it was a cobalt earth mixed with copper, since it dissolved in nitric acid to a green solution. Wallerius (see p. 171) thought it contained cobalt, iron, and arsenic. Nickel was discovered by Cronstedt (1751), who[8] proved that kupfernickel contains a peculiar metal, which in 1754 he called nickel. He obtained it as a silver-white feebly magnetic regulus by reducing the soluble green efflorescence which forms on the mineral in moist air. He showed that although, like copper, it forms green solutions in acids, especially nitric acid, which become blue with ammonia, it differs from copper in not being precipitated by iron or zinc. Before the blowpipe it forms a brown borax bead. The metal was further investigated by Bergman (see p. 190) and by Richter (see p. 688).

[1] KAH, 1748, ix, 99 (nativ regulus antimonii, eller Spets-Glas-Kung); Recueil, 1764, i, 166.
[2] KAH, 1758, xix, 282; Recueil, ii, 434.   [3] Opuscula, ii, 311; Essays, 1788, ii, 316.
[4] Scheffers Föreläsningar, 1775, § 329, Anm. 3.
[5] Pyrology, or Fire Chemistry; A Science interesting to the General Philosopher, and an Art of infinite importance . . . , 4°, London, 1875, 12 f.
[6] Gmelin, (1), ii, 572; Poggendorff, (1), i, 499.
[7] Phil. Trans., 1727, xxxiv, 192–203 (Brevis Commentatio de Cobalto).
[8] KAH, 1751, xii, 287; 1754, xv, 38; Recueil, 1764, i, 212, 218.

Sage[1] tried to show that kupfernickel was composed of iron, copper, cobalt and arsenic; and Monnet[2] that cobalt and nickel were the same. Cronstedt[3] remarked that: 'It would perhaps be more useful to discover more of these metals, than idly to lose our time . . . in order to discover the constituent parts of the metals already known.'

Cronstedt gave the name *zeolite* (ζέω, I boil, λίθος, a stone) to a mineral species which appears to boil before the blowpipe.[4] He described three new ores of iron,[5] and published on gypsum,[6] platinum,[7] and the manufacture of lime.[8] In his work on mineralogy, first published anonymously in Swedish in 1758, Cronstedt divided minerals into four groups: earths, salts, bitumens, and metals (see p. 171), heavy spar (*marmor metallicum*) being classed as a species:

I. Försök till Mineralogie eller Mineral-Rikets upställning, 8°, Stockholm, 1758, (251 pp.).
II. German tr. by G. Wiedman: Versuch einer neuen Mineralogie aus dem Schwedischen übersetzt, Kopenhagen, 1760 (Ross, Pyrology, 1875, p. xiv, thought this was the first issue); the pref. says the book was regarded in Sweden as Cronstedt's.
III. German tr. by A. G. Werner: Versuch einer neuen Mineralogie, aufs neue aus dem Schwedischen übersetzt, Bd. I, Theil i (all publ.), 8°, Leipzig, 1780.
IV. French tr. by Dreux 'fils': Essai d'une nouvelle Minéralogie, traduit du Suédois et de l'Allemand de M. Wiedmann, 8°, Paris, 1771 (389 pp.).
V. English tr. by von Engeström (see p. 179), which contains an account of blowpipe analysis: An Essay towards a System of Mineralogy by Axel Frederic Cronstedt. Translated from the Original Swedish, with Notes, by Gustav von Engestrom. To which is added, A Treatise on the Pocket-Laboratory, containing An Easy Method, used by the Author, for Trying Mineral Bodies, Written by the Translator. The Whole Revised and Corrected, with Some Additional Notes By Emanuel Mendes da Costa, 8°, London, 1770; do., with an Appendix by Prof. M. T. Brunnich, London, 1772 (in both eds. the work on the blowpipe begins with sep. pagin. 175 f., after p. 272 of text, and is accompanied by plates).
VI. Do., The Second Edition, greatly enlarged and improved . . . by John Hyacinth de Magellan . . . , 2 vols. 8°, London, 1788. Magellan says the treatise on the blowpipe was first published in English by Engeström: it is not in I–IV. An English tr. of 1765 is mentioned by Poggendorff, (1), i, 670.
VII. English V retr. by Beck into Swedish: Beskrifning af ett mineralogiskt fick laboratorium, och isynnerhet nyttan af blåsröret uti mineralogien, Stockholm, 1773 (Gmelin, (1), ii, 574, dates it 1772; Poggendorff, and Landauer, Ber., 1893, xxvi, 898, date it 1773; I have not seen it).

Bergman[9] says the blowpipe was first used in chemical analysis by Andreas von Swab about 1738, but Andreas von Swab died in 1731 and Anton von Swab (d. 28 January 1768) is meant. Bergman says the use was perfected by Cronstedt, Rinman, von Engeström, Quist, Gahn, and Scheele, and von Engeström wrote on it first in English. Linnæus thought the part dealing with the blowpipe was by Swab.

A very exhaustive history of the blowpipe, with many references, was given

---

[1] *Éléments de minéralogie docimastique*, 1772; Neumann, Z. angew. Chem., 1903, xvi, 225 (history of nickel).
[2] *Traité de la dissolution des métaux*, 1775.   [3] *System of Mineralogy*, 1788, ii, 847.
[4] KAH, 1756, xvii, 120; *Recueil*, ii, 430.   [5] KAH, 1751, xii, 226; *Recueil*, i, 247.
[6] KAH, 1753, xiv, 144; *Recueil*, ii, 337.
[7] KAH, 1764, xxv, 221 (Platina del Pinto; the identity of the metal he calls *caracoli* is doubtful).
[8] KAH, 1761, xxii, 197.
[9] *Opuscula*, Uppsala, 1780, ii, 455: primus, ni fallor, adhibuit Celebris noster metallurgus Andreas a Swab . . . circa annum 1738.

by Weigel.[1] Swab published his work on blowpipe analysis in 1748 in his paper on cobalt,[2] but was preceded by Rinman[3] and the blowpipe was then, in fact, well known. Berzelius[4] says Gahn's blowpipe was the best pattern, and Thomson[5] says this part of Berzelius's book is based on material supplied by Gahn. Engeström describes the use of soda, borax, and microcosmic salt as fluxes.

SCHEFFER

Henrik Theophilus Scheffer (Stockholm; 29 December 1710–10 August 1759), an assayer and technical chemist in Stockholm, gave courses of lectures published by Bergman from notes taken in 1749–50–51 by Jonas Alströmer (1685–1761), a Stockholm merchant, with important additions by Bergman:

I. Framledne Direct. och Kongl: Vet. Acad. Ledamots Herr H. T. Scheffers Chemiske Föreläsningar, Rörande Salter, Jordarter, Vatten, Fetmor, Metaller och Färgning, Samlade, i ordning stälde och med Anmärkningar utgifne, 8°, M. Swederus, Upsala, 1775 (pref. dated 7 November 1774, engr. t.p., xiv, 450 pp., 2 copperplates (symbols, and affinity tables)); 2 ed., Uppsala, 1779; 3 ed. revised by P. J. H.[jelm], Stockholm, 1796 (pref. dated 5 January 1796, pp. xvi, 509, xix, 2 pl.).

II. German tr. by Weigel: Herrn H. T. Scheffer . . . Chemische Vorlesungen, über die Salze, Erdarten, Wässer, entzündliche Körper, Metalle und das Färben; gesammlet, in Ordnung gestellt und mit Anmerkungen herausgegeben, vom Herrn Professor und Ritter Torb. Bergmann (sic). Aus dem Schwedischen übersetzt von D. Christian Ehrenfried Weigel, 8°, Greifswald, 1779 (pp. xxvi, 724, ii Errata, 2 plates).

III. Scheffer's Essai sur l'Art de la Teinture, . . . commenté et développé par le célèbre Bergman avec Mémoire sur l'Indigo, Paris, 1787 (228 pp.; the last part of the work; Scheffer had an expert knowledge of dyeing).

Scheffer defines an acid as a substance which effervesces with alkali, turns syrup of violets and litmus red, and precipitates what is dissolved in alkali.[6] He still thought that Epsom salt was a compound of lime and muriatic acid with some vitriolic acid.[7] He says that turbith mineral (basic mercuric sulphate) when heated with resin gave mercury, not vermilion (mercuric sulphide).[8] Although he reports that Roman vitriol was no longer made,[9] Bergman says[10] it was still made at Monte Fiascone and contained copper. Iron can be precipitated from solution by lime water.[11] Dutch white lead makers die after three years, even the dust being poisonous.[12] In an experiment on the conversion of water into earth, Scheffer[13] says that on heating the water in a pelican for two years, no more earth is deposited than at the beginning of the heating, when it is formed from the dust in the water (this is incorrect). He describes methods of water analysis,[14] gives a long account of the preparation of

---

[1] Crell's *Beyträge*, 1790, iv, 262, 393; 1794, v, 6, 198 (Versuch einer Geschichte des Blaserohrs und seine Anwendungen); also by Landauer, *Ber.*, 1893, xxvi, 898.

[2] KAH, 1748, ix, 99.   [3] KAH, 1746, vii, 176: see 178.

[4] *Traité de Chimie*, 1833, viii, 140.   [5] (1), ii, 246.   [6] I, § 8.

[7] I, § 73; II, p. 154; Bergman corrects this in a note.   [8] I, § 82; II, p. 76.

[9] I, § 85; II, p. 82.   [10] I, § 86, Anm.; II, p. 187.

[11] I, § 114; II, p. 219, contradicting Pott and Brandt.

[12] I, § 125 b; II, p. 233.

[13] I, § 181; II, p. 314.   [14] I, § 185 f.; II, p. 321 f.

ether,[1] and describes the methods of extracting essential oils,[2] including oil of cloves by the method of distillation *per descensum*.[3]

In a long memoir on the methods of separating metals (1752)[4] Scheffer remarks that (hot) concentrated sulphuric acid will dissolve silver from its alloy with gold, but says this acid was then more expensive than aqua fortis. If fixed alkali (potassium carbonate) solution is added to a solution of silver in aqua fortis and the bottle at once stoppered, there is no precipitate; but if the stopper is removed there is a brisk effervescence and a precipitate is formed.[5] Pure silver is obtained by fusing precipitated silver chloride with fixed alkali and a little nitre.[6]

Scheffer also investigated platinum (1752 and 1757),[7] which he called white gold (hvitt guld, aurum album) but recognised as a peculiar metal. It was investigated by Marggraf in 1757 (Vol. II, p. 728). Claude Morin,[8] and J. L. Fournier,[9] recognised it as a separate metal. Scheffer prepared an alloy of platinum and arsenic which was later important in the metallurgy of platinum. He says[10] he obtained the platinum from Brandt, and it was obtained in 1750 by Assessor Rudenschöld from the West Indies.

Scaliger[11] said there was a kind of brass found in Mexico which no fire or arts of the Spaniards can liquefy (inter Mexicum et Dariem fodinas esse orichalci: quod nullo igni, nullis Hispanicis artibus hactenus liquescere potuit), and this would be platinum. It is mentioned again by the mathematician Don Antonio de Ulloa (who visited Mexico in 1735)[12] in describing the gold and silver mines of Quito. He says several mines had been abandoned because of the platina (donde la *Platina*), which is so hard that it is not easily broken on an anvil and is not calcinable, so that the metal enclosed in it cannot be extracted without great expense and labour.

Specimens of native platinum were brought from Carthagena to Europe in 1741 by Charles Wood; the Spaniards called it platina de pinto. Experiments with it were made by Brownrigg[13] and by Lewis,[14] but Scheffer's was the first accurate examination of the metal.

Buffon[15] still thought that platinum was a natural alloy of gold and silver containing iron, and Richter (see p. 675) used the symbol $)\odot$ for it. The name platinum is used by J. L. Fournier.[9] Thomson[16] says the name 'platina' was changed to 'platinum' by Linnæus, this name being adopted by Bergman,

[1] I, § 212 f.; II, p. 381 f.   [2] I, § 218; II, p. 399.   [3] I, § 220; II, p. 403.
[4] KAH, 1753, xiv, 1; *Recueil*, i, 268 f., 295.
[5] *Recueil*, i, 300: perhaps a soluble silver bicarbonate is formed.   [6] *Ib.*, 299.
[7] KAH, 1752, xiii, 269, 276; 1757, xviii, 314.
[8] *Le platine, l'or blanc, ou le huitième metal*, 12°, Paris, 1758 (BN); Fourcroy, (3), 1790, ii, 550.
[9] *Dissertatio inauguralis chemico-medica de Metallis*, Vienna, 1777, 33.
[10] I, § 240; II, p. 456.   [11] *Exotericarum Exercitationum*, Exerc. 88; Paris, 1557, f. 134 *v.*
[12] *Relacion historica del Viage a la America Meridional*, 2 vols. 4°, Madrid, 1748, i, 606; tr., *A Voyage to South America*, 2 ed. 2 vols., London, 1760, ii, 471.
[13] *Phil. Trans.*, 1750, xliv, 584, 594 (communicated by W. Watson); Watson, *ib.*, 590.
[14] *Phil. Trans.*, 1754, xlviii, 638; 1757, l, 148; *id.*, tr. Neumann, *Chemical Works*, 1759, 43; *id.*, *Commercium Philosophico-Technicum*, London, 1763, ii, 443; Russell-Wood, *Ann. Sci.*, 1951, vii, 199.
[15] *Histoire Naturelle des Minéraux*, 4°, Paris, 1783, iii, 316–58; 1884, iii, 402.
[16] *Ency. Brit. Suppl.*, 1801, I, i, 22; (2), 1802, i, 93.

but Bergman[1] still used the name 'platina'. Platinum was found at Choco, New Granada, and near the coast of Barbacoas; it was never found near Cartha-gena. The price in Mexico in 1811 was 40 francs per lb., in Paris 130–150 francs.[2]

Scheffer[3] found by many experiments that metals gain in weight as 'phlo-giston is removed' from them and decrease in weight when 'phlogiston com-bines' with them; iron when melted in the absence of phlogiston loses much of its own phlogiston and increases in weight, since an equal weight is contained in a smaller space. He does not say that phlogiston has a negative weight, as Kopp[4] asserted.

Scheffer described[5] a method for the separation of gold from silver by boil-ing with concentrated sulphuric acid. He dealt with Chinese *petunse* (felspar, which he thought was gypsum),[6] sal ammoniac,[7] the different kinds of potash (cineres clavellati, cendre gravellée, Blau-krone, crude, brown, refined, etc.),[8] and the manufacture of pinchbeck from 5 pts. of copper and 2 of zinc (used as calamine and charcoal).[9] He gives a description of zinc[10] and says a poisonous white alloy of copper and arsenic was used in Germany to make tea-spoons.[11]

FAGGOT. FUNCK

Jacob Faggot (Holferbo-gård, 13 March 1699–Stockholm, 28 February 1777) investigated the fire-proofing of wood by vitriol solution,[12] the analysis of gunpowder (krut) by the hydrostatic balance and chemical tests (Swedish gunpowder contained 75 saltpetre, 16 sulphur, and 9 charcoal),[13] gave a table of specific gravities of solutions of various kinds of potash as determined by the hydrostatic balance,[14] and described the use of a hydrometer as an alcoholo-meter in determining the strength of wine and brandy.[15]

Alexander Funck (? –Stockholm, 8 November 1797) wrote on zinc ores,[16] pointing out blende as a true ore of zinc, usually mixed with some lead ore. Zinc is a true metal, not a semi-metal, and the copper, iron and lead found in it are only impurities from the ore.

BROWALL. BERGIUS

Johan Browall (Brevall, Brovallius) (Vesterås, 30 August 1707–Åbo, 25 July 1755) was professor in Åbo, Finland, and later bishop. He classed arsenic, which he obtained by heating arsenical pyrites, or white arsenic with soap (see Albertus Magnus, Vol. I), as a metal, and recognised that arsenic occurs

---

[1] KAH, 1777, xxxviii, 317: a particular metal.
[2] Humboldt, *Essai politique sur le Royaume de la Nouvelle Espagne*, Paris, 1811, iii, 351; iv, 205; McDonald, *Platinum Metals Review*, 1960, iv, 27.
[3] KAH, 1757, xviii, 314.   [4] (1), iii, 149.   [5] KAH, 1753, xiv, 1.
[6] KAH, 1753, xiv, 220.   [7] KAH, 1751, xii, 265.
[8] KAH, 1759, xx, 1; *Recueil*, ii, 521.   [9] KAH, 1760, xxi, 291; *Recueil*, ii, 601.
[10] I, § 326; II, p. 602.   [11] I, § 314; II, p. 590.
[12] KAH, 1741, i, 160; *Recueil*, i, 50.   [13] KAH, 1755, xvi, 96; *Recueil*, ii, 404.
[14] KAH, 1759, xx, 31; *Recueil*, ii, 541.
[15] KAH, 1770, xxxi, 255.   [16] KAH, 1744, v, 57; *Recueil*, i, 129.

frequently in minerals as well as sulphur.[1] He divided minerals into salts, sulphurs, and metals.[2]

Petter Jonas Bergius (Småland, 6 July 1730–Stockholm, 10 July 1790),[3] professor of medicine and pharmacy in the Carolinian Institute, Stockholm, was active mostly in botany, but investigated soluble tartar (neutral potassium tartrate) and borax,[4] baking bread,[5] human milk,[6] urinary calculi,[7] and the manufacture of brandy.[8]

RINMAN

Sven Rinman (Uppsala, 12 June 1720–Eskilstuna, 20 December 1792 or 1794) investigated minerals before the blowpipe, including a tin ore,[9] and discovered the green pigment (Rinman's green) formed by heating zinc oxide with cobalt salts.[10] He wrote on iron ores[11] and on the manufacture of iron and steel (which, with Stahl (see Vol. II, p. 682), he regarded as phlogisticated iron).[12] Bergman (see p. 193) and J. C. F. Meyer[13] also experimented on the supposed different contents of phlogiston in cast iron and steel.

Rinman's theory of the increase in weight of metals on calcination[14] is described later. He noticed the red solution (colloidal ?) of oxide of iron in alkali,[15] and the formation of potassium ferrate, soluble to a red solution in water, on heating iron filings and saltpetre (cf. Stahl, Vol. II, p. 682).[16] He showed that iron will rust in water on exposure to air, which he thought showed that the metal contained an acid; rusting is accelerated in presence of aërial acid (carbon dioxide), and inflammable air (hydrogen) is evolved from iron acting on a solution of aërial acid.[17] Cast iron is converted into steel, and steel into malleable iron, by successive loss of phlogiston.[18]

Bergman[19] says Rinman heated the alum pans at Garphytta with burning alum shale as fuel instead of wood. He says the reddish alum from Brunswick contained cobalt; Chinese alum was free from iron.[20]

---

[1] KAH, 1744, v, 20; Recueil, 1764, i, 133.

[2] Komppa, Z. angew. Chem., 1927, xl, 1431; V. Ojala and E. R. Schierz, J. Chem. Educ., 1937, xiv, 1413.

[3] Poggendorff, (1), i, 150; portr. in Zekert, C. W. Scheele, Mittenwald, 1933, vii, 266.

[4] Nova Acta Acad. Nat. Curios., 1770, iv, 95.   [5] KAH, 1773, xxxiv, 27.

[6] KAH, 1772, xxxiii, 43.   [7] KAH, 1777, xxxviii, 304.

[8] KAH, 1776, xxxvii, 257.   [9] KAH, 1746, vii, 176.

[10] KAH, 1780, i, 163; 1781, ii, 3.   [11] KAH, 1754, xv, 282; Recueil, i, 318.

[12] Försök till Järnets Historia med Tillämpning för Slögder och Handtwerk, 2 pts. 4°, Stockholm, 1782; tr. by J. G. Georgi, Versuch einer Geschichte des Eisens mit Anwendung für Gewerbe und Handwerker, 2 vols. 8°, Berlin, 1785, with notes by C. J. B. Karsten; new tr. by Karsten, 2 vols. 8°, Liegnitz, 1814; Gmelin, (1), ii, 573. The last work contains a large number of original experiments. It also deals (vol. i) with the making of magnets and compass needles.

[13] Schriften Berlin. Ges. Naturforsch. Freunde, 1783, iv, 274–90.

[14] Versuch, 1785, i, § 64 f., p. 211 f.   [15] Ib., ii, § 230, p. 225; § 249, p. 260.

[16] Ib., ii, § 253, p. 268.

[17] Ib., ii, §§ 213–16, pp. 160–72; this was fairly recently announced as a new discovery in the National Chemical Laboratory, Teddington.

[18] Ib., ii, §§ 266, 275, 281, 299, pp. 322, 366, 393, 443; cf. Bergman, p. 193.

[19] Scheffers Chemiske Föreläsningar, 1775, § 75, n. 2; tr. Weigel, p. 159.

[20] Ib., § 75, n. 3; tr., p. 160.

ENGESTRÖM

Gustaf von Engeström (Lund, 1 August 1738–Uppsala, 12 August 1813), warden of the Stockholm Mint, published on the blowpipe (see p. 174), on native soda (*kien*) from China[1] and borax (*poun-xa*) from Tibet,[2] pyrolusite,[3] Chinese zinc ore,[4] Chinese *paktong*,[5] iron and steel,[6] the separation of metals by means of liver of sulphur,[7] the separation of silver from silver chloride by fusion with potassium carbonate,[8] and the recovery of mercury from glass mirrors.[9]

GADD

Peter Adrian Gadd (Birkala, 12 April 1727–Åbo, 11 August 1797) was professor of physics, chemistry and economics in Åbo, Finland.[10] His many publications, often in the form of dissertations by students (the British Museum has 36 of these), cover a variety of topics: historical and general,[11] on physical chemistry,[12] on peat fuel,[13] on mineralogy and metallurgy,[14] on salts,[15] agriculture,[16] on the conversion of water into earth,[17] and saltpetre.[18]

Gadd's papers on colours of flowers,[19] various dyes,[20] silkworms,[21] water hemlock,[22] lime and cements,[23] and alum[24] are unimportant.

BERGMAN

Torbern Olof Bergman (he never used the second name) (Catherineberg, West Gothland, 20 (O.S. 9) March 1735–Medevi, 8 July 1784), the son of a tax-collector, entered the University of Uppsala to study, at the wish of his father, theology or law. He spent so much time clandestinely studying mathematics and science that his health failed and for an interval he went home, where, in the open air, he studied botany and natural history. On his return to

---

[1] KAH, 1772, xxxiii, 172.   [2] KAH, 1772, xxxiii, 322.   [3] KAH, 1774, xxxv, 196.
[4] KAH, 1775, xxxvi, 78.   [5] KAH, 1776, xxxvii, 35.   [6] KAH, 1774, xxxv, 3.
[7] KAH, 1775, xxxvi, 206.   [8] KAH, 1783, iv, 3.   [9] KAH, 1788, ix, 98.
[10] Gmelin, (1), ii, 576, 718; iii, 50; Poggendorff, (1), i, 826; Komppa, *Z. angew. Chem.*, 1927, xl, 1431.
[11] *De fatis scientiæ chemicæ sub epocha patrum* (diss. J. Erling), 4°, Åbo, 1763; *De sacerdote chimico*, 4°, Åbo, 1769; *De sale sodomitico*, 4°, Åbo, 1778; *Remoræ incrementorum scientiæ chemicæ* (diss. C. Avellan), 4°, Åbo, 1763; *Inventa quaedam chemica recentiora* (diss. J. Grââ), 4°, Åbo, 1763; *Leisten om chemiens tillåmpning til ylle manufacturers förbättring*, 4°, Åbo, 1764.
[12] *Observationes chemico-physicæ de originaria corporum mineralium electricitate*, 4°, Åbo, 1769; *Tentamen speciminis chemicæ opticæ*, 4°, Åbo, 1772.
[13] *Om brännetorf*, 4°, Åbo, 1759.
[14] *Observationes mineral. metallurgicæ de monte cuprifero Tilas-Wuari*, 4°, Åbo, 1769; *Om Järnets förwandling til stål* (diss. G. Korsemann), 4°, Åbo, 1760; *Om tennets och dess malmers beskaffenhet* (diss. A. Nordenskiöld), 4°, Stockholm and Åbo, 1772.
[15] *De sale calcis muriatico* (diss. Sourander), 4°, Åbo, 1773.
[16] *Åkerbrukets chymiska grunder om akerjordmonernes rätta kiännig och förbättring*, 4 pts. 4°, Åbo, 1761–4.
[17] *Disquis. chemica hypotheseos de transmutatione aquae in terram* (diss. S. Heuerlin), 4°, Åbo, 1763.
[18] *Om medel til salpeter-syuderierner förbättring och upkomst i riket* (diss. A. Grant), 4°, Åbo, 1763.
[19] KAH, 1762, xxiii, 115.   [20] KAH, 1767, xxviii, 134.   [21] KAH, 1773, xxxiv, 281.
[22] KAH, 1774, xxxv, 231: *cicuta*. [23] KAH, 1770, xxxi, 189.   [24] KAH, 1768, xxix, 125.

the university, by arrangement with his father, his studies of law were supplemented by mathematics, physics, chemistry, botany, and entomology. He made important discoveries in the last two subjects, especially entomology, attracting the attention of Linnæus.

In 1758 he qualified for the master's degree (Phil. Mag.) with a thesis in pure mathematics and was appointed magister docens (a post peculiar to Uppsala, a kind of assistant to the professor) in natural philosophy. In 1760 (or 1761) he became adjunct (assistant professor) in mathematics and physics. In this period he published on the rainbow, the aurora, the electrical properties of tourmaline, etc. He also made researches in electricity and drew up a table of bodies, each of which when rubbed with a preceding one became negative, but with a subsequent one positive, the strength of the electrification increasing the further apart were the two bodies in the series,[1] an anticipation in frictional electricity of Volta's contact series (see Vol. IV).

He became a member of the Swedish Academy in 1764 and in 1766 published an important treatise on physical geography.[2] In 1767 he succeeded J. G. Wallerius as professor of chemistry and pharmacy at Uppsala. He had studied chemistry but had then published nothing on that subject. The friends of Wallerius, who had another nominee, violently attacked[3] Bergman's first chemical publication, on the preparation of alum,[4] which contained quantitative experiments. Thomson[5] says feelingly: 'Such men unhappily exist in all colleges, and the more eminent a professor is, the more is he exposed to their malignant activity . . . they seldom succeed, unless from some want of prudence or steadiness in the individual whom they assail.' Fortunately, the Crown Prince, the Chancellor of the University, insisted (on the representation of Von Swab) on a proper enquiry, to the discomfiture of Bergman's opponents. When asked by Frederick the Great in 1776 to go to Berlin, Bergman remembered this and declined out of respect for his friend, who was then King of Sweden. In 1769 Bergman's health failed (no doubt from early overwork), and from 1780 he retired from active work until his death in 1784. His work on affinity (see p. 184), which concludes the last volume of his collected works published by himself, was left incomplete since, as he says, he did not expect to live long (vitæ præterea breve est curriculum, prosperamque valetudinem incertam . . . fiet autem quam brevissime),[6] and he died a year later, at the early age of 49, at Medevi near the Wetter Lake, East Gothland, where he had gone to take the mineral waters.

Bergman was for a period Rector of the University of Uppsala, 'a kind of republic', in which he preserved peace between the two parties, one the

[1] *Phil. Trans.*, 1764, liv, 84.
[2] *Werldsbeskrifning Andra Del eller Physisk Beskrifning öfver Jord-klotet*, 8°, Uppsala, 1766; tr. L. H. Röhl (and F. Mallett), *Physikalische Beschreibung der Erdkugel, auf Veranlassung der cosmographischen Gesellschaft verfasset von Torbern Bergman*, 2 vols. 8°, Greifswald, 1769–74; 3 enlarged ed., 1791 (Roy. Geograph. Soc. Library); ch. 5 tr. by A. Guichelin, *J. des Mines*, An IV (1795–6), iii, no. xv, 55–79; no. xvi, 21–66; summary in A. Wolf, *A History of Science, Technology and Philosophy*, 1938, ii, 420.
[3] Faggot, KAH, 1767, xxviii, 80.
[4] KAH, 1767, xxviii, 73; *Opuscula*, 1779, i, 279.   [5] (1), ii, 33.
[6] *De Attractionibus Electivis*, § 11; tr. Beddoes, *A Dissertation on Elective Attractions*, London, 1785, 70.

faculties of theology and law, and the other the scientific professors, and also
maintained discipline among the numerous young students. He was a member
of the Academies of Uppsala, Stockholm, Berlin, Göttingen, Turin and Paris,
and F.R.S. in 1765. Crell says he was a man of the highest character: 'Eitelkeit
kannte er nicht.'

By courtesy of the Curator of the Art Collection of Uppsala University

FIG. 16. TORBERN BERGMAN, 1735–84.
(From an oil-painting (1778) by Laurent Pasch.

On his appointment, Bergman formed a chemical library, a mineral collection (that purchased by the University from Swab being incomplete and not
arranged) and (at considerable sacrifice of his income) a collection of models of
machines used in chemical arts (purchased from Aurivillius), furnaces, and
metallurgical apparatus, for the instruction of students.[1] Thomson, who saw

[1] Thomson, (5), 104, 181 f., 183.

it, says the collection of models was very small. He visited Bergman's house and his laboratory, which was small but well-fitted.

Bergman's two children died in infancy. His widow received an annuity in return for handing over his library and apparatus to the Royal Society of Uppsala, which presumably still has them.[1] The Uppsala University Library has a large collection of letters to Bergman.[2] Fourcroy[3] arranged Bergman's publications in eight classes, dealing with: (i) acids, (ii) earths and stones, (iii) mineral waters, (iv) metals, (v) chemical attractions, (vi) new methods of analysis, (vii) applications of chemistry to mineralogy, the sciences and the arts, (viii) the history of chemistry.

The dissertations and memoirs printed (revised) in the *Opuscula* (see A below) are numbered I–LXXII but in irregular order of dates; many are dissertations by candidates named in the following list, rearranged in chronological order:

I. De confectione aluminis (G. Soedelius), 1767.
II. De calce auri fulminante (C. A. Plomgren), 1769.
III. De connubio hydrargyri cum acido salis, 1769.
IV. De aquis Upsaliensibus (P. Dube), 1770.
V. De laterum coctione rite instituenda, 1771.
VI. De terris geoponicis, 1773.
VII. De tartaro antimoniato (I. A. Level), 1773.
VIII. De formis crystallorum, præsertim e spatho ortis, 1773.
IX. De fonte acidulari Danemarkensi (C. H. Wertmüller), 1773.
X. De mineris ferri albis (P. J. Hielm), 1774.
XI. De acido aëreo, 1774.
XII. De attractionibus electivis, 1775 (extended in 1783, see p. 184).
XIII. De aquis medicatis frigidis arte parandis, 1775.
XIV. De magnesia (C. Norell), 1775.
XV. De niccolo (J. Afzelius Arvidsson), 1775.
XVI. De acido sacchari (J. Afzelius Arvidsson), 1776.
XVII. Observationes nonnullæ de calculis urinaris, 1776.
XVIII. Producta ignis subterranei chemice considerata, 1777.
XIX. De aqua pelagica, 1777.
XX. De lapide hydrophano, 1777.
XXI. De terra gemmarum, 1777.
XXII. De platina, 1777.
XXIII. De arsenico (A. Pihl), 1777.
XXIV. De magnesia nitri, 1777.
XXV. De nuperrimis chemiæ incrementis, 1777.
XXVI. De analysi aquarum (J. P. Scharenberg), 1778.
XXVII. De aquis medicatis calidis arte parandis, 1778.
XXVIII. Introitus de indagando vero, 1779 (Intr. to *Opusc.* i).
XXIX. De tubo ferruminatorio, ejusdem usu in explorandis corporibus, præsertim mineralibus, 1779.
XXX. De terra silicea (K. A. Grönlund), 1779.
XXXI. De terra turmalini, 1779.

[1] Condorcet, AdS, 1784, h 31; *id.*, *Oeuvres*, 1847, iii, 139–61 (b. 20 March); Crell, *Ann.*, 1784, II, 378; 1787, I, 74–96; Gmelin, (1), iii, 261; Hoefer, (1), ii, 423; Kopp, (1), i, 245; P.A.S. in *Biographiskt Lexicon öfver Namnkunnige Svenska Män*, Uppsala, 1836, ii, 191–203; Thomson, (1), ii, 27, 190; *id.*, *Ann. Phil.*, 1818, xii, 321; Vicq d'Azyr, 1805, i, 209 (b. 20 March, from autobiography); V.R. in NBU, 1853, v, 520; portrs. in Scherer's *Allgem. J. Chem.*, 1798, i; *Phil. Mag.*, 1801, ix; Zekert, *Carl Wilhelm Scheele*, Mittenwald, 1931–3, vi, 156; P. J.Hjelm, *Åminnelse-Tal öfver Herr Torbern Olof Bergman*, Stockholm, 1786 (104 pp.); B. Moström, *Torbern Bergman A Bibliography of his Works*, Stockholm, 1957.
[2] Nordenskiöld, *C. W. Scheele, Nachgelassene Briefe*, Stockholm, 1892, p. iii.   [3] (2), iii, 512.

XXXII. De mineris zinci (B. R. Geyer), 1779.
XXXIII. De primordiis chemiæ (J. Paulin), 1779.
XXXIV. De præcipitatis metallicis, 1780.
XXXV. De minerarum docimasia humida (P. Castorin), 1780.
XXXVI. De cobalto, niccolo, platina et magnesia, eorumque per præcipitationes investigata indole, 1780.
XXXVII. Analysis chemica pigmenti indici, 1780.
XXXVIII. De analysi ferri (J. Gadolin), 1781.
XXXIX. De causa fragilitatis ferri frigidi, 1781.
XL. De acidis metallicis, 1781 (extended).
XLI. De stanno sulphurato, 1781.
XLII. De antimonialibus sulphuratis (F. W. Mannecrantz), 1782.
XLIII. Historiæ chemiæ medium seu obscurum ævum, a medio seculi VII ad medium seculi XVII (P. Afzelius Arvidson), 1782.
XLIV. De analysi lithomargæ (C. D. Hjerta), 1782.
XLV. De terra asbestina (C. G. Robsahm), 1782.
XLVI. De aquis acidulatis Medviensibus, 1782.
XLVII. De diversa phlogisti quantitate in metallis, 1782.
XLVIII. De fontibus medicatis Lokanis, 1783.
XLIX. Meditationes de systemate fossilium naturali, 1784.
L. Observationes mineralogicæ, 1784.

The works in the above list are reprinted (many revised) in the *Opuscula Physica et Chemica* (A), the first three volumes edited by Bergman, with a prefatory essay (XXVIII) *On the Investigation of Truth*. Three more volumes, making six in all, were published in Leipzig with a reprint of the first three volumes.

A. Torberni Bergman . . . Opuscula Physica et Chemica, pleraque antea seorsim edita, jam ab Auctore collecta, revisa et aucta. Cum Tabulis Ænæis, 3 vols. 8°: I Cum Privilegio S. Elect. Saxoniæ, Holmiæ, Upsaliæ & Aboæ, In Officinis Librariis Magni Swederi, Regg. Acadd. Bibliop., 1779 (iii ll., xvi, 412 pp., 2 plates); II Upsaliæ, Litteris Direct. Johan. Edman, 1780 (iii ll., 510 pp., 2 plates); III Cum Privilegio S. Electoris Saxoniæ. Lipsiæ in Officina libr. Jo. Godof. Mülleriana prostat. Upsaliæ, Litteris Direct. Johan Edman, 1783 (iii ll., 490 (mispr. 290) pp., 3 plates). The vols. are dedicated, respectively, to the Royal Society of London, and the Royal Academies of Berlin and Paris.

B. Complete ed., 6 vols. 8°, Leipzig, I. G. Müller (BM 955. h. 23–5; 1035. i. 7–9; BN R 28280–2, 28283–5; CUL L. 47. 8). Vol. I, Editio nova emendatior (anon. pref.), 1788; II, 1792; III, editio noua, correctior, pref. by N. D. Leske, 1786; last three vols. ed. Hebenstreit: Opuscula Physica et Chemica pleraque seorsim antea edita nunc collecta et revisa. Editionis curam post Auctoris mortem gessit Ernestus Benjamin. Gottl. Hebenstreit; Vol. IV, 1787; V, 1788; VI, with index, 1790.

   Hebenstreit (Leipzig; 10 February 1758–12 December 1802), M.D., was assistant professor of general medicine (1785), then of anatomy and surgery (1793), in Leipzig.

C. Partial French tr.:

   Opuscules Chymiques et Physiques de M. T. Bergman . . . recueillis, revus, et augmentés par lui-meme, traduits par M. de Morveau, avec des Notes, 2 vols. 8°, Dijon, 1780–5 (I: pp. xxxi, 446, iii; II (very rare), pp. xvi, 525; Smeaton, *Ambix*, 1957, vi, 18); the tr. is by Mme. Picardet, supervised by Guyton de Morveau, who added the notes.

D. Partial English tr.:

   Physical and Chemical Essays: translated from the original Latin of Sir Torbern Bergman, . . . By Edmund Cullen, M.D. Fellow of the Royal College of Physicians at Dublin. To which are added Notes and Illustrations by the Translator, 2 vols. 8°, London, 1784 and again 1788; vol. iii (v. scarce), Edinburgh, 1791, translator anonymous. Cullen omitted many footnotes in orig. but added de Morveau's notes and some initialled B., i.e. Beddoes;[1] the tr. (especially of vol. iii) is unsatisfactory.

[1] Stock, *Memoirs of the Life of Thomas Beddoes*, 1811, 12.

E. German tr.:

Torbern Bergmann [*sic*] . . . Kleine Physische und Chemische Werke . . . Mit
einigen Kupfern aus dem Lateinischen übersetzt von Heinrich Tabor Med. Doct.,
6 vols. 8°, Frankfurt, 1782–90 (vols. iv–vi scarce; Gmelin, who ments. only 3 vols.,
says the tr. is unsatisfactory).

F. An Essay on the General Usefulness of Chemistry, and its Application to the
Various Occasions of Life, 8°, London, 1783 (iv, 163 pp., i. l. errata; BM T. 243.
(4.); in Swedish, and German, 1779; includes a 'general view, medical, œcono-
mical, and technical chemistry, halurgy, geurgy, theiurgy', etc., salts, earths,
inflammable substances, metals, waters, and airs).

Not printed in the Opuscula is Bergman's classification of minerals based on the
chemical composition:

G. (*a*) Sciagraphia Regni Mineralis secundum principia proxima digesta, 8°, Leipzig
and Dresden, 1782 (pp. 166, ii errata), Florence, 1783 (London Chem. Soc.),
London, 1783 (Duveen, 67).

(*b*) Outlines of Mineralogy, translated from the Original of Sir Torbern Bergman
by William Withering, 8°, Birmingham, 1783 (pp. iv, iii, 128).

(*c*) Manuel du Minéralogiste, ou, Sciagraphie du Règne Minéral, distribuée
d'après l'Analyse Chimique . . . mis au jour par M. Ferber . . . traduite et
augmenté de notes par M. Mongez, 8°, Paris, 1784 (pp. lxxx, viii, 343, plate);
nouvelle éd., considérablement augmentée par J. C. Delamétherie, 2 vols. 8°,
Paris, 1792 (I: pp. cxx, 359, plate of blowpipe; II: pp. 443, plate of crystals).

(*d*) German tr. in J. H. Pfingsten, Bibliotheck ausländischer Chemisten, Mineralogen, und mit Mineralien beschäftigter Fabrikanten, Nürnburg, 1783, iii, 507 f.

H. Bergman's ed. of Scheffer's lectures (see p. 175):

(*a*) Scheffers Chemiske Föreläsningar, 8°, Uppsala, 1775, 2 ed. 1779 (BN R
50340–1), 3 ed. revised by P. J. Hjelm, Stockholm, 1796;

(*b*) tr. by C. E. Weigel: Scheffer . . . Chemische Vorlesungen . . . herausgegeben
von . . . Torb. Bergmann [*sic*], Aus dem Schwedischen übersetzt, 8°, Greifswald, 1779.

Bergman's ed. of these lectures was intended for use as a text-book by students
at Uppsala.

J. (*a*) De attractionibus electivis disquisitio, *Nova Acta Reg. Soc. Sci. Upsaliensis*,
1775, ii, 159–248 (50 tables in two sheets): extended in A, 1783, iii, 291–470
(59 tables). A preliminary account is given in H (pref. dated November 1774).

(*b*) A Dissertation on Elective Attractions. By Torbern Bergmann [*sic*]. . . .
Translated from the Latin by the Translator of Spallanzani's Dissertations
[T. Beddoes], 8°, London, 1785, xvi, 382 pp., 1 leaf emendata, 1 table of
symbols, 7 folding plates (in which, it is said, some figures in the originals are
corrected).

(*c*) Traité des Affinités Chymiques, ou Attractions Électives; Traduit du Latin,
sur la derniere Edition de Bergman. Augmenté d'un Supplément & de Notes.
Avec des Planches, 8°, Paris, 1788, pp. 1–259 and Supplément, 260–444,
7 plates. Approbation signed by de Fourcroy, 8 October 1787; the Privilege du
Roi speaks of the *Traité* as 'traduit de l'Anglois'. The translator was François
Joseph Bonjour (see p. 505), assistant to Berthollet. The notes are antiphlogistic and include unpublished material from Berthollet.

Fourcroy[1] says that Bergman was self-taught in chemistry and evolved his
own method, based on the precision and severity of mathematics combined
with the observational method of natural history, two sciences of which he
was previously master. The course of his chemical career can be followed by
his published dissertations (1767–84): 'il n'a jamais rien écrit de vague . . . ne
saurais-je trop en recommander la lecture repétée, & l'étude approfondie à
ceux qui veulent faire de véritables progrès en chimie.' Fourcroy says Bergman's most important contributions are: (1) his improvement of qualitative

[1] (2), 1796, iii, 502 f.

and quantitative analysis, which he applied to minerals,[1] volcanic products,[2] and mineral waters;[3] (2) his chemical classification of minerals (following Cronstedt, 1758, see p. 174), and (3) his work on elective affinity.[4]

Special features of Bergman's essays are the very complete historical introductions, partly compiled from Pott (see Vol. II, p. 718), and the attempt to make them intelligible to non-specialists, so that they are very readable. The two essays on the history of chemistry (XXXIII and XLIII)[5] and the Stockholm lecture of 1777 (XXV)[6] contain much information not easily found elsewhere. In a discussion of accounts of transmutations,[7] Bergman says that 'although most of them are deceptive and many uncertain, some bear such character and testimony that, unless we reject all historical evidence, we must allow them to be entitled to confidence'. The essay *On the Investigation of Truth*[8] contains a vigorous defence of the experimental method as exemplified by Newton, and a criticism of the speculative method as represented by the Cartesians: it also points out some common sources of error in chemical experiments.

Bergman's *Sciagraphia* (G) contains a chemical classification of minerals. Buffon[9] laid almost exclusive stress on the crystal form and neglected the chemical composition. Bergman in the last year of his life (1784) also wrote a long essay, *Thoughts on a Natural System of Minerals*,[10] in which he enlarges upon the advantages of a chemical study of minerals. Following Cronstedt (1758, see p. 174) he divided minerals into four classes: saline, earthy, inflammable, and metallic, earths soluble in water being called saline earths (our alkaline earths).[11] Bergman's essay on the shapes of crystals, particularly Iceland spar, went some distance on the way afterwards taken by Haüy (see Vol. IV).[12] Thomson says the derivation from simple primary forms was really discovered by Gahn, who is mentioned by Bergman (primus vidit . . . Dom. J. G. Gahn).[13]

Bergman made much use of the blowpipe, which is mentioned in his first chemical paper (I), on alum, in 1767, and he learned of it from Gahn. He used charcoal as a support both with and without a cavity, and a silver or gold spoon for fusion. He recognised the oxidising and reducing flames and used borax, microcosmic salt (which he says contains soda, ammonia, and phosphoric acid) and soda as fluxes and for beads (*sphærula*).[14] The blowpipe is mentioned in Bergman's edition of Scheffer's lectures.[15] A manuscript of an essay on the blowpipe sent to Baron Born (see Vol. II, p. 731) in 1777 was printed in 1779.[16]

[1] XXXV (1780); A, ii, 399.   [2] XVIII (1777); A, iii, 184.
[3] XXVI (1778); A, i, 68.   [4] XII (1775–83); A, iii, 291.
[5] B, iv, 1, 85; tr. in Wiegleb, (1) and (2); very inaccurate tr. in D, iii, 1–158.
[6] B, vi, 65–95.   [7] XLIII; B, iv, 127.
[8] XXVIII; A, I, i–xvi; D, I, xxi–xliv.
[9] *Histoire Naturelle des Minéraux*, 9 vols. 8°, Paris, 1783–8, i, 4 f., 11 f.
[10] XLIX; 8°, Florence, 1784; B, iv, 180–278; D, iii, 205–316.
[11] XXIX (1777); A, ii, 462.   [12] VIII (1773); A, ii, 1.   [13] A, ii, 9.
[14] XXI, 1777; XXIX; A, ii, 72, 455, and plates; Engeström, in Cronstedt, *System of Mineralogy*, London, 1788, ii, 945–8, says microcosmic salt was so expensive that it was 'still very little in use'.
[15] H (*a*), 1775, xi; H (*b*), 1779, xxi.
[16] XXIX; *Commentatio de Tvbo Ferrvminatorio, ejusdemque usu in explorandis corporibus, præsertim mineralibus*, 8°, Vienna, 1779 (64 pp.); in A, ii, 455–506; Italian tr. in Amoretti and

In general analysis Bergman used as indicators (giving Boyle credit for pioneering work) litmus tincture, and decoction of Brazil wood; he says[1] that syrup of violets imported into Sweden was so often adulterated that he used instead paper stained with logwood (fernbok) or turmeric. As general reagents he used tincture of galls for iron, prussiate of potash (potassium ferrocyanide; blue with iron, brown with copper, white with manganese), sulphuric acid for baryta (precipitate) and carbonates (effervescence), nitric acid for sulphides (precipitation of sulphur), white arsenic for sulphuretted hydrogen (yellow precipitate), oxalic acid for lime, fixed and caustic alkalis for metal precipitates, ammonia for copper; lime or baryta water for carbon dioxide, barium nitrate for sulphates, silver nitrate for chlorides and sulphides. In water analysis it is sometimes necessary to detect 1 part in 100,000. He used alcohol to separate salts, also cold and hot water. Less certain reagents were solutions of nitrate of mercury, corrosive sublimate, iron vitriol, lead acetate, liver of sulphur, and tincture of soap (used in water testing); a pure water should not give precipitates, according to the prevailing methods.[2]

Bergman emphasised the need for using purified reagents.[3] He developed wet tests for metals, e.g. precipitates with mild and caustic alkalis, which sometimes changed colour on heating. Finely powdered minerals insoluble in hydrochloric acid were fused with alkali. He gives tests for gold, silver, platinum, copper, lead, mercury, tin, bismuth, arsenic, antimony, zinc, cobalt, nickel, and manganese. He points out that precipitates formed from metal solutions by mild alkali (alkali carbonate) are often heavier than those formed by caustic alkali (hydroxide).[4]

In his *De praecipitatis metallicis* (1780)[5] Bergman gives the weights of the precipitates obtained with caustic, mild, and phlogisticated (ferrocyanide) alkalis (and with green vitriol in the case of gold, etc.) from 100 parts of gold, platinum, silver, mercury, lead, copper, iron, tin, bismuth, nickel, arsenic, cobalt, zinc, antimony, and manganese, dissolved in acids. He points out that the weight of the calx is greater than that of the metal, hence it is probable that the matter of heat is attached to the calx. The calces sometimes retain part of the acid, 'but if the mode of operation be always the same, the results of the experiments will be constant'; thus 'a foundation is laid for the art of assaying by the wet way from the bare knowledge of the weights'. He hints that the weight of a metal precipitated by another may make it possible to determine 'the unequal quantities of phlogiston in different metals' (see p. 196). Analysis of minerals by precipitation is extended in his *De minerarum docimasia humida* (1780),[6] the precipitates after washing with distilled water being dried

Soave, *Opusculi Scelti sulle Scienze e sulle Arti*, Milan, 1780, iii, 387, and plate; French tr. in *Obs. Phys.*, 1781, xviii, 207, 467, and plate opp. 253; for forms of blowpipes see also de Saussure, *ib.*, 1785, xxvi, 409, and plate; Hassenfratz, *ib.*, 1786, xxviii, 345, and plate.

[1] H (*a*), § 31, n. 3; H (*b*), 59.

[2] XXVI, 1778; A, i, 68; Thomson says this essay 'is entitled to much praise', as it laid the foundations of water analysis.

[3] XXI, 1777; A, ii, 85.

[4] XXVIII; A, I, viii: alkali aëratum in quibusdam casibus longe ponderosiorem exhibet calcem, quam causticum.

[5] XXXIV; KAH, 1780, i, 282; A, ii, 391.   [6] XXXV; A, ii, 399, 406.

at 100° on the filter paper free from alum before weighing. Iron in minerals was determined by fusion with alkali, treating with acid (when silica remained), and precipitating the iron as Prussian blue, one-sixth of the weight of which was taken as iron. Lime, baryta, magnesia and alumina were precipitated with potash (potassium carbonate), ignited and weighed, then extracted with cold acetic acid, which left the alumina. The filtrate was precipitated with potash and the precipitate treated with dilute sulphuric acid; magnesia dissolves, lime forms gypsum soluble in much water, baryta forms an insoluble salt. In this way he quantitatively analysed emerald, sapphire, topaz, hyacinth and ruby, finding alumina, silica, lime and iron:[1]

	alumina	silica	lime	iron
emerald	60	24	8	6
sapphire	58	35	5	2
topaz	46	39	8	6
hyacinth	40	25	20	13
ruby	40	39	9	10

Swedish weights and measures used by Bergman are:[2] 1 Swedish foot = 10 inches, 1 inch (= 1·238435 English in.) = 10 lines. The kanne is 100 Swedish cu. in. or 188·9413 English cu. in. (about 3·1 litres), equal to 8 quadrans, and 1 quadran = 12½ Swedish cu. in. The Swedish pound is, like the English Apothecaries' pound, divided into 12 ounces (1 ounce approximately 30 grams), the pound being 6556 Swedish Troy grains, the English Troy grain being 1·138194 Swedish grains. The Swedish lod (German loth) is $\frac{1}{32}$ Swedish pound (about ½ oz. English). The hundredweight (centenarius) used by Bergman is the assay weight of 60 Swedish or 63 English grains, the assay pound being derived from it.

In quantitative analysis Bergman introduced the important method of separating and weighing the substance to be determined in the form of a well-defined compound, and he necessarily assumed the truth of the law of constant composition. In 1775–84 he analysed a large number of compounds, but the results, on account of the imperfections of the methods at that time, are not very accurate although Bergman's great reputation caused them to be preferred to better results of other chemists.[3] Crell says Bergman often experimented far into the night, but Thomson thought most of his published work was done by assistants, which explains its lack of accuracy.

In the analysis of mineral waters Bergman expelled the gases by boiling and collected them over mercury for analysis. In the analysis of stones he fused them with potassium carbonate in an iron crucible or a small platinum dish.[4]

Insoluble particles remain suspended in a liquid when they 'acquire a surface so large in proportion to their weight that the friction to be overcome in their descent is equal to or greater than the difference in specific gravity between the particles and water, which is the force causing them to sink'.[5] Bergman observed the formation of soluble (colloidal) silicic acid by adding acid to a dilute solution of alkali silicate, and explained the 'very remarkable'

[1] XXI (1777); A, ii, 92 f.   [2] Thomson, *Ann. Phil.*, 1813, i, 452.
[3] Kopp, (1), ii, 71.
[4] XXI (1777); A, ii, 72.   [5] XXVI, § iv; A, i, 84.

fact by the above theory.[1] The fact was previously stated by Bergman[2] and by J. C. F. Meyer,[3] and Scheffer[4] also stated that when silica is precipitated from soluble glass by an acid, the saturation (neutralisation) point must not be exceeded, as otherwise the earth will dissolve in the acid (och kan qvartsjorden fällas med syror, men saturations puncten bör noga i agt tagas, ty om förmycket syra tilkommer löses åter jorden). He thought the solution formed alum.

Bergman, in his examination of volcanic minerals, noticed the gelatinisation of silica when some silicates (zeolites) are treated with acids.[5] He showed that the waters of several springs contain dissolved silica.[6] He obtained artificial quartz crystals by letting powdered quartz stand in a corked bottle for two years with hydrofluoric acid (containing hydrofluosilicic acid), and he emphasised that the precipitate (potassium or sodium fluosilicate) formed from the solution by vegetable or mineral alkali (potash or soda) is 'a triple salt of a peculiar kind, composed of siliceous earth, fluor acid, and fixed alkali, which dissolves with difficulty in warm water', whilst the precipitate with ammonia is pure silica.[7]

The percentage compositions of salts as found by Bergman[8] are given in the table below, the dry compounds being denoted by modern symbols. It will be seen that Bergman supposed that some anhydrous salts (K_2SO_4, KCl, NaCl) contain small quantities of water; perhaps he estimated this by difference. His results should be compared with those of Wenzel (p. 672).

	K_2SO_4	Na_2SO_4	$NaNO_3$	KCl	NaCl	$CaSO_4$
Base	52	15	49	61	42	32
Acid	40	27	33	31	52	46
Water	8	58	18	8	6	22

	$MgSO_4$	$Al_2(SO_4)_3$	$Ca(NO_3)_2$	$Mg(NO_3)_2$	$CaCl_2$	$MgCl_2$
Base	19	18	32	27	44	41
Acid	33	38	43	43	31	34
Water	48	44	25	30	25	25

	$CuSO_4$	$FeSO_4$	$ZnSO_4$
Metal	26	23	20
Acid	46	39	40
Water	28	38	40

[1] XXX (1779); A, ii, 36.   [2] XII, § vii; A, iii, 314.
[3] Beschäft. Berlin. Ges. naturforsch. Freunde, 1775, i, 267–91; 1777, iii, 219–25 (Versuche mit der Auflösung der Kieselerde in Säuren).
[4] Chemiske Föreläsningar, § 178b; 1775, p. 187; 1796, p. 217.
[5] XVIII (1777); A, iii, 185 (227): peculiari gaudent facultate acida gelatinam coagulandi.
[6] IV (1770); A, i, 149 f., 154, 159, etc.   [7] XXX (1779), § 3; A, ii, 33.
[8] XXVI (1778), § xi; KAH, 1778, xxxix, 219; A, i, 133 f.; D, i, 177 f., where Kirwan's figures are given by the translator in comparison, with the explanation that 'Mr. Kirwan considers the acids as pure, and totally free from water; whereas Professor Bergman considers them in a state of considerable concentration' but still 'containing a very large proportion of water'; Kirwan's results are given later, p. 668; Kopp, (1), ii, 314.

Kirwan said that crystalline magnesium chloride cannot be dried without losing much acid and that copper sulphate (blue vitriol) loses 28 per cent. of water by slight calcination. In his essay on zinc (1779)[1] Bergman gives the composition stated in the table but speaks of 20 parts of calx of zinc instead of metallic zinc (see p. 191).

Bergman nearly always gives the solubilities in water and alcohol of salts (and of other substances with which he worked, e.g. oxalic acid) at different (specified) temperatures, and also describes carefully the crystal forms and habits. He determined the composition of calcium oxalate as 46 lime, 48 acid and 6 water, and made use of this in determining lime.[2] He showed that concentrated sulphuric acid removes the water of crystallisation of salts (aquam crystallisationis eripere valet).[3]

In 1774[4] Bergman published his work, going back to 1770, on fixed air (carbon dioxide), which had been carefully investigated by Cavendish in 1766 (see p. 312). He called it the aerial acid (acidum aëreum), determining its density (1·5 that of air), solubility, action on litmus, absorption by alkali, presence in the atmosphere, solvent action on zinc, iron, manganese, limestone, mild magnesia, etc. He also describes the preparation and crystalline form of potassium bicarbonate. Bergman speaks of the chemistry of gases as 'transcendental' and complains that chemists who do not understand it tend to neglect it as of little importance.[5] He does not mention Black or Cavendish, but says 'the celebrated Dr. Priestley' mentioned him in 1772. Priestley says: 'It is not improbable but that fixed air itself may be of the nature of an acid, though of a weak and peculiar sort. Mr. Bergman of Upsal, who honoured me with a letter upon the subject, calls it the aerial acid; and among other experiments to prove it to be an acid, he says that it changes the blue juice of tournesole into red.'[6] Although Black distinctly says fixed air behaves as an acid[7] he does not mention its action upon litmus; Scheele had discovered this in 1770.[8] As late as 1785, George Fordyce[9] says: 'This Gas has been considered by some as an Acid yet nevertheless we cannot very well rank it among Acids, it has most and undoubtedly many of their properties but their most essential ones it has not.'

Bergman calls the solution 'aerated water' (aqua aërata . . . sit venia novo vocabulo), a name used by Venel in 1755 (see p. 78). He says that by adding suitable salts 'we may perfectly imitate the Seltzer, Spa, and Pyrmont waters. Such artificial waters I have now been using for eight years with signal advantage'. Hoefer[10] pointed out that the discovery of aerated water, used as a medicinal water, goes back at least to 1766 (=1774–8), and Priestley is in error in claiming this discovery, which he regarded as of immense benefit to humanity (see p. 247).

Bergman[11] also showed that the white ores of iron (ferrous carbonate) contain the aerial acid. He prepared several metallic carbonates synthetically. He later

---

[1] A, ii, 328.   [2] XVI (1776); A, i, 262; compositions of other oxalates.
[3] I (1767); A, i, 319.
[4] Om Luftsyra, KAH, 1774, xxxiv, 170; De acido aërëo commentatio, Nova Acta Reg. Soc. Sci. Upsal., 1775, ii, 108; A, i, 1.
[5] F, 1783, 17.   [6] Phil. Trans., 1772, lxx, 153.   [7] ACR, i, 22.
[8] Nordenskiöld, Scheele, Nachgelassene Briefe, 1892, 42; Gahn's note.
[9] Unpublished Lectures, Lect. 97.   [10] (1), ii, 436.   [11] X (1774); A, ii, 184.

explained the hardening of mortar as due to the absorption of carbon dioxide from the atmosphere by the lime, with the formation of crystals of calcium carbonate (ex atmosphæra acidum aëreum attrahit, quo ad saturationem hausto, particulæ solutæ crystallisando secernuntur).[1]

In collecting gases Bergman used a pneumatic trough with a perforated shelf above the water level (see p. 126), generating bottles or flasks or a Woulfe's bottle with a funnel for adding acid closed by a glass rod. The delivery tubes were fitted through corks, and he also used rubber tubing (tubo resina elastica).[2] Bergman clearly distinguished carbon dioxide (aerial acid) and sulphur dioxide (phlogisticated vitriolic acid), which he says had been 'miserably confused' by some.[3] He showed[4] that sulphuretted hydrogen generated from liver of sulphur is the same as that present in mineral waters, and pointed out its reactions with solutions of metallic salts and with litmus, although he thought only the unwashed gas showed an acid reaction.

Bergman's dissertations on manganese (1774),[5] magnesia (1775),[6] nickel (1775),[7] arsenic (1777),[8] platinum (which he obtained malleable) (1777),[9] zinc (1779),[10] and cobalt (1780),[11] contain useful observations. In his dissertation on manganese he says he had suspected for many years that 'black magnesia' contained a peculiar metal but all his attempts to reduce it failed; Gahn first obtained the metal by means of a most intense heat, without knowing of Bergman's experiments (see p. 201). Bergman also says that metallic manganese remained unchanged in a dry well-corked bottle for six months, but he remarks that in the open air it tarnished and became friable in two days; 'moisture, but particularly the access of the aerial acid, assists this operation.' He found a similar result with arsenic. In his dissertation on the ores of zinc[12] he says, mistakenly, that the metal was not known so much as by name by the ancient Greeks and Arabians. He still called it a semi-metal.

In his essay on nickel he gives a history of the metal; describes his experiments on the very difficult process of separating arsenic from the crude metal by repeated roasting, etc.; and purification by heating with liver of sulphur, nitre, and sal ammoniac, and by various processes in the wet way. He found that nickel obstinately retains cobalt. After obtaining pure salts, he showed by numerous tests that nickel is a distinct metal, and obtained its salts with common acids as well as nickel formate. He found that pure nickel salts give hyacinth-coloured borax and microcosmic salt beads. Bergman emphasised that manganese, nickel, cobalt, and platinum are peculiar metals different from all others.[13] He recognised native cobalt arsenate (cobaltum sæpe egregias exhibet *efflorescentias rubras* ... interdum pulcherrimæ crystalli ex eodem centro stellarum instar radiant).[14]

---

[1] XVIII (1777); A, iii, 195.
[2] XIII; KAH, 1775, xxxvi, 8; A, i, 215; Feldhaus, (1), 1914, 487, says rubber tubing was made by Grossart soon after the publication of Hérissant and Macquer, AdS, 1768, h 58, m 209; Priestley used leather tubes, see p. 251.

[3] XII, § xxxvi; A, iii, 383.
[4] XXVII (1778); A, ii, 218.
[5] X; A, ii, 184.
[6] XIV; A, i, 378.
[7] XV; A, ii, 231.
[8] XXIII; KAH, 1777, xxxviii, 25; A, ii, 272.
[9] XXII; KAH, 1777, xxxviii, 317; A, ii, 166.
[10] XXXII; A, ii, 309.
[11] XXXVI; B, iv, 371.
[12] XXXII (1779); A, ii, 309; D, ii, 314.
[13] XXXVI; B, iv, 371.
[14] XXXV; A, ii, 446.

An earth must be insoluble in at least a thousand times its weight of boiling water. As earths Bergman recognised baryta (terra ponderosa), magnesia, lime (calx), alumina (terra argillacea), and silica (terra silicea).[1] Baryta, on account of its high density and its precipitation by prussiate (ferrocyanide) of potash, is probably a metallic calx.[2] He says baryta and lime were first differentiated by Gahn and Scheele; Bergman found that salts of baryta precipitate prussiate of potash;[3] J. C. F. Meyer[4] incorrectly assumed from this that the prussiate contained sulphate. Bergman obtained magnesium ammonium sulphate (alkali volatile cum magnesia et acido vitrioli arctissime copulatur in hoc vero sale triplo);[5] his 'triple salt' is what is now called a 'double salt' (see below).

Bergman (1777) at first supposed[6] that diamond is a peculiar earth (terra nobilis), but he later (1782)[7] classed it among the combustible bitumens along with amber (which he calls petroleum acido succini adunatum).

A salt must be soluble in not more than two hundred parts of water.[8] One salt may increase the solubility of another.[9] When salt solutions crystallise the temperature rises, since when the particles aggregate the matter of fire is set free.[10] Scheffer[11] made neutral (neutrales) and middle salts (medelsalter) synonymous. Bergman classified salts into neutral (to litmus) compounds of acids and alkalis, and middle salts, compounds of acids with metals or earths.[12] As well as neutral or 'complete' (perfecta) salts he speaks of 'incomplete' (imperfecta), i.e. basic (alkaliske) and acid (sura) salts as imperfect double salts (sales imperfecta duplices) or middle salts. His triple salts (sales perfecta triplices), such as microcosmic salt (with two bases) are our double salts.[13] Double salts (sales duplices), compounds of acid and base, are our simple salts; triple salts (sales triplices) are formed with salts of magnesia and some metals, and alkalis including ammonia, or compounds (our double salts) or mixtures of Epsom salt and green vitriol, or blue vitriol and green vitriol.[14]

Bergman[15] emphasised that acids form salts with metallic calces (oxides), not with the metals as such, or at least from them only with some loss of phlogiston, whilst Stahl and others had supposed that the acids unite with the reguline metals. This theory in its more modern shape, that salts are formed from acidic and basic oxides, was supported by Lavoisier in his memoir on the solution of metals in acids (1785) (see p. 460).

Bergman was not altogether clear on the composition of alum. In his first chemical paper (1767)[16] he thought the addition of potash or ammonia caused crystallisation because it neutralised some excess of acid, and he repeated this in 1776.[17] Thomson says Bergman adopted this view because he was told that no alkali was added in the alum works at Hönsöter in West Gothland, where

[1] XXI; A, ii, 86; G (a), 1782, § 86; G (b), 1783, 38.   [2] XLIX, § 76; B, iv, 212.
[3] XII, § 40; J (b), 180; G (a), §§ 87–91; G (b), 40 f.   [4] Crell's *Ann.*, 1786, II, 142.
[5] XIV; A, i, 378.   [6] XXI; A, ii, 72.   [7] G, § 142; (a), 1782, 96; (b), 1783, 68.
[8] H (a), § 1; H (b), 1779, 4.   [9] H (a), § 51, n. 9; H (b), 113–14.
[10] H (a), § 51, n. 5; H (b), 108.   [11] H (a), §§ 3 f., 50; H (b), 108–12.
[12] G (a), 21 f.   [13] H (a), §§ 3 f., 50, 51 c Anm. 8, 67, 71; XLIX, § 67; B, iv, 208.
[14] XII, § 8, J (b), 46; G (a), 1782, 53.
[15] XXXIV (1780); XLVII (1782); A, ii, 354; iii, 135.
[16] I; A, i, 279.   [17] KAH, 1776, xxxvii, 176.

in fact this was not necessary, since the material used there was alunite, or basic aluminium potassium sulphate. Yet Bergman concluded from many experiments that 'it is certain that alum [i.e. aluminium sulphate] and vitriolated vegetable alkali [potassium sulphate] easily unite and form a triple salt (quo sal oritur triplex)'.[1]

Mention should be made of Bergman's chemical symbols,[2] which are adapted from Stahl's, and his attempts to improve chemical nomenclature. He introduced[3] the names potassinum, natrum and ammoniacum for the alkalis; acidum nitreum and acidum nitrosum for nitrous and nitric acids; and speaks of salts by such names as vitriolicum potassinatum (potassium sulphate), vitriolicum calcareatum (calcium sulphate), cuprum vitriolatum (copper sulphate), ferrum vitriolatum (ferrous sulphate), but also uses older names[4] such as alkali vegetabile vitriolatum (K_2SO_4), nitratum (KNO_3), salitum (KCl); alkali minerale vitriolatum (Na_2SO_4), etc.; calx vitriolata ($CaSO_4$), nitrata ($Ca(NO_3)_2$), salita ($CaCl_2$), etc.; magnesia vitriolata ($MgSO_4$), etc.; argilla vitriolata ($Al_2(SO_4)_3$); alkali minerale aëratum (Na_2CO_3); terra ponderosa vitriolata ($BaSO_4$); etc. Tables of names of salts are given in his edition of Scheffer's lectures.[5] Instead of using separate names for varieties of acids Bergman called them 'concentrated' and 'dilute', e.g. for sulphuric acid (instead of oil of vitriol, spirit of vitriol), nitric acid (instead of Glauber's Saltpetergeist, Scheidewasser) and muriatic acid (instead of Glauber's spirit of salt, muriatic acid).[6]

Bergman regarded nitric acid as a vegetable acid dephlogisticated by putrefaction, on account of its formation in nitrification.[7] He says[8] red fuming nitric acid becomes green, blue and colourless on progressive dilution. He says the colour is due to phlogiston and that Scheele had found the colourless acid became yellow on exposure to light. He thought[9] the phosphoric acid in animal bones, etc., is probably derived from the vegetables used as food. He mentions plastic sulphur.[10]

In his dissertation on fulminating gold (1769)[11] Bergman showed that it is formed only in the presence of ammonia, inferred that it is a compound of ammonia and calx (oxide) of gold, explained its explosion as due to the sudden evolution of gas by the decomposition of the ammonia by removal of its phlogiston (its hydrogen; see Berthollet, p. 502), and proved that the gas evolved was not fixed air, as Black had supposed (see p. 140), but the gaseous residue of ammonia when its hydrogen is removed, i.e. nitrogen. By adding turpeth mineral (basic mercuric sulphate) and gold to a microsmic salt bead before the blowpipe, a red or purple bead was formed.[12]

In his dissertation on tartar emetic (1773)[13] (tartarus emeticus, stibiatus, antimoniatus) Bergman gave a history of the substance and described several

---

[1] I; A, i, 326, perhaps an addition, since Scheele, De aëre et igne (1777) is q. on the same page.
[2] XII, plates; XLIX, § 74 f.   [3] XLIX, § 194; B, iv, 263.   [4] G (a); XXVI; A, i, 128 f.
[5] H (a), §§ 51 c Anm. 8, 71, 80; 1796, 74, 121 f.   [6] H (a), §§ 9, 15, 22.
[7] G (a), §§ 28, 45; G (b), 16, 23.   [8] H (a), § 20 d, n.; H (b), 32.
[9] H (a), § 30 n.; H (b), 1779, 56.   [10] H (a), § 194; H (b), 337.
[11] A, ii, 133, with a history of the subject.   [12] XXIX (1779); A, ii, 488.   [13] VII; A, i, 338.

methods of preparation, obtaining it pure in octahedral or tetrahedral crystals. He recognised that it is a compound of calx of antimony, potash, and tartaric acid. He also recognised that white lead is a carbonate (calx plumbi aërata), not an acetate like verdigris, although vinegar is used in its manufacture.[1] He distinguished between the soluble mercurous and mercuric salts, but he thought there were three compounds of mercury and muriatic acid: corrosive sublimate (mercuric chloride) and precipitated and sublimed calomel (mercurous chloride), with decreasing proportions of acid.[2] He noticed that fixed alkali (potassium carbonate) gives a brown precipitate with mercuric salts, but if the alkali is exposed to air it absorbs aërial acid (carbon dioxide) and the product (potassium bicarbonate) gives a white precipitate.[3] The brown precipitate becomes white when treated with ammonia.[4] Bergman found that copper dissolves to a brown solution in very concentrated muriatic acid.[5]

In his essay on the analysis of iron[6] Bergman distinguished cold-short [containing phosphorus] and hot-short [containing sulphur] iron. The impurities of iron are sulphur, plumbago, arsenic, zinc and especially manganese (magnesium). He postulated two kinds of phlogiston in metals, the metallising (phlogiston reducens) evolved by the action of acids, and the coagulative, and attempted to determine the former by measuring the volume of gas (hydrogen) evolved when cast iron, steel, and malleable iron are dissolved in dilute sulphuric acid or hydrochloric acid. With dilute nitric acid much less gas was obtained. The volumes of gas were compared with the weight of silver reduced from moist silver oxide by the various specimens of iron.

The conclusion reached was that cast iron, steel and malleable iron contain increasing amounts of phlogiston, but decreasing amounts of the matter of heat (measured by the rise in temperature on solution in acid) and of plumbago. The residue after dissolving in acid decreased in the order cast iron, steel and malleable iron: it consisted of silica and plumbago. Hot-shortness was thought to be partly due to sulphuric acid (really sulphur) but mostly to impure phlogiston. The composition of different kinds of iron is given in percentages:

	cast iron	steel	malleable iron	hot-short iron	cold-short iron
Silica	1–3·4	0·3–0·9	0·05–0·3	0·8	0·05–0·5
Plumbago	1–3·3	0·2–0·8	0·05–0·2	0·7	0·05–0·4
Manganese	0·5–30·0	0·5–30·0	0·50–30·0	0·5	0·50–4·0
Iron	63·3–97·5	68·3–99·0	99·50–99·4	98·0	95·40–99·4

J. C. F. Meyer[7] also attempted to compare the quantities of phlogiston in cast iron and steel. In this memoir[8] Bergman records the important observation

[1] XI; A, i, 38.
[2] III; KAH, 1770, xxxi, 79; 1771, xxxii, 294; 1772, xxxiii, 193; B, iv, 279; H (a), § 110 n.; H (b), 212.
[3] H (a), § 32, n. 1.   [4] H (a), § 43, n. 2.   [5] H (a), § 113; H (b), 217.
[6] XXXVIII (1781); Analyse du Fer, tr. (with four other memoirs on metallurgy) by Grignon, Paris, 1783 (pp. xvi, 268); A, iii, 1; E, 1785, iii, 3; cf. XII, § 70, A, iii, 466.
[7] Schrift. Berlin. Ges. Naturforsch. Freunde, 1783, iv, 274–90.   [8] A, iii, 82, 93, 95.

(really made by Scheele, see p. 208) that inflammable air (hydrogen) is slowly evolved by the action of water on iron filings, which are converted into a black powder (limaturi martis sub aqua aëris inflammabilis portionem promat, in pulverem nigrum sensim fatiscens).

Bergman's method of determining manganese in iron, by treating the ignited oxides with nitric acid and sugar,[1] gave too high results, by up to 30 per cent. When cold-short iron was dissolved in dilute sulphuric acid, and the solution exposed to air, a white residue (basic ferrous phosphate ?) was obtained. In his essay on the cause of cold-shortness of iron[2] Bergman tried to show that this white 'earth' was the cause of cold-shortness. He fused it with charcoal and a flux and obtained a white brittle metal which he called siderum. J. C. F. Meyer[3] also regarded it as a new metal (hydrosiderum, or Wassereisen), but later Meyer himself,[4] Klaproth[5] by synthesis, and Scheele[6] by analysis, showed that it is iron phosphide.

Bergman accepted the phlogiston theory till the end of his life, regarding the metals as compounds of phlogiston with the calces (oxides) as elements, and supposing that combustibles contain phlogiston. His views on combustion, however, were modified by increasing knowledge of gases and especially Scheele's discoveries and opinions.[7] The subtle principle phlogiston can never, so far as is known, be collected pure and alone, but always requires a suitable base. In order that a body shall be inflammable, it must contain a certain proportion of phlogiston connected with the base in so loose a manner that the surrounding pure air may dissolve the union (ut ambiens aër purus nexum rumpere queat).[8] He says[9] phlogiston is 'so subtle, indeed, that, were it not for its combination with other substances, it would be imperceptible to our senses. It can, however, be made to migrate from one body into another, according to the laws of elective attraction'. The existence of phlogiston he regarded as proved by the experiments of Priestley and Kirwan, and in another place Bergman regarded hydrogen as pure phlogiston (aër inflammabilis e metallis phlogiston fere purum putum in forme aërea continet),[10] and supposed that phlogiston could exist free as such and also in combination (ligatum, quod proprie phlogiston audit, variis liberari potest).[11]

Bergman's theory of combustion[12] is a modification of Scheele's:

'fire is therefore neither more nor less than the state of inflammable bodies, in which the greater part of the phlogiston, which enters into their composition, is torn away by means of this pure air [oxygen] with great force and violence from those particles with which it was before combined.'

Light is heat combined with more phlogiston. Light, heat, oxygen, fixed air (carbon dioxide), nitric oxide, and nitrogen dioxide are compounds of phlogiston with increasing proportions of nitric acid, which contains very little

[1] X; A, ii, 225.   [2] XXXIX (1781); A, iii, 109.
[3] *Schriften Berlin. Ges. Naturforsch. Freunde*, 1781, ii, 334–48; 1782, iii, 380–93.
[4] Crell's *Ann.*, 1784, I, 195.   [5] Crell's *Ann.*, 1784, I, 390.
[6] KAH, 1785, vi, 134; *Collected Papers*, ed. Dobbin, 1931, 275.
[7] See XXXIV, § 3; A, ii, 353–78; tr. in full in Fourcroy, (2), iii, 519 f. (mispaged).
[8] XXIX (1777); A, ii, 481.   [9] F, 1783, 102.
[10] XII, § 46; A, iii, 408.   [11] XII, § 47; A, iii, 413.
[12] XII, §§ 46–7; A, iii, 401–18; J (*b*), 204, 219; F, 140.

phlogiston. Nitrogen is nitric acid rendered gaseous by combination with phlogiston.[1] Bergman, like Black, regarded heat as material; the theory which supposed it to consist in the intestine motion of the parts of bodies is 'at present held to be totally improbable'.[2] Nitric acid attracts phlogiston and forms nitrous air [NO]; further addition of phlogiston and specific heat may form vital air [O_2].[3]

Bergman says he repeated with success the principal experiments of Scheele on oxygen, which he calls dephlogisticated air (*aër dephlogisticatus*) and mentions that a glowing chip (*bacillus ligneus*) or a candle with a glowing wick when put in the gas 'is instantly kindled with a bright coruscation and, as it were, explosion (extempore & cum quadam explosione lucidissima sponte accenditur flamma)'.[4]

Specific heat is not proportional to specific gravity or to volume, but to 'the compound ratio of the peculiar attraction and the surfaces', including the internal surfaces of the invisible pores, the heat inside a body surrounding its atoms as atmospheres. When gases expand their particles separate, heat is absorbed, and the gas cools.[5] Some consider that light is the matter of heat (elementary heat), others that elementary fire is different from phlogiston and one expels the other, whilst Scheele thought the matter of heat is a compound of phlogiston and vital air.[6] The matter of heat has a very small weight. Lavoisier, in experiments on the increase in weight of phosphorus and sulphur on combustion, assumed that the increase in weight was exactly equal to the weight of vital air which he justly concluded was absorbed. The specific heats of sulphur and concentrated vitriolic (sulphuric) acid, o·183 and o·758, are in the ratio 1 to 4, but that of vitriolic acid deprived of water would be reduced to 3 at least. When vitriolic acid is set at liberty by the combustion of sulphur its specific heat ought to be increased in the ratio of 3 to 1. 'Does not then this matter of heat coincide with the combination of vital air and phlogiston?', as Scheele assumed, and after enumerating ways in which heat is produced Bergman concluded that 'there is no heat produced without vital air, which is more or less diminished, and phlogiston is present in them all'.[7]

Bergman supposed (with Scheele) that dephlogisticated air (oxygen) absorbed the phlogiston of the burning body, forming heat, a very subtle matter which passed through the vessels (evanescet fluidum elasticum, vitro coërcendum, calorem generans et vasa penetrans).[8] Metals contain heat which escapes when they dissolve in acids. The vital air [oxygen] formed by heat from calces impregnated with nitric acid[9] comes partly from the heat employed, partly from the phlogistication of the acid. Calces of noble metals are reduced by attracting phlogiston from heat and setting free the vital air (see p. 220).[10]

Fourcroy says[11] such theories, based on Scheele's views, are quite incom-

[1] XII, § 46; J (*b*), 208; XXXIV; A, ii, 368 f.   [2] XXXII (1779), § 10; A, ii, 341 f.
[3] XII, § 46; A, iii, 403.
[4] XXXIV (1780), § iii C; A, 1780, ii, 361; the 'glowing splint' test, first described by Priestley (see p. 258); Leonhardi, *Macquer's Chymisches Wörterbuch*, Leipzig, 1790, vi, 614, wrongly says Bergman first used it.
[5] XII, § 48; A, iii, 423 f.   [6] XII, § 48; A, iii, 418 f.
[7] XII, § 48; A, iii, 428 f., 436.   [8] XXXIV (1780); A, ii, 363.
[9] Priestley's experiments, see p. 260.   [10] XXXIV; A, ii, 367 f., 375.   [11] (2), iii, 517, 521.

patible with Lavoisier's experiments, which seem to have had little attention from Bergman, but Guyton-Morveau,[1] reports that Bergman wrote to him on 13 May, 1783, saying: 'Je ne regarde pas l'hypothèse de Scheele comme démontrée, mais comme probable . . . au reste cela ne peut rester long-temps indécis.'

Bergman[2] says air contains three fluids mixed together, 'that which is called in England dephlogisticated air' serving to support combustion and respiration; this forms $\frac{1}{4}$ or at most $\frac{1}{3}$ of the volume, the rest is foul air (aër corruptus) with $\frac{1}{16}$ at most of acid air (CO_2).

The increase in weight of metals on calcination is given as: lead 0·12, copper 0·16, zinc 0·17, iron 0·36.[3] From the analogy with arsenic, white arsenic (arsenious oxide), and the arsenic acid investigated by Scheele, Bergman thought that 'it is highly probable that the metals are only different acids coagulated by a large quantity of phlogiston'.[4] He gave a brief description of the molybdic and tungstic acids discovered by Scheele, and says the same phlogiston combines with different calces to form specific metals.[5] Bergman's important memoir on the different quantities of phlogiston in metals[6] is undated. Nordenskiöld,[7] probably mistaking it for XXXIV, dated it 1780, but Berzelius[8] had pointed out that it was published in 1782 as an Uppsala dissertation.[9] The research had the object of determining the quantity of phlogiston which each metal contains. Bergman came to the conclusion that the quantities of phlogiston are inversely as the weights of the metals (phlogisti mutuas quantitates praecipitantis et praecipitandi ponderibus esse inverse proportionales). If, as Lavoisier did (see p. 460), we take phlogiston = − oxygen, this means that the two metals require identical weights of oxygen in order to neutralise identical weights of acid.

To precipitate 100 of silver required 135 of mercury, 234 of lead, 31 of copper, 64 of nickel, 92 of arsenic, 37 of cobalt, 55 of zinc, 83 of antimony, etc. from nitric acid solution. Iron precipitated silver incompletely from nitric acid solution or remained quite unattacked (passivity), but 100 of silver required 29 parts of iron for precipitation from sulphuric acid solution. In many cases precipitation was incomplete. Only 30 parts of copper were required to precipitate 100 of silver from the sulphate solution, which shows the greater strength of nitric acid, which causes it to attract phlogiston more strongly than sulphuric acid (qua phlogiston prae vitriolico arripit).

If the quantity of phlogiston in 100 of silver is put equal to 100, the quantities in 100 of other metals are, on the hypothesis stated: mercury 74, lead 43, copper 323, iron 342, tin 114, bismuth 57, nickel 156, arsenic 109, cobalt 270, zinc 182, antimony 120 and manganese 196. From the number for zinc, those

[1] Ency. Méthod., Chymie, 1786, i, 629.   [2] XII, § 46; A, iii, 401: aër vitalis.
[3] XXXII (1779); A, ii, 330.   [4] XXIII (1777), XXXV (1780); A, ii, 287, 442.
[5] XL (1781); A, iii, 124.   [6] XLVII; A, 1783, iii, 132.
[7] Scheele, Nachgelassene Briefe, Stockholm, 1892, 323.
[8] Lehrbuch der Chemie, 1828, III, i, 18.
[9] Obs. Phys., 1783, xxii, 109–21: Dissertation chimique sur les diverses proportions dans lesquelles les Métaux contiennent le phlogistique, soutenue par M. Nicolas Tunborg, M. Tobern Bergmann [sic] Président; Fourcroy, (2), iii, 504, 517, mistakenly dated it 1783.

for 100 parts of other metals precipitated by zinc are calculated as: gold 394, platinum 756, mercury 80, lead 47, copper 290, bismuth 64, antimony 127.[1]

Bergman knew that some calx (oxide) of the precipitating metal is often mixed with the precipitated metal, and that the results are inaccurate when hydrogen is evolved. He says 234 parts of lead are needed to precipitate 100 of silver, 'but this quantity of lead requires more nitric acid than is combined with 100 of silver, hence some dephlogisticated lead [oxide] is thrown down by that dissolving, in order to generate sufficient phlogiston (plumbum itaque dephlogisticatum novo solvendo deturbetur oportet, ut satis prodeat phlogisti.)'

Bergman made an attempt to calculate the quantities of phlogiston in metals. He found that one part of pine charcoal detonated with three of nitre[2] to form alkali (potassium carbonate) and 1 part of wrought iron 'alkalises' $\frac{1}{2}$ a part of nitre;[3] hence 1 lb. of charcoal contains as much phlogiston as 2 lb. of iron. Since 2 lb. of iron gave $\frac{11}{100}$ lb. of inflammable air, this contains $\frac{5}{100}$ lb. of phlogiston and $(11-5)/100=\frac{6}{100}$ lb. of matter of heat. Now 100 assay lb. of charcoal distilled with oil of vitriol gave 82 cu. in. of aerial acid, weighing 82 assay lb. Adding 3 to correspond with the ash of the charcoal, this gives 85 lb. of fixed air, leaving $100-85=15$ of phlogiston.[4] Hence the phlogiston in 100 of iron is $15 \div 6 = 2 \cdot 5$. The relative number is 342, hence the absolute weight of phlogiston in other metals is calculated.[5] For 100 parts: copper 2·12–2·34, zinc 1·33, tin 0·83, silver 0·733, mercury 0·54–0·585, bismuth 0·42–0·47, lead 0·31–0·34.

From the analysis of charcoal it is found that a cu. in. of inflammable air contains $\frac{63}{1000}$ assay lb. of phlogiston, and it contains as much phlogiston as 2 lb. of forged iron, i.e. $\frac{5}{100}$; therefore the weight of specific heat (caloris specifici) necessary to give it the aerial form is $(63-50)/1000=\frac{13}{1000}$.[6]

In 1775 Bergman placed the metals in the columns of the acids in the affinity tables, but in his revised work[7] he says he had observed that the series of metals is the same for all acids and suspected that 'the precipitation of metals depended, not on the election of the acids, but on some other principle, which I now certainly know to be the attractive power of the dissolved calces for the phlogiston of the precipitating metal', and he excluded metals from the tables.

Bergman[8] mentions Guyton-Morveau's theory (see p. 611) that phlogiston is lighter than air and its escape makes metals heavier on calcination: he says that Lavoisier maintained that instead of phlogiston separating in the calcination of metals, fixed air or aerial acid (carbon dioxide) is absorbed from the atmosphere, causing the increase in weight, and the calcination is limited in closed vessels (see p. 392).

Bergman found that 'phosphorus is consumed only very slowly in vital air without the assistance of heat, and hardly at all unless water is present to aid

[1] Table in G (b), 1783, 71. [2] XII, § 48; A, iii, 440. [3] XXXVII; A, iii, 24, 51 f.
[4] XII, § 48; A, iii, 440. [5] A, iii, 480, Addenda. [6] XII, § 47; A, iii, 413.
[7] XII; A, iii, 338. [8] H (a), § 269 n. 2; H (b), 364.

the decomposition by a double affinity'.[1] He mentions the liquid appearance of heated gypsum powder, due to the escape of water vapour, and suggests by analogy that liquids may be regarded as aggregates of subtle solid molecules surrounded by atmospheres of heat.[2]

Bergman divided bodies into organic and inorganic (omnia corpora in duas classes ample distributa notantur; quarum prima *Organica*, altera *Inorganica* continet).[3] Many publications by Bergman on subjects of inorganic chemistry include essays on tin sulphide (1781),[4] antimony sulphide (1782),[5] volcanic products (1777),[6] in which he gives an analysis of basalt (silica 52, alumina 15, calcium carbonate 8, iron 25); lithomarge (1782),[7] asbestos (1782),[8] the hydrophane (*oculus mundi*) (1777),[9] tourmaline (1779),[10] tin from Siberia (1781),[11] the Loka Springs (1783),[12] observations on minerals (1784),[13] brick-making (1771),[14] mineral waters of Medevi (1782),[15] the precipitation of cobalt, nickel, platinum, and manganese (1780),[16] soil (1773),[17] magnesia nitrate (1777),[18] and the metallic acids, molybdic (*acidum molybdænæ*) and tungstic (*acidum lapidis ponderosi*) (1781).[19]

Bergman's work was mostly in inorganic chemistry. In connection with some organic substances, he says that the specific gravity of strong spirit of wine is 0·820 (which shows that it still contained water),[20] and still gave Geoffroy's method (p. 56) for finding the strength, viz. burning in a silver cylinder and measuring the residual water, although he says the hydrometer is more delicate.[21] He distinguishes between ether and oil of wine, which Scheffer had confused;[22] in the preparation of ether from alcohol and sulphuric acid, he thought the alcohol lost water and took up phlogiston.[23] Bergman mentions from Sage (see p. 97) that potassium ferrocyanide, which he thought was alkali loaded with phlogiston (belastadt med phlogiston), could be obtained in crystals.[24]

Bergman's essay on oxalic acid (acidum sacchari) (1776)[25] is in the form of a thesis supported by Johann Afzelius (Arfedson; see p. 200), but the real dis-coverer of the preparation of oxalic acid from sugar by the action of nitric acid was Scheele, mention of whom was omitted by an oversight.[26] The acid of sugar was obtained by boiling sugar with nitric acid and crystallising the solution. Several of its salts, and the impure ethyl ester, are described.

Bergman says the gas evolved on heating acid of sugar (oxalic acid) is half

[1] XII, § 46 C; A, iii, 409.   [2] XII, § 45; A, iii, 398.
[3] XLIX, Florence, 1784, 5; B, 1787, iv, 180, 'anorganica'.
[4] XLI; A, iii, 157.   [5] XLII; A, iii, 164.   [6] XVIII; A, iii, 184–290.
[7] XLIV; B, iv, 142.   [8] XLV; B, iv, 160.
[9] XX; KAH, 1777, xxxviii, 347; A, ii, 54.   [10] XXXI; KAH, 1779, xl, 224; A, ii, 118.
[11] KAH, 1781, ii, 328.   [12] XLVII; KAH, 1783, iv, 256; B, iv, 359.
[13] XLIX; KAH, 1784, v, 109; B, v, 98.   [14] V; B, iv, 336.
[15] XLVI; KAH, 1782, iii, 288; B, iv, 346.   [16] XXXVI; KAH, 1780, i, 282; B, iv, 371.
[17] VI; B, v, 59.   [18] XXIV; KAH, 1777, xxxviii, 213; B, v, 111.
[19] XL; KAH, 1781, ii, 95; A, iii, 124.   [20] H (a), § 210, Anm. 1; 1796, 265.
[21] Ib., § 210, Anm. 3; 1796, 265.   [22] Ib., § 212, Anm.; 1796, 269.
[23] Ib., § 213, Anm. 6; 1796, 272.   [24] Ib., § 165 g, Anm. 4; 1775, 161; 1796, 187.
[25] XVI; A, i, 251.
[26] Zekert, *C. W. Scheele*, Vienna, 1936, 49; Thomson, (4), 1831, ii, 15, quotes Erhart, one of Scheele's intimate friends, as saying in Elwert's *Magazin für Apotheker, Chemisten und Materi-alisten*, Nürnberg, 1785, i, 54, that Scheele was the real discoverer, and Thomson says Hermb-städt and Westrumb also assign the discovery to Scheele.

aërial acid (carbon dioxide), easily separated by lime water, and half a gas burning with a blue flame (dimidiam partem acido aëreo constat, aqua calcis facile separandam, qua alteram vero flamma mox accenditur et cærulea ardet),[1] so that he discovered carbon monoxide independently of Priestley (see p. 271) and Lassone (1776, see p. 95).

Oxalic acid is said to be mentioned by F. P. Savary,[2] who knew that salt of sorrel is the potash salt of an acid which he did not isolate. He obtained the neutral oxalate and also, by crystallising from dilute sulphuric or nitric acid, the quadroxalate (rediscovered by Wollaston, see p. 701).

Bergman's dissertation on indigo (1776)[3] describes its solution in concentrated sulphuric acid, which gave a blue solution in water which was slowly decolorised by nitric acid, caustic alkali, and green vitriol (ferrous sulphate). He thought the colour was due to phlogiston. Concentrated nitric acid dissolved indigo with the evolution of much heat (very concentrated nitric acid caused inflammation); on dilution a brown solution was formed. He concluded that indigo contains mucilage soluble in water, resin soluble in alcohol, earth soluble in acetic acid, calx of iron soluble in muriatic acid, and the rest a blue pigment giving ammonia on distillation. Most of the facts had been published by Woulfe,[4] who is not mentioned; perhaps Bergman (F.R.S. 1765) did not read the *Philosophical Transactions*. He described the natural history of American cochineal[5] and South European kermes.[6]

Fermentation (gäsning), Bergman defined as an internal motion of a mass whereby a spirituous, acid, or ammoniacal body (putrefaction) is produced which was not obvious before.[7] The smell of raw corn spirit is called 'finkellukt (Fuselgeruch)'.[8] The methods of testing essential oils[9] are described. He says ammonium acetate can be crystallised if the solution is evaporated to a syrup.[10] He suggested that astringent vegetable materials contain an acid.[11] He distinguished formic acid (acidum formicarum) from acetic acid (acetum).[12] His agricultural essay on soil[13] was awarded a prize by the Academy of Sciences at Montpellier in 1773; he published an essay on a urinary calculus (1776).[14] He described the preparation of tartaric acid by boiling a solution of tartar with chalk, decomposing the precipitate with diluted sulphuric acid, decanting, and evaporating.[15] He distinguished acid of sorrel (acidum acetosellæ) from acid of sugar (acidum sacchari)[16] although both are oxalic acid. He says tartar was purified only in Venice (with albumen) and Montpellier (with a kind of clay).[17]

---

[1] A, i, 259.
[2] *Dissertatio de sale essentiali acetosellæ*, Strasbourg, 1773; Gren, 1794, ii, 85; Kopp, (1), iv, 354.
[3] XXXVII; AdS, *Mém. div. Sav.*, 1780, ix, 121–64 (analyse et examen chimique de l'indigo); B, v, 1.
[4] *Phil. Trans.*, 1771, lxi, 114.   [5] H (a), § 354, n. 4; H (b), 656.
[6] H (a), § 362, n. 3; H (b), 671.   [7] H (a), § 207, n. 2; H (b), 371.
[8] H (a), § 209, n.; H (b), 373.   [9] H (a), § 218, n. 4; H (b), 399.
[10] H (a), § 62; H (b), 136.   [11] H (a), § 382 g, n. 2; H (b), 496.
[12] XIV (1775); A, i, 389.   [13] VI; B, v, 59.
[14] XVII; KAH, 1776, xxxvii, 333; B, iv, 387; appendix to a memoir by Scheele, KAH, 1776, xxxvii, 327–32.
[15] XII, § 23; A, iii, 367.   [16] XII, §§ 22, 24; A, iii, 363, 370.
[17] H (a), § 66; H (b), 139.

RETZIUS

Anders Jahan Retzius (Christianstad, 3 October 1742–Stockholm, 6 October 1821) was demonstrator (1764) in Lund. He left for Stockholm in 1768, but returned to Lund in 1772. He was a friend of Scheele in Stockholm in 1768–1770. Retzius became professor of chemistry in the Carolinian Institute in Stockholm in 1798. He was probably the last phlogistonist.[1] He published on tartaric acid,[2] oxalic acid, and citric acid in solution,[3] embodying results obtained by Scheele (to whom he gives credit), and on corrosive sublimate.[4] He also published on botany (the species Retzia was named after him by Thunberg) and zoology. His son Carl Gustaf Retzius (Lund, 28 April 1798–Stockholm, 28 February 1833) was demonstrator in chemistry in Lund, later professor in the Veterinary School in Stockholm; he published on minerals. Anders Adolf (1796–1860) and Magnus Christian (1795–1871) Retzius were physicians.

AFZELIUS

Johann Afzelius (also called Arvidson, with various spellings, from his father's Christian name Arvid, Arfved, etc.; the name Afzelius is common in Sweden) (Larss Församling, Skara Stift, 13 June 1753–Uppsala, 20 May 1837) graduated Phil.Mag. (1776) in Uppsala. In 1780 he was adjunct and from 1784 until 1820 professor of chemistry, metallurgy, and pharmacy at the University of Uppsala, and the teacher of Berzelius, on phlogistic principles. He was a pupil of Bergman, under whom he published dissertations on nickel (1775) and oxalic acid (1776),[5] and with Peter Öhrn a dissertation on formic acid (1777).[6]

By distilling 1 lb. of ants they obtained $7\frac{1}{2}$ oz. of acid of s.g. 1·0075 at $-15°$ and on rectification formic acid of s.g. 1·0011. They proved that it is a peculiar acid distinct from acetic acid. Afzelius also published on heavy spar (baroselenite)[7] and pisolite (1800). It was in a specimen of a mineral sent to him by Afzelius that Berzelius found selenium (see Vol. IV). Thomson[8] on his visit to Uppsala found Prof. Afzelius infirm and nearly blind but lecturing at 9 a.m. and conducting laboratory classes on Wednesday and Saturday. His brother Adam Afzelius (8 October 1750–30 January 1836) was a distinguished botanist.[9]

[1] KAH, 1822, 462–7 (bibl.); Nordenskiöld, Scheele Nachgelassene Briefe, 1892, i; Zekert, Carl Wilhelm Scheele, Mittenwald, 1933, iii, 113 (portr.).
[2] KAH, 1770, xxxi, 207 (Försök med Vinsten och dess Syra).
[3] KAH, 1776, xxxvii, 130 (växtsyra).   [4] KAH, 1770, xxxi, 110.
[5] Nos. XV and XVI in the list on p. 182.
[6] Afzelius, Dissertatio de Niccolo, Præs. T. Bergman, 4°, Uppsala, 1775, BM B. 398. (6.); Dissertatio de acido Sacchari, Præs. T. Bergman, 4°, Uppsala, 1776, BM B. 385. (22.); Dissertatio de acido formicarum, 4°, Uppsala, [1777], BM B. 385. (23.); Guyton de Morveau, Ency. Méthod., Chymie, 1786, i, 61 (formic acid); the dates 1777, 1780, 1781, and 1782 are given for the last dissertation by Gmelin, Wiegleb, and Thomson, who had not seen it.
[7] Crell's Ann., 1788, II, 198–205.   [8] (5), 1813, 166.   [9] KAH, 1836 (1838), 342.

GAHN

Johan Gottlieb Gahn (Voxna ironworks (S. Helsingland), 19 or 17 August 1745–Stockholm, 8 December 1818)[1] was (1760–70) Bergman's assistant in Uppsala. In 1770 he went into industry at Fahlun to improve the copper smelting process, and soon after became manager of the Stora-Kopparberg, where he studied the technical application of minerals and founded several new branches of industry. He was appointed Assessor of the mining college at Stockholm in 1784. Gahn made many experiments and discoveries in all branches of chemistry, but published hardly anything, so that his reputation (also injured by his intense liberalism) was much less than he deserved. His essays on the blowpipe and on the balance (with a rider moved by hand) are reproduced by Berzelius.[2] In a short paper which Thomson persuaded him to write, Gahn[3] describes the blue colour formed by heating alumina with cobalt nitrate (the blowpipe test), better known as Thenard's blue. The mineral gahnite (zinc spinel $ZnAl_2O_4$) was named after him by von Moll. He discovered metallic manganese in 1774 (see p. 190).

Science owes Gahn an inestimable debt of honour for the care with which he preserved the notes, papers, and letters of his friend Scheele. Thomson, who visited him in 1812 at Fahlun, speaks of Gahn with warm admiration, saying that he was 'one whose manners were the most simple, unaffected, and pleasing, of all the men of science with whom I ever came in contact'. He showed Thomson Scheele's papers and laboratory notes. Although aged 68, Gahn was very active and well up in the latest advances in science. He had a good collection of platinum apparatus.[4] He lent Berzelius a platinum crucible which was too heavy for his balance.

LOMONOSOV

Mikhail Vasilyevich Lomonosov (Deniskova, nr. Archangel, 1711–St. Petersburg (Leningrad), 4 April 1765) studied science in Moscow (1731) and then went to Germany to study science, philosophy (under J. C. Wolf in Marburg), and also metallurgy in Freiberg (1735). He returned to Russia in 1741, becoming a member of the Academy of Sciences in St. Petersburg, founded in 1724, where he built a laboratory for teaching and research. He also set up a factory for making coloured glass and mosaics. Lomonosov worked at astronomy and was a grammarian, poet, historian and man of affairs as well as a scientist.[5] Although not mentioned by Kopp or E. von Meyer, he

[1] Thomson, *Ann. Phil.*, 1824, viii, 1; *id.*, (1), ii, 242; Eggertz, *J. Chem.* (Schweigger), 1822, xxxiv, 140–7; Poggendorff, (1), i, 828 (publs.); de Fère, NBG, 1857, xix, 169; portr. in Zekert, *C. W. Scheele*, Mittenwald, 1933, vii, 252, and Berzelius, *Bref*, 1922, IIA.

[2] *Lehrbuch der Chemie*, Dresden, 1831, IV, ii, 905, 1052; Speter, *Z. Instr.*, 1930, l, 204.

[3] *Ann. Phil.*, 1818, xi, 40 (7 pp.); tr. with intr. by Büchner, *J. f. Chem.* (Schweigger), 1820, xxix, 295.

[4] Thomson, (1), ii, 242; (5), 76, 222.

[5] T. L. Davis, *J. Chem. Educ.*, 1938, xv, 203–9 (illustr.); Prince A. Galitzin, NBG, 1860, xxxi, 542; Gmelin, (1), ii, 449, 577, 696; Hoefer, (1), ii, 367; B. N. Menschutkin, *Chem. News*, 1912, cv, 73, 85; *id.*, *J. Chem. Educ.*, 1927, iv, 1079; *id.*, *Isis*, 1928, xi, 462; 1938, xxviii, 556;

was quoted with appreciation by Demachy and by Hoefer (who thought the chemist and the poet were different persons). B. N. Menschutkin published an account of his work in 1904, excerpts from his writings in 1910,[1] and a book based on some unpublished sources in 1952.[2] Euler said of him:

Toutes ses pièces sont non-seulement bonnes, mais très excellentes; car elles traitent les matières de la physique et de la chimie les plus intéressantes et qui sont tout à fait inconnues et inexplicables aux plus grands génies, avec tant de solidité, que je suis tout à fait convaincu de la justesse de ses explications.[3]

Lomonosov's first scientific publication was on electricity.[4] He emphasised the importance of the study and application of chemistry in Russia.[5] Some important memoirs by Lomonosov were published by the St. Petersburg Academy.

(I) Meditationes de caloris et frigoris Causa, *Novi Commentarii Academiae Scientiarum Imperialis Petropolitanae*, St. Petersburg, 1750, i, 206–29 (written 1744, read 1745). (II) Tentamen Theoriae de Vis Aeris Elastica, *ib.*, 230 (presented in definitive form 1748); Supplementum ad Meditationes de Vis Aeris Elastica, *ib.*, 307 (written in 1749, condensed tr. in Ostwald's *Klassiker* clxxviii, 34); (III) De Motu Aeris in Fodinis Observato, *ib.*, 267; (IV) Dissertatio de Actione Menstruorum Chymicorum in genera, *ib.*, 245; 1788, vii, 182 (not in Ostwald's *Klassiker* clxxviii). Summaries of these, in Russian and in Latin, are given at the beginning of vol. i (pp. $\mathcal{X}$ 51 $\mathcal{X}$– $\mathcal{X}$ 57 $\mathcal{X}$). The Supplementum ad Meditationes de Vis Aeris Elastica deals with a criticism of the kinetic theory of D. Bernoulli (referring to *Hydrodynamica*, p. 243), on the question as to whether air from exploded gunpowder is the same as common air; see Vol. II, p. 631.

Some of the papers were tr. by Münter in *Physikalische und medizinische Abhandlungen der kaiserlichen Akademie der Wissenschaften in Petersburg*, Riga, 1782, i; and in Crell's *N. Chemisches Archiv*, 1788, vii, 174 (causes of heat and cold), 178 (theory of the elasticity of air), 182 (the action of chemical solvents).

Extracts of some works translated in Ostwald's *Klassiker*, 1910, clxxviii, are:

1. Elements of Mathematical Chemistry, 1741 (in MS.), 6 f.

2. On the insensible physical particles constituting natural bodies, 1742–3 (in MS.), 12 f. (De particulis physicis insensibilibus, corpora naturalia constituentibus, in quibus qualitatum particularium ratio sufficens continetur), the usual ideas of corpuscles (from Boyle, etc.); an atomic-molecular theory of matter foreseeing the possibility of isomerism.

3. Thoughts on the Causes of Heat and Cold, 1744–7, 18 f.; heat is motion; Lomonosov at first thought mercury could not be frozen but in 1759 he experimented with Braun and froze it.

4. Research on the Elastic Power of Air, 1748, 28 f.

5. On the Uses of Chemistry, 1751.

6. Course in True Physical Chemistry, 1752.

Menschutkin and Speter, Ostwald's *Klassiker*, 1910, clxxviii; Sarton, *Rev. gén. Sci.*, 1912, xxiii, 300; *id.*, *Isis*, 1936, xxv, 153; Speter, Lavoisier und seine Vorläufer, in *Samml. chem. u. chem.-techn. Vorträge*, 1910, xv, 160, 201; Sutton, *Isis*, 1952, xliii, 371. Galitzin says the works of Lomonosov were published by the Academy of Sciences, St. Petersburg, 6 vols. 4°, 1794; another sumptuous ed. has recently been published by the Soviet Government, vols. vi and vii on his scientific works; see on the Academy of Science from 1725, Pogodin, *Bull. Acad. Sci. U.R.S.S.*, 1945, 179; Zelinsky, *ib.*, 195.

[1] Ostwald's *Klassiker*, 1910, clxxviii.

[2] B. N. Menschutkin, *Russia's Lomonosov. Chemist, Courtier, Physicist, Poet*, tr. by J. E. Thal and W. C. Webster under the direction of W. C. Huntington, Princeton and London, 1952 (ix, 208 pp., 5 plates); see *Nature*, 1953, clxxi, 138.

[3] Galitzin, 543.

[4] *Oratio de Meteoris Vi Electrica ortis, cum Responsione et de Meteoris Isolitis sibi observatis*, 4°, St. Petersburg, 1754 (68 pp.; Sotheran *Cat.* 195 (1956), 83, no. 1072).

[5] *Oratio de Utilitate Chemiæ in publico conventu Imperialis Academiæ Scientiarum Instituto . . . Ex Rossica autem in Latinam linguam conversa a Gregorio Kositzki*, 4°, Petropoli, 1751 (30 pp., Duveen, 366; in German in Ostwald's *Klassiker*, clxxviii).

Demachy[1] in dealing with the increase in weight of metals on calcination, says: On peut voir dans le quinzième volume des Mémoires de l'Académie de Pétersbourg, une très-belle Dissertation à ce sujet, de M. Lomonosow. This is the first memoir (I) named above (vol. i of the *Novi Comment.* follows vol. xiv of the *Commentarii*), the matter being dealt with on pp. 225–6. This was read two years before Beraut's book (see p. 607) appeared. It mentions the increase in weight when lead is converted into minium (et pondus eius cum lucro artificum auget), and gives a criticism of Boyle's explanation that it is due to the fixation of ponderable fire:

An esto, quod præter partes corporis accensi vel particulas in aere circumuolitans, qui super calcinata continuo fluit, accedat metallis calcinatione durante quaedam alia materia, quae pondus calcium auget . . . accedit igitur calcinationis actu materia quaedam corporibus, verum non illa, quæ igne propria esse prædicatur. Cur enim ea in calcibus naturae suæ obtiuisceratur, non video. . . . Firma igitur non sunt etiam illa argumenta, quæ ad peculiarem igni materiam vindicandam ex augmento ponderis calcinatorum corporum asseruntur.

It is probable that Lomonosov's interest in this subject was aroused by a previous publication in the same memoirs by Johann Georg Gmelin (Tübingen; 12 June 1709–20 May 1755), the son of an apothecary in Tübingen (1674–1728) who had been a pupil of Hiärne,[2] went to St. Petersburg in 1727 and was professor of chemistry and natural history (1731) there, later (1749) professor of medicine in Tübingen. He is best known for his travels of 1733–43 with F. Müller and De l'Isle de la Croyère in Siberia.[3] In 1738 he published a memoir on the increase in weight of metals on calcination (*De augmento ponderis quod capiunt quædam corpora, dum igne calcinatur*),[4] mentioning Boyle's experiments (see Vol. II, p. 529) and the explanation of Boyle, Kunckel (see Vol. II, p. 374) and Freind[5] that the increase is due to the fixation of particles of fire. Gmelin thought that air might play some part, which could be decided by heating the metal in a vacuum with a burning glass, and he describes an experiment which gave an indecisive result (the vacuum was imperfect).

Lomonosov thought that weight may not be a true measure of mass, and weight might change in the same place if particles of an aggregate were separated so as to expose more surface to the action of gravity. He used this idea to explain Boyle's (incorrect) result that there is an increase in weight when a metal is calcined in a *sealed* retort, which Boyle explained by the fixation of ponderable fire-particles. Lomonosov thought the increase in weight when a metal is calcined in air is normally due to the fixation of air particles by the metal, but Boyle's result, if correct, could be explained by the increase in surface on calcination leading to an increase in weight. In a letter to Euler of 5 July 1748, Lomonosov said the theory that weight is not proportional to mass:

disposed of the beliefs about fixed fire in calcined bodies. There can be no doubt that the air particles which always flow over the calcined body combine with it and increase its weight. If reference is made to the experiments in which the burning of bodies in a

---

[1] Tr. of Juncker, *Élémens de Chymie*, 1757, iii, 134.   [2] Gmelin, (1), ii, 639.
[3] *Reise durch Siberien*, 4 vols., Göttingen, 1751–2.
[4] *Comment. Petropol.*, 1738, v, 263–73.   [5] *Chymical Lectures*, 2 ed., 1737, 25.

sealed vessel yet caused an increase in weight, these experiments could be explained by assuming that, after heating, the cohesion of the particles is removed and that their sides which were formerly in contact are now freely exposed to gravity (Schwere) and hence are more powerfully urged (gedrückt) to the centre of the earth.

Lomonosov said that in Boyle's experiments the sealed retort should have been weighed before it was opened (as Cherubin d'Orléans had said in 1679, see Vol. II, p. 530), and he showed by experiment in 1756 that there is no increase in weight when a metal is heated in a sealed retort;[1] this observation, which was not published, anticipated Lavoisier's (see p. 399). Lavoisier probably saw Lomonosov's papers in the *Novi Commentarii*, 1750, i, since he refers[2] to a paper by Richmann in the same volume and close to Lomonosov's paper criticising Boyle's experiments on calcination.[3]

Lomonosov argued against the material nature of heat and regarded it as a form of motion. His theory of gases (1748–9; de Vis Aeris Elastica) assumed that the particles are rotating and that motion is transmitted from particle to particle by friction between their rough surfaces. It is less correct than that of D. Bernoulli,[4] who was in St. Petersburg in 1738. Lomonosov made some experiments in 1752 on the expansion of air by heat, using tubes, and found the coefficient of expansion 0·003,[5] which is roughly correct.

In an outline of a course in 'true physical chemistry' for the use of young students,[6] Lomonosov says this is 'a science which explains on the basis of the laws and experiments of physics what occurs in compound bodies by means of chemical operations', and the experimental part includes the determination of melting points and the solubilities of salts. A programme for research included the determination of the specific heats and viscosities of solutions.[7] Lomonosov, who had a good mathematical training, emphasised that chemistry should be developed on mathematical lines, as had been done by Keill in 1708 and Freind in 1709 (see Vol. II, p. 478), not to mention the book by Swedenborg (see p. 165) of 1721 on the explanation of chemistry by geometry.

In his memoir on solutions (*Dissertatio de Actione Menstruorum*; IV) Lomonosov supposed that air is present in solids, and this air, together with that contained in the solvent, regains its former elasticity and tears the solid to pieces, the particles of the dissolving body repelling one another by a vibratory motion. There is a glimmering here of the gaseous theory of solutions of van't Hoff, and a departure from the view that solutions are chemical compounds.[8]

Lomonosov was a man of genius and had many good ideas which, if he had worked them out in detail, might have notably advanced science, but his duties as an academician, his variety of interests, and his irregular mode of life, hampered his progress in scientific research. The country of his birth, which has produced so many distinguished chemists, has every right to be proud of such an original and talented man.

[1] Ostwald's *Klassiker*, clxxviii, 26, 50.   [2] AdS, 1777 (1784), m 420.
[3] Leicester, *Chymia*, 1959, v, 138.   [4] *Hydrodynamica*, Strasbourg, 1738.
[5] Ostwald's *Klassiker*, clxxviii, 55.
[6] *Tentament Chymiæ physicæ in usum studiosæ juventutis adornatum. Dromus ad veram Chymiam Physicam. Prolegomena*, Ostwald's *Klassiker*, clxxviii, 39.
[7] Ostwald's *Klassiker*, clxxviii, 43.
[8] Y. I. Solovyev, *History of Solutions* (in Russian), Moscow, 1959, 8, 13, 91.

CHAPTER VI

CHEMISTRY IN SCANDINAVIA. II. SCHEELE

Carl Wilhelm Scheele (Stralsund, 9 or 19 December 1742–Köping, 21 or 26 May 1786) was born at Stralsund, then the chief town of Swedish Pomerania (it became German in 1815). The date of birth of 9 December was given by J. C. Wilcke, the Secretary of the Swedish Academy of Sciences, whose

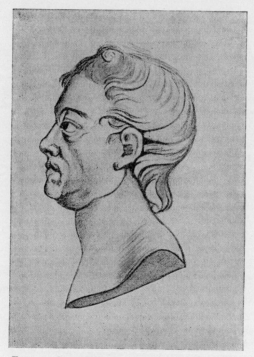

FIG. 17. CARL WILHELM SCHEELE, 1742–1786.

mother was Anna Scheele, a female connection of the family. Wilcke on his death in 1796 left a MS. of 226 pages, which was the basis of the notice by C. G. Sjöstén, Secretary of the Academy. This date is preferred by Vicq d'Azyr, Cleve, and Nordenskiöld. The date 19 December was given by Crell and is preferred by Hoefer, Blomstrand, Poggendorff, Zekert,[1] and Walden, who point out that the entry of Scheele's baptism is dated 21 December. Fredga thought either date was possible. The country of origin of the family is

[1] (1), 1932, ii, 12.

doubtful. Nordenskiöld thought it was Sweden; Thomson[1] and Zekert that it was North Germany, where his ancestors included an admiral and a bishop, Fredga thought it was Hannover. Thomson found no portrait of Scheele in Sweden, no trace of him in Köping, and no personal remains except the col-

FIG. 18. C. W. SCHEELE, 1742–1786.
(From a posthumous portrait by Falander.)

lection of his letters then in Gahn's possession. Thomson thought Scheele wrote his papers in German but Dobbin found that many were written originally in Swedish.

The portrait in Fig. 17[2] is from a medal struck in 1789 by the Swedish Academy of Sciences; it is the frontispiece in Scherer's *Allgemeines Journal der Chemie*, 1801, v, and *Z. phys. Chem.*, 1897, xxiv. The posthumous portrait by Falander (Fig. 18) shows him in later life, and Zekert[3] says it is not very satisfactory. The statue of Scheele in Stockholm depicted in Nordenskiöld is based on a projected one shown in Cleve's memoir.[4]

[1] (5), 76–9, 222.
[2] Partington, *Everyday Chemistry*, 1929, 96, Nordenskiöld, vii; Zekert, (1), ii, 34.
[3] (1), ii, 31.
[4] Anon. in *Pharm. Rundschau* (New York), 1886, iv, 143, 162; Anon. in *Pharm. J.*, 1893, xxiii, 568 (sep. reprint, 1893, with portr. by Falander); Anon., *ib.*, 1895, xxv, 621; J. Black, *Lectures on Chemistry*, Edinburgh, 1803, i, 396; C. W. Blomstrand, *Carl Wilhelm Scheele. Minnesteckning föredragen inför Kongl. Vetensk. Akad. på 100: de årsdagen af Scheeles död*, 1886 (not seen); U. Boklund, *C. W. Scheele Bruna Boken*, Stockholm, 1961; Browne, *J. Chem. Educ.*, 1940, xvii, 53 (Scheele's laboratories); Cap, 1864, ii, 233–72; P. T. Cleve, *Carl Wilhelm Scheele;*

Scheele's father was Joachim Christian Scheele (Stralsund; 1703–76), a merchant; his mother Margaretha Eleanora Warnecros (Stralsund; 11 July 1713–1 April 1788) survived him. He was the seventh of a family of eleven; the eldest became an apothecary, the youngest, Paul Joachim, became M.D. Halle in 1773. (In the Stralsund church register the father's name and those of the children are entered as 'Scheel'.)[1]

Scheele had a good elementary education. In 1757 at the age of fourteen he entered the apothecary's business of Martin Anders Bauch in Gothenburg, whose name deserves mention since he provided Scheele with opportunities for study, when he read Caspar Neumann's *Prælectiones Chemicæ*, Lemery's *Cours de Chymie*, Boerhaave's *Elementa Chemiae*, Kunckel's *Laboratorium Chymicum* (which he greatly prized), and Rothe's *Anleitung zur Chymie*, all books of considerable merit. He also made chemical experiments. Bauch's shop had a good collection of chemicals, most of which form the subjects of Scheele's later investigations. A MS. of 1748 of Scheele's brother Johann Martin gives the contents of a Gothenburg pharmacy and contains a most detailed and extensive list, showing the wide range of apparatus and chemicals available.[2]

In 1765 Scheele moved to Malmö, where his master P. M. Kjellström

Ett Minnesblad på hundrade årsdagen af hans död, Köping [1886] (portrait by Falander); Cornell, *Ann. Sci.*, 1936, i, 219; Crell, *Ann.*, 1787, i, 175–92 (reprod. in Hermbstädt's ed. of Scheele's *Sämmtliche physische und chemische Werke*, Berlin, 1793, i, xix f.; English (with Scheele's essays), in Crell's *Chemical Journal*, 3 vols., London, 1791–3); H. Davy, (1), *Elements of Chemical Philosophy*, 1812, i, 38; (2), *Works*, 1840, vii, 118; *id.*, in J. Davy, *Memoirs of Sir H. Davy*, 1836, i, 225; Van Deventer, *Chem. Weekblad*, 1928, xxv, 101 (Scheele's synthesis of KCN); L. Dobbin, *Collected Papers of Carl Wilhelm Scheele*, translated from the Swedish and German Originals, London, 1931 (intro.); Dumas, (2), 1878, 94; F. A. Flückiger, *Arch. Pharm.*, 1886, xxiv, 369, 417; *Pharm. Rundschau* (New York), 1886, iv, 188, 208; Fourcroy, (2), 1796, iii, 524–41; A. Fredga, *Carl Wilhelm Scheele, Levnadstekningar över K. Svenska Vetenskapsakademiens ledmöter*, 119, Stockholm, 1943; Gmelin, (1), iii, 257; Grimaux, *Rev. gén. Sci.*, 1890, i, 1 (letter from Scheele to Lavoisier); Hildebrand, *Lychnos*, 1936, i, 76 (b. 9 December); E. Hjelt, *Chem. Ztg.*, 1913, xxxvii, 277 (letters of Black on Scheele); Hoefer, (1), ii, 450–72; Jörgensen, *Samml. chem. u. chem. techn. Vorträge* (ed. Herz), 1909, xiv, 111–72; Kopp, (1), i, 255; *Lefnadsteckningar öfver Kongl. Svenska Vetensk. Akad. efter år 1854 aflidna ledamöter*, Stockholm, 1891, iii, 1–38 (not seen); G. Lockemann, in G. Bugge, *Das Buch der grossen Chemiker*, Berlin, 1929, i, 274; *id.*, *Pharm. Ztg.*, 1936, lxxxi, 604–8; *id.*, *Geschichte der Chemie*, Berlin, 1950, i, 115 (b. 21 December 1742); J. G. Macintosh, *Scheele's Chemical Essays, with additions and life*, etc., London, 1901; A. E. Nordenskiöld, *Karl Wilhelm Scheele; Nachgelassene Briefe und Aufzeichnungen*, Stockholm, 1892 (another edition in Swedish, *Efterlemnade Bref och Anteckningar*, Stockholm, 1892) (vii (life), xxxv–xli (list of Scheele's printed works), xlii–iii (list of biographies); 491 pp., 2 pp. symbols, iv ll. facsim., contents); Baron Nils Adolf Erik von Nordenskiöld (Helsingfors, 18 November 1832–1901), was at first professor of chemistry and mineralogy in the Carolinian Institute in Stockholm, then the famous explorer; Nordström, *Lychnos*, 1942, vii, 177 (letters, etc.; important); C. W. Oseen, (1) *Torbern Bergman och Carl Wilhelm Scheele*, Stockholm, 1940 (not seen); (2) *Carl Wilhelm Scheele Manuskript 1756–1777. Tolkning av C. W. Oseen*, Stockholm, 1942 (173 pp.) and vol. of reproductions (Ljustryck, 182 pp.); Partington, *Nature*, 1931, cxxviii, 1023; Poggendorff, (1), ii, 776, 1439; C. G. Sjöstén, *Åminnelsetal . . . öfver . . . C. Vilhelm Scheele den 14 Oct. 1799*, Stockholm, 1801 (not seen); T. Thomson, *Ann. Phil.*, 1814, iv, 16, 311; *id.*, (1), ii, 54; *id.*, (5), 1813, 76–8; *id.*, *Heat and Electricity*, 1840, 276 ('a model in chemical researches'); Thorpe, *Essays*, 1902, 60; Tilden, *Famous Chemists*, 1921, 53 f.; Vicq d'Azyr, 1805, ii, 19–47 (the result of some months of work, *ib.*, i, 68); Walden, *Z. anorg. Chem.*, 1943, ccl, 230 (b. 19, not 9, December 1742); O. Zekert, (1) *Carl Wilhelm Scheele sein Leben und seine Werke*, Mittenwald (Bavaria), 7 parts, 1931, 1932 (pts. i–ii, pp. 7–39) and (pts. iii–vii, sep. pagin., 3–303) 1933; issued in complete form in 1934 (*Isis*, 1935, xxiv, 226); medallion portr. of Scheele aged about 25, ii, 34; (2) *id.*, *Pharm. Monatshefte*, 1936, xvii, 105–7; 1937, xviii, 107 (papers in vol. for 1920 not available); (3) *id.*, *Carl Wilhelm Scheele*, Vienna, 1936 (with Falander's portr.).

[1] Poggendorff, (1), ii, 1439.   [2] Zekert, (1), iii–vii, 3–84.

again allowed him facilities for study and practical research. Kjellström says Scheele read books saying: 'that may be; that is wrong; I will try that.' Here he became acquainted with Anders Jahan Retzius (see p. 200), afterwards professor in Lund, with whom Scheele maintained a friendship for the rest of his life. Retzius used to say that Scheele read a book only once or twice, when, so good was his memory, he never needed to refer to it again.[1]

In 1768 Scheele was in Stockholm in a shop, not the laboratory, but he carried out research on tartaric acid with Retzius (who had followed him to Stockholm) and utilised a sunny window of the shop to study the effect of light on silver salts. If it is correct, as Retzius says, that Scheele made at this time most of the experiments described in his book *On Air and Fire*, he must have had the use of a laboratory. Scheele's name first appears in print in a memoir on tartaric acid by Retzius, published in 1770,[2] in which credit is given to Scheele for his part in the research on the preparation of the acid from cream of tartar.

Whilst he was in Stockholm Scheele got to know Johann Gottlieb Gahn (see p. 201), Bergman's assistant in Uppsala, and when Scheele moved to Uppsala in 1770 Gahn introduced him to Bergman. The biographers of Scheele say (with somewhat varying details) that Bergman had complained that a specimen of saltpetre bought from the shop where Scheele worked gave off red vapours with acid. Neither the apothecary, Lokk, nor Gahn could explain this, but Scheele told Gahn that he had found that saltpetre on heating forms the salt of another acid, giving the reaction in question.[3] Scheele was then introduced by Gahn to Bergman, who was impressed by his knowledge, advised him to investigate pyrolusite (leading to the discovery of chlorine in 1774), and took care that his researches should be published.[4] Bergman in 1775[5] stated (without mentioning Scheele) that nitre on heating becomes phlogisticated and the residue gives up its acid with vinegar.

A paper on salt of sorrel (acid potassium oxalate) which Scheele had sent to the Swedish Academy had been read but, owing to some unintentional negligence on Bergman's part, had not been printed,[6] and this is said to have led at first to some disinclination on the part of Scheele to be introduced to Bergman, who had a high regard for Scheele's genius, and did everything in his power to bring him to the notice of the scientific world. Scheele owed to Bergman, as Faraday did later to Davy, his transition from obscurity to a leading position in the world of science. Retzius[7] says Scheele had previously sent to the Swedish Academy an ill-digested paper on a pharmaceutical preparation of iron (globuli martiales) made by boiling iron powder with a solution of cream of tartar, which contained the important observations that hydrogen (phlogiston elasticum) is evolved by the action of organic acids on iron, or even of water alone on iron filings,[8] whilst Cavendish[9] said: 'I know of only three metallic substances, namely, zinc, iron and tin, that generate in-

[1] Zekert, (1), iii, 115.   [2] Försök med vinsten och dess syra, KAH, 1770, xxxi, 207.
[3] Letters to Retzius, VI (see p. 211), 4 f., 9 f., dated 1767.   [4] VI, xix.
[5] *Scheffers Föreläsningar*, § 55, n. 6; tr. Weigel, 1779, 126.   [6] VI, xvii.
[7] VI, xvi.   [8] Letter to Gahn, *c.* 1770; VI, 50-4.
[9] *Phil. Trans.*, 1766, lvi, 141; *Scientific Papers*, 1921, ii, 78.

flammable air by solution in acids; and those only by solution in the diluted vitriolic acid, or spirit of salt.' Retzius says Scheele's memoir was not published and: 'ich weiss nicht anderes, als dass diese Untersuchung in Bergmans Hände kam und verschwand.' Bergman published the observation on iron and water in 1781,[1] without mentioning Scheele.

In his position at Uppsala Scheele again had a considerate master, Lokk, who gave him one day a week for research. In February 1775, at a meeting at which the King was present, Scheele, on the proposal of Prof. Bergius, was elected a member of the Royal Academy of Sciences of Sweden, an unprecedented honour for an apothecary's assistant,[2] and in the same year he moved to Köping to act as superintendent of the pharmacy. At Köping, in spite of early disappointments and offers of happier and more lucrative posts, he remained for the rest of his life. He had an offer from Frederick the Great in Berlin in 1777, the matter beginning with a letter to him from D'Alembert of 15 December 1775, recommending Scheele as Marggraf's successor.[3] A letter from his brother Christian Scheele to Wilcke states that Scheele received an offer in 1776 with a proposal of a salary of 1200 Reichsthalers.[4] Thomson[5] refers to a statement by Crell[6] that Scheele was invited by the English ministry to an easy and advantageous position in England, but after full enquiry he could find no evidence of this; Thorpe suggests that the offer may have come through Lord Shelburne.[7] French[8] said Scheele was 'a foreign member of the Royal Society' but his name does not appear in Thomson's list.

Scheele's death was brought about by a complication of disorders, including rheumatism contracted by work in unfavourable circumstances, and later, gout: 'no apothecary', he said, 'escapes the gout.' His laboratory was at first a cold and draughty wooden shed.[9] In the presence of death his unselfishness did not desert him; he was married to the widow of his predecessor at the pharmacy in order that the apothecary's privilege should remain with her; two years later she married again, in accordance with his wish. The pursuit of scientific truth, undeflected alike by disappointment or success, was the one object of Scheele's brief life. His circumstances were too modest to expose him to jealousy or malice, and his work was done without such hindrances. In a letter to Gahn, he said: 'how glad is the enquirer when discovery rewards his diligence; then his heart rejoices', and if Scheele's reward in discoveries was rich, it was abundantly deserved.

Beddoes[10] says a near relation of Bergman told him that 'the greatest of Bergman's discoveries was the discovery of Scheele', a trivial remark long afterwards associated with Davy and Faraday. Dumas says 'when it is only a question of facts, Scheele is infallible'. In theory, Scheele was in much the same position as his contemporaries: he followed the great error of Stahl, and held to the theory of phlogiston to the end of his life. Even here, however, he

---

[1] *Opuscula*, iii, 82, 93, 95.   [2] Zekert, (1), vi, 159.
[3] *Oeuvres de Frédéric le Grand*, Berlin, 1854, xxv, 32 (Correspondance, t. x).
[4] Tilden, 58; Zeckert, (1), iii, 217 f., 294.   [5] (1), ii, 60.
[6] *Ann.*, 1787, I, 175.   [7] See *Lychnos*, 1942, vii, 280.
[8] *Torch and Crucible*, Princeton, 1941, 102.   [9] Zekert, (1), vii, 203.
[10] *The Chemical Essays of Charles William Scheele*, London, 1786, pref. vi.

showed originality, and it is especially noteworthy that, unlike many of Priestley's, his experimental researches were always carefully planned and the results expected. He wrote in 1777 to Bergman: 'ohne Theorie wollte ich wohl nicht experimentiren',[1] and his publications are certainly more systematic than Priestley's.

The contributions made to chemistry by Scheele, especially in view of his limited opportunities, are astonishing both in number and importance. R. Lubbock[2] says of Scheele: cum ob suam simplicitatem tum ob methodum qua ordinantur experimenta, nulli videtur secunda. Davy[3] said of him: 'nothing could damp the ardour of his mind or chill the fire of his genius: with very small means he accomplished very great things.'[4]

Besides being the first discoverer of oxygen, Scheele made a number of other most important discoveries:

1. Chlorine, manganese and baryta in an investigation on 'black magnesia' (native manganese dioxide) (1774).
2. Silicon fluoride and hydrofluoric acid from fluorspar (1771, 1780, 1786).
3. Phosphorus from bone ash, and phosphoric acid by the action of nitric acid on phosphorus (1774, 1777; phosphoric acid was discovered in bone ash in 1770–71 by Gahn).
4. Arsenic acid (1775), molybdic acid (1778), tungstic acid (1781). Distinction between molybdenite (MoS_2) and graphite (1779). Arsenic hydride (1775), copper arsenite ('Scheele's green') (1778).
5. Several organic acids: tartaric (1770), mucic (1780), lactic (1780), uric (1780), prussic (1782–3), oxalic (1776, 1784–5), citric (1784), malic (1785), gallic and pyrogallic (1786); also glycerol (1783–4), murexide (1780), several esters (1782), aldehyde (1782), and casein (1780).
6. Action of light on silver salts (1777).
7. Hydrogen sulphide ('stinking sulphurous air') and crude hydrogen persulphide (1777).
8. Distinction between nitrous and nitric acids (1767); nitric oxide, nitrous acid (N_2O_3), nitrogen dioxide, and nitric acid contain decreasing amounts of phlogiston (increasing amounts of oxygen) (1777).
9. Formation of cyanide by the action of ammonia on a mixture of charcoal or graphite and potassium carbonate (1783).

Scheele's publications, apart from his book (p. 211), are to be found in Swedish in the memoirs of the Stockholm Academy (1770–86) and in German in Crell's *Annalen* (1784–7): they have been collected and translated:

I. Carl Wilhelm Scheele . . . Sämmtliche Physische und Chemische Werke, nach dem Tode des Verfassers gesammlet, und in deutscher Sprache herausgegeben von D. Sigismund Friedrich Hermbstädt, 2 vols. 8°, Berlin, 1793 (I, pp. xxxii, 264, 1 plate; II, 446 pp.); Crell, *Ann.*, 1793, II, 181, says this was published 'aus reinen Gesinnung der Verehrung und Dankbarkeit gegen den unsterblichen Scheele', at a low price within the means of students (2 thl. 8 gr.). It is the standard text, but Dobbin, V, says it is not altogether satisfactory.

II. Caroli Guil. Scheele Opuscula chemica et physica. Latine vertit G. H. Schaefer. Edidit et præfatus est E. B. G. Hebenstreit, 2 vols. 8°, Leipzig, 1788–9 (I, pp. viii, 284, 1 plate; II, vi, 284, xxii; BM 954. e. 27.).

III. Mémoires de Chymie . . . tirés des Mémoires de l'Acad. Royale des Sciences de

---

[1] VI, 284; Fourcroy, (2), iii, 525, said: Livré tout entier à la solution d'un problème, il ne suivoit qu'un certain ordre d'expériences, correspondant à une ordre d'idées uniques, jusqu'à ce qu'il eut trouvé ce qu'il cherchoit.
[2] *Dissertatio Physico-chemica Inauguralis, de Principio Sorbile*, Edinburgh, 1784, 18.
[3] (1), 38.   [4] Hoefer, (2), 1843, ii, 460: avec de petites ressources, il fit de grandes choses.

Stockholm, traduites du Suédois et de l'Allemand, 2 pts. 8°, Dijon, 1785 (21 memoirs); the tr. is by Mme. Picardet revised by Guyton de Morveau (BM 236. i. 20).

IV. The Chemical Essays of Charles-William Scheele. Translated from the Transactions of the Academy of Sciences at Stockholm. With additions [by T. Beddoes], 8°, London, 1786; reprinted with a sketch of the life of Scheele by J. G. M. M'Intosh, and index, 8°, London, 1901.

V. Collected Papers of Carl Wilhelm Scheele, translated from the Swedish and German Originals, by L. Dobbin, London, 1931 (with introduction); apart from the originals, this is the most accurate and complete form of Scheele's memoirs.

Scheele's book *On Air and Fire* (1777) is dealt with below (VII). It is contained in I, II, and V. Since Scheele's letters, etc., published by Nordenskiöld, are frequently referred to, this volume (full title in bibliography, p. 207) is given a reference number:

VI. C. W. Scheele, Nachgelassene Briefe und Aufzeichnungen, ed. A. E. Nordenskiöld, Stockholm, 1892.

VII. Carl Wilhelm Scheele's . . . Chemische Abhandlung von der Luft und dem Feuer. Nebst einem Vorbericht von Torbern Bergman, . . . Upsala und Leipzig, Verlegt von Magn. Swederus, Buchhändler, sm. 8°, 1777 (pp. vi, 16, 155: list of books publ. by Swederus; engraved f.p., plate; BM 1035. c. 14). Zweite verbesserte Ausgabe, sm. 8°, Leipzig, 1782 (pp. xxxii, 286, 2 plates, Zekert, (1), vii, 258; Goldschmidt, *Cat.* 51 (1939), no. 216; contains a letter from Priestley dated 1780, and a new treatise by Scheele on the purity of air). The illustration of a laboratory on the t.p. of VII is on the t.p. of Bergman's ed. of Scheffer's Chemiske Föreläsningar, 1775, also publ. by Swederus. Both eds. of VII are very rare.

VIIA. French tr.:

Traité Chimique de l'Air et du Feu. Avec une Introduction de Torbern Bergmann (*sic*) . . . traduit de l'Allemand par le Baron de Dietrich, 12°, Paris, 1781 (pp. xliv, 45–268, plate, very rare); 2 ed., 12°, Paris, 1787 (pp. xliv, 45–268, plate).

VIIB. Supplément au Traité Chimique de l'Air et du Feu de M. Scheele, Contenant un Tableau abrégé des nouvelles découvertes sur les diverses espèces d'Air, par Jean-Godefroi Léonhardy; des Notes de M. Richard Kirwan, & une Lettre du Docteur Priestley . . . sur l'Ouvrage de M. Scheele; Traduit et Augmenté De Notes, & du Complément du Tableau abrégé de ce qui a été publié jusqu'aujourd'hui sur les différentes espèces d'Air: Par M. le Baron de Dietrich . . . Avec la Traduction, par MM. de l'Académie de Dijon, des expériences de M. Scheele sur la quantité d'air pur qui se trouve dans l'atmosphère, 12°, Paris, 1785 (pp. xiv, i l., pp. 14–214; v. scarce).

VIIC. English tr.:

Chemical Observations and Experiments on Air and Fire. By Charles-William Scheele . . . Translated from the German by J. R. Forster . . . To which are added Notes By Richard Kirwan, Esq. F.R.S. with a letter to him from Joseph Priestley, L.L.D. F.R.S., 8°, London, 1780 (f.p., pp. xl, incl. fulsome dedication to Priestley and depreciatory note on Mayow, 259). Scheele complained that the tr. is inaccurate, VI, 318.

Partial eds. of VII in ACR, 1894, viii; Ostwald's *Klassiker*, 1894, lviii; full in I, i, 1–244 (with notes), II, and V, 85–178.

John Reinold Forster, F.R.S. (Dirschau, W. Prussia, 1729– Halle, 1798) was a professor in Warrington Academy (where Priestley taught) in 1766–7 and from 1780 in Halle. He was aided by Freemasons and unpopular in all quarters.[1]

Baron de Dietrich was Paul Thierry (Edesheim, Palatinate, *c.* 6 December 1723–Paris, 21 June (or January) 1789), whose grandfather Johann Jacob Hollbach was a notary and whose uncle Franz Adam Hollbach went to Paris and in 1722 became a knight as Eques ab Holbach. He brought up Paul and the latter became Paul Heinrich Dietrich Baron d'Holbach, 'Dietrich' being

[1] Ersch and Gruber, *Allgemeine Encyclopädie*, 1847, xlvi, 376.

'Thierry' and 'Heinrich' apparently inserted for effect.[1] He wrote the atheistical *Système de la Nature* (1770) and translated works of Kunckel, Gellert, Lehmann, Wallerius, Stahl, Henckel, Orschall, and Scheele. He was very wealthy and his friends included Rouelle, D'Alembert, Diderot, Buffon, and Rousseau, but Voltaire opposed him. Several of his books are anonymous or pseudonymous. His house in Paris was known as the 'Café de l'Europe'.

Manganese, Baryta, Chlorine

An early and important research by Scheele is that on 'black magnesia', i.e. native manganese dioxide or pyrolusite,[2] in which he discovered chlorine and recognised the existence of an earth (baryta) present (as an impurity) in the pyrolusite. Scheele found that pyrolusite has a strong attraction for phlogiston (is an oxidising agent) and forms colourless salts (manganous salts) with acids only in presence of phlogiston (a reducing agent). Solutions which do not contain phlogiston are coloured (manganic salts). Scheele prepared a number of manganous salts, including a solution of the dithionate (MnS_2O_6) by the action of sulphurous acid. He discovered manganese in plant ashes by the green colour (potassium manganate) formed on fusing them with nitre on a sheet of silver before the blowpipe. Bergman[3] thought this green colour was produced by iron. Scheele found that the green colour (manganate) turned red (permanganate) with acids. By distilling pyrolusite, sugar, and diluted sulphuric acid he obtained a 'very pure vinegar' (acetic acid). He later[4] obtained pyrophoric manganous oxide by heating manganous carbonate. Although Scheele suspected that pyrolusite contained a new metal (manganese), this was first isolated by Gahn in 1774, and later by Rinman, by strongly heating calcined pyrolusite with oil.[5] Irvine[6] had inferred in 1769 that pyrolusite is 'a metallic substance; whether a new metal, or a mixture of those already known'.

The name manganese (manganèse) was proposed by Guyton de Morveau[7] but had been used in 1599 by Imperato (see Vol. II, p. 95). Henry Gahn said that manganese was first prepared by his brother J. G. Gahn, who also isolated baryta from heavy spar.[8] Ignatius Godfrey Kaim (of Styria)[9] claimed to have

---

[1] A. Becker, *A. Nat.*, 1916, vii, 163; Lange, *Geschichte des Materialismus*, Iserlohn, 1882, 305; L. Vibert, *Ann. Chim. Anal.*, 1943, xxvi, 38; P. Naville, *Paul Thiry d'Holbach et la Philosophie Scientifique au XVIIIe Siècle*, 1943 (bibl.); Hippeau, NBG, 1858, xxiv, 925; Guerlac, *Chymia*, 1959, v, 73 (100); in NBG, 1855, xiv, 153, it is said he was born in Strasbourg in 1748 and guillotined in Paris on 28 December 1793.

[2] Om Brun-sten eller Magnesia nigra och dess Egenskaper, KAH, 1774, xxxv, 89, 177; I, ii, 35; V, 17; ACR no. 13.

[3] De mineris ferri albis, 1774; *Opuscula*, ii, 220.   [4] VII, § 65.

[5] VI, 125 (regulus magnesiæ), 271 (magnesium); Bergman, *Scheffers Föreläsningar*, § 337, Anmerk. 3; 1775, 390; 1796, 446; Gren, 1795, iii, 680; see also Bergman, KAH, 1774, xxxv, 194; von Engeström, *ib.*, 1774, xxxv, 196; Rinman, *ib.*, 1774, xxxv, 201; Hjelm, *ib.*, 1778, xxxix, 82; 1785, vi, 141; *id.*, Crell's *Ann.*, 1787, I, 158.

[6] *Essays, chiefly on Chemical Subjects*, 1805, pref. xviii.

[7] *Méthode de Nomenclature Chimique*, by de Morveau, Lavoisier, etc., 1787, 54.

[8] H. Gahn, in *Medical and Philosophical Commentaries by a Society in Edinburgh*, ed. Duncan, Edinburgh, 1783, vii, 438 (BM 48. b. 1): 'magnesia nigra is reducible to a new semi-metal; and that the marmor metallicum, or heavy spar, is a compound of vitriolic acid and a new species of earth, whose attraction to the vitriolic acid is very great. Both these have been made by my brother.'

[9] *Dissertatio Inauguralis Chemica de Metallis Dubiis*, Vienna, 1770 (on arsenic, cobalt, nickel, 'magnesia vitrariorum').

obtained a regulus from tungsten earth, molybdena, manganese, etc., by heating strongly with black flux, but his results were not favourably received.

Early in 1774 Scheele discovered in pyrolusite 'another earth' (baryta), from which he prepared the nitrate and chloride, showing that these gave a white precipitate with sulphuric acid and sulphates, and could be used as a test for these. He recognised that this earth (baryta) was contained in largest amount in crystals (of heavy spar) in the specimens of pyrolusite sent to him by Bergman, in which it was combined with sulphuric acid. The presence of this earth in crystals of heavy spar sent to him by Scheele was established by Gahn in 1774 (see p. 212) and this was confirmed by Scheele.[1] Gahn's discovery was published by Bergman.[2] Scheele in 1776 obtained pure baryta by heating the nitrate.[3]

The most important outcome of Scheele's research on manganese was the discovery of chlorine. This was announced in a letter to Gahn of 28 March 1773.[4] Scheele found that pyrolusite dissolved in cold acid of salt (hydrochloric acid) to form a dark brown solution (containing a higher chloride of manganese), which on warming in a retort gave off a greenish-yellow gas with a suffocating smell of aqua regia. He collected the gas in a bladder, which turned yellow, found that it corroded corks, and had a permanent bleaching action and was thereby converted into acid of salt. It attacked all metals, even gold, gave white fumes with ammonia, and with soda formed common salt. (It is strange that Scheele did not observe the formation of hypochlorite and chlorate in the last experiment.) Since the manganese ore readily takes up phlogiston in presence of acids and passes into solution, Scheele assumed that the new gas was *dephlogisticated acid of salt*, and since he regarded hydrogen as the same as phlogiston (see p. 224), this amounts to the assumption that the gas was *acid of salt — hydrogen*.

Silicon fluoride. Hydrofluoric acid

In 1671 John Ray announced to the Royal Society that Samuel Fisher had produced a liquid which made glass so soft that it could be shaved with a knife like horn and was reduced to a white calx.[5] A corrosive liquid which etched glass discovered by Heinrich Schwanhardt, mentioned by Sandrart,[6] has often been identified with hydrofluoric acid, but this is probably incorrect.[7] A mention of a liquid corroding glass made by adding powdered fluorspar to nitric acid was communicated by Pauli of Dresden to Weygand in 1725,[8] and the discovery is said to have come from England.[9]

[1] VI, 114, 116, 120, 243 (letter to Bergman before 16 May 1774); Scheele, On the Earth of Heavy Spar, *Beschäftigungen der Berlinischen Gesellschaft naturforschender Freunde*, 1779, iv, 611; I, ii, 177; V, 207; VII, § 95.
[2] *Scheffers Föreläsningar*, 1775, § 167, Anmerk. 3; 1796, 194.   [3] VI, 247.   [4] VI, 76.
[5] Birch, *History of the Royal Society*, 1756, ii, 495.
[6] *L'Academia Todesca oder Teutsche Academie*, 3 vols. f°, Nürnberg, 1675-9, i, 346.
[7] Partington, *Manchester Mem.*, 1923, lxvii, No. 6, 73; cf. Accum, *Nicholson's J.*, 1801, iv, 1.
[8] *Sammlung von Natur- und Medicin-Kunst- und Literatur Geschichten, Winter Quartel 1725 von Academ. Naturæ Curios. in Breslau*, Leipzig and Budissin, 1726, 107 (BM 431. b. 1).
[9] Halle, *Fortgesetzte Magie*, Berlin, 1788, 516.

Scheele published three important memoirs on the action of sulphuric acid on fluorspar.[1]

In 1771 he found that fluorspar lost its property of phosphorescence without change of weight on heating, and concluded that it is the lime salt of a peculiar acid, which he obtained in an impure state by distilling fluorspar with concentrated sulphuric acid in a glass retort. The retort was powerfully corroded (as Marggraf had found in 1768; see Vol. II, p. 728) and a gas was evolved which deposited gelatinous silica on contact with water. Scheele concluded that silica was a compound of the acid with water. The gas would be mostly silicon fluoride, which Scheele thus discovered (1771) some years before Priestley (see p. 267). Scheele describes many of the reactions of the acid (hydrofluoric acid mixed with hydrofluosilicic acid) and prepared several of its salts (fluorides). He showed in 1786 that fluorspar is decomposed on fusion with potassium carbonate.

Priestley[2] gave Scheele credit for his work and also mentions 'M. Boulanger, who has taken a great deal of pains with this subject, and is of opinion that this new acid is only the acid of salt, combined with an earthy substance'.[3] An account of 'the new-discovered Swedish Acid' with some additional experiments was given by John Hill in 1774.[4]

John Hill (Spalding, nr. Peterborough, 1716–London, 15 November 1775) who was an M.D. and a man of ability, disappointed at not being elected a Fellow, published *A Review of the Works of the Royal Society* (4°, 1751, 2 ed., 1780), pointing out errors and absurdities in the *Philosophical Transactions*. He was given the order of the Polar Star by the King of Sweden, assuming the title 'Sir'. He published several other works:[5] also plays and fiction and two papers.[6] His botany was in advance of his time (he knew the action of light in stimulating movements) but he left no permanent mark on the science.[7]

The use of metal, in place of glass, retorts in the distillation of fluorspar with sulphuric acid was suggested (but not tried) by Wiegleb in 1781;[8] in 1781

---

[1] KAH, 1771, xxxii, 120 (fluss-spat och dess Syra); Crell's *Chym. J.*, 1779, ii, 192; KAH, 1780, i, 18; Crell's *Ann.*, 1786, I, 3; V, 3, 209, 295; see J. R. Forster, *An Easy Method of Assaying and Classing Mineral Substances . . . To which is added, a Series of Experiments on the Fluor Spatosus, or Sparry Fluor. (By Charles William Scheele). Abstracted from the Memoirs of the Royal Swedish Academy of Sciences for the Year 1771*, London, 1772 (ii ll., 44, 24 pp.; at end: *Appendix to Cronstedt's Mineralogy*, containing additions and notes by Prof. M. T. Brunnich).

[2] E & O (see p. 244), 1790, ii, 339.

[3] Boullanger, *Expériences et Observations sur le Spath vitreux, ou Fluor spathique*, 8°, Paris, 1773 (32 pp.) (Duveen, 91). The author, who gives no initials to his name, is otherwise unknown. Lavoisier, *Traité de Chimie*, 1789, 263, says he was the Duc de Liancourt (La Rochefoucauld, 1747–1827); Kopp, (1), iii, 369, that he was the chemist D'Arcet.

[4] *Theophrastus's History of Stones*, 2 ed., 1774, 267–78; Berliner, *Science*, 1927, lxvi, 192.

[5] (1) Ed. of Pomet's *History of Drugs*, 4°, 1748; (2) *The Construction of Timber*, 8°, 1770; (3) *Fossils arranged according to their Obvious Characters; with their History and Description; Under the Articles of Form, Hardness, Weight, Surface, Colour, and Qualities; The Place of their Production, Their Uses, and Distinctive English, and Classical Latin Names*, 8°, 1771 (420 pp. and index); (4) *The Vegetable System*, 26 vols. f° and 1600 copperplates, 1759–75; Z in NBG, 1858, xxiv, 682; Barker, DNB, 1891, xxvi, 397–401; Woodruff, *American Naturalist*, 1926, lx, 417 (portr.).

[6] *Phil. Trans.*, 1746–7, xliv, 60 (the manner of seeding of mosses), 458 (Winsor loam).

[7] J. R. Green, *A History of Botany in the United Kingdom*, 1914, 222.

[8] Crell, *Neueste Entdeckungen*, 1781, I, 3.

J. C. F. Meyer[1] used an iron retort and obtained a fairly pure solution of hydrofluoric acid, from which he prepared ammonium fluoride (Flussspath Salmiak: the name suggests the relation of hydrofluoric to hydrochloric acid). Meyer mentions the use of metal vessels by Scheele, with whom he was in communication. A very detailed study of hydrofluoric acid was made by Wenzel:[2] he used a lead retort in two halves, soldered together when the powdered fluorspar and sulphuric acid were put in, and a lead receiver containing water. He made Flussspathsalmiak (ammonium fluoride), and by precipitating a solution of it with lime water obtained synthetic fluorspar. Scopoli[3] found the same result with a gilt silver retort and concluded that the 'earth' came from the glass.

Meyer's experiments were confirmed in 1781 by Scheele,[4] and in the same year Scheele used a cast-tin retort,[5] but the results were not published till his third memoir appeared in 1786: in this he mentions Meyer, but not Wenzel. A set of experiments (quantitative) on similar lines to Wiegleb's (which he mentions) was made by de Puymarin junr., of Toulouse,[6] who describes the process of engraving with hydrofluoric acid on glass coated with wax on which designs were scratched, and suggested its use in graduating glass instruments. He refers for this process to a previous letter from the Comte de G . . . [Garaye] communicated to Crell[7] by Klaproth.

Phosphorus

In a footnote in his first paper on fluorspar (1771, see p. 214) Scheele says: 'it has recently been discovered that the earth in bone and horn is lime, saturated with the acid of phosphorus.' Bergman says in one place (and probably correctly) that this discovery was made by Gahn in 1769, but in another place that it was made by Scheele.[8] Scheele[9] says it was discovered by Gahn and himself 'since 1770', but in another place he says they collaborated 'and finally Mr. Gahn discovered that the acid was identical with phosphoric acid'.[10] In 1777 Scheele obtained phosphoric acid by the action of nitric acid on phosphorus.[11]

Henry Gahn[12] says the presence of phosphoric acid in bones and the preparation of phosphorus from bones, by a process which he describes, were discovered by his brother J. G. Gahn. Guyton de Morveau[13] mentions that Crell, in a paper read to the Medical Society of Edinburgh and published (in German) at Altenburg in 1776, had communicated 'an article of M. Gahn of Stockholm which announced that phosphorus could be extracted from animal bones', but Crell could find no trace of Gahn's work

---

[1] Beiträge zur Kentniss des Flussspaths, in *Schrift. Berlin. Ges. Naturforsch. Freunde*, 1781, ii, 319–33; a full summary of the paper by Meyer and of Wenzel's pamphlet (see below) is given by Partington, *op. cit.*, p. 213.

[2] *Chemische Untersuchungen des Flussspaths*, 8°, Dresden, 1783.

[3] Crell's *Ann.*, 1784, I, 236–7.   [4] VI, 324: letter from Scheele to Bergman.

[5] VI, 325.   [6] *Obs. Phys.*, 1788, xxxii, 419.   [7] *Ann.*, 1786, II, 494.

[8] *Scheffers Föreläsningar*, § 173, Anmerk. (Gahn); § 206, Anmerk. 1. (Scheele); *ib.*, 1796, 208, 259; Bergman calls phosphoric acid 'urinsyra'.

[9] V, 311.

[10] Zekert, (1), i, 283; Speter, *Superphosphate*, 1933, vi, 125; 1935, viii, 149; VI, 37.

[11] VII, § 77; V, 144; see Marggraf, Vol. II, p. 725.

[12] *Medical and Philosophical Commentaries by a Society in Edinburgh*, ed. Duncan, Edinburgh, 1775, iii, 94.

[13] *Ency. Méthod., Chymie*, 1786, i, 210.

except a note in Scheele's paper on fluorspar (1771). Guyton de Morveau then refers to the statement by Bergman as establishing Gahn's priority.

Scheele in 1774[1] dissolved burnt hartshorn (containing calcium phosphate) in nitric acid, precipitated gypsum from the solution by sulphuric acid, filtered, evaporated to dryness, dissolved in water, filtered, evaporated to a syrup, mixed the phosphoric acid so obtained with charcoal powder, and distilled phosphorus in a coated glass retort. In 1777[2] Scheele treated the bone ash directly with sulphuric acid to obtain phosphoric acid. The important discovery that microcosmic salt contains soda is announced only in letters to Gahn of October, and Bergius of December, 1774:[3] 'es ist ein dreifaches Mittelsalz, aus alkali minerali fixo, alkali volatili und acido phosphori bestehend' (cf. Proust, p. 642). He also described magnesium ammonium sulphate (ein dreifaches Salz, bestehend aus acido vitrioli, alkali volatili und magnesia).[4]

Molybdenum

In 1778 Scheele clearly distinguished between two minerals which are very similar in appearance, viz. molybdenite (MoS_2) and graphite.[5] Bengt Andersson Qvist (? –? 14 October 1799) had investigated molybdenite in 1754[6] and concluded that it contained iron, tin, and much sulphur, but had not distinguished it from graphite. Scheele found that on boiling with nitric acid it formed a chalk-white powder (which Qvist had mistaken for oxide of tin), which he called 'earth of molybdena' (*terra molybdanæ*), of an acid nature,[7] giving crystals of a salt when boiled with potash solution. This 'earth' was molybdenum trioxide, MoO_3. Scheele was unable to reduce it to a coherent metal by strong heating with charcoal or oil, but obtained a black powder (probably metallic molybdenum). By heating the 'earth' with sulphur he obtained the original molybdenite. He obtained blue solutions of molybdenum salts by reduction of the acid solutions. In a letter to Bergman[8] Scheele says metallic molybdenum was obtained in 1781 by Hjelm, whose experiments were first published in 1790.[9]

Graphite

Scheele's investigation of graphite (plumbago) was published in 1779.[10] He showed that graphite when fused with nitre forms fixed air [carbon dioxide] and leaves a little oxide of iron, and concluded that it is 'a kind of mineral sulphur or charcoal, of which the constituents are aërial acid [carbon dioxide] united with a large quantity of phlogiston'. He correctly recognised that the iron is only an impurity, and he also found that the residue when pig-iron is dissolved in acid is graphite; he thought it contained less phlogiston than does plumbago (it contains more iron). The two minerals molybdenite and graphite, which are very similar in appearance and physical properties, had

[1] *Nya Lärda Tidningar*, 1774, 108; q. in V, 311.
[2] 'Chéel', *Obs. Phys.*, 1777, ix, 156; V, 312.
[3] VI, 144, 212.   [4] VI, 228 (Febr. 1775); cf. Fourcroy, p. 542.
[5] VI, 202 f.; KAH, 1778, xxxix, 247; V, 186.   [6] KAH, 1754, xv, 189: Rön om Bly-Erts.
[7] In 1777 he had suggested that 'all the earths are varieties of acids'; VII, §§ 73, 82.
[8] VI, 332; Bergman, De acidis metallicis, 1781; *Opuscula*, iii, 128.
[9] KAH, 1790, xi, 50, 81; *Ann. Phil.*, 1814, iv, 322.
[10] KAH, 1779, xl, 238; V, 202; it had been investigated by Gahn in 1778: VI, 204 f.

been confused until Scheele's investigation and he first clearly distinguished them and established their chemical composition.

W. Lewis (see Vol. II, p. 762)[1] had found that black-lead when calcined is slowly consumed, leaving a fourteenth part of its weight of rusty brown calx attracted by a magnet (iron oxide), and says: 'the remarkable dissipation . . . of a substance which in close vessels resists intense fires, may be somewhat illustrated by the known property of charcoal'; he emphasised the need for exposure to air. H. Colquhoun,[2] following up some experiments of Charles Macintosh (B.Pat. 5173/1825) in which rods of iron heated in a stream of 'carburetted hydrogen' (oil gas) were converted into steel, found that filaments of a 'new form of carbon' of metallic appearance and very pure were deposited, and this was probably the first formation of artificial graphite.

Tungsten

In 1781 Scheele[3] discovered tungsten trioxide (WO_3), which he obtained as a yellow powder by boiling a mineral now called *scheelite* (calcium tungstate, $CaWO_4$), formerly regarded as a mineral of iron or tin, with nitric acid. Scheelite had been named *lapis ponderosus* by Bergman, who confirmed Scheele's results[4] (the Swedish form, *tung sten*, 'heavy stone', is the origin of the name tungsten). Cronstedt thought it was an ore of iron (ferrum calciforme, terrâ quâdam icognita intime mixtum), whilst most German mineralogists thought it was a tin ore (Zinnspath).[5] Scheele isolated tungsten trioxide, showed that it is an acid and is combined with lime in the mineral, and he prepared several salts. He found that the precipitated acid is white, and that both molybdenum and tungsten trioxides become blue when reduced with zinc, tin, or iron in presence of spirit of salt.

Two Spanish chemists, the brothers Fausto (later Director-General of Mines in Mexico), and Juan Josef (who studied for six months under Bergman) De Elhuyar first obtained metallic tungsten and showed that the mineral wolfram is a tungstate of iron and manganese. The work was begun in 1782. A memoir 'par MM. d'Elhuyar freres' in French[6] has the title: 'sur la nature du wolfram et celle d'un nouveau métal qui entre dans sa composition.' A translation by Cullen was published in 1788:

A Chemical Analysis of Wolfram; and Examination of a New Metal, which enters into its Composition. By Don John Joseph and Don Fausto de Luyart. Translated from the Spanish By Charles Cullen, Esq. To which is prefixed A Translation of Mr. Scheele's Analysis of the Tungsten, or Heavy Stone; With Mr. Bergman's Supplemental Remarks, 8°, London, 1785 (ii ll., 67 pp.).[7]

[1] *Commercium Philosophico-Technicum*, London, 1763, ii, 326 f.
[2] *Ann. Phil.*, 1826, xii, 1–13.　　　　　[3] KAH, 1781, ii, 89; V, 225.
[4] KAH, 1781, ii, 95.　　　　　　　　　[5] Fourcroy, (3), 1790, ii, 207.
[6] *Mémoires tirés des Registres de l'Académie*, Toulouse, 1784 (1786), ii, 141–68, read 24 March 1784; Cullen says his translation (see above) was from 'the Transactions of the Royal Biscayan Society of Friends to their Country, for the year 1783', adding that: 'this society seems to have been instituted about twenty years ago, and has already published several volumes of Transactions; they meet in the cities of Bilbao, Vergara, and Vitoria, by turns.'
[7] Hadfield, *J. Iron and Steel Inst.*, 1903, lxiv, II, 14; Moles, *An. Fis. Quim.*, 1928, xxvi, 234 (life and portrait); Mourelo, in Diergart, 1909, 409; Weeks, *J. Chem. Educ.*, 1934, xi, 413; *id.*, *Isis*, 1935, xxiii, 526; *id.* (1), 255, 285. Moles says the original is *Extractos de las Juntas generales de la Sociedad Vascongada*, 1783, 46–88, the names being given there as D. Juan Josef and

They heated a mixture of 100 grains of tungsten trioxide and charcoal in a crucible in a strong fire for an hour and a half. A friable button of metal was formed, 60 grains in weight, 'a congeries of metallic globules, among which were some of the bigness of a pin's head, and when broke had a metallic appearance at the fracture in colour like steel.' The s.g. was 17·6. On heating in air it formed yellow tungsten trioxide, increasing 24 p.c. in weight.

Von Ruprecht and Tondy[1] in a letter to von Born claimed to have obtained molybdenum, tungsten (mentioning Hjelm) and also metals from baryta, magnesia, and silica, by reducing the oxides with carbon at a high temperature, but their work was criticised by Klaproth.[2] Raspe (1785) showed that the metals from wolfram and scheelite were the same (see Vol. II, p. 734).

The metal was called *wolfram* (the present German name), the name *tungsten* (tungstène) being proposed by Guyton de Morveau[3] and adopted by Berzelius,[4] who says the name *scheelium* had been proposed, but 'I have found it best, however, to retain the name Wolfram', adding in the French translation[5] 'et en français celui de tungstène'. The origin of the name wolfram for the mineral is supposed to be the German Wolf-Rahm, *spuma lupi*, since it hindered the smelting of tin ores (with which it sometimes occurs): 'Es reisst das Zinn fort und frisst es, wie der Wolf das Schaf.'[6]

Arsenic

A third 'metallic acid' discovered by Scheele was arsenic acid (H_3AsO_4) in 1775; he obtained it by the action of chlorine water or nitric acid on white arsenic (As_2O_3) dissolved in spirit of salt.[7] He described some of its salts, the arsenates, and the gas (containing arsenic hydride) obtained by the action of a solution of the acid on zinc, which deposits a black 'regulus of arsenic' when exploded mixed with air, and is 'inflammable air which holds regulus of arsenic dissolved'. This long and detailed memoir contains a large number of experiments. The green pigment copper arsenite, later called 'Scheele's green', is first mentioned in it; the details of its preparation as 'a new green colour' were published in 1778.[8]

Soda from Salt

About 1770 Scheele[9] discovered the preparation of soda by the litharge process, giving lead oxychloride as a by-product; this was announced by Berg-

D. Fausto de Lhuyart. According to Sir Robert Hadfield, 'Captain Diaz, of the Spanish Embassy in London, kindly made inquiries at one of the Royal Libraries in Madrid. It was there found that the correct name is De Elhuyar.' Fredga and Rydén, *Lychnos*, 1959, 161.

[1] Von Ruprecht, Crell's *Ann.*, 1790, II, 3, 91, 195, 291; von Born, *ib.*, 1790, II, 483.
[2] Crell's *Ann.*, 1790, II, 128; cf. G. Candida, *Sulla formazione del molibdeno. Lettera al Signor Vincento Petagna*, Naples, 1785 (61 pp.).
[3] *Méthode de Nomenclature Chimique*, by de Morveau, Lavoisier, etc., 1787, 54.
[4] *Lehrbuch der Chemie*, 1826, II, i, 83: Tungstenum.
[5] *Traité de Chimie*, Paris, 1830, ii, 483.
[6] Gmelin, *Handbuch der Chemie*, 1933, no. 54, 1; Mellor, *Treatise*, xi, 673, who says the mineral was called wolfram by Cronstedt, 'although Ercker called it wolferam and Agricola called it *lupus spuma*' (!).
[7] Om Arsenik och dess Syra: KAH, 1775, xxxvi, 263; I, ii, 99; V, 53.
[8] KAH, 1778, xxxix, 327; V, 195; for a letter on it from Scheele to Gahn in 1777, see VI, 192.
[9] VI, 57; in Gahn's papers.

man in Scheffer's lectures (1775):[1] powdered litharge was percolated in a funnel with common salt solution and the solution of caustic soda formed was carbonated by exposure to air. The yellow lead oxychloride so formed was patented as a pigment (*Turner's yellow*) by James Turner in 1780.[2] Fourcroy[3] said 'several people in England possess the secret of obtaining soda from marine salt in the great way, and practise it in considerable extent', but the translator (Nicholson) states that it was not much practised, and J. Murray[4] that the expense was to be defrayed by the sale of the yellow pigment, but the demand was insufficient to allow the process to be successful on the large scale. It appears from his letters that Black was interested in the process.

Bergman[5] mentions that Scheele had obtained soda from common salt by the action of iron in presence of air and water, when sodium carbonate was formed as an efflorescence. Scheele found soda in the efflorescence formed on a paste of quicklime and salt brine.[6]

The Discovery of Oxygen

Scheele's most important discovery was oxygen, and Scheele's priority is established by his laboratory notes and letters published by Nordenskiöld in 1892 (see p. 211), which show that his discovery was made in Uppsala between 1770 and 1773. Some of the material published by Nordenskiöld was shown by Gahn to Thomson in 1812.[7] Scheele's manuscript was published in facsimile by the Swedish Academy of Sciences[8] and some readings in the old transcript made by Mme. Elin Bergsten for Nordenskiöld can now be corrected. Scheele's discovery of oxygen is described in two manuscripts numbered 52 (old 181) and 53. The first is undated.

Nordenskiöld deduced from the manuscript that most of the work on oxygen was completed in 1773 and some of the experiments, including the preparation of oxygen by heating saltpetre, go back to 1770.[9] Oseen[10] concluded from the contents of MS. 52 that Nordenskiöld's date 1771–2 was too early, and he proposed for it the autumn of 1772, or more probably early in 1773; the 'vitriol air', however, appears in MS. 53, of the period 1770–1,[11] and Nordenskiöld's date may be correct.

Oxygen is mentioned as vitriol air (in symbols aer vitriolicus; Vitriol-Luft) in MS. 52 of the Uppsala period to which Nordenskiöld assigned the date 1771–2.[12] Then, or soon after, Scheele obtained it by heating mercuric oxide, silver carbonate, magnesium nitrate, saltpetre, and arsenic acid with pyrolusite (magnesia nigra; manganese dioxide), finding that the gas is odourless and tasteless and supports the combustion of a candle much better than common

---

[1] *Scheffers Föreläsningar*, § 59, Anm. 2; 1796, 91.
[2] *Repertory of Arts and Manufactures*, etc., 1800, xii, 157; Aikin, *A Dictionary of Chemistry and Mineralogy*, 1807, ii, 28; Clapham, *Chem. News*, 1870, xxi, 148; see Chaptal, p. 563.
[3] (3), 1790, i, 438.   [4] 1806, ii, 538.   [5] *Scheffers Föreläsningar*, § 41, Anm.; 1796, p. 57.
[6] KAH, 1779, xl, 158; V, 200.   [7] Thomson, (5), 76–9, 222; *id.*, (1), ii, 43.
[8] *Lychnos*, 1942, vii, 254; C. W. Oseen, (2).
[9] VI, xxi, 466; Zekert, (1), vi, 164 f.; vii, 250 f., 289 f.
[10] (2), 1942, 168 f., 171; reprod., 132–43.   [11] *Ib.*, 123, 171.   [12] VI, 458 f., 466.

air. The name fire air (Feuerluft) occurs in a letter to Gahn in October 1775.[1]

Scheele in his notes represents oxygen gas by symbols meaning 'vitriol air', perhaps because he obtained it by heating manganese dioxide with sulphuric acid, although this is not mentioned in the printed paper on manganese, completed by the end of 1771 or the beginning of 1772, sent to Bergman in November 1773 and printed early in 1774.[2] Other preparations are given, e.g. by heating magnesium nitrate:[3]

Als magnesia alba [magnesium carbonate] mit spiritu nitri saturirt und destillirt wurde, ging auf die Letzte das acidum nitri von der magn. alb. in eine mit mixt. calcis vivae angefeuchtete Blase, und eine gute Quantität Luft, welche der Vitriolluft in allem gleich war. Das Feuer brannte sehr schön in selbiger.

He writes in symbols: 'red precipitate of mercury heated in a retort gave much vitriolic air, no fixed air, very little sublimate (yellowish-red), and metallic mercury.'[4] Scheele[5] mentions his memoir on arsenic,[6] saying that he 'showed how this acid can be sublimed into ordinary arsenic simply by continued heat; and although I clearly perceived the reason for this, even at that time, still I was unwilling to mention it there in order to avoid prolixity'. He found that when arsenic acid is very strongly heated it melted, 'boiled', and white arsenic sublimed.

A summary of Scheele's experiments and theory was given by Bergman in 1775,[7] saying that oxygen (aër nudus, or aër purus) is formed by heating calces (oxides) of mercury, silver, and gold, that it supports combustion and respiration better than common air, and that Scheele regarded heat as a compound of it and phlogiston. He had repeated Scheele's preparation by heating mercuric oxide but modified it by collecting the gas over water (see Fig. 12, p. 126):

'demonstrabit experimentis D. Scheele materiam caloris nihil esse aliud, quam phlogiston aëri puro intime unitum'. Mercuric oxide on heating gives an air: 'qui nullo modo aquam calcis turbavit, sed igni respirationique maxime idoneus.... Unde jam hic aër? Ex calore decomposito, qui per vasis poros penetrans suum calci metallicæ præbuit phlogiston, quo facto aër liberatus vitrum penetranseundi facultatem perdit.'

Priestley also published his discovery of oxygen in 1775 (see p. 256).

Scheele on Air and Fire

Scheele's book On Air and Fire (VII) was written in Köping in the autumn of 1775.[8] The manuscript was sent to the printer, Swederus in Uppsala, in December 1775, and he sent it to Bergman early in 1776.[9] A summary of it, dated November 1775, was among Gahn's papers.[10] The book was published

---

[1] VI, 166.   [2] VI, 95, 458; see p. 212.   [3] VI, 465.   [4] VI, 458, and plate.
[5] VII, § 41.   [6] KAH, 1775, xxxvi, 263; V, 56.
[7] Nova Acta Reg. Soc. Sci. Upsal., 1775, ii, 159 (232–4); information kindly supplied by Prof. G. Malmquist (18 Oct., 1961), Secretary of the Royal Society of Uppsala, leaves little doubt that the vol. was published in 1775.
[8] Fredga, 1943, 11.   [9] VI, 172, 178.   [10] VI, xxv, 79–86, 166.

between 13 July and 22 August 1777.[1] The book[2] contains a long introduction
by Bergman dated 13 July 1777, in which he says that he had repeated and
confirmed many of the experiments, and states that Scheele's discovery preceded Priestley's publications. Scheele blamed the printer and publisher for
the delay in publication. In letters to Gahn and to Bergman (who informed
him of Priestley's work) Scheele said in 1776: 'it will be said I have drawn
from their papers and only altered them somewhat. For all this I have
Swederus to thank.'[3] He refers to Priestley's work in a letter to Gahn of
27 November 1775, in which he says he is working all night writing the
book.[4]

J. C. Wilke[5] wrote to Scheele

I still think Priestley had heard of your theory and fire air in a letter from Bergman
before he made his researches. Yet I can only think this between ourselves (doch
darf ich's nur unter uns so denken). If you know better, let me know.

Bergman did correspond with Priestley (see p. 189) but Wilcke's suggestion
(which Zekert thinks is not outside the bounds of possibility) does not
square with Priestley's categorical statement that he was 'not conscious of
having concealed the least hint that was suggested to me by any person
whatever' (see p. 260).

It appears from his correspondence with Bergman that Scheele's first
knowledge of Priestley's discovery of oxygen was obtained from a letter from
Bergman in August 1776. Scheele blamed Swederus for the delay in the publication of his book, and in October 1776 he told Bergman that he thought he
would ask for his manuscript to be returned. The printer had sent Scheele
proofs of the first part of the book in May 1776, and it was complete in type in
May 1777. Bergman's introduction is dated 13 July 1777 and the printer was
waiting for this before the book could be completed. As stated, publication
was achieved in August, and there was no undue delay. If Bergman had not
been involved the book might well have been published in 1776.

In the preface to his book Scheele states that he had completed the greater
part of his experiments before he 'obtained sight of Priestley's elegant observations (Ich hatte bereits den Haupttheil dieser Versuche ausgearbeitet, als
ich die schönen Erfahrungen des Herrn Priestleys zu Gesichte bekam)'. He
said in a letter to Gahn on 9 February 1777 that he had not yet seen Priestley's
book, and could not read it unless it was in French.[6] Scheele had also obtained
hydrogen chloride and perhaps ammonia in the gaseous state in 1770, before
Priestley.[7] He repeated most of the experiments described in his book in
Köping in 1775.[8]

Scheele's book *Chemische Abhandlung von der Luft und dem Feuer*, 1777,
is divided into 97 numbered paragraphs to which reference is made below.

[1] Zekert, (1), vii, 257.
[2] VII; I, i, 3–27; Bergman says the book was completed in 1775.
[3] VI, xxvi, 178, 264, 268, 273 (Zekert, (1), vii, 257, says the correct date is 27 June 1777).
[4] VI, 167.   [5] Zekert, (1), vii, 241, 282.   [6] VI, 195.
[7] VI, 42 f., 49: Gahn's notes.
[8] Letter to Bergman, Jan. 1776; VI, 246.

Thomson said: 'there is no chemical book in existence which contains a greater number of new and important facts . . . at the time it was published.' A summary of it will now be given.

Air is very elastic, possesses weight, and is always mixed with water vapour and aerial acid (CO_2) produced by the putrefaction or combustion of organised bodies (§ 4). All bodies at a high temperature could probably be converted into air-like vapours (§ 5).[1]

The properties of ordinary air are: (1) fire must burn for a certain time in a given quantity of air; (2) if this fire does not produce any fluid resembling air, then after the fire has gone out of itself, the quantity of air must be diminished by $\frac{1}{3}$ to $\frac{1}{4}$ (the correct figure is $\frac{1}{5}$); (3) it must not unite with water; (4) all kinds of animals must live a certain time in a confined volume; (5) seeds, e.g. peas, must strike root in a confined volume and, with the aid of some water and a moderate heat, must attain a certain height (§ 7).

In his first set of experiments to prove that 'air must be composed of two kinds of elastic fluids' (§§ 8–15), Scheele exposed a confined volume of air to liver of sulphur, a solution of sulphur in lime water, rags dipped in alkali and then exposed to the fumes of burning sulphur, nitrous air (NO) in a bladder, oil of turpentine, Dippel's animal oil (see Vol. II, p. 378), 'green calx of iron' (ferrous hydroxide) precipitated by alkali from green vitriol, moist iron filings, and a solution of iron in vinegar. In all cases the material is rich in phlogiston or 'the simple inflammable substance (der einfache brennbare Grundstoff)', which is the same in all bodies (§ 66); a given quantity of air can unite with and saturate only a certain quantity of the inflammable principle, and there is a contraction of $\frac{1}{3}$ to $\frac{1}{4}$. If the residual air contained the inflammable substance, then, since there has been contraction, it should be heavier than ordinary air; but 'a very thin flask which was filled with this air and most accurately weighed, not only did not counterpoise an equal bulk of ordinary air, but was even somewhat lighter'. (He says 'phlogiston is a material substance, which always presupposes some weight', § 24). He was unable to separate the lost air again (e.g. as fixed air) from the materials employed, hence (§ 16):

the air consists of two fluids differing from each other, the one of which does not manifest in the least the property of attracting phlogiston, whilst the other, which composes between the third and the fourth part of the whole mass of the air, is peculiarly disposed to such attraction.

die Luft aus zwey von einander unterschiedenen Flüssigkeiten bestehet, von welchen die eine die Eigenschaft, das Phlogiston anzuziehen, gar nicht aüssert, die andere aber zu solcher Attraktion eigentlich aufgeleget ist, und welche zwischen dem dritten und vierten Theil von der ganzen Luftmasse ausmacht.

He calls these two elastic fluids 'verdorbene Luft' (*skamd luft* in Swedish) and 'Feuerluft' (*elds luft* in Swedish), the latter because 'it is required for the origination of fire' (§ 29). The literal translations are 'spoiled' or 'vitiated air', and 'fire air'. Forster gave 'foul air' and 'empyreal air', the first of which is usually retained (although it is a poor translation) but the second is always

---

[1] Priestley, E & O, 1777, iii, 329, also said: I believe there is no substance in nature but what is capable of assuming that form [a dry or permanently elastic vapour], in a certain degree of heat; emphasised by Hartog, *J. Chem. Soc.*, 1933, 899.

replaced by 'fire air'. Scheele is rather indefinite in his views on the nature of foul air. The name 'vitiated air' had been used by Bergman, and Scheele refers to it as 'already known' (§ 29).

Scheele noted that the yellow solution of liver of sulphur (potassium polysulphide) is converted on exposure to air into a colourless solution of vitriolated tartar (potassium sulphate), so that the alkali has attracted the acid of sulphur and the air the phlogiston (§ 16).

Scheele next placed a little phosphorus in a thin flask, corked the flask, and warmed it till the phosphorus took fire, producing a white cloud which attached itself to the sides of the flask in white flowers of 'dry acid of phosphorus' (which can be sublimed by gentle heat, § 73). On opening the inverted flask under water, 'the external air pressed the water into the flask' and this occupied rather less than one-third ($\frac{9}{30}$). The same result was obtained when phosphorus was allowed to stand for six weeks in the same flask, until it no longer glowed (§§ 17–18).

Scheele generated hydrogen from iron filings and dilute sulphuric acid in a bottle A (Fig. 19) standing in hot water to promote a brisk evolution of gas. The hydrogen flame was burning at the top of a tube fixed to the bottle and over it a glass flask was inverted. The water rose in the flask to D, corresponding with one-fifth of the volume, when the flame went out and the water began to sink again. No fixed air was formed (§ 19).[1]

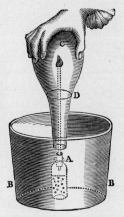

A small candle fixed to a wire rising from a plastic mass of wax, resin and turpentine in a dish, was lighted and a flask inverted over it and pressed into the mass. (This arrangement is not so neat as Mayow's siphon, Vol. II.) The dish was filled with water. When the flame went out and the flask was cold, water was allowed to enter, but occupied only $\frac{1}{80}$ of the volume of the air. Practically the same result was found by burning spirit of wine or red-hot charcoal on a support (§ 21).

Scheele thought this small contraction was due to the heat of the flame expanding the air before the flask could be pressed on the wax. The contraction was the same, 2 oz., for flasks of 160 oz. and 20 oz. of water capacity, whereas 'had the former 2 oz. measure of air been absorbed, then there should only have been 2

FIG. 19. COMBUSTION OF HYDROGEN IN AIR: SCHEELE'S EXPERIMENT.

THE HYDROGEN WAS GENERATED IN THE BOTTLE A, IMMERSED IN A TUB OF HOT WATER B, AND THE HYDROGEN FLAME C BURNT INSIDE THE INVERTED FLASK D. THE WATER ROSE IN THE FLASK.

drachms measure absorbed with the 20 oz. flask'. He says: 'these experiments seem to prove that the transference of phlogiston to the air does not always diminish its bulk, which, however, the experiments in §§ 8–16 show distinctly. But the following will show that that portion of the air which unites with the inflammable substance and is absorbed by it, is replaced by the newly formed aerial acid.' This was proved (§ 22) by shaking with lime water,

[1] Warltire published an account of a similar experiment in 1777; Priestley, E & O, 1777, iii, Appendix, 367.

when $\frac{1}{19}$ was lost. This small contraction (as compared with that with phosphorus) was explained; since 'one part of aerial acid mixed with ten parts of ordinary air extinguishes fire', the candle, etc., was extinguished before all the fire air was removed. Burning sulphur, followed by exposure to lime water, removed $\frac{1}{6}$ of the air, nearly as much as the phosphorus (§ 23).

Scheele now considered the result of the hydrogen experiment and sought for the lost fire air and phlogiston (inflammable air). The product was not in the water, nor could it be in the residual air, which he had found was lighter than ordinary air; hence he assumed that it had escaped in the form of heat, which 'has gone through the fine pores of the glass and dispersed itself far and wide in the air' (§ 24). Since he worked over hot water, Scheele missed the dew condensed on the flask. He thus assumed that fire air combined with the 'inflammable substance' to form heat: *fire air + phlogiston* (ϕ) = *heat*. In another place (§ 81) he says inflammable air is phlogiston combined with a little heat.

In order to decompose heat into fire air and the inflammable substance (ϕ), Scheele recalled that nitric acid has a great attraction for phlogiston, forming red fumes. He heated saltpetre in an 8 oz. glass retort with oil of vitriol (Fig. 20). At first the nitric acid went over red, then it became colourless, and finally

FIG. 20. SCHEELE'S ISOLATION OF FIRE AIR.

'all became red again'. The receiver was then removed and the red fumes were received in a bladder containing some milk of lime (which absorbed the red fumes) fixed to the neck of the retort. The bladder gradually filled with a gas, which was transferred to a bottle filled with water and tied to the neck of the bladder. On inverting the bottle, water ran from it into the bladder, displacing the gas, which collected in the bottle (§§ 25–9). Scheele collected gases in bladders, which were permeated by them when moist but not when dry, except that inflammable air (hydrogen) penetrated both dry and moist bladders (§ 30).

Scheele actually says (§ 29): 'Ich nahm eine gläserne Retorte, welche acht Unzen Wasser fassen konnte, und destillirte die rauchende Salpetersäure nach der gewöhnlichen Methode.' He had previously said (§ 25): 'Wie oft haben nich die Chemisten die rauchende Salpetersäure aus Vitriol und Salpeter destillirt.' Forster[1] translated liter-

[1] VII C, 34.

ally: 'I . . . distilled fuming spirit of nitre according to the usual method.' It is clear, however, that Scheele had in the retort not fuming nitric acid but a mixture of nitre and oil of vitriol.[1] By distilling 1 oz. of nitre with 1 oz. of pure concentrated vitriolic acid, Keir obtained, 'besides the usual quantity of nitrous acid, thirty ounce measures of pure air [oxygen].'[2]

Of the new gas (fire air, i.e. oxygen) Scheele says: 'I then placed a small lighted candle in it; scarcely had this been done than the candle began to burn with a large flame, whereby it gave out such a bright light that it was sufficient to dazzle the eyes' (§ 29). By mixing 1 vol. of this fire air with 3 parts 'of that kind of air in which fire would not burn', ordinary air was formed (§ 29). Scheele prepared fire air (oxygen) in many other ways (§§ 31–41). He heated calx of mercury (mercuric oxide), which on his theory decomposed the heat, combining with the phlogiston to form mercury and setting free the fire air, which was 'pure' (§ 80):

$$\text{calx of mercury} + (\phi + \text{fire air}) = (\text{calx of mercury} + \phi) + \text{fire air.}$$
$$\qquad\qquad\qquad\quad \text{heat} \qquad\qquad\qquad\quad \text{mercury}$$

Fire air was also obtained by heating 'black manganese' (manganese dioxide) with concentrated sulphuric acid or phosphoric acid at a red-heat,[3] or saltpetre (the best and cheapest method), or the 'calces' of gold, silver, and mercury, precipitated by alkali (potassium carbonate), the aerial acid (carbon dioxide) also formed (except with gold calx, which would be the oxide) being absorbed with milk of lime, and by heating magnesium and mercurous nitrates.

Fourcroy[4] said that Scheele's theory, although erroneous, is 'l'ouvrage de génie', and his experiments are 'fines et déliées'.

The preparation of 'pure air' (aër purus) by heating black manganese with concentrated sulphuric acid, and the explanation by Scheele's theory of the decomposition of heat, were given by Bergman,[5] who says that on evaporating with somewhat diluted sulphuric acid, a red salt (manganic sulphate), containing less phlogiston, is obtained. Scheele's theory of combustion is sketched in a letter from him to Gahn in November 1775,[6] in which he also gives the experiments on which it was based. A good summary of it was given by Elliot in his translation of Fourcroy's book.[7]

Scheele found that fire air is *completely* absorbed by liver of sulphur, etc. When he burnt phosphorus in a thin flask of it, this collapsed on cooling. With a thicker flask, the cork could not be taken out under water but could be pushed in, when water rushed in and filled the flask. A hydrogen flame continued burning in the gas until seven-eighths were absorbed. By weighing it in a thin flask he found that a volume of fire air occupying 20 oz. of water weighed 2 grains more than the same volume of common air (§§ 42–9). The weights

[1] J. C. Fischer, 1806, vii, 773: der Destillation der rauchenden Salpetersäure aus Vitriolöl und Salpeter.
[2] Keir, *A Treatise on the Various Kinds of Permanently Elastic Fluids, or Gases,* 2 ed., London, 1779, 30.
[3] The laboratory notes give a mixture of black manganese and arsenic acid; VI, 465.
[4] (2), iii, 536.   [5] *Opuscula,* 1780, ii, 214.   [6] VI, 79.
[7] *Elementary Lectures on Chemistry and Natural History,* Edinburgh, 1785, i, 86 f.

used by Scheele were: 1 Swedish ounce=480 grains=29·69 grams. This means that 29·69 c.c. of oxygen weigh 0·123 gm. (correct value dry and at S.T.P.=0·080 gm.) more than this volume of common air. Priestley had arrived at a similar result by weighing the gas in a bladder (see p. 263).

Scheele found that there is a rise in temperature when substances containing phlogiston withdraw fire air from air (§§ 50–4). He confined animals and insects in air, care being taken to provide their appropriate foods. They ultimately died, aerial acid (carbon dioxide) being formed with contraction of the air, and the residual air extinguished a flame (§§ 83–5). Two large bees were placed in a bottle of fire air over milk of lime, some honey being 'provided for their stay'. After eight days the bees were dead and the bottle was almost completely filled with liquid (§ 91). Fermenting peas absorbed fire air and formed aerial acid (§ 86), but peas would not grow in pure fire air (§ 92). Fire air is partly dissolved out of common air when this stands over water which has been boiled. A candle burns more brightly in the air expelled from the water by boiling than in common air: 'fire air, dissolved in water, must be as indispensable for aquatic animals as for those that live upon the earth' (§ 94).

Scheele was, apparently, the first to use the name 'radiant heat (strahlende Hitze)' and to distinguish it from light, which it otherwise closely resembles, and he describes many of its characteristics, e.g. its reflection from metallic surfaces but absorption by glass (§§ 56–8). In experiments with light he showed that it decomposes the vapour of nitric acid in a partly filled bottle, colouring the acid yellow (§ 62), and in 1786[1] he showed that fire air is liberated in the reaction. Pure nitric acid is colourless and the yellow colour of the ordinary acid is separated as red vapours (phlogisticated nitric acid) on heating (§§ 25, 27). These red vapours, less phlogisticated (containing more oxygen) than nitrous air (nitric oxide, NO), can unite with alkalis and earths and be expelled again by vegetable acids: the same salt is formed when nitre is heated to redness (§ 27).

Scheele then knew that nitric oxide, nitrous anhydride, nitrogen dioxide (which he says is formed from nitric oxide and air with diminution of volume and evolution of heat: sie sich nehmlich nicht allein vermindert, sondern auch warm wird), and colourless nitric acid contain less phlogiston (more oxygen) in this order, and he seems to think that the last is free from phlogiston (§ 27). In 1767 he had distinguished nitrous and nitric acids but he then confused nitrous acid with nitric oxide, evolved in colourless bubbles on acidifying a solution of potassium nitrite.[2] In a letter to Bergman[3] of 2 January 1784, he wrote that nitric acid 'aus dephlogistirtem *aere vitali* und verdorbener Luft besteht', a statement of its composition from oxygen and nitrogen a year before Cavendish's publication.[4]

Scheele thought that light was not pure phlogiston but a compound of fire air with more phlogiston than is contained in heat, and that radiant heat contains an intermediate amount of phlogiston (§§ 66 f.). Silver chloride (horn-

[1] *J. de Phys.*, 1786, xxix, 231; Crell's *Ann.*, 1786, I, 332; V, 342.
[2] VI, 9 f.   [3] VI, 368.   [4] *Phil. Trans.*, 1785, lxxv, 372.

silver) is turned violet by light: it is the violet rays (which he thought consist of smaller particles than the red, and are richer in phlogiston) which act most powerfully (§§ 63, 66, 69, 76). When the blackened silver chloride is treated with ammonia, the unchanged salt is dissolved and metallic silver remains, and 'as every particle of the horn-silver is converted on the surface into silver, just so much acid of salt must separate' (§ 63). Heat evolved by hammering or bending metals is driven out by constriction of the pores (§ 76). Metals are composed of specific earths combined with phlogiston and some heat. The earth is attracted by acids and the phlogiston and heat are expelled as inflammable air (§ 96).

By the explosion of fulminating gold an air is evolved (nitrogen) which is insoluble in water, extinguishes a flame, and does not precipitate lime water. This air comes from the volatile alkali (ammonia), used to make the fulminating gold, which alkali consists of this air combined with phlogiston, i.e. of nitrogen and hydrogen (§ 82). This was before Berthollet's publication in 1785.

Scheele noticed that metals combine with sulphur in absence of air, with evolution of heat and light (§ 81). Fixed air (carbon dioxide) confined over oil is not absorbed by quicklime unless water is added (§ 95). A pyrophorus made by calcining vitriolated tartar (potassium sulphate) with charcoal inflames in ordinary air but not in air in a bottle which had been dried by quicklime (§ 81); 'in thoroughly dry air no pyrophorus takes fire; moisture must meet with it.'[1] Bucquet's observation that dry carbon dioxide is not absorbed by quicklime was made in 1773 and published in 1780,[2] but Scheele's seems to be the first for a combustion reaction.

A test for fire air dissolved in water used by Scheele was to precipitate green vitriol dissolved in it by adding alkali, when the green precipitate soon becomes yellow. Water in which a leech had died in a closed bottle did not give this reaction (§ 94). 'All acids derive their origin from fire air' (alle Säuren ihren Ursprung von der Feuerluft erhalten) (§ 93).

Although he was unable to repeat Priestley's (incorrect) experiments of converting vitiated or inflammable air into common air by agitation with water (see p. 252), Scheele thought he had converted inflammable air into foul (vitiated) air by respiration of it (which he found difficult) (§ 93). The respirability of inflammable air was at first doubted by Fontana, but later he confirmed Scheele's experiment, although sometimes he was made ill[3] — probably from impurities in the gas. Scheele says: 'it is by means of fire air that the circulation of the blood and of the juices in animals and plants is so fully maintained', but he thought that insects and (germinating) plants convert fire air into aerial acid (carbon dioxide), while respiration of animals converts it into foul air (§§ 90–3; he goes astray here). He thought that blood became more red in the lungs by absorption of phlogiston, and his views on respiration are incorrect. He points out that 'a green resin' (chlorophyll) is soon formed by the action of sunlight on plants bleached in a dark cellar (§ 93).

[1] Crell's *Ann.*, 1786, I, 483.
[2] AdS, *Mém. div. Sav.*, 1780, ix, 563.   [3] *Phil. Trans.*, 1779, lxix, 337.

In 1779 Scheele published a supplement to his book on Air and Fire[1] in which he records experiments made in 1778 on the action of a mixture of iron filings and sulphur supported on a stand in air confined over water (or, in very cold weather, brandy) in a jar graduated on the lower part by a varnished label. He concluded that 'our atmosphere must always contain, though sometimes with a little variation, the same quantity of fire air or pure air, viz. nine thirty-thirds'. This (27 per cent.) is a more accurate result than the one-third found in 1777.

In 1785, Scheele revised his views on the nature of air and fire[2] as a result of Lavoisier's observations on the increase in weight on burning phosphorus in air. He says he had also often observed the formation of water on the explosion of a mixture of inflammable air (hydrogen) and fire air in a bottle, but had thought the moisture was in the gases (as Priestley had done in 1781 (see p. 328)). Scheele says:[3]

It is only the exact observation of Lavoisier which has helped me out of the dream. How often have I not burned the mixture of inflammable [air] and fire air, and likewise always observed moisture in the bottle as soon as the kindling had taken place; but I believed that, as the air continually carries moisture with it, so the inflammable air could also carry some moisture with it, from the vitriolic acid; indeed, the flame of the candle might even supply moisture from itself on the kindling of this air.

He now ('although I do not at all doubt the truth of the observations of Lavoisier and Cavendish') confirmed that moisture was deposited even with dry gases. He adopts Cavendish's theory (see p. 334), but thought there would be a slight loss in weight owing to escape of fire. He now regards fire air as a compound of a fixed saline principle (principium salinum) with phlogiston and some water. The saline principle is probably anhydrous nitric acid, and heat and light are compounds of this principle with phlogiston. Inflammable air is the saline principle with much phlogiston, or heat and phlogiston. On combustion, the saline principle of the fire air attracts the phlogiston of the inflammable air, forming heat and light, which escape through the glass, whilst the water, 'abandoned by the fire air and the saline principle', collects into drops.[4]

In 1777 Scheele said that metals heated in air are calcined and increase in weight, either because their phlogiston attracts fire air and forms heat, or their phlogiston is handed to the air and heat attracted from the fire: 'enough! there is fire air present in these calces which must occasion the excess of weight' (VII, § 95). In 1785[5] he says that he had 'attributed the increased weight of the metallic calces to the heat attracted', but 'experienced a little dissatisfaction afterwards concerning this opinion'. Other cases of combustion[6] are now explained by a complicated theory. Acids and earths when deprived of phlogiston attract water strongly. Phosphorus on burning gives up phlogiston to the saline

[1] KAH, 1779, xl, 50 (Rön, om rena Luftens mängd); *J. de Phys.*, 1782, xix, 79, and plate II; published in *Supplément au Traité Chimique de l'Air et du Feu*, Paris, 1785 (this does not contain the plate); VIIB; V, 196.
[2] Crell's *Ann.*, 1785, I, 229, 291 (Neuere Bemerkungen über Luft und Feuer und die Wasser-Erzeugung); V, 283.
[3] Crell's *Ann.*, 1785, I, 229 (231).
[4] *Ib.*, 235.
[5] Crell's *Ann.*, 1785, I, 229; V, 284.
[6] *Ib.*; cf. letter to Bergman, 1779; VI, 296.

principle of the fire air, forming heat, whilst the water of the fire air combines with the acid of phosphorus and increases its weight:

$$(\phi + \text{acid}) + (\text{water} + \text{saline ppl.} + \phi) = (\phi + \text{saline ppl.}) + (\text{acid} + \text{water})$$

| combustible | fire air | | heat | prod. of combustion |

Scheele's earlier theory (1777) was criticised in detail in 1784 by Lavoisier,[1] who generously admitted that Scheele's book:

'n'en aura pas moins le plus grand mérite aux yeux des physiciens et des chimistes, par la multitude d'expériences intéressantes qu'il contient, par la simplicité des appareils, par la précision des résultats qu'il a obtenus dans plusieurs circonstances.'

Miscellaneous Observations

About 1770 Scheele obtained hydrogen by the action of water or vegetable acids on iron.[2] He found in 1779 that manganese evolves inflammable air on dissolving in dilute *nitric* acid,[3] and he found that inflammable air (hydrogen) is generated by heating zinc with caustic alkali (independently of Lassone in 1776: see p. 95) or ammonia, or by heating charcoal with caustic alkali. The charcoal is 'a sulphur composed of phlogiston and aerial acid'.[4] Inflammable air from burning charcoal (carbon monoxide) produces headache and is 'absorbed in the blood', whilst that from metals (hydrogen) does not act in these ways.[5] Scheele first accurately describes the preparation and properties of sulphuretted hydrogen,[6] which he calls 'inflammable sulphurous air (brennende Schwefelluft)' or 'fetid sulphurous air (stinkende Schwefelluft)'; it is a compound of phlogiston (hydrogen), sulphur, and heat. He obtained it by the action of acids on sulphides (best of all ferrous sulphide), or by heating sulphur in hydrogen (the first synthesis of the gas), showed that it is soluble in water, does not precipitate lime water, is decomposed by nitric acid with separation of some sulphur, and it precipitates orpiment (arsenic sulphide) from a solution of arsenic. Bergman[7] (1778) called the gas hepatic air, showed that it is contained in solution in some mineral waters, and, like Scheele, regarded it as a compound of sulphur and phlogiston, or sulphur, phlogiston and heat (1779).[8] Scheele also obtained hydrogen persulphide (VII, § 97):

'if much acid be poured at once into a solution of sulphur in alkali, less stinking air is formed and a thin oil may be observed in the mixture; still, this oil does not remain permanently fluid, but in the open air soon becomes thick and hard.'

He had observed this in 1768.[9]

In 1768 Scheele obtained solid nitrososulphuric acid (chamber crystals) in crystals 'like ice on a window' by the action of nitrous fumes on concentrated sulphuric acid; it is decomposed on exposure to air.[10] He distinguished clearly in 1770 between potassium carbonate and bicarbonate (alkali fixo crystallisato aëre fixo saturato),[11] and he distinguished acid, neutral and basic salts very clearly in 1771.[12]

Scheele used the blowpipe (blassruhr) only with difficulty, as he told Gahn

---

[1] AdS, 1781 (1784), m 396; *Oeuvres*, ii, 391–402.   [2] VI, 50 f.   [3] VI, 380.
[4] VII, § 96.   [5] VI, 169.   [6] VII, § 97.   [7] *Opuscula*, i, 233.   [8] *Ib.*, ii, 342.
[9] VI, 22.   [10] VI, 19; see Priestley, p. 290.   [11] VI, 90.   [12] *Ib.*, 67.

in 1771;[1] in 1772 he pointed out that the colour of the borax bead produced by a metal depends on the presence of reducing agents.[2] He distinguished in 1774 the oxidising and reducing parts of the blowpipe flame: the inner flame is richer in phlogiston.[3]

Scheele in 1773 noticed that when a drop of blue solution was put on paper, the blue colour precipitated and a clear ring of water spread from the spot: 'the blue particles are attracted by the tiny capillaries (Haarröhrlein)' and it is doubtful if the mechanism of dyeing can be explained chemically.[4] Bergman[5] says Scheele discovered that writing with cobalt chloride (sympathetic ink) became blue in air dried by quicklime or concentrated sulphuric acid in a flask, as well as on heating.

Scheele had a very good knowledge of the different oxides and corresponding salts of the metals iron, copper, manganese, mercury and lead before 1775;[6] e.g. he says the crystals from a solution of mercury in cold nitric acid (mercurous nitrate) give a precipitate with sulphuric acid (1775).[7] He recognised in 1777 that iron formed sulphates in two degrees of 'phlogistication' (ferrous and ferric) and that ferrous and ammonium sulphates form a soluble double salt (ferrous ammonium sulphate).[8] He showed by experiments that white lead (cerussa) is formed from lead and acetic acid only in presence of air and carbon dioxide and gives a clear and correct account of the reactions (1776).[9] He obtained lead dioxide by the action of nitric acid on red lead, showed that it dissolves in nitric acid in presence of sugar, and knew that it is the highest oxide of lead (vollständig dephlogistisirter Bleikalk) (1782–4).[10] Acids combine with metallic oxides, not with the metals themselves (1776) (es sind nicht ganze Metalle, welche sich mit acidis verbinden, sondern nur metallische Erden),[11] and Scheele explained metallic precipitation in the manner afterwards published by Bergman (see p. 196), viz. attraction of the calx for phlogiston. Bergman (1775)[12] mentions the different crystalline salts obtained with mercury and cold and hot nitric acid, etc., probably from a communication sent to the Swedish Academy by Monnet in 1770.[13]

In a letter to Bergius in January 1775[14] Scheele announced that silica is not converted into alumina when fused with an alkali, as Baumé (1770) had asserted (see p. 93). The alumina came from the clay crucible and Scheele proved that it is not formed when an iron crucible is used. He remarks: 'my practice with chemical statements is never to believe any of them unless I have proved them by making experiments.'

In a letter to J. C. F. Meyer in 1781[15] Scheele adopts Black's theory (p. 135) of fixed air and after giving reasons says: 'These observations will, I hope, convince you, most worthy friend, that Black's doctrine not only agrees with all experiments but that it will also maintain its ground at all times on the

[1] Zekert, (1), vi, 169.   [2] VI, 97, 99.   [3] VI, 142 and diagram.
[4] VI, 107: adsorption.   [5] Scheffers Föreläsningar, § 119, Anm.; 1796, p. 160.
[6] VI, 114, 161, 179, 231, 276 f., 295.   [7] VI, 181.   [8] VI, 281.
[9] VI, 190; V, 349 (letter to Gadolin, 1788).   [10] VI, 349, 366, 369.
[11] VI, 261, 321; Bergman's theory, see p. 191.
[12] Scheffers Föreläsningar, § 82, § 95, Anm. 1; 1796, 127, 140.   [13] Oseen, 164.
[14] VI, 216; Scheele, KAH, 1776, xxxvii, 30; V, 77.
[15] Crell, Neueste Entdeck., 1781, i, 30; V, 318.

main question and that it is consequently true.' (J. C. F. Meyer was not the J. F. Meyer who had proposed the theory of *acidum pingue*, see p. 145.) Scheele[1] also criticised Weber's pamphlet on quicklime (see p. 152). He criticised the experiments of Kirwan, who claimed to have obtained fixed air by heating calx of mercury with iron filings, by pointing out that the fixed air comes from plumbago in the iron, which combines with the fire air; and he also criticised Landriani's view that fixed air is the source of all other acids.[2] He published a detailed criticism of Wenzel's book, *Lehre von der Verwandt-schaft der Körper* (1777), saying (among other things) that he had never found that iron precipitates zinc from its solution in spirit of salt, nor that lime by strong ignition is converted into a vitreous earth.[3]

Scheele was an independent discoverer of the adsorption of gases by char-coal,[4] using recently ignited charcoal and a mixture of carbon dioxide and nitrogen. He had been anticipated in publication by Priestley (1775) (see p. 296).

Minor papers by Scheele deal with the preparation of calomel by precipi-tating a solution of mercurous nitrate with common salt,[5] the preparation of powder of algaroth,[6] *sal perlatum* (in which he proved that Meyer's supposed new metal, *hydrosiderum*, from cold-short iron, is iron phosphide),[7] and the preparation of magnesia alba in which Glauber's salt is obtained, by crystal-lisation from a solution of Epsom salt and common salt, as a by-product.[8]

In a series of short letters to Crell, Scheele reports some interesting obser-vations. By boiling Glauber's salt with milk of lime a very little caustic soda is formed but most of the Glauber's salt remains: 'if this were boiled again, some alkali would be obtained, and so on indefinitely' (mass action).[9] Silver nitrate containing copper nitrate is purified by fusion, and on dissolving in water the copper calx (oxide) remains as a black powder.[9] Fulminating gold cannot be formed unless ammonia is present.[10] Lead amalgam on standing in a bottle filled with water containing dissolved air removes the fire air (oxygen) from the water.[11] The disagreeable taste of raw grain spirit is not due to acid of vinegar (acetic acid) but to an oil (fusel oil) which separates during very severe cold.[12] In a letter to Bergius[13] Scheele describes, with a figure, a method of making oxygen on a large scale for medicinal use by heating a mixture of nitre and slaked lime in an iron retort.

Organic Compounds

Scheele's researches in Organic Chemistry are of the same fundamental character as in other branches of the science. One of his earliest discoveries, the preparation of a solution of tartaric acid from crude tartar by precipitating

[1] Crell's *Ann.*, 1785, II, 220.   [2] Scheele, Crell's *Ann.*, 1785, I, 153; V, 331.
[3] Scheele, Crell's *Journal*, 1780, iv, 78; V, 313.
[4] Letter to Gahn, March, 1773: VI, 112; VII, § 96.
[5] KAH, 1778, xxxix, 70; Crell's *Ann.*, 1788, I, 59; V, 181, 330; Chaptal, *Elements of Chemistry*, 1791, ii, 421, says he had communicated the process of making calomel by precipitation to the Society of Sciences at Montpellier two years before Scheele made it known.
[6] KAH, 1778, xxxix, 141; V, 183; Klaproth, Crell's *Ann.*, 1785, I, 238.
[7] KAH, 1785, vi, 134; V, 275.   [8] KAH, 1785, vi, 172; V, 282.
[9] Crell's *Ann.*, 1784, II, 123; V, 328.   [10] Crell's *Ann.*, 1785, I, 59; V, 329.
[11] Crell's *Ann.*, 1785, I, 455; V, 334.   [12] Crell's *Ann.*, 1785, I, 59; V, 330.
[13] *Vecko-skrift för Läkare och Naturforskare*, 1786, vii, 288; V, 346.

calcium tartrate and decomposing this with sulphuric acid, was published by Retzius,[1] who gives Scheele full credit.[2] Scheele prepared pyrotartaric acid in 1774 by heating tartaric acid.[3] The method he had used with tartaric acid was applied by Scheele as a general method for the preparation of organic acids, the calcium salt being decomposed by hydrochloric acid when the organic acid was sparingly soluble, as in the preparation of benzoic acid ('salt of benzoin') in the wet way (1775),[4] or with sulphuric acid, gypsum being precipitated, when the acid was soluble. Another general method used by Scheele was to precipitate the lead salt of the acid and decompose this with sulphuric acid; this could be used with acids the calcium salts of which are soluble but the lead salt insoluble.

A clarified concentrated lemon juice, essentially a solution of citric acid, was described by Georgius,[5] and Retzius[6] also described the preparation of a solution, but crystalline citric acid was first prepared by Scheele, by boiling the lemon juice with chalk, decomposing the precipitated calcium citrate with diluted sulphuric acid, filtering, and evaporating; he says a sweetened solution of citric acid makes a good artificial lemonade, and describes some metallic citrates.[7]

Oxalic acid, separated from sorrel through the lead salt, was shown (1784–1785) to exist in rhubarb and other vegetables as the calcium salt ('earth of rhubarb'),[8] and was proved to be the same as the acid formed by the action of nitric acid on malic acid or cane sugar.[9] By oxidising milk sugar with nitric acid Scheele in 1780 obtained both oxalic acid and a new insoluble acid (acidum sacchari lactis; acidum galacto-saccharinum), viz. mucic acid, and by heating mucic acid, a sublimate of pyromucic acid.[10]

From sour fruit juices (gooseberries, sour apples, cranberries, and 16 other fruits, but not from unripe grapes) Scheele (1785) obtained citric acid and another acid (malic acid), which he called 'acid of apples',[11] and showed that it formed oxalic acid with nitric acid, and a well-crystallising zinc salt. He says 'it cannot easily be obtained in crystals but is always deliquescent (lässt sich nicht leicht in Krystallen bringen, sondern zerfliesst beständig)'.

According to Gmelin[12] Scheele obtained only 'a thick brown uncrystallisable syrup, drying to a varnish in warm air', but Scheele does not say this; pure crystalline malic acid, Gmelin says, was first prepared by Donovan[13] from mountain-ash berries; he called it 'sorbic acid', but Braconnot[14] showed that it was malic acid. (The modern sorbic acid is a different substance, also present in mountain-ash berries.)

[1] KAH, 1770, xxxi, 207; Crell, Chym. J., 1779, ii, 179.
[2] Thomson, Ann. Phil., 1814, iv, 310; VI, xvi, 391 (Gahn's notes); V, xv, 351; Retzius seems to have obtained crystals of impure tartaric acid; Kopp, (1), iv, 349.
[3] VI, 154.   [4] KAH, 1775, xxxvi, 128; Crell's Ann., 1784, II, 123; V, 49, 327.
[5] KAH, 1774, xxxv, 245.   [6] KAH, 1776, xxxvii, 130.
[7] KAH, 1784, v, 105; Crell's Ann., 1785, II, 437; V, 259, 340.
[8] KAH, 1784, v, 180; 1785, vi, 171; Crell's Ann., 1785, I, 513; 1786, I, 439; V, 262, 281, 341–2.
[9] KAH, 1785, vi, 17; V, 267; VI, 253 ('acid of sorrel', 1776); the discovery of the 'acid of sugar' was published by Bergman in 1776; see p. 198.
[10] KAH, 1780, i, 269; V, 221.
[11] KAH, 1785, vi, 17; I, ii, 373; V, 267; see the table in Chaptal, Elements of Chemistry, 1791, iii, 131.
[12] Handbook of Chemistry, 1856, x, 206, 211.
[13] Phil. Trans., 1815, cv, 231; Ann. Chim., 1816, i, 281.
[14] Ann. Chim., 1817, vi, 239 (acide sorbique); 1818, viii, 149; 1832, li, 328.

From sour milk Scheele (1780) obtained lactic acid (acidum lactis) by decomposing the lime salt with oxalic acid,[1] and he also described the properties of casein, first definitely recognised as a peculiar substance by Berzelius (1812).[2] Scheele found that if vinegar is heated in bottles in a pan of boiling water for an hour it will keep good for years, even if the bottle is only half filled and contains air ('Pasteurising').[3]

A 'previously unknown concrete acid (*calculus*)' was separated by Scheele from urinary calculi (uric acid) and shown to be present in small quantities in urine. The red colour (murexide) formed on evaporating it with nitric acid was observed.[4] By heating uric acid he obtained a sublimate (afterwards called pyrouric acid) which he thought was similar to succinic acid; it is really cyanuric acid.[5]

By exposing a solution of nut-galls (tannin) to air for several weeks Scheele obtained a sediment of 'essential salt of galls or gall-nut salt' (gallic acid), and on heating this a crystalline sublimate (pyrogallic acid) was formed.[6] Gallic and pyrogallic acids were clearly distinguished and named by Braconnot (1831).[7]

In 1783–4 Scheele obtained a 'sweet principle of oils and fats' (Oelsüss), i.e. glycerol, by heating the oil with water and litharge, when a lead soap (lead plaster) was formed, and the sweet principle remained in solution and was obtained as a thick syrup on evaporation. He says it decomposes on distillation. He found that, like sugar, it gave oxalic acid on boiling with nitric acid.[8] He had shown that oils give fixed air and water on combustion, and considered that they were compounds of these and phlogiston.[9]

Scheele considered that alcohol is composed of oil, fire, water, and phlogiston. He obtained 'ethers' (esters) of acetic, benzoic, and other organic acids by distilling alcohol with the acid and sulphuric acid; also ethyl chloride. He showed that they are decomposed by alkali into alcohol and a salt of the acid. From alcohol, sulphuric acid, and manganese dioxide he obtained a distillate with 'a fine smell', which would be aldehyde, and on increasing the fire vinegar came over.[10] Lauraguais[11] said he had obtained acetic ether by distilling alcohol and acetic acid, but Scheele could not obtain it without adding sulphuric acid, and Bergman had informed him that Poerner had failed with Lauraguais' process; acetic ester is in fact formed, but only slowly and an equilibrium is reached, with concentrated acetic acid.

Scheele had begun to work on Prussian blue in 1765,[12] and his researches (1782–3) on it led to the discovery of hydrocyanic acid.[13] By distilling potassium

[1] KAH, 1780, i, 116; V, 215.   [2] *J. f. Chem.* (Schweigger), 1814, xi, 261.
[3] KAH, 1782, iii, 120; V, 237.
[4] KAH, 1776, xxxvii, 327; V, 80; VI, 268 (letter of Oct., 1776, to Bergman).
[5] Berzelius, *Lehrbuch der Chemie*, 1833, ii, 172.
[6] KAH, 1786, vii, 30; V, 306; Nierenstein, *Incunabula of Tannin Chemistry*, 1932, 37; this was Scheele's last published research, but Gahn's notes show that Scheele's work on gallic and pyrogallic acids goes back to the earliest period, about 1770; VI, 37, 40.
[7] *Ann. Chim.*, 1831, xlvi, 206.
[8] KAH, 1783, iv, 324; Crell's *Ann.*, 1784, II, 328; V, 255, 328.   [9] VII, § 74; V, 139.
[10] KAH, 1782, iii, 35; Crell's *Ann.*, 1785, I, 549; V, 229, 334.
[11] *J. des Sçav.*, Amsterdam, 1759, xliv, 318.   [12] VI, 16, 26 (1768).
[13] KAH, 1782, iii, 264; 1783, iv, 33; Crell's *Ann.*, 1784, I, 525; V, 238, 326 (Experiments concerning the Colouring Principle in Prussian Blue).

ferrocyanide with diluted sulphuric acid he noticed a strong smell (hydrocyanic acid). He did not know the acid was poisonous; he says it had 'a
peculiar, not unpleasant smell', and 'a taste which almost borders slightly on
sweet and is somewhat heating in the mouth' (all pharmacists taste substances
to recognise them). It is difficult to understand how he escaped with his life.
Bohm,[1] Schrader,[2] Gehlen,[3] and Vauquelin,[4] all obtained prussic acid by distilling bitter almonds, peach kernels, laurel leaves, etc., with water, and inferred the poisonous properties of the acid from those of laurel water. Scheele
found that the vapour of prussic acid (which he calls throughout 'the colouring
principle') is inflammable, and fixed air (carbon dioxide) is produced on its
combustion. As evidence of his care in experimenting it may be mentioned
that he kindled the gas with a little burning sulphur, since the fixed air from a
burning taper could have produced the effect on lime water observed.

By distilling Prussian blue he obtained some ammonia, and in 1783 he
obtained potassium cyanide by adding sal ammonic to a red-hot mixture of
charcoal or plumbago and potassium carbonate. This is the first synthesis of a
cyanogen compound.[5] Scheele concluded that prussic acid is a compound of
volatile alkali (ammonia), fixed air, and phlogiston. He obtained a solution of
mercuric cyanide (which he also tasted) by boiling mercuric oxide with
Prussian blue and water, and ammonium cyanide from the acid and ammonia,
or by distilling Prussian blue with ammonia. Scheele, of course, was not in a
position to clear up the relationship of the cyanogen compounds, but he got as
far as saying that in potassium ferrocyanide ('the neutral salt known in
chemistry') the iron is 'a means of attaching the colouring principle to the
alkali', and he remarks that solutions of cyanides are alkaline in reaction. He
obtained silver cyanide by precipitation, and found it soluble in excess of
calcium cyanide solution. In a letter to Bergman in March, 1783[6] Scheele says
'acidum berolinense' (hydrocyanic acid) is 'probably the weakest acid, weaker
than aerial acid' (Luftsäure; carbonic acid).

Every chemist who has attempted research will look over the record of
Scheele's discoveries outlined above with astonishment and admiration.
Astonishment at the great volume of discoveries which he made in his short
life in such disadvantageous circumstances; admiration of the way in which he
carried out his work and the fundamental importance of it all. Crell in his biography truly said:

Aus der Vorzeit lässt sich, in der Menge unerwarteter grosser und wichtiger Entdeckungen, kein Scheidekünstler nur irgend mit ihm vergleichen: auch wohl keiner
seiner Zeitgenossen, darf ich hinzusetzen: ich kann vermuthen, vielleicht keiner seiner
Nachfolger.

GADOLIN

Johan Gadolin (Åbo, 5 June 1760–Wirmo, 15 August 1852), the son of a
professor of physics and theology (afterwards a bishop), studied under Berg-

[1] *Allgem. J. Chem.* (Scherer), 1803, x, 126.
[2] *N. allgem. J. Chem.*, 1803, i, 392; *Ann. Chim.*, 1804, li, 179.
[3] *N. allgem. J. Chem.*, 1803, i, 95.   [4] *Ann. Chim.*, 1803, lv, 206.
[5] Van Deventer, *Chem. Weekbl.*, 1928, xxv, 101.   [6] VI, 364.

man in Uppsala (1778), travelled in Germany, Holland, England and Ireland (1786–8), and became acquainted with Crell, Kirwan and Crawford. On his return he became extraordinary (1785) and ordinary (1797) professor of chemistry in Åbo (Finnish, Turku), retiring in 1822. His laboratory and mineralogical collection were destroyed in a great fire which burnt down the university in 1827.[1]

His theory of combustion,[2] his researches on heat,[3] and his discovery of the yttria earths in a mineral afterwards called gadolinite,[4] are his best-known contributions to science. He taught the antiphlogistic theory from 1789,[5] and his small text-book[6] was the first in Swedish to teach the new system and did much to procure its adoption. He published an important dissertation on affinity.[7]

The mineral in which he discovered the new earth yttria (really a mixture of several rare earths) was brought from Ytterby, near Stockholm, by Lieut. Arhenius in 1787 and was described by Geijer in 1788.[8]

Gadolin,[9] criticising Crawford's calculation of the absolute zero (see p. 156), made accurate determinations of the specific heat (0·5315) and latent heat of fusion (81·1) of ice (which he showed to be the same as that of snow).[10] In a work on chemical mineralogy[11] he criticised Berzelius's classification of minerals on the basis of the electrochemical theory (see Vol. IV).

A large collection of Åbo dissertations in which Gadolin acted is bound up in a quarto volume for Sir Joseph Banks, in the British Museum (B. 387):

De theoria calcinationis, 1792 (J. H. Mennander; adopts oxygen theory); De theoria solutionis chemicae, 1795 (M. Harfvellin); De speciebus solutiones chemicae, 1797 (M. Sylvèn); De acido carbonico, 1798 (H. G. Alcenius); De silica ex solutione alkalina per calcem præcipitata, 1798 (J. Holstius); Animadversiones celeberrimi Gmelin in theoriam Lavoisierianum de natura acidorum examinans, 1801 (E. O. Sellin, reply to Gmelin, Crell's *Ann.*, 1796, I, 291); De silica ex solutione alkalina per barytum præcipitata, 1801 (H. Jajanus); De theoria caloris corporum specifici, 1784 (N. Maconius); Animadversiones celeberrimi Gmelin in theoriam Lavoisierianum de natura acidi carbonici examinans, 1801 (J. A. Montén); ditto de natura acidi nitrici examinans, 1801 (J. J. Erling); ditto de natura acidi sulphurici examinans, 1802 (J. M. Lindenmarck); ditto de natura acidi phosphorici examinans, 1802 (J. J. Björksten); Animadversiones in commentationem nobilissimi von Crell de notione carbonii, 1801 (J.

[1] Hjelt, in Diergart, 1909, 517–23; Edv. Hjelt and R. Tigerstedt, *Johan Gadolin 1760–1852. In Memoriam. Wissenschaftliche Abhandlungen Johan Gadolins in Auswahl*, Leipzig, n.d. [1911]; Komppa, *Z. angew. Chem.*, 1927, xl, 1431; Poggendorff, (1), i, 827; T. E. T[horpe]., *Nature*, 1911, lxxxvi, 48; K. R. Webb, *J. Roy. Inst. Chem.*, 1960, lxxxiv, 349; on Finnish chemists (incl. Gadolin) see V. Ojala and E. R. Schierz, *J. Chem. Education*, 1937, xiv, 161; Tomula, *Suomen Kemistilheti*, Helsingfors, 1936, ixA, 25; 1937, xA, 106; on Gadolin's electrochemical theory see Söderbaum, *Meddel. K. Vetensk. Nobelinst.*, 1919, v, no. 9.
[2] Crell's *Ann.*, 1788, I, 15, 328; see p. 628.
[3] KAH, 1784, v, 218 (Rön och Anmärkningar om Kroppars absoluta Varma); Gadolin and Nicolaus Maconi, *Dissertatio Chemico-physica de Theoria Caloris Corporum Specifici*, 4°, Åbo, 1784 (BM B. 277. (3.)); Crell's *Ann.*, 1788, I, 328 (on Crawford); McKie and Heathcote, *The Discovery of Specific and Latent Heats*, 1935, 108–21, 135 f. (portr.).
[4] KAH, 1794, xv, 137 (Undersökning af en svart tung Stenart ifrän Ytterby); Crell's *Ann.*, 1796, I, 313.
[5] Hjelt and Tigerstedt, *op. cit.*
[6] *Inledning til Chemien*, Åbo, 1798 (150 pp., BM B. 672. (7.)), 17 f.
[7] *Dissertatio academia historiam doctrinæ de affinitatibus chemicis exhibens*, 4°, Åbo, 1815 (BM B. 387. (28.)).
[8] Crell's *Ann.*, 1788, I, 229.   [9] *Nova Acta Reg. Soc. Sci. Upsal.*, 1792, v, 1–49.
[10] Ångström, *Ann. Phys.*, 1853, xc, 509.
[11] *Systema Fossilium analysibus chemicis examinatorum secundum partium constitutivarum rationes ordinatorum*, 4°, Berlin, 1825 (240 pp., 1 errata; BM 445. d. 17).

Montén); De sulphatæ potassæ, 1802 (H. Hartwich); De sulphatæ potassæ acidulo, 1802 (E. Wenell); Historia doctrinæ de affinitatibus chemicis (contin. pagin. but sep. t.ps.), 1815, with M. Baeck (1–12; Newton), P. A. Bonsdorff (13–26; Geoffroy, de Morveau), C. D. von Haartman (27–42; Grosse, Gellert, Rüdiger), C. E. Eklund (43–66; Baron, Sage, Marherr, Machy), G. J. Costiander (67–76; Bergman), E. V. Sylvander (77–94; Bergman), G. W. Enquist (95–110; Bergman), V. R. Brummer (111–24; Grén).

Hjelm

Petter Jacob Hjelm (Sunnerbo, Hårad, 2 October 1746–Stockholm, 7 October 1813), Keeper of the Mint at Stockholm,[1] studied at Uppsala in 1763, and besides his discovery of molybdenum (see p. 216) published researches on mineralogy, metallurgy, and technical chemistry. He obtained metallic manganese in 1778,[2] but this had been done by Gahn in 1774, who did not publish the result (see p. 190), if not in 1770 by J. G. Kaim.[3]

Ekeberg

Anders Gustaf Ekeberg (Stockholm, 16 January 1767–Uppsala, 11 February 1813), a poet, and assistant professor of chemistry at Uppsala from 1794, continued to teach there although in his later years he was very deaf and nearly blind.[4] He discovered tantalum in an analysis of a mineral from Ytterby, in the course of which he confirmed Gadolin's discovery of yttria.[5] In a research on the mineral gadolinite[6] he found that on fusion with potash before the blow-pipe it gives a red mass, but this was not due to manganese. On dissolving in water, the red solution became green (likt den bekante Chamæleon) and deposited red ferric oxide; he proved that this result could be obtained with oxide of iron, and thus rediscovered potassium ferrate, which had been obtained by Stahl (see Vol. II). Ekeberg investigated calcium phosphate in bones,[7] mentioning that Proust in 1790 had announced the unexpected discovery of this 'animal earth' in mineral form in Estramadura.[8] Ekeberg published other analyses of minerals[9] and was examiner of Berzelius's dissertation on a mineral water.[10]

[1] KAH, 1813, 280; Ann. Phil., 1814, iv, 321.
[2] Hjelm, KAH, 1778, xxxix, 82; 1785, vi, 141; Crell's Ann., 1787, I, 158.
[3] Dissertatio de metallis dubiis, Vienna, 1770, 48.
[4] KAH, 1813, 276; Thomson, (5), 168, 181; Ann. Phil., 1814, iv, 241.
[5] Af den svarta Stenarten från Ytterby och den dari funda egna jord: KAH, 1797, xviii, 156; Crell's Ann., 1799, II, 63.
[6] Om Yetterjordens, KAH, 1802, xxiii, 68 (76); Allgem. J. Chem. (Scherer), 1802, ix, 597; Ann. Chim., 1802, xliii, 276; Nicholson's J., 1802, iii, 251.
[7] Crell's Ann., 1798, I, 323.
[8] Giving the reference to 'Crell's Annalen, 1790, II', where there is nothing on the matter, although the same reference is given in the general index to Crell's Ann.; the paper is said to be An. Hist. Nat. Madrid, 1799, i, 127, 138 (Sobra la piedra fosforica de Estramadura); I know only the publication in Obs. Phys., 1788, xxxii, 241.
[9] Poggendorff, (1), i, 655.
[10] Nova analysis aquarum Medeviensium, Disp. præs. A. G. Ekeberg, 4°, Uppsala, 1800.

CHAPTER VII

PRIESTLEY

Joseph Priestley (Fieldhead, nr. Leeds, 24 (13 O.S.) March 1733–Northumberland, Pa., U.S.A., 6 February 1804) was the son of a cloth finisher, Jonas Priestley (apparently of substance, since his father, another Joseph Priestley, employed at least thirty hands); his mother, who died in 1739, was the daughter of a farmer. In 1742 he was adopted by his aunt Mrs. Keighley who, until her death in 1764, was in every way a parent to him. The Keighleys were people of substance; Mrs. Keighley was widowed soon after Priestley went to live with them. She was a strict Nonconformist and he acquired his religious convictions at that time. He was educated partly by private study and partly at 'a large free school', supposed to be at Batley. At the age of sixteen he was sickly but he recovered. He acquired a knowledge of Latin and some Greek, and somewhat later he learned the elements of Hebrew. At one time he contemplated going into business and therefore learnt some French, Italian, and German. With the help of a Dissenting minister he learnt something of geometry, mathematics, and natural philosophy, and the rudiments of the Chaldee (Aramaic) and Syriac languages. He also knew some Arabic. He then decided to study for the Nonconformist ministry and, at the age of nineteen, entered the famous Dissenting Academy at Daventry to study under Dr. Ashworth, the successor of Dr. Doddridge.

Priestley developed steadily in heterodoxy. From Calvinism he passed to Arminianism, from this to Arianism, and in 1767 came to rest only in Socinianism. In each step he convinced himself that he was coming nearer the truth, his sincerity is unquestionable, and he and his friend Lindsey were pioneers of Unitarianism. Priestley had a knowledge of Greek and Hebrew which enabled him to read the Scriptures in the original tongues, and theological learning which enabled him to meet on more than equal terms his more orthodox brethren, with whom he was in continual dispute. His political opinions were of an advanced kind and were fearlessly expressed in a stream of pamphlets.

He was somewhat conservative in heterodoxy, speaking of Methodists as not acquainted 'with the sentiments and wants of the *proper Dissenters*, by which I mean, in this case, the Dissenters of some standing'. The Arians in 18-cent. England recognised Christ's pre-existence and agency in creation, but denied His deity as identical with that of the Father. The Socinians (followers of Fausto Sozzini, 1539–1604) denied His pre-existence and granted Him no nature beyond the human.

Priestley left Daventry in 1755 after three years of fruitful study. His first ministry, for three years, was at a small chapel at Needham Market, in Suffolk, where his stipend was £30 a year, to which he added the fees from a small

school which he set up. For his teaching he bought a pair of globes (made by
John Senex, F.R.S.). At Needham Market he was treated coldly by the dissenting clergy but was friendly with a Quaker, S. Alexander, the owner of a good

FIG. 21. JOSEPH PRIESTLEY (1733–1804).

library to which Priestley had access. Thus, a member of the Society of Friends
was as helpful to Priestley as another, Gough, was later to Dalton.[1]

[1] Anon., *Brit. Quart. Rev.*, 1845, ii, 253 (Priestley 'babbled and prattled'); Anon., *Nature*,
1904, lxix, 348 (a Priestley club); Anon., *Pharm. J.*, 1894, xxv, 521; W. R. Aykroyd, *Three
Philosophers (Lavoisier, Priestley, and Cavendish)*, London, 1935; T. Belsham, *Dr. J. Priestley.
Discourse on his Death, with a Memoir and Letter from his Son*, 1804 (Grant, *Cat.*, Edinburgh,
1927, 947); H. C. Bolton, *Scientific Correspondence of Joseph Priestley. Ninety seven letters
addressed to Josiah Wedgwood, etc., with an Appendix*, New York, 1892 (vii, 240 pp., privately
printed; portr., list of contents of laboratory, list of portraits, etc.; BM 010920. l. 2): thirty-
eight of these letters were known to and used by Wilson, *Life of Cavendish*, 1851, 90 f.;
J. Bostock, *An Essay on Respiration*, Liverpool, 1804, 208; Lord Brougham, *Lives of Philosophers of the Time of George III*, London and Glasgow, 1855 (or Edinburgh, 1872), 68–90;
C. A. Browne, *J. Chem. Educ.*, 1933, x, 443 (b. 24 March 1733); Caven, *Joseph Priestley*,
Institute of Chemistry, London, 1933; Conklin, *Proc. Amer. Phil. Soc.*, 1950, xciv, 127 (P's
expts. on spontaneous generation); Cooper, see *Memoirs*; J. Corry, *Life of Priestley*, Birmingham, 1804; Cuvier, *Éloges historiques*, Paris, 1860, 35; *id., Recueil des Éloges historiques lus
dans les Séances Publiques de l'Institut Royal de France*, 3 vols. Paris, 1819, i, 189; *id.*, AdS,
1806, vi, h 29–58; T. L. Davis, in *Studien zur Geschichte der Chemie, Festgabe E. O. von Lippmann*, ed. J. Ruska, Berlin, 1927, 132 (The Last Stand of Phlogiston); *id., J. Chem. Educ.*,
1927, iv, 176; *id., Isis*, 1928, x, 178; R. A. M. Dixon, *J. Chem. Educ.*, 1933, x, 149; 1934, xi, 284;
De Luc, *Idées sur la Météorologie*, London, 1787, ii, 204 f. (letters of Priestley; visits to Priestley
at Calne, end of 1773, and Birmingham, 1782); Dumas, (1), 1837, 111 f.; England, *Amer. J.
Pharm.*, 1932, civ, 594 (Franklin and Priestley); Faujas Saint-Fond, *Voyages en Angleterre*,
etc., 1797, ii, 398 (in Smiles, *op. cit.*, 354; P's laboratory in 1785); W. de Fonvielle, *Célébration
du premier centenaire de la découverte de l'oxygène 1er Août 1774. La vie et les travaux du*

In 1751 Priestley moved to a ministry at Nantwich in Cheshire. Here he supplemented his small stipend by opening a school and giving lectures, buying an air pump and an electrical machine (which were then expensive). He also married the daughter of the ironmaster Isaac Wilkinson of Wrexham, who had originally been a small farmer and foreman in an ironworks at Clifton in Cumberland.[1]

In 1761 he was appointed tutor in languages at the Dissenting Academy at Warrington. There he taught the theory of languages, oratory and criticism; the history, laws, and constitution of England; logic, and Hebrew (the last two

docteur Priestley, Paris, 1875 (36 pp.); Fourcroy, (2), iii, 379, 412, 457; J. F. Fulton and C. H. Peters, bibliography in *Papers of the Bibliographical Society of America*, 1936, xxx, 150 (issued in 1938); *id.*, *Works of Joseph Priestley, 1733–1804. Preliminary Short Title List*, New Haven, Conn., 1937 (mimeographed, 20 pp., books and pamphlets only); *Gentleman's Magazine*, 1794, lxiv, I, 428 (P's departure for America); Gmelin, (1), iii, 158, 270, 317; Goldschmidt, *J. Chem. Educ.*, 1927, iv, 145; P. G. Hartog, (1), DNB, 1896, xlvi, 357; (2) *id.*, *Chem. News*, 1931, cxliii, 281, 285; (3) *id.*, *Proc. Roy. Inst.*, 1931, xxvi, 395–430 (and repr.); (4) *id.*, *J. Chem. Soc.*, 1933, 896; (5) *id.*, *Ann. Sci.*, 1941, v, 1; H. Hartley, *J. Chem. Soc.*, 1933, 915; W. Henry, *An estimate of the philosophical character of Dr. Priestley, read to the first meeting of the British Association . . . at York, September 28th, 1831*, York, 1832 (from *B.A. Report*, 1833, i, 60–71); *id.*, *Amer. J. Sci.*, 1833, xxiv, 28; Hepburn, *J. Franklin Inst.*, 1947, ccxliv, 63, 95 (P in America; 67 refs.); Hoefer, (1), ii, 472–87; Anne Holt, *A Life of Joseph Priestley*, London, 1931 (bibl., portr. without wig); G. L. Hume, *Chemical Attraction. An Essay in Five Chapters*, Cambridge, 1835, 59 ('if Dr. Priestley had lived in the times of persecution against Christianity, his life would willingly have been given up by him for her cause'); T. H. Huxley, (1) *The Priestley Memorial*, 1875; (2) *id.*, *Science and Culture*, 1881, 94; (3) *id.*, *Collected Essays*, 1893, iii, 1; Jörgensen, *Samml. chem.-u. chem.-techn. Vorträge*, Stuttgart, 1909, xiv, 111–72; O. Lodge in J. H. Muirhead, *Nine Famous Birmingham Men*, 1909 (BM 10803. bbb. 35); Loewenfeld, *Manchester Mem.*, 1913, lvii, no. 19 (p. 31, early portr., and caricatures, of P); Louisy, NBG, 1862, xli, 27; D. McKie, *Sci. Progr.*, 1933, xxviii, 17; H. Maclachlan, *English Education under the Test Act*, Manchester, 1931; *id.*, *The Warrington Academy, its History and Influences*, Manchester, 1943; J. F. Marsh, *Trans. Hist. Soc. Lancashire and Cheshire*, 1855, vii, 65–81 (correspondence of P in Warrington Museum and Library); Harriet Martineau, *Retrospect of Western Travel*, 3 vols., London, 1838, i, 175–98 (visit to P's grave); C. Matignon, *Bull. Soc. Chim.*, 1935, liii, 1313; A. N. Meldrum, (1) *The Eighteenth Century Revolution in Science*, Calcutta, 1930; (2) *id.*, *J. Chem. Soc.*, 1933, 902; *Memoirs of Dr. Joseph Priestley to the Year 1795, written by himself, with a Continuation to the time of his Decease, by his Son*, 2 vols., London, 1805 (with observations by Cooper and Christie), also London, 1806–7, 1809. Vol. ii contains a list of Priestley's publications (the notes on Chemistry are by Judge Thomas Cooper, Penn., U.S.A., formerly of Manchester, England, who was proposed, unsuccessfully, by Priestley for the F.R.S.); M. M. Pattison Muir, *Heroes of Science. Chemists*, London, 1883, 52–76; Newell, *J. Chem. Educ.*, 1933, x, 151; R. E. Oesper, Priestley, Lavoisier and Trudaine de Montigny, *J. Chem. Educ.*, 1936, xiii, 403; Partington, *Nature*, 1933, cxxxi, 348; Peacock, *Joseph Priestley*, London, 1920 (63 pp.; portr.); *Phil. Mag.*, 1833, ii, 158, 317, 383–402 (speeches at centenary dinner, Monday 26 March 1833); H. W. Picton, *The Story of Chemistry*, 1889, 185; Poggendorff, (1), ii, 528; *The Priestley Memorial at Birmingham, August, 1874*, London 1875; J. D. Reuss, *Alphabetical Register of all the Authors Actually Living in Great Britain . . . Gelehrte England, oder Lexicon der jetz-lebenden Schriftsteller in Grossbritannien . . .*, Berlin and Stettin, 1791, 327–32; Rodwell, *Nature*, 1882, xxvii, 8 (P 'discovered' oxygen in March, 1775; Lavoisier's part); J. T. Rutt, *Life and Correspondence of Joseph Priestley, Ll.D., F.R.S.*, 2 vols., London, 1832 (vols. 25 and 26 of Rutt's ed. of Priestley's *Theological and Miscellaneous Works*, repr. in 1831–32 from an American ed., 1809 (?)); list of works in ii, 535 f.; R. E. Schofield, *Ann. Sci.*, 1957 (1959), xiii, 148–63 (P's scientific background); Sellers and Sellers, *J. Franklin Inst.*, 1920, cxc, 877 (P's air pump; plate); S. Smiles, 1874, 292 f.; *ib.*, 1904, 339 f.; Edgar Fahs Smith, *Priestley in America, 1794–1804*, Philadelphia, 1920; *id.*, *Science*, 1926, lxiv, 317; *id.*, *Ind. Eng. Chem.*, 1919, xi, 405; 1923, xv, 465; T. Thomson, *Ann. Phil.*, 1813, i, 81; *id.*, (1), ii, 1; *id.*, (3), 472; T. E. Thorpe, (1), *Joseph Priestley*, in *Science Lectures for the People*, Manchester, 1874; (2) *id.*, *Essays*, 1902, 32; (3) *id.*, *Joseph Priestley*, London, 1906; (4) *id.*, in *Sir Henry Roscoe*, London, 1916, 39 f. (reminiscences of Mrs. M. Roscoe); Tilden, *Famous Chemists*, 1921, 32 (pastel portr. of P without wig by Mrs. Sharples in Nat. Portrait Gallery); Var. authors in 'Priestley number', *J. Chem. Educ.*, 1927, iv, 145 f.; *Isis*, 1928, ix, 201; W. Cameron Walker, (1) *Nature*, 1933, cxxxi, 876; *id.*, (2) *Proc. Leeds Phil. Soc.*, 1934, ii, 549; *id.*, (3) *Isis*, 1934, xxi, 81 (P's early career; early portr.); Weatherby, *J. Chem. Educ.*, 1926, iii, 129 (alchemical MS. in P's library); Whewell, (1), 1857, iii, 110.
[1] A. S. Davies, *Trans. Newcomen Soc.*, 1951–3 (1956), xxviii, 203–5.

being after a year or two exchanged with Dr. Aikin for civil law); and in one
year he gave a course of lectures on anatomy. He probably prepared himself
adequately for all these courses, and the Academy had a high standard.[1]

It is characteristic of Priestley that, although he had a stammer and a poor

FIG. 22. JOSEPH PRIESTLEY (1733–1804).

delivery, he taught oratory and published a book on the subject. He had himself had the equivalent of a good university education. He published some
charts of history and biography:

(1) A Chart of Universal History, London, 1753, single engraved oblong f° sheet
(BM Cup. 1250. e. 18).

(2) A New Chart of History, London, 1769, single engraved oblong f° sheet (BM
Cup. 1253. c. 12); reduced before t.p. of History of Electricity, 2 ed., 1769.

(3) A Chart of Biography, Warrington, 1765, single f° sheet (BM 611. l. 19). A
Biographical Chart (folding) before t.p. of History of Vision, Light, and Colours, 1772, i.

(4) A Description of a Chart of Biography, 8°, Warrington, 1765 (BM 611. d. 30).
There are many later issues in BM.

On the basis of these mediocre productions he was awarded the degree of
Ll.D. of Edinburgh in 1765; thereafter he was always 'Dr. Priestley'. In
February 1766 Priestley wrote to Canton saying that he wished to become a
Fellow of the Royal Society and he was elected in June. Thorpe[2] says incor-
rectly that this was in recognition of his History of Electricity, not published
until 1767.[3] The president was then James, Earl of Morton. Election to the

[1] Maclachlan, 1931, 209 (on Daventry, 152).   [2] (2), 1906, 62, 65.   [3] Walker, (3).

Royal Society was then largely in the hands of the Secretaries, and 'whoever wished to add the title of F.R.S. to his name, as author of a book, or as a Divine seeking preferment, or as a Physician in quest of practice, had only to become acquainted with these officers, and obtain their good will'.[1]

About 1765 Priestley began to spend a month every year in London, where he became acquainted with Dr. Price, Canton, Watson, and Benjamin Franklin.

John Canton (Stroud, Glos., 31 July 1718–London, 22 March 1772), F.R.S. 1749, was head of a private school in Spital Square, London. He wrote on electrical and magnetic subjects and first measured the compressibility of water.[2] Canton[3] prepared phosphorescent calcium sulphide and made some experiments depending on the formation of ultraviolet rays, intercepted by glass, by the electric spark, but he did not explain the results.[4]

About this time Priestley began to write his *History of Electricity*, which Franklin encouraged him to finish, and it was published in 1767, in which year Priestley moved to Leeds to take up a ministry in Mill Hill Chapel. At Leeds he began his experiments on gases. He had an elementary knowledge of chemistry, dating back to his days at Warrington. He said[5] that he and other members of the class made some experiments with Dr. Turner at Warrington, e.g. the preparation of nitric acid. He also read some of Boerhaave's *Elements of Chemistry*.[6] Dr. Turner, of Liverpool, afterwards wrote (under the name of Hammon) a reply to Priestley's *Letters to a Philosophical Unbeliever*.[7]

Priestley in 1773 went as 'literary companion' to Lord Shelburne, afterwards first Marquis of Lansdowne, Prime Minister in 1782, the first English statesman to hold free trade principles. Shelburne in 1771 had met Baron d'Holbach and Morellet in Paris and by them, as well as Adam Smith, he was much influenced. Priestley lived in a house near Lord Shelburne's seat Bowood in Calne, Wiltshire, and in winter in a house near to Lord Shelburne's London house. He had a salary of £250 a year, the use of a splendid library, plenty of leisure for his own work, and the promise of an annual pension of £150 on retirement.[8] He says Lord Shelburne treated him as a friend. In the autumn of 1774 Priestley travelled with Lord Shelburne on the Continent and met Lavoisier in Paris; Priestley had then just discovered oxygen in Calne.

In 1779 Priestley parted amicably from Lord Shelburne at the latter's suggestion, and began to draw his pension.[9] One reason why he left Lord Shelburne was probably Priestley's expressed opposition to his patron's political opinions, and Shelburne also did not care for controversial divinity; one of Priestley's friends said: 'I could only stop a publication for six months, though it was to hurt his patron with the public and the court, appear when it would.' Priestley now found difficulty in supporting an increasing family, but he received substantial gifts from friends, and in 1780 settled in Birmingham, where he continued his experiments. He was indebted to Josiah Wedgwood, the potter, for many gifts of apparatus and funds for his work and was helped

[1] Brougham, 1855, 357. [2] *Phil. Trans.*, 1762, lii, 640; 1764, liv, 261.
[3] *Phil. Trans.*, 1768, lviii, 337.
[4] Priestley, *History of Vision, Light and Colours*, 1772, ii, 434.
[5] *Philosophical Empiricism*, 1775, 45. [6] *Memoirs*, 1806, 183.
[7] *Memoirs*, 1806, 61. [8] Rutt, i, 201. [9] Rutt, i, 206.

by Boulton, Erasmus Darwin and others. He had a large and well-stocked laboratory.[1]

Priestley's freely expressed religious and political opinions gave offence in many quarters. He was attacked in the House of Commons by Edmund Burke, who was on friendly terms with Priestley and took an interest in his scientific work,[2] and Priestley replied in a pamphlet. On 14 July 1791, when a decorous dinner was held in the afternoon in Birmingham to celebrate the fall of the Bastille, the mob pillaged Priestley's house and laboratory, although he himself was not present at the dinner and had nothing to do with it. For three days Birmingham was the scene of an orgy of political violence and bestiality which has rarely been equalled in England. 'Persons in the habit of gentlemen' were seen rummaging among his papers in the vain hope of finding incriminating documents.[3] A claim for £4083 10s. 3d. (other figures are given) was made by Priestley for the damage to his house and laboratory,[4] and he received about half this sum. A large item, £84 10s. 0d., was for the contents of the wine cellar; the claim for books and manuscripts was £853 10s. The total damage in Birmingham was about £50,000, about half of which was made good by a rate levied on the district, including the town itself.[5] Priestley, the unsubduable pamphleteer, wrote on the Birmingham riots,[6] and there is a profuse pamphlet literature by various authors in 1791–3.[7]

Priestley made a dignified protest and several of the ringleaders were afterwards severely dealt with. He found it desirable to escape in disguise to Worcester, from where he went to London, where he taught at New College, Hackney[8] and seems to have lived quite happily for a time. It is said that he was ostracised by some fellows of the Royal Society, but he did not resign his Fellowship.[9] He felt lonely, and in April 1794 he followed his sons to America, where he settled on the banks of the Susquehanna and established a laboratory and library.[10] He took no steps to become an American citizen and was regarded with suspicion in America as in England. Priestley before leaving England wrote:[11]

I cannot refrain from repeating again, that I leave my native country with real regret, never expecting to find anywhere else society so suited to my disposition and habits. . . . Still less can I expect to resume my favourite pursuits with anything like the advantages I enjoy here. . . . I can, however, truly say that I leave it without any resentment or ill-will. On the contrary, I sincerely wish my countrymen all happiness;

[1] Smiles, 1874, 299.   [2] Armytage, Ann. Sci., 1956 (1957), xii, 160.
[3] Rutt, ii, 116 f.; Corry, 1804, 28.
[4] S. Timmins, Dr. Priestley's Laboratory, 1791, London, 1890 (BM 8709. bb. 2.c.5.1); McKie, Notes and Records of the Royal Society, 1956, xi, 114.
[5] Thorpe, (3), 146.
[6] An Appeal to the Public on the Subject of the Riots in Birmingham, Dublin, 1792; 2 ed., Birmingham, 1792.
[7] Views of the Ruins of the principal Houses destroyed during the Riots at Birmingham, 1791, London, 1792, showing the burning of Priestley's house; reprod. in Smiles, 1874, 333; S. H. Jeyes, The Russells of Birmingham, 1911, 25 f., 44 f., plate of the burning of Priestley's house, from an oil painting; copy corrected by T. H. Russell in London University Library.
[8] Priestley, Heads of Lectures on a Course of Experimental Philosophy, particularly including Chemistry, delivered at . . . Hackney, London, 1794.
[9] Rutt, ii, 119, 274, 280; cf. Kopp, (1), iv, 238; R. A. M. Dixon, J. Chem. Educ., 1934, xi, 284.
[10] Rutt, ii, 230.   [11] Thorpe, (2), 39.

and when the time for reflection (which my absence may accelerate) shall come, they will, I am confident, do me more justice. . . . In this case I shall look with satisfaction to the time when, if my life be prolonged, I may visit my friends in this country; and perhaps I may, notwithstanding my removal for the present, find a grave (as I believe is naturally the wish of every man) in the land that gave me birth.

He never returned to England. He died in Northumberland, Pennsylvania, after two years of painful illness and his remains lie there.

He was elected professor of chemistry in the University of Pennsylvania in 1794 but declined, feeling that 'though I have made discoveries in some branches of chemistry, I never gave much attention to the routine of it'. He also declined the charge of a Unitarian chapel in New York.[1]

With many gifts from friends, including £10,000 from a brother-in-law, and his pension from Lord Shelburne, Priestley was always well provided for, and had ample means for his scientific researches. He was blamed[2] for seeking and accepting benefactions from friends which enabled him to decline an offer to procure a pension from the Government, so as to 'preserve himself independent of everything connected with the court', but he has been defended against this censure.[3] The gifts continued when he was in America. The money was used not only for his 'philosophical and theological studies' but also for the education of his children and to defray the costs of housekeeping and entertainment, 'exceeding twice his own income.'

Lord Brougham,[4] who had not a very high opinion of Priestley's character, said he 'was a perfectly conscientious man in all the opinions which he embraced, and sincere in all he published respecting other subjects . . . upright and honourable in all his dealings, and justly beloved by his family and friends as a man spotless in all the relations of life'. In private life Priestley was a courteous gentleman of attractive and winning personality. His theological and political writings made him many enemies, though whether the fault lay with him or with his opponents has been disputed.[5] Even in 1839, the President of the British Association[6] could say that a charge had been brought against it because an account of Priestley[7] had 'formed a part of its early transactions'. It has been said that 'as a controversialist, Priestley is not enjoyable. He is bad-tempered and superior, his ridicule heavy, and the reader tires of his frequent phrase, "I flatter myself".' His pamphlets usually start moderately, but he soon lashes himself into a passion.[8] He was of an equable temper and always able to work, 'all seasons have been equal to me, early or late, before dinner and after'; he could write by the fireside with his family, 'nothing but reading aloud, or speaking without interruption' interfered with his work. He was a man of prodigious industry: he says he often wrote till he could hardly hold the pen. In 1800 he began to learn Chinese,[9] and in 1802[10] he was experimenting with the newly discovered voltaic battery. In science he was somewhat of an amateur, and his defective knowledge of general chemistry exposed him to many mistakes.

[1] Miles, *Chymia*, 1953, iv, 37 (66); Smiles, 1874, 297; 1904, 419; E. F. Smith, 1920.
[2] Brougham, 1872, i, 81.   [3] Smiles, 1904, 344; Bolton, 1892, 26.
[4] 1872, i, 90.   [5] Rutt, i, 344.   [6] Harcourt, *B.A. Report*, 1839, 15.
[7] W. Henry, *B.A. Report*, 1833, i, 60–71; read by Phillips.
[8] Holt, 1931, 112.   [9] Rutt, i, 115; ii, 464, 496.   [10] *Nicholson's J.*, 1802, i, 198.

Priestley published about fifty works on theology, thirteen on education and history, eighteen on political, social, and metaphysical subjects, and twelve books and about fifty papers on scientific subjects. When he was once asked how many books he had written, he replied: 'Many more, Sir, than I should like to read.'[1] The following are of interest to us; in the quotations Priestley's copious use of italics is generally disregarded:

I. The History and Present State of Electricity, with Original Experiments, 4°, London, 1767, 2 ed. enlarged, 4°, 1769 (ded. to James Earl of Morton, P.R.S.): in the Advertisement to the 2 ed. Priestley says he had learnt German, a language hardly known to English writers.

II. Familiar Introduction to the Study of Electricity, 4°, London, 1768 (51 pp. and 4 plates) with an advertisement of electrical machines to be made under Priestley's direction; the plates are numbered 2, 3, 6, and 7, taken unchanged from I.

III. The History and Present State of Discoveries relating to Vision, Light, and Colours, 2 vols. 4°, London, 1772 (dedic. to the Duke of Northumberland, Earl Percy, saying 'without that knowledge about which it is conversant, rank and fortune would be of little value'; 6 p. list of subscribers, with supplementary list, incl. R. Watson, later Bishop of Llandaff, list of Priestley's books; contin. pagin., 812 pp.). This book was not very successful; he says he proposed to continue the series but in 1772 he began his experiments on gases which turned his attention into a different channel (see p. 249).

IV. Experiments and Observations on Different Kinds of Air, 3 vols. 8°, London, 1774–5–7; 2 ed. Vol. I, 1775, Vol. II, 1776 (corrected) and 1784, Vol. III, 1777; 3 ed. Vol. I, 1781. The first vol. of the original ed. is not called 'Vol. I' and Priestley perhaps did not anticipate in 1774 that he would publish further vols.

French tr. by Jacques Gibelin:

Expériences et Observations sur différentes Expèces d'Air, 5 vols. 12°, Paris, I–III, 1777; IV–V (usually missing), 1780; including a general index and notes by Gibelin; Sotheran, *Cat.* 832 (1932), No. 5633; full analysis of contents in Fourcroy, (2), iii, 459 f.

V. Experiments and Observations relating to Various Branches of Natural Philosophy, 3 vols. 8°, London, 1779–81–86. The 3 vols. of V are sometimes (and by Priestley himself) called vols. iv–vi of IV.

French tr. by J. Gibelin:

Expériences et Observations sur différentes Branches de la Physique avec une Continuation des Observations sur l'Air, 4 vols. 12°, Paris, 1782–7, with a long preface.

VI. Experiments and Observations on Different Kinds of Air and other Branches of Natural Philosophy, 3 vols. 8°, Birmingham, 1790 (revised and abridged from IV and V, with additions).

VII. Philosophical Empiricism: containing Remarks on a Charge of Plagiarism respecting Dr. H—s [Bryan Higgins], interspersed With various Observations relating to different kinds of Air, London, 1775 (see p. 728).

VIII. Experiments and Observations relating to the Generation of Air from Water, 8°, London, 1793 (39 pp.; BM 8704. de. 11. (1.)), from *Phil. Trans.*, 1791, lxxxi, 213; answered at some length by Pearson, A Translation of the Table of Chemical Nomenclature, 1794, 47 f.

IX. Experiments and Observations relating to the Analysis of Atmospherical Air; also, Farther Experiments relating to the Generation of Air from Water . . . to which are added, Considerations on the Doctrine of Phlogiston and the Decomposition of Water. Addressed to Messrs. Berthollet, &c., 8°, Philadelphia (printed in London), 1796; repr. for J. Johnson: in this Priestley complains that the new theory of chemistry was taught in all the American schools. It was tr. and answered by Adet: Réflexions sur la doctrine du Phlogistique et la décomposition de l'Air . . . traduit de l'Anglais & suivi d'une réponse par P. A. Adet, 8°, Philadelphia, 1797; Paris, 1798 (Duveen and Klickstein, *Isis*, 1954, xlv, 278 (290)); German tr. with notes by Crell, *Ann.*, 1801, I, 143–63.

X. Considerations on the Doctrine of Phlogiston, and The Decomposition of Water, Philadelphia, printed by Thomas Dobson, 1796; reprinted with 'Two Lectures

[1] Holt, 175.

on Combustion: Supplementary to a Course of Lectures on Chemistry. Read at Nassau-Hall. Containing an Examination of D.ʳ Priestley's Considerations on the Doctrine of Phlogiston, and The Decomposition of Water,' by John Maclean [1771–1814], Professor of Mathematics and Natural Philosophy, in the College of New-Jersey [Princeton], Philadelphia, 1797; reissued with an account of Maclean by Prof. W. Foster, Princeton, 1929.

XI. The Doctrine of Phlogiston Established and that of the Composition of Water Refuted, 8°, Northumberland (U.S.A.), 1800 (xv, 90 pp., 1 leaf, folding plate of soda-water app.); 2 ed. with additions, and Observations on the Conversion of Iron into Steel, in a letter to Mr. Nicholson, 8°, Northumberland and Philadelphia, 1803.

Priestley's *History of Electricity* gives a good account of the subject, largely based on original sources, and is still of value. It contains a proof of the inverse square law by a method suggested by Franklin, depending on the absence of force inside a hollow charged conductor.[1] The mathematical argument applies to a hollow spherical shell,[2] afterwards used by Cavendish (see p. 305), but Priestley used a cup or cylindrical vessel. He says: 'May we not infer from this experiment, that the attraction of electricity is subject to the same laws with that of gravitation, and is therefore according to the squares of the distances.'

The mathematical deduction of the inverse square law from the result follows simply only with a sphere over which the charge is uniformly distributed, but the experimental result is found with hollow conducting vessels of any shape, as in the 'ice-pail experiment' made by Faraday.[3]

D. Bernoulli in 1760 had stated the inverse square law for electric force (in actione reciproca quadrata distantium id fieri, si vis electricitas maneat idem) on the basis of some experiments with a floating hydrometer used as a balance.[4] Robison in 1769 made some experiments which showed that the repulsive force varied inversely as the 2·06 power of the distance and the attractive force inversely as a power less than 2, inferring that the true law was the inverse square, but these were not published until 1822.[5]

Priestley[6] discovered that hot glass is a conductor, and his book contains some views on the philosophy and method of science, based on Franklin's.[7]

It is Priestley's chemical work which is of interest to us. He says[8] that he was not 'a professed chemist' and was 'attending only to such articles in that branch of knowledge as my own pursuits are particularly connected with', 'not being a practical chemist.'[9] Several of his experiments were suggested to him by his 'chemical friends';[10] he frequently mentions Woulfe as having provided materials, given advice, and suggested experiments. Scheele[11] (1786), in correcting one of Priestley's mistakes, said: 'this excellent philosopher . . . does not profess himself to be a chemist.' Berthollet[12] says: 'The celebrated Priestley himself often set us the example, by rectifying the results of some of his numerous experiments.'[13]

[1] I, 1769, 711.   [2] Maxwell, *A Treatise on Electricity and Magnetism*, Oxford, 1892, i, 83.
[3] *Phil. Mag.*, 1843, xxii, 200; *Experimental Researches*, 1844, ii, 279.
[4] Burkhardt, *Ann. Phys.*, 1869, cxxxvi, 634.
[5] Robison, *Elements of Mechanical Philosophy*, ed. Brewster, Edinburgh, 1822, iv, 73.
[6] I, 1769, 577.   [7] Hartog, (5).   [8] V, i, 39.   [9] IV, ii, 1.   [10] See, e.g., VI, 1790, i, 87.
[11] *Collected Papers*, 1931, 302.   [12] In Kirwan, *Essay on Phlogiston*, 1789, 124.
[13] Priestley, V, ii, 307–24: 'Remarks on certain passages in the preceding volumes, . . . explaining, or correcting them, by the help of subsequent experiments and observations.'

It is interesting to find Priestley writing to Franklin in 1777 that he 'did not quite despair of the philosopher's stone', and to find Franklin advising him in return, if he found it, 'to take care to lose it again.'[1] It was not quite in this sense, but with reference to his general outlook and method that Muir[2] said that 'Priestley was an alchemist, not a chemist'. Schofield attempted to rescue Priestley from the considered opinion of all who have written on him, that he had little real chemical background, but his own writings are perhaps the best evidence of this. A little more knowledge would have saved Priestley from making many mistakes.

Priestley said that his discoveries owed more 'to what we call *chance*, that is, philosophically speaking, to the observation of *events arising from unknown causes*, than to any proper design or preconceived *theory* in this business',[3] but John Bostock,[4] who was Priestley's pupil and assisted him in the laboratory, could not agree that Priestley's discoveries were 'accidental', and Priestley no doubt over-emphasised this aspect of his work. Whatever his method was, it certainly gave results. Priestley also compared natural philosophy with hunting, when a passer-by may sometimes blunder on the quarry while the serious experts 'weary themselves without starting any game'.[5]

Priestley[6] said:

'If we could content ourselves with the bare knowledge of new *facts*, and suspend our judgment with respect to their *causes*, till, by their analogy, we were led to the discovery of more facts, of a similar nature, we should be in a much surer way to the attainment of real knowledge . . . I think I have as little to reproach myself with on this head as most of my brethren; and whenever I have drawn general conclusions too soon, I have been very ready to abandon them.'

This, as will be seen below, is by no means the case, and a great number of his 'facts' were either not facts but disguised hypotheses or incorrect observations; although he certainly changed his opinions with rather bewildering frequency, he held fast to the cardinal errors of chemical theory to the end. He was, he says, disposed always 'to embrace what is generally called the heterodox side of every question',[7] but in chemistry he was most orthodox, and clung tenaciously to the last to the theory of phlogiston which his own experiments, if they had been properly interpreted, would have been the first to overthrow.

Fourcroy[8] reproached him for finding too many facts and not theorising enough — unlike Lavoisier. Hartog[9] claimed that Priestley, whose views on hypotheses were expounded in his *History of Electricity*, 'kept intact a light-hearted scepticism about every hypothesis that seemed to him unverifiable, and the hypothesis of phlogiston was one of them', and speaks of Priestley's 'good-humoured expression of doubt as to the existence of phlogiston'; whilst Meldrum[10] takes Priestley to task for his 'glib' discourse about phlogiston: 'there was no ruling purpose behind his work and there was no austerity in his thinking.' Priestley, like Faraday later,[11] wrote out accounts of his experiments in the order in which he made them, not rearranging or editing them,[12] and we

[1] Rutt, i, 297.   [2] *History of Chemical Theories and Laws*, 1907, 38.
[3] IV, ii, 29; cf. *ib.*, 39, 42, etc.; VI, ii, 102.   [4] *Phil. Mag.*, 1833, ii, 383 (389).
[5] IV, I, xi; V, I, xi.   [6] V, I, x–xi.   [7] Rutt, i, 24.
[8] (2), iii, 412 f.   [9] (5), 16.   [10] (1), 60.
[11] See Faraday, *Phil. Mag.*, 1833, ii, 383 (390).   [12] Bostock, 1804, 208.

always know exactly what he did. Priestley was a rapid worker, who accumulated facts which others were to turn to better use. Huxley[1] applied to him the description found in Lucretius:[2] 'one of the swift runners who hand over the torch of life (quasi cursores vitaï lampada tradunt).' He also published promptly, partly with a genuine desire to promote knowledge, and partly with the perfectly legitimate object of establishing priority. He told Silliman, whom he met in Philadelphia: 'when I made a discovery, I did not wait to perfect it by more elaborate research, but at once threw it out to the world, that I might establish my claim before I was anticipated. I subjected whatever came to hand to the action of fire or various chemical reagents, and the result was often fortunate in presenting some new discovery.'[3]

Priestley was not quite ignorant of chemistry when he began research; he had attended Dr. Turner's course at Warrington, had read books on the subject, and had done some practical work (see p. 241). His interest in chemistry is also shown in the chapter 'Experiments on mephitic air [carbon dioxide] and charcoal' in his *History of Electricity* (1767),[4] in which he speaks of 'having read, and finding by my own experiments, that a candle would not burn in air that had passed through a charcoal fire, or through the lungs of animals, or in any of that air which the chymists call mephitic'; he wonders if it could not be restored to its original state by violent agitation (he found this was not the case with electrification, etc.). He found that it was a non-conductor of electricity, like common air, and concluded 'from some experiments of my own, and others of Dr. Macbride, that this mephitic air was not anything that had been common air, but a fluid *sui generis*'.

Charcoal, however, he found to be a conductor, and calces of metals (non-conductors) become metals when heated with charcoal, perhaps by imbibing mephitic air, as supposed by 'the modern chymists', or phlogiston in a fixed state. He then, apparently, knew very little of contemporary chemistry in supposing that fixed air was identical with phlogiston, and he forgot that sulphur, supposedly rich in phlogiston, is a non-conductor. This idea is amplified in his first scientific paper, on charcoal.[5]

In 1770 Priestley wrote from Leeds to his friend the Rev. T. Lindsey, with whom he corresponded to the end of his life, saying: 'I am now taking up some of Dr. Hales's enquiries concerning air.'[6] He says he began his experiments on gases as a result of living in Leeds next to a public brewery, where he noticed that fixed air was evolved in the fermentation vats;[7] he tested the gas with a lighted candle, etc., and once, he tells us, a vat of beer was spoiled. As a result of his experiments Priestley later published a pamphlet on making an artificial mineral water by saturating water with fixed air:

Directions for Impregnating Water with Fixed Air in order to communicate to it the peculiar Spirit and Virtues of Pyrmont Water and other Mineral Waters of a similar Nature, London, 1772, price 1 shilling.

[1] (3), 1893, iii, 2.   [2] *De nat. rer.*, ii, 78.
[3] P. E. Browning, *J. Chem. Educ.*, 1934, xi, 170.
[4] I, 1767, 598–608; 2 ed., 1769, 566; Hartog, *op. cit.*
[5] *Phil. Trans.*, 1770, lx, 211; IV, ii, 241.   [6] Rutt, i, 113.
[7] Rutt, i, 75; IV, ii, 269; *Memoirs*, 1805, 255.

German tr.:

Auserlesene kleine Werke dreyer berühmter Englischer Chemysten. Priestley, Henry und Black, Die Schwängerung des gemeinen Wassers mit fixer Luft, die Magnesia und Kalkerde . . . betreffend, 8°, Copenhagen and Leipzig, 1774 (BM 1035. f. 33. Priestley pp. 1–28; Henry 29 f., Black 133 f.).

Priestley had read Brownrigg's paper (see p. 123) and uses the name 'spirit' for the gas dissolved in Pyrmont water. He persuaded the First Lord of the Admiralty to instal his aerated-water apparatus on two warships as a preventive of scurvy (for which it is useless), this idea being Macbride's, who knew that fresh vegetables prevented this disease and thought they did so because of the fixed air evolved in digestion.[1] The addition of a small quantity of carbonate of soda to the water seems to have been proposed first by Priestley's friend, the apothecary Richard Bewley of Great Massingham, the recipe for 'Mr. Bewley's julep' being given by Thomas Henry,[2] who used it mixed with brandy as a beverage.

Priestley's apparatus was criticised and improved by John Mervin Nooth M.D.,[3] who substituted an ivory or glass valve for the bladder used by Priestley, which, Nooth said, tainted the water. A large part of Priestley's second volume of IV is taken up by a discussion of the apparatus, of Nooth's criticism, and of the improvement of Nooth's apparatus by Parker. The polemical part is modified in the second edition,[4] where he says:[5] 'I have never recommended my own apparatus for the use of a family since I have been acquainted with his [Nooth's]', and in 1790[6] he calls Nooth's apparatus 'ingenious'.

William Falconer (b. Chester 1743), then a physician in Bath, proposed 'soda water' as a remedy for calculus:

Experiments and Observations, in three parts. Part I. On the dissolvent Power of Water impregnated with Fixable Air, compared with Simple Water, relative to Medicinable Substances. Part II. On the Dissolvent Power of Water impregnated with Fixable Air, on the Urinary Calculus. Part III. On the Antiseptic Power of Water impregnated with Fixable Air, . . . , 8°, London, 1776 (ii ll., 136 pp., dedic. to Priestley); On the Efficacy of the Aqua Mephitica Alkalina; or, Solution of Fixed Alkaline Salt, saturated with Fixible Air, in Calculous Disorders, 8°, Bath, 1787; 3 ed. London, 1789; 4 ed., London, 1792.

João Jacinto de Magalhaens (or Magelhaens), commonly called Magellan (Lisbon, 4 November 1722–London, 7 February 1790), an Augustinian prior in Lisbon who left for England and Protestantism in 1764, F.R.S. 1774, published an account of an improved apparatus in 1777:

A Description of a Glass Apparatus for making in a few minutes, and at a very small expence the best Mineral Waters . . . together with a Description of some new Eudiometers . . . , in a letter to the Rev. Dr. J. Priestley, 8°, London, 1777 (BM T. 312. (5.)); 2 ed., revised, 1779 (BM 7942. f. 21); 3 ed., enlarged by the author, the title now has 'two new Eudiometers' and concludes 'with an Examin of the Strictures of . . . T. Cavallo . . . upon these Eudiometers', London, 1783 (pp. viii, 80, and plate; BM 1034. h. 26. (8.), autographed copy); German tr. by Wenzel, Dresden, 1780; Gmelin, (1), iii, 331; Poggendorff, (1), ii, 10 (dates 1 ed. 1770 in error). Magellan also published:

---

[1] Macbride, *Experimental Essays*, 1764, 169 f.
[2] *Experiments and Observations*, London, 1773.
[3] *Phil. Trans.*, 1775, lxv, 59.   [4] IV, ii, 1776, 263–303.   [5] *Ib.*, 297.   [6] VI, i, 55.

Description et usage des nouveaux baromètres, 4°, London, 1779; Essai sur la Nouvelle Théorie du Feu élémentaire et de la Chaleur des Corps, 4°, London, 1780, containing the first table of specific heats (see p. 156).

A work on the medicinal uses of fixed air was published by Matthew Dobson.[1] Priestley[2] expelled fixed air from mineral waters by boiling and collected it over mercury. Air bubbling from Bath water contained $\frac{1}{20}$ vol. of fixed air and the rest was 'almost perfectly noxious' [nitrogen]. He recommended impregnating 'flat' beer with fixed air,[3] and artificial carbon dioxide is now much used for this purpose.

Priestley's first extensive paper on gases, 'Observations on Different Kinds of Air',[4] was read in March 1772, but additions were made to it until November.[5] On 30 November 1773 he was awarded a Copley Medal by the Royal Society for this work and that on electricity, and a discourse was delivered by the president, Sir John Pringle:

Sir John Pringle, Six Discourses delivered by Sir John Pringle, Bart. when President of the Royal Society; on occasion of Six Annual Assignments of Sir Godfrey Copley's Medal. To which is prefixed the Life of the Author. By Andrew Kippis, D.D. F.R.S. and S.A. London, 1783; 1 f.: A Discourse on the Different Kinds of Air, delivered Nov. 30, 1773; summary in Obs. Phys., 1774, iii, 161; Fourcroy, (2), iii, 387 (ib., 389–414 on apparatus used from Hales to Lavoisier); Gmelin, (1), ii, 730–9.

Pringle mentions Seip, Brownrigg, Black, Cavendish, Priestley, and Lowther (on fire-damp), and the very inadequate historical account given by Priestley in 1774[6] is taken from Pringle; he mentions Van Helmont and Cavendish but not Mayow or Black. He always used the name 'airs' and in his last book[7] he says: 'I saw no occasion for the term gas.'

John Pringle (Stichell, Roxburgh, 10 April 1707–London, 14 (or 18) January 1782), pupil of Boerhaave, army physician, a Unitarian, F.R.S. 1745, President 1772,[8] published memoirs on putrefaction, in which he examined the effects of a large number of substances on the process,[9] and remarks on Hales's ventilators.[10] Priestley,[11] who found that the air of marshes is inferior to common air, thought he had thus confirmed Pringle's theory that intermittent and low fevers are due to moist miasmata.

Priestley used Troy weights: 24 grains = 1 pennyweight (dwt.), 20 dwt. = 1 oz., 12 oz. = 1 lb. His 'ounce measure' is the volume of 1 Troy oz. = 480

[1] A Medical Commentary on Fixed Air, 8°, Chester, 1779; 2 ed. 1785 (by Falconer) with an appendix 'on the use of the solution and fixed Alkaline Salts saturated with fixable air, in the Stone and Gravel'; 3 ed. 1787. John Harrison published The remarkable effects of Fixed Air in Mortifications, 1788.
[2] IV, ii, 222 f.   [3] VI, i, 53.
[4] Phil. Trans., 1772, lxii, 147–267; mostly reprod. in IV, 1774, i, 23–162, but the plate altered; McKie, 1933.
[5] See Rutt, i, 185 (letter to Price, November, 1772); the paper was tr. in Obs. Phys., 1774, i, 292 (and plate), and summarised by Lavoisier, Opuscules Physiques et Chimiques, 1774 (1801), 111–53, and Fourcroy, (2), iii, 397 f.
[6] IV, i, 1–7; a longer account, partly identical with that of 1774, was given later by Priestley, IV, iii, 325; VI, i, 1; claiming his priority in the discovery of acid air (HCl) and alkaline air (NH₃).
[7] XI, 1800, 90; 1803, 118.
[8] Vicq-d'Azyr, 1805, iii, 171, 193; Mrs. Singer, Ann. Sci., 1949, vi, 127; 1950, vi, 229, 248.
[9] Phil. Trans., 1750, xlvi, 480, 525, 550.   [10] Phil. Trans., 1753, xlviii, 42.
[11] Phil. Trans., 1774, lxiv, 90; IV, 1774, i, 195–201; Price, Phil. Trans., 1774, lxiv, 96; Cooper, 1805, 256.

grains of pure water and is 1·898 English or 1·567 contemporary French cubic inches.[1] He says[2] he 'made it a rule, as much as possible, to throw nothing away, if I could make room for it'.

In his account of the apparatus he used in work on gases Priestley says it is 'the apparatus of Dr. Hales, Dr. Brownrigg and Mr. Cavendish, diversified,

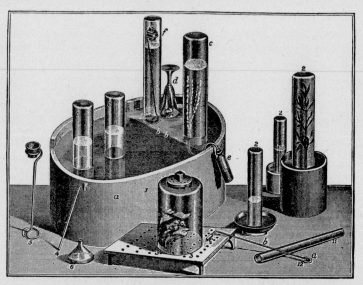

FIG. 23. PRIESTLEY'S PNEUMATIC TROUGH AND OTHER APPARATUS.
(From his *Experiments and Observations on Air*, vol. i, 1774.)

and made a little more simple'. Its successful use, however, requires much practice. He describes a trough (afterwards called a pneumatic trough) with a shelf for collecting gases over water, to some extent anticipated by Brownrigg's (see p. 125), whose trough had a shelf above the water level; Cavendish's trough (see p. 313) had no shelf. Priestley later[3] said the shelf of the trough was 'formed on the plan of that of the Duc de Chaulnes, with a small addition'; the funnels under holes in the shelf were 'an ingenious contrivance of the Duc de Chaulnes'.[4]

The 'beehive shelf' is depicted in Graham's *Elements of Chemistry*,[5] but may be earlier. The flat shelf with a hole, supported from the sides of a rectangular glass trough, is shown in Mitscherlich's *Lehrbuch der Chemie*.[6]

In his earlier experiments, Priestley seems to have used a basin of mercury

[1] IV, 1774, i, Advertisement, p. xxiv.   [2] VI, ii, 137.   [3] V, 1779, I, xxv; VI, i, 13.
[4] Marie Joseph Louis d'Albert d'Ailly, Duc de Chaulnes (Paris; 18 November 1741–after 1789), F.R.S. 1764, published: Mémoire et Expériences Sur l'Air Fixe qui se dégage de la Bière en fermentation, AdS, *Mém. div. Sav.*, 1780, ix, 521–50, and addition 551–62 (expts. at Longchamps brewery made in Sept. 1771; read 13 Dec. 1775; ments. Priestley on fixed air in vat, and Hey q. by Priestley); *Obs. Phys.*, 1777, ix, 287–91; Fourcroy, (2), iii, 479–81; Duc de Chaulnes, *Nouvelle méthode pour saturer d'air fixe, à la fois et en moins d'une minute, vingt-cent ou trente pintes d'eau . . .*, 4°, s.l.e.a. (Paris, 1778), 2 pp. and plate (BN Rz. 2481); preparation of fusible salt of urine (microcosmic salt) and transparent phosphoric acid, *Phil. Trans.*, 1783, lxxiii, 288 (in French).
[5] 1842, 247.   [6] 1831, i, 2, etc.

in which a tube filled with mercury was suspended by strings,[1] but in 1777[2] he describes a mercury trough of wood. He noticed[3] the leakage of air between a glass jar and mercury at different levels inside and out, which was prevented by a layer of water, and he correctly attributed it to imperfect contact. It occurs only with soiled mercury.[4]

FIG. 24. PART OF PRIESTLEY'S LABORATORY.
(From his *Experiments and Observations on Air*, vol. i, 1774, very slightly modified.)

Priestley used leather tubes for conveying gases; india rubber tubing was used by Bergman (see p. 190), and by Ingen Housz,[5] who made it from rubber sheet cut from caoutchouc 'bottles', the fresh edges being pressed together, as was done long afterwards.[6] 'Caoutchouc' was first sent to the Paris Academy in 1736 by de la Condamine, who described it in 1751.[7] Priestley[8] mentions as new its use as a pencil eraser; a ½-in. cube cost 3/–.

Priestley begins his paper of 1772 with an account of his early experiments with fixed air and the impregnation of water with it (the later 'soda water'), and his pamphlet on the artificial Pyrmont water (p. 247). He mentions Bergman's letter to him (see p. 252). He points out that fixed air is evolved in fermentation. It is expelled from solution on freezing. He made the gas by the action of diluted oil of vitriol on chalk. He says[9] Hey found that fixed air does not behave as an acid in changing the colour of syrup of violets, but Bewley[10] found that it changed the colour of litmus or scrapings of radishes, with which Hey[11] agreed, saying that he had later (1773) found that it changed the colour of litmus, fresh juice or syrup of violets, or scrapings of radishes.

[1] IV, 1774, i, item 7, plate II. See Fig. 24.   [2] IV, iii, 1.
[3] V, 1786, iii, 336.   [4] H. B. Dixon, *Chem. News*, 1886, liv, 227.
[5] *Experiments upon Vegetables*, London, 1779, 171.
[6] Faraday, *Chemical Manipulation*, 1842, 209–10.
[7] AdS, 1751, m 319; the specimens were obtained by Fresneau in Brazil.
[8] *A Familiar Introduction to the Theory and Practice of Perspective*, 1770, Pref., xv.
[9] IV, 1774, i, 288.   [10] IV, 1775, ii, 337.   [11] IV, 1777, iii, 383.

William Bewley (1725–83), a surgeon and apothecary in Great Massingham, Norfolk, was an opponent of Lavoisier's views.[1] Hey was a Leeds Surgeon. Priestley[2] says: 'Mr. Bergman of Upsal, who honoured me with a letter upon the subject, calls it the *aërial acid*, and, among other experiments to prove it to be an acid, he says that it changes the blue juice of tournesole into red. This Mr. Hey found to be true, and he moreover discovered that when water tinged blue with . . . tournesole, and then red with fixed air, has been exposed to the open air, it recovers its blue colour again.'

Priestley then[3] deals with 'air in which a candle, or brimstone, has burned out', pointing out that every other combustible he tried (wax or tallow candles, chips of wood, spirit of wine, and ether) except sulphur, when burnt in air, precipitated lime water, and reduced the volume $\frac{1}{15}$ or $\frac{1}{16}$ 'owing to the precipitation of the fixed air'. Hence 'flame disposes the common air to deposit the fixed air it contains'. The residual air is not heavier than common air, and an animal will live in air in which a candle has burnt out. The goodness is not restored by compression, and Priestley disproved Hales's idea that the diminution in volume of air in which combustion had occurred was due to a decrease in elasticity, since the specific gravity of air in which candles or sulphur had burnt was not considerably altered, and even slightly decreased.[4] Keir[5] also said the diminution in bulk of air in a receiver by the combustion of inflammable substances was due to a diminution of elasticity. Priestley found the air was not restored by cold, as the Count de Saluce[6] said it was. Air vitiated by the burning of candles is restored by growing vegetation, viz. a sprig of mint, or growing groundsel, or spinach (see p. 277). Leaves not growing (e.g. fresh cabbage leaf) did not do this, but vitiated the air.

The section on inflammable air[7] contains a repetition of Cavendish's experiments (see p. 312), but Priestley (unlike Cavendish) confused hydrogen with other inflammable airs made by heating 'any vegetable or animal substance whatever', or 'any mineral substance, that is inflammable'. Inflammable air (coal gas) was obtained by heating coal in a gun barrel and collecting it in a bladder or over mercury. On shaking it in a jar over water for a long time, inflammable air is converted into common air (a favourite mistake of Priestley's with most gases). Plants live in it, but it kills animals. Although Priestley supposed it to be 'air united to or loaded with phlogiston', inflammable air (which Cavendish thought was pure phlogiston) was not absorbed by oil of vitriol or nitric acid, but when mixed with nitric acid vapour it is explosive, as if mixed with common air.[8]

'Air infected with animal respiration, or putrefaction' is restored by exposure to growing plants, but not by exposure to light, or by heating, rarefaction or compression. Continued agitation in a trough of water 'never failed to restore any kind of noxious air on which I have tried it'. If a mouse was put

---

[1] *A Treatise on Air: . . . being a full investigation of Mr. Lavoisier's system*, London, 1791 (BM 954. k. 19).
[2] IV, 1774, i, 31.   [3] *Phil. Trans.*, 1772, lxii, 162 f.   [4] IV, 1774, i, 46, 267; 1775, ii, 94.
[5] *A Treatise on the Various Kinds of Permanently Elastic Fluids, or Gases*, 2 ed. 1779, 8.
[6] *Miscellanea Taurinensia*, 1759, i, 3 f. (41); see p. 127.
[7] *Phil. Trans.*, 1772, lxii, 170 f.   [8] *Ib.*, 181.

into a portion of air in which another mouse had been breathing but was still living, the mouse put in died at once. 'Air in which a mixture of brimstone and iron filings has stood'[1] was diminished in volume but was rather lighter than common air and was noxious to animals. He later[2] called this 'noxious air' by the new name 'phlogisticated air', using 'a new application of a term already in use among chymists'. It is 'produced by charging common air with phlogiston'.[3]

Priestley's discovery of *nitrous air*,[4] made on 4 June 1772, was based on an experiment of Hales (see p. 119) with nitric acid and Walton pyrites; Cavendish told Priestley that any kind of pyrites, or metals, would serve, and Priestley does not seem to have noticed that Hales had also used iron filings and aqua fortis.[5] Priestley used brass filings, iron, copper, tin, silver, mercury, bismuth, and nickel; he found that the nitrous air was not evolved with zinc, but was formed from platinum or antimony with aqua regia. The gas formed deep red fumes with air, and when the mixture was made over water 'about one-fifth of the common air, and as much of the nitrous air as is necessary to produce that effect' disappear. He found later[6] that:

if one measure of nitrous air be put to two measures of common air, in a few minutes . . . there will want about one-ninth of the original two measures; and if both the kinds of air be very pure, the diminution will still go on slowly, till in a day or two there will remain only one fifth of the original quantity of common air. . . . I hardly know any experiment that is more adapted to amaze and surprize than this is, which exhibits a quantity of air, which, as it were, devours a quantity of another kind of air half as large as itself, and yet is so far from gaining any addition to its bulk, that it is considerably diminished by it.

Over mercury the diminution was much less, so that water is necessary for it. Lime-water was not in his first experiments made turbid, but Priestley afterwards[7] thought he had shown that it was (a position he maintained stubbornly), and 'we have here another evidence of the deposition of fixed air from common air'. He says the diminution 'is peculiar to common air, or *air fit for respiration*; and . . . very nearly, if not exactly, in proportion to its fitness for this purpose; so that by this means the goodness of air may be distinguished much more accurately than it can be done by putting mice, or any other animals, to breathe in it', which 'was a most agreeable discovery to me'.

He disliked experiments on living animals, and when he discovered the test of the purity of air by nitrous air [nitric oxide], he said: 'every person of feeling will rejoice with me in the discovery of *nitrous air*, which supersedes many experiments with the respiration of animals.'[8] He always took pains to keep his mice warm and comfortable, and noticed with surprise that they 'live intirely without water'; during three or four months, although offered water, 'they would never taste it.'[9]

Priestley's method of testing the 'goodness' of air was to mix equal volumes of atmospheric air and nitrous air in a wide jar over water and, after contraction ceased, to transfer the gas remaining to a narrow graduated tube. A small phial,

[1] *Ib.*, 207.   [2] IV, 1774, i, 178.   [3] V, 1781, ii, 330.
[4] *Phil. Trans.*, 1772, lxii, 210.   [5] Hales, *Veg. Staticks*, 1727, 216, 217, 220.
[6] IV, 1774, i, 110–11.   [7] IV, 1774, i, 188.
[8] IV, 1774, i, 73; VI, iii, 258.   [9] IV, 1774, i, 9; VI, i, 17.

called an 'air measurer', of about 1 oz. capacity, was filled with the air, which was transferred to a jar about $1\frac{1}{2}$ in. diam. filled with water. The air measure was filled with nitrous air over water, and the gas emptied into the air in the jar. After standing for about 2 mins. the residual gas was transferred to a glass tube about 2 ft. long and $\frac{1}{3}$ in. wide, graduated in terms of the air measure and divided into tenth and hundredth parts. After adjusting the water levels, the volume of gas was read off and was called the 'standard of the air'. If 1·36 vols. remained from 1 vol. of air and 1 vol. of nitrous air, the standard was 1·36. For very small quantities, he used a narrow tube for mixing.[1]

He thought he could detect variations in the 'goodness' of various kinds of air, but he later found that 'the difference . . . is generally inconsiderable'; that between Manchester or Birmingham air and 'the very best air in this country [Wiltshire] . . . was very trifling'; and 'air may be very offensive to the nostrils, probably hurtful to the lungs . . . without the phlogiston being so far incorporated with it, as to be discoverable by the mixture of nitrous air'.[2]

The air from a crowded room, however, was 'much contaminated'; the goodness was 1·31, that of fresh air being 1·25 and that of air breathed till it just extinguished a candle 1·43.[3] Other observers found air from Bristol Hotwell water, and that expelled from sea water by boiling, rather better than common air: Becket found that 3 vols. of nitric oxide added to 5 vols. of common air over water left 5 vols. of gas.[4] Sigaud de la Fond[5] independently found that air from crowded rooms, hospitals, etc., differed little, if at all, in goodness from fresh air.

Priestley[6] said: 'I have frequently found air expelled from water to be much better than common air' (Scheele had previously found this, p. 226), and 'water imbibes dephlogisticated air from the atmosphere'. Many spring waters give fixed air only on long boiling, including even a petrifying spring, and Priestley recognised that this was due to the fixed air being united to the content of calcareous earth. Experiments with the nitric oxide eudiometer gave very inaccurate results until the careful investigations of Cavendish (see p. 321). Davidson had found that the air of Martinique in an epidemic of yellow fever contained 67 per cent. of oxygen,[7] confirming Mitchill's theory that dephlogisticated air (oxygen) was the cause of this and other fevers.

Nitrous air standing over a mixture of iron filings and brimstone made into a paste with water diminished to a quarter of its volume, and then smelt like common air in which the same mixture had stood (see p. 259). Nitrous air had practically the same density as common air. The antiseptic properties of nitrous air were later found to be less satisfactory than was thought in 1772, the flesh exposed to it having a peculiar taste and smell, although 'Mr. Magellan . . . had not so bad an opinion of this piece of cookery as I had'.[8] Priestley at first thought that nitrous air reddened litmus, but he later[9] found that this

---

[1] IV, 1774, i, 20; V, 1779, i, 77, 269 f.
[2] V, i, 269 f. (preface dated 1 March 1779); VI, i, 259; Ingen Housz, *Experiments upon Vegetables*, 1779, pref.
[3] V, i, 280.   [4] *Ib.*, 466 f.
[5] *Essai sur différentes espèces d'air*, 1779, 180 f. (approbation dated 19 January 1779).
[6] V, 1781, ii, 167, 325; VI, i, 56 f.
[7] Gmelin, (1), iii, 829, where other results are given.   [8] V, i, 69.   [9] V, iii, 307.

is not the case if the gas is pure; neither did it then make a cloud with alkaline air (ammonia), as he had thought.[1] Senebier[2] also noticed the white cloud (ammonium nitrate) formed when nitrous air is mixed with *air* and ammonia gas.

Priestley[3] found that 'Air infected with the fumes of burning charcoal' by heating charcoal in a jar of air over water or mercury by a burning glass, precipitated lime water. The section on 'The effect of the Calcination of Metals, and of the Effluvia of Paint made with White-Lead and Oil, on Air'[4] describes experiments in which pieces of lead and tin suspended in air in a jar were heated by means of a burning glass so as to make them fume; the effect was to diminish the volume by $\frac{1}{4}$ as a maximum, but lime water did not become turbid, 'the calx immediately seizing the precipitated fixed air', and 'air is, some way or other, diminished in consequence of being highly charged with phlogiston'. (There was, of course, no fixed air produced.) It is not necessary that the air saturated with phlogiston shall be inflammable, since this 'may depend upon some particular mode of combination, or degree of affinity, with which we are not acquainted'.

The 'acid air'[5] later called 'marine acid air',[6] viz. hydrochloric acid gas, was obtained by heating hydrochloric acid, with or without copper, in a phial and was collected over mercury, 'which I never failed to do in any case in which I suspected that air might either be absorbed by water, or be in any other manner affected by it.' He later[7] said: 'this manner of producing air from substances contained in small phials, and receiving the produce in quicksilver, . . . has never failed to strike every person to whom I have shewed it.' The gas extinguished flame, giving it a blue colour, was much heavier than air, was soluble in water, and liquefied ice. It *dissolved* in water and did not merely 'lose its elasticity', since a given quantity of water in a tube over mercury will take up only a given volume of the acid air and then becomes saturated. This air 'is, in fact, nothing more than the vapour, or fumes, of spirit of salt, which appear to be of such a nature, that they are not liable to be condensed by cold, like the vapour of water, and other fluids, and therefore may be very properly called an *acid air*,'[8] 'or more restrictively, the *marine acid air*.'[9] His curious distinction between a gas 'losing its elasticity' in contact with water, and 'dissolving' in water, is due to a misunderstanding, unconscious or otherwise, of Cavendish's description of an experiment (see p. 315). Priestley later obtained marine acid air by heating common salt with concentrated oil of vitriol.[10] Iron filings were rapidly dissolved by the acid air, half the volume disappearing and leaving half a volume of inflammable air;[11] sulphur slowly gave an inflammable air, burning with a blue flame.[12] Marine acid air displaced nitric acid from nitre and sulphuric acid from alum,[13] which is 'rather extraordinary', since the marine acid 'is reckoned the weakest of all the three mineral acids'.[14]

[1] IV, i, 171; VI, ii, 376.
[2] *Recherches sur l'Influence de la Lumière Solaire pour metamorphoser l'Air fixe en Air pur par la Végétation*, Geneva, 1783, 290.
[3] *Phil. Trans.*, 1772, lxii, 225.   [4] *Ib.*, 228.   [5] *Ib.*, 239; VI, ii, 275.
[6] IV, 1777, iii, 298.   [7] IV, 1775, ii, 5.   [8] IV, 1774, i, 147.
[9] VI, ii, 278.   [10] VI, ii, 279.   [11] IV, 1774, i, 149.
[12] *Ib.*, 152.   [13] IV, 1774, i, 153; VI, ii, 291.   [14] VI, ii, 318.

Priestley noticed (1772) that on heating concentrated hydrochloric acid with copper filings inflammable air (hydrogen) is slowly evolved; he later obtained hydrogen by the action of radical vinegar (glacial acetic acid) on iron or zinc,[1] or by the action of infusion of galls, or powdered galls and water, on iron filings.[2]

In some 'miscellaneous observations',[3] a quantity of air was made by heating saltpetre, and in it 'a candle burned just as in common air', or 'not only burned, but the flame was increased, and something was heard like a hissing, similar to the decrepitation of nitre in an open fire'. Priestley, as he later recognised,[4] had here obtained dephlogisticated air (oxygen) before November, 1772.

The Discovery of Oxygen

In 1775 Priestley wrote letters dated 15 March (to Sir John Pringle), 1 April (to Dr. Price), and 24 May (to Sir John Pringle, misdated 25 May in the printed paper), which were later printed in the *Philosophical Transactions*[5] as 'An Account of further Discoveries in Air', dealing with dephlogisticated air, vitriolic acid air (sulphur dioxide), nitrous air, and vegetable acid air (acetic acid vapour). The first letter, on dephlogisticated air, was read to the Royal Society on 23 March. The letter was reprinted, with additions, in Priestley's book,[6] from which the following account is taken.

After some general remarks, Priestley says that although the elementary nature of air was a philosophical maxim, he was in the course of his experiments 'soon satisfied that atmospherical air is not an unalterable thing', or an element, 'but a composition.' He then describes his famous experiment, made on Monday, 1 August 1774, at Calne. There has been an astonishing amount of discussion as to where Priestley made this experiment, yet he says himself that it was made at Calne.[7] The day has also often been said to have been Sunday. Priestley also begins by saying that his experiments 'furnish a very striking illustration of the truth of a remark . . . which can hardly be too often repeated . . . viz. that more is owing to what we call chance . . . than to any proper design, or preconceived theory in this business'; and (as if he foresaw the attempts which have been made to have us believe that Priestley was really a very systematic experimenter) he repeated in 1779[8] that he had experimented 'without any particular view, except that of extracting air from a variety of substances by means of a burning lens in quicksilver, which was then a new process with me, and which I was very fond of'. He says[9] that when he began these experiments:

'I was so far from having formed any hypothesis that led to the discoveries I made in pursuing them, that they would have appeared very improbable to me had I been

[1] IV, 1777, iii, 256; VI, i, 183.   [2] VI, i, 193 f.
[3] *Phil. Trans.*, 1772, lxii, 244; IV, 1774, i, 155.   [4] V, 1779, i, 192.
[5] *Phil. Trans.*, 1775, lxv, 384; for dates see Meldrum, (1), 1930, 49 f.; Hartog, *Nature*, 1933, cxxxii, 25; *id.*, (5), 31.
[6] IV, 1775, ii, 29–103; dedication dated Nov. 1775.
[7] IV, 1775, ii, 34; VI, 1790, ii, 106; *Philosophical Empiricism*, 1775, 48; Caven, *Nature*, 1933, cxxxii, 25; Hartog, *ib.*, 1933, cxxxii, 25; *id.*, (3); *id.*, (5); McKie, 1933; Holt, 1931, 69 f., 101: 'in the laboratory at Bowood, the small room at the end of the long library', but Priestley had his own house at Calne.
[8] V, i, 195.   [9] IV, ii, 29.

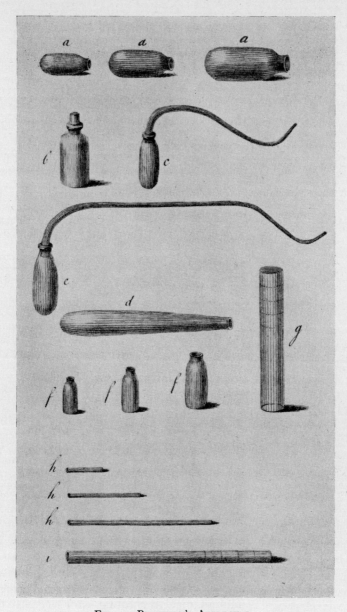

FIG. 25. PRIESTLEY'S APPARATUS.

told of them; and when the decisive facts did at length obtrude themselves upon my notice, it was very slowly, and with great hesitation, that I yielded to the evidence of my senses.'

Priestley's account of the experiment[1] is as follows:

'. . . having procured a lens of twelve inches diameter, and twenty inches focal distance, I proceeded with great alacrity to examine, by the help of it, what kind of air a great variety of substances, natural and factitious, would yield, putting them into the vessels

[1] IV, 1775, ii, 33; VI, ii, 102; ACR, vii.

represented fig. *a* (Fig. 25), which I filled with quicksilver, and kept inverted in a bason of the same. Mr. Warltire, a good chymist, and lecturer in natural philosophy, happening to be at that time in Calne, I . . . was furnished by him with many substances, which I could not otherwise have procured.'

The large lens was given to Priestley by the London instrument maker Parker and was destroyed in the Birmingham riot in 1791.[1] The statue of Priestley in Leeds (Fig. 26) shows a rather smaller lens.

'With this apparatus, after a variety of other experiments, . . . on the 1st of August, 1774, I endeavoured to extract air from *mercurius calcinatus per se*; and I presently found that, by means of this lens, air was expelled from it very readily. Having got about three or four times as much as the bulk of my materials, I admitted water to it, and found that it was not imbibed by it. But what surprized me more than I can well express, was, that a candle burned in this air with a remarkably vigorous flame, very much like that enlarged flame with which a candle burns in nitrous air, exposed to iron or liver of sulphur; but . . . as I knew no nitrous acid was used in the preparation of *mercurius calcinatus*, I was utterly at a loss how to account for it.'[2]
'In this case, also, though I did not give sufficient attention to the circumstance at that time, the flame of the candle, besides being larger, burned with more splendor and heat than in that species of nitrous air; and a piece of red-hot wood sparkled in it, exactly like paper dipped in a solution of nitre . . . ; an experiment which I had never thought of trying with nitrous air.'

FIG. 26. STATUE OF
PRIESTLEY IN LEEDS.

He says[3] that since red precipitate made *per se* (by heating mercury in air) gave the same 'air' as that made from mercury and spirit of nitre (nitric acid), he concluded that 'by exposing mercury to a certain degree of heat, when common air has access to it', the mercury 'had collected something of *nitre*, in that state of heat, from the atmosphere'. The first specimen of precipitate *per se* which Priestley used had been obtained from Warltire, who assured Priestley that it was genuine. When he visited Paris in October, Priestley obtained (through Magellan) another specimen from Cadet, and found that this gave more air on heating for a longer time than the first specimen. He had in his first experiments obtained the same air from red lead (minium), but part of this air was absorbed by water (probably carbon dioxide, from unchanged lead carbonate in the minium, made by heating white lead). He had then 'no suspicion that the air . . . was even wholesome, so far was I from knowing what it was that I had really found; taking it for granted, that it was nothing more than such kind of air as I had brought nitrous air to be by the process above mentioned',

[1] Bolton, 1892, 40; McKie, *Notes and Records of the Roy. Soc.*, 1956, xii, 114; *Archives*, 1956, ix, 117.
[2] The word 'surprize' occurs at least six times in about 12 pages, once 'utter astonishment'.
[3] *Ib.*, 35.

in which a candle would sometimes burn with an enlarged flame, 'and yet remain perfectly noxious.'[1]

On 19 November 1774 he found that the new air still supported combustion strongly even after agitation with water, whereas 'modified nitrous air' (nitrous oxide mixed with some nitric oxide) is so deprived of its power of supporting combustion.[2] It was unchanged when mixed with common air, and hence the residue was not nitrous air. On 1 March 1775 he found that on mixing with nitrous air over water it became red and 'diminished quite as much as common air'.[3] On 8 March he confined a mouse in 2 oz. measures of the new air and found that, although in common air it would have lived about a quarter of an hour, 'in this new air, however, my mouse lived a full half hour', and on being 'held to the fire, it presently revived and appeared not to have received any harm from the experiment'.[4] The residual air, left after the breathing of the mouse, was also much better than common air, by the test with nitrous air. Priestley says: 'I wish my reader be not quite tired with the frequent repetition of the word *surprize* . . . but I must go on in that style a little longer.' He found that the residue left after mixing the new gas with nitrous air over water still supported the respiration of a mouse perfectly, and, when the mouse was taken out alive, the air remaining was nearly as good as common air.[5]

In his test of common air Priestley added 1 vol. of nitrous air to 1 vol. of common air over water (see p. 253). With the new air he found that 5 vols. of nitrous air were received by 2 vols. 'without any increase of dimensions', and since common air 'takes about one half of its bulk of nitrous air, before it begins to receive any addition to its dimensions from more nitrous air', whilst the new air takes four or even five half-measures, 'I conclude that it was between four and five times as good as common air.' With air made from red lead he thought nearly six half-volumes of nitrous air could be added: 'I have since procured the air better than this, even between five and six times as good as the best common air that I have ever met with.' But when he reprinted this part in 1790[6] he says 'nearly three measures and a half [of nitrous air] saturated it', i.e. it was nearly 7 times as good as common air. This was too large a figure, 5 being correct. The new air, 'being capable of taking more phlogiston from nitrous air, it therefore originally contains less of this principle, my next enquiry was, by what means it comes to be so pure, or philosophically speaking, to be so much *dephlogisticated*.'[7] This is the origin of his name 'dephlogisticated air' for oxygen gas.

Priestley, in the preface,[8] says: 'I even think that I may flatter myself . . . that there is no history of experiments more truly ingenuous than mine, and especially the Section on the discovery of dephlogisticated air.' The description he gives of his discovery of oxygen is admirable; every step is clearly recorded. He also said:[9]

[1] *Ib.*, 37.   [2] *Ib.*, 39; see IV, 1774, i, 118, 189, 215; 1775, ii, 175.   [3] *Ib.*, 40.
[4] *Ib.*, 44.   [5] *Ib.*, 46.   [6] VI, ii, 119, 121.   [7] IV, 48-9.
[8] IV, II, ix; his prefaces are largely theological, moral, and political, and were curtailed in the French translations.
[9] IV, 1775, II, x.

'I am not conscious to myself of having concealed the least hint that was suggested to me by any person whatever, any kind of assistance that has been given me, or any views or hypotheses by which the experiments were directed, whether they were verified by the result or not.'

This is an important statement, showing that Priestley's discovery was entirely original as far as he was concerned.

In confusing oxygen with nitrous oxide until March 1775, Priestley overlooked two important differences between the two gases which he had then discovered, viz. (1) that nitrous oxide is appreciably soluble in water, whereas he says the new gas was not, and (2) the difference between the dazzling combustion in oxygen and the peculiar flame of a candle burning in nitrous oxide, which he had described rather minutely in 1774, when he says that treatment of nitrous air (nitric oxide) with iron 'makes it not only to admit a candle to burn in it, but enables it to burn with an enlarged flame, by another flame (extending every where to an equal distance from that of the candle, and often plainly distinguishable from it) adhering to it', and this property is removed by agitation with water.[1] On 19 November 1774 Priestley had shown that the air obtained from red precipitate *per se* obtained from Cadet, made without nitric acid, on repeated agitation with water still supported the combustion of a candle with a strong flame, and hence was not diminished nitrous air.[2] The third test distinguishing nitrous oxide from oxygen, viz. that nitrous oxide is not acted upon by nitric oxide whereas oxygen forms a red gas at once soluble in water, Priestley did not make until 1 March 1775, after his return from Paris. He says himself that he was unaware of the real nature of the new gas until this date,[3] but it is important to notice that by its 'real nature' he meant his 'discovery' that the gas was a compound of spirit of nitre (nitric acid) and earth. On 6 April he wrote: 'I have now discovered an air five or six times as good as common air',[4] saying that he had 'got it first from *mercurius calcinatus per se*, red lead, &c.; and now, from many substances, as quick-lime (and others that contain little phlogiston,) and spirit of nitre, and by a train of experiments demonstrate that the basis of our atmosphere is spirit of nitre. Nothing I ever did has surprized me more, or is more satisfactory'.

Priestley obtained dephlogisticated air by heating red lead which had been moistened with nitric acid and dried (which would contain lead nitrate), but not from red lead similarly treated with sulphuric and hydrochloric acids,[5] which seemed to confirm his idea. He says:[6] 'the same kind of air is produced by moistening with the spirit of nitre [nitric acid] any kind of earth that is free from phlogiston' and heating, and hence 'there remained no doubt in my mind but that *atmospherical air*, or the thing that we breathe, *consists of the nitrous acid and earth*, with so much phlogiston as is necessary to its elasticity; and likewise so much more as is required to bring it from its state of perfect purity to the mean condition in which we find it'.

As 'earths' he used flowers of zinc, chalk, marble, quicklime, slaked lime, magnesia, pipeclay, flint, potash, coal ash, and mica (mostly obtained from

[1] IV, 1774, i, 216; VI, ii, 55.   [2] IV, 1775, ii, 39.   [3] IV, 1775, ii, 40.
[4] Rutt, i, 268.   [5] IV, ii, 52 f.   [6] *Ib.*, 54.

Dr. Bryan Higgins), concluding that spirit of nitre and earth constitute respirable air.[1] He thought that by repeatedly moistening with nitric acid, all the earth would be exhausted. His hypothesis would suit 'exceedingly well' the generation and detonation of nitre. He[2] gives some 'processes for the production of dephlogisticated air', in which he mentions that sedative salt [boric acid] and slightly calcined Roman vitriol [copper sulphate] gave some dephlogisticated air when heated alone,[3] and he recalls that he had obtained it in 1772 by heating saltpetre;[4] he found that 'salt-petre, heated in a glass vessel, yields very pure dephlogisticated air; its own earth, and the spirit of nitre which it contains, being capable, by heat, of forming that kind of union of those two principles which the constitution of that air requires'.[5] In the experiments 'the greatest care should be taken to keep the instruments as clear as possible from all phlogistic matter, which is the very bane of purity with respect to air, they being exactly plus and minus to each other'.[6] Dephlogisticated air is produced 'from all kinds of earth mixed with spirit of nitre, only that a greater quantity of air is produced from some than from others; the advantage in this respect being on the side of the metallic and calcareous earths'.[7]

In 1777 he emphasised the 'fact' that the 'purest air' is obtained by distilling an earth with nitric acid, or by heating the residue from the evaporation of a solution of a metal in nitric acid, and he proceeds to determine the 'quantity of spirit of nitre in dephlogisticated air' by heating red lead, etc., with nitric acid.[8] He still thought that nitric acid is converted into fixed air by distilling it with earth such as wood ashes, which furnish phlogiston. Actually, of course, it was liberated by the action of an acid on a carbonate in the earth. Priestley's poor chemical knowledge shows up here. He says the purest air is a compound of 'spirit of nitre and earth . . . besides the phlogiston it may contain'.[9]

Priestley suggested that dephlogisticated air could be mixed with air 'in a room in which much company should be confined' either by bringing it 'into the room in casks' or generating it in an adjoining laboratory;[10] also its use in blowing fires, and his friend Michell 'observed that possibly platina might be melted by it'. Priestley suggested its use in medicine in diseases of the lungs; for normal respiration 'we might, as may be said, *live out too fast*' in it, and 'the air which nature has provided for us is as good as we deserve'.[11] After breathing it, he says, 'I fancied that my breast felt peculiarly light and easy for some time afterwards. Who can tell but that, in time, this pure air may become a fashionable article in luxury. Hitherto only two mice and myself have had the privilege of breathing it.'[12] Priestley later made oxygen in large quantities by heating nitre in a Wedgwood's earthenware retort.[13]

Harcourt,[14] Rodwell,[15] and Hartog[16] dated Priestley's 'effective' discovery of oxygen as March 1775, when he tested it with nitric oxide and by the respiration of a mouse and realised that it was much 'better' than common air. On 1 August 1774 Priestley had described the preparation of oxygen and

[1] *Ib.*, 55 f.   [2] *Ib.*, 62–90.   [3] *Ib.*, 86.   [4] IV, 1774, i, 155; 1775, ii, 87.
[5] IV, 1775, ii, 88.   [6] *Ib.*, 59.   [7] *Ib.*, 85.   [8] IV, 1777, iii, xxix, 5, 28, 41, 85.
[9] *Ib.*, 236.   [10] *Ib.*, 98.   [11] *Ib.*, 101.   [12] *Ib.*, 102.
[13] VI, 1790, ii, 173.   [14] *Phil. Mag.*, 1846, xxviii, 498.   [15] See p. 239   [16] (3), (5).

distinguished it correctly by two reactions, the flame test and the sparing solubility in water, from nitrous oxide. He said in 1775:[1]

'In this case, also, though I did not give sufficient attention to the circumstance at that time [1 August 1774], the flame of the candle, besides being larger, burned with more splendor and heat than in that species of nitrous air; and a piece of red-hot wood sparkled in it, exactly like paper dipped in a solution of nitre, and it consumed very fast; an experiment which I had never thought of trying with nitrous air.'

Priestley's later views on the nature of dephlogisticated air varied. In 1779[2] he thought it contained an earth and sulphuric, nitric, or some other acid; in 1786[3] that it was a compound of nitric acid and heat, or as Watt had led him to think, 'one of the constituent parts of water, combined with the element of heat', or as might be suggested 'to amuse us', 'to consist of a simple substance ... with the addition at least of the principle of heat', which is Lavoisier's theory; in this case: 'the only kind of air, that is now thought to be properly elementary and to consist of a simple substance, is dephlogisticated air.'[4]

In 1779[5] also, he thought that dephlogisticated air is a compound of earth and vitriolic (sulphuric) acid, since Landriani told him it is formed by heating turbith mineral (basic mercuric sulphate), and Priestley obtained it by heating green copperas (ferrous sulphate) and other vitriolic salts in small retorts. He also obtained it by heating manganese [dioxide].[6] The earth of iron may constitute the bulk of the atmosphere and account for the magnetism of the Earth.[7] This earth, however, might be 'a truly *primitive earth*, or an *earthy principle* common to all earths and all metallic calces whatever'.[8] Yet[9] it was 'an acid principle that is common to the vitriolic and nitrous acids' which combined with earth to form dephlogisticated air. In his book on Bryan Higgins[10] Priestley says: 'It is to be wished ... that you would prove ... the absolute inconvertibility of what you call *elements* into each other ... especially that *earth* is not convertible into *air*, as I assert, and you deny.'

Priestley says he at first considered that common air consisted of marine [hydrochloric] acid air and phlogiston, since:

the union of this acid vapour and phlogiston made inflammable air; and inflammable air by agitation in water, ceases to be inflammable, and becomes respirable ...[11] though I could never make it quite so good as common air. ... Upon this, which no person can say was an improbable supposition, was founded my conjecture, of volcanos having given birth to the atmosphere of this planet, supplying it with a permanent air, first inflammable, then deprived of its inflammability by agitation in water, and farther purified by vegetation.

It is not easy to extract from his conflicting statements Priestley's considered views (if he had any) on the nature of oxygen and nitrogen; Thomson[12] says: 'Common air he considered as a compound of oxygen and phlogiston. Oxygen, in his opinion, was air quite free from phlogiston, or air in a simple

[1] IV, ii, 35.   [2] V, i, 198, 260.   [3] V, iii, 290.
[4] V, 1786, iii, 290, 402.   [5] V, i, 197 f., 213, 226 f., 236 f.   [6] *Ib*., 203 f.
[7] *Ib*., 225.   [8] V, 1781, ii, 148.   [9] V, 1781, ii, 318.   [10] VII, 1775, 71.
[11] In shaking the jar, the hydrogen escaped and was replaced by common air; this was one of Priestley's favourite mistakes.
[12] (1), ii, 22.

and pure state; while azotic gas [nitrogen] . . . was air saturated with phlogiston. Hence he called oxygen *dephlogisticated* and azote *phlogisticated air*.' The function of air in combustion is to draw phlogiston from the burning body. In 1790, Priestley was still doubtful as to the correct way of regarding the composition of air. Sometimes he seems to regard it as a mixture of dephlogisticated and phlogisticated air,[1] sometimes he speaks of it as becoming 'phlogisticated';[2] at other times[3] he says it is equally possible to suppose that air 'consists of two distinct parts', one removed by substances containing phlogiston and leaving the other, or the whole air is an element and becomes phlogisticated.

Nitrogen

Nitrogen (mephitic air) had been clearly distinguished from fixed air (carbon dioxide) by Cavendish, who communicated the result to Priestley,[4] who reported this in his 1772 paper, but does not give Cavendish's conclusion quite correctly (typical of him). Priestley found[5] that common air phlogisticated by exposure to a moist mixture of brimstone and iron filings, although it contracted in volume, was rather lighter than common air. He said:[6]

In what *manner* air is diminished by phlogiston, independent of the precipitation of any of its constituent parts, is not easy to conceive; unless air thus diminished be heavier than air not diminished, which I did not find to be the case. It deserves, however, to be tried with more attention. That phlogiston should communicate absolute *levity* to the bodies with which it is combined, is a supposition that I am not willing to have recourse to, though it would afford an easy solution of this difficulty.

Since 'the diminution of the air was, in some way or other, the consequence of the air becoming overcharged with phlogiston . . . it might not be amiss to call the air that has been diminished, and made noxious . . . by the common appellation of *phlogisticated air*'. He later[7] said 'the reason why I called this species of air *phlogisticated* was my supposition of its being atmospherical air, affected by phlogiston. But whether this be the case, or the air of the atmosphere consist of two distinct parts, and substances containing phlogiston, attract one of those, viz. the *dephlogisticated*, and leave the other, this other part may still be called *phlogisticated air*'.

In 1775 Priestley weighed some gases in a bladder (which he says is Cavendish's method) containing 55 oz. measures (1 oz. measure is the volume of 1 Troy oz. of water) 'or one pennyweight nine grains of common air', and he gives:

'The bladder, filled with				dwts.	gr.	gr.
phlogisticated air, weighed	-	-	-	7	15	183
nitrous air	-	-	-	-	-	7	16	184
common air	-	-	-	-	-	7	17	185
dephlogisticated air	-	-	-	-	7	19	187'

[1] VI, iii, 378 f., 380: 'the two constituent parts' are perhaps not 'loosely mixed' but 'have some principle of union'.
[2] *Ib.*, iii, 385.   [3] *Ib.*, ii, 188.
[4] Harcourt, *B.A. Rep.*, 1839, 31, 63 f.; *id.*, *Phil. Mag.*, 1846, xxviii, 498; G. Wilson, *Life of Cavendish*, 1851, 28; see p. 318.
[5] *Phil. Trans.*, 1772, lxii, 208.   [6] IV, i, 267.   [7] VI, ii, 188.

so that 'nitrous air [nitric oxide], and air diminished by phlogistic processes [nitrogen], are both rather lighter than common air; and . . . dephlogisticated air appears to be a little heavier than common air'.[1] These are the *total* weights, and if the weight of the bladder in a vacuum, viz. (7 dwt. 17 gr.) — (1 dwt. 9 gr.) = 6 dwt. 8 gr., is subtracted, the weights of 55 oz. measures in grains are: N_2 31, NO 32, air 33, O_2 35, in the ratios 13·52 : 13·96 : 14·4 : 15·27 instead of 14 : 15 : 14·4 : 16. Considering the crude method, the results are quite good.

RUTHERFORD

Nitrogen was independently discovered by Scheele (p. 222) about 1771–2, and in 1772 by Daniel Rutherford (Edinburgh; 3 November 1749–15 November 1819), from 1786 professor of botany in Edinburgh and a pupil of Black. In his M.D. dissertation[2] Rutherford describes experiments in which mice were allowed to breathe in a confined volume of air and the fixed air (carbon dioxide) then removed by caustic potash solution. There was a residue of another noxious air (aer malignus) which killed animals and extinguished flame, but (unlike fixed air) did not precipitate lime water and was not absorbed by caustic alkalis. He says:[3]

Sed aer salubris et purus respiratione animali non modo ex parte fit mephiticus sed et aliam indolis suæ mutationem inde patitur. Postquam enim omnis aer mephiticus [carbon dioxide] ex eo, ope lixivii caustici secretus et abductus fuerit, qui tamen restat [N_2] nullo modo salubrior inde evadit; nam quamvis nullam ex aqua calcis præcipitationem faciat haud minus quam antea et flammam et vitam extinguit.

He seems to have thought it was given off by the lungs in respiration, and says that it is a compound of air and phlogiston:

Ex iisdem etiam deducere licet quod aer ille malignus [N_2] componitur ex aere atmospherico cum phlogisto unito et quasi saturato. Atque idem confirmatur eo, quod aer qui metallorum calcinationi jam inferviit, et phlogiston ab iis abripuit, ejusdem plane fit indolis.[4]

Rutherford found that the same gas is formed by passing air over red-hot charcoal and by burning sulphur and phosphorus in air; the precipitate with lime water in air in which phosphorus has burnt is due to the phosphoric acid formed:[5]

Aer qui per carbones ignitos folle adactus fuit, atque deinde ab omni aere mephitico [carbon dioxide] expurgatus, malignus tamen adhuc reperitur et omnino similis ei qui respiratione inquinatur. Immo ab experimentis patet, hanc solam esse aeris mutati-

[1] IV, ii, 93–4.
[2] *Dissertatio inauguralis de Aere fixo dicto, aut mephitico*, Edinburgh, 1772 (BM); faulty tr. in *Obs. Phys.*, 1774, i, 450; 1774, ii, 85 (copious corrections); partly tr. in Crell, *Neueste Entdeckungen*, 1784, xii, 187; complete tr. by Crum Brown in *J. Chem. Educ.*, 1935, xii, 370; on Rutherford, see Woodward, DNB, 1897, l, 5; W. Walker, 1862, 163; McKie, *Sci. Progr.*, 1934, xxix, 650; Weeks, *Rev. Scient.*, 1934, lxxii, 441 (portr.); Lockhart, *Memoirs of Sir Walter Scott*, 1900, i, 8, 117; iii, 342, 347 (Scott was Rutherford's nephew); Lockhart says Rutherford d. December 1819, a date also given in *Quart. J. Sci.*, 1820, ix, 214. Rutherford's dissertation is dated 12 September 1772, whilst Priestley's paper in *Phil. Trans.*, 1772, was read on 5, 12, 19, and 26 March 1772, and an appendix is dated 29 October 1772. It was, apparently, not printed till after 28 January 1773, this date appearing in a notice at the beginning of the volume.
[3] *Dissert.*, 17; Thomson, (2), 1802, i, 65; *ib.*, 1807, i, 102.
[4] *Dissert.*, 20.   [5] *Dissert.*, 19.

onem quæ inflammationi adscribi potest. Si enim accenditur materies quælibet quæ ex phlogisto et basi fixa atque simplici constat, aer inde natus ne minemam aeris mephitici quantitatem in se continere videtur. Sic aer in quo sulphur aut phosphorus urinæ combustus fuit, licet maxime malignus, calcem tamen ex aqua minime præcipitat. Interdum quidem si ex phosphoro natus fuerit, nubeculam aquæ calcis inducit sed tenuissimam, nec aeri mephitico attribuendam, sed potius acido illi quod in phosphoro inest, et quod, ut experimenta docuerunt, hoc singulari dote pollet.

Rutherford must be regarded as an independent discoverer of nitrogen but he did not give it a distinctive name and regarded it as common air charged with phlogiston.

Priestley on Soluble Gases

Priestley discovered hydrogen chloride gas (*acid air*) in 1772 by collecting it over mercury (see p. 255). In 1773–4[1] he obtained *alkaline air* (ammonia gas) by heating ammonia solution and collecting over mercury:

I procured some volatile spirit of sal ammoniac, and having put it into a thin phial, and heated it with the flame of a candle, I presently found that a great quantity of vapour was discharged from it; and being received in a vessel of quicksilver, standing in a bason of quicksilver, it continued in the form of a transparent and permanent air, not all all condensed by cold.

He also obtained it by heating a mixture of 1 part of sal ammoniac and 3 parts of slaked lime in a small phial or an iron tube. The water also evolved was condensed in a small vessel interposed between the apparatus and the mercury trough (*d*, 8, Fig. 24). The alkaline air was soluble in water, $1\frac{1}{4}$ grains of water taking up $\frac{1}{2}$ grain of gas, the saturated solution being more concentrated than ordinary 'spirit of sal ammoniac'. On mixing the gas with acid air (hydrogen chloride, discovered in 1772): 'a beautiful white cloud was formed . . . the quantity of air began to diminish, and . . . there appeared to be formed a solid white salt, which was found to be common sal ammoniac, or the marine acid united to the volatile alkali.'[2]

Fixed air formed a net-work of thin crystals, the 'same thing with the volatile alkalis which chemists get . . . by the distillation of sal ammoniac with fixed alkaline salts'. He later[3] found that 1 vol. of acid air [HCl] 'absorbs' $1\frac{1}{6}$ vols. of alkaline air. (Ammonia gas is difficult to dry.) Alkaline air is soluble in alcohol and ether, but not olive oil; charcoal 'seemed to condense this air upon [its] surface; for it began to diminish immediately'. A candle flame 'went out three or four times successively; but at each time the flame was considerably enlarged, by the addition of another flame, of a pale yellow colour; and at the last time this light flame descended from the top of the vessel to the bottom'. The gas was judged to be heavier than common inflammable air (hydrogen), but lighter than acid air. It liquefied a piece of ice, 'as fast as a hot fire can do it', marine acid air behaving similarly.

Alkaline air exposed to electric sparks increased in volume to three times its bulk of inflammable air $(N_2 + 3H_2)$,[4] an effect he afterwards produced by heat.[5] By heating massicot (lead monoxide) in 3 oz. measures of alkaline air it gave 1 oz. measure of phlogisticated air (nitrogen), but 100 oz. measures of alkaline air

[1] IV, 1774, i, 163–77; VI, ii, 368.   [2] IV, i, 170.   [3] IV, 1777, iii, 294; VI, ii, 387.
[4] IV, 1775, ii, 239 (qualitative); V, 1781, ii, 220–1; 1786, iii, 12.
[5] V, 1786, iii, 197; VI, ii, 389.

K

'revived' only 352 grains of lead, whilst an equal volume of 'inflammable air from iron' (hydrogen) would have revived 480 grains of lead. Alkaline air is 'resolvable into considerably more than twice its bulk of inflammable air', and hence 100 oz. measures should have revived at least 960 grains of lead, instead of 608 grains.[1] Hence, 'the inflammable air, into which alkaline air is resolvable, is not the same as that, which is procured from iron, and may contain much less phlogiston.' Priestley is unable to draw an obvious conclusion that it is a mixture of the inflammable air from iron and phlogisticated air. He thought the alkaline air absorbed phlogiston from the electric spark and became inflammable air, which is 'a compound of phlogiston and something else'.[2] Bewley[3] objected that 'volatile alkali in itself contains a very large portion of inflammable substance', and asked 'may not the electric spark, in this case, act merely by it's *heat*; and might not dry alkaline air, confined in a tube made red-hot, undergo some such change?' In 1789[4] Priestley showed that ammonia gas and nitric acid vapour are decomposed on passing through heated tubes, but ammonia to a less degree than by electric sparks. Calx of lead (lead oxide) heated in alkaline air is reduced to lead and a large residue ($3\frac{1}{2}$ oz. measures from $5\frac{1}{2}$ oz. measures of alkaline air) of phlogisticated air (nitrogen) is formed.[5] Alkaline air did not act on bright copper.[6]

Vitriolic acid air (sulphur dioxide) was obtained on 26 November 1774[7] mixed with fixed air by heating oil of vitriol with a little olive oil (at the suggestion of Lane) or charcoal, and collecting over mercury. By heating oil of vitriol in a small phial with a ground-in delivery tube (Fig. 25 *c*) with two candles, no air was evolved. On taking away the candles, the mercury was drawn in from the trough, 'a prodigious quantity of air was generated,' the apparatus broke, and 'part of the hot acid being spilled upon my hand, burned it terribly, so that the effect of it is visible to this day'. Priestley then heated mercury with the acid and collected the gas evolved over mercury. Copper and silver gave the same result; with iron and zinc some inflammable air was also evolved with the vitriolic acid air; gold and platinum gave no gas. Vitriolic acid air dissolved in water and ether and was absorbed by charcoal. It liquefied camphor, which was reprecipitated by water. The gas extinguished a candle, 'was found to be heavier than common air' and not liquefied by cold, which is 'a sufficiently proper criterion to distinguish *air* from *vapour* . . . the difference between them being in *degree* rather than in *kind*'. When mixed with alkaline air (ammonia) a white cloud was formed and 'the quicksilver rose almost to the top of the receiver', forming a 'vitriolic sal ammoniac' which was not examined; 1 vol. of vitriolic acid air 'saturates' 2 vols. of alkaline air.[8] On letting a mixture of vitriolic acid air and common air stand for two days and then adding water, 'the common air which remained appeared, by the test of nitrous air, to be considerably injured.'

[1] V, 1786, iii, 189; VI, ii, 396.   [2] V, 1781, ii, 218.
[3] *Ib.*, 385.   [4] *Phil. Trans.*, 1789, lxxix, 289.
[5] *Phil. Trans.*, 1783, lxxiii, 398 (405–6); read 26 June 1783; V, 1786, iii, 12 f.
[6] IV, ii, 232.   [7] IV, 1775, ii, 1–22; V, 1781, ii, 319.
[8] IV, 1777, iii, 292; V, 1781, ii, 347; VI, ii, 387 (the product would be ammonium amido-sulphite, $SO_2 + 2NH_3 = NH_4 . SO_2 . NH_2$).

Priestley regarded the gas as vitriolic acid 'divested of the water with which it is usually combined', although in another place he says 'some metals will part with their phlogiston to hot oil of vitriol, and thereby convert it into a permanent elastic air'. The gas obtained with charcoal is only partly soluble in water and the residue is fixed air, since it made lime water turbid. A saturated solution of vitriolic acid air when warmed with zinc filings, evolved inflammable air.[1] The *vegetable acid air*[2] he afterwards said was not a proper air; perhaps it was merely acetic acid vapour.

The *fluor acid air* (silicon fluoride) was (as Priestley says)[3] previously obtained by Scheele (p. 214). Priestley thought that 'the fluor acid' is 'the acid of vitriol, charged with so much phlogiston as is necessary to its taking the form of air, and also with much of the earthy matter of the spar'. He heated Derbyshire spar (calcium fluoride) and oil of vitriol in a glass vessel and collected the gas over mercury. He passed it through mercury covered with water and noticed that the bubbles rising through the water were covered with a film like 'a piece of thin white gauze', the experiment being so striking that, he says: 'I have met with few persons who are soon weary of looking at it; and some could sit by it almost a whole hour and be agreeably amused all the time.'[4] The water became gelatinous and very acid. The gas (silicon fluoride) extinguished flame. On mixing it with alkaline air (ammonia) a white solid formed, not soluble in water, being 'the stony substance only which had been held in solution in the acid air'. The gas dissolved in spirit of wine and ether without forming a precipitate. From a very concentrated solution of the gas, pressed from the precipitate (gelatinous silica), Priestley obtained on heating 'a great plenty of air; which by every test that I could think of applying, appeared to have the very same properties with the vitriolic acid air (sulphur dioxide)' and was absorbed by water without forming a crust. It is hard to think what Priestley could have been doing here, or in the experiment when he obtained fluor acid air from Canton's phosphorus (calcium sulphide) and oil of vitriol.[5] He later[6] rather reluctantly concluded that fluor acid air is perhaps different from vitriolic acid air. One volume of fluor acid air 'saturates' 2 vols. of alkaline air (ammonia).[7]

Priestley determined the volumes of alkaline air (ammonia) absorbed by 1 vol. of different acid airs to be:[8]

fluor acid air	$1\frac{19}{20}$	marine acid air	$1\frac{1}{6}$
vitriolic acid air	2	fixed air	$1\frac{6}{7}$

He says he did not allow for the 'weight of quicksilver in the jar above the level of the quicksilver without the jar', since to level the mercury he would have needed a deeper vessel. He does not seem to have thought of Boyle's law. W. Henry (1832) pointed out that these results, and his discoveries that 1 vol. of dephlogisticated air combines with about 2 vols. of nitrous air, and 1 vol.

[1] IV, 1777, iii, 273; VI, 1790, ii, 309. [2] IV, 1775, ii, 23, 324 f.; V, 1779, i, 448.
[3] IV, 1775, ii, 187–212 (before November 1775); VI, 1790, ii, 339.
[4] IV, 1775, ii, 193. [5] IV, 1775, ii, 212.
[6] IV, 1777, iii, 285, 360.
[7] IV, 1777, iii, 292; VI, ii, 385. [8] IV, iii, 292; VI, ii, 38.

of alkaline air gives 3 vols. of inflammable air, could have led Priestley to deduce Gay-Lussac's law of gaseous volumes.

The Nature of Phlogiston

In 1774[1] Priestley concluded that:

'the electric light [the electric spark] comes from the electric matter itself; and this being a modification of phlogiston, it is probable that *all light* is a modification of phlogiston also. Indeed, since no other substances besides such as contain phlogiston are capable of ignition, and consequently of becoming luminous, it was on this account pretty evident . . . that light and phlogiston are the same thing, in different forms or states.' Heat, however, 'is a state into which the parts of bodies are thrown by their action and reaction with respect to one another; and probably (as the English philosophers in general have supposed) the heated state of bodies may consist of a subtle vibratory motion of their parts.'

The theory that phlogiston is the matter of light was afterwards held by Macquer (see p. 85) and Priestley is in advance of Lavoisier (see p. 421) in his theory of heat. In 1783, however,[2] Priestley had adopted Cavendish's and Kirwan's theory that phlogiston is identical with inflammable air (hydrogen). He says it was thought that phlogiston 'could not be exhibited except in combination with other substances, and could not be made to assume separately either a fluid or solid form'. Some thought that phlogiston, so far from adding to the weight of bodies, made them lighter or is 'the principle of levity', an opinion that had great patrons. Lavoisier and others thought:

'the whole doctrine of phlogiston is founded on mistake, and that in all cases in which it was thought that bodies parted with the principle of phlogiston, they in fact lost nothing, but on the contrary acquired something, in most cases an addition of some kind of air, . . . and that the calx is produced not by the loss of phlogiston, or of any thing else, but by the acquisition of air. The arguments in favour of this opinion, especially those which are drawn from the experiments of Mr. Lavoisier made on mercury, are so specious, that I own I was myself much inclined to adopt it. My friend Mr. Kirwan, indeed, always held that phlogiston was the same thing with inflammable air.'

In March 1782 Priestley[3] investigated the reduction of calces of metals when heated in inflammable air (hydrogen) confined over water or mercury in a bell-jar, the calx being supported in a vertical spoon and heated by the sun's rays focused on it by a burning glass. By using red lead he obtained metallic lead and managed to cause the calx to absorb practically all the inflammable air. Since lead = calx + phlogiston, it would seem that inflammable air is identical with phlogiston. Priestley thought the metal should have weighed more than the calx, but as this was never the case he concluded that the loss in weight was due to the sublimation of some of the calx. He says:[4]

For seeing the metal to be actually revived, and that in considerable quantity, at the same time that the air was diminished, I could not doubt but that the calx was actually imbibing something from the air; and from its effects in making the calx into metal, it could be no other than that to which chemists had unanimously given the name of phlogiston.[5]

[1] IV, i, 280–81.
[2] *Phil. Trans.*, 1783, lxxiii, 398 (read 26 June 1783); V, 1786, iii, 1; VI, i, 248; letter to Wedgwood in Bolton, 1892, 33, 35.
[3] Letter to Wedgwood in Bolton, 1892, 33, 35.   [4] VI, i, 248 f., 276.   [5] *Ib.*, 251–2.

He found that 1 oz. of lead was revived by 108 oz. measures of inflammable air, and 1 oz. of tin by 377 oz. measures. But 1 oz. measure $= 1 \cdot 89$ cu. in., hence 108 oz. measures $= 204 \cdot 1$ cu. in. of hydrogen, at the ordinary temperature, weighing 4·4 grains. The correct result for litharge is 4·6 grains; and similarly the 377 oz. measures for the tin oxide correspond with 15·4 grains, the correct result for SnO_2 being 16·3 grains. Priestley's quantitative results, as they usually were, are very good.

Priestley concluded that phlogiston is present in a combined state in metals, just as fixed air is present in chalk, both being expelled again by acids. He repeated the experiment with calx of mercury, the inflammable air being confined over mercury, and observed that 'even though the inflammable air was previously well dried with fixed ammoniac' [calcium chloride], water was formed in 'sufficient quantity'.[1] He thought this water was contained in the gas and is deposited when 'this kind of air is decomposed'. Priestley was very undecided whether the water was contained in the calx or in the inflammable air or both, but the section is headed 'Experiments which prove that Water is a necessary ingredient in inflammable air'.

In 1785[2] Priestley repeated Lavoisier's experiment of decomposing steam by red-hot iron (see p. 445), saying:

I was for a long time of opinion that his conclusion was just, and that the inflammable air was really furnished by the water being decomposed in the process; but though I continued to be of this opinion for some time, the frequent repetition of the experiments, with the light which Mr. Watt's observations threw upon them, satisfied me at length that the inflammable air came from the charcoal or the iron.

In two of many experiments in which steam from water boiled in a glass retort was passed over red-hot iron in a copper or earthenware tube, he found:

with the addition of 267 grains to the quantity of iron and the loss of 336 grains of water, I procured 840 ounce measures of inflammable air; and with the addition of 140 grains to another quantity of iron, and the consumption of 254 grains of water, I got 420 ounce measures of air.

But 840 ounce measures of hydrogen at ordinary temperature weigh 34·3 grains, so that the gain of the iron was $267/34 \cdot 3 = 7 \cdot 78$ times the weight of inflammable air, instead of the correct figure 7·94, so that Priestley's quantitative experiment is better than Lavoisier's (see p. 447).

Priestley says Lavoisier had made 'a very valuable discovery which had escaped me', and it is a pity that Lavoisier could not follow Priestley in clearly giving credit where it was due instead of remaining silent or wrapping up his acknowledgments in such obscure language as to make them useless. Priestley adds that he 'had the assistance of Mr. Watt, who always thought that Mr. Lavoisier's experiments by no means favoured the conclusions that he drew from them'. Hartog[3] thought that, but for Watt, Priestley might have adopted Lavoisier's theory, but Priestley was not so easily diverted from his faith. He had then found that of the gas from steam and 'perfect charcoal . . . made with a very strong heat', $\frac{1}{5}$ was fixed air, 'and of the inflammable part nearly $\frac{1}{3}$ more appeared to be fixed air by decomposition [combustion]'. The confusion of the

---

[1] VI, i, 276.   [2] *Phil. Trans.*, 1785, lxxv, 279; V, iii, 70; VI, i, 282.   [3] (3), repr., 28.

inflammable air from metals and acids (hydrogen) with that from charcoal (carbon monoxide or a mixture of this with hydrogen) was a fruitful source of error at this time, yet Priestley himself was in a position to differentiate between them, which unfortunately he failed to do sufficiently.

In a letter to Wedgwood of 8 November 1784, Priestley says he heated calx of iron (from red-hot iron and steam) with charcoal when, 'instead of yielding water, as we all imagined it would, it yielded a prodigious quantity of inflammable air, but of a peculiar kind, for it is about as heavy as common air, owing, as I found, to its containing a great quantity of fixed air combined with it, so as not to be separated by lime water, but only by decomposition with pure air by the electric spark.' This would be mostly carbon monoxide.[1] In his paper of 1785 Priestley describes a quantitative experiment, obviously made under Lavoisier's influence. He calcined some dry iron turnings in dry oxygen over mercury by means of a burning glass, reducing 7 oz. measures of the oxygen to 0·65 oz. measures, and found 'no more water . . . than I imagined it had not been possible for me to exclude'. The residual gas was still dephlogisticated air with the phlogisticated air it originally contained as impurity. In other experiments, however, he found that $7\frac{1}{2}$ oz. of dephlogisticated air left $\frac{1}{2}$ oz. of which $\frac{1}{5}$ was fixed air, and 'to what circumstance the difference might be owing I cannot tell'. The iron had been converted into iron scale, 'into which it runs in a very intense heat, in an open fire.'

He now heated the iron calx by a burning glass in inflammable air over water and found that it was absorbed, but 'to my surprise . . . the iron had lost weight, instead of gaining any'. The 'iron' [oxide] lost $2\frac{1}{2}$ grains and $7\frac{1}{2}$ oz. of inflammable air disappeared, and as $2\frac{1}{2}$ grains corresponded with 4·1 oz. measures of dephlogisticated air, the ratio of the inflammable and dephlogisticated airs was $7·5 : 4·1 = 1·83$, which was 'very nearly in the proper proportion to saturate each other, when decomposed [sic] by the electric spark, viz. two measures of inflammable air to one of dephlogisticated air'. By working over mercury he found water formed, and 'it then appeared to me very evident that water, with or without fixed air, was the produce of the inflammable air, and the pure air let loose from the iron in this mode of operation; though I was afterwards taught by Mr. Watt to correct this hypothesis, and to account for this result in a different manner'. He collected the water 'by means of a piece of filtering paper' and 'found it to be, as nearly as possible, of the same weight with that which had been lost by the iron' — i.e. to the weight of the oxygen only. The loss in one experiment was 1·5 grains and the weight of water 1·7 grains, 'but perfect accuracy is not to be expected.' Although Hartog points out that the true ratio is 1·6 : 1·8, his suggestion is misleading, since Priestley obviously thought the weights should be equal.

A repetition of Lavoisier's experiments of passing steam over red-hot charcoal or iron, says Priestley, 'satisfied me at length that the inflammable air came principally from the charcoal, or the iron.' Hartog says 'Priestley henceforward displays what seems to us a perverse ingenuity in adapting the phlogiston theory to fit every new fact', and it would be tedious to follow him

[1] G. Wilson, *Life of Cavendish*, 1851, 99.

through this labyrinth of error. He concluded that 'calx of iron consists of the intimate union of the pure earth of iron and of water; and therefore when the same calx, thus saturated with water, is exposed to heat in inflammable air, this air enters into it, destroys the attraction between the water and the earth, and revives the iron, while the water is expelled in its proper form'. When steam is passed over heated iron 'nothing is necessary to be supposed but the entrance of the water, and the expulsion of the phlogiston belonging to the iron, no more phlogiston remaining in it than what the water brought along with it, and which is retained as a constituent part of the water, or of the new compound'.[1]

In 1781[2] Priestley drew up a 'summary view of all the most remarkable facts' which he had discovered up to that date. It was translated by Fourcroy,[3] who showed that many of the 'facts' were incorrect hypotheses.

In 1789[4] Priestley made a quantitative experiment on the calcination of iron in oxygen with the intention of proving that all the fixed air produced did not come from the plumbago in the iron (which, of course, it did). He did not weigh the iron, and *assumed* that 6 parts of iron would give 9 of 'finery cinder' (ferrosoferric oxide). Even in 1803[5] Priestley asserted that no water, or only a 'barely perceptible amount', is formed when mercuric oxide is reduced in inflammable air (he must have used carbon monoxide), and when zinc is calcined by heating in a tube in steam, when inflammable air is formed, the zinc does not increase in weight (which is simply wrong).

Discovery of Carbon Monoxide

Priestley's confusion of various inflammable gases goes back to his earliest work,[6] when he said that inflammable airs from metals and acid, and that formed by dry distillation of vegetable substances, minerals (including coal), and animal matters (including bone), are the same. Inflammable air is 'air united to or loaded with phlogiston', whilst the air which extinguishes flame [nitrogen] is air 'so much overloaded [with phlogiston] as to admit of no more'.[7] The confusion persisted till his last days.

By heating powdered chalk in an iron gun-barrel, Priestley obtained a mixture of equal volumes of fixed air and an air which was 'inflammable, sometimes very weakly, but sometimes pretty highly so'; this, he found 'burns blue, and not at all like that which is produced from iron or any other metal, by means of an acid' — which puzzled him, as he was fairly sure it came from the iron, though 'perhaps this inflammable principle may come from some remains of animals' in the chalk.[8] This would be carbon monoxide. Priestley,[9] however, thought the blue flame was due to admixture with fixed air.

In 1785,[10] 1794,[11] and 1799,[12] by heating charcoal with iron scales ('finery cinder') or carbonate of barytes, all the materials having previously been

[1] V, iii, 107–8.   [2] V, ii, 325–67.   [3] (2), iii, 464–76.
[4] *Phil. Trans.*, 1789, lxxix, 289.   [5] XI, 1803, 18, 55.
[6] *Phil. Trans.*, 1772, lxii, 170 f.; IV, i, 55 f.   [7] IV, i, 65, 68.
[8] *Phil. Trans.*, 1772, lxii, 159; IV, i, 38; ii, 110.   [9] V, 1781, ii, 337.
[10] *Phil. Trans.*, 1785, lxxv, 279; V, iii, 109.   [11] X; repr. 1929, 37.
[12] XI, 1800, 18 f.; 1803, 21 f.; Sect. III.

calcined, and so freed from water, Priestley obtained an inflammable gas which he regarded as the same as 'heavy inflammable air'. He persisted in saying that there is very little difference between the inflammable air from metals and charcoal gas, in spite of Cruickshank's experiments (see p. 273).[1] Priestley, whose views had not altered much since 1772, thought the experiment proved the existence of phlogiston in metals, or the phlogistication of water in the iron scales by the charcoal. He says:[2]

'This experiment seems to be decisive against the hypothesis of Mr. Lavoisier, and others, who say that the inflammable air procured by means of iron and charcoal comes from the water, and who think that by this means they can exclude phlogiston. For, according to them, neither the scales of iron, nor the charcoal, contain phlogiston, or any thing from which inflammable air can be made.'

The French chemists, to explain these experiments, were driven at first to assume that even well-calcined charcoal contains some hydrogen.[3] Priestley's arguments were refuted by John Maclean, originating in Scotland but from 1795 to 1812 professor of mathematics and natural philosophy in New-Jersey College (Princeton), d. 1814, in a pamphlet (1797).[4]

Priestley in his pamphlet (IX, 1796) tried to show that in every case of the diminution of air (by withdrawal of oxygen), phlogiston is emitted, e.g. by the action of iron filings and sulphur (when some hydrogen is formed), heating steel needles in air, when they did not gain in weight but the air was diminished and carbonic acid produced (from carbon in the steel), etc. When mercury is calcined in air it 'imbibed air, without parting with any or very little of its phlogiston' (since it forms mercury again on heating). Priestley's experiments and arguments were demolished in a long experimental paper by Theophilus Lewis Rupp.[5]

Priestley found that 'heavy inflammable air' is about 3 times lighter than common air, whilst 'light inflammable air from metals' (hydrogen) is 10 times lighter.[6] In an 'analysis of the different Kinds of inflammable Air'[7] he says:

'it was, indeed, my first opinion, that inflammable air consists of acid and phlogiston. Afterwards I adopted the opinion of Mr. Kirwan, viz. that it is pure phlogiston in the form of air, but at present I am fully satisfied with the opinion of Mr. Cavendish, that *water* is an essential ingredient in the constitution of this kind of air. It may, indeed, appear extraordinary that since, according to the hypothesis which at present seems to be well established, water itself consists of phlogiston and dephlogisticated air, this water should exist in inflammable air as an essential part of it; . . . no mere difficulty of conceiving how a thing can be, should be admitted as an argument against any conclusion fairly deduced from proper premises.'

Priestley distinguished between inflammable airs 'which burn with what may be called a *lambent flame* [Latin *lambo*, I lick], sometimes blue, sometimes yellow, and sometimes white', and 'another kind' which 'always burns with an *explosion*'. They have different specific gravities, 'the purest kind being about

[1] XI, 1803, 27.
[2] V, 1786, iii, 111 (footnote, not in the paper in *Phil. Trans.*, 1785, lxxv, 279).
[3] Berthollet, *Ann. Chim.*, 1789, iii, 63 (79); Priestley's reply, VI, 1790, iii, 554 f.
[4] X, 1797, repr. 1929, 99 f., 103; see *Isis*, 1927, ix, 165; 1928, x, 179; Edelstein, *Chymia*, 1959, v, 155.
[5] *Manchester Mem.*, 1798, v, 123–62.   [6] V, 1786, iii, 151; VI, i, 205.
[7] V, 1786, iii, 162, 406; VI, i, 308.

ten times lighter than common air, but some of the other kinds not more than twice as light.' He once thought this was due to fixed air, 'so intimately combined . . . as not to be discoverable by lime water' in the heavier airs, since these gave fixed air when exploded with dephlogisticated air, which the 'lightest kind' did not. (Some of the inflammable airs would not explode when sparked with common air.) But, since a greater weight of fixed air is sometimes formed than the weight of the inflammable air, there 'must have been a real generation of it, by an union of the inflammable and dephlogisticated air'.[1] By exploding equal volumes of inflammable air from finery cinder and charcoal [carbon monoxide] and dephlogisticated air he found the 2 vols. gave $1\cdot85$ vols., which by washing with lime water gave $1\cdot2$ vols. ($2CO + O_2 = 2CO_2$).[2]

Inflammable airs made by passing vapours of alcohol and ether through a red-hot tube, and by passing steam over heated sulphur, charcoal, coke, and bone charcoal, and wood gas freed from fixed air, all produced fixed air on explosion with oxygen. Slaked lime heated in an iron gun-barrel gave 'pure inflammable air of the explosive kind' (hydrogen) and no fixed air. Iron turnings heated in fixed air gave inflammable air burning with a lambent blue flame (carbon monoxide), which was formed from the fixed air and the phlogiston in the iron.[3] By heating cream of tartar with oil of vitriol, Priestley obtained at first a mixture of equal volumes of fixed air and an inflammable air 'burning with a lambent blue flame' (carbon monoxide), but later 'two-thirds of it was inflammable'. By heating cream of tartar alone, a similar mixture was evolved.[4]

Priestley said[5] 'there is an astonishing variety in the different kinds of inflammable air, the cause of which is very imperfectly known'. One important distinction was first made clear by Cruickshank.[6] William Cruickshank, Dipl. Roy. Coll. Surgeons (England), was Ordnance Chemist, Lecturer in Chemistry in the Royal Artillery Academy, Woolwich, Surgeon of Artillery, and Surgeon to the Ordnance Medical Department, F.R.S. 1802; he died in Scotland about 1810–11.[7] Cruickshank proved by many experiments that 'heavy inflammable air', which he prepared by passing carbon dioxide over heated iron, is an oxide of carbon and contains no hydrogen. He determined its composition nearly correctly as $8\cdot6$ carbon (instead of $7\cdot9$) and 21 oxygen, and also its density. He called it 'gaseous oxide of carbone', the name 'carbonic oxide' being proposed by Chenevix.[8] Carbon monoxide had been obtained from oxalic acid by Bergman in 1776 (see p. 199) and in the same year by Lassone (see p. 95).

James Woodhouse (Philadelphia; 17 November 1770–4 June 1809), professor of chemistry (1795) in Philadelphia College, published 'An Answer to Dr. J. Priestley's Considerations on the Doctrine of Phlogiston and the

[1] VI, i, 313.   [2] *Ib.*, 314.   [3] *Ib.*, 316–27.   [4] VI, i, 87.   [5] V, iii, 406.
[6] Some Observations on different Hydrocarbons and Combinations of Carbone with Oxygen, &c. . . . In reply to some of Dr. Priestley's late Objections to the New System of Chemistry; *Nicholson's J.*, 1801, v, 1, 201; 1802, ii, 42; *Ann. Chim.*, 1801, xxxix, 319 (abstr.).
[7] Coutts, *Notes and Queries*, 1955, ii, 131; *Ann. Sci.*, 1959 (1961), xv, 121; P. M. Sanderson and F. Kurzer, *Chem. and Ind.*, 1957, 456–60 (bibl.).
[8] *Remarks upon Chemical Nomenclature*, 1802, 94.

Decomposition of Water'.[1] Woodhouse found that fixed air is not formed on
heating mercury oxide in inflammable air (hydrogen), as Priestley had said.[2]
The inflammable air obtained by Priestley from hammer-scale (ferrosoferric
oxide) and charcoal is also formed on heating charcoal with oxides of zinc,
copper, lead, manganese, and bismuth, and these contain oxygen. Adet was
wrong in supposing that the inflammable air is hydrogen contained in the
charcoal (see IX, p. 244). The inflammable air contains carbon. Woodhouse,
however, concluded that the oxides contained water, and that his experiments
in general confirmed Priestley's theory. If hammer-scale is only iron and
oxygen, as Lavoisier said, it must form only carbonic acid and not inflammable
air. If Priestley could show that as much carbonic acid is formed from charcoal and water as from charcoal and metal oxides, the whole antiphlogistic
system would be disproved, but this has not happened.

Woodhouse sent his paper to the Paris Institut and Guyton de Morveau
gave an account of it, which, with an abstract of it, was published in 1801.[3]
Guyton says he had asked Desormes, a demonstrator in the École Polytechnique, to repeat the experiments; at the meeting of the Institut (à la séance
du 6), when Berthollet said his own experiments suggested that charcoal contains hydrogen, Guyton gave a summary of the experiments of Desormes and
Clement, who had shown that the gas from zinc oxide and charcoal detonated
feebly with oxygen, 'et qui en exige une plus grande quantité', no water being
formed.[4] Guyton says Desormes and Clement had found that the inflammable
gas is formed when carbonic acid gas is passed over red-hot charcoal. When
the paper was read the results 'ont été confirmés . . . par la note que lut le
citoyen Fourcroy, d'une expérience toute semblable qu'il avait faites, dans les
mêmes vues avec le cit. Thénart' (sic; Thenard), and Hassenfratz reported that
he had found on passing oxygen over heated charcoal a more or less heavy or
light, more or less combustible, gas was produced.[5]

Guyton then reported that the 'gaz oxide de carbone' is oxidised in the cold
by chlorine in presence of water, forming carbonic acid.[6] Desormes and
Clement[7] were not acquainted with Cruickshank's paper, which had not
then reached Paris,[8] but their results confirmed his. They obtained the gas
by heating zinc oxide with charcoal or graphite, or barium carbonate with
charcoal, and found that it could be exploded with oxygen over oil or mercury
in a eudiometer (it exploded only weakly), giving no water but only carbonic
acid gas, completely absorbed by lime water. An important experiment was

[1] Trans. Amer. Phil. Soc., 1799, iv, 452–75; Nicholson's J., 1802, ii, 150; on Woodhouse, see
Miles, Chymia, 1953, iv, 37 (72); Woodhouse also published 'Experiments and Observations
on the Vegetation of Plants', Nicholson's J., 1802, ii, 150; Miles says he was 'the best chemist
America produced up to the time of Robert Hare'.
[2] Trans. Amer. Phil. Soc., 1799, iv, 382: no water but only fixed air is formed, and he must
have used carbon monoxide.
[3] Ann. Chim., An IX (1801), xxxviii, 271–84.   [4] Ann. Chim., 1801, xxxviii, 285–90.
[5] Ann. Chim., 1801, xxxviii, 285 (288–9).
[6] Ann. Chim., 1801, xxxix, 18–25: Sur la combustion à froid du gaz oxide de carbone; read to
the Institut 6 messidor an 9.
[7] Ann. Chim., 1801, xxxix, 26–64; Sur la rêduction de l'oxide blanc de zinc par le charbon, et
sur le gaz oxide de carbone qui s'en dégage (they spell their names without accents); J. de
l'École Polytechnique, 1802, iv, 322.
[8] Ann. Chim., 1801, xxxix, 319–20.

the production of the gas by passing *dry* carbonic acid gas backwards and forwards over charcoal strongly heated in a porcelain tube. They concluded that the inflammable 'carbonous gas (gaz carboneux)' is a gaseous oxide of carbon (oxide de carbone gaseux) containing less oxygen than carbonic acid gas. Explosion with oxygen in a Volta's eudiometer gave the composition 41·6 carbon and 58·4 oxygen, but they thought the true figures should be 44 carbon and 56 oxygen. The quantitative results of the reduction of zinc oxide by charcoal were in satisfactory agreement (53·1, 46·9, and 52·9, 47·1).

As an average of nine experiments they found that 100 vols. of gaseous oxide of carbon exploded with 34 vols. of oxygen gave 81 vols. of carbonic acid gas. The density was 1·101 gm./lit., and the coefficient of expansion by heat was the same as that of air. They proved by the combustion of charcoal in oxygen that the composition of carbonic acid gas was 71·65 oxygen and 28·35 of carbon, agreeing with Lavoisier's result. Gaseous oxide of carbon is formed by heating wood or gum, also (as Chaussier had reported in 1780) by burning a mixture of 3 parts of saltpetre and 1 of charcoal powder in a closed vessel. It is also formed by burning potassium chlorate with excess of charcoal; by strongly heating barium sulphate and carbonate, and calcium carbonate, with charcoal; and from metallic oxides and charcoal, provided the oxide is not reduced below a red heat. It is quite different in properties from water gas (le gaz hydrogène carboné) formed by passing steam over red-hot charcoal, which is a mixture (un mélange) of hydrogen, carbonic acid gas, and gaseous oxide of carbon; also from the gas formed by passing alcohol vapour through a red-hot tube (which contains hardly any carbonic acid gas). They obtained 'hydrogène carboné' by passing hydrogen over charcoal in a red-hot iron tube seven or eight times.

Gaseous oxide of carbon kills a bird instantly, is unchanged by light, strong heating in a glass tube, or by electric sparks. It burns in air with a blue flame; a mixture with air in a Volta's eudiometer burns on sparking, a flat blue flame running down the tube. It explodes with oxygen, forming only carbonic acid gas. The explosion is much weaker than with hydrogen, and sometimes the mixture can be fired again by a second spark. With excess of oxygen it burns rapidly with a reddish flame. Gaseous oxide of carbon is probably the cause of the poisonous effect of the gas from burning charcoal.

A dry mixture of equal volumes of carbonic acid gas and hydrogen passed through a strongly heated glass tube deposited a mirror (émail) of carbon and formed water and hydrogen (since it burnt with a red flame). Mixed with 4 vols. of chlorine over water and left for 36 hours it disappeared, leaving only a little nitrogen. On passing oxygen over heated charcoal, only carbonic acid is formed; to obtain gaseous oxide of carbon the gas must stand for some time over heated charcoal.

Berthollet[1] still believed that the gas contained hydrogen; it is lighter than carbonic acid gas although it contains more carbon, and is lighter than oxygen, although no known gas is specifically lighter than a constituent (see p. 807).

---

[1] *Ann. Chim.*, 1802, xlii, 282 (288); *Phil. Mag.*, 1802, xiii, 276; *Mém. de l'Inst.*, 1803, iv, 9–324, 325–33; *Mém Soc. Arcueil*, 1809, ii, 68.

It is true that no water is formed on burning the gas, since it combines intimately with the carbonic acid. He later[1] supposed that water gas is not a mixture but an oxycarburetted hydrogen, a compound of carbon, hydrogen, and oxygen.

The Dutch chemists (Deiman, Paets van Troostwijk, Lauwerenburgh, and Vrolik)[2] supposed that the inflammable gas contains no oxygen and is a compound of carbon and hydrogen. Fourcroy[3] answered this, and in a further paper Clement and Desormes[4] emphasised their experiment on its formation from *dry* carbonic acid gas and heated charcoal. They had now to prove that ignited charcoal contains no hydrogen. In the course of this work they had discovered a new compound prepared from charcoal and sulphur, souffre carburé (carbon disulphide), which is free from hydrogen. Good charcoal from any source gives no water on combustion and all kinds give the same weight of carbonic acid on combustion (diamond may be an exception). In this paper they mention 'Crwishank'.

In reading the papers of Desormes and Clement after Priestley's contemporary publications we feel that we are in a new world. Cruickshank had just before them cleared up the confusion between the 'inflammable airs' which was the main source of Priestley's numerous errors, but Priestley's mind was closed. He objected[5] to Cruickshank's correct experiments and conclusions, and in a series of communications from 1798 to 1803 (to be mentioned later) to the *Medical Repository* he refused to accept a compromise by one of its editors, Mitchill, in which hydrogen was assumed to be a compound of phlogiston and heat (caloric), sulphur a 'phlogisture of sulphur', etc., and metals as elements.[6] Priestley had said with pride that: 'no person was ever more temperate, or more cautious, than I have been in the introduction of *new terms*, considering the number of *new facts* that I have discovered',[7] and 'inflammable air' was an example of one 'term' covering many different gases.

Samuel Latham Mitchill (North Hampstead, Long Island, N.Y., 20 August 1764–New York, 7 September 1831), M.D. Edinburgh 1786 (pupil of Black), professor of chemistry, natural history, and agriculture in Columbia College, New York (1792), was the first exponent of Lavoisier's theory in America.[8] He was also professor of chemistry and materia medica in the College of Physicians (1820–26). Mitchill's theory that nitrous oxide, which he called oxyd of septon, was the principle of contagion and very poisonous[9] was refuted by Davy (see Vol. IV).

[1] *Statique Chimique*, 1803, ii, 61 f., 92.   [2] *Ann. Chim.*, 1802, xliii, 113–32.
[3] *Ann. Chim.*, 1802, xliii, 132–6.   [4] *Ann. Chim.*, 1802, xlii, 121–52.
[5] *Nicholson's J.*, 1801, i, 181; 1802, ii, 69; 1803, iii, 52; 1803, iv, 65.
[6] Edelstein, *Chymia*, 1959, v, 155.   [7] VI, 1790, i, 9.
[8] *Nomenclature of the New Chemistry*, New York, 1794 (based on Girtanner); Duveen and Klickstein, *Isis*, 1954, xlv, 278–92, 368; NBG, 1862, xxxv, 679; C. Hall, *J. Chem. Educ.*, 1928, v, 253; id., *Isis*, 1929, xiii, 184; id., *A Scientist in the Early Republic, S. L. Mitchill*, New York, 1934; R. Siegfried, *Isis*, 1955, xlvi, 327 (Mitchill and Priestley).
[9] *Remarks on the Gaseous Oxyd of Azote and on the Effects it Produces*, New York, 1795.

Photosynthesis

In August 1771,[1] confirmed in May 1772, Priestley found that air which has been vitiated by putrefaction, the breathing of animals, or the burning of candles, is restored by growing green plants; and in 1778[2] he found dephlogisticated air (oxygen) in the bladders of seaweed, and showed that aquatic plants growing in water containing dissolved fixed air (carbon dioxide) give off dephlogisticated air (oxygen). He says[3] 'the injury which is continually done to the atmosphere by the respiration of such a large number of animals . . . and the putrefaction of vegetable and animal substances is, in part at least, repaired by the vegetable creation', almost the same being said in a note written about 1773.[4] Priestley did not at first appreciate the part played by light in the change, now called photosynthesis. He did not recognise this definitely until 1781,[5] although he had hinted at it in 1779,[6] when he said that: 'whatever air is naturally contained in water, or in substances dissolved in water, as calcareous matter, &c. becomes, after long standing, but especially when exposed to the sun, *depurated*, so as at length to become absolutely dephlogisticated', but he says nothing here of the action of plants. In 1779 this was first and definitely stated by Ingen Housz,[7] who published the main facts, including the action of light, but did not give a satisfactory explanation of them.

Priestley[8] thought the melioration of air by growing plants might be due either to 'the plants imbibing the phlogistic matter, as part of their nourishment', or because 'the phlogiston unites with the vapour that is continually exhaled from them', and 'of the two opinions I should incline to the former'. He definitely and incorrectly said that it is the phlogisticated air (nitrogen) and not the fixed air (carbon dioxide) which is 'restored' by vegetation,[9] and that the 'pure air is not *produced* by light or by plants, but only by the purification of the impure air to which the plants have access'.[10]

He found that fixed air (carbon dioxide) in a fairly pure state is injurious to plants,[11] and that water impregnated with fixed air has a harmful effect on plants with the *roots* immersed in it, although at first the growth seemed to be promoted. This was perhaps due to the *stimulus* only, and a similar effect was produced by 'a little common salt, or even a little spirit of nitre [nitric acid]' in the water. Air extracted from pure water is generally purer than atmospheric air.[12] Plants do not grow well in dephlogisticated air.[13]

Priestley had not satisfied himself until September 1779 that the 'green matter producing the pure air' was living vegetable matter formed from invisible seeds in the atmosphere, and that all plants produce the effect when they are healthy, and he did not previously mention the specific action of light.[14] In 1786,[15] and in one of his last papers,[16] Priestley denied 'equivocal', or (as he says Erasmus Darwin[17] called it) 'spontaneous', generation, maintaining

[1] *Phil. Trans.*, 1772, lxii, 160 f., 168, 193 f.; IV, 1774, i, 52, 87, 159; Rutt, i, 148 f.
[2] V, 1779, i, 313.   [3] V, 1779, i, 297.   [4] Rutt, i, 196.   [5] V, 1781, ii, 16.
[6] V, 1779, i, 347–8.   [7] *Experiments upon Vegetables*, 1779.   [8] V, 1779, i, 311.
[9] V, 1781, ii, 330.   [10] *Ib.*, 27, 29, 364.   [11] IV, 1777, iii, 306; V, 1779, i, 329.
[12] V, 1781, ii, 167, 325.   [13] V, 1779, i, 326.
[14] Rutt, i, 325; V, 1781, ii, pref., and 16.   [15] V, 1786, ii, 33.
[16] *Trans. Amer. Phil. Soc.*, 1804, vi, 119.   [17] *Temple of Nature*, 1803.

that the 'green matter' came from seeds in the air and was not generated *de novo* in the water. He quoted[1] Ingen Housz[2] as saying that: 'The water itself, or some substance in the water, is, as I think, changed into this vegetation, and undergoes, by the influence of the sun shining upon it, . . . such a metamorphosis, as to become what we now call dephlogisticated air', this being 'no more extraordinary than the change of grass and other vegetables into fat, in the body of a graminivorous animal'. Priestley added: 'But the change of *water*, into an *organized plant*, is a thing of a very different nature from these.'

Priestley[3] says Mr. Walker drew his attention to 'the green substance' or 'vegetable matter' found in a horse-trough at Harwich; after describing the emission of pure air from it, Priestley says he 'never found it except in circumstances in which the water had been exposed to light',[4] and later,[5] on the basis of a microscopic examination by Mr. Bewley, he concluded that the green substance could 'come most properly under the denomination of the *Conferva*'. Priestley, on account of his weak eyes, avoided the use of the microscope.[6]

INGEN HOUSZ

The experimental investigation of the action of light on vegetative processes, or *photosynthesis*, opened with the researches of the Dutch naturalist Jan Ingen Housz (Breda, 8 December 1730–Bowood, nr. Calne, 7 September 1799; his grave is lost).[7] These were first published in 1779 and were based on experiments completed in London:

A. Experiments upon Vegetables, discovering their great Power of purifying the Common Air in the Sun-shine, and of injuring it in the Shade and at Night. To which is joined a new method of examining the accurate Degree of Salubrity of the Atmosphere, 8°, London, 1779 (dedicated to Sir John Pringle).

B. French tr.: Expériences sur les Végétaux . . . traduit de l'Anglois par l'Auteur, 2 vols., Paris, 1787–9 (enlarged); Bolton, (1), 550, gives a Dutch tr., Amsterdam, 1780; Italian summary in Amoretti and Soave, *Opuscoli Scelti sulla Scienze e sulle Arti*, Milan, 1780, iii, 173.

C. German tr.: Vermischte Schriften Phisisch-Medizinischen Inhalts übersetzt [from an English original, which was not published] und herausgegeben von N. K. Molitor, Vienna, 1782.

D. French tr. by the author: Nouvelles Expériences et Observations sur divers Objets de Physique, 2 vols., Paris, 1785–9 (the expts are in 1789, ii, 6, 173, 316).

E. Versuche mit Pflanzen, hauptsächlich über die Eigenschaften, welche sie in einem höhen Grade besitzen, die Luft im Sonnenlicht zu reinigen und in die Nacht und Schatten zu verderben . . . übersetzt von J. A. Scherer, 3 vols., Vienna, 1786–90.

F. On the Nutrition of Plants and the Fruitfulness of the Earth, London, 1796; tr. by Humboldt, Über Ernährung der Pflanzen und Fruchtbarkeit des Bodens,

---

[1] V, 1781, ii, 33; VI, iii, 307.   [2] *Experiments Upon Vegetables*, 1779, 90–1.
[3] VI, iii, 271.   [4] V, 1781, i, 346.   [5] VI, iii, 306.
[6] VI, iii, 293; on the 'green matter' (an alga) see Lippmann, (6), 1933, 50, 78, 81.
[7] M. Garthshore, *Ann. Phil.*, 1817, x, 161; Thomson, *ib.*, 1819, xiii, 81; J. von Wiesner, *Jan Ingen-Housz. Sein Leben und seine Wirken als Naturforscher und Arzt*, Vienna, 1905; H. S. Reed, *Jean Ingenhousz . . . with a History of the Discovery of Photosynthesis*, in *Chronica Botanica*, Waltham, Mass., 1949, xi, nos. 5–6; R. Foregger, *Anesthiology*, 1956, xvii, 511, was informed by P. van der Pas that 'Ingen Housz never used the hyphen and the present living members of the family do not use the hyphen either'; the common English spelling, e.g. in DNB, is 'Ingenhousz'.

Leipzig, 1798. Ingen Housz also published on an inflammable air lamp,[1] an inflammable air pistol,[2] the preparation of dephlogisticated air,[3] the thermal conductivity of metals,[4] the combustion of metals (including iron in oxygen),[5] the relation between animals and vegetables,[6] manganese and chlorine,[7] and platinum.[8] His work on eudiometry is mentioned on p. 324.

That green leaves take up some nutriment from the atmosphere had been suggested by Malpighi (1628–94) in 1671.[9] Boyle (see Vol. II) had found that moist seeds do not germinate in a vacuum; Scheele[10] found that in germination fire air (oxygen) is absorbed from air and is replaced by an equal volume of fixed air.

Ingen Housz (1779) showed that *all* the *green* parts of plants purify 'bad air' by giving out dephlogisticated air, but only on exposure to light and in proportion to the intensity of the light. In the dark the opposite process occurs to a small extent and contaminates the air, especially from flowers, fruits, and roots. (It is now known that this process occurs to a small extent in light.)[11] Cooper[12] says that Priestley's experiments were probably communicated to Ingen Housz by Magellan, 'whose pleasure and whose occupation it was, to give information of new facts to his philosophical correspondents, and of this in particular to D! Ingenhouz then engaged in similar researches', and that Ingen Housz so anticipated Priestley in publication. Ingen Housz in a letter to Yeats[13] dated February 1798, complained of Priestley's 'profound silence' on Ingen Housz's discovery of 1779 on the influence of light on growing plants, which he says he was the first to 'announce'. The importance of the discovery 'could scarce fail of exciting an envy, in a mind so laudably fond of philosophical merit, as that of D! Priestley', who had used all possible ingenuity to make it appear that he had given the complete explanation without mentioning Ingen Housz. In a letter to Ingen Housz of November, 1787, Priestley says he had found that 'the green matter . . . produced pure air by means of *light*; and immediately after the publication of this fact, and before I saw your book, I had found that other whole plants did the same', but later he admits that Ingen Housz 'certainly published before' him.[14]

In his first publication (A, 1779) Ingen Housz says pump water freshly drawn must be used before it has 'parted with its own air'.[15] He always speaks of the conversion of 'bad air' into dephlogisticated air, testing the goodness by candles, living animals (chickens) and nitrous air (he used a new eudiometer of Fontana).[16] He speaks of leaves absorbing 'septic, noxious and phlogistic particles' formed in breathing, and 'pouring down a beneficial shower of purified or dephlogisticated air', which 'oozes out' of the leaves.[17] He nowhere

[1] D, 1785, i, 136.   [2] *Ib.*, 150.   [3] *Ib.*, 192, 441.   [4] *Ib.*, 380.
[5] *Ib.*, 391, 446.   [6] *Phil. Trans.*, 1782, lxxii, 426; D, 1789, ii, 296.
[7] D, 1789, ii, 465.   [8] *Ib.*, 505.
[9] *Anatomes Plantarum Idea*, 2 vols., London, 1675–79; Sachs, 1875, 394, 481, 494, 521.
[10] *On Air and Fire*, 1777, §§ 88 f.; Engl. tr., 1780, 151 f.
[11] Detailed summary in J. Murray, 1807, iv, 29 f.; brief summary in Harvey Gibson, 1919, 65.
[12] 1805, i, 260.
[13] Yeats, *Observations on the Claims of the Moderns, to Some Discoveries in Chemistry and Physiology*, London, 1798, 394 f.
[14] IX, London, 1793, 24.   [15] A, p. xxxix.   [16] A, 152 f.   [17] A, 137 f.

states that dephlogisticated air is *formed* from fixed air, vaguely saying that 'plants delight in foul air, probably because this air impregnated with phlogiston affords more proper nourishment, viz. phlogiston, to the plant':[1] plants live better in this 'foul air' than in 'pure air'. Leaves placed in water impregnated with fixed air do *not* give off dephlogisticated air so well as leaves in pump water do.[2] Flowers and fruits render air noxious.[3] Ingen Housz thought that green leaves could convert inflammable air (hydrogen) into dephlogisticated air. He never makes it clear that it is *fixed air* which is converted into dephlogisticated air, and Chaptal could say in 1790[4] that Priestley, Ingen Housz and Senebier had proved that *nitrogen* served as the food of plants.

In F (1796) Ingen Housz accepted Lavoisier's results and explained that the leafy shoots give off oxygen in light and carbonic acid gas in the dark, while the non-green parts give off carbonic acid gas both in the light and in the dark. He made the mistake of assuming that plants take up atmospheric nitrogen to form compounds with the carbohydrates.[5] The correct explanation of photosynthesis, that fixed air is converted into dephlogisticated air, was first given by Senebier (1782).

SENEBIER

Jean Senebier (Geneva; 6 May 1742–22 July 1809), evangelical pastor from 1765, librarian of Geneva from 1773, translated works of Spallanzani.[6] He was instructed in chemistry by Pierre François Tingry (Soissons, 1743–Geneva, 13 February 1821), professor in Geneva. He published a large number of works and papers, some of chemical interest.[7] Senebier wrote on plant physiology in the *Encyclopédie Méthodique* (1791) and republished the articles in a revised and extended form.[8] Although he often cites Lavoisier, Senebier was a firm supporter of the phlogiston theory,[9] and criticised Lavoisier's doctrines.[10] He also wrote on hygrometry[11] and eudiometry.[12] Senebier[13] supposed that inflammable air contains phlogiston, water, and some of the acid used in its preparation (Lavoisier's earlier idea), but Kirwan showed that the last is insignificant and only accidental. Senebier investigated the bleaching of yellow wax[14] and the action of oxygen on oils.[15]

---

[1] A, 64.   [2] A, 86, 245.   [3] A, 58.   [4] *Elements of Chemistry*, 1791, iii, 31.
[5] Sachs, 1875, 397, 483, 534, mistakenly says Ingen Housz found in his *earlier* work that 'green plants, under the influence of light, take up carbonic acid, separate the oxygen, and so assimilate carbon'.
[6] *Expériences pour servir à l'histoire de la génération des Animaux et des plantes*, Geneva, 1786; *Opuscules de Physique, Animale et Végétale*, 2 vols., Paris, 1787.
[7] J. P. Maunoire aîné, *Éloge Historique de M. Jean Senebier . . . Lu à la Soc. des Arts de Genève, le 19 décembre 1809*, Geneva, 1810 (60 pp., with list of publ. and unpubl. works); Thomson, *Ann. Phil.*, 1818, xii, 241.
[8] *Physiologie Végétale, contenant une description des organes des plantes, et une exposition des phénomènes produits par leur organisation*, 5 vols., 8°, Geneva, [1800].
[9] Mémoires sur le phlogistique, in *Obs. Phys.*, 1777, viii, 25–37; 1777, ix, 97–104, 366–76; 1778, xi, 326–38 (replying to a criticism of his earlier papers by Mme. de V***, *ib.*, 1777, x, 206–13).
[10] *Obs. Phys.*, 1786, xxx, 93–9.   [11] *Obs. Phys.*, 1778, xi, 421–39.
[12] *Obs. Phys.*, 1779, xiii, 303–6 (letter to Volta).
[13] *Recherches analytiques sur la natur de l'air inflammable*, 8°, Geneva, 1784; tr. by Crell with Kirwan's remarks, Leipzig, 1785; q. by J. C. Fischer, 1806, vii, 810.
[14] *Obs. Phys.*, 1791, xxxviii, 56–62.   [15] *Ann. Chim.*, 1791, xi, 89–95.

The formation of bubbles of air on leaves immersed in water and exposed to light was observed by Charles Bonnet (Geneva; 13 March 1720–20 June 1793),[1] who is often quoted by Senebier. Bonnet thought the bubbles were common air but in some cases they were probably oxygen. Senebier published several works dealing with photosynthesis:

A. Mémoires Physico-Chimiques, Sur l'influence de la lumière solaire pour modifier les êtres des trois règnes de la Nature, & sur-tout ceux du règne végétal, 3 vols., 8°, Geneva, 1782.
B. Recherches sur l'influence de la lumière solaire pour metamorphoser l'air fixe en air pur par la végétation, avec des expériences et des considérations propres à faire connoître ces substances aériformes, Geneva, 1783.
C. Expériences sur l'action de la lumière solaire dans la végétation, Geneva and Paris, 1788.
D. Rapport de l'air atmosphérique avec les êtres organisés, 3 vols., Geneva and Paris, 1807.

In 1782 he showed that leaves in water, in the absence of light, 'do not allow the air they contain to escape',[2] that the quantity of air produced is proportional to the light intensity (except during the first few hours),[3] and that all the green parts of plants, not only the leaves, furnish air.[4] He 'suspected' that 'the leaves produce more air as they draw more fixed air from the water'; water saturated with fixed air produces 'a prodigious quantity of air'; but boiled water gives very little, and the evolution is stopped if alkalis are added.[5] Experiments in which sulphuric, nitric, and marine (hydrochloric) acids were added to the water led to no results of interest.[6] Senebier proved by experiments with the nitric oxide eudiometer that the bubbles emitted under the influence of light consist of oxygen (dephlogisticated air),[7] and he proved that the leaves perform their function also when they are isolated from the plant.[8] He discussed the question as to how the fixed air is metamorphosed into dephlogisticated air;[9] the first is formed by the union of the second with phlogistic matters, and by the action of water and light the fixed air deposits its phlogiston on the calcareous earth (lime) and resin of the leaves and allows the dephlogisticated air to escape.[10]

He is wrong in thinking the lime in the leaves took part in the conversion of carbon dioxide into oxygen, but he probably meant by 'resin' the green colouring matter chlorophyll (Priestley's 'green matter'); Thomson[11] still called this 'the green resin, which constitutes the colouring matter of the leaves of trees, and almost all vegetables'. Senebier says the change of fixed air into dephlogisticated air occurs in the vessels of plants, where the fixed air 'est filtré & agité en mille manièrs, & ou il trouve des corps avide de phlogistique'.[12] He analysed the gas formed by means of Fontana's nitric oxide eudiometer.[13]

The solid parts of plants are not formed by the conversion of water into earth, as Van Helmont, Boyle, and Du Hamel asserted, but from water and fixed air under the influence of light.[14]

[1] Recherches sur l'usage des Feuilles dans les Plantes, et sur quelques autres Sujets relatifs à l'Histoire de la Végétation, Göttingen and Leyden, 1754, 24; Oeuvres, Neuchatel, 1779, iv, 46; Sachs, 1875, 525.
[2] A, i, 54.   [3] A, i, 66.   [4] A, i, 151.   [5] A, i, 173 f., 187, 216 f.
[6] A, i, 216 f.   [7] A, i, 181.   [8] A, i, 101 f.   [9] A, i, 343 f.   [10] A, i, 344; iii, 403 f.
[11] (2), 1817, iv, 141.   [12] B, 383.   [13] A, i, 274 f.   [14] A, iii, 378–86.

Since Senebier never says clearly that fixed air is a compound of carbon and oxygen, he cannot reach a correct idea of carbon assimilation. He also made a number of experiments on growing plants in inflammable air,[1] showing that they perish in this unless it is mixed with common air.[2] He gives a long summarising table of his quantitative experiments.[3] His conclusion[4] is that the leaves furnish much 'air' which, mixing in the atmosphere with the phlogiston contained in the latter, 'precipitates' a large quantity of fixed air and in this way diminishes the amount of harmful phlogisticated matter in the atmosphere. The fixed air is then absorbed by the plants together with water and some phlogiston, and it is decomposed in the presence of light into dephlogisticated air, which is given out, and phlogiston which is retained by the plant. He gives analyses made by Tingry by the distillation of green and of etiolated plants which seemed to show that the first contain more phlogiston and volatile alkali than the second.[5]

Senebier[6] says he had communicated his ideas in a letter of 10 May 1779 to Bonnet before he saw Ingen Housz's book, although he admits that he made use of the latter. He mentions Ingen Housz only in passing,[7] and in a footnote[8] he says Ingen Housz 'établit la plupart des mêmes faits' as Priestley. Harvey Gibson[9] says that 'many of Senebier's conclusions are merely restatements of those of Ingen-Housz, with whom he keeps up a constant polemic'; the main point of Senebier's work was his recognition that it is *fixed air* and not merely 'bad' or 'phlogisticated' air which is decomposed, and this was never recognised by Ingen Housz. Senebier was undoubtedly hampered by Priestley's confused phlogistic ideas. Pfeffer[10] thought Senebier 'established the fact that organic substance is produced from carbonic acid gas and water, while oxygen is excreted', and was the first to 'make it clear that the exhalation of oxygen was accompanied by a corresponding decomposition of carbon dioxide'; and Sachs[11] emphasised Senebier's part in showing the great influence of light in the growth and the production of the green colour of plants.

Harvey Gibson[12] thought that Senebier had only a 'vague idea' that fixed air has an important relation to the vital economy of the plant and 'fails to grasp the fact that the oxygen comes from the carbon dioxide, for he thinks that the leaf in the sunlight can change nitrogen into oxygen and that fixed air may also be transformed into oxygen'. There is no evidence that he was either 'the discoverer or even the co-discoverer of carbon assimilation'. Although Harvey Gibson criticises Sachs and Pfeffer severely, I think that if allowance is made for Senebier's phlogistic ideas he probably got further than Harvey Gibson thought, and that Sachs and Pfeffer were not so wide of the mark as he supposed they were.[13] Priestley and Senebier, both ministers of religion, seem to have been anxious to give Ingen Housz as little credit for his work as they possibly could.

[1] A, i, 224 f.   [2] A, ii, 136 f.   [3] A, i, 356–71.   [4] A, i, 373 f.; ii, 140 f., 207 f.
[5] A, ii, 160–75.   [6] A, i, 1–5.   [7] A, i, 33, 76, 234, 274.   [8] B, 265–6.
[9] 1919, 67–8.   [10] *Pflanzenphysiologie*, Leipzig, 1881, i, 186; 2 ed., Leipzig, 1897, i, 289.
[11] 1875, 398, 535.   [12] 1919, 67–8.
[13] See A. Tröndle, Geschichte des Atmungs- und Ernährungsproblems bei den Pflanzen, *Veröffentl. Schweitz. Ges. f. Gesch. Medizin u. Naturwiss.*, 1925, iv, q. in *Isis*, 1926, viii, 806; Stiles, *Sci. Progr.*, 1894, xxxv, 577 (review).

Senebier's experiments were repeated and confirmed by Ingen Housz.[1] Ingen Housz, however, found[2] that too much fixed air dissolved in the water is injurious. Rumford had asserted[3] that oxygen is also evolved from such materials as silk, cotton, and linen, in water exposed to light, but Ingen Housz[4] showed that the effect is produced by green matter formed in the water on standing. Draper[5] said it was due to air dissolved in the water. Thos. Henry[6] mentions experiments by Percival many years before, showing that fixed air is 'a pabulum for plants', and Henry found, as Priestley had done, that plants die in pure fixed air.

The amelioration of impure air by absorption of it and emission of oxygen was denied by Rumford, J. Woodhouse,[7] and Harrup,[8] and was doubted by Erasmus Darwin.[9] Hassenfratz[10] tried to show by inaccurate experiments and faulty theories that carbonic acid does not play any appreciable part in the growth of plants; since he thought (with Lavoisier) that there is a contraction when carbon burns in oxygen he supposed that a volume of air containing carbonic acid gas should increase when this is converted into oxygen by a growing plant, whilst it does not. Again, much heat should be absorbed in the decomposition of carbonic acid gas, whereas growing plants evolve heat. Senebier[11] replied to Hassenfratz.

DE SAUSSURE

Nicolas Theodore de Saussure (Geneva; 14 October 1767–18 April 1845) investigated photosynthesis quantitatively.[12] His first paper on this subject[13] attracted great attention and led to his election as corresponding member of the Paris Institut. Although professor of mineralogy and geology in the Geneva Academy he never seems to have lectured. His important organic analyses are mentioned later (Vol. IV).

He found that a proportion of carbon dioxide exceeding $\frac{1}{12}$ by volume of the air was injurious. The volume of oxygen evolved in photosynthesis was less than the carbon dioxide absorbed, the difference being made up by nitrogen which de Saussure thought was given out by the plant. He was clear that the carbon from the carbon dioxide was assimilated by the plant, he thought together with some of its oxygen, the rest of the oxygen being

[1] B, 1789, ii, 78. [2] B, i, 290; ii, 282, 296, 408.
[3] Phil. Trans., 1787, lxxvii, 84–124. [4] B, ii, 362.
[5] Scientific Memoirs, 1878, 182. [6] Manchester Mem., 1785, ii, 341; read in 1784.
[7] Nicholson's J., 1802, ii, 150–62: Experiments and Observations on the Vegetation of Plants, which shew that the common Opinion of the Amelioration of the Atmosphere, by Vegetation in Solar Light, is ill founded; the paper is addressed in London.
[8] Nicholson's J., 1803, v, 184.
[9] Phytologia or the Philosophy of Agriculture and Gardening, 1800, 40.
[10] Ann. Chim., 1792, xiii, 318.
[11] Obs. Phys., 1792, xl, 173–89 (Les végétaux ont-ils une chaleur qui leur soit propre?); ib., 1792, xli, 205 (Sur la grande probabilité qu'il y a que le Gaz acide carbonique est décomposé par les Plantes dans l'acte de la Végétation).
[12] Recherches Chimiques sur la Végétation, Paris, 1804; Ostwald's Klassiker, 1890, xv, xvi; see Murray, 1807, iv, 43 f.; Berzelius, Lehrbuch der Chemie, 1827, III, i, 199 f.; Sachs, 1875, 537; Pfeffer, Pflanzenphysiologie, Leipzig, 1881; Bayliss, General Physiology, 1915, 558 f.
[13] La formation de l'acide carbonique est-elle essentielle à la végétation?; J. de Phys., 1798, xlvi, 191.

'exhaled' (his expression), and he proved the increase in carbon in the plant by experiments in which the plants were carbonised. The absorption of oxygen and production of carbon dioxide in the shade were confirmed. De Saussure also proved that the mineral constituents of plants come from the soil and are not generated *de novo*, as had been assumed. De Saussure says:[1]

> When green plants are exposed to atmospheric air in the successive action of day and night they inspire and expire alternately oxygen mixed with carbonic acid gas. The oxygen which green plants inspire is not directly assimilated by them; it is changed on inspiration into carbonic acid gas. They decompose this gas in the act of expiration, and it is only by this decomposition (which is only partial) that they are able to assimilate the oxygen which is present in the atmosphere.

All plants, whether cultivated in water or in air, obtain *all* their carbon from carbon dioxide.[2] A plant grown in a glass vessel containing quicklime, which absorbs carbon dioxide formed by the plant, droops and its leaves fall off in a few days, and the air is free from carbon dioxide; hence plants deprived of carbon dioxide do not grow in light. Some oxygen was removed from the air. A plant grew in air free from carbon dioxide in the dark, oxygen being removed.[3] Plants do not assimilate nitrogen gas,[4] and they do not decompose water.[5] De Saussure thought that atmospheric air has an 'affinity' for carbon dioxide.[6]

> In one experiment, the atmosphere surrounding the plant contained initially 4199 c.c. nitrogen, 1116 c.c. oxygen, and 431 c.c. carbon dioxide; at the end it contained 4338 c.c. nitrogen, 1408 c.c. oxygen, and no carbon dioxide. The seven portions of *Vinca pervinca* weighing 2·707 gm. gave on dry distillation 0·528 gm. charcoal, and after respiration gave 0·649 gm. charcoal, an increase of 0·120 gm. 'from the carbonic acid gas'. In air free from carbon dioxide the plant lost some carbon. The first experiment showed that the 431 c.c. of carbon dioxide were replaced by only 291 c.c. of oxygen, so that 139 c.c. had been absorbed and had liberated 139 c.c. of nitrogen.[7] Many similar experiments with other plants were made.

Priestley on Respiration

In a note written about 1773 Priestley says air becomes unfit for respiration and combustion 'by being overcharged with that principle which the chemists call *phlogiston*, which decomposes the common air, and makes it deposit the fixed air which entered into its constitution'.[8] He explains Black's experiment of blowing into lime water (see p. 141):[9]

> It now being pretty clearly determined, that common air is made to deposit the fixed air which entered into the constitution of it, by means of phlogiston, in all cases of diminished air, it will follow, that in the precipitation of lime, by breathing into lime water, the fixed air, which incorporates with the lime, comes not from the lungs, but from the common air, decomposed by the phlogiston exhaled from them, and discharged, after having been taken in with the aliment, and having performed its function in the animal system. Thus my conjecture is more confirmed, that the cause of the death of animals in confined air is not owing to the want of any *pabulum vitæ*, which the air had been supposed to contain, but to the want of a discharge of the phlogistic matter, with which the system was loaded; the air, when once saturated with it, being no sufficient *menstruum* to take it up.

[1] *Recherches*, 1804, 133.　　　[2] *Ib.*, 49 f., 58.　　　[3] *Ib.*, 34 f.　　　[4] *Ib.*, 207, 216.
[5] *Ib.*, 237.　　　[6] *Ib.*, 78; for experiments, *ib.*, 76 f., 92 f.; long table of results, *ib.*, 99–103.
[7] *Ib.*, 40 f.　　　[8] Rutt, i, 195.　　　[9] IV, 1774, i, 194: he does not mention Black.

Mayow is never mentioned by name but Priestley is certainly criticising him when he says[1] that when animals die when put in air in which other animals have died, 'the cause of their death is not the want of any *pabulum vitæ*, which has been supposed to be contained in the air, but on account of the air being impregnated with something stimulating to their lungs; for they almost always die in convulsions'; or, alternatively[2] to 'the want of a discharge of the phlogistic matter, with which the system was loaded', although 'I still think . . . owing to some *stimulus*, which, by causing immediate, universal, and violent convulsion, exhausts the whole of the *vis vitæ* at once'.

Priestley's paper, 'Observations on Respiration, and the Use of the Blood', read 25 January 1776,[3] was, according to Jörgensen:[4] 'as far as I know, the first attempt to bring the phenomena of respiration into agreement with the phlogiston theory.' When he reprinted it in 1790[5] Priestley said: 'I supposed the phlogistication, as I called it, of air, to be the effect of phlogiston, emitting [*sic*] by the phlogisticating substance, and . . . had no idea of the absorption of dephlogisticated air, which was the discovery of Mr. Lavoisier.'[6]

In his paper (1776) Priestley says the reason why air contributes to animal life 'seems not to have been discovered by any of the many philosophers and physicians who have professedly written upon the subject', but 'it discovered itself, without any trouble or thought, in the course of my researches into the properties of different kinds of air'. He gives a concise history of the theories of respiration, taken from Haller,[7] Hales's *Haemastaticks*, and the memoir of Cigna,[8] and quotes from Hewson[9] that, since nitre produces the same effect on the colour of blood as air does, 'some have attributed the difference in colour in the arterial and venous blood to nitre, which they supposed was absorbed from the air whilst in the lungs. But we know that this is a mere hypothesis, for air contains no nitre.' This hint was wasted on Priestley, who says it is 'something extraordinary, that among such a variety of opinions concerning the use of respiration, the right one should never have been so much as conjectured', this one being his own theory. He confidently asserts that his experiments showed that:

'respiration is a *phlogistic process*, affecting air in the very same manner as every other phlogistic process (*viz*. putrefaction, the effervescence of iron filings and sulphur, or the calcination of metals, &c.) affects it, diminishing the quantity of it in a certain proportion, lessening its specific gravity, and rendering it unfit for respiration or inflammation, but leaving it in a state capable of being restored to a tolerable degree of purity by agitation in water [his favourite error], &c. Having discovered this, I concluded that the use of the lungs is to carry off a putrid effluvium, or to discharge that phlogiston, which had been taken into the system with the aliment, and was become, as it were, effete; the air that is respired serving as a menstruum for that purpose . . . effected by means of the blood, . . . wonderfully formed to imbibe, and part with, that

[1] IV, 1774, i, 71.   [2] IV, 1774, i, 194.
[3] *Phil. Trans.*, 1776, lxvi, 226; IV, 1777, iii, 55–84; Rutt, i, 288.   [4] 1909, 168.
[5] VI, iii, 348.   [6] Lavoisier, AdS, 1777 (1780), m 185 (read 3 May 1777); *Oeuvres*, ii, 174.
[7] *Elementa Physiologiæ*, Lausanne, 1761, iii, 313–65 (which often mentions Mayow).
[8] *Miscell. Taurinensia*, 1759, i, 22, 51 (*Comment.*); 1760, ii, 168–203; see p. 401.
[9] W. Hewson, Experiments on the Blood, *Phil. Trans.*, 1770, lx, 368–413 (373); repr. in his *Experimental Inquiries: Part the First. Being a Second Edition of an Inquiry into the Properties of the Blood*, 1772, 10; *The Works of William Hewson*, ed. G. Gulliver, 1846, 11 (the note says 'perhaps Mayow's nitro-aerial spirit may be here confounded with nitre').

principle which the chemists call phlogiston, and changing its colour in consequence of being charged with it, or being freed from it; and affecting air in the very same manner, both out of the body and in the lungs; and even notwithstanding the interposition of various substances, which prevent its coming into immediate contact with the air.'

He showed that air can act upon blood through a piece of bladder, or through a layer of serum or milk over coagulated blood.

Thus, 'one great use of the blood must be to discharge the phlogiston with which the animal system abounds, imbibing it in the course of its circulation, and imparting it to the air, with which it is brought into contact, in the lungs.' Goodwyn[1] had shown that dephlogisticated air passed through the wall of a vein into the blood, but Priestley[2] asserted that phlogiston, which Goodwyn had neglected, at the same time passed out. He found by quantitative experiments that much more dephlogisticated air is absorbed in each inspiration than is necessary to form the fixed air given out in expiration, and hence some must have been absorbed by the blood.[3] He supposed from experiments on the composition of inspired and expired air, that phlogisticated air (nitrogen) is also absorbed by the blood in respiration, and Davy[4] thought he had confirmed this.

Experiments on Oxides of Nitrogen

Some of Priestley's best later work was on the oxides of nitrogen and nitric acid.[5] He found that when electric sparks are passed through air confined over litmus solution an acid is formed and the air contracts; when the experiment was performed over lime water a precipitate was formed, hence he concluded, incorrectly, that the acid is fixed air (carbonic acid).[6] This must have been formed from dust, etc., in the apparatus. In these experiments he used a straight sparking tube (16), Fig. 24, but in order to be sure that the metal wire was not 'contributing to the effect' he repeated them in a bent tube (19) with each leg in a cup of mercury, an apparatus later used by Cavendish (see p. 339), who showed that the acid is not fixed air but nitrous and nitric acids.

Priestley[7] says that Woulfe, 'Phil. Trans. Vol. XVII. p. 178', had found 'a very great absorption of air' in distilling nitric acid from nitre and oil of vitriol. Woulfe[8] really says there is an *evolution* of air. Priestley, using 'a most commodious apparatus' furnished by Woulfe, found that much air, much purer than common air, was *evolved*, which dephlogisticated air came 'unquestionably' from 'the earth of the nitre, united to a part of its [nitric] acid'. In the distillation[9] the nitric acid first came over pale and strong, but effervescing and giving nitrous air with water; this was followed by a paler acid, then a brown, and finally a deep orange, the last two making no effervescence with water. The changes of colour of the vapour during distillation are accurately described.[10] He thought this was because there was no steam present

---

[1] Edmund Goodwyn, M.D., *The Connexion of Life with Respiration; Or, an Experimental Inquiry into the Effects of Submersion, Strangulation, and the Several Kinds of Noxious Airs on Living Animals* . . . , 8°, London, 1788; he mentions Lower, p. 55, but not Mayow.
[2] *Phil. Trans.*, 1790, lxxx, 106; VI, iii, 376.   [3] The respiratory quotient.
[4] *Researches Concerning Nitrous Oxide*, 1800, 429, 436, 447.   [5] Meldrum, (2).
[6] IV, i, 183–7; V, i, 284.   [7] IV, 1777, iii, 234; VI, iii, 1.   [8] *Phil. Trans.*, 1767, lvii, 517.
[9] IV, 1777, iii, 190, 243; VI, iii, 9.   [10] VI, iii, 120.

at the end of the distillation. He later[1] found that the orange colour is produced by heat only, which develops, 'as it were, the phlogiston it contained
before, and put it in *a new state*', not, as he had thought, that 'pure nitrous
vapour may be necessarily red, except when combined with water, or some
other substance'.[2] He describes in some detail the action of water on nitrous
vapour.[3] Many of the observations, which are accurate, have since been forgotten, but they are of considerable present-day interest.

Nitric acid vapour is decomposed by heating in a glass tube or on passing
through a red-hot glazed earthenware tube, and dephlogisticated air is
evolved.[4] It is decomposed by light and becomes 'phlogisticated' and coloured
strong orange, this being dissolved by the liquid acid and also colouring it; in a
bottle quite filled with liquid acid, the change did not occur.[5] Since fixed air is
evolved from nitric acid and spirit of wine, fixed air must be a modification of
nitrous air — a typical piece of false logic.[6]

Nitrous (nitric) acid was 'extracted' from nitrous air by filling a phial containing some water and air with nitrous air from a bladder, when a 'decomposition of nitrous air' by common or dephlogisticated air occurs, and a
solution of the acid is formed.[7] In 1786[8] Priestley admitted 'the proper generation of phlogisticated air from nitrous air and phlogiston, agreeably to that
most valuable discovery of Mr. Cavendish, who has actually produced nitrous
acid from phlogisticated air'.

The production of nitrous air (nitric oxide) from copper and dilute nitric
acid is much diminished unless there is brisk effervescence[9] — a correct
observation. On mixing 2 vols. of nitrous air and 1 vol. of dephlogisticated air
over water, a residue of only $\frac{3}{100}$ vol. of gas remained. Priestley did not connect
this with the diminution with common air, but compared it with the formation
of sal ammoniac from acid and alkaline airs, the product, 'whatever it be',
dissolving in the water.[10] By heating iron by means of a burning glass in
nitrous air he obtained about half the volume of phlogisticated air (nitrogen),[11]
a good result.

Nitrous air was absorbed by nitric acid, the latter becoming orange-red
when concentrated and greenish-blue if more dilute, and about half the liquid
acid disappeared.[12] This also occurs when copper or mercury dissolves in the
concentrated acid.[13] The solution of nitrous air in a solution of green vitriol
(ferrous sulphate) forms a black liquid, red by transmitted light.[14]

'Nitrous acid vapour' (nitrogen dioxide, NO_2) was made by the action of
concentrated nitric acid on bismuth and 'shut up' in dry glass phials with
ground glass stoppers, being collected by displacement of air (perhaps the first
use of this process), the delivery tube being 'bent downwards, in order to be
inserted into the mouths of the phials that were to receive the vapour'. It could
not be collected over mercury, which absorbed it and was attacked. Nitrous

[1] V, 1779, i, 1.   [2] IV, 1777, iii, 190.   [3] IV, 1777, iii, 194; VI, i, 335; iii, 129.
[4] *Phil. Trans.*, 1789, lxxix, 139, 289; VI, 1790, iii, 198.
[5] V, 1786, iii, 342; VI, iii, 126; see Scheele, p. 226.
[6] IV, 1777, iii, 215, 349; VI, i, 133.   [7] IV, 1777, iii, 159; VI, ii, 29.
[8] V, 1786, iii, 322.   [9] IV, 1777, iii, 165.   [10] V, 1779, i, 245.
[11] V, 1786, iii, 304; VI, ii, 50.   [12] IV, 1777, iii, 121 f.; VI, i, 381.
[13] V, 1779, i, 41; VI, i, 402.   [14] V, 1779, i, 45; VI, ii, 6.

acid vapour is contained in the red vapour evolved in the last stage of the preparation of nitric acid by distilling nitre with sulphuric acid. Priestley noticed the pronounced darkening in colour of the gas when heated in a glass tube, the colour again becoming lighter at higher temperatures, and he (correctly) supposed that it would become colourless at a high temperature (at which the glass softened).[1] He describes its action on water, which became blue and deep green, and on shaking became 'sparkling' from evolution of nitrous air.[2] By its action on spirit of wine, a 'genuine nitrous ether' swam on the surface.[3] With spirit of salt (hydrochloric acid) it gave a deep-orange liquid which dissolved gold in the cold, and was 'a cheap aqua regia'; at the same time 'an acid air of a very peculiar kind, partaking both of the nitrous and marine acid' was evolved (this would be nitrosyl chloride).[4]

Nitrous vapour converts red lead into a white solid (lead nitrate), and on heating this 'white minium' in a glass tube it emitted red vapour and then dephlogisticated air, leaving a yellow residue (PbO).[5] Red lead darkens (from formation of lead dioxide) with nitric acid, but when exposed to 'nitrous acid vapour' it formed a white 'nitre of lead' (lead nitrate), also formed by dissolving lead in diluted nitric acid, which on heating in a glass tube again evolved nitrous acid vapour, this being a convenient method of preparation of the latter.[6] 'Lead ore' (presumably galena, PbS) when moistened with nitric acid and heated in a gun-barrel, detonated with great violence:[7] this would be a mixture of lead nitrate and lead sulphide.

Priestley passed nitrous vapour into a solution of caustic alkali, which absorbed a great quantity, 'but seeing nothing remarkable in the appearance of the liquor, I did not prosecute the experiment',[8] thus missing the discovery of potassium nitrite. He was puzzled by the fact that if the nitrous vapour generated from nitric acid and bismuth was passed into water, the solution (containing nitrous acid) gave more nitrous air (NO) with copper than the original nitric acid would have done.[9] Volatile alkali (ammonia) is formed by the action of iron on dilute copper nitrate solution.[10] He filled a large jar with pieces of iron wire:

and having repeatedly poured upon them a diluted solution of copper in the nitrous acid, at length a thick incrustation was formed upon them; and having no occasion to make use of the jar for several months, I took no notice of it till I found the jar was burst by the swelling of that saline incrustation . . . being the calx of iron; but there was mixed with it a quantity of green matter, which when broken had a strong smell of volatile alkali . . . the calx of iron being supersaturated with phlogiston from the nitrous air, decomposed by it, the alkali, of which this and other metallic calces consists, uniting with it, becomes volatile alkali.

Priestley was not very happy with this completely erroneous explanation, being 'far from disposed to question the truth of the common opinion, that metals consist of phlogiston and a peculiar earth'. Olive oil and turpentine solidify in contact with 'nitrous fumes'.[11]

[1] IV, iii, 184 f.; V, 1779, i, 1 f.; VI, iii, 113.   [2] IV, iii, 194; VI, iii, 129.
[3] IV, iii, 213; VI, iii, 136 f.   [4] IV, iii, 219, 225; VI, iii, 151.
[5] V, 1779, i, 35; 1781, ii, 243.
[6] VI, iii, 166 f., 175: 'nitrated calx of lead', 'white minium'.
[7] IV, 1775, ii, 67; VI, iii, 206.   [8] IV, 1777, iii, 228.   [9] IV, 1777, iii, 250.
[10] V, 1781, ii, 301; VI, i, 41; cf. Higgins, p. 746.
[11] IV, 1777, iii, 115, 174, 208; VI, i, 372; iii, 106, 136.

Priestley, in the same year as Wenzel (see p. 671), described the passivity of iron in concentrated nitric acid:[1]

When I put a thick piece of iron into a quantity of very strong spirit of nitre, it was not at all affected by it; but by the application of a boiling heat it yielded nitrous air. . . . When a quantity of water was poured upon the spirit of nitre and iron, it became of a beautiful green or blue colour, and no motion was perceived in it for about a minute, when it burst out all at once into the most violent effervescence imaginable, and a prodigious quantity of nitrous air was instantly produced.

Priestley found that a candle burned in nitrous air diminished by iron or by liver of sulphur (nitrous oxide) but not in that diminished by a mixture of iron and sulphur, although he later found the latter to give the same result.[2] What he calls 'inflammable nitrous air', in which a candle burns with an enlarged flame, was obtained by the solution of zinc in dilute nitric acid.[3] The processes by which nitrous air is brought to the state in which a candle burns in it with an enlarged flame include the solution of iron, zinc, and tin in dilute nitric acid, exposure of nitrous air to iron, a mixture of iron filings and sulphur, and liver of sulphur, when the volume of nitrous air is diminished: a mixture of the residual gas with inflammable air is explosive.[4] He later found that water is necessary when iron is used, and called the gas 'dephlogisticated nitrous air'; a rapid method of preparing it is to dissolve iron in a dilute solution of copper nitrate.[5] The properties of the gas evolved by the action of zinc on nitric acid varied in different experiments; once, with very strong acid, the gas was not affected by common air or nitrous air and extinguished a candle, although part was absorbed by water (this would be a mixture of nitrous oxide and nitrogen). In another lot, tried immediately, a candle burned with an enlarged flame in the first part and with a natural flame in the second part evolved.[6] Very weak acid gave only the gas in which a candle burnt with an enlarged flame, and it was the same at the beginning and the end of the experiment: 'this looks as if there was more phlogiston than acid in this kind of air.'[7]

Dephlogisticated nitrous air (nitrous oxide) was purified by dissolving it in water and then expelling it by heat; at first it was found that the residual water was acid,[8] but later that the water does not become acid.[9] Priestley regarded it as 'fatal to animal life',[10] but on trying it on a mouse 'was surprized to find that it continued perfectly at its ease five minutes', although the gas was not affected by nitrous air, so that 'in this very singular case, nitrous air fails to be a test of the respirability of air'.[11] He repeated later that 'though this air agrees with dephlogisticated air in admitting a candle to burn in it, and sometimes [sic] with peculiar brilliancy, it is as fatal to animals as the most perfectly phlogisticated air'.[12] By heating iron strongly in the gas by a burning glass, $3\frac{1}{2}$ vols. became 2 vols. which extinguished a candle.[13] This would correspond with nitrous oxide mixed with some nitric oxide.

[1] IV, iii, 169; VI, i, 333.   [2] IV, 1774, i, 217 f.; VI, ii, 70 f.   [3] IV, iii, 21.
[4] IV, iii, 132, 140; V, 1781, ii, 174, 192, 209; VI, ii, 6, 58, 70.
[5] V, 1781, ii, 192, 203, 304; 1786, iii, 315; VI, ii, 62, 76, 97.   [6] IV, iii, 137.
[7] IV, iii, 139.   [8] IV, iii, 140 f.; V, 1781, ii, 213, 345; 1786, iii, 324; VI, ii, 81.
[9] V, iii, 327.   [10] V, ii, 193.   [11] V, ii, 374.
[12] V, iii, 321; cf. VI, 1790, ii, 97: 'a candle burns in this kind of air, and an animal dies in it.'
[13] VI, ii, 86.

In 1786[1] *'nitrous air*, according to the long established hypothesis, consists of nitrous acid and phlogiston', but more correctly 'it consists of a dephlogisticated nitrous vapour, and phlogiston', the addition of dephlogisticated air and water being necessary to make it nitrous acid. 'Dephlogisticated nitrous air, I take to be dephlogisticated nitrous vapour only, and therefore, perhaps, an elementary substance, as well as dephlogisticated air. It seems to be produced by depriving nitrous air of its phlogiston.' It is converted into common air by the addition of latent heat;[2] i.e. by decomposition.

Priestley obtained nitrososulphuric acid; nitrous vapours disposed sulphuric acid to crystallisation,[3] and most of the sulphuric acid solidified to ice-like crystals, which became green and evolved nitrous vapour (in contact with moist air?). The crystals melted on warming but solidified again on cooling. Separate crystals were in the shape of a feather, of beautiful appearance; 'I am afraid I shall never see the like again.' The supernatant liquid behaved as if it were pure nitric acid $(2NO_2 + H_2SO_4 = (NO)HSO_4 + HNO_3)$. The impregnated acid readily dissolved mercury and silver but would not touch gold.[4] Bernhardt[5] had obtained crystals, the properties of which he described, by distilling nitre and calcined green vitriol in a retort connected with a receiver containing some water. Priestley found that nitrous air gives a purple colour to concentrated sulphuric acid.[6]

Miscellaneous Observations

Priestley,[7] at the suggestion of Woulfe, investigated the action of manganese on spirit of salt, Woulfe having cautioned him of the dangerous 'vapours that would issue from it'; he found that 'air, or vapour, was expelled; but it was instantly seized by the quick-silver'. This was chlorine, already discovered by Scheele (p. 212). In 1789[8] he tried the effect of passing hydrogen chloride and chlorine gases through heated tubes. He seems to have obtained chlorine (or nitrosyl chloride) as 'an *acid air* of a very peculiar kind', which corroded mercury, and in which a candle 'was both extinguished and lighted again with a most beautiful deep blue flame', by 'distilling to dryness a solution of gold in marine acid impregnated with nitrous vapour'.[9] Although Scheele's paper on chlorine was published in 1774 and in English in 1786,[10] Priestley never seems to have seen or heard of it. Sulphuric acid vapour heated in a sealed glass tube or passed through a red-hot glazed earthenware tube is decomposed into vitriolic acid air (sulphur dioxide) and dephlogisticated air.[11] Steam passed over heated 'arsenic' gave fixed air and a 'strongly inflammable air', the smell of which 'could not be distinguished from that of phosphorus';[12] this would contain arsenic hydride, but Priestley survived.

In contradiction to 'the opinion of those who make steel', Priestley correctly found that there is a small increase in weight when iron is converted into steel

[1] V, iii, 407–8.   [2] *Ib.*, 415.   [3] V, i, 26, 450; VI, iii, 156.
[4] IV, 1777, iii, 223; no mention of crystals then.
[5] *Chymische Versuche und Erfahrungen*, Leipzig, 1755; Guyton de Morveau, *Ency. Méthod.*, *Chymie*, 1786, i, 185 (also mentioning Cornette); Thomson, (2), 1807, ii, 218.
[6] IV, iii, 129.   [7] V, 1781, ii, 251.   [8] *Phil. Trans.*, 1789, lxxix, 289.
[9] IV, 1777, iii, 225.   [10] *The Chemical Essays*, 1786, 67 f.
[11] *Phil. Trans.*, 1789, lxxix, 289; VI, iii, 195.   [12] VI, i, 204.

by cementation in contact with carbon, 72 grains gaining 3 grains.[1] 'Finery cinder' (Fe_3O_4) may, like scales of iron, be 'considered as iron increased about one third in weight (it should be $\frac{8}{21}$) by imbibing pure air, or rather water, though with the loss of its own phlogiston';[2] this is Cavendish's theory (see p. 350). When inflammable air is heated in tubes of flint glass they are blackened because the lead in the glass attracted phlogiston from the inflammable air.[3]

Witherite (terra ponderosa aerata, barium carbonate) evolves fixed air when heated in a current of steam, and (as Priestley did not discover that hydrated baryta is formed) this shows that 'fixed air consists of about half the weight of water'.[4] Hope[5] found that fixed air is evolved without the action of steam only at the temperature of a smith's forge. Priestley correctly found that lime water heated in a sealed tube deposited lime, which is less soluble in hot than in cold water.[6]

Priestley wrongly thought that fixed air is always formed when sulphur burns in dephlogisticated air: $6\frac{1}{2}$ oz. measures of dephlogisticated air were reduced to 6 oz. by the combustion, 'much vitriolic acid' being formed; on adding water $2\frac{1}{2}$ oz. of air remained, of which $\frac{1}{2}$ oz. was fixed air and the rest very pure dephlogisticated air, 'a decisive proof of the real production of fixed air from phlogiston and dephlogisticated air.'[7] A 'considerable quantity of fixed air' is also formed by burning phosphorus in dephlogisticated air, and 'Mr. Kirwan had a similar result from phosphorus confined in atmospheric air';[8] both were wrong, the precipitate is calcium phosphate, as Rutherford proved in 1772.[9]

The production of fixed air occurs when either inflammable or dephlogisticated air is presented to the other 'in what may be called its *nascent state*', e.g. in the above experiments or when red precipitate is heated in inflammable air,[10] and Priestley was the first to recognise nascent hydrogen. In the calcination of metals, 'it appears, from the experiments of Mr. Lavoisier, that the dephlogisticated part of common air is imbibed, . . . and from my own later experiments, that the phlogiston of the metals uniting with another part of it makes fixed air.'[11]

Priestley[12] thought, as did Lavoisier (p. 418), that 'a red colour' is 'the criterion of dephlogistication, both in the calx of iron, and of mercury', and the red colour of blood is due to the same cause.[13] Red lead moistened with nitric acid became deep brown.[14] Oil of turpentine absorbed three-quarters or even five-sixths of a volume of air, the residue being phlogisticated air, whilst in other cases only one-fourth of the air was absorbed,[15] a 'fact' at which he was 'exceedingly surprized'. He found that in a vacuum the liquid 'discharged air in great plenty'.

[1] V, 1786, iii, 370.   [2] V, 1786, iii, 375.   [3] V, 1779, i, 368; VI, i, 234.
[4] *Phil. Trans.*, 1788, lxxviii, 147 (152); VI, i, 130; X, 1796, repr., 1929, 36.
[5] *Trans. Roy. Soc. Edin.*, 1798, iv, 34 f.   [6] V, 1779, i, 413; see Dalton, p. 822.
[7] VI, i, 162–3.   [8] VI, 1790, i, 170–1.
[9] See p. 264; Lavoisier, AdS, 1777 (1780), m 65; *Oeuvres*, ii, 139.
[10] V, 1781, ii, 84, 87, 95; VI, i, 168, 171, 187, 189, 268 ('newly formed'); Watt, *Phil. Trans.*, 1784, lxxiv, 329 (334).
[11] VI, ii, 210.   [12] V, 1781, ii, 145.   [13] VI, ii, 222.
[14] V, 1775, ii, 53; see p. 288.   [15] IV, 1777, iii, 92; VI, ii, 232.

In one or two places, Priestley seems to hint that atmospheric air is a *mixture* of dephlogisticated air and phlogisticated air, saying that: 'it is pleasing to observe how readily and perfectly dephlogisticated air mixes with phlogisticated air, . . . each tempering the other, so that the purity of the mixture may be accurately known from the quantity and quality of the two kinds of air before mixture.'[1] Priestley[2] tried to repeat Lavoisier's experiment, which he criticises, of converting mercury into red precipitate and decomposing this by heat, but he obtained a smaller weight of mercury than the original. In the calcination of mercury in 'pure air', Priestley says:[3]

the phlogiston belonging to the metal unites with that air, so as together to form *fixed air*; and therefore the calx may be said to be the metal united to fixed air. Then, in a greater degree of heat . . . this factitious fixed air is again decomposed; the phlogiston in it reviving the metal, whilst the pure air is set loose. . . . Since, therefore, this fact *can* be accounted for without excluding phlogiston, the supposition of which is exceedingly convenient, if not absolutely necessary, to the explanation of many other facts in chemistry, it is at least adviseable not to abandon it.

Mercury revived from its calx in inflammable air, he says incorrectly, 'contains more phlogiston than that revived from the same calx by mere heat.'[4]

'If it be admitted that there is a principle in inflammable air, which, being imbibed by the calx of a metal, converts it into a metallic substance, it will follow that the same principle is contained in charcoal, and other combustible substances; because they will all produce the same effect, and therefore that the principle of inflammability, or phlogiston, is the same in them all.'[5]

It is only fair to say[6] that Priestley 'remained a "sceptical chymist"[7] to the end'. In his 'Observations relating to Theory' in 1786,[8] after remarking that 'I am at present even less able to give such a theory as shall satisfy myself, than I was some years ago; new difficulties having arisen, which unhinge former theories, and more experiments being necessary to establish new ones', says he proposes to discuss the constituent parts of all the kinds of air known, 'and a more particular account of the hypothesis concerning phlogiston. . . . The sketch that I shall give will at least serve, like our former theories, to amuse us when we look back upon it, after having gained a more perfect knowledge of the subject. . . . Dephlogisticated air appears to be one of the elements of water, of fixed air, of all the acids, and of many other substances, which till lately, have been thought to be simple.'[9] He says[10] 'there exists a principle, or cause of heat, whether it consist in the mere change of state in the parts of the heated body (as, for instance, in their being thrown into a vibratory motion) or there be such a *substance* (in the same sense in which air, or water, are substances) infused into a body when it is heated, and withdrawn when it is cold', and 'I do not know of any case in which phlogiston has been supposed to enter into a body, but there is room to suppose, that something does enter into it;

[1] IV, 1775, ii, 97, 160; cf. VI, ii, 177, footnote (where he says the air may 'consist of two distinct parts'), 445 (where the two parts do not separate by gravity).
[2] IV, 1777, iii, xiv f., xxviii, xxx; V, 1779, i, 260.   [3] V, iii, 420.
[4] X, 1796 (1929), 25.   [5] *Ib.*, 33.   [6] Hartog, (5), 2, 47–8.
[7] Boyle's name for his famous book, see Vol. II.
[8] V, iii, 400–26; altered in VI, iii, 533–40.   [9] V, iii, 401–3.   [10] *Ib.*, 418.

and in other cases, and especially some of my own late experiments, something certainly does'. But 'it is known that *light* contains phlogiston, if there be any such thing'.[1] In 1790, in 'a more particular Answer to the Objections of the Antiphlogistians,'[2] he reiterates his opinions, but then says that he would 'not feel much reluctance to adopt the new doctrine, provided any new and stronger evidence be produced for it'. Even his last work, *The Doctrine of Phlogiston Established* (1800), is less dogmatic than the title suggests. He says in it:[3] 'I may have overlooked some circumstances which have impressed the minds of others, and their sagacity is at least equal to mine. Tho' the title of this work expresses perfect confidence in the principles for which I contend, I shall still be ready publicly to adopt those of my opponents, if it appears to me that they are able to support them'; and in criticising Davy's *Essays*, just published, he speaks (as he did in 1786) of 'phlogiston, if there be such a thing as phlogiston'.

It has been pointed out (p. 270) that Priestley's retention of the phlogiston theory was largely a result of his confusion of different kinds of 'inflammable air' and some of his experiments and conclusions in this field[4] had previously been rectified by Kirwan.[5]

Priestley's later views on calcination were based on Cavendish's theory,[6] that the metals gave out phlogiston whilst at the same time the calx absorbed water or fixed air, both produced by the phlogistication of air. Beddoes[7] said it now remained to find if in the calcination of metals 'a quantity of water, equal to the difference of weight, is generated during calcination'.

In a letter to Lindsey in January 1800, Priestley said: 'I feel perfectly confident of the ground I stand upon . . . though nearly alone, I am under no apprehension of defeat';[8] and in July 1801 he said Watt and Kirwan, 'as good chemists as any in Europe', favoured the phlogiston theory, and 'truth will in time prevail over any error';[9] this was certainly the case, but not in the way Priestley expected. In his 'Experiments on the Pile of Volta'[10] he found varying amounts of oxygen and hydrogen in the electrolysis of water, and concluded that the gases were not formed by decomposition but were already dissolved in the water; the 'modern hypothesis of the decomposition of water . . . I consider as wholly chimerical'.

Priestley's later papers, published after he went to America, are of little or no interest and are mostly inaccurate. A short tabular summary (not otherwise easily accessible) is given:[11]

    I. *Nicholson's Journal* (new series):

        1802, i, 181: Reply to Cruickshank on carbon monoxide.
        1802, i, 198: Experiments on the Pile of Volta.
        1802, ii, 233: On the conversion of iron into steel.
        1802, iii, 52: On air from finery cinder and charcoal.
        1803, iv, 65: Further reply to Cruickshank.

[1] *Ib.*, 421.   [2] VI, iii, 554.   [3] XI, 1800, 77.
[4] V, iii, 417–26; VI, iii, 540.
[5] *Phil. Trans.*, 1783, lxxiii, 179.   [6] *Phil. Trans.*, 1784, lxxiv, 119 (151).
[7] Tr. of Bergman, *A Dissertation on Elective Attractions*, 1785, 345.
[8] Rutt, ii, 426.   [9] Rutt, ii, 468.   [10] *Nicholson's J.*, 1802, i, 198.
[11] Incomplete list in *Memoirs*, 1805, 290 f.; Edelstein, *Chymia*, 1959, v, 155.

II. *Transactions of the American Philosophical Society*:

1799, iv, 1: Experiments and observations relating to the analysis of atmospherical air: heating black bones, steel needles, etc., in air; inflammable air exposed to iron forms phlogisticated air.

1799, iv, 11: Farther experiments relating to the generation of air from water: air is *always* generated by boiling water; water absorbs dephlogisticated air in preference to phlogisticated air; Priestley still thought air is *generated* from water.

1799, iv, 382: On Phlogiston: red precipitate heated in inflammable air does not form water but fixed air; phlogiston can penetrate glass.

1802, v, 1: Experiments on the transmission of Acids and other Liquors in the Form of Vapour, over several Substances in a hot earthen Tube: air evolved on heating water is 'worse' [less oxygen] than atmospheric air.

1802, v, 14: Experiments on the change of Place in different kinds of Air through several interposing Substances: diffusion through an earthen vessel of fine texture, bladder, etc.

1802, v, 21: Experiments relating to the absorption of air by Water: the air is 'completely phlogisticated'.

1802, v, 28: Miscellaneous Experiments relating to the Doctrine of Phlogiston: denies that the fixed air formed on heating red precipitate and iron comes from plumbago in the iron, since plumbago heated in steam forms no fixed air but 'inflammable air of the purest kind, exactly resembling that from iron by the acid of vitriol'; much fixed air is formed on calcining *any* metal in common air: all incorrect.

1802, v, 36: Experiments on the Production of Air by the Freezing of Water: air is formed from melting ice, hence it is not dissolved air; water converted into vapour forms phlogisticated air.[1]

1802, v, 42: Experiments on Air exposed to Heat in metallic Tubes: a mixture of hydrogen and oxygen does not explode on heating to redness in earthenware, copper, iron, silver, or gold tubes, but explodes in glass tubes.

1804, vi, 129: The Discovery of Nitre in Common Salt frequently mixed with Snow: common salt repeatedly mixed with snow used to make a freezing-mixture becomes charged with nitre and makes a touch-paper (dated 21 November 1803 and perhaps Priestley's last scientific publication); incorrect.

III. *Medical Repository* (New York, ed. by S. L. Mitchill):[2]

1798, i, 521, 541: letters to Mitchill.

1799, ii, 48: letter to Mitchill.

163: On Red Precipitate of Mercury as favourable to the doctrine of Phlogiston (20 July 1798).

166: Objections to the Antiphlogistic Doctrine of Water.

263: Experiments relating to the Calcination of Metals (11 October 1798).

269: On some Experiments made with Ivory Black and also with Diamonds (11 October 1798).

383, 388: On the Phlogistic Theory (17 January and 1 February 1799).

1800, iii, 116 (18 July 1799), 121 (24 July 1799), 124 (26 July 1799): Dr. Priestley's reply to his Antiphlogistian opponents.

305: Singular Effects of Gaseous oxyd of Septon (nitrous oxide, 30 January 1800).

379: review of P's *The Doctrine of Phlogiston Established*.

422: Air Produced, without Limitation, from Water by freezing.

---

[1] Priestley, *Nicholson's J.*, 1800, iv, 193, found that nitrogen is evolved when ice from air-free water is melted; even when frozen nine times without exposure to air, the same water when the ice was melted gave nearly the same amount of nitrogen. His erroneous experiments on the conversion of water into air are dealt with later (p. 345).

[2] Several of these papers in the *Medical Repository* were also published in *Nicholson's Journal* and are included in the second ed. (1803) of Priestley's *The Doctrine of Phlogiston Established*, which has a new preface referring to them. In it (p. 117) he refers to Davy's *Essays* published by Beddoes (see Vol. IV) and says (p. 118) 'Mr. Davy's *nitrogen*, I suspect, will be no longer lived than the French *hydrogen*', probably meaning the name.

Priestley's Observations on Physics

Priestley's experiments on gaseous diffusion[1] showed that 'when two kinds of air have been mixed, it is not possible to separate them again by any method of decanting ... but they will remain equally diffused through the mass of each other'. But, 'notwithstanding these experiments, I do not say but that if two kinds of air, of very different specific gravities, were put into the same vessel, with very great care, without the least agitation that might mix or blend them together, they might continue separate, as with the same care *wine* and *water* may be made to do.' He recommended that gases should be kept in corked inverted bottles containing a little water above the cork, since otherwise corks will not confine them, and they also escape through bladders.[2] Inflammable air passed out through a bladder into dephlogisticated air, and the latter entered the bladder.[3] Some experiments on the expansions of gases by heat gave very different values.[4] The intensity of sound in different gases increases with the density, being very feeble in hydrogen.[5]

Priestley[6] tried to measure the refractive powers of nitrous and inflammable air in a hollow glass prism, and found them equal; he afterwards printed a letter from Warltire describing some more experiments by the same method, showing that the refractive power of inflammable air was greater than that of common air.[7] Some experiments on the conducting power for heat of various gases made by immersing a glass globe containing the gas, with a thermometer bulb at the centre, in hot water and then in cold, showed that inflammable air conducted 'much better than any other kind of air', about twice as well as common air.[8]

Priestley[9] seems to have been the first to notice the detonation wave set up when an explosive gaseous mixture is kindled at one end of a tube closed at both ends. The greatest force of the explosion was felt at the other end: 'the air [gas] at the opposite end is first condensed, in consequence of the

---

[1] IV, 1777, iii, 301; V, 1786, iii, 390; VI, ii, 441.   [2] IV, 1774, i, 62.
[3] V, 1786, iii, 377 f.   [4] IV, 1777, iii, 345 (table); V, 1781, ii, 359.
[5] V, 1781, ii, 295; Watt informed Priestley that steam conducts sound, *ib.*, 388.
[6] IV, 1775, ii, 235.   [7] IV, iii, 365; V, 1781, ii, 338.
[8] V, ii, 375; VI, ii, 457.   [9] VI, iii, 64.

inflammation and expansion of the air at the other end, so that the air is there fired in a condensed state; and hence its greater force.' Even the flat end of a $\frac{1}{10}$ in. thick copper vessel 'was in time made quite convex' by the force of the explosion, and tinned iron vessels 'swelled out at that end, and at length burst'.

Priestley frequently mentions the colour of the electric spark in various gases; in fixed air (CO_2) it is 'exceedingly white', in inflammable air (H_2) it is red or purple (which he regarded as characteristic).[1] He found that water impregnated with fixed air 'is by no means so good a conductor of electricity as water impregnated with any of the mineral acids'.[2]

Priestley[3] noticed that sulphur dioxide and ammonia gas are taken up by charcoal over mercury, and says 'the air had only been, as it were, condensed on its surface', a theory later adopted by Faraday (see Vol. IV). The effect was independently discovered by the Abbé Fontana, and he communicated his results to Priestley[4] who in 1779 said: 'The absorption of all kinds of air by charcoal is a capital discovery of the Abbé Fontana, which he has been so obliging as to give me leave to mention.' Fontana published his experiments in 1782.[5] In 1784 Fontana[6] says of 'mes expériences sur le charbon', that: 'Je les ai faites dès les premiers tems de mon séjour à Paris', and in 1779[7] that he worked in Paris in 1777–8. Ostwald[8] says Fontana was the first to describe the experiment of quenching a piece of red-hot charcoal in mercury and passing it into a tube of gas over mercury, when the gas is taken up and the mercury rises in the tube. Kopp[9] dates Fontana's discovery in 1777, a date generally given. Scheele had published the discovery in 1777 (see p. 231). Priestley's words imply that Fontana's work was unpublished in 1779.

Priestley defines an atom as 'an ultimate component part of any gross body'; it is 'wholly impervious to any other atom', has a determinate form, and is infinitely hard, although 'it must be divisible, and therefore have parts', these being held together by 'powers of mutual attraction infinitely strong'.[10] Matter 'has no properties but those of attraction and repulsion'; its properties are all explained by the theory of Boscovich, also adopted by Michell, of centres of attractive and repulsive forces.[11]

Priestley's *Experiments and Observations relating to the Generation of Air from Water* (London, 1793, 39 pp.) is dedicated to 'The Members of the Lunar Society at Birmingham', with the explanation that 'the members held their meetings every month, on the Monday that was nearest to the full moon, in order to have the benefit of its light on returning home'. There seems to be some doubt as to who the other members were;[12] the Society was founded

[1] VI, i, 232.   [2] VI, i, 115.   [3] IV, 1775, ii, 13.   [4] V, 1779, i, 62; 1786, iii, 237.
[5] *Mem. Mat. Fis. Soc. Ital.*, 1782, i, 648–706, dated 20 October 1781; the observations are on p. 679 f. and he quotes the above passage from the French tr. of Priestley by Gibelin.
[6] *Opuscules Physiques et Chymiques*, Paris, 1784, 76.   [7] *Phil. Trans.*, 1779, lxix, 432.
[8] *Lehrbuch* (1906), II, iii, 218.
[9] (1), iii, 289.   [10] *Disquisitions on Matter and Spirit*, 1777, 5–6.
[11] *Ib.*, 18–23; III, 1772, i, 390; Daubeny, *Atomic Theory*, Oxford, 1850, 41, 465.
[12] Bolton, 1892; Dickinson, *James Watt*, Cambridge, 1936, 119, 157; A. Holt, 1931, 127; E. Robinson, *Ann. Sci.*, 1956 (1957), xii, 296; 1957 (1958), xiii, 1; R. E. Schofield, *ib.*, 1956 (1957), xii, 118; S. Smiles, 1874, 292; 1904, 336; Thorpe, (3), 94.

about 1766, it is said by Boulton and Erasmus Darwin, and became extinct as the members gradually died off.

WEDGWOOD

One of Priestley's friends was Josiah Wedgwood (Burslem, 12 July 1730–Etruria (Staffs.), 3 January 1795),[1] founder of the Etruria pottery works, F.R.S. 1784. He invented a pyrometer depending on the shrinkage of cylinders of prepared clay in the furnace or kiln,[2] the temperatures found by it being much too high, e.g. 18,000° F. for the melting-point of cast iron.[3] Wedgwood also communicated papers on black wad (manganese dioxide),[4] and on a supposed new earth from New South Wales,[5] which was examined by Klaproth,[6] and was called Austral sand, sydneia, etc. Hatchett[7] showed that it was a silicate of alumina and iron mixed with graphite, Wedgwood having 'employed the common acids of the shops, without having previously examined and purified them'. Wedgwood introduced the use of native barium carbonate (witherite) and sulphate (cawk, heavy spar) in making ceramic bodies (jasper ware).

Josiah's fourth son Thomas Wedgwood (Etruria, 14 May 1771–Gunville, nr. Blandford, Dorset, 10 July 1805)[8] made observations on the production of light by the action of heat and attrition on various minerals and solids; he found that blue fluorspar, which gives a fetid smell when rubbed, gives a green light becoming purple or lilac, when heated,[9] and Black[10] thought these experiments showed that the fluorspar 'emits a luminous matter'. Wedgwood also found that when a piece of earthenware was gilded in lines, luted to the end of an earthenware tube, and this end gradually heated to redness in a crucible, no difference in appearance between the gold and earthenware could be seen on looking down the tube: 'may it not be inferred that almost all bodies begin to shine at the same temperature?' He was on the way to discovering Kirchhoff's radiation law. He made experiments on the action of light on silver compounds which are of interest in the history of photography (see Vol. IV).[11]

KEIR

Captain James Keir (Edinburgh, 29 September 1735–Birmingham, 11 October 1820) graduated M.D. at Edinburgh with a dissertation *de attractione*

[1] G. Marryat, *A History of Pottery and Porcelain*, 2 ed., 1857, 151; Church, DNB, 1899, lx, 140; *Wedgwood's Letters to Bentley, 1762–1780*, 2 vols., 1903; *Correspondence of Josiah Wedgwood, 1781–1794*, 1906; E. Robinson, *Ann. Sci.*, 1957 (1958), xiii, 1; Schofield, *Chymia*, 1959, v, 180; Priestley's letters to Wedgwood in the period 1781–92, and to Keir in the period 1782–1788, are described and quoted by G. Wilson, *Life of Cavendish*, 1851, 90–106; the Wedgwood Museum is at Barlaston, Stoke-on-Trent.

[2] *Phil. Trans.*, 1782, lxxii, 305; 1784, lxxiv, 358; 1786, lxxvi, 390.

[3] J. Murray, 1806, i, 490.

[4] *Phil. Trans.*, 1783, lxxiii, 284.   [5] *Phil. Trans.*, 1790, lxxx, 306.

[6] *Beiträge zur chemischen Kenntniss der Mineralkörper*, Posen and Berlin, 1797, ii, 66.

[7] *Phil. Trans.*, 1798, lxxxviii, 110.

[8] R. B. Litchfield, *Tom Wedgwood the First Photographer*, 1903 (Wedgwood himself always signed his letters 'Thomas').

[9] *Phil. Trans.*, 1792, lxxxii, 28, 270.   [10] *Lectures*, 1803, ii, 126.

[11] *Journals of the Royal Institution*, 1802, i, 171; H. Davy, *Works*, 1839, ii, 240–5.

chemica (1778). He became an army physician in the West Indies. From 1770 he lived in Birmingham; he established a glass factory at Stourbridge in 1775, and soon afterwards had sole charge of Boulton and Watt's works at Soho, Birmingham; he became F.R.S. in 1785. In partnership with Blair, a brother officer, he set up an alkali and soap works near Dudley, afterwards making litharge, etc. He invented an alloy of copper and zinc almost identical with Muntz metal. Keir was a friend of Erasmus Darwin in Edinburgh and Birmingham.[1] Keir translated Macquer's *Dictionary of Chemistry*, 2 vols., 1771 — a favourite book of Josiah Wedgwood[2] — and published a treatise on gases and part of a dictionary of chemistry:

I. A Dictionary of Chemistry . . . Translated from the French . . . 2 vols., 1771; *ib.*, The Second Edition . . . To which is added, as An Appendix, A Treatise on the Various Kinds of Permanently Elastic Fluids, or Gases, 3 vols. 8°, London, 1777. The Appendix is in Vol. 3, with separate t.p. and pagination; plate of Priestly's (*sic*) trough; theory on pp. 79 f., where it is said most known gases are compounds of acids and phlogiston; on p. 105 Lavoisier's experiment on the combustion of phosphorus is mentioned.

II. A Treatise on the Various Kinds of Permanently Elastic Fluids, or Gases, 8°, London, 1777 (pp. viii, 108); 2 ed., 1779 (pp. xvi, 120); 'intended as an appendix to the second English Edition of Macquer's Dictionary of Chemistry'.

III. The first Part of a Dictionary of Chemistry, etc., 4°, Birmingham, 1789; London, 1790 (218 pp.).

In II Keir uses Van Helmont's name 'gas', gives an appreciative account of Helmont's ideas on gases, and emphasises that he differentiated these from air. Keir also describes an experimental verification of Boyle's law for carbon dioxide.[3] In III Keir expressed dissatisfaction with Lavoisier's theory, particularly of the composition of water (probably under Watt's influence). Thomson[4] says it did not sell and Keir, probably feeling, as he proceeded, that his defence of phlogiston was hopeless, 'renounced the undertaking, and abandoned altogether the pursuit of chemistry.' Keir's argument against the elementary nature of nitrogen was answered by Berthollet.[5] According to Thomson,[6] Keir in the article 'Air' in his translation of Macquer's *Dictionary* first suggested that fixed air is an acid and called it *calcareous acid*. Keir[7] found that a solution of 1 lb. of nitre in 8 to 10 lb. of sulphuric acid on gentle heating dissolved silver from plated copper without dissolving copper. In this paper he mentions iron rendered 'passive' by nitric acid, but this had been noticed by Stahl (see Vol. II, p. 675), by Wenzel (1777) (see p. 671), and Priestley.[8] The phenomenon was rediscovered by Wetzlar,[9] whereupon

[1] Goodwin, DNB, 1892, xxx, 313; *Sketch of the Life of James Keir, Esq., F.R.S., with a selection from his Correspondence. Printed for Private Circulation*, n.d. (Goodwin, and the Cambridge University Library Catalogue, date it 1859); the Cambridge copy (Zz. 37. 58), presented to Erasmus Darwin, has the date 'Jan. 24 1869' pencilled on the fly-leaf, and Bolton, 1892, 16, dates it 1868: it contains many interesting letters from contemporary scientists. It was published by his grandson Jas. Keir Moilliet, with an intr. by Amelia Moilliet.
[2] *Letters to Bentley*, 1903, i, 443.   [3] II, 1779, 84.   [4] (1) ii, 140.
[5] *Ann. Chim.*, 1791, x, 131.   [6] *Ency. Brit. Suppl.*, 1801, I, i, 320.
[7] *Phil. Trans.*, 1790, lxxx, 359.
[8] IV, 1777, iii, 170; further literature, see Abegg, *Handbuch der anorganischen Chemie*, 1933, IV, iii, pt. 2A, 337.
[9] *J. Chem. Phys.* (Schweigger), 1827, xlix, 470; 1827, l, 88, 129.

Fechner[1] drew attention to Keir's work and published a translation of his paper.

Keir discovered the crystalline hydrate of sulphuric acid H_2SO_4, H_2O, the m.p. of which he found to be 45° F.[2] He also published on native soda from Bengal,[3] nitric acid,[4] the decomposition of common salt and sal ammoniac by copper,[5] the crystallisation of glass,[6] and the production of brandy in Chatra (Ramgur) from the flowers of a tree (*māhwah*).[7]

DARWIN

Erasmus Darwin (Elston Hall, Nottinghamshire, 12 December 1731–nr. Derby, 18 April 1802), physician and poet, introduced much science into his writings. In his poem *The Temple of Nature; or, the Origin of Society*, 1803, there is a note on a chemical theory of electricity and magnetism. His *Botanic Garden* in two parts, *The Economy of Vegetation* and *The Loves of the Plants* (1791), also contains sections on chemistry.[8]

Darwin[9] was unable to confirm Mayow's observation that arterial blood frothed under an air-pump receiver.

WITHERING

William Withering (Wellington, Shropshire, 28 March 1741–Birmingham, 6 October 1799), a medical practitioner in Birmingham (he lived at Edgbaston Hall) discovered native barium carbonate (*terra ponderosa aerata*),[10] later named after him witherite. He says the specimen (sp. gr. 4·338) came from Alston Moor, Cumberland, but it probably came from Anglezark, near Chorley, Lancs.; it was in Boulton's collection.[11] Withering[12] calls it 'a new acquisition to mineralogy', since Bergman had said it did not occur native. Withering also refers to 'heavy gypsum' (barytes, or native barium sulphate), found in Derbyshire lead mines and called 'cauk' (or 'cawk').[13] He says the *precipitated* carbonate can be decomposed by heat (probably because it contains water) into a 'heavy lime', which makes a kind of lime water, whilst the native kind is not decomposed by strong heat but fluxes with the matter of the crucible. He distinguished talc from mica,[14] and with Bergman's approval

[1] *J. Chem. Phys.*, 1828, liii, 151.   [2] *Phil. Trans.*, 1787, lxxvii, 267.

[3] *Trans. Soc. for Encouragement of Arts Manufactures and Commerce*, 1788, vi, 133–48.

[4] *Obs. Phys.*, 1789, xxxiv, 142.   [5] Dollfuss, in Crell's *Ann.*, 1788, II, 510.

[6] *Phil. Trans.*, 1776, lxvi, 530–42.

[7] *Asiatick Researches, or, Transactions of the Society instituted in Bengal for inquiring into the History etc. of Asia*, Calcutta, 1788, i, 309–19; on the tree, C. Hamilton, *ib.*, 300–8; Keir is called 'Archibald' in the paper.

[8] Krause, *Erasmus Darwin*, tr. Dallas, 1879, 2 ed. 1887; Pearson, *D^r. Darwin*, 1930; Robinson, *Ann. Sci.*, 1954, x, 314; Seward, *Memoirs of the Life of Erasmus Darwin*, 1804; Shurlock, *Sci. Progr.*, 1924, xviii, 447 (portr.).

[9] *Phil. Trans.*, 1774, lxiv, 345.   [10] *Phil. Trans.*, 1784, lxxiv, 293; he became F.R.S. in 1784.

[11] Watt, *Manchester Mem.*, 1790, iii, 599; Crell's *Ann.*, 1790, I, 511; Parkes, *Chemical Essays*, 1823, i, 313; Fowles, *Chem. News*, 1927, cxxxv, 309 (repeats that it came from Alston Moor).

[12] Tr. of Bergman's *Sciagraphia*, as *Outlines of Mineralogy*, Birmingham, 1783, 28.

[13] Martyn, *Phil. Trans.*, 1729, xxxvi, 22: 'a coarse talcky spar'; see R. Watson, *Chemical Essays*, 1793, i, 46; 1796, iii, 285.

[14] Tr. of Bergman, *Outlines of Mineralogy*, 1783, 58.

changed the name of manganese from 'magnesium' to 'manganesium'.[1] He devised a soda-water apparatus.[2] Withering is best known as a botanist; his work on the foxglove is a classic.[3]

CAVALLO

Tiberius Cavallo (Naples, 30 March 1749–London, 21 (or 26) December 1809), who left Italy when young and came to London, where he was a successful instrument maker, is notable for his work on electricity.[4] He became F.R.S. in 1779. He published two works on gases:

I. A Treatise on the Nature and Properties of Air, and other Permanently Elastic Fluids. To which is prefixed, an Introduction to Chymistry, 4°, London, 1781 (printed for the Author).
II. Essay on the Medicinal Properties of Factitious Airs, with an Appendix on the Nature of Blood, 8°, London, 1798 (printed for the Author); tr. with notes and addition by A. N. Scherer, Versuch über die medicinische Anwendung der Gasarten nebst Anhängen über das Blut, über Watt's medicinisch-pneumatischen Apparat, und Fischer's Bibliographie der Respiration, 8°, Leipzig, 1799.

I deals with chemistry, hydrostatics, and pneumatics, examines critically most of Priestley's experiments, and adds new work on the atmosphere and on fixed and inflammable airs. It accepts the phlogiston theory, but quotes Lavoisier's opinions. It also describes some extensions of the experiments by Ingen Housz on the influence of light on the growth of plants. II deals with oxygen, hydrogen, nitrogen, carbon dioxide, etc.

Cavallo also published thermometrical experiments (with a black-bulb thermometer),[5] on the cold produced by evaporation and a method of purifying ether,[6] describing the solubility of caoutchouc in washed ether discovered by Macquer,[7] and a new air pump[8] with oiled silk valves.

WOULFE

Peter Woulfe (? 1727–London, 1803 or 1805) lived partly in Paris and partly in Barnard's Inn, London, where he had an untidy but well-stocked laboratory, to which his friends were invited at very inconvenient times in the night. If he took a dislike to an acquaintance he presented him with a specimen of some very rare chemical and never invited him again. He had very eccentric

---

[1] Ib., 33.   [2] Priestley, V, 1781, ii, 389.

[3] An Account of the Foxglove and some of its Medical Properties, London, 1785; A Botanical Arrangement of all the Vegetables naturally growing in Great Britain, 2 vols., London, 1766, and later eds.; on Withering see Boulger, DNB, 1900, lxii, 268; F. A. Crew, Life, in Withering Memorial Lecture, Univ. Birmingham, London, 1927; Faujas Saint-Fond, Voyages en Angleterre, etc., Paris, 1797, ii, 393; L. Roddis, Ann. Med. Hist., 1936, viii, 93; id., William Withering, New York, 1936 (Isis, 1937, xxvii, 379); W. Withering, Miscellaneous Tracts, with a Memoir of his Life, by his Son, 2 vols., London, 1822; T. C. Allbutt, Greek Medicine in Rome, 1921, 262, makes Withering speak of 'that monster phlogiston', and says he wrote an essay on 'The Death and Burial of Phlogiston'.

[4] A Complete Treatise of Electricity in Theory and Practice; with Original Experiments, London, 1777 (412 pp., 3 plates); 2 ed. 1782; 3 ed., 3 vols. 1786–95; On the multiplier of electricity, Nicholson's J., 1797, i, 394; The Elements of Natural and Experimental Philosophy, 4 vols., London, 1803; Hunt, DNB, 1887, ix, 337.

[5] Phil. Trans., 1780, lxx, 585.   [6] Phil. Trans., 1781, lxxi, 509.

[7] See p. 89; Faujas Saint-Fond, Voyages, 1797, i, 29–41.

[8] Phil. Trans., 1783, lxxiii, 453.

habits and carried out experiments on transmutation, affixing prayers to his apparatus.[1]

An improved distillation apparatus described by Langrish[2] was a fore-runner of Woulfe's,[3] which was used for ammonia, hydrochloric acid, and nitric acid, and for distilling and collecting acids in fractions. By distilling hydrochloric acid and alcohol separately, mixing the vapours, and condensing, Woulfe obtained 'marine ether', i.e. ethyl chloride.

The difficult arrangement of apparatus (pierced receivers, etc.) for distillation before Woulfe's was used is emphasised by Fourcroy,[4] who says Woulfe's apparatus was used in Paris from about 1773, when it was described by J. B. Bucquet.[5] The 'Woulfe's bottle' is not shown in the plate in Woulfe's paper of 1767; Fourcroy says it was used in Paris from about 1773 (apparently by Bucquet). It is depicted (with two, and three, necks) in Lavoisier's treatise.[6] It is also described and depicted in Jacquin's book.[7]

Woulfe introduced the method of purifying phosphorus by pressing the liquid through chamois leather.[8] He gave recipes for the preparation of crystalline stannic sulphide[9] or 'mosaic gold'; this had been described in a 14-cent. Naples MS.[10] and fully by William Lewis,[11] who implies that the process was well known. In the same paper Woulfe described the preparation of a blue solution of indigo in concentrated sulphuric acid (previously known) and says that with indigo and nitric acid a yellow colour was formed, which dyed silk or wool. Very concentrated nitric acid inflamed indigo (see Bergman, p. 199). The yellow substance was picric acid. Woulfe[12] described a white tin ore and other minerals. An unpublished Bakerian Lecture by him is in the Royal Society papers.[13]

[1] *Allgemeines Journal der Chemie* (Scherer), 1801, v, 128; Brande, 1848, i, p. xvii; H. Davy, *Works*, 1840, ix, 367; Hartog, DNB, lxiii, 63.
[2] *Phil. Trans.*, 1744, xliii, 254.   [3] *Phil. Trans.*, 1767, lvii, 517.
[4] *Ency. Méthod.*, *Chimie*, iii, 408 f.
[5] *Introduction à l'étude des corps naturels tirés du règne végétal*, 1773, ii, plate.
[6] *Traité élémentaire de Chimie*, 1789, plate IV; in the text, p. 450, he speaks of the apparatus of 'Hales, Rouelle, Woulfe, and many other celebrated chemists'; on p. 451 of 'la bouteille . . . tubulée', without mentioning Woulfe.
[7] *Lehrbuch der allgemeinen und medicinischen Chemie*, 2 vols., Vienna, 1793; tr. Stutzer, *Elements of Chemistry*, London, 1799 (folding plate) (Duveen, 307); see W. A. Campbell, *Chem. and Ind.*, 1957, 1182.
[8] Pelletier, 1785; *Memoires et Observations de Chimie*, 1798, i, 252: comme M. Woulfe me l'avoit indiqué il y a environ trois ans.
[9] *Phil. Trans.*, 1771, lxi, 114; Partington, *Isis*, 1934, xxi, 203.
[10] Partington, *loc. cit.*; see Vol. I.   [11] *Commercium Philosophico-Technicum*, 1765, i, 222.
[12] *Phil. Trans.*, 1779, lxix, 11–34.   [13] Church, *Proc. Roy. Soc.*, 1908, lxxxi, 462.

CHAPTER VIII

CAVENDISH

Henry Cavendish (Nice, 10 October 1731–London, 28 February 1810), the elder of two sons of Lord Charles Cavendish, the fifth son of the second Duke of Devonshire, was born in Nice, where his mother, the fourth daughter of Henry Duke of Kent, was then living on account of poor health. She died when Henry was only two years of age. He was at first educated in a private school in Hackney, then went in 1749 to Peterhouse College, Cambridge, leaving without a degree (perhaps on religious grounds) early in 1753. It is said that his family wished him to take part in public life. His father was not rich for a nobleman in his position but provided for his son with as much as he could afford. After a tour of the Continent with his brother, Cavendish lived in London with his father until the latter's death in 1783. His father carried out important research in heat, electricity, and magnetism, and his son assisted him. Much of his chemical and electrical work was done in this period. Thomson[1] says that when he lived with his father in Great Marlborough Street, Cavendish's 'apartments were a set of stables, fitted up for his accommodation', but Maxwell[2] points out that a room in which Cavendish carried out his early electrical experiments was 14 ft. high. He became F.R.S. in 1760 but his first published paper is in the *Philosophical Transactions* in 1766. He later became very rich (from the bequest of which of his relatives is not clear), but he retained the frugal habits of his early life. Although very retiring in disposition he could be sociable with scientific friends and he collaborated with other Fellows of the Royal Society on committees, e.g. on lightning conductors and did his full share of the work. On the whole, however, he can truthfully be described as a recluse.[3]

[1] (1), i, 336.   [2] In Cavendish, *Scientific Papers*, 1921, i, 2.
[3] Anon., *Brit. Quart. Rev.*, 1845, ii, 197, 243; Anon., *Pharm. J.*, 1894, xxv, 661; Aykroyd, *Three Philosophers (Lavoisier, Priestley, Cavendish)*, London, 1935; J. Barrow, *Sketches of the Royal Society and the Royal Society Club*, 1849, 140 (does not call him 'Hon.'); A. J. Berry, *Henry Cavendish. His Life and Scientific Work*, London, 1960; Biot, *Biographie Universelle*, 1844, vii, 272; Brougham, 1855 (or 1872), i, 91–106, 312–16, 327; F. Cajori, *History of Physics*, New York, 1929, 134; Cuvier, AdS, 1814, xii, II, cxxvi–cxliv (éloge, 1812); *id.*, (1) *Recueil des Éloges*, 1819, ii, 75 (not very accurate but containing material not found elsewhere); *id.*, (2) *Éloges Historiques*, 1860, 139 (Wilson, 1851, 159, says considerable importance attaches to Cuvier's statements); Dains, *J. Chem. Educ.*, 1934, xi, 153; H. Davy, *Works*, 1840, vii, 127–45 (and notes by J. Davy); Getman, *Osiris*, 1937, iii (1), 69; Rev. W. Vernon Harcourt, (1) *B.A. Rep.*, 1839 (1840), 3–68, and 60 pp. lithographed facsimiles; *id.*, (2) *Phil. Mag.*, 1846, xxviii, 106; Hoefer, (1), ii, 535; *id.* (anon.), NBG, 1854, ix, 293; Hunt, DNB, 1887, ii, 348; Kopp, (1), i, 230; *id.*, (2), iii, 235–310; J. P. Muirhead, *Correspondence of the Late James Watt*, London, 1846; Partington, *The Composition of Water*, 1928, 5, 26, 30; T. Thomson, (1), i, 336; *id.*, *Ann. Phil.*, 1813, i, 5; T. E. Thorpe, (1) *Science Lectures delivered in Manchester*, Manchester, 1875, vii, 89; *id.*, (2) *Essays*, 1902, 79; (3) *id.*, in Cavendish, *Scientific Papers*, Cambridge, 1921, ii, 1 f. (the account of Cavendish's unpublished chemical work is defective; it does not even reproduce in ordinary type the parts of Cavendish's diary lithographed by Harcourt, (1), and

Cavendish's house on Clapham Common had a laboratory in the drawing-room, with a smith's forge in an adjoining room, the upper part being an observatory. He frequently worked on Sunday. His town house had a large library, which was open to his friends; he himself filled up a ticket when he borrowed a book, and on the death of his librarian, he himself issued and received the books. He was a bachelor and had an aversion to women; his domestic servants had orders to keep out of his sight, on pain of dismissal. His dinner was ordered by a note placed daily on the hall table, and when he had one or two guests he always provided a leg of mutton. On being told this would not be enough for one party, he replied in his shrill, thin voice: 'then get two.' Although he regularly attended meetings of the Royal Society and the President's (Sir Joseph Banks's) weekly conversaziones, and conversed with the other Fellows at the Society's dinners at the Crown and Anchor in the Strand, he was very shy. When Ingen Housz was pompously introducing a foreign scientist at Sir Joseph Banks's, Cavendish looked anxiously for a gap in the crowd and bolted from the room. He refused to sit for his portrait and the only one (by Alexander) in existence (now in the British Museum Print Room), Fig. 27, was sketched surreptitiously by the artist, the clothes being drawn first and the face inserted when he had the chance of seeing his subject for a few minutes.[1] One account[2] says that Cavendish dressed in a faded violet suit and wore a knocker-tailed periwig. Lord Brougham[3] says: 'His dress was in the oldest fashion, a greyish-green coat and waistcoat, with flaps, a small cocked hat, and his hair dressed like a wig (which possibly it was) with a thick clubbed tail. . . . He probably uttered fewer words in the course of his life than any man who lived to fourscore years.' Lord Brougham recollected 'the shrill cry he uttered as he shuffled quickly from room to room' at meetings of the Royal Society, 'seeming to be annoyed if looked at.'

Although a very wealthy man, Cavendish spent very little on himself and took no steps to increase his fortune. His large balance accumulated at the bank, and when it was suggested that he should invest it, Cavendish replied that if it was inconvenient he could go to another banker.[4] He was not miserly, contributing to charities and to the promotion of science, and he settled an annuity of £500 on Sir Charles Blagden, who was his assistant from 1782/3 to 1789, leaving him £15,000 in his will, although Thomson says they did not get on very well together. Cavendish became a Corresponding Member of the Paris Institut in 1802.

The accounts of the death of Cavendish vary.[5] In one it is said that he called his servant and said: 'Mind what I say — I am going to die. When I am dead,

the reports of the work on arsenic and tartaric acid are very sketchy); Tilden, *Famous Chemists*, 1921, 41; W. Walker, *Memoirs of Distinguished Men of Science*, 1862, 38; G. Wilson, (1) *Life of the Honble Henry Cavendish, including Abstracts of his more important Scientific Papers, and a critical inquiry into the claims of all the alleged Discoverers of the Composition of Water*, 1851 (dated 1849 on binding); Wilson 'corrected' the punctuation, parts in italics, etc., of letters or parts of memoirs, and Harcourt and Muirhead are more reliable in this respect; *id.*, (2) *Proc. Roy. Soc. Edin.*, 1859, iv, 205; T. Young, biogr., repr. in Cavendish, *Scientific Papers*, 1921, ii, 435.
[1] Wilson, *Life of the Honble Henry Cavendish*, 1851, 171.
[2] Wilson, *Life*, 1851, 167.   [3] 1872, 91 f.   [4] Wilson, (1), 127 f.
[5] Thomson, (1), i, 338; Davy, *Works*, vii, 139; Wilson, (1), 182.

but not till then, go to Lord George Cavendish and tell him. Go.' In half an hour the servant returned and found his master dead. Sir Everard Home the surgeon, however, says he was called by Cavendish's servant and stayed with Cavendish all night till his death early next morning. Cavendish was buried in the Devonshire family vault in All Saints' Church, Derby. No slab or monu-

FIG. 27. HENRY CAVENDISH, 1731–1810.
(From the portrait in the British Museum.)

ment marks the place of his sepulchre: a proposal to provide one was made in 1927.[1] His large fortune, of the order of £1,000,000, was left to his relatives. Unlike Priestley, Cavendish was thoroughly educated in mathematics and physics, and devoted his life entirely to scientific investigation. Davy says: 'Of all the philosophers of the present age, Mr. Cavendish was the one who combined, in the highest degree, a depth and extent of mathematical knowledge with delicacy and precision in the methods of experimental research.' His apparatus was never complicated, but it was capable of giving the best results which could be achieved in his time. Like Newton and unlike Priestley (who thrived on it) Cavendish avoided controversy and was upset by it: on the only occasion when he occupied himself with it, in dealing with Kirwan,[2] he apologised for wasting the time of the Royal Society. His literary style is simple, concise, and modest, conveying his meaning quite unambiguously.

[1] Anon., *Nature*, 1927, cxix, 899.   [2] *Phil. Trans.*, 1784, lxxiv, 170.

Cavendish's scientific work, published by him and unpublished, is available in a convenient form:

The Scientific Papers of the Honourable [*sic*] Henry Cavendish, F.R.S. Volume I The Electrical Researches Edited from the Published Papers, and the Cavendish Manuscripts in the possession of . . . the Duke of Devonshire . . . by James Clerk Maxwell . . . Revised by Sir Joseph Larmor; Volume II Chemical and Dynamical. Edited from the Published Papers, and the Cavendish Manuscripts in the possession of . . . the Duke of Devonshire . . . by Sir Edward Thorpe . . . , etc., 2 vols., Cambridge, 1921. Referred to as *Sci. Pap.*[1]

Cavendish published 18 papers in the *Philosophical Transactions*, 10 on chemistry, 2 on electricity, 2 on meteorology, 3 on astronomy, and one (his last) on a method of dividing astronomical instruments. He also left a large amount of unpublished work. His published and unpublished electrical researches were edited by Clerk Maxwell,[2] who spent much time and trouble in carrying out many mathematical calculations and performing experiments. The valuable material in Cavendish's unpublished papers was first revealed by Vernon Harcourt at the Birmingham meeting of the British Association in 1839 (see p. 302).

Electrical Researches

Cavendish[3] clearly distinguished between quantity of electricity and potential (intensity), which he called 'degree of electrification'; and he was the first to make quantitative experiments on the capacities of charged bodies, realising that capacities could be expressed as lengths. Faraday[4] said: 'The beautiful explication of these variations afforded by Cavendish's theory of quantity and intensity requires no support at present, as it is not supposed to be doubted.' Cavendish[5] gave an experimental proof of the inverse-square law of electrical forces, by showing that there is no charge inside a hollow charged spherical conductor; Priestley, following a hint from Franklin, had pointed out this consequence of the law (see p. 245). Cavendish, unknown to Faraday, had discovered the different specific inductive capacities of insulating materials, and measured some of them,[6] but he did not publish this. He compared the electrical conductivities of solutions of salts containing the same fractions of the chemical equivalents in equal volumes, by passing discharges from a Leyden jar through tubes of the solutions and using the shock as a measure of the current. For dilute solutions he found the ratio of the conductivity and the

---

[1] The designation 'Honourable' is also used by Wilson and Hunt but the Errata vol. of DNB, 1904, 58, says this is erroneous. The books of Peterhouse College, Cambridge, call him 'Honorabilis Henricus Cavendish . . . filius natu maximus' (the eldest son) but a statement in Wilson, (1), 13, 17, suggests that his brother Frederick was also entered as 'Honourable'. This appears also in letters to him, including one from his brother in 1780: *Sci. Pap.*, ii, 69. Berry, 12, says the style 'Hon.' 'would not be correct according to present-day usage', adding that 'a few of his earlier papers in the *Philosophical Transactions* are entitled as "By the Hon. Henry Cavendish", but the later ones are designated as "By Henry Cavendish Esq" '. Cuvier, 1860, 139, refers to him as 'Cadet d'une branche cadette'.

[2] *Electrical Researches of Henry Cavendish*, ed. J. C. Maxwell, Cambridge, 1879; Cavendish, *Sci. Pap.*, i.

[3] *Phil. Trans.*, 1771, lxi, 584; 1776, lxvi, I, 196; *Sci. Pap.*, i, 18, 66, 194; Berry, 89.

[4] *Phil. Trans.*, 1833, cxxiii, 23 (28); *Experimental Researches*, 1849, i, 81.

[5] *Sci. Pap.*, i, 118, and Maxwell's note.   [6] *Sci. Pap.*, i, 21, 389, 418.

percentage of salt nearly constant. The results compare favourably with the accurate ones found by Kohlrausch.[1]

Cavendish made experiments to find 'what power of the velocity the resistance is proportional to'. By 'resistance' he meant the whole force which resists the current, and by 'velocity' the strength of the current through unit cross-section of the conductor. In four different series of experiments with salt solutions in wide and narrow tubes, he found that the 'resistance' varied very nearly as the first power of the 'velocity', and this result, found in January 1781, is really Ohm's law.[2] His experiments on divided circuits also anticipated Kirchhoff's application of Ohm's law to them.[3] These experiments, it should be noticed, were carried out with frictional electricity not with currents from a battery, and the current strength was determined by comparisons of the shocks given to the body,[4] although Cavendish made use of electrometers in other researches.

The electric shock of the torpedo fish ($\nu\acute{\alpha}\rho\kappa\eta$) is mentioned by Plato, Aristotle, and Theophrastos.[5] John Walsh[6] showed that the effect is electrical, although he was unable to obtain the smallest spark with 'the torpedinal fluid'. Walsh's memoir is addressed to Benjamin Franklin: 'He, who predicted and showed that electricity wings the formidable bolt of the atmosphere, will hear with attention that in the deep it speeds a humbler bolt, silent and invisible.' Cavendish[7] made an 'artificial torpedo' from wood, metal, and leather, and imitated with it, suitably electrified, the properties of the fish. He related the electrical effect with the 'prismatical columns of which the electrical organ is composed', as disclosed by the dissection by John Hunter (1773), and supposed that 'the quantity of electric fluid, transferred from one side of the torpedo to the other, must be extremely great'.

Dynamics, etc.

Cavendish[8] determined the mean density of the earth by the torsion balance method, using apparatus which had been partly constructed by Rev. John Michell: his result, recalculated by Baily (correcting an arithmetical error), was 5·45. The modern value is 5·53 gm./cm.[3]. In some notes on dynamics Cavendish[9] clearly distinguished 'ordinary momentum' mv from 'mechanical momentum', vis viva, mv^2. In some unpublished experiments made in October 1788:[10] 'It was tried whether the *vis inertiae* of phlogisticated was the same in proport. to its weight as that of common air by noting the time in which a given quantity passed through a given hole when urged by a given pressure' (the apparatus is described):

'with common air it was	2·15 running out
a second time	2·12½

---

[1] *Sci. Pap.*, i, 26 f., 286 f., 311 f., 349 f.; Berry, *From Classical to Modern Chemistry*, Cambridge, 1954, 53; *id.*, 1960, 122.
[2] *Sci. Pap.*, i, 25.   [3] *Ib.*, i, 302.   [4] *Ib.*, i, 202, 423.
[5] Fragm. 178; *Opera*, ed. Wimmer, Paris, 1866, 461.
[6] On the Electrical Property of the Torpedo; *Phil Trans.*, 1773, lxiii, 461.
[7] *Phil. Trans.*, 1776, lxvi, 196–225; *Sci. Pap.*, i, 194.
[8] *Phil. Trans.*, 1798, lxxxviii, 469; *Sci. Pap.*, ii, 249; Berry, 1960, 160.
[9] *Sci. Pap.*, ii, 407, 415.   [10] Harcourt, (1), 67–8; Cavendish, *Sci. Pap.*, ii, 320.

With air phlog. by liv. sulphur   2·7
With com. air   2·9'
The sp. gr. of the gas [nitrogen] was
'$\frac{1}{47}$ less than that of common air'.

This work anticipated that published by Faraday.[1] Cavendish's paper on the Royal Society's instruments[2] dealt not only with thermometers but also with the effect of capillarity on the height of mercury in a barometer tube and the correction for temperature, the rain-gauge, hygrometer, dipping needle, and variation compass. It contains careful observations on the construction and calibration of mercury thermometers. Lord Charles Cavendish[3] had previously described what is essentially a Beckmann thermometer with a variable zero. Cavendish constructed an ingenious registering (maximum and minimum) thermometer, which is now in the Royal Institution.[4]

Experiments on Heat

In his MS. treatise on heat, written in finished form and dated February 1765, Cavendish twice refers to Black, and must have had some knowledge of some of his work at least — Black did not publish it.[5] The experiments, Wilson supposed, were begun in 1764. Cavendish measured the temperature change on mixing hot and cold water; hot water with cold mercury (in which he found the specific heat of mercury 1/30·42 that of water, but adopted $\frac{1}{30}$=0·033); and hot mercury with spirit of wine, dilute sulphuric acid, and solutions of common salt and potassium carbonate. Various solids (iron, lead, tin, sand, glass, marble, coal, sulphur, and charcoal) were mixed with hot water. An attempt was made to find the specific heat of air by passing cold air through a metal worm-tube in hot water, or hot air and cold water; the specific heat of air was found to be 1/5·5 or 1/9·2, but the temperature changes were so small that the measurement of the effect was considered very imperfect. He calls specific heat the 'effect of substance in heating or cooling others' and drew up a table of specific heats. If Cavendish had published this work in 1765 he would have anticipated Irvine, Crawford, Wilcke, and Lavoisier and Laplace.

Cavendish made some good experiments on latent heats of evaporation and fusion. He says that 'all bodies changing from a solid state to a fluid state, or from a non-elastic state to the state of an elastic fluid, generate cold, and by the contrary change they generate heat'. Cullen's and Black's experiments are mentioned. Cavendish made experiments in which water was boiled with a multiple-wick spirit lamp below a tin vessel containing a weighed quantity of water and enclosed in a metal jacket. He concluded that 'there is as much heat lost by converting any quantity of water into steam, as is sufficient to raise that

---

[1] *Quart. J. Sci.*, 1817, iii, 354; 1819, vii, 106; *Experimental Researches in Chemistry and Physics*, 1859, 5, 6.
[2] *Phil. Trans.*, 1776, lxvi, 375–401.
[3] *Phil. Trans.*, 1757, l, 300; Menzies, *J.A.C.S.*, 1921, xliii, 2309.
[4] Wilson, (1), 477; *Sci. Pap.*, ii, 395.
[5] Wilson, (1), 446; Harcourt, (1), 45 f.; *Sci. Pap.*, ii, 326; McKie and Heathcote, *The Discovery of Specific and Latent Heats*, 1935, 52.

quantity of water 982° [F.]'. Experiments in which steam was passed into a worm immersed in cold water gave 920° F. He preferred 960° F., i.e. 535° C. (modern value 536). Cavendish also measured the difference in heat evolved on neutralising (i) alkali carbonates and (ii) caustic alkalis with acids, to find 'the cold generated by the emission of fixed air', which really assumes Hess's law of constant heat summation.[1]

Experiments on the fusion of ice (snow), spermaceti, tin, lead, bismuth, and mixtures of the metals, in which the method of mixtures was used, and in which the changes of temperature were recorded by a thermometer in the solidifying liquid, showed that heat is absorbed on melting and evolved on solidification, the temperature (except with the mixed metals) remaining constant. The latent heat of fusion of ice is given as 154°, 151°, 142°, 154°, the value of 'rather more than 150° F.' (=83·3° C.) being afterwards adopted.[2] The modern value is 80° C.

In his papers on the freezing-point of mercury[3] Cavendish took the freezing-point as −39·26° C. Heat evolved in solidification is said to be 'generated', and he says:

> I am informed, that Dr. Black . . . instead of using the expression, heat is generated or produced, . . . says, latent heat is evolved or set free; but as this expression relates to an hypothesis depending on the supposition, that the heat of bodies is owing to their containing more or less of a substance called the matter of heat; and as I think Sir Isaac Newton's opinion, that heat consists in the internal motion of the particles of bodies, much the most probable, I chose to use the expression, heat is generated.

The hypothesis attributed to Newton is, of course, really due to Francis Bacon (Vol. II, p. 393). Blagden, in his paper, says Cavendish was the first in England to freeze mercury, in a mixture of pounded ice or snow and dilute nitric acid, on 26 February 1783.

Cavendish[4] in some notes on a 'theory of boiling' adopted Halley's and Le Roy's theory (p. 380) that evaporation is a 'solution' of water in air, 'just as water does salt', but boiling 'may be performed without any assistance from the air'; the temperature of boiling depends on 'the pressure acting on the water'. He determined the pressure of aqueous vapour at various temperatures (extending earlier work by his father, Lord Charles Cavendish), using first (like Dalton, p. 768) a barometer tube containing water and later (1777–9) what was long afterwards called an isotensiscope.[5] He explained the results by a modification of Boscovich's theory of attractive and repulsive forces between the particles of water, and says the boiling point should be larger in capillary tubes or in contact with a solid. A few results found by Cavendish, compared with Regnault's (1847)[6] are:

[1] Sci. Pap., ii, 347.   [2] Phil. Trans., 1783, lxxiii, 303 (312).

[3] Observations on Mr Hutchins's Experiments for determining the Degree of Cold at which Quicksilver freezes; Phil. Trans., 1783, lxxiii, 303; Sci. Pap., 1921, ii, 145; see also Black's instructions, q. by Hutchins; the paper by Hutchins is printed before Cavendish's in Phil. Trans., 1783, lxxiii, 303* (asterisked pages), and Blagden's paper, giving a history of the subject, in ib., 1783, lxxiii, 329.

[4] Sci. Pap., ii, 354–80.

[5] Chapman Jones, J. Chem. Soc., 1878, xxxiii, 175; Smith and Menzies, Ann. Phys., 1910, xxxiii, 971.

[6] AdS, 1847, xxi, m 465; Berry, 1960, 133.

° F.	11·0	31·0	52·0	92·0	122	182	244·3	248·6	308·07
in. Hg (C.)	0·065	0·174	0·384	1·467	3·573	15·647	54·21	58·37	153·25
in. Hg (R.)	0·071	0·174	0·388	1·500	3·621	15·92	55·16	59·42	154·40

Cavendish's results, especially at higher temperatures (for which Dalton's figures were obtained by an incorrect method of extrapolation) are, in general, more accurate than Dalton's (1805). In experiments made in 1778 on the effect of water vapour on the compressibility of air, Cavendish concluded that 'the increase of pressure which perfectly dry air will sustain by the addition of water, supposing the bulk to remain unaltered, is equal to the depression of the barometer by water', which is the law of partial pressures.[1] Experiments made in 1779–80[2] on the expansion of different 'airs' by heat (common air, nitric oxide, carbon dioxide, 'heavy inflammable air' [water gas or carbon monoxide ?], nitrogen, oxygen, and hydrogen) gave too large results for the coefficients of expansion for 1° F. ($\frac{1}{390}-\frac{1}{347}$), probably because the gases were moist, but could have led to the conclusion (which he does not state) that the values were the same within the limits of experimental error. He used a U-tube containing mercury with a bulb containing the gas on one side, heated in a water bath. If he had published this work he would have anticipated the experiments of Charles (see p. 771).

Cavendish's reports[3] on the freezing of solutions of nitric and sulphuric acids are of great interest in the history of Physical Chemistry, since they disclose the existence of eutectic points and maxima on the freezing-point curves of binary liquid systems, and relate the positions of these to the compositions of the solutions with astonishing precision. Bottles of the acids of various strengths, some ordinary alcohol, and some calibrated thermometers, were sent to McNab at Hudson's Bay, with instructions. The bottles were to be exposed to cold and the temperatures of freezing ascertained. The liquid part remaining was to be decanted into another bottle and returned to Cavendish. McNab gave minute details of the appearances during freezing. Nitric acid solutions could freeze either as a whole or in part only (when ice or the watery part solidified). A 'point of easiest freezing' (eutectic point) was observed, and Cavendish distinguished the 'aqueous' and 'spirituous congelations', i.e. on the water-rich and acid-rich sides. The results correspond with the separation of various hydrates of nitric and sulphuric acids reported by modern workers. In the second paper, Cavendish refers to experiments by Keir[4] which showed that 'oil of vitriol has a strength of easiest freezing [corresponding with the hydrate H_2SO_4, H_2O, of 45° F.] and that at that point a remarkably slight degree of cold is sufficient for its congelation'. Cavendish showed that there is a second such point for a higher acid strength.

Experiments on freezing mixtures, which really determine eutectic temperatures of solutions of salts, were made by Richard Walker, Apothecary in Radcliffe Infirmary, Oxford.[5]

[1] Sci. Pap., ii, 372, 376. [2] Ib., ii, 374–80.
[3] Phil. Trans., 1786, lxxvi, 241; 1788, lxxviii, 166; Sci. Pap., ii, 59, 195, 214.
[4] Phil. Trans., 1787, lxxvii, 267.
[5] Phil. Trans., 1788, lxxviii, 395; 1789, lxxix, 199; 1795, lxxxv, 270; 1801, xci, 120; An Account of some Remarkable Discoveries in the Production of Artificial Cold; with experiments on

Chemical Work

The very high opinion of Cavendish as a chemist formed by his contemporaries such as Thomas Thomson and Davy was based on his published
work alone. In addition, he left several unpublished manuscripts and had in
his possession a great deal of material which, if he had published it, would have
advanced chemistry very materially.[1] He had anticipated Scheele's discovery
(in 1775) of arsenic acid, was aware of the true composition of cream of tartar
before Scheele's discovery of tartaric acid in 1769, and had made a quantitative
investigation of gaseous explosions. He was the first to show that potash has a
stronger affinity for acids than soda, his experiments being given in papers by
W. Heberden and Donald Monro on mineral waters.[2] The potassium salts
crystallised on cooling solutions of sodium sulphate, nitrate, and chloride in
which potassium carbonate had been dissolved by heating.

The experiments on arsenic,[3] dated December 1764, show that Cavendish
had (before Scheele) prepared arsenic acid (which he calls 'arsenical acid'). He
first repeated Macquer's experiments (see p. 87) of preparing what was
called 'neutral arsenical salt' by heating a mixture of nitre and arsenious oxide
and crystallising the product from hot water. Cavendish showed that the salt
(probably KH_2AsO_4) was not strictly neutral, as Macquer supposed, since it
dissolved alkali carbonates and showed a feebly acid reaction with litmus. He
obtained arsenic acid by dissolving arsenious oxide in hot nitric acid and
evaporating to dryness on a sand-bath. On heating the residue strongly 'no
arsenic sublimed' and no red fumes were evolved (arsenic pentoxide is fairly
stable). The product weighed 'about $\frac{1}{6}$th part more than the arsen. from which
it was made due to the arsen. retaining some of the matter of the aq. fort. used
in making it'. (5 pts. of As_2O_3 give 5·87 of As_2O_5 instead of 6.)

The 'calcarious arsenical salt' (calcium arsenate), prepared from the acid
and whiting, was insoluble; the acid 'also unites to the earth of alum, which
last the sedative salt [boric acid] & sulphur (substances which possess some of
the properties of acids, but not all) are not able to do'. Cavendish says 'the
only difference between plain arsenic [arsenious oxide] & the arsen. acid is that
the latter is more thoroughly deprived of its phlogiston [more oxidised] than
the former', and 'arsen. acid differs from plain arsen. much in the same manner
as that does from the regulus of arsenic [metallic arsenic]'. Whereas white
arsenic 'has a very evident affinity to f[ixed] alk[ali]., thereby manifesting something of an acid property: the arsen. acid is much more dissoluble in water than
white arsen., has a strong affinity to f. alk. & seems in all respects a real acid'.
It 'is easily reduced into regulus by subliming it with inflammable substances',
as when sublimed in 'an apothecary's vial with about $\frac{1}{2}$ its weight of linseed
oil'. On heating '3·4 [3 oz. 4 dr.] of arsen. acid' in a small vial in sand in a

---

the congelation of Quicksilver, and the best methods of producing Artificial Cold, Oxford, 1796,
96 pp. and plate.
[1] Wilson, (1), 19, 446 f.; Cavendish, Sci. Pap., ii, 297–492 (incomplete).
[2] Heberden, Phil. Trans., 1765, lv, 57; Monro, ib., 1771, lxi, 567; Thomson, Ann. Phil.,
1813, i, 13.
[3] Harcourt, (1), 31, 50 f.; Wilson, (1), 21; Sci. Pap., ii, 298.

crucible so as to soften the glass, 'the arsen. acid was not melted & lost but 6 gr. of its weight, which very likely were only water'.

In this work Cavendish distinguished nitrous gas (NO) and nitrous acid vapour (NO₂) before Priestley (see p. 287):

the red fumes which issue . . . can be nothing else, I imagine, than the nitrous acid combined with & volatilized by the phlogiston of the arsen., though I am quite ignorant why they should differ so much both in colour & their greater degree of vola-tility from the same acid impregnated with phlogiston by dissolving other metallic substances in it . . . though in general the nitrous acid has the least affinity to metallic substances of any acid, yet it dissolves them with the greatest ease of any: this has been with great reason attributed to the great affinity of the nitrous acid to phlogiston, part of the acid laying hold of the phlogist. of the metals, & thereby preparing them for dis-solution, whilst the remainder dissolves them.

Cavendish determined the composition of potassium arsenate as follows. He says 3·18·16 (i.e. 3 oz. 18 dwt. 16 gr.)[1] of a solution of dry pearl ashes (K_2CO_3) in an equal weight of water were 'saturated' by 2·18·11 of aqua fortis of sp. gr. 1·398. The loss on mixing in a Florence flask was 10·9. On evaporation 2·11·19 of dry crystals of nitre were obtained, so that '1 part of saltpetre con-tains ·936 of aqua fortis, ·759 of dry pearl ashes, & ·559 of ditto freed from air [carbon dioxide]'. 20·0·0 of nitre distilled with the same quantity of arsenic gave a cake of 30·0·0 of dry salt and 3·9·4 of arsenic [As_2O_3] sublimed. Thus 16·10·20 of arsenic remained in the salt, and '1 part of neut. arsen. salt con-tains ·506 of dry f. alk. saturated with air or ·373 of the same alcali deprived of air, & ·551 of arsen.'.

Since the precipitates of mercury and silver produced by alkali from solutions of the metals in concentrated sulphuric acid are 'reducible without the help of inflammable matters . . . there seems no reason to think that the purest f. alk., or even lime, is intirely free from phlogiston'. He wrongly supposed that phlogiston is necessary to convert arsenic oxide into arsenious oxide, not knowing that oxygen is evolved.

In work on tartar[2] carried out at two different (unknown) periods, Caven-dish discovered the true nature of cream of tartar (potassium hydrogen tartrate) and its relation to 'soluble tartar' (normal potassium tartrate) obtained from cream of tartar and lime. By the action of nitric acid on cream of tartar he obtained nitre, showing that cream of tartar contains potash. Sulphuric acid liberated tartaric acid, isolated by evaporation on a water-bath. By heating a solution of cream of tartar with chalk, fixed air was evolved, 'soluble tartar' went into solution, and 'tartareous selenite' (calcium tartrate) was precipitated. The reaction was:

$$2C_4H_4O_6KH + CaCO_3 = C_4H_4O_6K_2 + C_4H_4O_6Ca + CO_2 + H_2O.$$

To the filtrate from the calcium tartrate he added dilute nitric acid and found that cream of tartar was precipitated. From 2370 grains of cream of tartar he

---

[1] Cavendish used Troy weights: 24 grains (gr.) = 1 pennyweight (dwt.), 20 dwt. = 1 ounce (oz.), 12 oz. = 1 pound (lb.). 1 grain = 0·0648 gram, 1 Troy lb. = 373·248 grams. The 'ounce measure' was the volume of 1 Troy oz. of water, or 31·11 c.c.

[2] Sci. Pap., ii, 301.

obtained 1050 (should be 1185) grains of cream of tartar in this way together with 573 grains of nitre. The reaction is:

$$C_4H_4O_6K_2 + HNO_3 = C_4H_4O_6KH + KNO_3,$$

and the ratio $C_4H_4O_6KH$ to KNO_3 which he found is $1050/573 = 1\cdot83$, the theoretical being $188/101 = 1\cdot87$.[1]

On triturating the calcium tartrate with dilute sulphuric acid, gypsum was precipitated and on evaporating the filtrate to a syrup, crystals, which were tartaric acid, 'shot on cooling.' By adding a solution of barilla (sodium carbonate), acid and neutral sodium tartrates were prepared from the acid. Ammonium tartrate crystals were prepared and distilled, and the formation of pyrotartaric acid and tartaric anhydride seems to have been detected. Cavendish found that a solution of calcium tartrate becomes turbid on heating, indicating a decrease of solubility with rise of temperature.

All these experiments were quantitative, weights being given, and the conclusion was drawn that the amount of alkali required to convert a given weight of tartaric acid into 'soluble tartar' is at least twice that to convert it into cream of tartar; it is actually just twice and Cavendish was very near to the law of multiple proportions and the recognition that tartaric acid is dibasic. Although a remarkably accurate experimenter, he was lacking in ability to draw far-reaching generalisations from his results, which Lavoisier and Dalton possessed in a pre-eminent degree. This will also appear again in his work on the composition of water, discussed later. Other examples have been pointed out previously.

Experiments on Gases

Cavendish's first *published* chemical memoir,[2] is entitled 'Three Papers, containing Experiments on factitious Airs', a 'factitious air' being 'in general any kind of air which is contained in other bodies in an unelastic state, and is produced from thence by art'. They were read on 29 May, 6 November, and 13 November 1766. Part 1 deals with inflammable air (hydrogen), part 2 with fixed air (CO$_2$), and part 3 with 'air produced by fermentation and putrefaction'. A part 4 was written but not published (see p. 318).

Cavendish's apparatus for collecting gases was simple (Fig. 28). A jar filled with water was suspended mouth downwards in a tub of water and supported by strings. The gas was generated in a bottle fitted by grinding with a glass delivery tube passing beneath the jar in the trough. Gas was decanted from one jar to another through a funnel, and passed from a jar to a bladder by means of a siphon tube attached to the latter, the other end passing inside the jar, which was depressed under a head of water in the trough, a bit of wax being stuck on the end of the pipe and rubbed off against the side of the bottle, so that no water got into the tube.

Cavendish studied the properties of *fixed air* (carbon dioxide) which had been named by Black (who published scarcely anything on it) and *inflammable*

---

[1] Berry, 1960, 66.   [2] *Phil. Trans.*, 1766, lvi, 141; *Sci. Pap.*, ii, 77.

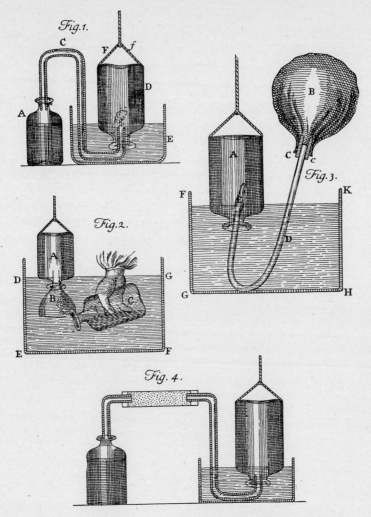

FIG. 28. CAVENDISH'S APPARATUS FOR MANIPULATION OF GASES.

air (hydrogen), which had been investigated by Boyle (see Vol. II), who did not clearly distinguish it as a peculiar gas entirely different from common air. Maud[1] had obtained inflammable air from iron and dilute sulphuric acid, collected it in a bladder, and showed that its mixture with air was explosive when kindled; this may have suggested Cavendish's work.[2] Lowther[3] collected fire-damp from a Whitehaven coal mine in bladders and kindled the gas at a meeting of the Royal Society. Pringle in 1773[4] regarded the gases from mines, sewers, and neglected privies, fire-damp from coal pits, and inflammable air (hydrogen) as more or less the same.

Cavendish found that from the same weight of a particular metal, zinc, iron,

[1] *Phil. Trans.*, 1736, xxxix, 282.   [2] Cooper, *Memoirs of Dr. Priestley*, 1805, 224.
[3] *Phil. Trans.*, 1733, xxxviii, 109.   [4] *Six Discourses*, 1783, 23.

or tin, the same volume of inflammable air was obtained with either hydro-chloric or sulphuric acid: 'the air is the same and of the same amount which-ever acid is used to dissolve the same weight of any particular metal', and hence he concluded that it came from the metal and not the acid. He calls it 'the inflammable air from metals'. The origin in the metal was also supported by the production of an inflammable air by the distillation of vegetable, and the putrefaction of animal, substances, i.e. materials rich in phlogiston. The fact that Black regarded fixed air as fixed in *solids*, not in liquids (although con-tained in solutions of mild alkalis) may possibly have influenced Cavendish in thinking that the gas came from the metal.[1] Cavendish says that when zinc, iron and tin dissolve in spirit of salt or dilute vitriolic acid, 'their phlogiston flies off, without having its nature changed by the acid, and forms the inflam-mable air', and he seems[2] to have been the first, at least in England, to advance the view that inflammable air is phlogiston, afterwards taken up by Priestley and Kirwan, to whom he himself afterwards attributed it (see p. 334): they all changed their views later. Cavendish would represent the action of an acid on a metal as:

$$\underbrace{calx + \phi}_{metal} + acid = \underbrace{calx + acid}_{salt} + \underbrace{\phi}_{inflammable\ air}.$$

In describing its combustion mixed with air in bottles he does not mention any production of moisture.

The inflammable air differed from fixed air in being insoluble in water and

alkali. Cavendish found that it formed an explosive mix-ture with air, the most violent detonation being with a mixture of three volumes of inflammable air with seven volumes of common air (he did not try the ratio 2 : 5). He determined its density in two ways. In the first, he filled a weighed bladder of 80 fluid oz. capacity (by measurement of the circumference) with the air and found it lost 41 grains at 50° F. and $29\frac{3}{4}$ in. of mercury, whence he calculated that inflammable air was either 7 or $10\frac{8}{10}$ times lighter than common air, according to the figure taken from previous experimenters for the density of common air. (The correct figure is 14·4.) In the second method he used the apparatus of Fig. 29, finding the loss in weight when a known weight of metal is dis-solved in acid. The drying tube was filled with pearl-ash (potassium carbonate) which kept back both moisture and acid spray, any carbon dioxide evolved from the pearl-ash by the acid being fixed as potassium bicarbon-ate. By special experiments he proved that inflammable air is not absorbed by pearl-ash. Cavendish was ap-parently the first to use a drying tube for gases.[3] In this case the tube was fixed in the bottle by a lute of almond powder and glue, well beaten with a hammer.

FIG. 29. CAVENDISH'S APPARATUS FOR FIND-ING THE WEIGHT OF GAS EVOLVED IN A REACTION.

[1] Wilson, (1), 26–7.   [2] Wilson, (1), 198–9.   [3] Wilson, (1), 201.

From these experiments, Cavendish found that inflammable air is eleven times lighter than common air.

Hales[1] had tried unsuccessfully to weigh a gas ('air of tartar') in a pear-shaped glass vessel closed with bladder. Hauksbee[2] and Isaac Greenwood of Cambridge, Mass.,[3] had attempted to weigh different gases, but found no great difference from air. Cavendish, therefore, seems to have been the first to publish the fact that different gases have different densities, and to give quantitative results.[4]

The volumes in ounce measures of inflammable air evolved from 1 oz. of metal, measured at 50° F. and 30 in. barometer, were: zinc 356, iron 412, tin 202. The experiments on the loss in weight of the bottle on dissolving the metals in acids gave (after correction for the air displaced from the bottle):

$$254 \text{ grains of zinc gave } 10\tfrac{3}{4} \text{ grains inflammable air}$$
$$250\tfrac{1}{2} \text{ ,, ,, iron ,, } 11\tfrac{3}{8} \text{ ,, ,, ,,}$$
$$607 \text{ ,, ,, tin ,, } 13\tfrac{3}{4} \text{ ,, ,, ,,}$$

The volume results gave for the weights of metals producing equal volumes of hydrogen: zinc 29, iron 24·3, tin 49·5, whilst the modern equivalent weights are 32·7, 28, and 59·4. Cavendish's figures are in the correct ratios, though accurate values could not be expected in the circumstances and the metals were probably far from pure. The weight results give for the weights of metals producing 1 grain of hydrogen: zinc 23·6, iron 22·0, tin 44·5, again in the correct order.

When zinc, iron, and tin were dissolved in hot undiluted acid of vitriol they evolved uninflammable vapours smelling strongly of 'the volatile sulphureous acid' (sulphur dioxide), and 'in this case their phlogiston unites to the acid; for it is well known, that the volatile sulphureous acid consists of the plain vitriolic acid united to phlogiston'. In nitrous (nitric) acid the metals evolved red fumes, produced by the phlogiston uniting with the acid. In a footnote Cavendish says: 'if oil of vitriol be distilled, from sulphur, the liquor which comes over, will be the volatile sulphureous acid.'

By heating copper wire with spirit of salt until all the air was expelled from the vessel, Cavendish found that 'on a sudden, without any sensible alteration of the heat, the water rushed violently . . . into the bottle and filled it almost entirely full'. He remarks that the vapour 'loses its elasticity as soon as it comes in contact with the water'. This gave Priestley the hint which enabled him to collect the 'acid air' (HCl) over mercury. For some reason, Priestley[5] mistook Cavendish's words 'loses its elasticity' to mean a contact action and not a solution of the gas in water.

Cavendish now investigated fixed air (carbon dioxide), 'or that species of factitious air, which is produced from alkaline substances, by solution in acids, or by calcination.' He prepared it by dissolving marble in spirit of salt (hydrochloric acid) and collected it over water, as usual. The air was slowly and

[1] *Vegetable Staticks*, 1727, 184.   [2] *Phil. Trans.*, 1710, xxvii, 196, no. 328.
[3] *Phil. Trans.*, 1729, xxxvi, 184, no. 411; Harcourt, (2), 106 (120).
[4] Kopp, (1), i, 231; Wilson, (1), 202.   [5] *Phil. Trans.*, 1772, lxii, 239.

nearly completely absorbed on standing over water, and the water then precipitated lime water. The fixed air extinguished a candle flame. These properties were known to Black. The times in seconds a small candle would burn
in a closed jar were: in common air 80; in 1 fixed air + 19 common air 51; in air
containing $\frac{3}{40}$ fixed air 23; in air containing $\frac{1}{10}$ fixed air 11; in air containing $\frac{1}{9}$
fixed air 0 (immediately extinguished). A large flame burns longer, but 'the
power which common air has of keeping fire alive, is very much diminished
by a small mixture of fixed air'. When air contains about one-ninth its volume
of fixed air it ceases to support the combustion of a small candle.

By collecting fixed air from the generating bottle over mercury in a graduated cylinder, then introducing rain water purged of air by boiling so that the
mercury fell out of the cylinder, and allowing to stand for a day or two,
Cavendish found that water absorbs rather more than its own volume of fixed
air at room temperature (55° F.) and more when cold, and that boiling expels
it; and that spirit of wine absorbs $2\frac{1}{4}$ times its volume of fixed air. He noted its
solubility in alkalis, but does not refer to its acidic reaction.[1]

Cavendish's result that fixed air is a mixture 'of substances of different
natures, part of it being more soluble in water than the rest', was correctly
explained by Black[2] as due to 'the common air which water contains, and
which arises with the fixed air', and the same explanation was given by Dalton
later. This effect frequently misled Priestley. Cavendish said later in a footnote: 'Pearl ashes [potassium carbonate] deprived of their fixed air, i.e. sope
leys [potassium hydroxide], will absorb the whole of the air discharged from
marble: as I know by experience.' Yet he still thought the gas is not homogeneous. In 1784[3] Cavendish correctly stated that if a mixture of common air
and fixed air is shaken with water, only part of the fixed air is absorbed ($\frac{1}{2}$ from
a mixture with 10 vols. of common air, shaken with an equal volume of distilled water). He failed to deduce the law of partial pressures, first stated by
Dalton.

The weight of fixed air expelled by acids from limestone, marble, pearl-ash,
etc., was determined with the apparatus shown in Fig. 29, the acid being first
put in and the bottle and tube weighed. The weighed solid was then put in
and the drying tube fixed in with a lute of almond paste and glue. The drying
tube now contained 'shreds of filtering paper' (since pearl-ash absorbs fixed
air). The gas leaving the vessel would still be saturated with water vapour,
and Priestley seems to have first used calcium chloride for drying gases (see
p. 269).

The weights of fixed air contained in 1000 parts of the alkalis and marble
were found to be: marble 407, 408 (440); 'volatile sal ammoniac' (carbonate of ammonia; a special apparatus was used with this) 528, 533
(559.3 if $2(NH_4)_2O, 3CO_2$); pearl ash 284, 287 (318); bicarbonate of potash 423
(440), the correct figures being in brackets. Cavendish appreciated that differ-

---

[1] Thorpe, 1902, 87, had correctly said that Cavendish both *collected* and stored fixed air over
mercury before Priestley used mercury. It has often been said, incorrectly, that Cavendish only
'stored' soluble gases over mercury and Priestley first 'collected' them; e.g. McKie, *Lavoisier*,
1952, 40–1.

[2] *Lectures on Chemistry*, 1803, ii, 91.   [3] *Phil. Trans.*, 1784, lxxiv, 121–2.

ent specimens of volatile sal ammoniac would probably give different proportions of fixed air.

Cavendish described (Expt. XV) the preparation of bicarbonate of potash by shaking a solution of the carbonate (pearl ash) in a bottle to the neck of which was attached a bladder filled with fixed air. The crystals obtained were not deliquescent and dissolved in about 4 times their weight of water at room temperature. Cavendish mentions Black's statement that on exposing a solution of salt of tartar (potassium carbonate) to the air for a long time, crystals separated which 'seemed to be composed only of the alkali, and of a larger quantity of air than is usually contained in that salt'.[1]

The Duc de Chaulnes, in a paper communicated in December 1775, described experiments on fixed air made in 1771–3,[2] including its acid reaction and the formation of a crystalline salt (potassium bicarbonate) by the action of fixed air on solutions of potassium carbonate and hydroxide. Sodium bicarbonate was discovered by Valentin Rose junr. in 1801.[3]

Cavendish explained the effervescence when a solution of calcium chloride is added to one of carbonate of ammonia as due to the excess of fixed air in the latter, and the non-precipitation of a salt of magnesia as due to the solution of magnesium carbonate in the excess of fixed air. Cavendish found that the following weights of alkalis 'saturated' the same weight of acid as 1000 of marble (his standard): volatile sal ammoniac 1680, bicarbonate of potash 2035, pearl ash 1588. By weighing a 100 oz. volume bladder filled with fixed air directly from the generating apparatus, and then squeezing out the fixed air, it was found to lose 34 grains at 45° F., and hence it was calculated (air being $\frac{1}{800}$ the density of water) that fixed air was $1\frac{57}{100}$ times heavier than common air (which is rather too large). At 65° F. it was less than this, in the ratio of 511 : 563. The figure taken for the density of air is too small; it should be 1/767·4.

Macbride, at Black's suggestion (he wrote to Hutcheson, lecturer on chemistry at Trinity College, Dublin), had found that fermentation and putrefaction evolve fixed air.[4] Cavendish, in the third part of his paper, confirmed this for the vinous fermentation of sugar and apple juice, the gas being completely absorbed by caustic potash solution, and having the same density, action on flame, and solubility in water, as the gas from marble. He found that sugar by fermentation gave off 57 per cent. of its weight of fixed air, which is too high (some alcohol was probably lost as vapour).[5] Experiments were made on the fermentation of apple juice but in this case the final liquid was very sour and 'had gone beyond the vinous fermentation'. Gas from the putrefaction of gravy broth at 96° F. was partly fixed air and the residue 1 of common air and 4·7 vols. of inflammable air, somewhat heavier than inflammable air from metals in the ratio $4\frac{3}{4} : 4\frac{1}{2}$ (it would probably contain methane), and hence 'not

[1] Black, *Essays and Obs. . . . read before a Society in Edinburgh*, 1756, ii, 218; ACR, i, 42 (see p. 139).

[2] AdS, *Mém. div. Sav.*, 1780, ix, 521, 551.

[3] *Allgem. J. Chem.* (Scherer), 1801, vi, 50.

[4] Macbride, *Experimental Essays*, 1764, 10, 22, 27 f., 33 f.; Black, *Lectures on Chemistry*, 1803, ii, 89.

[5] Berry, 1960, 52.

exactly the same, or else mixed with some air heavier than it'. In determining the densitites of small quantities of these gases Cavendish used 'a piece of ox-gut furnished with a small brass cock' as more convenient than a bladder.

A continuation of the paper, called 'Part IV', was prepared for publication by the Royal Society, probably not later than 1767, but is incomplete and was not published.[1] It deals with the gases formed on distilling wainscot (raspings of Norway oak), tartar, and hartshorn shavings. These gases were similar but differed in specific gravity and in explosive power when mixed with air. Cavendish then deflagrated the *caput mortuum* (residue) of the distillation with nitre and found, contrary to expectation, that the weight of fixed air produced (and retained by the alkali) is greater than that of the charcoal consumed: 'I must be mistaken in supposing that all the fixed air in the alcali proceeded from the caput mortuum.' This difficulty probably led Cavendish to defer publication. He clearly recognised that the inflammable air obtained by these processes is quite different from that (hydrogen) obtained by dissolving metals in acids. It was denser and required more air to make it explosive. The gas, after removal of carbon dioxide, must have been a mixture of hydrogen, methane, and carbon monoxide. He says the flame of it 'was blue, in colour like that of burning sulphur'. If this part had been published it might (although this is doubtful) have saved Priestley from confusing hydrogen with other inflammable gases such as carbon monoxide. Nitrogen (phlogisticated air) was clearly distinguished from carbon dioxide (fixed air) by Cavendish before 1772. The manuscript is marked 'Communicated to Dr. Priestley' and says[2] that there were probably many kinds of mephitic air which suffocate animals:

I am sure there are 2, namely, fixed air, & common air in which candles have burnt, or which has passed thro' the fire. Air which has passed thro' a charcoal fire contains a great deal of fixed air, which is generated from the charcoal, but consists principally of common air, which has suffered a change in its nature from the fire.

In an experiment air was passed from one receiver to another through a tube of red-hot charcoal; 180 oz. measures of air from the first receiver gave 190 oz. measures in the second, but when:

some sope leys was mixed with the water in the bason, into which the mouth of this 2nd receiver was immersed; it was thereby reduced to 168 oz. . . . therefore 14 oz. of common air were absorbed by the fumes of burning charcoal, agreeable to what Dr. Hales and others have observed, that all burning bodies absorb air.

A further 4 oz. was absorbed after a second passage over the charcoal.

The specific gravity of this [residual] air was found to differ very little from that of common air; of the two it seemed rather lighter. It extinguished flame, & rendered common air unfit for making bodies burn, in the same manner as fixed air, but in a less degree, as a candle which burnt about 80" in pure common air, & which went out immediately in common air mixed with $\frac{6}{55}$ of fixed air, burnt about 26" in common air mixed with the same portion of this burnt air.

Cavendish gave no special name to this 'air', generally calling it 'mephitic air'. As he said, this work was communicated to Priestley, who gave an account of it

[1] Harcourt, (1), 32 f., 58 f.; Cavendish, *Sci. Pap.*, 1921, ii, 307 f.
[2] Harcourt, (1), 31, 63 f.; *id.*, (2), 500; Wilson, (1), 28.

in 1772[1] which is not wholly accurate, and says that, with 'a small variation of circumstances', he found 'nearly the same result'.

Water Analysis

In a paper on pump-water from Rathbone Place, London,[2] Cavendish says that in 1765 he noticed the deposition of calcareous earth on boiling the water, which also separated as a scurf on the surface of the water on exposure to air. On adding a solution of corrosive sublimate a precipitate was formed, a property which 'does not take place, in any considerable degree, in most of the London waters'. He proved that the 'calcareous earth' (calcium carbonate) was held in solution by fixed air:

the suspension [solution] of the earth [calcium carbonate] in the Rathbone-place water, is owing merely to its being united to more than its natural proportion of fixed air: as we have shewn that this earth is actually united to more than double its natural proportion of fixed air, and also that it is immediately precipitated, either by driving off the superfluous fixed air by heat, or absorbing it by the addition of a proper quantity of lime water.

He found some magnesia in the deposit formed on boiling. Finding similar results with other waters, which gave a precipitate with lime water, he thought it 'reasonable to conclude, that the unneutralised earth, in all waters, is suspended merely by being united to more than its natural proportion of fixed air', viz. 'more than double its natural proportion', and precipitated by boiling or by the addition of a proper proportion of lime water.

He refers to Brownrigg's observation 'that a great deal of fixed air is contained in Spa water',[3] and collected the gas contained in Rathbone Place water by heating 411 oz. of the water in a large tin pan occupied by a dome-shaped funnel with the upper narrow end still under water, a bottle filled with the water being inverted over it. On heating the water in the pan bubbles passed into the bottle, which was taken off by putting a small ladle under its mouth. The gas was found to be 66 oz. measures of fixed air with $8\frac{3}{4}$ oz. of common air, the latter detected by the noise of its explosion with hydrogen and its specific gravity. The analysis of 1 pint or 7315 grains of the water was (as recalculated by Wilson): solid residue 17·5 gr. containing volatile alkali equivalent to carbonate of ammonia 0·9, carbonate of lime (and a little magnesia) 8·4, free carbon dioxide 4·65, sulphate of lime 1·2, chloride of sodium and sulphate of magnesia 7·9. This is an early water analysis.

Cavendish found no nitrate, although he says 'many waters contain a good deal of neutral salt composed of the nitrous acid, united to a calcareous earth' (calcium nitrate); other London waters had been found 'to contain a considerable proportion of nitrous salt'. The distillate from the water contained a little volatile alkali (ammonia); on redistilling this in a small retort a smell of ammonia was observed.

Cavendish does not record the experiment of passing an excess of fixed air

---

[1] *Phil. Trans.*, 1772, lxii, 162; E & O, 1774, i, 129.
[2] Experiments on Rathbone Place Water: *Phil. Trans.*, 1767, lvii, 92–108; recd. 11 December 1766, read 19 February 1767; *Sci. Pap.*, ii, 102; Wilson, (1), 209 f.
[3] *Phil. Trans.*, 1765, lv, 218; see p. 123 and Van Helmont, Vol. II, p. 228.

into lime water, but he saturated rain water with fixed air and added 11 oz. of this solution to $6\frac{1}{2}$ oz. of lime water, when: 'the mixture became turbid on first mixing, but quickly recovered its transparency on shaking, and has remained so for upwards of a year.' He found that it was precipitated by adding lime water and says the solution contains twice as much fixed air as normally saturates the lime contained in it.

Lassone (De Lasône) found that Vichy water contained an absorbent earth, a ferruginous matter, and a 'spirituous principle' which perhaps keeps them in solution and causes the water to effervesce with acids:[1]

un principe spiritueux . . . qui vrai-semblablement est le principal agent qui tient cette terre suspendue . . . enfin que ce même principe aërien est la cause d'une partie de l'effervescence qui ces eaux font avec tous les acides.

A quantitative analysis of Kilburn water, containing hydrogen sulphide, was made by Schmeisser.[2] After Cavendish's work, Lane,[3] at the suggestion of Dr. Watson junr.,[4] showed that iron is similarly held in solution by fixed air. Lane exposed a wide-mouthed bottle containing half a pint of distilled water and 60 grains of steel filings over fermenting molasses, so that the fixed air entered the bottle. The clear liquor decanted had a ferruginous taste, turned an inky colour with infusion of galls or green tea, and on exposure to air deposited an ochry sediment. Lane's experiment thus proved that iron can be held in solution (as ferrous bicarbonate) in chalybeate water.

Timothy Lane (June 1734–5 July 1807), F.R.S. 1770, a London apothecary, also carried out electrical researches, inventing an electrometer;[5] and published short papers on human calculi[6] and magnetic oxide of iron.[7]

Equivalents

In his analysis of Rathbone Place water (1767; see p. 319) Cavendish[8] speaks of using in an experiment 'as much fixed alcali, as was equivalent to $46\frac{8}{10}$ grains of calcareous earth, i.e. which would saturate as much acid', thus introducing the name 'equivalent'. In 1788[9] Cavendish determined the strength of oil of vitriol by precipitating lead sulphate (plumbum vitriolatum) by lead acetate (sugar of lead), and says he computed the strength 'on the supposition that a quantity of oil of vitriol, sufficient to produce 100 parts of plumbum vitriolatum, will dissolve 33 of marble; as I found by experiment that so much oil of vitriol would saturate as much fixed alkali [potash] as a quantity of nitrous [nitric] acid sufficient to dissolve 33 of marble'. Since the molecular weights of lead sulphate and calcium carbonate are 303 and 100, the ratio is $PbSO_4/CaCO_3 = 100/33$, as Cavendish found. This is a recognition of the law of reciprocal or equivalent proportions before its publication by Richter in

[1] AdS, 1771, h 41, m 1.
[2] Phil. Trans., 1792, lxxxii, 115; Johann Gottfried Schmeisser, Osterode, Harz, 24 June 1767–Hamburg, 5 February 1837, lived for some years in London and travelled in Scotland; he also published on strontianite, Phil. Trans., 1794, lxxxiv, 418.
[3] Phil. Trans., 1769, lix, 216.   [4] Pringle, Six Discourses, 1783, 16.
[5] Phil. Trans., 1767, lvii, 451; Priestley, History of Electricity, 2 ed., 1769, 499.
[6] Phil. Trans., 1791, lxxxi, 223.   [7] Ib., 1805, xcv, 281.   [8] Sci. Pap., ii, 108.
[9] Experiments on the Freezing of Acids; Phil. Trans., 1788, lxxviii, 166; Sci. Pap., ii, 221.

1792 (see p. 676). Cavendish failed to generalise the result and gives no hint that the determination of other equivalents would be important.

Maxwell[1] noted that the weights of salts taken as equivalent in making up solutions for determining the electrical conductivities (p. 305) are numerically nearly the same as the values on the standard $H = 1$, except in the case of common salt, probably because Cavendish took 100 grains of marble as standard, the molecular weight being $CaCO_3 = 100$. It is improbable that he took $H = 1$, since his own experiments 'left it doubtful whether inflammable air was always of the same kind'. These experiments were made in January 1777.

Name used by Cavendish	Modern symbol	Weight used by Cavendish	Modern equivalent
Sea salt	NaCl	37·2	58·5
Sal Sylvii	KCl	74	74·5
Sal ammoniac	NH_4Cl	51	53·5
Calcined Glauber's salt	$\frac{1}{2}Na_2SO_4$	69	71
Quadrangular nitre	$NaNO_3$	89	85
Calc. S.S.A.	$\frac{1}{2}NaCO_3$?	346	$\frac{1}{4} \times 332$
f[ixed] alk[ali]	$\frac{1}{2}K_2CO_3$	139	$\frac{1}{2} \times 138$
Oil of vitriol	$\frac{1}{2}H_2SO_4$	48	49
Spirit of salt	$HCl + xH_2O$	130	$36·5 + 18x$

The identity of 'Calc. S.S.A.' is doubtful; it was taken as 'Calcined salsola soda alkali' by P. T. Main,[2] but it may mean 'sal soda Alicante'. His specimen was probably crude. Cavendish says the weights of the salts were 'such that the quantity of acid in each should be equivalent to that in a solution of salt in 29 of water'.

Eudiometry

In 'An Account of a New Eudiometer'[3] Cavendish examined the great discrepancies in the results of various investigations on the 'goodness' of air as determined by Priestley's method (see p. 259) of measuring the contraction ensuing when air is mixed over water with nitrous gas (nitric oxide). He refers to the Abbé Fontana's eudiometer (see p. 323) and showed that the differences resulted from variations in the method of mixing the gases and the time the gases are allowed to stand before shaking with the water. This, in turn, depended on the fact that 'the same quantity of nitrous air goes further in phlogisticating a given quantity of respirable air' when the nitric oxide is added to the atmospheric air than when the air is added to the nitric oxide, and the nitric acid formed may be more or less phlogisticated (in modern terminology, in different degrees of oxidation). Cavendish says: 'we may safely conclude, that it is this circumstance of the nitrous air going further in phlogisticating common air in some circumstances than in others, which is the cause that the diminution in trying the purity of air by the nitrous test is so much greater in some methods of mixing them than in others.' The purity of

[1] Cavendish, Sci. Pap., i, 28, 430; see 320 for facsimile of Cavendish's note.
[2] Maxwell, in Cavendish, Sci. Pap., i, 431.
[3] Phil. Trans., 1783, lxxiii, 106; Sci. Pap., ii, 127.

the water and of the nitrous air also influenced the results. He worked out a standard method, using distilled water and nitrous air from copper and nitric acid, and says that: 'During the last half of the year 1781, I tried the air of near 60 different days, in order to find whether it was sensibly more phlogisticated at one time than another; but found no difference that I could be sure of, though the wind and weather on those days were very various; some of them being very fair and clear, others very wet, and others very foggy.' In some cases 'the air of London appeared rather the purest, and sometimes that of Kensington [then in the country]; but the difference was never more than might proceed from the error of the experiment'.

Phlogisticated air (nitrogen) was prepared for use in these experiments by shaking air with a solution of liver of sulphur (which he made by boiling fixed alkali, lime, and flowers of sulphur with water), or by allowing air to stand in contact with a mixture of iron filings and sulphur; but these methods were not used by Cavendish in testing the goodness of common air. He determined the quantities of the gases used by weighing the vessels containing them immersed in water, the nitrous air being put into a globular glass vessel by a small glass measuring jar with a handle, and the atmospheric air contained in a small cylinder from which it was forced by water to pass in small bubbles through a stopcock into the nitrous air, which was kept shaken. One vol. of common air was mixed with $1\frac{1}{4}$ vols. of nitrous air. When the nitrous air was added to the common air, equal volumes were used:

When a small quantity of nitrous air comes in contact with a large quantity of common air, it is more completely deprived of its phlogiston [is more oxidised], and is absorbed by the water in a more dephlogisticated state than when a small quantity of common air comes in contact with a large quantity of nitrous. . . . As to the common air, as it is completely phlogisticated [has its oxygen removed] in both methods, it most likely suffers an equal diminution in both . . . and if the nitrous air is added slowly to the common, without being in contact with water, the mixture will be found to be still more phlogisticated [the nitric oxide more oxidised] than in the method, where the two airs are in contact with water at the time of mixing.

Cavendish called the diminution in volume on mixing the air and nitric oxide the *test* of the air:

The highest test I ever observed was 1·100, the lowest 1·068, the mean 1·082. . . . Thus, if the test of any air [gas] is found to be the same as that of a mixture of equal parts of common and phlogisticated air [nitrogen], I would say that it was half as good as common air; or, for shortness, I would say, that its standard was $\frac{1}{2}$: and, in general, if its test was the same as that of a mixture of one part of common air and x of phlogisticated air, I would say, that its standard was $1/(1+x)$. In like manner, if one part of this air would bear to be mixed with x of phlogisticated air, in order to make its test the same as that of common air, I would say, that it was $1+x$ times as good as common air, or that its standard was $1+x$; consequently, if common air, as Mr. Scheele and La Voisier suppose, consists of a mixture of dephlogisticated and phlogisticated air, the standard of any air is in proportion to the quantity of pure dephlogisticated air in it. . . . Suppose the test of a mixture of D parts of dephlogisticated air with P of phlogisticated air is the same as that of common air, then is the standard of the dephlogisticated air $(D+P)/D$. Now let δ parts of this dephlogisticated air be mixed with ϕ parts of phlogisticated air, the standard of the mixture will be $[(D+P)/D] \times [\delta/(\delta+\phi)]$.

The standard of pure phlogisticated air is zero, that of pure dephlogisticated air was found to be 4·8, and $100/4·8 = 20·83$, which is the percentage by volume of oxygen. Scheele and Lavoisier had found 25 per cent, and Priestley nearly as much, whilst Cavendish's result is very near the correct value. Cavendish also was the first, in 1784, to analyse air brought from the upper atmosphere by a balloon, finding it practically the same as that at ground level.[1]

The name *eudiometer* (Greek, ϵὐδία, fine weather, μέτρον, measure) was introduced[2] by Count Marsiglio Landriani (Milan ?–Vienna before 1816), the Court Marshal of the Duke of Saxony-Teschen in Vienna, who published papers on chemistry, heat, electricity, meteorology, etc.; with Moscati on several species of factitious air and the preparation of dephlogisticated air.[3] Landriani made a 'eudiometrical tour' through Italy, and wrote on 17 November 1776 to Priestley[4] that he had found reputedly bad air 'to be so, to a very great degree of exactness, by this instrument of mine', the air on mountains being purer than that in valleys. H. B. de Saussure, on the other hand, found with a nitric oxide eudiometer the air better in the valleys among the Alps, and at Geneva purer than that on the tops of high mountains.[5]

The most accurate eudiometer was said to be that of the Abbé Fontana, in which the graduated tube was long and narrow, and provided with a wide-necked funnel through which the air and nitric oxide were rapidly passed.[6] Fontana[7] found little variation in the salubrity of air in different places, and ascribed previous varying results of others to experimental errors. He found that air expelled from water is somewhat richer in dephlogisticated air than atmospheric air.

Felice Fontana (Pomarolo, nr. Roverto, 15 April 1730–Florence, 11 January 1805) also published experiments on fixed air,[8] and the solution of mercury in nitric acid and the evolution of oxygen on heating the residue,[9] in which he showed that nitrous air (NO) does not redden litmus. He found[10] that 2 vols. of dephlogisticated air and 5 vols. of nitrous air mixed over water diminished by $5\frac{1}{2}$ measures, and 2 vols. of common air and 1 vol. of nitrous air by 1 measure. He described[11] quantitative experiments on heating red precipitate of mercury, the loss of weight being approximately the weight of the dephlogisticated air, and the original weight of mercury used in making the red precipitate was

[1] *Sci. Pap.*, ii, 22; Biot and Gay-Lussac, *J. de Phys.*, 1804, lix, 314; *Nicholson's J.*, 1805, x, 278, found the same result.
[2] *Ricerche Fisiche intorno alla Salubrità dell'Aria*, 8°, Milan, 1775 (BN R. 12797); German tr., 8°, Basel, 1778 (Poggendorff, (1), i, 1366; Wiegleb, (2), 1791, ii, 175); Black, *Lectures*, 1803, ii, 523; Thomson, (2), 1807, iv, 56; Murray, 1806, ii, 43 f., 458 f., 481 f.; J. C. Fischer, 1806, vii, 1006 f. A history of eudiometry is given by Göttling, *Praktische Anleitung zur prüfenden und zerlegenden Chemie*, Jena, 1802, 217 f., and *Elementarbuch der chemischen Experimentir-kunst*, Jena, 1808, i, 44 f.
[3] Amoretti and Soave, *Opuscoli Scelti sulle scienze e sulle Arti*, 4°, Milan, 1780, iii, 122; Landriani, *Opuscoli fisico-chimici*, 8°, Milan, 1781 (with section: Della formazione dell' aria senza flogisto, con gli acidi minerali).
[4] E & O, 1777, iii, 380 (Appendix).
[5] *Voyages dans les Alpes*, 4°, Neuchatel, 1779, i, 514–17; in Amoretti and Soave, *Opuscoli*, Milan, 1780, iii, 383.
[6] Fontana, *Descrizioni ed usi di alcuni stromenti per misurare la salubrità dell' aria*, 4°, Florence, 1774; *id.*, *Obs. Phys.*, 1785, xxvi, 339; Priestley, E & O, 1777, iii, p. xi; Kopp, (1), iii, 209.
[7] *Phil. Trans.*, 1779, lxix, 337, 432.   [8] *Obs. Phys.*, 1775, vi, 280.
[9] *Recherches physiques sur la Nature de l'Air Nitreux et de l'Air Déphlogistiqué*, Paris, 1776 (184 pp.).
[10] *Ib.*, 55.   [11] *Ib.*, 117–21.

recovered. Fontana thought[1] that metals gain weight on calcination in air by losing phlogiston and at the same time taking up a 'third substance', which is not common air but can be transformed into air when deprived of its natural phlogiston.

Fontana also published on formic acid and vegetable acids,[2] potash and soda,[3] the analysis of malachite,[4] inflammable air,[5] and bile.[6] His measurements on the densities of gases[7] were important but his most outstanding work was a series of experiments on respiration, the calcination of metals, adsorption of gases by charcoal (see p. 296), the production of inflammable gas from water and heated charcoal, etc., in which, e.g., he showed that the weight remains constant in chemical reactions, and that different gases follow Boyle's law.[8]

Ingen Housz[9] described some eudiometers which he thought better than Fontana's, involving the use of an india-rubber bottle, but the experiments seem to be very crude and the results (none are given) would be worthless. Ingen Housz, with a nitric oxide eudiometer,[10] found that air above the sea and on the sea coast was appreciably better than ordinary air, a result welcomed by proprietors of boarding establishments in seaside towns. Magellan[11] put two or more equal measures of air and nitric oxide over water in a wide vessel, and measured the gaseous residue, remarking that 'Mr. Cavallo . . . and other Fontanists . . . throw one air after another into a narrow tube'. Cavallo[12] used a tube 16–17 in. long and $\frac{1}{2}$–$\frac{2}{3}$ in. diameter, sealed at one end and with a funnel at the other.

Senebier[13] showed that the nitric oxide eudiometer is inexact, even when operated over mercury (although he desisted in these experiments because of the effect of the cold mercury on his hands, which were affected by rheumatism); he found that the results depended on the time of contact, extending over months.

Johann Friederich Luz[14] improved Fontana's method. Berthollet[15] and T. de

[1] Ib., 128, 155.   [2] Obs. Phys., 1778, xii, 64.   [3] Obs. Phys., 1778, xii, 376.
[4] Obs. Phys., 1778, xi, 509.   [5] Amoretti and Soave, Opuscoli scelti, 1780, iii, 334–47.
[6] Mém. Acad. Turin, 1786–7 (1788), iii, 397.
[7] In Cavallo, A Treatise on the Nature and Properties of Air and other Permanently Elastic Fluids, London, 1781, 422.
[8] Mem. Mat. Fis. Soc. Ital., 1782, i, 648–706 (dated 20 October 1781); on Fontana, see Vitali, NBG, 1857, xviii, 103; Guaraschi, in Diergart, 1909, 477 f.
[9] Phil. Trans., 1776, lxvi, 257–67 (letter to Pringle); 1790, lxxx, 354; Obs. Phys., 1785, xxvi, 339–59; Expériences sur les Végétaux, 1780.
[10] Nouvelles Expériences et Observations sur divers Objets de Physique, Paris, 1785–9, i, 289; ii, 137, 227.
[11] Description of a Glass Apparatus . . . together with a Description of two New Eudiometers. Examination of the Strictures of Mr. T. Cavallo, F.R.S., upon these Eudiometers, 3 ed., 1783, 67; Priestley, E & O, 1777, iii, 379; Magellan's eudiometer is described by Girardin, Obs. Phys., 1778, xi, 248 (plate).
[12] A Treatise on the Nature and Properties of Air, 4°, London, 1781, 344: 'The Author's method of determining the degree of purity of air.'
[13] Recherches sur l'influence de la lumière solaire pour metamorphoser l'air fixe en air pur par la végétation, Geneva, 1783, 297 f. (Expériences nouvelles, propres à fair voir l'inexactitude & peut-être l'inutilité des Eudiomètres qui exigent l'usage de l'air nitreux).
[14] Anweisung das Eudiometer des Herrn Abt von Fontana zu verfertigen und zum Gebrauch bequemer zu machen ingleichen durch eine sehr einfache Einrichtung in kurzer Zeit Mineralwasser zu verfertigen, Nürnberg and Leipzig, 1784 (78 pp. and plate, BM).
[15] Statique Chimique, Paris, 1803, i, 514 (with summary).

Saussure[1] found with glowing phosphorus that there is an expansion after the oxygen is removed owing to the evolution of phosphorus vapour; but de Saussure obtained good results with the maximum contraction. Cavendish noticed in 1781 that pure oxygen is scarcely acted upon by cold phosphorus:[2] 'The test by new Eud. large bott. was 5·088 . . . 3193 of this air were put into a bott. & a bit of my fathers phosphorus stick on pointed glass kept in it for a day when it was found that only 25 gra. were absorbed.'

Burning phosphorus was used by Achard,[3] Scheele,[4] Seguin,[5] Reboul,[6] and T. de Saussure.[7] Alkali sulphide solution was used by Scheele,[8] Guyton de Morveau,[9] Marti,[10] Hope,[11] and in a modification of Hope's apparatus by W. Henry.[12] Adam Wilhelm von Hauch (Copenhagen; 1755–1838) described a new eudiometer.[13] F. Humboldt[14] found that 1000 vols. of air contain 274 of oxygen, 718 of nitrogen, and 8 of carbon dioxide. He believed that the slow oxidation of phosphorus does not remove the oxygen completely; the rest is removed by nitric oxide but some oxygen is lost in the form of 'phosphures d'azote oxydées', formed from the phosphorus and air. This conclusion was contested by Parrot,[15] who invented an 'oxygenometer or new phosphorus eudiometer' consisting of a vertical tube with a wider piece at the top, closed by an iron screw, containing a stick of phosphorus, and standing over mercury.

The Composition of Water

Early in 1775 Priestley found that when inflammable air (hydrogen) is exploded with dephlogisticated air, the report is much louder than with common air;[16] 'the effect far exceeded my expectations, and it has never failed to surprize every person before whom I have made the experiment.' He used a $1\frac{1}{2}$ oz. bottle with a $\frac{1}{4}$ in. opening and amused himself by carrying these corked or stoppered bottles about and exploding them. 'The repercussion is very considerable; and the heat produced by the explosion very sensible to the hand' holding the phial, which must be 'a very strong one; otherwise it will certainly burst with the explosion'. With a mixture of 1 vol. of 'highly dephlogisticated air' and 2 of inflammable air the report was 'not less than forty or fifty times as loud as with common air', judged from the distances when the sound was heard.

Macquer[17] reported that the detonation of a mixture of hydrogen and oxygen

[1] *Recherches Chimiques sur la Végétation*, Paris, 1804, p. v.
[2] Harcourt, (1), lithogr. diary, p. 56 [p. 26] 17 June 1781.
[3] *Mém. Acad. Berlin*, 1778, 91.   [4] KAH, 1779, xl, 50; see p. 222.
[5] *Ann. Chim.*, 1791, ix, 243; *J. der Phys.* (Gren), 1792, vi, 148.
[6] *Ann. Chim.*, 1792, xiii, 38; *N. J. der Phys.* (Gren), 1795, i, 374.
[7] *Recherches Chimiques sur la Végétation*, Paris, 1804, p. v.
[8] *On Air and Fire*, 1777, §§ 8–11, 42.
[9] Nicholson's *J.*, 1797, i, 268; *Phil. Mag.*, 1799, iii, 191.   [10] *J. de Phys.*, 1801, lii, 173.
[11] Nicholson's *J.*, 1803, vi, 61, 210.   [12] *Elements of Experimental Chemistry*, 9 ed., 1823, i, 290.
[13] Bestrivelse af en nye Luftprøber eller Eudiometer: *Skrifter Videns. Selsk., Nye Saml.* (Copenhagen), 1793, iv, 537–44.
[14] *Versuche über die chemische Zerlegung des Luftkreises und über einige andere Gegenstände der Naturlehre*, Brunswick, 1799, 67; *Ann. Chim.*, 1798, xxvii, 141–60.
[15] Voigt's *Magazin für d. neus. Zustand der Naturkde.*, 1802, iv, 75; *Ann. Phys.*, 1802, x, 193; long account in J. C. Fischer, 1806, vii, 1039.
[16] *Philosophical Empiricism*, 1775, 21; E & O, 1775, ii, 98.
[17] *Dictionnaire de Chymie*, 1778, ii, 312.

(air très pur) was very violent, and it is wise to wrap even a thick glass bottle with a thick cloth before firing the mixture. Macquer used a pint bottle and says that, judging by the effect, the explosion of 12 to 15 pints would equal that of a large piece of artillery and would have to be carried out in an iron or brass vessel as strong as a cannon or mortar. He makes no mention of firing the gas in a closed vessel.

Priestley (1779) speaks of 'the mode of experimenting introduced by that excellent philosopher Mr. Volta; who fires inflammable air in common air, by the electric spark, and consequently can determine the exact proportion of the inflammable air decomposed in a given quantity of common air'. In 1777 he printed a letter of 10 December 1776 from Volta, who said he was sending a pamphlet on inflammable air and its explosion with common air (see p. 814).[1] The experiments of firing mixtures of inflammable air with common air or dephlogisticated air in closed glass or metal vessels by an electric spark, made by Priestley, Warltire, and Cavendish, thus go back to Volta's researches.[2]

Volta in letters of 8, 14 and 15 January 1777 described an 'electric pistol' in which a cork was forcibly blown out of a closed tube by the explosion by an electric spark of a mixture of hydrogen and oxygen.[3] Volta also invented what he calls in a letter to Priestley 'a new eudiometer' (un nuovo eudiometro) (Fig. 30).[4] The letter (November) describes the inflammation of a mixture of common air and inflammable air in a closed graduated glass eudiometer provided with stopcocks and a brass wire for passing the electric spark. A second letter to Priestley[5] describes experiments on the limits of inflammation of mixtures of hydrogen with air and oxygen, and the contraction on explosion, with explanations based on the phlogiston theory. An improved graduated glass eudiometer with a funnel and a metal stopcock below, and a metal cap with an insulated sparking wire at the top (Fig. 31), was described by Volta in 1790.[6]

FIG. 30. VOLTA'S
FIRST EUDIOMETER.

In an unpublished research made about 1781 on the 'strength' of gaseous explosions, Cavendish fired the mixture by an electric spark in a brass cylinder attached to a lever. A hole in the bottom of the cylinder was closed loosely by a fixed peg. The height which the suitably weighted cylinder rose was measured. 'There

[1] Priestley, E & O, 1777, iii, 381; E & O Nat. Phil., 1779, i, 381; Harcourt, (1), 35.

[2] Arago, Ann. Chim., 1833, liv, 402 (in Éloge of Volta, 396–444): Volta est le premier qui les ait répétées dans des vas clos (1777). C'est donc à lui qu'appartient l'appareil dont Cavendish se servait en 1781 pour opérer la synthèse de l'eau, pour egendre ce liquide à l'aide de ses deux principes constituans gazeux.

[3] Lettres de M. A. Volta ... sur l'air inflammable des marais; aux quelles on a ajouté trois lettres du même auteur tirées du Journal de Milan, Strasbourg, 1778; Opere, 1816, iii, 131; Opere, Milan, 1928, vi, 103, 121; summary in Amoretti and Soave, Opuscoli Scelti, 4°, Milan, 1784, iii, 121.

[4] Volta, in Amoretti and Soave, op. cit., 1784, iii, 432–9; Obs. Phys., 1778, xii, 365 (November) and plate III; Opere, 1816, iii, 176; Opere, Milan, 1928, vi, 176, 291, 393 (photograph of Volta's eudiometer in Como); 1929, vii, 61, 173.

[5] Obs. Phys., 1779, xiii, 278–303, and Plate I (April).

[6] Annali di Chimica, 1790, i, 171; J. de Phys., 1805, xiii, 151; Opere, 1816, iii, 195, and Plate II.

seemed to be some minute interval of time between the electric spark and the explosion.'[1]

In 1781 Watt suspected that an engine announced by the Hornblowers was worked by heated air or gas, or was 'a caloric air engine', and set Boulton experimenting with the assistance of Priestley. About that time Boulton fitted up a laboratory for experiments on gases. In a letter to Watt of 28 July 1781, Boulton said Priestley had proceeded with the experiments and had come to the conclusion that 'there is nothing to be feared from any of the tribe of gases which cannot be procured nearly so cheap as steam'.[2] Priestley in the same year (1781) had learned of some experiments made by Warltire.

John Warltire, whom Priestley[3] calls 'a good chymist', was born about 1738–9 in Wolverhampton, near Birmingham, died in Tamworth, and was buried on 23 August 1810. He spent most of his life lecturing for a living. He was one of the first 45 honorary members of the Manchester Literary and Philosophical Society. He published several semi-popular works, mostly lectures or intended for use in his lectures, and also supplied chemicals (he provided Priestley with the red precipitate from which he first obtained oxygen, see p. 258) and apparatus.[4] Erasmus Darwin[5] says he was assisted in his experiments by 'Mr. Warltire, a celebrated itinerant philosopher', and Josiah Wedgwood[6] said in 1779 that Warltire was 'a warm admirer of the Docters [Priestley], & personally acquainted with him. He often mentions him in his lectures with every mark of honor & respect, calling him the Newton of the age'.

Warltire published in London and Nottingham a small pamphlet:

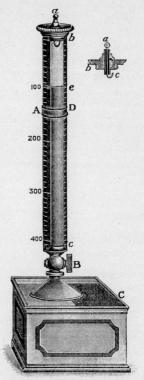

FIG. 31. VOLTA'S IMPROVED EUDIOMETER.

The gas was collected through the funnel at the base over water in C. The ring AD was used to read off the level *e* on the graduated scale. Details of the sparking device are shown at *abc*.

Concise Essays upon various Philosophical & Chemical Subjects proper to be read before or after attending Courses of Chemistry or Experimental Philosophy. Under the following heads, viz. Matter and Motion, Chemical Principles and Processes, Useful Tables, And A Vocabulary; Nottingham; Printed for the author by H. Cox MDCCLXXXI; pp. 61, vii (unnumbered), 69, 70 (London Library); another ed., London, n.d. but probably after 1775 (not 1770, as in BM *Cat.*); on the last page it is stated that: 'All the instruments contained in the 3 plates are introduced in the author's courses, with his other extensive apparatus', but there were no plates in the Nottingham ed.

[1] *Sci. Pap.*, ii, 318.   [2] Smiles, 1874, 236, 238, 298.
[3] E & O, 1775, ii, 34; McKie, *Endeavour*, 1951, x, 46.
[4] H. Maclachlan, *English Education under the Test Acts*, Manchester, 1931, 203, mentions that Warltire, who 'has been a lecturer for about 50 years on these subjects' (natural philosophy), had given a course in 1803 at Rotherham.
[5] *Phil. Trans.*, 1788, lxxviii, 43.   [6] *Correspondence, 1772–80*, 1903, ii, 371.

In this[1] he says 'Explosive mixtures are made by burning pure air [oxygen] and inflammable air [hydrogen] together; the best proportion is pure air *one* and inflammable air *two*'. Warltire's earliest 'very curious' experiments are reported in a letter to Priestley dated 3 January 1777.[2] He burnt a jet of inflammable air at the end of a bent tube two inches under water and rising four inches above the water in a bell jar (see Scheele, p. 223):

'A receiver, such as for an air-pump, is to be brought over the burning air, and its edge sunk in the water upon the bend of the tube. The inflammable air continues to burn as long as there is common air in the receiver capable of supporting the flame. . . . About as much inflammable air vanishes as is equal to the bulk of the common air . . . the common air is contracted full a fifth part of its original dimensions; immediately after the flame is extinguished, there appears through almost the whole of the receiver, a fine powdery substance like a whitish cloud, and the air in the glass is left perfectly noxious.'

In a letter to Priestley dated Birmingham 18 April 1781 Warltire says he exploded inflammable and common airs in a copper globe holding 3 wine pints, with a screw stopper, by an electric spark; on weighing after cooling:

'a loss of weight was always found, but not constantly the same; upon an average it was two grains . . . I have fired air in glass vessels since I saw you [Priestley] venture to do it, and I have observed, as you did, that, though the glass was clean and dry before, it became dewey, and was lined with a sooty substance.'

Priestley was, therefore, the first to observe the deposition of moisture. Priestley comments:

'I do not think . . . that so very bold an opinion as that of the latent heat of bodies contributing to the weight, should be received without more experiments, and made upon a still larger scale. . . . I must add, that the moment he [Warltire] saw the *moisture* on the inside of the close glass vessel, in which I afterwards fired the inflammable air, he said that it confirmed an opinion he had long entertained, viz. that common air deposits its moisture when it is phlogisticated. With me it was a mere random experiment, made to entertain a few philosophical friends [of the Lunar Society] . . . After we had fired the mixture of *common* and inflammable air, we did the same with dephlogisticated and inflammable air; and though, in this case, the light was much more intense, and the heat much greater, the explosion was not so violent, but that a glass tube about an inch in diameter, and not exceeding one tenth of an inch in thickness, bore it without injury. It is evident . . . that little is to be expected from the firing of inflammable air in comparison with the effects of gunpowder, besides that after firing of inflammable air, there is a great diminution of the bulk of air, whereas in the firing of gunpowder there is a production of air.'[3]

Priestley does not then say water is deposited with inflammable air and *dephlogisticated* air. Even in 1801 Thomson[4] thought 'from analogy' that there might be a slight loss in weight on exploding hydrogen and oxygen, 'but the difference, if it exists, can scarcely be sensible.'

[1] Nottingham, 1781, 44. [2] Priestley, E & O, 1777, iii, 365.
[3] Priestley, E & O *Nat. Phil.*, 1781, ii, *395–8; these starred pages are not bound up in all copies (they are not in mine), and were apparently issued when, or perhaps after, the book had been printed; the material is reprod. in full in Muirhead, pp. xxx–xxxiii; Brougham, i, 57; the passage in Cavendish's paper, *Phil. Trans.*, 1784, lxxiv, 126, quoted in the text on p. 330, is ambiguous as between Priestley and Warltire; see Wilson, (1), 81, 108, 281.
[4] *Ency. Brit., Suppl.*, 1801, I, i, 293.

Cavendish's Synthesis of Water

In considering Cavendish's experiments in which water was formed quantitatively from measured volumes of hydrogen and oxygen (or air) his nomenclature must be kept in mind:

dephlogisticated air = oxygen
inflammable air   = hydrogen
phlogisticated air   = nitrogen
nitrous air   = nitric oxide
nitrous acid   = nitric acid
dephlogistication   = oxidation.

Cavendish begins his paper, 'Experiments on Air',[1] by saying:

The following experiments were made principally with a view to find out the cause of the diminution which common air is well known to suffer by all the various ways in which it is phlogisticated, and to discover what becomes of the air thus lost or condensed.

At that time air was believed to be 'phlogisticated' in six different ways, by: (i) the calcination of metals, (ii) the burning of sulphur or phosphorus, (iii) mixture with nitrous air, (iv) respiration, (v) explosion with inflammable air, and (vi) by the electric spark. Cavendish doubts the last process. He points out that previous experimenters (Priestley and Lavoisier) had proved that no fixed air is formed by the calcination of metals; he had 'never heard of any fixed air being produced by the burning of sulphur and phosphorus', and he found that none is formed on mixing common air and nitrous air if they are first washed with lime water.[2] He showed that when common or dephlogisticated air and inflammable air (first washed with lime water) are exploded, 'not the least cloud was produced in the lime-water, when the inflammable air was mixed with common air, and only a very slight one, or rather diminution of transparency, when it was combined with dephlogisticated air.' He showed that no nitric acid is formed (as Priestley thought possible) when sulphur was burnt in air over lime water, or when a solution of sulphur in milk of lime was shaken with air. He calls the calcium salts formed in these experiments 'selenite'; in the first it would be calcium sulphite and in the second thiosulphate.[3] Cavendish remarks that the two salts (which he does not distinguish) differ from gypsum (calcium sulphate) in solubility and a bitter taste. No vitriolic (sulphuric) acid was formed by mixing nitrous air with common air over distilled water, as was shown by neutralising with potash, when no potassium sulphate was formed.

Cavendish next proceeds to the process of exploding inflammable air with common air. He says the inflammable air was always made with zinc, except in two experiments when it was made with iron, the two giving the same results. In *all* cases, therefore, he used hydrogen, and not the miscellaneous

---

[1] *Phil. Trans.*, 1784, lxxiv, 119–53, read 15 January (the whole of the volume is dated 1784); *Sci. Pap.*, ii, 161–81; ACR, iii.
[2] Cf. Cavendish, *Ib.*, 170; *Sci. Pap.*, ii, 182.   [3] Wilson, (1), 233.

combustible gases afterwards used by Priestley (see p. 348). He mentions from Priestley:

'an experiment of Mr. Warltire's, in which it is said that, on firing a mixture of common and inflammable air by electricity in a close copper vessel holding about three pints, a loss of weight was always perceived, on an average about two grains. . . . It is also related, that on repeating the experiment in glass vessels, the inside of the glass, though clean and dry before, immediately became dewy; which confirmed an opinion he had long entertained [the ambiguous statement], that common air deposits its moisture by phlogistication.'

Cavendish repeated the experiment of exploding inflammable air and common air in a glass vessel, and says regarding the loss in weight:

it did not succeed with me; for though the vessel I used held more than Mr. Warltire's, namely, 24,000 grains of water [1·555 lit. or 2¾ pints], and though the experiment was repeated several times with different proportions of common and inflammable air, I could never perceive a loss of weight of more than one-fifth of a grain, and commonly none at all.

In his laboratory notes Cavendish records a loss of $\frac{2}{10}$ grain on firing and a further $\frac{1}{10}$ grain on standing; whenever there was a change in weight, it was always a slight *loss*.[1] In the paper he says: 'Dr. Priestley, I am informed, has since found the experiment not to succeed.' In all the experiments 'the inside of the glass globe became dewy, as observed by Mr. Warltire, but not the least sooty matter could be perceived'.

Cavendish gives a small table of the results of these experiments,[2] 'the bulk of the inflammable air being expressed in decimals of the common air':

Common air	Inflammable air	Diminution	Air remaining after the explosion	Test of this air in first method	Standard
	1,241	,686	1,555	,055	,0
1	1,055	,642	1,413	,063	,0
	,706	,647	1,059	,066	,0
	,423	,612	,811	,097	,03
	,331	,476	,855	,339	,27
	,206	,294	,912	,648	,58

The 'test of this air in first method' and 'standard' refer to the earlier paper dealing with the analysis of air by the eudiometer.[3]

Cavendish in his notes[4] says: 'From the 4th mixt it should seem as if 44 of infl. were suff to phlogist 100 of common in which case infl is very little more than $\frac{3}{10}$ of whole & the bulk mixt should be 0·803 of com. air.' In the paper[5] he says:

From the fourth experiment it appears, that 423 measures of inflammable air are nearly sufficient to completely phlogisticate 1000 of common air; and that the bulk of the air remaining after the explosion is then very little more than four-fifths of the common air employed; so that as common air cannot be reduced to a much less bulk than that by any method of phlogistication, we may safely conclude, that when they are

[1] Muirhead, xxxv.
[2] The original in Cavendish's note-book is reproduced by Harcourt, (1), 119 lithogr.
[3] *Phil. Trans.*, 1783, lxxiii, 106; *Sci. Pap.*, ii, 127; see p. 322.
[4] Harcourt, (1), 119 lithogr.   [5] *Phil. Trans.*, 1784, lxxiv, 128.

mixed in this proportion, and exploded, almost all the inflammable air, and about one-fifth of the common air, lose their elasticity, and are condensed into the dew which lines the glass.

Cavendish says:[1]

'There is the utmost reason to think, that dephlogisticated and phlogisticated air, as M. Lavoisier and Scheele suppose, are quite distinct substances, and not differing only in their degree of phlogistication; and that common air is a mixture of the two.'

Cavendish's analysis of air (see p. 322) corresponded with 20·83 per cent by volume of oxygen; the 1 vol. of common air contained 0·2083 vols. of oxygen, and the ratio of the combining volumes of hydrogen and oxygen will be 0·423/0·2083 = 2·03. Taking the modern figure 0·210 for the oxygen in air the result is 423/210 = 2·014. The figure 0·03 in the last column of the table shows that there was still a trace of oxygen in the final gas, and the figure 2·014 should, therefore, be slightly raised, say to 2·02. These experiments were made in a $2\frac{3}{4}$ pint globe.

'The better to examine the nature of this dew, 500,000 grain measures [$32\frac{1}{2}$ lit.] of inflammable air were burnt with about $2\frac{1}{2}$ times that quantity of common air, and the burnt air made to pass through a glass cylinder eight feet long and three-quarters of an inch in diameter, in order to deposit the dew.[2] The two airs were conveyed slowly into this cylinder by separate copper pipes, passing through a brass plate which stopped up the end of the cylinder; and as neither inflammable air nor common air can burn by themselves, there was no danger of the flame spreading into the magazines from which they were conveyed. Each of these magazines consisted of a large tin vessel, inverted into another vessel just big enough to receive it. The inner vessel communicated with the copper pipe, and the air was forced out of it by pouring water into the outer vessel; and in order that the quantity of common air expelled should be $2\frac{1}{2}$ times that of the inflammable, the water was let into the outer vessel by two holes in the bottom of the same tin pan, the hole which conveyed the water into that vessel in which the common air was confined being $2\frac{1}{2}$ times as big as the other. . . . By this means upwards of 135 grains of water were condensed in the cylinder, which had no taste nor smell, and which left no sensible sediment when evaporated to dryness; neither did it yield any pungent smell during the evaporation; in short, it seemed pure water . . . by this experiment it appears, that this dew is plain water, and consequently that almost all the inflammable air, and about one-fifth of the common air, are turned into pure water.'

The next step was to examine the combustion of inflammable air with dephlogisticated air:

'In order to examine the nature of the matter condensed on firing a mixture of dephlogisticated and inflammable air, I took a glass globe, holding 8800 grain measures [570 c.c.], furnished with a brass cock, and an apparatus for firing air by electricity. This globe was well exhausted by an air-pump, and then filled with a mixture of inflammable and dephlogisticated air, by shutting the cock, fastening a bent glass tube to its mouth, and letting up the end of it into a glass jar inverted into water, and containing a mixture of 19500 grain measures [1268 c.c.] of dephlogisticated air, and 37000 [2505 c.c.] of inflammable air; so that, upon opening the cock, some of this mixed air rushed through the bent tube, and filled the globe. In order to prevent any water from getting into this tube, while dipped under water to let it up into the glass jar, a bit of wax was stuck upon the end of it, which was rubbed off when raised above the surface of the water. The cock was then shut, and the included air fired by electricity, by which means almost all of it lost its elasticity. The cock was then again opened, so as to let in more of the same air, to supply the place of that destroyed by the explosion, which was again fired, and the operation continued till almost the whole of

[1] *Ib.*, 141.   [2] A sketch of this is in his note book; Harcourt, (1), 126 lithogr.

the mixture was let into the globe and exploded. By this means, though the globe held not more than the sixth part of the mixture, almost the whole of it was exploded therein, without any fresh exhaustion of the globe.'

By attaching a larger exhausted globe to the firing globe and opening the taps between them, the residual 'air' rushed from the firing globe into the larger globe until the pressure was equalised. By opening the larger globe under water the amount of 'burnt air' in it was found, and a simple proportion then gave 'the whole quantity of the burnt air' as 2950 grain measures (188·5 c.c.) of 'standard' 1·85 (i.e. containing 39 per cent of oxygen, since $1·85 \times 21 = 38·85$). Cavendish did not dry the gases admitted to the globe, and since the exhaustion was imperfect and the air contained in the bent tube was admitted to the globe, the globe at the end must have contained some nitrogen as well as the excess of oxygen. The residual 'burnt air', therefore, contained 1151 grain measures of oxygen and 1799 grain measures of nitrogen. This nitrogen must have come partly from the oxygen and hydrogen gases used, and if we assume that each gas contained the same percentage of impurity, and neglect the air in the tube and the nitrogen burnt by the excess oxygen, the hydrogen contained $(37000/56500) \times 1799 = 1178$, and the oxygen $(19500/56500) \times 1799 = 621$, volumes of nitrogen. The volumes of pure oxygen and hydrogen combining are therefore $(19500 - 1151 - 621) = 17728$ of oxygen and $(37000 - 1178) = 35822$ of hydrogen. The ratio of the combining volumes is thus $35822/17728 = 2·02$, in agreement with the first result (p. 331).

Cavendish had now proved that hydrogen and oxygen gases (called by any names we wish), mixed in proper proportions (practically 2 vols. to 1), can be completely converted into *their own weight* of water. He was the first to discover this experimental *fact*.[1] He could have published this result in 1781, but did not for the following reason. He says:

The liquor condensed in the globe, in weight about 30 grains, was sensibly acid to the taste, and by saturation with fixed alkali, and evaporation, yielded near two grains of nitre; so that it consisted of water united to a small quantity of nitrous acid. No sooty matter was deposited in the globe. The dephlogisticated air used in this experiment was procured from red precipitate, that is, from a solution of quicksilver in spirit of nitre distilled till it acquires a red colour.

Other specimens of dephlogisticated air, however, also gave an acid liquid, even that procured from the leaves of plants 'in the manner of Doctors Ingenhousz and Priestley'. The more dephlogisticated air was used in excess, the more acid was the liquid. When excess of inflammable air was used, or when common air was exploded with inflammable air, the liquid was not acid. The production of acid when excess of oxygen was used, and its non-production when excess of hydrogen was used, gave the clue. Its non-production when air was used instead of oxygen was because 'the explosion is too weak, and not accompanied with sufficient heat'. The acid was recognised as proceeding from some impurity in the gases: 'if those airs could be obtained perfectly pure, the whole would be condensed.' The true cause of the production of acid was established by later experiments, which Cavendish published in 1785 (see p. 338).

[1] Wilson, (1), 81.

Cavendish's paper of 1784 contains no diagram of his glass firing globe, but a long tradition has sketched in the lineaments of his famous 'eudiometer', a name which he himself never gave to the apparatus. His description of it corresponds with a thick glass bulb of 570 c.c. capacity, fitted with a brass stopcock and firing wires. There is a piece of apparatus in the Chemistry Department of the University of Manchester (Fig. 32) the pedigree of which is fairly complete, and it is highly probable that it is the apparatus made by Newman, Cavendish's instrument maker, and the one described in Cavendish's paper. Wilson[1] says:

'Cavendish left behind him an immense amount of apparatus, which was inherited by Lord George Cavendish. From him it passed into the possession of various parties, but the Earl of Burlington, Sir Humphry Davy, and Mr. Newman of Regent Street, obtained the greater part of it. By them or their heirs it has to a great extent been dispersed among those likely to value it.'

H. B. Dixon[2] said the Manchester globe:

'was given to him 40 years ago by the Rev. T. H. W. Hopkins, Fellow of Magdalen, with this history: It was originally made by Newman for Cavendish, and was brought back by Newman after Cavendish's death; it was purchased from Newman as Cavendish's instrument by Professor Daubeny, of Oxford, who left it to his friend Hopkins.'

The vessel is pear-shaped, of heavy nearly colourless glass, the lower neck thicker than the upper part. The lower neck has a heavy glass stopcock, below which is a brass stopcock with a screw for attaching to an air-pump plate or other apparatus. The glass stopcock is not mentioned by Cavendish.

FIG. 32. CAVENDISH'S FIRING GLOBE ('EUDIOMETER').

(From a photograph of what is believed to be the original apparatus in the University of Manchester.)

The upper part of the globe has a thick glass stopper ground to fit accurately. Through this stopper are cemented two wires, now apparently of brass (Dixon says 'platinum'), for firing the gas, and the stopper is held in place by a brass clamp with two screws, this clamp being attached to a collar passing round the upper part of the globe. Cavendish gives the capacity as 'about 8800 grain measures' or about 570 c.c., much less than the 'glass globe holding about three pints' which Roscoe and Schorlemmer[3] declare was used. They repeat a statement by Wilson[4] that: 'Cavendish . . . would not recognise the modern instrument as resembling any part of his apparatus, and it would startle him to hear it called his eudiometer.' Wilson[5] says he was unable to trace the glass globe-eudiometers described in Cavendish's paper of 1784.

A cylindrical brass vessel presented by Davy to the Royal Institution (where it still is)[6] is a brass cylinder about 6 in. by 2 in., closed at one end by a perforated plate, perhaps

[1] (1), 475.   [2] J. Soc. Chem. Ind., 1921, xl, 243R.
[3] Treatise on Chemistry, 1920, i, 20.   [4] (1), 42.   [5] (1), 475.
[6] Wilson, (1), 476; Partington, The Composition of Water, 1928, 27–8, and plate III.

for a stopcock, and fitted at the other end by a tapering stopcock. By the side of the opening in the plate is another opening through which is screwed a perforated nut containing a short piece of thermometer tube, the bore of which is filled with a wire passing into the cylinder and perhaps for passing a spark through a gas in the cylinder. Cavendish gives no description of this apparatus and the use which he made of it is not known.

We should have expected Cavendish to have concluded that: 'When in-flammable air and dephlogisticated air unite together they produce water, which is a compound of these two substances', but he was under the influence of the phlogiston theory, and what he says[1] is:

'I think we must allow that dephlogisticated air is in reality nothing but dephlogisti-cated water, or water deprived of its phlogiston; or, in other words, that water consists of dephlogisticated air united to phlogiston; and that inflammable air is either pure phlogiston, as Dr. Priestley and Mr. Kirwan suppose, or else water united to phlogis-ton; since, according to this supposition, these substances united together to form pure water . . . there seems the utmost reason to think, that dephlogisticated air is only water deprived of its phlogiston, and that inflammable air, as was before said, is either phlogisticated water, or else pure phlogiston; but in all probability the former.'

In a footnote he gives the reason for this preference. Whereas common or dephlogisticated air combines at the ordinary temperature with nitrous air (nitric oxide), taking the phlogiston from it (*i.e.*, oxidising it) and forming red fumes of 'phlogisticated nitrous acid', yet dephlogisticated air will not act upon inflammable air below a red heat. Hence it is improbable that inflammable air can be pure phlogiston, which might be expected to unite at once with dephlogisticated air.

That hydrogen and oxygen do not combine unless heated was explained by Priestley[2] by supposing that 'the two kinds of air, when formed at the same time and in the same vessel, can unite in their *nascent* state; but that when fully formed, they are incapable of acting upon one another, unless they are first set in motion by external heat'.

Hartog[3] said: 'Chemical composition for Cavendish had a different conno-tation from that which we attach to it. What it was I confess I cannot fathom, at present.' I will attempt to explain Cavendish's meaning. He seems to have represented his results as follows. Let ϕ stand for phlogiston. Inflammable air is (*water* $+\phi$), dephlogisticated air is (*water* $-\phi$). When the two gases combine the reaction is:

$$(\text{water} + \phi) + (\text{water} - \phi) = 2 \text{ water}.$$

The water pre-exists in both gases, and is deposited as a result of a re-distribution of phlogiston. Cavendish's explanation is quite consistent with the view that water is an element. Paul[4] said the water was 'the result of a mutual and compensating alteration of the two kinds of air, both of which he supposed to be, at the same time, equally air and also equally water'. The

[1] *Phil. Trans.*, 1784, lxxiv, 137, 140.
[2] Quoted by Watt, *Phil. Trans.*, 1784, lxxiv, 334–5; see Priestley, E & O *Nat. Phil.*, 1781, ii, 84, for 'nascent state'.
[3] *Ann. Sci.*, 1941, v, 1 (44).   [4] In Watts, *Dict. of Chem.*, 1872, ii, 780.

above interpretation of Cavendish's words was given by H. B. Dixon in his lectures and by Berzelius[1] who said:

'oxygen gas is water deprived of phlogiston, and hydrogen gas is water supersaturated with the same hypothetical substance, and by the mutual combination of these gases, the water reappears in its primitive state. According to this explanation, water was still a simple body, containing the ponderable parts of oxygen gas and hydrogen gas.'

Wilson[2] objected to this interpretation, but he failed to recognise, what he emphasised in other places,[3] that Cavendish had changed his opinion of 1766 that hydrogen was phlogiston. Wilson[4] thought Cavendish regarded inflammable air as 'hydrate of anhydrous hydrogen' (taking $\phi = H$), which on oxidation '*produced* one quantity of water, and set free another which had pre-existed in it', and Thorpe[5] says Cavendish 'did not regard hydrogen as a simple substance, in the modern sense'. For Priestley,[6] fixed air and water were both 'analysed into the same principles', phlogiston and dephlogisticated air, but water:

'is the union not of pure phlogiston but of inflammable air and dephlogisticated air. *Inflammable air* seems now to consist of water and inflammable air, which, however, seems extraordinary, as the two substances are hereby made to involve each other, one of the constituent parts of water being inflammable air, and one of the constituent parts of inflammable air being water; and, therefore, if the experiments would favour it (but I do not see that they do so) it would be more natural to suppose that water, like fixed air, consists of phlogiston and dephlogisticated air, in some different mode of combination.'

Cavendish, in 1784, was aware that another explanation was possible. In a part of the paper added by Cavendish himself before printing he says:[7]

'There are several memoirs of Mr. Lavoisier . . . in which he intirely discards phlogiston, and explains those phaenomena which have been usually attributed to the loss or attraction of that substance, by the absorption or expulsion of dephlogisticated air; and . . . According to this hypothesis, we must suppose, that water consists of inflammable air united to dephlogisticated air; . . . and indeed, as adding dephlogisticated air to a body comes to the same thing as depriving it of its phlogiston and adding water to it, and as there are, perhaps, no bodies entirely destitute of water, and as I know no way by which phlogiston can be transferred from one body to another, without leaving it uncertain whether water is not at the same time transferred, it will be very difficult to determine by experiment which of these opinions is the truest; but as the commonly received principle of phlogiston explains all phaenomena, at least as well as Mr. Lavoisier's, I have adhered to that.'

Since Cavendish's new hypothesis was given widespread attention it should be pointed out that he did not regard the oxidation of a substance A as occurring by the reaction:

(1) $A + (\text{water} - \phi)$, which would be correct if $\phi = H$, but by the reaction:
(2) $(A - \phi) + \text{water}$.

If A is mercury, $(A - \phi) = $ mercuric oxide, and hence the product of oxidation of mercury is hydrate of mercuric oxide, and so on. Cavendish says:[8]

---

[1] *Traité de Chimie*, 1845, i, 354. [2] (1), 328. [3] (1), 199, 325, 411.
[4] (1), 387–9. [5] Cavendish, *Sci. Pap.*, ii, 35. [6] E & O *Nat. Phil.*, 1786, iii, 405.
[7] *Phil. Trans.*, 1784, lxxiv, 150–3; Wilson, (1), 77 f., 137 f., 251 f., 413 f.; Muirhead, 147 f. (alters several words and changes the punctuation).
[8] *Phil. Trans.*, 1784, lxxiv, 143–4.

red precipitate may be considered, either as quicksilver deprived of part of its phlogiston, and united to a certain proportion of water, or as quicksilver united to dephlogisticated air; after which, on further increasing the heat, the water in it rises deprived of its
phlogiston, that is, in the form of dephlogisticated air, and at the same time the quicksilver distils over in its metallic form. . . . Mercurius calcinatus appears to be only
quicksilver which has absorbed dephlogisticated air from the atmosphere during its
preparation; accordingly, by giving it a sufficient heat, the dephlogisticated air is
driven off, and the quicksilver acquires its original form . . . but yet, as uniting dephlogisticated air to a metal comes to the same thing as depriving it of part of its
phlogiston and adding water to it, the quicksilver may still be considered as deprived
of its phlogiston. . . . In procuring dephlogisticated air from nitre . . . upon heating
red-hot, the dephlogisticated air rises mixed with a little nitrous acid, and at the same
time the acid remaining in the nitre becomes very much phlogisticated [forming
nitrite]; which shews that the acid absorbs phlogiston from the water in the nitre, and
becomes phlogisticated, while the water is thereby turned into dephlogisticated air. . . .
This phlogistication of the acid in nitre by heat has been observed by Mr. Scheele.[1]

A similar theory was held by Watt:[2] 'the acid acts upon the water, and
dephlogisticates it; and the fire supplies the *humor* with the due quantity of
heat to constitute it air, under which form it immediately issues.' Watt
adopted De Luc's name *humor* for 'dephlogisticated water, or . . . the basis of
water and air', i.e. what Lavoisier called the 'base' of oxygen gas (p. 421).
Berzelius[3] pointed out that Cavendish's and Watt's theories were essentially
the same, but Cavendish did not make any use of a 'quantity of heat'. Cavendish says:

Another thing which Mr. Lavoisier endeavours to prove is, that dephlogisticated air
is the acidifying principle. From what has been explained it appears, that this is no
more than saying, that acids lose their acidity by uniting to phlogiston, which with
regard to the nitrous, vitriolic, phosphoric, and arsenical acids is certainly true. . . .
But as to the marine acid [hydrochloric acid] and acid of tartar, it does not appear that
they are capable of losing their acidity by any union with phlogiston.

Cavendish does not point out that oxygen does not act as an acidifying
principle in the formation of water, which is a neutral substance, but he
appreciated what is really a weak point in Lavoisier's theory. Davy in 1810 was
to show that marine acid does not contain any oxygen. Besides this, Cavendish
also rejected a central part of Lavoisier's theory, the materiality of heat (see
p. 308).[4]

Cavendish, like Priestley,[5] disliked the 'new set of terms' invented by
Lavoisier and his associates. In a letter to Blagden Cavendish says:

I have been reading La V. [Lavoisier's] preface. It has only served the more to convince me of the impropriety of systematic names in chemistry . . . distinguishing the
neutral salts of less common use by names expressive of the substances they are
composed of, the case is different; for their number is so great, that it would be endless to attempt to distinguish them otherwise; but as to those in common use, or which
are found naturally existing, I think it would be better retaining the old names . . . I do
not imagine, indeed, that their nomenclature will ever come into use; but I am much
afraid it will do mischief, by setting people's minds afloat, & increasing the present
rage of name-making.[6]

---

[1] Neither red precipitate nor nitre contains any water.
[2] *Phil. Trans.*, 1784, lxxiv, 336.   [3] *Traité de Chimie*, 1845, i, 354.
[4] Harcourt, (1), 10, 13.   [5] E & O, 1790, iii, 543.
[6] Harcourt, (1), 66–7; no date given.

It has been supposed that Cavendish (like Priestley) never abandoned the phlogiston theory, but Fourcroy[1] names Black, Kirwan, and *Cavendish* as having 'renoncé absolument à l'hypothèse du phlogistique'.

Cavendish gives Lavoisier the credit for stating the composition of water in terms of the new theory, since Lavoisier had *published* this in 1783 (see p. 438), and there has never been any question that he was entitled to it. Cavendish regarded the theory as quite different from his own. Cavendish's paper was read on 15 January 1784 and printed in the *Philosophical Transactions* for that year. The reprints of the paper are dated in error 'read Jan. 15, 1783' and this date is given in the French translation by Pelletier.[2] Cavendish corrected this in a letter to the French editor, Mongez, dated 22 February 1785,[3] which was not published. A long summary in German published by Crell[4] refers to 'Experiments on Air, London, by J. Nichols, 1784, 4 Mai', and 'p. 37' is quoted, showing that it was one of the separately paged reprints, but the correct date 1784 is given. Kirwan's paper and Cavendish's reply (see p. 338) are also incorrectly dated in the French translations,[5] and Cavendish complained to Mongez of inaccuracies in the translation of his first paper.

The dates when the various parts of Cavendish's research were carried out can be ascertained from his MS. laboratory note-book.[6] The first examination of Warltire's experiment was made on 3–6 July 1781, the densities of the residual gases (not given in the paper) being determined. The first reference to the production of water in the *globe* is on 4 August 1781, but the formation of 135 gr. of 'pure water' by burning hydrogen and air in the tube was observed on 'Sun[day]. July'. Preliminary experiments with oxygen were made in June–July, but the first record of their explosion is in September 1781, when 3 grains of acid water were produced, giving 2 gr. of nitre with potash; on 28 September, with washed oxygen, 50 gr. of acid water were obtained; another experiment was made on 20 October. Cavendish's assertion in the 1784 paper that the experiments justifying his conclusion as to the nature of water were made in 1781 is correct, but he had not then found the cause of the acidity.

He turned to his eudiometer experiments (p. 321) until October 1782, when he began to work on the cause of acidity, the experiments continuing till 24 January 1783. In 1783 he investigated whether air formed nitrous acid when phlogisticated with liver of sulphur, whether red precipitate contains any nitrous acid, the preparation of oxygen from turbith mineral and its explosion with hydrogen, the detonation of nitre with charcoal, and the gas formed by the distillation of charcoal.[7] In December 1783 he refers to the growth of vegetables, etc., and the work recorded in the paper read on 15 January 1784 was probably not completed until Christmas 1783. Cavendish was thus not slow in communicating his results. An abstract of Priestley's paper of 1783

[1] (2), 1797, iii, 711.   [2] *Obs. Phys.*, 1784, xxv, 417–29 (December); 1785, xxvi, 38–51.
[3] Harcourt, (1), 41, 65; Wilson, (1), 423.
[4] *Ann.*, 1785, I, 323.   [5] *Obs. Phys.*, 1785, xxvi, 414, 425.
[6] Harcourt, (1), 36 f.; and lithogr. pp.; summarised (with references to other parts not lithographed and printed by Harcourt) in Wilson, (1), 353–404, who altered some punctuation; the MS., in sheets, 1778–85, was paged and indexed by Cavendish himself: Harcourt, 32.
[7] *Phil. Trans.*, 1784, lxxiv, 134–5.

made by the Secretary of the Royal Society refers to 'an experiment of Mr.
Cavendish . . . in which pure dephlogisticated air and inflammable air decomposed by an electric explosion . . . yielded a deposit of water equal in
weight to the decomposed air'.[1]

De Luc[2] reported a conversation in 1782 in which Priestley told him about
Cavendish's *quantitative* experiments, and Wilson remarks that this was before
Watt had drawn the conclusion, in 1783, in which he claimed to have anticipated
Cavendish (see p. 354). The priority of Cavendish's *experiments* over Watt's
theory and Lavoisier's experiments (see below) is unquestionable.[3] De Luc in
a long section entitled: 'Anecdotes relatives à la découverte de l'Eau sous la
forme d'Air',[4] reports that at the beginning of 1773 he met Priestley in Calne
and found him busy with experiments on various kinds of air, which were
published in 1774. He then says:[5]

Vers la fin de l'année 1782 j'allai à Birmingham, ou le Dr. Priestley s'étoit établi
depuis quelques années. Il me communiqua alors; que M. Cavendish, d'après une
remarque de M. Warltire; qui avoit toujours trouvé de l'Eau dans les Vases où il avoit
brûlé un mélange d'Air inflammable & d'Air atmosphérique; s'étoit appliqué à découvrir la Source de cette Eau, & qu'il avoit trouvé: qu'un mélange d'Air inflammable
& d'Air dephlogistiqué en proportion convenable, étant allumé par l'étincelle éleq-
trique, se convertissoit tout entier en Eau.

Kirwan[6] said that in all 'phlogistic processes', such as:

'the calcination of metals, the decomposition of nitrous by mixture with respirable air,
the phlogistication of respirable air by the electric spark, and, lastly, that effected by
amalgamation. . . . Mr. Cavendish is of opinion, that the diminution of respirable air is
owing to the production of water, which, according to him, is formed by the union of
the phlogiston, disengaged in those processes, with the dephlogisticated part of
common air.'

In a reply to Kirwan, Cavendish[7] says he does not agree that the electric spark
phlogisticates air, or that any fixed air is produced in the other processes. The
formation of fixed air in the combustion of iron, reported by Kirwan, is due
to the presence, as Bergman had proved, of plumbago in the iron, which, in
common with other carbonaceous substances, is well known to afford fixed air
on combustion. He does not deny the theory attributed to him by Kirwan, but
says he will not 'endeavour to point out any inconsistencies or false reasonings,
should any such have crept into' Kirwan's paper.

The Composition of Nitric Acid

In his paper of 1784 Cavendish said, with regard to the presence of acid in
the water, either: (1) dephlogisticated air contains a little nitrous acid which,
'when the inflammable air is in a sufficient proportion, unites to the phlogiston,

[1] Harcourt, (1), 44.
[2] *Idées sur la Météorologie*, London, 1787, ii, 206–7; Wilson, *Proc. Roy. Soc. Edin.*, 1859, iv,
205 (206–7).
[3] Harcourt, (1), 38.   [4] *Idées*, 1787, ii, 204–66.
[5] *Ib.*, 206–7; see also 223–4 (Blagden's conversation with Lavoisier), 224–7 (on Watt), 273 f.
(on Lavoisier's views on air), 283–96 (on Cavendish's experiments), 298 f. (on Priestley's
experiments).
[6] *Phil. Trans.*, 1784, lxxiv, 154 (5 February 1784).
[7] *Phil. Trans.*, 1784, lxxiv, 170 (4 March 1784); *Sci. Pap.*, ii, 182; a short reply by Kirwan,
Phil. Trans., 1784, lxxiv, 178–80, was ignored by Cavendish.

and is turned into phlogisticated air [nitrogen]; but does not when the inflammable air is in too small a proportion'; or (2) when the dephlogisticated air 'is in a sufficient proportion, part of the phlogisticated air with which it is debased, is, by the strong affinity of phlogiston to dephlogisticated air, deprived of its phlogiston and turned into nitrous acid', whilst if there is no excess of dephlogisticated air, this all goes to the inflammable air. The second explanation Cavendish shows by three reasons is 'much the most likely'; one reason, 'almost decisive', is that more acid is formed 'by mixing the air to be exploded with a little phlogisticated air'. Cavendish's second paper on 'Experiments on Air' (read 2 June 1785),[1] deals with the possible phlogistication of air by the electric spark, which he had left undecided. The experiments showed that the diminution in volume of air on sparking is not due to 'the burning of some inflammable matter in the apparatus', but 'the real cause of the diminution is very different from what I suspected, and depends upon the conversion of phlogisticated air into nitrous acid'.

The apparatus consisted of a bent tube M (Fig. 1 in Fig. 33) filled with

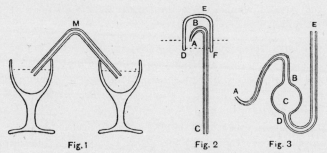

Fig.1   Fig. 2   Fig. 3

FIG. 33. CAVENDISH'S APPARATUS FOR THE SYNTHESIS OF NITRIC ACID.

mercury and inverted in two glasses of the same (really Priestley's apparatus, see p. 286), into which gas was introduced by a bent piece of thermometer tube ABC (Fig. 2):

'the bent end of which, after being previously filled with quicksilver, was introduced under the glass DEF, inverted into water, the end C of the tube being kept stopped by the finger; then, on removing the finger from C, the quicksilver in the tube descended in the leg BC, and its place was supplied with air from the glass DEF. Having thus got the proper quantity of air into the tube ABC, it was held with the end C uppermost, and stopped with the finger; and the end A, made smaller for that purpose, being introduced into one end of the bent tube M, the air, on removing the finger from C, was forced into that tube by the pressure of the quicksilver in the leg BC. By these means I was enabled to introduce the exact quantity I pleased of any kind of air into the tube M; and, by the same means, I could let up any quantity of soap-lees [potash solution], or any other liquor which I wanted to be in contact with the air. . . . The bore of the tube M . . . was about one tenth of an inch; and the length of the column of air . . . in general from $1\frac{1}{2}$ to $\frac{3}{4}$ of an inch.

It is scarcely necessary to inform any one used to electrical experiments, that in order to force an electrical spark through the tube, it was necessary, not to make a communication between the tube and the conductor, but to place an insulated ball at such

[1] Phil. Trans., 1785, lxxv, 372; Sci. Pap., ii, 187.

a distance from the conductor as to receive a spark from it, and to make a communication between the ball and the quicksilver in one of the glasses, while the quicksilver
in the other glass communicated with the ground.'

Litmus solution in the tube became red, and the air was diminished on
sparking, 'conformably to what was observed by Dr. Priestley', but with lime
water no cloudiness was observed, although the air was diminished by one-
third, and hence no fixed air was produced. With oxygen in the tube there was
only a very slight diminution and the litmus was bleached (probably owing to
the formation of ozone). After sparking over litmus, fixed air was formed, as
shown by the lime water test. With soap-lees (caustic potash solution) in the
tube the absorption in the case of air was more rapid than with water.

'I accordingly made some experiments to determine what degree of purity the air
should be of, in order to be diminished most readily, and to the greatest degree; and I
found that, when . . . perfectly phlogisticated air [nitrogen] was used, no sensible
diminution took place; but when five parts of pure dephlogisticated air [oxygen] were
mixed with three parts of common air, almost the whole of the air was made to disappear. It must be considered, that common air consists of one part of dephlogisticated
air, mixed with four of phlogisticated; so that a mixture of five parts of pure dephlogisticated air, and three of common air, is the same thing as a mixture of seven parts of
dephlogisticated air with three of phlogisticated.'

(As Wilson[1] says, this calculation is erroneous, the ratio being $5 \cdot 6 : 2 \cdot 4$; he
should have taken 5 of common air and 9 of dephlogisticated air to obtain
$2N + 5O$.) When 'air' was to be repeatedly introduced into the tube Cavendish
used the apparatus Fig. 3 (Fig. 33), first filled with mercury, then C and AB
with gas by introducing A into gas over water, drawing mercury from ED by a
siphon, putting A into one end of M (Fig. 1) and forcing down ED a wooden
cylinder, more mercury being put into ED as required. The apparatus was
weighed at first and after each operation, when the volume of gas transferred
was 'equal in bulk to a quantity of quicksilver, whose weight was equal to the
increase in weight of the apparatus'.

The gas in M was sparked and fresh quantities added till no further
diminution took place, a little dephlogisticated air, and after that a little
common air, being added to make sure the contraction was ended. The solution separated from the mercury was neutral and contained nitre, 'as appeared
from the manner in which paper, impregnated with the solution of it, burned.'
A larger quantity was made in a larger tube and tested with barium chloride
and silver nitrate, which showed that no more vitriolic or marine acid was
present than the soap-lees contained, 'and there is no reason to think that any
other acid entered into it, except the nitrous.' The solution precipitated silver
nitrate but Cavendish recognised that this was due to 'phlogisticated nitrous
acid' (nitrite). He showed that when nitre is strongly heated 'in an earthen
retort, till it had yielded a good deal of dephlogisticated air', the solution, made
sensibly acid with pure nitric acid, gave 'a very copious precipitate' with silver
nitrate. This 'property of phlogisticated nitre is worth the attention of
chemists; as otherwise they may sometimes be led into mistakes, in investi-

[1] (1), 256.

gating the presence of marine acid by a solution of silver'. This warning did not prevent Berthollet[1] from making the mistake. Cavendish said:

We may safely conclude that in the present experiments the phlogisticated air was enabled, by means of the electrical spark, to unite to, or form a chemical combination with, the dephlogisticated air, and was thereby reduced to nitrous acid, which united to the soap-lees, and formed a solution of nitre; for in these experiments those two airs actually disappeared, and nitrous acid was actually formed in their room.

In two experiments he found that 416 grain measures of phlogisticated air and 914 of dephlogisticated air, and 1920 of phlogisticated air and 4860 of dephlogisticated air, were absorbed. But 'in both experiments some air remained in the tube uncondensed, whose degree of purity I had no way of trying; so that the proportion of each species of air absorbed is not known with much exactness'. These figures correspond with the formulae $N_2O_{4.39}$ and $N_2O_{4.61}$, the formula for nitric acid being N_2O_5. A little of the product was probably potassium nitrite (corresponding with N_2O_3). Cavendish pointed out that his explanation in 1784:

is confirmed in a remarkable manner by the foregoing experiments; as from them it is evident, that dephlogisticated air is able to deprive phlogisticated air of its phlogiston, and reduce it into acid, when assisted by the electric spark; and therefore it is not extraordinary that it should do so, when assisted by the heat of the explosion.

Cavendish found that although most of the oxygen and nitrogen gases were absorbed by sparking over alkali, there was a small residue. By repeated sparking of a given volume of nitrogen with oxygen Cavendish diminished it as far as possible and then absorbed the excess of oxygen by liver of sulphur (potassium sulphide) solution:

after which only a small bubble of air remained unabsorbed, which certainly was not more than $\frac{1}{120}$ of the bulk of the phlogisticated air let up into the tube; so that if there is any part of the phlogisticated air of our atmosphere which differs from the rest, and cannot be reduced to nitrous acid, we may safely conclude, that it is not more than $\frac{1}{120}$ part of the whole.

In 1894 Lord Rayleigh discovered that this small residue, prepared in the same manner as by Cavendish, did differ from the rest and that atmospheric nitrogen contains about 1 per cent of a new gas, argon.

Cavendish had said[2] that: 'phlogisticated air appears to be nothing else than the nitrous acid united to phlogiston, for when nitre is deflagrated with charcoal, the acid is almost completely converted into this kind of air'; and 'it is well known, that nitrous acid is also converted by phlogistication into nitrous air [nitric oxide]'. Thus, he believed that nitrous air is a compound of nitric acid and phlogiston, and phlogisticated air is a compound of nitric acid with still more phlogiston. Nitrous air is phlogisticated nitrous acid, phlogisticated air is perphlogisticated nitrous acid. He now says:[3]

phlogisticated air ought to be reduced to nitrous acid by being deprived of its phlogiston. But as dephlogisticated air is only water deprived of phlogiston, it is plain, that adding dephlogisticated air to a body, is equivalent to depriving it of phlogiston, and adding water to it; and therefore, phlogisticated air ought also to be reduced to nitrous

[1] *Statique Chimique*, 1803, ii, 27.
[2] *Phil. Trans.*, 1784, lxxiv, 135.
[3] *Phil. Trans.*, 1785, lxxv, 372.

acid, by being made to unite to, or form a chemical combination with, dephlogisticated air; only the acid formed in this way will be more dilute, than if the phlogisticated air was simply deprived of phlogiston,

i.e.   phlogisticated air + dephlogisticated air = nitric acid + water.
              nitric acid + ϕ water – ϕ

Cavendish believed that a universal product of oxidation, whether of hydrogen, carbon, sulphur, nitrogen, metals, etc., was water, so that every oxidisable body contains hydrogen, and every oxidation yields water as one product.[1]

Priestley[2] had found that an acid is formed by sparking air over litmus solution and there was a contraction of the air, the residual air no longer giving an acid on sparking, and he used both a straight tube fitted with a wire, and a bent tube containing mercury and solution and dipping into cups of mercury, as in Cavendish's apparatus. He found, however, that the reddened litmus recovered its blue colour on exposure to air 'exactly as water, tinged with the same blue, and impregnated with fixed air, will do'; on sparking air over lime water 'the lime was precipitated as the air was diminished', and hence the acid produced is fixed air (carbon dioxide). Priestley[3] also thought that phlogisticated air (nitrogen) is formed by heating red precipitate (mercuric oxide) with charcoal (his red precipitate must have contained some nitrate).

'Perhaps some part of the difficulty may be relieved, by making a little alteration in the hypothesis [sic] of Mr. Cavendish, and supposing, agreeably to the same experiments recited in this volume, that the *acid principle* is supplied by the dephlogisticated air, whilst the nitrous air gives the base of the nitrous acid, and phlogiston; and then this air may perhaps be considered as phlogiston combined not with all the necessary elements of nitrous acid, but only what may be called the base of it, viz. the dephlogisticated nitrous vapour, or something which, when united to dephlogisticated air, will constitute nitrous acid.'

Priestley tried several times without success to repeat Cavendish's experiment on the formation of nitric acid on exploding inflammable and dephlogisticated airs, either carelessly or wilfully omitting the essential conditions clearly set out by Cavendish, but in 1802[4] he found acid produced by exploding 100 of inflammable air with 51 of dephlogisticated air but not with 47 of it.

Van Marum[5] described the action of sparks or a brush discharge from a great electrical machine in the Teyler's Museum in Haarlem on a number of gases confined over mercury in a tube. Dephlogisticated air (oxygen) 'took a very strong odour, which seemed to us clearly the smell of the electric matter, but much stronger than we have experienced before', and the mercury was tarnished;[6] this would be due to the formation of ozone. Nitrous gas (NO) diminished to half its volume, leaving phlogisticated air whilst the mercury was attacked, and red precipitate was formed on heating the powder pro-

[1] Wilson, (1), 86–7, 326 f.   [2] E & O, 1774, i, 183, 186.
[3] E & O *Nat. Phil.*, 1786, iii, 404.   [4] *Trans. Amer. Phil. Soc.*, 1802, v, 28.
[5] Bevattende de Beschryving van eene ongemeen groote Electrizeer-Machine, in *Verhandelingen uitgeeven door Teyler's II Genootschap*, Haarlem, 1785, iii (pp. xxxi, 205), 112 f.; 1787, iv, 1, 180 f., 196 f.; Ostwald, *Elektrochemie*, 1896, 17; the great electrical machine was constructed by John Cuthbertson, of 54 Poland St., London; for the description and illustration of it see Van Marum, *op. cit.*, 1787, iv, suppl.
[6] *Ib.*, 1785, iii, 118.

duced; inflammable air was unchanged; ethylene expanded to three times its volume and left inflammable air; fixed air increased slightly in volume; ammonia increased in volume and gave an inflammable gas. Other gases were little affected (vitriolic acid air, marine acid air); atmospheric air sparked over litmus solution gave very little acid but was slightly phlogisticated.

Van Marum and Van Troostwyk,[1] even with the enormous electrical machine, were unable to confirm Cavendish's experiments on the formation of nitric acid. Cavendish said that Lavoisier and Hassenfratz, and Monge, also unaccountably failed in what is not really very difficult, so that in 1788[2] Cavendish reported some experiments made at his direction by Gilpin, clerk of the Royal Society, and witnessed by several fellows (including the President) in which his experiment on the formation of nitric acid was confirmed. Cavendish says the others must have failed for 'want of patience', and the reaction is a slow one.

The synthesis of nitric acid by Cavendish formed the basis of the 'arc process' for the manufacture of the acid,[3] which in turn has given way to the oxidation of ammonia, discovered by Milner in 1789.

MILNER

The modern process for making nitric acid, by the oxidation of ammonia to nitric oxide, is based on a discovery by Isaac Milner, D.D. (1750–1820), President of Queens' College, Cambridge, F.R.S. 1780, by passing ammonia gas over manganese dioxide heated in a tube.[4] Milner was the first Jacksonian professor of chemistry (1783–92); he published a syllabus of his lectures.[5] In his paper, written in the third person, he says:

Some time in the month of March, 1788 . . . he crammed a gun-barrel full of powdered manganese; and to one end of the tube he applied a small retort, containing the caustic volatile alkali. As soon as the manganese was heated red-hot, a lighted candle was placed under the retort, and the vapour of the boiling volatile alkali forced through the gun-barrel. Symptoms of nitrous fumes and of nitrous air soon discovered themselves, and by a little perseverence he was enabled to collect considerable quantities of air, which on trial proved highly nitrous. . . . The volatile alkali . . . will frequently pass over in great quantities undecomposed. . . . On admitting the atmospherical air, the nitrous air is decomposed, and the red nitrous fumes instantly combine with the volatile alkali. The receivers are presently filled with white clouds of nitrous ammoniac; and in this manner a wrong conclusion may easily be drawn, from the want of the orange colour of the nitrous fumes . . . by applying repeatedly fresh portions of strong volatile alkali . . . he often collected large jars of air, which was proved to be highly nitrous by mixture with atmospherical or with dephlogisticated air.

No nitric oxide was formed with red lead, but some with calcined green vitriol (ferric oxide).

[1] Ib., 1787, iv, 180.   [2] Phil. Trans., 1788, lxxviii, 261–76.
[3] Partington and Parker, The Nitrogen Industry, London, 1922.
[4] Phil. Trans., 1789, lxxix, 300; Obs. Phys., 1790, xxxvi, 171–9; Crell's Ann., 1790, II, 115; Ann. Chim., 1790, iv, 15.
[5] A Plan of a Course of Chemical Lectures, Cambridge, 1784, 1788 (still using the phlogiston theory); A Plan of a Course of Experimental Lectures Introductory to the Study of Chemistry and other Branches of Natural Philosophy, Cambridge n.d. (1780 ?); Mary Milner, Life of Isaac Milner, D.D., F.R.S., London and Cambridge, 1842; Clark, DNB, 1909, xiii, 456; Coleby, Ann. Sci., 1954, x, 234.

Black[1] says the newspapers in January 1796, 'inform us that the French chemists procured saltpetre for the army, by blowing alkaline gas, and even putrid steams, through red hot substances [manganese] which readily yield oxygen'; and Robison there vaguely suggests the use of ammonia and air. A letter from Bishop Watson to Milner (18 February 1796) also says the French were using the process to make nitre and suggests that it should be adopted in England, using ammonia from animal matter.[2] Milner's process was repeated under Vauquelin's supervision.[3] C. F. Kuhlmann invented the modern process of passing a mixture of ammonia gas and air over heated platinum, which acts as a catalyst.[4] Charles Frederic Kuhlmann (Kühlmann) (Colmar, Alsace, 22 May 1803–Lille, 27 January 1881) was professor of applied chemistry (1823–54) and director of the Mint at Lille, then owner of several chemical factories, finally the Société anonyme de manufacture des produits chimiques at Lille; he published many papers on chemical and geological subjects as well as on chemical industries.[5]

The Water Controversy

The time has come to say something of the so-called 'Water Controversy', which concerns the claims of Cavendish, Watt, and Lavoisier to have been discoverers of the composition of water. The title 'water controversy' was introduced by Wilson,[6] who gave a detailed and careful account of the matter, favouring the claims of Cavendish; J. P. Muirhead[7] gave the arguments in favour of Watt and reprinted the publications of Watt, Cavendish, Lavoisier and Monge. Wilson and Muirhead change the punctuation and sometimes the wording of the originals. Summaries were given by Kopp,[8] Thorpe,[9] and the author.[10]

The controversy began effectively with statements made in 1834 in his *éloge* of James Watt written for the Paris Academy by D. F. Arago,[11] who had read the published memoirs and Watt's correspondence of 1782–84. A summary of the controversy published anonymously in 1848[12] was, according to Wilson,[13] written by Lord Jeffrey. Lord Brougham[14] intervened in favour of Watt. For the present, Cavendish and Watt only will be considered, the much easier question of Lavoisier's claims being dealt with later (see p. 436).

[1] *Lectures on Chemistry*, Edinburgh, 1803, ii, 245, 455, 732.
[2] *Life of Isaac Milner*, 1842, 109.
[3] *J. de l'École Polytechn.*, An III (1794–5), Cahier iii, 174.
[4] *Mém. Soc. Roy. Sci. Lille*, 1838, iii, 88–107; abstr. in *Compt. Rend.*, 1838, vii, 1107; *Ann.*, 1839, xxxix, 272.
[5] Poggendorff, (1), 1863, i, 1327; 1898, iii, 756; portr. in Mittasch and Theis, *Von Davy und Döbereiner bis Deacon*, 1932, 192; Kuhlmann, *Recherches Scientifiques et Publications diverses*, Paris, 1877 (784 pp.); Sotheran *Cat.* 894 (1951), 58.
[6] (1), 265–445.
[7] *Correspondence of the late James Watt on his Discovery of the Composition of Water*, London and Edinburgh, 1846.
[8] (2), iii, 235–310; (3) 185–95.
[9] *Essays*, 1902, 98 f., 163 f.; *id.*, in Cavendish, *Sci Pap.*, ii, 31.   [10] (2), 30; (3), 1960, 142.
[11] AdS, 1840, XVII, lxj–clxxxvij; *Biographies of Distinguished Scientific Men*, London, 1857, 519 f., 596 f.; *Oeuvres*, Paris, 1854, i, 371 f., composition of water, 452 f.; *id.*, *Historical Éloge of James Watt*, 8°, London, 1839; *id.*, *Life of James Watt*, 3 ed., Edinburgh, 1839.
[12] *Edinburgh Review*, 1848, lxxxvii, 67–137.   [13] (1), 274.
[14] 1855, 95 f., 312 f., 473 f.

WATT

James Watt (Greenock, Scotland, 19 January 1736–Heathfield, Stafford-shire, 25 August 1819) had a good education at school and worked in Glasgow and London making instruments. As London did not agree with him, he returned to Glasgow and opened a shop as an instrument maker in the University. There he became acquainted with Black, Adam Smith, and Robison. It was when repairing the University model of a Newcomen engine in 1764 that Watt conceived the ideas for the improvements of the steam engine which were his life's work.[1]

During his earlier struggles, Watt was helped by Black with a loan of £1000, afterwards repaid. He became F.R.S. in 1785. Watt never attended Black's lectures,[2] but he was no stranger to chemistry; his work on bleaching with chlorine will be mentioned later (p. 508). He was good at languages, read extensively, and knew something of law. Davy[3] testified that Watt had a 'profound knowledge' of chemistry. He invented copying-ink in 1779,[4] and (or perhaps Murdock) the cement of iron filings, sulphur, and sal ammoniac.[5] Watt published a short paper on 'a test liquor' (indicator),[6] in which he states that 'the infusion of tournesol, or an artificial preparation called litmus' is not satisfactory with nitrous acid, for 'a mixture of phlogisticated nitrous acid [nitrous acid] with an alkali will appear to be acid, by the test of litmus, when other tests, such as the infusion of the petals of the scarlet rose, of the blue iris, of violets, and of other flowers, will show the same liquor to be alkaline, by turning green'. He found that an infusion of red cabbage leaves in dilute sulphuric acid, neutralised before use with chalk or potash, filtered and mixed with alcohol, gives a blue liquid, which becomes red with acid and green with alkali, and the reaction is not vitiated by nitrous acid. This indicator was long in use.[7] Watt proposed a decimal division of an international pound in 1783.[8] His experiments on the latent heat of steam were probably made in 1763–4 before he had heard of Black's unpublished researches made in 1761.[9]

Watt, like Cavendish (see p. 325), began with some experiments made by Priestley, but they were different experiments in the two cases. In December 1782 Priestley found that water boiled in a Wedgwood earthenware retort produced *atmospheric* air continuously,[10] and he communicated these results by letters to Watt, who had then arrived at a theory that it should be possible to convert water into air.

The basis of Watt's idea seems to have been his experimental discovery that

[1] Arago, AdS, 1840, XVII, h lxj–clxxxvij; *id.*, *Oeuvres*, 1854, i, 371 f.; Bramwell, DNB, 1899, lx, 51; H. W. Dickinson, *James Watt, Craftsman and Engineer*, Cambridge, 1936, 119, 157–9; Smiles, 1866 or 1904; Watt, in Robison, *System of Mechanical Philosophy*, revised by James Watt and ed. by Brewster, Edinburgh, 1822, II, ii–x, 113–21.

[2] Watt, in Robison, II, ii–x; Harcourt, (2), 111.   [3] *Works*, 1840, vii, 141.

[4] Dickinson, 116.   [5] Dickinson, 130.   [6] *Phil. Trans.*, 1784, lxxiv, 419.

[7] Faraday, *Chemical Manipulation*, 3 ed., 1842, 275: 'the only substance of the kind perhaps worth keeping.'

[8] Dickinson, 157.

[9] Robison, ii, 5, 35, 160; Harcourt, (2), 1846, 112; Muirhead, 18; Dickinson, 35.

[10] Priestley, *Phil. Trans.*, 1783, lxxiii, 398 (dated Birmingham, 21 April, read 26 June 1783); E & O *Nat. Phil.*, 1786, iii, 29 (32); Muirhead, 3, 4, 8, 13, 17.

the latent heat of evaporation of water decreases with rise of temperature, and his work on the coefficient of expansion of steam, the change in volume of water on conversion into steam, and the effect of pressure on boiling point,[1] which led him to 'a theory' that:

as steam parts with its latent heat as it acquires sensible heat, or is more compressed, . . . when it arrives at a certain point it will have no latent heat, and may, under proper compression, be an elastic fluid nearly as specifically heavy as water; at which point I conceive it will again change its state and become something else than steam or water. My opinion then has been that it would then become air, which many things had led me to conclude, and which is confirmed by an experiment which Dr. Priestley made the other day, in his usual way of groping about.[2]

Watt never claimed anything more than his 'opinion'. Priestley[3] said Watt had 'thought that if steam could be made red-hot, so that all its latent heat should be converted into sensible heat', there would be a 'possibility of the conversion of water, or steam, into permanent air'. Watt had, in fact, arrived at the idea of a *critical temperature* of water, but he went astray in supposing that the water was converted into air. He wrote to Boulton on 10 December 1782:

I have often said that if water could be heated red hot or something more, it would probably be converted into some kind of air, because steam would in that case have lost all its latent heat and that it would have been turned solely into sensible heat, and probably a total change of the nature of the fluid would ensue. Dr. Priestley has proved this by experiment.[4]

As a result of Priestley's further experiments and discussion with him, Watt abandoned this old idea (which was essentially correct) and by bringing in phlogiston he reversed the *rôles* of the latent and sensible heat, so reaching the theory which he later maintained. In his earlier view water was, to all intents, an element,[5] and 'air', on the basis of Priestley's experiments, was atmospheric air. Watt[6] said that in Priestley's experiment 'the clay vessels attract the phlogiston from water, and transmit it from particle to particle, until it comes to the outside, where they give it off to the external air', which it probably phlogisticates (i.e. converts into nitrogen).

The true explanation of Priestley's supposed conversion of water into air had been suggested to him in a letter of 23 January 1783 by Josiah Wedgwood (who made him a present of the retorts): 'If water passes through the retort outwards, may not air pass inwards?', which Priestley would not then admit.[7] In a letter of 29 April 1783, Priestley informed Watt that he had made a mistake; he says with relish: 'Behold with surprise and indignation the figure of an apparatus that has utterly ruined your beautiful hypothesis';[8] the experiment is described in Priestley's paper,[9] and must have been added after this was sent to the Royal Society on 21 April 1783.

Priestley had now surrounded the earthenware retort containing water by a

[1] Watt, in Robison, 1822, ii, 5 f., 35, 160; Muirhead, 18.
[2] Muirhead, 6 (letter to Black, 13 December 1783).
[3] *Phil. Trans.*, 1783, lxxiii, 398 f.; E & O *Nat. Phil.*, 1786, iii, 29 f., 32.
[4] Bolton, *Correspondence of Priestley*, New York, 1892, 45.   [5] Wilson, (1), 331.
[6] Muirhead, 22 (letter of 26 April 1783, to De Luc).
[7] Wilson, (1), 93; for the process, see Graham, *Elements of Chemistry*, 2 ed., 1850, i, 85.
[8] Muirhead, 25.   [9] *Phil. Trans.*, 1783, lxxiii, 431.

bell-jar of air, and boiled the water by 'throwing the heat of Mr. Parker's excellent lens upon the bulb', when air passed out of the retort, as usual, but 'the water ascended within the receiver . . . till more than three-quarters of the internal air disappeared'. The air collected was a 'mere trifle' better than atmospheric air, but that remaining in the bell-jar a little worse. Priestley could not then explain the process, but he afterwards correctly put it down to an exchange of air and steam through the earthenware retort, although he still made the mistake of thinking the steam was converted into air in the process. Watt in a letter to Black dated 23 June 1783[1] calls this 'an ugly experiment the said Dr. Priestley tried at my desire'.

The conversion of water into air, however, was later claimed by others. Achard[2] found that steam passed through red-hot earthenware *or metal* tubes is converted into nitrogen; Westrumb[3] found the same, and concluded that nitrogen is a compound of water and heat. Wiegleb[4] tried to prove this by arguments and experiments. Deiman, Troostwyck, and Lauwerenburgh[5] repeated Priestley's experiment and found that no gas is formed unless a porous tube is used. Wiegleb had used a red-hot tobacco pipe; the Dutch chemists found that no gas is collected if a metal or glass tube is used, unless the tube is cracked, that the gas collected is the same as that outside the tube, carbon dioxide and nitrogen if the tube is heated in a charcoal fire, or common air if the tube is taken from the fire. Although Wiegleb[6] tried to answer these objections by new experiments he did not succeed, and was himself doubtful.

Girtanner[7] from experiments similar to Wiegleb's concluded that nitrogen is formed from water vapour in contact with clay, and is a compound of hydrogen and oxygen containing less oxygen than water. His experiments were repeated by Berthollet and Bouillon Lagrange[8] who obtained no trace of nitrogen; either Girtanner never performed the experiments or was misled. Wurzer[9] obtained nitrogen by passing steam through heated glass or metal tubes. A. W. von Hauch[10] showed that the results are not obtained with glass or metal tubes and are due to the use of porous tubes.

Watt did not accept Priestley's suggestion that his hypothesis was disproved: 'It is not founded on so brittle a basis as an earthenware retort, nor its converting water into air; I founded it on other facts, and was obliged to stretch it a good deal before it would fit this experiment.' He thought Priestley had perhaps made some mistake.[11]

Cavendish says he communicated his results, with the exception of those 'on the cause of the acid found in the water', to Priestley, and in Priestley's paper (sent in on 21 April 1783, read 26 June),[12] he speaks of giving 'particular attention to an experiment of Mr. Cavendish's, concerning the re-conversion of air into water, by decomposing it in conjunction with inflammable air'. The abstract of Priestley's paper by Maty, Secretary of the Royal Society, in the Journal Book says: 'These arguments received no small confirmation from an experiment of Mr. Cavendish tending to prove the reconversion of air into water, in which pure dephlogisticated air and inflammable air were

[1] Muirhead, 30.   [2] Crell's *Ann.*, 1785, I, 304.
[3] Crell's *Ann.*, 1785, II, 499.   [4] Crell's *Ann.*, 1796, II, 467.
[5] *Ann. Chim.*, 1798, xxvi, 310–34.   [6] Crell's *Ann.*, 1799, I, 45.
[7] *Ann. Chim.*, An VIII (1799–1800), xxxiv, 3–40.
[8] Berthollet, *Ann. Chim.*, An VIII, xxxv, 23–31.
[9] Crell's *Ann.*, 1798, I, 179, 273.
[10] Undersøgelse af Vandets Bestanddele, in *Skrifter Videns. Selsk., Nye Saml.* (Copenhagen), 1793, iv, 517–28; *ib., Skrifter*, 1800, i, 201–16 (refuting Wurzer).
[11] Muirhead, 26.
[12] *Phil. Trans.*, 1783, lxxiii, 398–434 (426); E & O *Nat. Phil.*, 1786, iii, 50.

decomposed by an electric explosion, and yielded a deposit of water equal in weight to the decomposed air.'[1] Wilson[2] concluded that Cavendish's results were communicated to Priestley before 26 March 1783, when Watt mentioned in a letter[3] for the first time that Priestley had made fixed air (*sic*) by exploding dephlogisticated and inflammable air and 'finds on the side of the vessel a quantity of water, equal in weight to the air employed'.

What Priestley thought was a repetition of Cavendish's experiment was really quite a different process. He says: 'Still hearing of many objections to the conversion of water into air, I now gave particular attention to an experiment of Mr. Cavendish's, concerning the re-conversion of air into water, by decomposing it in conjunction with inflammable air.'[4]

On 23 March 1783, Priestley wrote to Wedgwood:[5] 'By the electric explosion I decompose dephlogisticated and inflammable air, and I find the weight of the latter in the *water* I get from it.'[6] In order to obtain the gases free from water, Priestley made the inflammable air by heating bits of charcoal in an earthenware retort, so that it would contain carbon monoxide, and his dephlogisticated air by heating nitre, so that it would contain some nitrogen.[7] On exploding them together he obtained fixed air and nitric acid, as we should expect. The weight of water formed by the explosion was determined by mopping it off the globe with filtering-paper and reweighing, and Priestley says he was not very satisfied and 'wished to have had a nicer balance', but 'always found, as nearly as I could judge, the weight of the decomposed air in the moisture acquired by the paper'.[8] This is the central point of the whole controversy. When Watt speaks of 'inflammable air' or 'phlogiston' (with which he identified it) he means Priestley's inflammable air, not hydrogen. Priestley's 'inflammable air', evolved from 'perfectly made charcoal' heated in a Wedgwood earthen retort, 'without any appearance of termination', so that he must have had a continual leakage of fire-gases into the retort, was a mixture of hydrogen, carbon monoxide, carbon dioxide, and water vapour. He could not possibly have 'obtained the weight of the decomposed air in the moisture', and 'he employed the wrong gas; he must have weighed inaccurately; and he either did not analyse, or failed to analyse sufficiently, the so-called water . . . He . . . deceived himself, and for a long period he . . . led others astray'.[9]

De Luc[10] quotes a letter from Priestley of 11 December 1782 saying that he had converted water into air by heating it in an earthen retort impervious to air. In March (1783) Priestley in Birmingham:

'me communiqa aussi alors les Expériences qu'il avoit faites, d'après M. Cavendish, sur la production de l'Eau, par la combustion de l'air déphlogistiqué avec l'Air inflammable. Il avoit réussi à employer ces Airs en telles proportions, qu'ils se détruisoient presque entièrement, & fournissoient une quantité d'Eau égale à leur

[1] Harcourt, (1), 44.   [2] (1), 60, 285 f.
[3] Muirhead, 17.   [4] *Phil. Trans.*, 1783, lxxiii, 431.
[5] Wilson, (1), 94, 285; the same is reported by Watt in a letter of 26 March 1783, to Hamilton, in Muirhead, 17.
[6] Watt says 'equal in weight to the air employed'.   [7] Harcourt, (1), 27.
[8] *Phil. Trans.*, 1783, lxxiii, 398–434 (414); E & O *Nat. Phil.*, 1786, iii, 50; Wilson, (1), 286.
[9] Harcourt, (1), 14 f.; Wilson, (1), 289.   [10] *Idées sur la Météorologie*, 1787, ii, 207–12.

Poids; ce qu'il eut la bonté de me montrer, en répétant cette opération en ma présence. M. Watt avoit pris aussi beaucoup d'intérêt à ces nouveaux Phénomènes sur l'Eau & l'Air, & il en avoit conclu une Théorie, qu'il se proposoit de vérifier par des Expériences immediates.'

Cavendish says he prepared his inflammable air from zinc (in two cases iron), presumably dissolved in dilute sulphuric acid, so that it must have been hydrogen. Priestley's 'inflammable air' could have been, according to his own definition:[1] 'that kind of air which takes fire, and explodes on the approach of flame', and his later list of 'inflammable air' (sic) includes hydrogen, marsh gas, hydrogen sulphide, ethylene, oil gas, a mixture of hydrogen and nitrogen, and various mixtures of hydrocarbon gases;[2] he first confused hydrogen and carbon monoxide under this name, and later he included water gas, the gas from heated charcoal, and any inflammable gas.

Watt had sent Priestley a letter dated 26 April 1783, which was to accompany Priestley's account of his experiments when it was read and to give an explanation of them. When he heard from Priestley, three days later, that his experiments on the supposed conversion of water into air were incorrect, Watt, understandably, informed Priestley that he did not wish his letter to be read with Priestley's paper. Watt told Sir Joseph Banks in a letter of 12 April 1784 that he had withdrawn his communication, partly because he had attempted to explain some experiments by Priestley which he had later found erroneous, and partly because he had been told 'that that theory was considered too bold and not sufficiently supported by facts'; he would like more time to consider it more maturely and to make more experiments. Watt told De Luc that the theory was thought to be too bold because 'a substance such as water, till then considered as of the nature of an element, was there placed in the class of compounds'. De Luc says:[3]

Mais M. Watt souhaita ensuite, que cette Lettre ne fut pas lus dans l'Assemblée de la Société; parce qu'il apprit, qu'on trouvoit sa Théorie trop hardie, en ce qu'une Substance telle que l'*Eau*, considérée jusqu'alors comme *élémentaire*, y étoit placée au rang des *Mixtes*: de sorte qu'il desira de pouvoir accompagner cette Théorie: du résultat de quelques Expériences qu'il projettoit.

De Luc who had *previously* thought that water was a compound (Mixte) which it would be very important to analyse, urged Watt to publish the letter, but Priestley's latest experiments on the earthen retort had thrown doubt on the earlier ones.[4] Watt in April 1783 had thus clearly stated that he now regarded water as a *compound*, and De Luc seems to have reached this conclusion before him. Lavoisier had not reached this conclusion until the end of June and had not published it until December, 1783 (see p. 438).

Priestley's paper, containing (as was usual with him) all the erroneous early experiments as well as the later ones correcting them, was sent from Birmingham on 21 April, read to the Royal Society on 26 June 1783, and printed in the *Philosophical Transactions*. Priestley thought charcoal could be converted

---

[1] E & O, 1790, i, 8; repeated from E & O, 1774, i, 23.
[2] E & O *Nat. Phil.*, 1781, ii, 335.
[3] *Idées sur la Météorologie*, London, 1787, ii, 216.
[4] De Luc, *op. cit.*; Harcourt, (1), 8; Muirhead, liv.

almost completely into inflammable air by heating it in a vacuum by a burning glass, apart from a grain of ash from many pounds, and that the inflammable air so made was quite free from fixed air. He also obtained inflammable air by heating dry iron filings in a gun-barrel.[1] In 1785, however, Priestley said[2] he had been misled because he overlooked the wet leather on which the receiver had stood, which would produce water vapour in the receiver, and Cavendish 'had told me that . . . *water* was essential to the production of it [inflammable air], and even entered into it as a constituent principle', and Priestley says he had discovered that 'notwithstanding these *facts*, it will appear from my subsequent experiments, that water was necessary'.[3] Thus Cavendish not only set Priestley right on his supposed 'facts' but also provided him with a theory which Priestley was later to use in maintaining the phlogistic interpretation of his results.[4] The printed version of Priestley's 1783 paper was altered after it was submitted, since the sub-section is entitled 'Experiments relating to the seeming Conversion of Water into Air' (the word 'seeming' being omitted in the *cross-headings* of the pages in the reprint of 1786), and a section added at the end describes some experiments on diffusion which preceded Graham's by many years. Priestley reprinted his almost completely erroneous statements in 1786,[5] merely stating in two small footnotes that: 'It will appear, however, that the air must have entered by the pores, but by means of a power very different from that of *pressure*, and able to counteract it.'

In a letter of 13 December 1782 to De Luc,[6] Watt mentions Priestley's early experiments with the porous retorts and says there is 'one element [air] dismissed from the list'. In letters of 22 April 1783 to Gilbert Hamilton, and 26 April 1783 to De Luc,[7] Watt says 'pure inflammable air is phlogiston itself' and 'water is dephlogisticated air deprived of part of its latent heat, and united to a large dose of phlogiston'. This follows because 'pure dry dephlogisticated air [Priestley's gas from nitre] and pure dry inflammable air [Priestley's charcoal gas] fired together, leave no residuum, except a small quantity of water equal to their weight' (Priestley's erroneous result). In a letter to Black of 21 April 1783[8] Watt also says: 'water is composed of dephlogisticated and inflammable air, or phlogiston, deprived of part of their latent or elementary heat.' He says that Priestley had exploded quite dry pure inflammable air ('the thing called phlogiston') and quite dry pure dephlogisticated air by an electric spark in a close glass vessel, and found:

'after the vessel is cold, a quantity of water adhering to the vessel, equal, or very nearly equal, to the weight of the whole air; and when he opens the vessel under water, or mercury, it is filled within $\frac{1}{200}$ part of its whole contents, which remainder is phlogisticated air, probably contained as an impurity in the other airs.'

Watt repeated this in his paper.[9] Priestley himself, however, makes no mention of such an experiment.[10] In a letter to De Luc of 18 May 1783 Watt says that

[1] *Phil. Trans.*, 1783, lxxiii, 398.
[2] *Phil. Trans.*, 1785, lxxv, 279 (288–9) (read 24 February 1785); E & O *Nat. Phil.*, 1786, iii, 24, 87.
[3] Cavendish, *Phil. Trans.*, 1784, lxxiv, 137.
[4] Harcourt, (1), 12.
[5] E & O *Nat. Phil.*, 1786, iii, 39, 62.
[6] Muirhead, 4.
[7] Muirhead, 20, 21.
[8] Muirhead, 19.
[9] *Phil. Trans.*, 1784, lxxiv, 329 (332).
[10] Wilson, (1), 307.

Priestley's mistake in supposing he had converted water into atmospheric air by boiling it in a porous clay retort:

'does not disprove my theory. . . . My assertion was simply, *that air was water deprived of its phlogiston, and united to heat* [italics in original]; — which I grounded on the decomposition of air by inflammation with inflammable air, the residuum, or product of which, is only water and heat.'[1]

Watt now asserts that *before* he had received Priestley's correction of his early experiments he had formed the theory of the composition of water which he states. Priestley's correcting letter was dated 29 April, but De Luc's statement (see p. 348) implies that Watt had arrived at his theory in March 1783. It seems, therefore, as if Watt's theory was based, not on Priestley's experiment but on Cavendish's work, which had been communicated to Priestley before 26 March 1783 (see p. 348).

Priestley's announcement on 28 June 1783 (the paper is dated Birmingham, 21 April 1783)[2] of Cavendish's result, that certain proportions of inflammable air and dephlogisticated air are converted into an equal weight of water as the sole product, made this public six months before Cavendish read his paper in January 1784. Watt mentioned Priestley's experiment in which he obtained from dry dephlogisticated air and dry inflammable air (Priestley's charcoal gas) by kindling in a closed vessel an equal weight of water, in letters of 26 March, 21 April, 22 April, 26 April, and 28 April, 1783,[3] i.e. *before* Priestley's letter of 29 April, and had stated his theory, so that the latter did not depend only on Priestley's supposed conversion of water into air and he told Priestley this (see p. 347).

De Luc

Jean André De Luc (Geneva, 8 February 1727–Windsor, 7 November 1817) was from 1770 Reader to Queen Charlotte (wife of George III) at Windsor. In 1798 he was appointed professor of philosophy and geology in the University of Göttingen, but never lived there, travelling between London, Berlin, Hannover, and Brunswick. He became F.R.S. in 1773, but rarely attended meetings. He published a large number of books and papers,[4] e.g. on evaporation,[5] on heat, water, fire, liquefaction and evaporation,[6] a criticism of Lavoisier's theory of vapours,[7] a general criticism of 'modern chemistry' in a letter to Fourcroy,[8] on the electric fluid,[9] and on water, phlogiston, acids, and airs, criticising Cavendish.[10] His book on meteorology[11] contains a criticism of de Saussure's views on the subject, with digressions on heat and combustion[12] (in which he says a combustible substance on burning is resolved into inflammable air and fixed air), on the Argand lamp, with numerous experiments and speculations on electricity, including a discussion of the Lichtenberg figures.[13]

[1] Muirhead, 29.   [2] *Phil. Trans.*, 1783, lxxiii, 398–434; Wilson, (1), 122.
[3] Muirhead, 17–25.
[4] Poggendorff, (1), i, 545–6; NBG, 1860, xxxii, 111; Harrison, DNB, 1888, xiv, 328; Roy. Soc. *Cat. of Sci. Papers*, 1868, ii, 232.
[5] *Phil. Trans.*, 1792, lxxxii, 400.   [6] *Obs. Phys.*, 1790, xxxvi, 193.
[7] *Ib.*, 1790, xxxvi, 276.   [8] *Ib.*, 1791, xxxviii, 460.
[9] *Ib.*, 1790, xxxvi, 450.   [10] *Ib.*, 1790, xxxvi, 144.
[11] *Idées sur la Météorologie* (2 vols., London, 1786–7).   [12] *Ib.*, i, 155 f.   [13] *Ib.*, i, 490.

De Luc's work on electricity is perhaps his best; it includes the invention of the 'dry pile',[1] afterwards improved by Zamboni, etc. (see Vol. IV). He had a confused theory that rain is produced by the action of electricity on a mixture of hydrogen and oxygen in the atmosphere.[2]

De Luc[3] visited Priestley at Calne at the end of 1773 and in Birmingham (where he also met Warltire) in 1782. He gives a long account of the matter now under discussion and gives some letters from Priestley.[4] De Luc was very well acquainted with Watt, in whose laboratory in Birmingham he made experiments on the latent heat of steam in the Spring of 1783, on which the so-called 'Watt's law' is based.[5]

Wilson,[6] whilst emphasising that De Luc was 'an upright, intelligent observer, a most indefatigable worker, and a sincerely religious man', points out that his lack of knowledge of chemistry, and his weakness in the English language and character, were a handicap to him, and that he acted hastily; but Wilson's statement that he was a 'deliberate mischiefmaker' in his letters to Watt (see below) is open to question. It is true that De Luc told Watt in 1782 that Crawford was trying to 'rob' Black of his discoveries in heat, this being passed on to Black.[7] De Luc himself was accused by Robison[8] of robbing Black of the theory of latent heat, and extricated himself with some difficulty.[9] De Luc did not understand British scientists very well, and probably acted with honest intention.

De Luc was in Paris when Cavendish's paper was read on 15 January 1784; he heard of it on his return to England in February, and asked Cavendish's permission to see it, which was granted. While De Luc was writing to Watt on 1 March 1784, the paper arrived (etant ici de ma lettre, j'ai reçu le mémoire), and after a glance at it De Luc informed Watt: 'In short, he expounds and proves your system, word for word (mot pour mot), and says nothing of you.' On 4 March De Luc sent Watt a transcript of parts of Cavendish's paper, says that Cavendish had used 'your actual words (vos propres termes) in your letter of April to Dr. Priestley, given as something new', and that this letter was known to Blagden: 'but keep this between ourselves.'[10] Blagden's part will be dealt with later. De Luc advised Watt to be careful, 'in view of your position, in order to draw from your discoveries [i.e. of the steam engine] practical consequences for your fortune, you must avoid causing jealousy (il faut éviter de vous fair des jaloux).' He suggested that the quickest way of clearing up the whole matter would be for Watt to allow De Luc to send a letter to Sir Joseph Banks, President of the Royal Society, in which Watt (who was not then a Fellow) should say that:

'having heard the Society is occupied with experiments on air, you beg that, if he agrees, two letters should be read, the one you wrote to D.r Priestley at such a date,

[1] *Nicholson's J.*, 1810, xxvii, 81, and plate: the 'Electric column'.
[2] J. C. Fischer, 1808, viii, 118 f.   [3] *Idées*, 1787, ii, 204 f., 211 f.
[4] Muirhead, 46 (March 1784); Wilson, (2).
[5] Muirhead, 18 (Watt's letter to Black, 21 April 1783); Robison, *System of Mechanical Philosophy*, Edinburgh, 1822, ii, 5, 35, 160.
[6] (1), 64 f., 70 f., 407 f.   [7] Muirhead, 5.   [8] Black, *Lectures on Chemistry*, 1803, i, 524.
[9] Muirhead, 10.   [10] Muirhead, 43–4.

and the other to me at such a date . . . , as having a close relation to the subject treated. I do not think he can refuse that, and nobody would have anything to complain of.'

To this quite sound advice Watt replied on 6 March 1784:[1]

'On the slight glance I have been able to give your extract of the paper, I think his theory very different from mine; which of the two is right I cannot say; his is more likely to be so, as he has made many more experiments, and, consequently, has more facts to argue upon. . . . As to making myself "des jaloux", that idea would weigh little . . . for although I am dependent on the favour of the public, I am not on Mr. C. or his friends.'

Watt was sensitive and pessimistic, in poor health, and a victim of unscrupulous treatment by business rivals. He said he felt it hard that 'in the first attempt I have made to lay anything before the public, I should be thus anticipated'.[2] He was 'diffident, because I am seldom certain that I am in the right'; Black told him in February 1783 that if he wrote up his own work, 'you would do it in such a cold and modest manner, that blockheads would conclude there is nothing in it.'[3]

In a letter to Sir Joseph Banks, dated Birmingham, 14 December 1783,[4] Priestley said, after referring to 'Lavoisier's paper':

'Mr. Watt is the person who is properly concerned in this business. For the idea of water consisting of pure air and phlogiston was his, I believe, before I knew him; and you will find it in the letter which he addressed to me, which was delivered along with the last paper which I sent to the Royal Society, but which he afterwards withdrew. This letter he now wishes to be put into the hands of Mr. De Luc, who will make some use of it. You will oblige us both, therefore, if you will give orders to have this letter delivered to Mr. De Luc, who will wait upon you for the purpose.'

Sir Joseph Banks, the President of the Royal Society, called on Watt in London, asking him in a 'very civil manner' to have the letters read to the Royal Society. Watt asked De Luc, a Fellow, and well known to him, to act on his behalf, telling him he had informed Sir Joseph Banks that there would be 'a few alterations' and that De Luc could 'show him the original letter, if doubts should arise concerning the date of any part of it'.[5] Owing to Watt's ill-health and the pressing 'attention to business', the preparation of the material in the interval 17 April to 2 May 1784 was necessarily hurried and rather confused, but the two papers were read on 29 April and 6 May 1784, Sir Joseph Banks informing Watt that: 'Both appeared to meet with great approbation from large meetings of Fellows.' John Davy[6] says Watt's letter was read on 6 May 1784 before it came before the Committee of Papers on 20 May, when it was ordered to be printed together with a postscript. Cavendish was not then a member of the Council of the Royal Society, being first elected in 1785.

Blagden, as a Secretary of the Royal Society, then corresponded with Watt on the form the printed paper should take, and after receiving Watt's directions (he saying that 'on some other accounts I would rather have wished it to be suppressed'), Blagden prepared the paper. He wrote on 9 August 1784

[1] Muirhead, 46-8.   [2] Muirhead, 49.   [3] Muirhead, 15, 50.
[4] Edelstein, *Chymia*, 1948, i, 123.   [5] Muirhead, 49-58.
[6] *Works of Sir Humphry Davy*, 1840, vii, 129-39 (138).

asking if Watt wished to see proofs and offering to send them to Birmingham, but Watt replied on 11 August that he had no wish for this, and left it to Blagden.[1] The courtesy and friendliness of Sir Joseph Banks and the willing assistance of Blagden throughout are particularly noteworthy, and were appreciated by Watt.

Watt supplied five versions of his theory: (α) the letter to Priestley of 26 April 1783; (β) 'another copy' sent on 28 April 1783 because of 'some inaccuracies in language, and some inconsistencies' in (α);[2] (γ) a letter to De Luc of 26 November 1783;[3] (δ) a revised copy sent on 17 April 1784 to De Luc; and (ϵ) a postscript of 30 April 1784 sent to De Luc.[4] The final form and title of the printed paper were suggested by Watt himself to Blagden. The letter of 26 April, printed in its original form by Schofield,[5] does not differ significantly from the version in Watt's published paper.

The *reprints* of Watt's letter were ready before 11 November 1784. The paper was printed, and later an addition to it.[6] The papers are described as letters from Watt to De Luc. The first is entitled 'Thoughts on the constituent parts of water and of dephlogisticated air; with an account of some experiments on that subject'; the second 'Sequel to the thoughts on the constituent parts of water and of dephlogisticated air'. The first is headed 'Read April 29, 1784' and is dated 'Birmingham, November 26, 1784' which is a mistake for 1783, put right in the errata of the volume ('for 1784 read 1783'). The second part, dealing with 'some necessary cautions to those who may choose to repeat the experiments' in the paper of '26th of November last' is dated Birmingham, 30 April 1784, and was read on 6 May 1784. It was not until 27 June 1786 that Watt drew De Luc's attention to the errors of dating in the reprints of the papers by Cavendish (see p. 337) and himself.[7] Watt's letter to Priestley of 26 April 1783 is in the first paper embodied in a much longer letter to De Luc, but the original date is given at the head of the paper.

A large part of Watt's paper describes his quantitative experiments on heating various nitrates, including potassium nitrate (nitre), which he thought contained 'besides its water of crystallization, a quantity of water as one of its elementary [*sic*] parts, which water adheres to the other parts of the nitre with a force sufficient to enable it to sustain a red heat, when the acid acts on the water and dephlogisticates it; and the fire supplies the humor [see p. 336] with the due quantity of heat to constitute it air'. This is the same, except the last part, as Cavendish's theory (see p. 336). The second paper deals entirely with these experiments.

In a letter to Blagden of 27 May 1784 Watt says the letter of 26 April 1783 was 'received' by Priestley:

at London and, after showing it to several Members of the Royal Society, he [Priestley] delivered it to Sir Joseph Banks, the President, with a request that it might be read at some of the public meetings of the Society; but before that could be complied with, the author, having heard of Dr. Priestley's new experiments, begged that the reading

[1] Muirhead, 58–68.   [2] Muirhead, 23.
[3] Muirhead, 32; Wilson, (1), 316.   [4] Muirhead, 54; Wilson, (1), 316.
[5] *Ann. Sci.*, 1954, x, 294.
[6] *Phil. Trans.*, 1784, lxxiv, 329, 354; Muirhead, 77–110.   [7] Muirhead, 70.

might be delayed. The letter, therefore, was reserved until the 22nd April last; when at the author's request, it was read to the Society. It has been judged unnecessary to print that letter, as the essential parts of it are repeated, almost *verbatim*, in this letter to Mr. De Luc; but, to authenticate the date of the author's ideas, the parts of it which are contained in the present letter are marked with double commas.[1]

John Davy[2] said Watt's printed paper was altered and extended from the original version of 1783, but these parts are clearly marked (at Watt's request) by double inverted commas. In spite of Watt's statement it is possible that his letter to Priestley was sent from Birmingham on 21 April 1783 to Sir Joseph Banks (the letter of 26 April was to De Luc). The date 26 April is corrected in two places in the MS. to 21 April.[3] De Luc[4] says Watt:

persista à desirer, que la lettre qu'il avoit écrite ne fut pas [*sic*] lu à la Société royale; quoiqu'elle eût pour objet principal, la production de l'*Eau* par la décomposition de l'*Air dephlogistiqué* avec l'*Air inflammable*, & que ce grand Fait se trouvât établi, par des Expériences certaines, contenues dans le Mémoire que le Dr. Priestley communiqua alors à la Société.

Watt's paper begins by saying that it was known for some time that inflammable air contains much phlogiston. Priestley had by experiments found that it was either wholly phlogiston or contains no apparent mixture of any other matter, and Kirwan had also proved that it was probably 'the real phlogiston, in an aerial form'. Watt, however, was of the opinion that it contains a small quantity of water and much elementary heat. Priestley's experiments are those on the reduction of calces by inflammable air (hydrogen) (see p. 268). He then refers to Priestley's experiments with pure dry dephlogisticated air and pure dry inflammable air (charcoal gas, see p. 348), which when exploded by a spark became red hot and on cooling the vessel 'a mist or visible vapour appeared in it, which was condensed on the glass in the form of moisture or dew', a footnote (a pencil note added to the original just before it was sent in) saying: 'I believe that Mr. Cavendish was the first who discovered that the combustion of dephlogisticated and inflammable air produced moisture on the sides of the glass in which they were fired', which is incorrect, since it was Priestley (see p. 328). Watt goes on to say that in Priestley's experiment, after the glass was cooled to atmospheric temperature, it 'was opened with its mouth immersed in water or mercury, so much of these liquids entered, as was sufficient to fill the glass within about $\frac{1}{200}$ part of its whole contents; and this small residuum may safely be concluded to have been occasioned by some impurity in one or both kinds of air'. Priestley never mentions such an experiment, nor does Cavendish. Watt in one of the additions to the paper says De Luc informed him of experiments made in Paris (Lavoisier's) in which a mixture of the two airs when ignited produced 'a quantity of water equal in weight to the airs; and that the water thus produced appeared, by every test, to be pure water', but it was Cavendish who did this (finding, it is true, correctly that the water could be acid). Watt says:[5]

[1] Muirhead, 63, 78.   [2] *Edin. N. Phil. J.*, 1849, xlviii, 42.
[3] Harcourt, (1), 44; Muirhead, 21, refers to 'Watt's letter to Priestley, dated 26 April 1783' but he does not reproduce it.
[4] *Idées sur la Météorologie*, 1787, ii, 223.   [5] *Phil. Trans.*, 1784, lxxiv, 333.

Are we not, then, authorized to conclude that water is composed of dephlogisticated air and phlogiston, deprived of part of their latent or elementary heat; that dephlogisticated or pure air is composed of water deprived of its phlogiston and united to elementary heat and light; and that the latter are contained in it in a latent state, so as not to be sensible to the thermometer or to the eye; and if light be only a modification of heat, or a circumstance attending it, or a component part of the inflammable air, then pure or dephlogisticated air is composed of water deprived of its phlogiston and united to elementary heat.

In a letter to Black of 3 February 1783,[1] Watt said that Priestley 'produces very pure inflammable air' by heating olive oil, or oil of turpentine, in an earthen retort, and on 2 May 1783, he asked Priestley to try 'inflammable air produced from spirit of wine, and oils, or the air $[N_2 + 3H_2]$ from the volatile alkali'.[2]

In Watt's paper[3] it is Priestley who had found that 'dephlogisticated air unites completely with about twice its bulk of the inflammable air from metals'. Priestley had not used 'inflammable air from metals' but charcoal-gas; still, the carbon monoxide in Priestley's gas would also unite with about half its volume of oxygen $(2CO + O_2 = 2CO_2)$ and produce the 'fixed air' which Priestley says he found. Watt says that 'phlogisticated air [nitrogen] seems to be another composition of phlogiston and dephlogisticated air', and that Priestley[4] had shown that 'charcoal, when freed from fixed air, and other air which it imbibes from the atmosphere, is almost wholly convertible into inflammable air'. Priestley, he says, had also shown that, in some circumstances, 'dephlogisticated air can unite, in certain degrees, with phlogiston, without being changed into water', since clean iron filings heated with red precipitate of mercury, give fixed air.

Although phlogiston for Watt could mean hydrogen, it could also mean any kind of inflammable air, including carbon monoxide, as it did for Priestley,[5] whereas Cavendish[6] had clearly stated that the gas from charcoal is 'a different kind of inflammable air' from that (hydrogen) which he used, and he had also disproved Priestley's conclusion from the experiment with iron filings and red precipitate.[7] If the most favourable interpretation is given to Watt's statements, he believed that:

$$\text{hydrogen} = \text{phlogiston} = \phi$$
$$\text{oxygen} \quad = \text{water} - \phi + \text{heat} = \text{water} - \text{hydrogen} + \text{heat};$$

whilst Cavendish took:

$$\text{oxygen} \quad = \text{water} - \phi$$
$$\text{hydrogen} = \text{water} + \phi.$$

Watt's statement is half of Cavendish's plus half of Lavoisier's, the latter believing that *all* gases contain combined heat.

Watt[8] thought that fixed air contains a greater quantity of phlogiston than phlogisticated air does, because it has a greater specific gravity, and because it has more affinity with water, and 'the attraction of the particles of matter to

[1] Muirhead, 14.   [2] Muirhead, 27.   [3] *Phil. Trans.*, 1784, lxxiv, § 17, 349.
[4] *Phil. Trans.*, 1783, lxxiii, 411.   [5] E & O, 1790, i, 8.
[6] *Phil. Trans.*, 1784, lxxiv, 135; ACR, iii, 20.
[7] Wilson, (1), 284, 297, 436.   [8] *Phil. Trans.*, 1784, lxxiv, 335, 351-2.

one another . . . is increased by phlogiston, and bodies are thereby rendered specifically heavier'. Also[1] that 'dephlogisticated water has a more powerful attraction for phlogiston than it has for latent heat', as Harcourt said[2] 'a principle which chemistry has no means of investigating', although if 'phlogiston' is hydrogen and 'latent heat' is 'caloric' it is Lavoisier's theory. Hermbstädt[3] recognised a distinction between Lavoisier's and Watt's theories of the nature of oxygen and thought Watt's was superior.

An addition to Cavendish's paper after it was read, in Blagden's handwriting, says:

Mr. Watt, in a paper lately read before this Society, supposes water to consist of dephlogisticated air and phlogiston deprived of part of their latent heat, whereas I take no notice of the latter circumstance, . . . If there be any such thing as elementary heat, it must be allowed that what Mr. Watt says is true; but . . . there are very few [chemical combinations] which are not attended with some increase or diminution of heat. I have chosen to avoid this form of speaking, both because I think it more likely that there is no such thing as elementary heat, and because saying so in this instance, without using similar expressions in speaking of other chemical unions, would be improper, and would lead to false ideas; and . . . doing it in general would . . . cause more trouble and perplexity than it is worth.

A large part of Muirhead's essay is devoted to a personal attack on Blagden; he was deliberately responsible for the incorrect dates on Watt's paper and on the reprints of Cavendish's paper; his letter in Crell's *Annalen* in 1786 (see p. 414), although mentioning Watt, deliberately tried to give the impression that his theory was later than Cavendish's; Blagden had 'added a passage' (that just quoted) to Cavendish's paper (which he could hardly do without Cavendish's consent) intended to deprive Watt of his priority; and finally, that Cavendish gave Blagden a considerable annuity and left him a legacy of £15,000.[4] These fantastic charges are partly based on a statement on 4 March 1784 by De Luc that Blagden had seen Watt's letter of April 1783 and, by implication, passed on its contents to Cavendish.[5] Something has been said above (p. 351) on De Luc, and a little may now be said about Blagden.

Charles Blagden (Wooton under Edge, Gloucestershire, baptised 19 April 1748–Arcueil, near Paris (in Berthollet's house), 26 March 1820; he is buried in Paris) was originally an army surgeon, F.R.S. 1772, Cavendish's assistant from 1782 or early in 1783 till about 1789, a Secretary of the Royal Society in 1784 and a friend of the President, Sir Joseph Banks, knighted 1792; he was often in Paris and knew most French scientists (particularly Berthollet) well, and was highly respected by them. He was an unsuccessful suitor of Mme. Lavoisier, who married Count Rumford (see p. 365). He was a formal man, of quite considerable scientific ability and complete integrity. He seems to have had a friendly disposition; Dr. Johnson called him a 'delightful fellow'.[6] He published important papers on the freezing of mercury,[7] the supercooling of

---

[1] *Ib.*, 334.   [2] (1), 29.
[3] *Physikalisch-chemische Versuche und Beobachtungen*, Berlin, 1786, i, 255.
[4] Muirhead, xxxvii, lv, lx, lxiii, cxxv.   [5] *Ib.*, lx, 46.
[6] Getman, *Osiris*, 1937, III, i, 69; Harrison, DNB, 1908, ii, 617; Thorpe, *Nature*, 1890, xliii, 3; Wilson, (1), 126–46; Blagden's letters were acquired by the Royal Society in 1947.
[7] *Phil. Trans.*, 1783, lxxiii, 329.

water,[1] and the freezing points of salt solutions,[2] as well as other papers, e.g. on restoring ancient ink.[3]

Cavendish and Watt showed no ill-feeling towards one another; they met at one of Sir Joseph Banks's soirées in 1786 and in the same year Cavendish, on one of his geological tours, visited Watt in Birmingham.[4]

Both Muirhead[5] and Wilson[6] agree that Cavendish had priority in the *experiments* (Watt made no experiments on the subject), but they differ on the priority of the *conclusions*. Wilson says: (i) Cavendish in his paper admits no obligation to Watt for his conclusions; (ii) although there are no conclusions in Cavendish's laboratory journal this is entirely a record of facts; the conclusions were formed in January 1783 and may go back to 1781; (iii) Cavendish gave an account of his experiments to Priestley in 1781, and may have told him then that water was formed by the combustion of inflammable and dephlogisticated airs, although Priestley never said this;[7] (iv) Watt first stated clearly that water is not an element and gave the ingredients from which it could be prepared; (v) Watt stated that one ingredient is oxygen and the other a combustible gas which he called 'phlogiston', and this included various inflammable gases as well as hydrogen; (vi) Lavoisier called this combustible gas 'aqueous inflammable air', later 'hydrogen', and first made both the elements of water (not merely ingredients) manifest and tangible.

Muirhead thought (i) if Cavendish had formed his theory in 1781 he would have mentioned it before 1784 or even 1783, and Blagden would have been more precise than 'the Spring of 1783' as he said in 1786:[8] 'about the same time the news was brought to London, that Mr. Watt of Birmingham had been induced by some observations to form a similar opinion' to that communicated by Cavendish to Blagden and other 'particular friends in the Spring of 1783'; (ii) Blagden had seen Watt's letter to Priestley, sent to Sir Joseph Banks, and had given Cavendish an account of Watt's theory.

Arago[9] also thought Blagden's statement too imprecise; he and Robison[10] favoured Watt. Nicholson,[11] and Murray,[12] favoured Cavendish; Dumas[13] and William Henry[14] decided in favour of Watt. Thomson[15] says: 'Mr. Watt had previously drawn the same conclusion from the experiments of Dr. Priestley and Mr. Warltire; but his opinions were unknown to Mr. Cavendish, when he laid his paper on the subject before the Royal Society.'

James Watt junr[16], asserted that Watt had the hypothesis of the composition of water in mind before December 1782, but Watt's letter of 26 March 1783, that Priestley's experiment (admittedly made as a repetition of Cavendish's) was 'new to him',[17] suggests that Watt had not formulated his hypothesis before Cavendish had told Priestley of his results. Lord Brougham[18] suggested

[1] *Ib.*, 1788, lxxviii, 125.   [2] *Ib.*, 1788, lxxviii, 277.   [3] *Ib.*, 1787, lxxvii, 451.
[4] Wilson, (1), 146.   [5] Pp. lxvii, lxix f., xciii, ciii.   [6] (1), 353–404, 437 f.
[7] Priestley may have thought his and Warltire's experiments had established it.
[8] Crell's *Ann.*, 1786, I, pt. i, 58–61; see p. 441.
[9] *Oeuvres*, 1854, i, 452 f.; Muirhead, 221; Harcourt, (1), 22; Wilson, (1), 297, 314.
[10] In Black, *Elements of Chemistry*, 1803, ii, 233; Harcourt, (1), 41.
[11] *Dictionary of Chemistry*, 1795, ii, 1019.   [12] *System of Chemistry*, 1806, ii, 159.
[13] *Compt. Rend.*, 1840, x, 109–11.   [14] Letter of 1820, in Muirhead, xcvii–xcix.
[15] (3), 1812, 471; cf. *id.*, (2), 1817, ii, 20.   [16] Muirhead, 257.
[17] Muirhead, cxxv, 17.   [18] *Works*, 1872, i, 64, 99, 312 f., 473 f.; in Muirhead, 257.

that: (i) Watt 'formed his theory during the few months or weeks preceding April 1783', (ii) it was known among some members of the Royal Society eight months before Cavendish's paper was read, (iii) it is doubtful if Cavendish had heard of it before he had drawn his own conclusions, (iv) Cavendish discovered 'the composition of water' before Watt's claim was made, and without any previous knowledge of Watt's reasoning, (v) although Cavendish's experiments were made before Watt's inferences, 'yet Mr. Cavendish's conclusion was not drawn even privately by himself, till after Mr. Watt's inference had been made known to many others'.

Davy[1] in 1799 said Watt and Keir 'are still phlogistians'. Berzelius[2] concluded that *if* Watt's phlogiston could be regarded as synonymous with hydrogen, his statement of the composition of water would be correct, but it is obscure and this does not follow directly from it, and when he said phlogiston is identical with hydrogen Lavoisier's memoir (mentioned in his paper) had been published and the whole question decided. Kopp[3] concluded that: 'Cavendish was the first to establish the fact from which the knowledge of the composition of water proceeded' but did not state the components of water; Watt 'first concluded from these facts that water is a compound, but without reaching a true knowledge of the components'; Lavoisier, from the same facts 'and with the recognition of the compound nature of water, first gave the correct determination and the exact statement of the components'. I think that this is a correct view.

Wilson[4] speaks of 'the endless contradictory statements regarding the products of the combustion of inflammable air, which are scattered through Priestley's volumes' and summarises Priestley's views.[5]

In a letter to Wedgwood of 24 July 1784, Priestley[6] says 'Watt[7] still thinks it is water that furnishes the air' when nitre is heated. Watt said this, and so did Cavendish:[8] 'the acid absorbs phlogiston from the water in the nitre, and becomes phlogisticated, while the water is thereby turned into dephlogisticated air.' Priestley adopted this view and asserted that 'air is dephlogisticated water'.[9] In 1785 (probably in reply to the historical note inserted in Cavendish's paper) Priestley said:[10]

In the experiments of which I shall now give an account, I was principally guided by a view to the opinions which have lately been advanced by Mr. Cavendish, Mr. Watt, and M. Lavoisier [the order is significant]. Mr. Cavendish was of opinion, that when *air* is decomposed, *water* only is produced; and Mr. Watt concluded from some experiment, of which I gave an account to the Society, and also from some observations of his own, that water consists of dephlogisticated and inflammable air, in which Mr. Cavendish and M. Lavoisier concur with him: but M. Lavoisier is well known to maintain, that there is no such thing as what has been called *phlogiston*, affirming inflammable air to be nothing else but one of the elements or constituent parts of water.

This statement, it will be seen, contains some errors.

[1] Paris, *Life of Davy*, 1831, i, 79.   [2] *Jahres-Ber.*, 1841, II, 43–51.
[3] (2), iii, 309; Thorpe, *Essays*, 1902, 149 f.   [4] (1), 312.   [5] *Ib.*, 92 f., 96, 106 f.
[6] Wilson, (1), 95.   [7] *Phil. Trans.*, 1784, lxxiv, 336.
[8] *Phil. Trans.*, 1784, lxxiv, 144.   [9] Wilson, 97 (letter to Wedgwood, 23 January 1784).
[10] *Phil. Trans.*, 1785, lxxv, 279–309 (read 24 February 1785); repr. in E & O *Nat. Phil.*, 1786, iii, 71, and E & O, 1790, i, 280; Wilson, (i), 85–6, 96, 106 f.

Priestley[1] in 1786 says: 'I also procured water when I decomposed dephlogisticated air and inflammable air from iron by an electric spark in a close
vessel, which is an experiment similar to those that were made by Mr.
Lavoisier in Paris', although it was Cavendish and not Lavoisier who made
such experiments. From a mixture of 1·25 and 2·50 oz. measures, respectively,
of the airs Priestley obtained 1 grain of moisture, and the dephlogisticated air
in this mixture would have weighed little more than 0·75 grain. By repeating
the experiment with half as much dephlogisticated as inflammable air 'I could
not perceive any water after the experiment'. By heating red precipitate in an
inflammable air which gave water with iron scales he obtained no water. A
number of other inaccurate experiments are described. He says 'Mr. Watt has
led me to think, that there is no acid whatever in dephlogisticated air, and that
it consists of nothing more than one of the constituent parts [of] water, combined with the element of heat; the other constituent part of water being
inflammable air. In this opinion I for the present acquiesce'.[2] In the end[3]
Priestley says: 'the weight of the water produced is never, I believe, found
quite equal to that of both kinds of air. May not the *light*, therefore, emitted
from the flame, be part of the phlogiston of the inflammable air, united to the
principle of *heat*?' He is now back to Warltire's idea of 1781, that the loss of
weight is due to the escape of ponderable heat (see p. 328).

Priestley in 1788[4] exploded dephlogisticated and 'inflammable' air in a
copper vessel by a spark (the inflammable air being 'from iron', perhaps by
passing steam over heated iron, or from iron and acid, and hence hydrogen) and
obtained a green liquid, which Keir showed contained copper nitrate. Hence,
says Priestley: 'I concluded that an acid was the necessary result of the union
of those two kinds of air, and not water only; which is an hypothesis that has
been maintained by Mr. Lavoisier and others, and which has been made the
basis of an intirely new system of chemistry.' Priestley says the 'supposition of
water entering into the constitution of all the kinds of air . . . makes it unnecessary to suppose, as myself as well as others have done, that water consists
of dephlogisticated air and inflammable air, or that it has ever been either
composed or decomposed in any of our processes'. Probably Priestley's
oxygen contained some nitrogen. Berthollet[5] found that ordinary red precipitate on heating gave oxygen containing a third of its volume of phlogisticated
air.

In 1788[6] Priestley says the product of 'decomposition' of dephlogisticated
and inflammable airs is always '*acid*, which Dr. Withering finds to be as yet in
all cases the nitrous . . . the great quantity of *water* that has been found in this
case is nothing more than was either diffused through the airs, or was necessary for their aerial form', and Cavendish's explanation of the formation of
acid (see p. 334) is 'doubtful'.

In 1790[7] Priestley says:

[1] E & O *Nat. Phil.*, 1786, iii, 126   [2] *Ib.*, 291.   [3] *Ib.*, 407.
[4] *Phil. Trans.*, 1788, lxxviii, 147; 1791, lxxxi, 213; E & O, 1790, iii, 54.
[5] *Ann. Chim.*, 1789, iii, 63 (94).
[6] Wilson, (1), 100: letter to Wedgwood, 8 January 1788.   [7] E & O, 1790, i, 266 f.

'At first I had no suspicion that water was any part of inflammable air. . . . That water in great quantities is sometimes [sic] produced from burning inflammable air and dephlogisticated air seemed to be evident from the experiments of Mr. Cavendish and Mr. Lavoisier. I have also frequently collected considerable quantities of water in this way, though never quite so much as the weight of the two kinds of air decomposed.'

He describes an apparatus consisting of a glass globe with a tubulure passing into an empty tube, and a jet of inflammable air burning inside the globe, but he realised that some 'vapour . . . very different from steam' might escape. He had reflected 'particularly' on 'Mr. Cavendish's ideas on the subject'. Also:[1] 'I have never been able to find the full weight of the air decomposed in the water produced by the decomposition [i.e., combination]; and . . . I apprehend it will not be denied, that the produce of this decomposition is not mere water, but always some acid.' In 1791[2] Priestley again says the water formed, which always contains nitrous acid, was contained in the two 'airs', but 'the doctrine of *phlogiston* stands firm, and it only appears it is one element in the composition of water'.

In 1794[3] he says the experiments alleged to prove the resolving of water into dephlogisticated and inflammable air 'do not satisfy me', and it could be supposed that water was a 'simple element' but for very recent experiments which show that 'by means of heat . . . it seems to be resolvable into such air as that of which the atmosphere consists, viz. dephlogisticated and phlogisticated, only with a greater proportion of the former'.

In 1794[4] Priestley says:

'when dephlogisticated and inflammable airs, in the proportion of a little more than one measure of the former to two of the latter, both so pure as to contain no sensible quantity of phlogisticated air, are inclosed in a glass or copper vessel, and decomposed by taking an electric spark in it, a highly phlogisticated nitrous acid is instantly produced; and the purer the airs are, the stronger the acid is found to be . . . a peculiarly *dense vapour* is formed, which the eye can easily distinguish not to be mere vapour of *water*, and if the juice of turnsole [litmus] be put into the vessel, it immediately becomes of a deep red, which shows that it was an acid vapour.'

If an excess of inflammable air is used, no acid is formed, 'but in the place of it there will be a quantity of phlogisticated air.' He said later:[5] 'Tho' I have not gallons of this liquor, I have some ounces, which no antiphlogistian would care to drink.' Priestley maintained in his last papers[6] that air is generated from boiling water, i.e. water is convertible into atmospheric air, or[7] into phlogisticated air.

In a letter to Black of June 1788[8] Watt refers to the experiments of 1788 (see p. 360), producing a green water containing nitric acid saying: 'I think it highly probable that the acid proceeds from the inflammable air, and that the D[d] [dephlogisticated] air acts the same part that it does in the burning of sulphur and phosphorus.' Also, 'water probably in its own form constitutes

[1] E & O, 1790, iii, 555.   [2] Wilson, (1), 103: letter to Wedgwood, 26 February 1791.
[3] *Lectures on Experimental Philosophy*, 1794, 44.
[4] *Considerations on the Doctrine of Phlogiston*, 1794; reprint, Princeton, 1929, 34–6.
[5] *The Doctrine of Phlogiston Established*, 1803, 67.
[6] *Trans. Amer. Phil. Soc.*, 1799, iv, 11.   [7] *Ib.*, 1802, v, 36.
[8] Ramsay, *Life and Letters of Joseph Black*, 1918, 89–90.

the greater part of the mass of all sorts of air.' In a book by Beddoes and Watt[1] there is a letter of Watt dated 2 September 1794, which says: 'no species of artificial air is obtained except water is obviously present, or that there is reason to suspect it may be contained as an element, or part of one of the substances concerned.' In the 1796 edition Watt describes the preparation of various kinds of 'Inflammable, or Hydrogene Airs', in which he includes gases prepared from zinc and iron by the action of water, 'heavy inflammable air' from water and charcoal heated to redness, and 'animal inflammable air' by heating animal substances, all varieties of 'inflammable air'.

[1] *Considerations on the Medicinal Use and on the Production of Factitious Airs*, 1796, 114.

CHAPTER IX

LAVOISIER

Venel, the author of most of the chemical articles in the *Encyclopédie* of Diderot and D'Alembert,[1] said that chemistry was little cultivated in France, the chemists 'forment un peuple distinct, très-peu nombreux, ayant sa langue, ses loix, ses mystères, et vivant presque isolés'. There was a prejudice against it and its aims were misunderstood.

Even the great names of Becher and Stahl were hardly known; although Jean Bernoulli's work on fermentation and Boerhaave's on fire were praised, the 'far greater views of Stahl on the same subjects' existed only for a few chemists. 'The revolution which would raise chemistry to the rank it merits, and place it on a level with mathematical physics, can be accomplished only by a clever, enthusiastic, and bold chemist, who finds himself in a favourable position and profits by happy circumstances.' Venel awaited the appearance of 'this new Paracelsus'. He could hardly have hoped that, in so short a time, this role would be filled by his countryman, Lavoisier.[2]

[1] *Ency.*, 1753, iii (art. 'Chymie'); repr. in *Ency. Méthod., Chimie*, 1796, iii, 262.
[2] Anon., *Pharm. J.*, 1895, xxv, 857; W. R. Aykroyd, *Three Philosophers. Lavoisier, Priestley, Cavendish*, London, 1935; T. Andrews, *B.A. Rep.*, 1871, i, 189 (three letters from Lavoisier to Black); M. Berthelot, (1) *Revue Scientifique*, 1890, xlvi, 513–14; *id.*, (2) *Nature*, 1890, xliii, 1 (the discovery of oxygen); *id.* (3) Notice historique sur Lavoisier, in *Mém. Acad. Sci.*, n.d., XLV, xix–lxxij (read 1889); *id.* (4) *La Révolution Chimique. Lavoisier*, Paris, 1890; *id.* (5) *Compt. Rend.*, 1902, cxxxv, 549–57 (vol. ii of L's laboratory notes); G. Bertrand, *Compt. Rend.*, 1943, ccxvii, 633–40; 1947, ccxxv, 833–5 (Priestley-Lavoisier priority; reply to Hartley, *q.v.*, superficial); *id.*, in Commémoration du Bicentenaire de la Naissance de Lavoisier, in *Bull. Soc. Chim.*, 1944, xi, Appendix, 2–6; Boatner, *Osiris*, 1936, i, 176 (letters of L); O. Boillot, *De la Combustion . . . Phénomènes Générales. Modification apportée à la Théorie de Lavoisier*, Paris, 1869 (BM); W. T. Brande, 1848, I, lxxxv–xci; H. Brocard, *Compt. Rend.*, 1902, cxxxv, 574–5 (recovery of lost laboratory notes of Lavoisier in Perpignan); Lord Brougham, 1855 or 1872, 290–333; F. Cajori, *Isis*, 1922, iv, 483 (on caloric); Clerc, *Ann. Chim. Anal.*, 1943, xlv, 63 (Lavoisier and the Tribune); J. A. Cochrane, *Lavoisier*, London, 1931, 1934 (pp. xiii, 264); J. B. Cohen, *Chemical World*, 1914, iii, 247; A. Crum Brown, *The Development of the Idea of Chemical Composition, Inaug. lect.*, Edinburgh, 1869, 25 f.; G. Cuvier, *Rapport Historique sur les Progrès des Sciences Naturelles*, 1828, 66 f.; M. Daumas, (1) *Lavoisier*, Paris, 1941 (259 pp.); *id.* (2) *Chymia*, 1950, iii, 45; *id.* (3) *Lavoisier, théoricien et expérimenteur*, Paris, 1955 (180 pp., 4 pls.); Delambre, *Mém. de l'Inst.* (AdS), 1812 (read 1814, publ. 1816), II, h lxvij; J. B. Dumas, (2), 135–214; Du Pont, Bertrand, Darmois, Polovski, Javillier, and Jolibois, in *Commémoration du Bicentenaire de la Naissance de Lavoisier, Soc. Chim. France*, 1945 (19 pp.); Du Pont, *The Autobiography of an American Enterprise. The Story of E. I. Du Pont de Nemours and Company published in commemoration of the 150th Anniversary of the Founding of the Company on July 19, 1802*, New York, 1952, pp. vi, 138 (a refugee from France, Eleuthère Irénée Du Pont, had been a pupil of Lavoisier); D. I. Duveen, (1) *Chymia*, 1953, iv, 13 (Mme. Lavoisier); (2) *id.*, *Ann. Sci.*, 1955 (1956), xi, 103, 271 (L and Benj. Franklin); (3) *id. ib.*, 1957 (1958), xiii, 30; (4) *id.*, *Isis*, 1956, xlvii, 84; (5) *id.* and H. S. Klickstein, *A Bibliography of the Works of A. L. Lavoisier*, New York, 1954 (see Guerlac, (2)); A. F. de Fourcroy, *Notice sur la vie et les travaux de Lavoisier, précédée d'un discours* [by Mulot] *sur les funérailles et suivie d'une ode* [by Désaudray] *sur l'immortalité de l'âme*, Paris, An IV (1796) (60, 7 pp.); *id.*, (1), 1801, i, 36 f. (list of L's publs.); *id.*, (2), iii, 414 f.; S. L. French, *Torch and Crucible. The Life and Death of Antoine Lavoisier*, Princeton, 1941 (*J. Phys. Chem.*, 1942, xlvi, 336); R. Fric, *Catalogue*

Antoine Laurent Lavoisier (Paris; 26 August 1743–8 May 1794) was the
son of a Paris lawyer who had several scientific friends. In a genealogical tree[1]
his oldest ancestor is Antoine Lavoisier, d. 1620, a groom in the king's stables
at Villers-Cotteret, a position which his son united with that of postmaster
there. Lavoisier's father, Jean Antoine (Paris, 16 January 1715–Bourges, 16

préliminaire de la Correspondance de Lavoisier, s.l.e.a. (c. 1953), see p. 374; J. F. Gmelin, (1),
iii, 276 f.; id., Vitas nonnullorum Candidatorum . . . Præmittuntur Nonnulla de Primis Chemiæ
Pneumaticæ Originibus, 4°, Göttingen, 1797; J. A. Gregory, Combustion from Heracleitos to
Lavoisier, London, 1934; E. Grimaux, Lavoisier 1743–1794 d'après sa Correspondance, ses
Manuscrits, ses Papiers de Famille et d'autres documents inédits, Paris, 1888; I. Guareschi,
Lavoisier, sua vita e sue opere, 4°, Turin, 1903 (160 pp.); id., in Atti del Congresso Internazionale
di Scienza Storiche (Rome, April, 1903), Rome, 1904 (xii, pp. 115–50) (charges of plagiarism
made against Lavoisier); H. Guerlac, (1) Lavoisier and his Biographers, Isis, 1954, xlv, 51–62;
(2) id. ib., 1956, xlvii, 85, 211–16; (3) id., Archives, 1959, xii, 113–35 (L's work on combustion);
H. Hartley, Proc. Roy. Soc., 1947, cxxxiv B, 348; P. J. Hartog, Ann. Sci., 1941, v, 1–56;
A. Heller, 1884, ii, 516–25; J. C. Hemmeter, Janus, 1921, xxv, 1–22, 57–86; F. Hoefer, (1),
1869, ii, 489; id., NBG, 1859, xxx, 1; id., La Chimie enseignée par la Biographie de ses Fonda-
teurs, 1865, 71; E. J. Holmyard, Nature, 1932, cxxx, 97 (letter of Lavoisier); S. M. Jörgensen,
Die Entdeckung des Sauerstoffes, tr. from the Danish by Ortwed and Speter, in Samml.
chem.- und chem.-techn. Vörtrage, ed. W. Herz, Stuttgart, 1909, xiv, Heft 4; G. W. A. Kahlbaum and A. Hoffmann, Die Einführung der Lavoisier'schen Theorie in Besonderen in Deutsch-
land, Kahlbaum's Monographien aus der Geschichte der Chemie, Heft I, Leipzig, 1897 (full of
incorrect references; see 206 f., list of publications with dates); H. Kopp, (1), i, 299; id., (3),
85–91, 128–33, 134–206; A. Ladenburg, 1905, 22 f.; J. Lalande, Magasin Encyclopédique, ou
Journal des Sciences, des Lettres et des Arts, 1795, v, 174–88; ib., tr. as Lavoisier's Leben und
Schriften, in A. N. Scherer, Nachträge zu den Grundzügen der neuern chemischen Theorie,
Jena, 1796 (BM 956. i. 36); ib., tr. Phil. Mag., 1801, ix, 78–85 (Joseph Jérôme Le Français de
Lalande, 1732–1807, was the famous astronomer); Lemay, Bull. Soc. Franç. Hist. Med., 1934,
xxviii, 146, 156, 194, q. in Isis, 1935, xxiii, 520 f.; L. and L. Leroux, Lavoisier, Paris, 1928
(123 pp., q. in Chimie et Industrie, 1928, xix, 1177); Loewenfeld, Manchester Mem., 1913,
lvii, no. 19; D. McKie, (1) Lavoisier, London, 1935; (2) id., Antoine Lavoisier. Scientist,
Economist, Social Reformer, London, 1952; J. C. Marignac, Arch. Sci. Phys. Nat., 1920, ii,
81–98 (MS. of 1875 lecture); A. N. Meldrum, (1) The Eighteenth Century Revolution in
Science — The First Phase, Calcutta, n.d. (1930, pref. dated Oct. 1929; Winderlich, A. Nat.,
1930–1, xiii, 221–2); (2) id., Archeion, 1932, xiv, 15; (3) id., Isis, 1933, xix, 330–63; (4) id. ib.,
1934, xx, 396–425; Mémoires de Lavoisier: L'air et l'eau, Paris, A. Colin, 1923 (pp. xvi, 136);
Helène Metzger, (1) Archeion, 1932, xiv, 31–50; (2) id., La philosophie de la matière chez
Lavoisier, in Actualités scientifiques et industrielles, Paris, 1935, no. 218; A. Mieli, Lavoisier,
2 ed., Rome, 1926; id., Archeion, 1932, xiv, 51–6; M. M. Pattison Muir, Heroes of Science.
Chemists, 1883, 79–100; M. Nierenstein, Chem. and Ind., 1932, li, 438 R (Guyton de Morveau
and Lavoisier); R. E. Oesper, Priestley, Lavoisier and Trudaine de Montigny, J. Chem.
Educ., 1936, xiii, 403–12; Partington, (1), Sci. Progr., 1936, xxxi, 385; id., (2) Nature, 1943,
clii, 207; 1956, clxxviii, 1360; id., (3) Ann. Sci., 1952, viii, 399; id., (4) Bull. Brit. Soc. Hist.
Sci., 1951, i, 129; G. F. Rodwell, Nature, 1882, xxvii, 8; L. Scheler, Lavoisier et la Révolution
française, i, Le Lycée des Arts, revised ed., 1957; id. and W. A. Smeaton, Ann. Sci., 1958 (1960),
xiv, 148 (L's religion); A. N. Scherer: see Lalande; E. Schultze, Lavoisier, der 'Begründer der
Chemie', Samml. gemeinverständlicher wissenschaftlicher Vorträge, ed. Virchow and Watten-
bach, 1894, Heft 212, 723–60; W. A. Smeaton, (1) The Early Years of the Lycée and the Lycée
des Arts, in Ann. Sci., 1955 (1957), xi, 308; (2) id., Lavoisier's membership of the Société
Royale de Médecine, ib., 1956 (1957), xii, 228; (3) id., Lavoisier's membership of the Société
Royale d'Agriculture, ib., 1956 (1957), xii, 267; (4) id., The Library, 1956, xi, 130–3 (review of
Duveen and Klickstein); (5) id., Ann. Sci., 1957 (1959), xiii, 219 (early publs. of L), 235
(membership of Commune 1789–90); M. Speter, (1) Lavoisier und seine Vorläufer, in
Samml. chem.- und chem.-techn. Vorträge, ed. W. Herz, Stuttgart, 1910, xv, 109–218 (also
separate, repaginated); (2) id., Z. angew. Chem., 1926, xxxix, 578 (origins of L's system, criticising Berthelot); (3) id., Chem. Weekblad, 1927, xxiv, 232 (Lavoisier and Rey); (4) id. ib.,
1931, xxviii, 79 (influence of de Morveau and Mitouard); (5) id., Chem. Ztg., 1931, lv, 993;
(6) id., Angew. Chem., 1932, xlv, 104 (Lavoisier's note in Academy archives on combustion of
phosphorus in terms of phlogiston theory); (7) id., Z. f. Instrumentenkunde, 1934, liv, 56–61
(L's balances and weights); T. Thomson, Ann. Phil., 1813, ii, 81 (list of L's publs., 85 f.); id.,
(1), ii, 75–141; L. Thorndike, Isis, 1924–5, vi, 361–86 (L'Encyclopédie); T. E. Thorpe, (1)
Essays in Historical Chemistry, 1902, 123, 149, 176; (2) id., Nature, 1890, xlii, 313; 1890, xliii,
1; (3) id., Revue Scientifique, 1890, xlvi, 515–23; Van Deventer, Chem. Weekblad, 1927, xxiv,
234; Van Klooster, J. Chem. Educ., 1946, xxiii, 210 (Lavoisier's apparatus, illustr.).
    [1] J. C. Hemmeter, Janus, 1921, xxv, 1–22, 57–86.

November 1775) is also described[1] as a rich merchant (un riche commerçant). His mother, whose maiden name was Punctis and who had inherited wealth, died when he was five years old and he was brought up by a young aunt, who remained single in order to devote herself to this task. He was educated at the Collège Mazarin, where he gained prizes, and then studied law, taking the degree of Bachelor in 1763 and Licenciate in 1764. At some indefinite period he studied mathematics and astronomy under La Caille, botany under Jussieu, and chemistry (it is said) under Rouelle.[2] He assisted Guettard, curator of a cabinet of natural history of the Duc d'Orléans, for three years in geological work. Guettard and Monnet later published the work.[3]

In 1766 Lavoisier submitted an essay based on a large number of experiments for a prize of 2000 livres offered by the Paris chief of police, de Sartine, for the best description of a method of illuminating a large city; the essay did not win the prize but it was ordered to be printed by the Academy and the King directed that a gold medal should be awarded to Lavoisier, which was done at a public sitting of the Academy in 1766. In 1768 he became assistant to the Fermier Général Baudon, and in 1780 he became a Fermier Général himself, a step which later led to his execution. In 1768 he also became a candidate for the Académie des Sciences, on the death of Baron. His rival was an older man Gabriel Jars, well known for work in metallurgy, who rendered valuable services to the State. The Academy recommended Lavoisier, who seems to have had a small majority of votes, but the King was advised to elect Jars and give Lavoisier a provisional place, which was done. Jars died in 1769 and Lavoisier's place was automatically normalised. He became an 'assistant', in 1772 an 'associate', and in 1778 'pensionnaire', receiving a salary. In 1785 he became director. Lavoisier in 1767 had anticipated his election in 1768 by autographing his copy of Agricola's *De Re Metallica*: 'Regiae Scientiarum Academiae socius anno 1767.'[4] He became F.R.S. in 1788.

In 1771 Lavoisier married Marie-Anne Paulze, then aged nearly fourteen, the daughter of a Fermier Général. She later assisted him by making translations from English and other foreign publications (Lavoisier was poor at languages) and in making all the drawings for the attractive plates in his *Traité de Chimie*. She survived him and afterwards married Count Rumford, with whom she lived on very bad terms until they separated.[5] Guizot, an intimate friend of 'Mme. Lavoisier de Rumford', described her charm, but Tyndall[6] found it difficult to forget that after a disagreement with Count Rumford she poured boiling water over his favourite flowers; in later life she became less attractive.[7] She occupies most of the space in the idealised portrait of Lavoisier by David, now in the Rockefeller Institute in New York,[8] which has been reproduced many times.[9]

[1] Hoefer, NBG, 1859, xxx, 1.   [2] Guerlac, (2), 211–16.
[3] *Atlas et Description Mineralogique de la France, entrepris par orde du Roi*, Paris, 1780, with 31 maps.
[4] Duveen, *Bibliotheca*, 1949, 5.
[5] Ellis, *Memoir of Sir Benjamin Thompson, Count Rumford*, Boston, 1871, 576.
[6] *New Fragments*, 1892, 147.   [7] Duveen, (1).   [8] Oesper, *J. Chem. Educ.*, 1936, xiii, 403.
[9] In colour in McKie, *Notes and Records of the Royal Society*, 1949–50, vii, 1; for other portraits see T. L. Davis, *J. Chem. Educ.*, 1934, xi, 211; McKie, (2); *Phil. Mag.*, 1798, i,

Lavoisier set apart a piece of land on his estate at Vendôme near Blois for agricultural experiments.[1] In 1771 Lavoisier investigated the water supply of Paris.[2] In 1776 he was commissioned by Turgot to inspect the manufacture of gunpowder and he increased the range from 90 to 120 toises. During the war

FIG. 34. A. L. LAVOISIER, 1743–1794.

of the American Revolution the French gunpowder was much superior to the British, but during the war of the French Revolution the quality of the powder of the two nations was reversed.[3] In 1790 Lavoisier was a member of the commission which introduced the metric system,[4] and in 1791, as a Commissioner to the Treasury, he presented a report on the *Richesse Territoriale du Royaume de France*, an extract from which appeared as a 48-page pamphlet in 1791 and 1819.[5]

Lavoisier's international reputation as a scientist and his valuable services to France were as dust in the balance when weighed against his profession as a Fermier-Général. In 1793 he and other members of the Ferme were arrested on

frontisp.; Colson, in Hanotaux, *Histoire de la Nation Française*, 1924, xiv, 429 ('le vielle de sa morte d'apres un tableau de la collection Louis David ayant appartenu à Raspail').

[1] *Ann. Chim.*, 1792, xv, 267; *Oeuvres*, ii, 812; Brougham, 1872, 322; Lenglen, *Lavoisier Agronome*, Paris, 1936.

[2] AdS 1771 (1774), m 17; *Oeuvres*, iii, 227.   [3] Thomson, (1), ii, 79.

[4] *Oeuvres*, vi, 670 f.; Hellmann, *Osiris*, 1936, i, 314.

[5] *Oeuvres*, vi, 403–63; Dujarric de la Rivière, *Lavoisier économiste*, Paris, 1949 (120 pp.; rev. in *Archives*, 1951, iv, 226).

the charge of having mixed water and other ingredients harmful to the health of citizens in snuff. He had taken refuge in the Arsenal, where he had a laboratory,[1] but on hearing that this might compromise others he gave himself up. He was tried by jury, was found guilty of conspiracy with the enemies of France,[2] legally condemned to death, and guillotined on 8 May 1794.

A courageous citizen, Hallé, read a detailed account of Lavoisier's discoveries and his services to his country before the Tribunal, but without result. Many legends soon appeared about his trial, e.g. that Coffinhal, presiding over the Tribunal, when asked to spare a man of science said: 'The Republic has no need of savants; justice must take its course.'[3] These stories are probably apocryphal.[4]

Antoine Dupin, who in 1793 had secured the appointment of a commission to examine the accounts of the Fermiers and was appointed to present a report to the National Convention, was in 1794 approached through his sister-in-law by Pluvinet, an obscure man who had sold materials to Lavoisier for his laboratory. Dupin promised that Lavoisier would be separated from the other Fermiers and put in another prison, and that his report on him would not be in any way unfavourable. He pointed out that Mme. Lavoisier, whilst intriguing with other aristocrats, had not troubled to approach him or call on him. Mme. Lavoisier called on Dupin, but instead of following up the good work of Pluvinet she took a different line, asserting among other things, that only scoundrels could accuse her husband (des scelerats seul peuvent l'accuser).[5] Dupin took no further steps. Lavoisier's furniture, laboratory equipment, books, and most of his papers, which had been confiscated, were returned to Mme. Lavoisier in 1796. He died childless and apparently had few personal and intimate friends.

The abstract of Seguin and Lavoisier's memoir on the transpiration of animals[6] says: Les expériences de ce mémoire, aussi nombreuse que difficiles doivent bien faire regretter la perte de l'auteur, qui devoit continuer ces utiles recherches, ainsi que beaucoup d'autres.

Lavoisier's execution, it is unnecessary to say, was regretted by all who wrote on him and condemned by many. It must be kept in mind that he suffered as a member of a community of officials and not as a scientist, and that the French, never particularly fond of tax collectors, had just cause before the Revolution to dislike them more than ever. In 1789 (the year of the Revolution), the memoir on respiration by Lavoisier and Seguin[7] puts forward very advanced social opinions; the lot of the manual worker was to be ameliorated, and praise is accorded to 'wise institutions which will tend to equalise fortunes, raise the price of labour and assure it a just recompense, and present to all classes of society, and above all the indigent classes, more happiness and

[1] On L's residences see Duveen, *Isis*, 1951, xlii, 233.
[2] See McKie, *Notes and Records of the Royal Society*, 1949–50, vii, 1; Guerlac, (1).
[3] Girtanner, *Anfangsgründe der antiphlogistischen Chemie*, Berlin, 1795, 8, makes Robespierre say directly to Lavoisier: 'Fort mit Dir; wir brauchen jetz keine Gelehrte mehr'; see also *Allgem. J. Chem.* (Scherer), 1802, ix, 357.
[4] Guerlac, (1).   [5] Grimaux, 289.
[6] AdS, 1790 (1797), h xij.   [7] AdS, 1789, m 568; *Oeuvres*, ii, 698.

more prosperity'. Lavoisier might well have adapted himself to the changed conditions, had he been spared to continue his valuable services to the state.

In 1777[1] Lavoisier analysed some rubbish deposited in the streets, spent wood-ashes from bleachers, which were collected by poor women and sold to saltpetre makers for 2 sous 6 deniers a bushel. He showed that they were worth only 1 sou 6 deniers, but we do not know whether the poor women lost anything as a result.

The statue of Lavoisier later erected behind the Madeleine[2] disappeared in World War II. It has been said to be of Condorcet (also the bust in the Louvre),[3] but the marble bust at Versailles (1801) is of Lavoisier. The statue showed the famous mercury experiment and was obviously intended to be Lavoisier's.[4]

Lalande (who must have known him well) says 'Lavoisier was of large stature; affability and penetration were displayed in his countenance; his behaviour was mild, civil, and polite, and his activity knew no bounds'. Girtanner, who had many acquaintances in Paris and lived there for a time, said in 1786:[5]

Lavoisier is Fermier Général and has much business connected with this, so that access to him is difficult, as I have myself found. I am told that, with his great wealth and little time, he has many of his experiments arranged and executed by others (von anderen machen und ordnen lassen).

Arthur Young, F.R.S., who visited Lavoisier at the Arsenal in October 1787[6] found him 'splendidly lodged, and with every appearance of a man of considerable fortune'; Mme. Lavoisier, 'a woman of understanding, that works with her husband in his laboratory', was then translating Kirwan's Essay on Phlogiston (see p. 662).

Fourcroy[7] said Lavoisier performed his experiments many times before his colleagues and invited their rigorous criticisms; they were all willing to help and support him, but his discoveries were his own. Lavoisier took young men of promise into his laboratory and trained them in research, but his important experiments he usually made himself. Berthelot[8] says: 'c'était un homme doux, prudent, avisé, entendent fort bien les affaires.' Y. G. Dorfman[9] called him 'a business man in the worst sense', but there is no evidence that in his public and private life Lavoisier was otherwise than scrupulously honourable.

Publications

The *Mémoires* of the Académie des Sciences from 1768 to 1790 contain more than sixty papers by Lavoisier.[10] The following list is compiled from the originals; the date in brackets is that of publication:

[1] Expériences sur le Cendre qu'employait les Salpêtriers de Paris & sur son usage dans la fabrication du Salpêtre; AdS 1777 (1780), h 33, m 123 (12 March 1777); *Oeuvres*, ii, 160.
[2] Davis, *J. Chem. Educ.*, 1934, xi, 211–12.
[3] *Le Courrier Médical*, 18 March 1934, 23 June 1935.
[4] Hemmeter, *Janus*, 1921, xxv, 1, plate.   [5] Crell, *Ann.*, 1786, I, 525.
[6] *Travels in France*, ed. C. Maxwell, Cambridge, 1929, 81 f.
[7] (2), iii, 426 f.   [8] *Mém. Acad. Sci.*, n.d., XLV, xix (xxiv).
[9] *Lavoisier*, publ. by Acad. Sci. U.S.S.R., Moscow and Leningrad, 1948 (in Russian); q. by Leicester, *Isis*, 1958, xlix, 97.
[10] Fourcroy, (1), i, 36–45; Grimaux, 1888, 336–58; summary of the earlier memoirs, to 1771, in Meldrum, (3) and (4).

I. (1) 1765 AdS *Mém. div. Sav.*, 1768, v, 341–57 (Analyse du Gypse).

(2) 1770 (1773) h 5, m 73: Sur la nature de l'Eau et sur les Expériences par les-quelles on a pretendu prouver la possibilité de son Changement en Terre.

(3) 1772 (1776) m 555: Sur l'usage de l'Esprit-de-vin dans l'analyse des Eaux minérales;

(4) m 564: Premier Mémoire sur la destruction du Diamant par le feu (read 29 April 1772).

(5) 1774 (1778) m 62 (with Trudaine de Montigny, Macquer, Cadet and Brisson): Premier essai du grand Verre ardent de M. Trudaine (read 12 Nov. 1774);

(6) m 351: Mémoire sur la calcination de l'Étain dans les vaisseaux fermés; & sur la cause de l'augmentation du poids qu'acquiert ce metal pendant cette opération (read 'S. Martin [Nov.], 1774', remis 10 Mai 1777).

(7) 1775 (1778) m 520: Mémoire sur la nature du Principe qui se combine avec les Métaux pendant leur calcination, & qui en augmentent le poids (read Pâques [Easter] 1775. Relû 8 Août 1778).

(8) 1776 (1779) m 671: Mémoir sur l'existence de l'air dans l'acide nitreux, & sur les moyens de décomposer & de recomposer cet acide (lu 20 Avril 1776. Remis Décembre 1777).

1777 (1780):

(9) h 25, m 65: Sur la combustion du Phosphore de Kunckel, & sur la nature de l'acide qui résulte de cette combustion (présenté 21 Mars 1777. Lû 16 Avril);

(10) m 92: Analyse de quelques Eaux rapportées d'Italie par M. Cassini le fils (2 Juillet 1777);

(11) h 33, m 123: Expériences sur la Cendre qu'emploient les Salpêtriers de Paris, & sur son usage dans la fabrication du Salpêtre (12 Mars 1777);

(12) h 30, m 185: Expériences sur la Respiration des animaux, & sur les changemens qui arrive à l'air en passant par leur poumon (3 Mai 1777);

(13) h 29, m 195: Mémoire sur la combustion des Chandelles dans l'air atmospherique, & dans l'air éminemment respirable (n.d.);

(14) h 28, m 324: Mémoire sur la dissolution du Mercure dans l'acide vitriolique, &c. (n.d.);

(15) h 26, m 363: Expériences sur la combinaison de l'Alaun avec les matières charbonneuses, &c. (Lû 5 Sept. 1777);

(16) h 27, m 398: Mémoire sur la vitriolisation des Pyrites martiales (5 Sept. 1777);

(17) h 31, m 420: De la Combinaison de la matière du feu avec les fluides évaporables, & de la formation des fluides élastiques aëriformes (5 Sept. 1777);

(18) h 1, m 505 (with Bézout and Vandermonde): Expériences faites par ordre de l'Académie, sur le Froid de l'année 1776 (read in extract 1776);

(19) h 32, m 592: Mémoire sur la Combustion en général (5 Sept. 1777).

1778 (1781):

(20) m 69 (with Macquer and Sage): Analyse de l'eau du lac Asphaltite;

(21) m 433 (with Guettard): Expériences sur une espèce de Stéatite blanche, qui se convertit seule au feu en un beau biscuit de Porcelaine (read 15 Sept. 1777);

(22) m 435 (with Guettard): Description des deux Mines de Charbon de Terre, situées au pied des montagnes de Voyes;

(23) m 535: Considérations générales sur la nature des Acides, & sur les principes dont ils sont composés (Présenté 5 Sept. 1777. Lû 23 Nov. 1779).

1780 (1784):

(24)   h 26, m 334: Mémoire sur quelques Fluides qu'on peut obtenir dans
                 l'état aériforme, à un degré de chaleur peu supérieur à la
                 temperature moyenne de la Terre (a note says the 'preceding
                 memoir' referred to was read in 1777 and 'n'a point été
                 imprimé');

(25)   h 32, m 343: Second Mémoire sur différentes combinaisons de l'Acide
                 phosphorique (Lû 18 Nov. 1780);

(26)   h 32, m 349: Mémoire sur un Procédé particulier pour convertir le
                 Phosphore en Acide phosphorique sans combustion (Lû
                 2 Mars 1780);

(27)   h 3, m 355 (with Laplace): Mémoir sur la Chaleur (18 Juin 1783);
(28)   m 409: Report on Prisons (by du Hamel, de Montigny, Le Roy,
                 Tendon, Tillet, and Lavoisier).

1781 (1784):

(29)   h 21, m 269 (with Meusnier): Mémoire ou l'on prouve par la décompo-
                 sition de l'Eau, que ce Fluide n'est point une substance
                 simple (Lû 21 Avril 1784);

(30)   h 6, m 292 (with Laplace): Mémoire sur l'Électricité qu'absorbent les
                 corps qui se réduisent en vapeurs;

(31)   h 5, m 379: Expériences sur l'effet comparé de différens combustibles;
(32)   m 396: Réflexions sur la Calcination & la Combustion, à l'occasion
                 d'un Ouvrage de M. Scheele, intitulé Traité Chimique de
                 l'Air & du Feu (perhaps written in 1781–2);

(33)   m 409: On the lighting of threatres;
(34)   h 25, m 448: Mémoire sur la formation de l'Acide nommé Air fixe ou
                 Acide crayeux, & que je désignerai desormais sous le nom
                 d'Acide du Charbon;

(35)   m 468: Mémoire dans lequel on a pour objet de prouver que l'Eau
                 n'est point une substance simple, un élément proprement dit,
                 mais qu'elle est susceptible de décomposition & de recom-
                 position (Lû St. Martin 1783; additions later).

1782 (1785):

(36)   h 28, m 457: Mémoire sur un Moyen d'augmenter considérablement
                 l'action du Feu & de la Chaleur dans les Opérations
                 chimiques (Nov. 1782);

(37)   m 466 (by Meusnier only): Description d'un Appareil propre à
                 manœuvrer les différentes espèces d'airs;

(38)   m 476: Mémoire sur l'effet que produit sur les Pierres précieuses
                 un degré de feu très-violent (Nov. 1782);

(39)   m 486: Memoire sur la combinaison de l'Air nitreux avec les Airs
                 respirables, & sur les conséquences qu'on en peut tirer,
                 relativement à leur degré de salubrité (Présenté 20 Dec.
                 1783);

(40)   h 33, m 492: Considérations générales sur la dissolution des Métaux
                 dans les Acides (n.d.);

(41)   h 36, m 512: Mémoire sur la précipitation des Substances métalliques,
                 les unes par les autres (Présenté 20 Dec. 1783: in h 36 the
                 title is: Sur les quantités de Principe oxygine, combinées
                 dans les Précipités metalliques);

(42)   h 39, m 530: Mémoire sur l'affinité du Principe oxygine avec les
                 differentes Substances auxquelles il est susceptible de s'unir
                 (20 Dec. 1783);

(43)   h 37, m 541: Mémoire sur l'union du Principe oxygine avec le Fer
                 (Présenté 20 Dec. 1783);

(44)   m 560: Mémoire sur la nature des Fluides élastiques aériformes,
                 qui se dégagent de quelques Matières animales en fermenta-
                 tion (n.d.).

1783 (1786):

(45)   m 416: Nouvelles Réflexions sur l'augmentation de poids qu'acquièrent, en brûlant, le Soufre & le Phosphore; & sur la cause à laquelle on doit l'attribuer (n.d.);

(46)   m 505: Réflexions sur le Phlogistique, Pour servir de développment à la théorie de la Combustion & de la Calcination, publiée en 1777 (n.d.);

(47)   m 563: De l'Action du Feu, animé par l'air vital, sur les substances minérales les plus réfractaires (n.d.).

(48) 1784 (1787): m 593: Mémoire sur la Combinaison du Principe oxygine avec l'Esprit-de-vin, l'Huile, & différens Corps combustibles (n.d.).

(49) 1786 (1788): m 590: Réflexions sur la décomposition de l'eau par les substances végétales & animales (n.d.).

(50) 1789 (1793): h xxj, m 566 (with Seguin): Premier mémoire sur la respiration des animaux (read 17 November 1790).

(51) 1790 (1797): h xij, m 601 (with Seguin): Premier Mémoire sur la transpiration des animaux (read 10 June 1791).

Nine memoirs were translated in 1783 by Thomas Henry:

II. Essays, on the Effects Produced by Various Processes on Atmospheric Air; with a Particular View to an Investigation of the Constitution of the Acids. By M. Lavoisier ... Translated from the French, by Thomas Henry, F.R.S. Warrington, Printed by W. Eyres, for J. Johnson, no. 72 St. Paul's Churchyard, 8°, London, 1783, 20 + 142 pp.; preface on the controversy between Priestley and Lavoisier. BM T. 243. 16.

A German translation of many of Lavoisier's publications (which I have not seen) appeared in five volumes:

III. Physikalisch-chemische Schriften, Greifswald, vols. i–iii, 1783–5 ed. by Weigel, vols. iv–v, 1792–4 by H. F. Link, with notes (often very critical). Complete table of contents in Duveen and Klickstein (5), 360–8. The first part of this includes the *Opuscules Physiques et Chimiques* (1774), the second and third the memoirs published by the Academy; there is an appendix of extracts from publications which 'Herrn Lavoisier nicht unbekannt gewesen sein könnten' but 'von ihm mit Fleiss übergangen wären'; q. by Speter, *Samml. chem.- und chem.-techn. Vorträge*, 1910, xv, 193; the first vol. was reviewed by Crell, *Ann.*, 1784, I, 373.

In 1792 Lavoisier began to prepare a collection of memoirs by himself and collaborators in which the published material was to be presented in a revised form and some unpublished material added. Part was collected later by Mme. Lavoisier in two volumes from sheets printed just before Lavoisier's execution in 1794. They contain also memoirs by Seguin, who was asked to write a preface condemning Lavoisier's execution but declined to do so:

IV. There are half-titles: *Mémoires de Chimie. Tome Premier [Second]* and an unpaged leaf of introduction by Mme. Lavoisier saying the work would form about eight volumes. Vol. i contains 416 pp., ending in an incomplete sentence; vol. ii contains 413 pp. in parts 2 and 3 (p. 413 has *Fin du second Volume*), and 64 pp. of part 4 (Des principaux phénomènes de l'economie animale), also ending in an incomplete sentence (CUL Hh. 55. 60–61).

The volumes are usually said[1] to have been published in 1805.

Grimaux[2] says they were published (publiées) in 1803, but earlier[3] gave two dates, 1805 and 1806. The date 1805 is in a sale catalogue of Mme. Lavoisier's library in 1836

---

[1] McKie, (1), 300; (2), 324.   [2] VIII, vi, 711.   [3] *Lavoisier*, 1888, 333, 355.

by Galliot.[1] The book is quoted by volume and page ('tom II, p. 309') in 1803 by Berthollet.[2] Apparently copies were given previously to friends by Mme. Lavoisier. The book is very rare; Thomson[3] had not seen it. It is not reprinted in the *Oeuvres*.

Lavoisier was the author of two books and joint author of one:

V. Opuscules Physiques et Chimiques, 8°, Paris, 1774. First ed. ('Tom. 1') issued in two forms: (A) with cancel leaves of pp. 255–6, 5–6, 283–4, 193–4, 307–8, 257–8 bound between pp. 434–5 and the original leaves in their places, showing only minor altera- tions of text (BM 232. f. 10); (B) with text in revised form. A and B both have 30 pp. (with first leaf dedication to Trudaine de Montigny duplicated in A), 436 pp., 3 folding plates. The second ed. is also in two forms: (A') a re-issue of the 1774 ed. with new half-title and t.p., ii ll., sub-title, 436 pp., the original imprint dated 1774 being at the end on p. 436, but the dedication to Trudaine de Montigny omitted, (B') entirely re-set, 30 pp., 443 pp.; both A' and B' were published by Deterville, Paris, and both are described as 'Second Edition' and dated An IX (1801). My copy is (B'). Reprinted in *Oeuvres*, i, 437–680, with reports. (C) publ. by Longchamp with works of Rey and Bayen, with a life of Bayen, Bibliothèque du Chimiste, tome VII, Epoque Pneuma- tique, Paris, 1834. (D) Engl. tr. by Thomas Henry: Essays Physical and Chemical. By M. Lavoisier . . . Volume the First. Translated . . . with Notes and an Appendix, 8°, London, 1776 (pp. xxxii, 475); the tr. is not good but Henry often corrects mistakes made in the tr. of Priestley's paper (1772) by Lavoisier. (E) German tr. by C. E. Weigel: Physikalisch-chemische Schriften, 8°, Greifswald, 1783; with Appendix: Bey- träge zur Geschichte der Luftarten, in Auszügen, 8°, Greifswald, 1784.

VI. Méthode de Nomenclature Chimique, Proposée par MM. de Morveau, Lavoisier, Bertholet [*sic*], & de Fourcroy. On y a joint Un nouveau Systême de Carac- tères Chimiques, adaptés à cette Nomenclature, par MM. Hassenfratz & Adet. Paris, chez Cuchet, 1787. Sous le Privilége de l'Académie des Sciences (pp. 314, 6 plates; 2 issues).

VIA. Nomenclature chimique, ou Synonymie ancienne et moderne, pour servir à l'intelligence des auteurs. Nouvelle Édition à laquelle on a joint différens Mémoires et Rapports de MM. Lavoisier, Fourcroy, Morveau, Cadet, Baumé, d'Arcet et Sage . . . , Paris, 1789, 2 issues; forming vol. iii of the second ed. of the *Traité*, VII; also issued as vol. iii of the last French ed. of VII, 1805, the same sheets being probably used. See de Morveau's announcement in Crell's *Ann.*, 1787, II, 54.

VIB. Method of Chymical Nomenclature, proposed by Messrs De Morveau Lavoisier, Berthollet and Fourcroy, . . . Translated by James St. John, M.D., 8°, London, 1788 (xvi, 238 pp.).

VIC. A Translation of the Table of Chemical Nomenclature . . . with additions and alterations: To which are prefixed an alteration of the Terms, and some Observations on the New System of Chemistry, by Geo. Pearson, 4°, London, 1794 (BM 457. d. 29, catal. as by Guyton de Morveau).

VIC'. 2 ed. enlarged and corrected. . . . To which are subjoined, Tables of Single Elective Attraction, Tables of Chemical Symbols, Tables of the Precise Forces of Chemical Attractions; and Schemes and Explanations of Cases of Single and Double Elective Attractions, 4°, London, 1799 (BM 462. k. 19) (elective attraction tables, pp. 98 f., incl. Cullen's diagrams).

For American eds. see Bolton, (1), 77; Duveen and Klickstein, *Isis*, 1954, xlv, 278, 368; Lyman Spalding, A New Nomenclature of Chemistry proposed by De Morveau, Lavoisier, Berthollet and Fourcroy, with additions and improvements, sm. oblong f°, Hanover (N.H., U.S.A.), 1799 (12 pp.); chart included in W. Nicholson's tr. of Four- croy, Elements of Natural History and Chemistry, 3 ed., 3 vols. London, 1790, pirated in America, 1791; S. L. Mitchill, Explanation of the Synopsis of Chemical Nomencla- ture and Arrangement, N.Y., 1801 (44 pp. and large folding chart), replaced 'hydrogen' by 'phlogiston' and caloric by 'anticroun' (from αντικρουω, I repel or keep at a distance), and his own 'septon' for nitrogen also appears (Duveen and Klickstein, (5), 377).

[1] Duveen, (5), 201: 1100 exemplaires. Mémoires de chimie par M. Lavoisier, Paris, 1805, 2 vol. in-8. br. Cet ouvrage dont tous les volumes n'ont qu'un faux titre n'a pas été publié; Smeaton, *The Library*, 1956, xi, 130 (132–3).
[2] *Statique Chimique*, An XI, 1803, ii, 25; Partington, *Chem. and Ind.*, 1955, 1475 (12 Nov.).
[3] *Ann. Phil.*, 1813, ii, 92.

VID. Methode der chemischen Nomenclatur für das antiphlogistische System. Aus dem Französischen, 8°, Vienna, 1793 (Bolton, (1), 58); Kahlbaum and Hoffmann, 1897, 189, do not give this but: Karl von Meidinger, System der chemischen Zeichen für die antiphlogistische Chemie und ihre Nomenklatur von Herrn Hassenfratz und Adet, Vienna, 1793.

VIE. Chenevix, Remarks upon Chemical Nomenclature, according to the Principles of the French Neologists, 8°, London, 1802 (pp. 246, i errata); mainly a criticism of Pearson's tr. VIC.

VII. Traité Élémentaire de Chimie, présenté dans un Ordre nouveau et d'après les Découvertes modernes, 8°, Paris, Chez Cuchet, 2 vols., 1789, pagination continuous but 3 title-pages: xliv, 1–322, viii (half-title, t.p., contents of Tome second), 323–558 (Fin), 559 half-title Tables à l'usage des Chimistes, 560 blank, 561–91, index 592–619; Extrait des Registres de l'Académie, 4 February 1789, 620–28 (signed by d'Arcet and Bertholet (sic) and certified 7 February by Condorcet); Extrait des Registres de la Société Royale de Médecine, 6 February 1789, 629–50 (signed by de Horne and Four-croy, certified by Vicq d'Azyr, 7 February); Extrait des Registres de la Société Royale d'Agriculture, 5 February 1789, 650–3 (signed by de Fourcroy and Cadet de Vaux, certified 6 February by Broussonet), ii errata and additions, i blank, 13 plates, 2 folding tables (the ed. used).

VIIA. . . . Nouvelle édition, à laquelle on a joint la Nomenclature Ancienne & Moderne, . . . différens Mémoires de MM. Fourcroy et Morveau, & le Rapport de MM. Baumé, Cadet, Darcet & Sage, sur la nécessité de réformer & de perfectionner la Nomenclature Chimique, 8°, Paris, chez Cuchet, 3 vols., 1789 (the 2 vols. of the Traité Élémentaire are now paged separately: xliv, 322 pp.; viii, 326 pp., 13 plates, 3 fold. tables; includes reports of Baumé, etc.; vol. iii is a reissue of VI).

VIIB. . . . Seconde [troisième] Édition, 3 vols. Paris, 1793 (an unauthorised reprint of VIIA).

VIIC. . . . Troisième [quatrième] Édition, 3 vols., Paris, An IX (1801), the last sep. ed.; contains memoirs on respiration.

VIID. Reprint of VIIA in Oeuvres, i, 1–435, contents 667–80, index 681–702.

VIIE. Traité Élémentaire de Chimie, partial reissue with introduction by Le Chatelier, in Les Classiques de la Découverte Scientifique, Paris (Gauthier-Villars), 1937 (pp. xxxviii, 191, 2 plates): first part in full; second part (tables) omitted; third part abridged.

VIIF. English tr.: Elements of Chemistry, in a New Systematic Order, containing all the Modern Discoveries, tr. by Robert Kerr, 8°, Edinburgh, 1790 (BM 1035. g. 16; l, 511 pp.); revised eds. 1793, 1796, 1799, 1801.

VIIG. German tr.: Des Herrn Lavoisier . . . System der antiphlogistischen Chemie. Aus dem Französischen übersetzt und mit Anmerkungen und Zusätzen begleitet von Sigismund Friedrich Hermbstädt, 2 vols. 8°, Berlin and Stettin, 1792 (10 plates), with extensive notes and additions by Hermbstädt; 2 ed.: System der antiphlogistischen Chemie von Anton Lorenz Lavoisier . . . übersetzt . . . von D. S. F. Hermbstädt, 2 vols., Berlin and Stettin, 1803: Duveen and Klickstein, (5), 190–2.

VIIH. Italian tr.: Trattato Elementare di Chimica Presentato in un ordine nuovo dietro le scoperte moderne . . . Recato dalla Francese nell' Italiana favella e corredato di annotazione da Vincenzo Dandolo, 4 vols. (vol. 3 containing Esame delle Affinità Chimiche . . . Opera del Sig. Morveau, and vol. 4 a Dizionarii vecchi e nuovo di Nomenclatura di chimica, by Dandolo), 8°, Venice, 1791 (2 fold. tables, 13 plates). Supplemento alla prima edizione, containing trs. of dissertations on respiration and transpiration together with a new ed. of the Trattato, 4 vols., Venice, 1792; 3 ed., 4 vols., Venice, 1796 (Sotheran Cat. 832 (1932), nos. 5437–8; Duveen and Klickstein, (5), 194–8).

VIIJ. A sketch of a contents published by Nieuwland: Schets van het scheikundige Leerstelsel van Lavoisier, Amsterdam, 1791; the only Dutch tr. proper is: Grond-beginselen der Scheikunde, vertaald en met Aanmerkingen en Byvoegselen vermeer-derd door N. C. de Fremery en P. van Werkhoven, 2 vols. 8°, Utrecht, 1800 (Sotheran Cat. 832 (1932), no. 5439, correcting Bolton, (1), 607; Duveen and Klickstein, (5), 193).

VIIK. Spanish trs.: Tratado Elemental de Chémica . . . Tomo Primero, Mexico, 1797; Tratado Elemental de Química, tr. J. M. Munarriz, 2 vols. 8°, Madrid, 1798 (Duveen and Klickstein, (5), 198).

Dumas promised in 1835 to edit Lavoisier's complete works.[1] In 1846 the Government undertook to provide the funds and in 1861 Dumas was appointed editor. Six volumes appeared at the instance of the Minister of Education in 1862–93, the last two being edited by Grimaux:

VIII. OEuvres de Lavoisier publiées par les soins de son Excellence le Ministre de l'Instruction Publique [et des Cultes; omitted from Vol. iii on], Paris, Imprimerie Impériale [Nationale from Vol. v], 6 vols., 1864–62–65–68–92–93.
Berthelot, (3), xxviij, said most of the material filling up vols. iii–vi is of mediocre interest, only vol. ii containing outstanding memoirs; vol. i contains a reprint of VIA from the second ed.
IX. Œuvres de Lavoisier Correspondance . . . publié sous le Patronage de l'Académie des Sciences, ed. R. Fric, Paris, A. Michel, Fascicule I (1763–9), 1955; II (1770–1775), 1957.

Thirteen volumes of the laboratory notebooks of Lavoisier are in the Archives of the Institut; the fourteenth (the second of the series), wrongly said to be missing,[2] is in the Library of Perpignan (MS. 61, ancien 59), where it was deposited by Arago.

It consists of 122 leaves, covering the period 9 September 1773 to 5 March 1774; a note by Arago says: 'Ce cahier renferme les célèbres experiences sur la calcination des métaux en vases clos, et les premières tentatives de Lavoisier sur le combustion du diamant.' Arago (who was born in Perpignan) wrote on the document: 'offert respectieusement à la Bibliothèque publique de la ville de Perpignan, par F. Arago'.[3] As a result of Brocard's discovery, Berthelot[4] gave an account of the contents of the volume. It would be desirable to have the thirteen volumes published; for the present, references are given to the extracts in Berthelot, (4).

The chronology of Lavoisier's memoirs (I) is confused, since the *Mémoires* of the Academy were frequently published up to four years in arrear, although the correct dates of publication appear on the title-pages. The volume for 1772, for example, consists of two parts published in 1775 and 1776; and papers classed in one year, such as 1772, were sometimes actually read a year or two later. The volume for 1776 contains a paper by Lavoisier printed in September 1778 and read in November 1779; the volume for 1774, published in 1778, contains a paper read in 1774 but 'relû' in 1777; and so on.[5]

Lavoisier, to ensure priority, quite properly published summaries of memoirs in the journal *Observations sur la Physique*, which appeared monthly. When, some years later in many cases, the work was published in the *Mémoires* of the Academy it had often been extensively altered. When Lavoisier began to collect his memoirs for publication (see p. 371) he altered them again. Meldrum said[6] Lavoisier:

[1] (1), 1837, 186: 'je publierai cette édition des œuvres de Lavoisier.'
[2] Berthelot, (4), 209 f., 213 f.; McKie, (1), 109.
[3] H. Brocard, *Compt. Rend.*, 1902, cxxxv, 574–5, giving a list of libraries in France containing documents by Lavoisier; he had not seen the volume in Perpignan. Partington, *Nature*, 1956, clxxviii, 1360.
[4] *Compt. Rend.*, 1902, cxxxv, 549–57; characteristically printed *before* Brocard's note was published.
[5] Brougham, 1872, 295 f.; many of the dates in Fourcroy, (1), i, 36 f., are incorrect.
[6] (1), 2–3, 40.

was deficient in historical instinct: his methods arouse distrust and defeat his purpose.
. . . He omitted and altered and inserted sentences . . . all of which belong to a time
that is years later than he ascribed to them. . . . In studying Lavoisier's memoirs it is
necessary to use circumspection. He could write with perfect simplicity at will and he
could produce a complicated effect over a simple matter.

Lavoisier had studied law — at one time he was intended for the legal profession, and his statements sometimes convey, without being actually untrue,
a meaning which can deceive an unsophisticated reader. Instead of saying 'I
published this in 1784' he will say 'I published this in the *Mémoires* of the
Academy, 1781' (not 'for 1781'), which appeared in 1784, etc. He says in a
review of Scheele's work (published in 1777, translated in 1781) in the
Mémoires for 1781 (published in 1784) that he (Lavoisier) had already announced some of the results in the '*Mémoires* . . . année 1777', which were
actually published in 1780; or that he had 'given in 1773' some of Scheele's
experiments, whereas these appeared in his *Opuscules* published in 1774, etc.[1]
He will also say[2] in 1776 that oxygen gas is what 'j'avais retiré de la chaux de
mercure . . . *mercure precipité per se*, et que M. Prisley [*sic*] a retiré d'un grand
nombre de substances, en le traitant par l'esprit de nitre'; this is legally true
but it is not the whole truth, since although Lavoisier *had* prepared oxygen
from red precipitate, Priestley had done so in August 1774, had told Lavoisier
in October 1774 that he had done this, and had published it in 1775.

We know from his extant memoranda that Lavoisier himself wrote some of
the summaries of his memoirs which should normally have been prepared by
the Secretary of the Academy, and some reports on them which are signed by
referees appointed by the Academy.

Lavoisier, either directly or by suggestion, in some cases laid claim to discoveries of others. Kopp,[3] an unprejudiced historian of chemistry, collected
some examples and said they form a shadow on his scientific character,
'welche keine oratorische Schönfärberi, wie diese auch versucht worden ist,
wegzuschaffen vermocht hat.' Brande[4] said: 'Lavoisier's character has, in some
measure, suffered by the misguided zeal of his admiring commentators,' but
even without their panegyrics, 'enough remains in Lavoisier's own writings to
cause serious misgivings.'

Early in 1773 Lavoisier had planned an extensive course of research on
gases, on which then very little was known (see p. 387). He published part of
this early in 1774 (see p. 388). Simultaneously, Priestley was beginning his
researches in the same field and he was able to tell Lavoisier in October 1774
of his discovery of oxygen, and had previously published his discovery of
several other gases. Lavoisier may have felt that if he had been given time he
would have made the discoveries himself, and allowance must be made for his
disappointment.

Before Galileo's time the sun was regarded as perfect; his revelation of its
spots by the telescope gave great offence, and it is said that some of the old
school refused to look at the blemishes through the new instrument. We need

[1] AdS 1781 (1784), m 396; VIII, ii, 391; Kopp, (3), 180, had drawn attention to this.
[2] AdS 1776 (1779), m 671. See also Vol. II, p. 648.
[3] (3), 141–4.   [4] 1848, I, lxxxv.

have no such reticence in scrutinising Lavoisier, and the sun, with or without spots, remains the sun.

Lavoisier's work was pre-eminently quantitative, but before him Van Helmont, Boyle, Black, Bergman, Cavendish, Priestley, and others had made quantitative experiments. His purely physical investigations were important, and even more significant was his use of physical methods in chemistry: he was essentially what we call a physical chemist.[1] He emphasised that when several causes or circumstances operate, it is necessary to remove them all but one, and investigate each separately.[2] His training in keeping accounts and preparing balance-sheets as a Fermier Général influenced his scientific work, and there is a close resemblance in form between his official memoranda (printed in the *Oeuvres*, especially in Vol. vi) and his scientific memoirs. His apparatus (which perhaps followed the ideas of the instrument makers) tended to be unnecessarily complicated and expensive; he aimed at accurate results, but seldom achieved them.[3] His work forms a connected whole and he had a thorough knowledge of previous work, a feature which had appeared in Pott's and Bergman's publications. He does not always give enough credit to this, and perhaps he thought that he could himself have made all the discoveries if he had had the opportunity.[4] When he mentions previous work he tends to omit researches which anticipated his own, or else mentions them as if he had come across them only when his own work had been completed, or quotes them quite inadequately (see p. 378). His style is clear but rather colourless, giving the impression (confirmed by the extensively altered drafts remaining in his papers) of laborious composition and a meticulous effort to choose words which would say what he intended they should and no more (see p. 375). He was a slow thinker and unwilling to admit mistakes. In admitting a mistake he says:[5]

> On conçoit qu'il a dû m'en coûter pour abandonner mes premières idées; aussi n'est-ce qu'après plusieurs années de réflexions, & d'après une longue suite d'expériences et d'observations . . . que je m'y suis detérminé.

Lavoisier discovered no new substances and practically the only new method of preparation he (if it was not his collaborator Meusnier) discovered was that of hydrogen by the action of steam on red-hot iron (p. 445). Thomson[6] said: 'It is not those who collect the stones, and the timber, and the mortar, but he who lays the plan, and shows how to put the materials together, that is in reality the builder of the house'; and Brande[7] that: 'Lavoisier, though a great architect in the science, labored little in the quarry; his materials were chiefly shaped to his hand, and his skill was displayed in their arrangement and combination.'[8] Lavoisier's main contributions were: (i) his recognition and experimental proof that combustion, calcination, and respiration involve the taking up of the 'ponderable' part of oxygen gas (the 'imponderable' part

[1] Kopp, (1), i, 273, 283, 295, 313; Heller, 1884, ii, 519.
[2] AdS, 1786 (1788), m 590; VIII, ii, 656.   [3] Daumas, *Chymia*, 1950, iii, 45.
[4] Thomson, (1), ii, 78; Kopp, (1), i, 302.   [5] VII, 151.
[6] *Ency. Brit. Suppl.*, 1801, I, i, 277.   [7] 1848, I, lxxxv.
[8] Cuvier, 1828, 69; Kopp, (1), i, 305; and Brougham, 1872, 326, say the same thing.

being the imaginary matter of heat); (ii) his proof of the composition of sulphuric, phosphoric, and carbonic acids, and of the composition of the atmosphere; (iii) his clear statement, from the results of Cavendish, of the true composition of water. Among his major mistakes were his assumptions: (i) that all acids contain oxygen, (ii) that combustion occurs only in oxygen gas, and (iii) that the heat and light evolved in combustion come from an imponderable element (caloric) combined with the base of oxygen in oxygen gas. His work, including his mistakes, brought about the ruin of the phlogiston theory and set chemistry on the road it has followed ever since. Kekulé[1] called Lavoisier 'the true founder of scientific chemistry (der eigentlichen Begründer wissenschaftlicher Chemie)', but 'modern chemistry' would be more correct.

The weights and measures used by Bayen and Lavoisier are compared with the metric standards as follows (the French and English grains were different):

1 litre = 50·4124 Paris cu. in.; 1 cu. in. = 19·84 c.c.
1 kg. = 18827·15 old French grains; 1 g. = 18·827 grains
1 lb. (livre) old French (poids de marc) = 16 onces = 489·5058 g.
1 once = 8 gros (drachm) = 576 gr.; 1 gros = 72 grains = 3·82 g., 1 grain = 0·0531 g.[2]

Law of Conservation of Matter

In quantitative experiments Lavoisier assumed the truth of the law of conservation of matter. He was not responsible for first stating this principle, which goes back to Classical antiquity (see Vol. I) and was often mentioned before his time.[3] Chardenon in 1764[4] said:

c'est un principe généralement adopté, que la pesanteur absolue d'un corps ne peut être augmentée que par l'addition de nouvelles parties de matiere. La loi des contraires indique donc qu'il ne peut devenir plus léger que par la soustraction de ces mêmes parties.

Still earlier, Mariotte[5] said it is a 'maxime ou regle naturelle' that 'la nature ne fait rien de rien, & la matiére ne se perd point'.

Lavoisier[6] said the principle may be stated that in every operation there is an equal quantity of matter at the beginning and end, that the elements are qualitatively and quantitatively conserved, and there are only changes and modifications:

'on peut poser en principe que dans toute opération, il y a une égale quantité de matière avant et après l'opération; que la qualité et la quantité des principes est la même, et qu'il n'y a que des changements, des modifications.

[1] *Lehrbuch der organischen Chemie*, Erlangen, 1861, i, 59.
[2] Hultsch, *Griechische und Römische Metrologie*, 1882, 24; Jörgensen, 1909, 142, 149; lists of obsolete weights in Spielmann, *Institutes de Chymie*, tr. Cadet, 1770, i, 82; Gren, *Handbuch der Chemie*, 1794, i, 123; tables of decimals of the French pound in Lavoisier, *Traité*, 1789, 561; tables of conversions of French to English weights in Kerr's tr., *Elements of Chemistry*, 1796, 562; results of French experiments are recalculated to the metric system by Riffault, tr. of T. Thomson, *Système de Chimie*, 1809, ii, 480 f.
[3] Walden, Mass, Zahl und Gewicht in der Chemie der Vergangenheit, in Ahren's *Samml. chem.- und chem.-techn. Vorträge*, Stuttgart, 1931, viii, 47–55; Hooykaas, *Chem. Weekbl.*, 1947, xliii, 244.
[4] Mémoire sur l'augmentation de poids des métaux calcinés. Lu le 15 Juillet 1763, & le 9 Décemb. 1764; *Mém. Acad. Dijon*, 1769, iA, 314.
[5] *Essai de logique* (anon., Paris, 1678); *Oeuvres*, 1717, ii, 656.　　[6] VII, 140; VIIF, 1796, 187.

'C'est sur ce principe qu'est fondé tout l'art de faire des expériences en Chimie: on est obligé de supposer dans toutes une véritable égalité ou équation entre les principes [elements] du corps qu'on examine, et ceux qu'on en retire par l'analyse.'[1]

Ladenburg,[2] Speter,[3] and Metzger[4] all say that Lavoisier never formally stated the principle, but the above quotation shows that he did, and Scherer[5] in 1795 explicitly stated the principle as an integral part of Lavoisier's system, translating the above passage (see p. 430).

Gypsum

Lavoisier's two memoirs on gypsum were read in February 1765 and March 1766. The first was published in 1768.[6] The work was begun in November 1764 and continued until 1766. In the first memoir he mentions Pott (see Vol. II, p. 718) and in a footnote says he had not seen some remarks by Baumé in an obscure publication until his own memoir was completely finished, and the conformity of Baumé's results and his own had disconcerted him. At the end, in a note added after reading, Lavoisier says he had just heard (j'ai appris) of the memoir of Marggraf in the *Memoirs* of the Berlin Academy for 1750; a French translation of this was published in 1762 (see Vol. II), in which Lavoisier could have seen that practically all his own results had been anticipated.

Lavoisier does mention 'M. Cromsted, dans les *Mémoires de l'Académie d'Upsal*', i.e. Cronstedt, whose memoir was in the proceedings of the Swedish Academy of Stockholm, not the Royal Society of Uppsala,[7] and a French translation was published in 1764,[8] a year before Lavoisier read his first paper. Marggraf and Cronstedt had established that gypsum is a compound of sulphuric acid and lime. Lavoisier quotes the memoir by Antoine de Jussieu,[9] but does not name him or give any indication of its contents. De Jussieu had concluded that gypsum contains water and sulphuric acid, pointed out that it is the same as selenite (lapis specularis), described some microscopic examination of the crystals, and suggested that plaster of Paris is formed from it by loss of water. De Jussieu's brother Bernard was, it is said, a teacher of Lavoisier (see p. 365).

Lavoisier showed that the hardening of plaster of Paris is due to its combination with water, which becomes 'the water of crystallisation of gypsum (eau de cristallisation du gypse)'. Marggraf had also shown that gypsum contains water. Lavoisier says he had discovered that gypsum is 'a true neutral salt . . . which results from the combination of the vitriolic acid with the calcareous earth . . . in no way different from selenite', existing in nature in numerous forms. The geological data are fully reported. Lavoisier incorrectly thought that nitric acid combined with gypsum to form 'a singular being, composed of two acids and one base'. He determined the solubilities of gyp-

---

[1] Hartog, 1941, 41, thought the word 'equation', as applied to chemistry, was first used here; in 1785 Lavoisier used the name 'formule': AdS, 1782 (1785), m 492; VIII, ii, 509.
[2] 1905, 22.   [3] (1), 46; (5).   [4] (2), 20.
[5] *Grundzüge der neuern chemischen Theorie*, Jena, 1795, 6.
[6] I, (1); VIII, iii, 106, 111.   [7] KAH, 1753, xiv, 144.
[8] *Recueil des Mémoires . . . contenues dans les Actes de l'Académie d'Upsal et dans les Mémoires de l'Académie . . . de Stockholm*, 2 vols., Paris, 1764, ii, 337.
[9] Sur la nature du gypse, AdS 1719, h 10, m 82–93.

sum and plaster of Paris and thought, incorrectly, that they were the same (in terms of $CaSO_4$). He says he could explain why 'dead-burnt' plaster ($CaSO_4$) does not rehydrate, but thought this would be out of place in a memoir on chemistry, 'où il n'est jamais permis de marcher que l'expérience à la main.'

The second memoir, presented in 1766 and approved by the Academy, was first published in 1865.[1] It describes the formation of gypsum from chalk and sulphuric acid. The solubility of selenite was found to be 1 part in 476 of water, alabaster the same, but different kinds had different solubilities, which he incorrectly thought were due to different proportions of acid and base. There are some geological speculations, partly vitiated by the above assumption. He confirmed Baumé's experiment,[2] communicated in 1760 ('M. Rouelle, le cadet, l'avait déjà proposé en problème dès 1752'), of converting vitriolated tartar (potassium sulphate) into nitre (potassium nitrate) by heating with nitric acid.

Conversion of Water into Earth

Lavoisier's memoir 'on the nature of water and on experiments which have been supposed to demonstrate the possibility of its conversion into earth' was read on 14 November 1770. An anonymous summary was published in the *Avant Coureur* in 1770,[3] and in 1771.[4] The remarks in this about 'ces ouvrages précieux' and the 'style claire et précise de M. Lavoisier', etc., were very probably written by Lavoisier himself. The memoir was published in 1773.[5] It says that since Van Helmont (see Vol. II, p. 223) many chemists such as Boyle, Trieval (Triewald), Eller, Gleditsch and Bonnet, Krafft, Alston, Borrichius, Marggraf, and others, had shown that distilled water always leaves a slight earthy residue when evaported to dryness in a glass vessel, even if it has been repeatedly distilled.[6]

Lavoisier weighed a glass vessel called a *pelican* (Fig. 35), an alembic provided with tubes returning to the body the distillate collecting in the head. He put into it a weighed quantity of water which had been distilled eight times. The vessel was slowly heated and the stopper closing the head lifted from time to time. It was then sealed down and the whole weighed. The vessel was then kept at a temperature of $60°–70°$ Re. for 101 days. A white solid slowly separated in the water, which increased in amount as time went on. The apparatus was cooled and weighed. There was no change in total weight. The water was poured out and the pelican dried and weighed. It had lost $17\frac{4}{10}$ grains. The white powder, when dried, weighed only $4\frac{9}{10}$ grains. The water was then evaporated in a glass alembic and finally in a weighed dish, and left a

FIG. 35. A PELICAN.

[1] Duveen, (5), 14; VIII, iii, 128 (Sur le gypse).
[2] AdS, *Mém. div Sav.*, 1774, vi, 231; see p. 92.
[3] Smeaton, *Ann. Sci.*, 1957 (1959), xiii, 219 (227).
[4] *Intr. Obs. Phys.*, 1771 (1777), i, 78–83: L'eau la plus pure contient-elle de la terre, & cette eau peut-elle être changée en terre?
[5] AdS, 1770 (1773), h 5, m 73, 90; VIII, ii, 1.
[6] See the summary in J. C. Fischer, 1804, v, 259–64, giving other names, including Le Roy.

residue of $15\frac{1}{2}$ grains. But $4\frac{9}{10} + 15\frac{1}{2} = 20\frac{4}{10}$ grains, which is 3 grains more than the loss in weight of the pelican. This excess was explained as due to water combined in the solid and to matter dissolved from the glass alembic used to evaporate the water.[1] Lavoisier concluded that the 'earth' had been dissolved by the water from the glass vessel and had not come from the water itself. This was later confirmed by Scheele by qualitative analysis of the 'earth', which was consistent with its origin from the glass.[2]

The volume of the *Observations* in which Lavoisier's abstract appears contains a long paper by Ferner[3] (in Sweden) claiming the conversion of water into earth. Le Roi (*sic*), while Lavoisier's work was in progress, submitted a memoir to the Academy, only the abstract of which by De Fouchy was printed,[4] giving a history of experiments on the conversion of water into earth and describing his own experiments. He disputed the conversion, since he thought that salts would distil with water on evaporation, so that water free from dissolved earth could not be obtained by distillation. A paper claiming the conversion of water into earth by Demachy appeared in 1775,[5] but Fontana[6] suggested, from his own experiments, that the earth came from atmospheric dust, and supported Lavoisier's conclusion.

Priestley,[7] in his book on him, says Bryan Higgins 'pretends to have considered the experiments of Boyle, Borrichius, Wallerius, Margraaff [*sic*], Eller, and Lavoisier (which is calculated to convey an idea of his extensive reading)', but 'he has overlooked the more decisive experiments of his countryman, the ingenious Mr. Godfrey, who converted the whole mass of a considerable quantity of distilled water into a perfectly dry earth'. Priestley tested some of this earth given to him by Godfrey, and made by his 'grand-father, the contemporary and fellow-labourer of Boyle', and found that it gave fixed air on heating and by the action of acids. This was presumably the earth made by Ambrose Godfrey junr. in 1740 (see Vol. II, p. 761).

Bishop Watson[8] gives a detailed history of the subject and mentions an experiment in which he found that water slowly distilled in a silver retort tarnished a polished silver plate on which it was evaporated; although 'M. Lavoisier's experiment staggers the confidence I had reposed in the conclusions of Marggraf . . . it must be repeated with success before it will utterly subvert it'. He was 'rather disposed to believe that water is converted into earth; though I own that no experiment has yet been produced, to which reasonable objections may not be made'. Evidently Lavoisier's proof was not completely convincing, and Thomson[9] mentions experiments by Schrader in a 'Preisschrift' crowned by the Berlin Academy in 1800,[10] in which vegetables were grown from seeds in flowers of sulphur and in oxides of zinc and antimony, supplied only with distilled water, and the vegetables were found to contain more earth than the seeds. Thomson says this may have come from atmo-

---

[1] Meldrum, (4), thought that this was due to atmospheric carbon dioxide absorbed by the alkali extracted by the water from the glass. Meldrum describes the various forms of the memoir.
[2] Scheele, *Air and Fire*, 1777, Pref.; *Collected Papers*, ed. Dobbin, 1931, 88.
[3] *Intr. Obs. Phys.*, 1771 (1777), i, 5.   [4] AdS, 1767 (1770), h 14.
[5] *Obs. Phys.*, 1775, iv, 37.   [6] *Obs. Phys.*, 1779, xiii, 161; 1782, xix, 396.
[7] *Philosophical Empiricism*, 1775, Advertisement A2, 57.
[8] *Essays*, 1786 (1796), iv, 257 f., 293, 306.   [9] (1), ii, 83.
[10] Summary in *N. Allgem. J. Chem.* (Gehlen), 1804, iii, 523–48.

spheric dust, but the question was still open then (in 1830). Thus, although it has been said[1] that 'Lavoisier had refuted a theory held for twenty centuries', his contemporaries did not think he had.

Mineral Waters

In Lavoisier's work on the analysis of mineral waters[2] eight different mixtures of alcohol and water were used to separate the salts formed on evaporation, a method used by Macquer (see p. 87). The results are of no interest. Lavoisier then believed there were only two mineral acids, sulphuric and hydrochloric; the nature of nitric acid is unknown and the idea (Sage's) that phosphoric acid is a peculiar acid is not sufficiently demonstrated. Several other articles by Lavoisier on the analyses of natural waters[3] mention the statement by Le Roy[4] that earth can pass over with water on distillation, and Lavoisier believed that true salts would volatilise with water more readily than earth. He described determinations of density by a hydrometer (aréomètre) and unsuccessful attempts to calculate the composition of solutions from the density. The composition was correctly related to the nature of the strata of the earth through which the waters had passed. A constant-immersion hydrometer is fully described in an article on the determination of specific gravity.[5] Lavoisier had some idea that purely physical methods might replace chemical analysis of waters, and as Thomson[6] said, chemical analyses 'were not the investigations in which Lavoisier excelled'.

In a paper on the analysis of mineral water from a place near an alum mine in Italy[7] Lavoisier reports that the compound of alumina and sulphuric acid does not crystallise well, that to form true alum it is necessary, 'as M. Marggraf observed', to add fixed alkali (potash), and that 'the base of alum is not a simple earth, as all chemists have hitherto supposed, but a compound of an earth, with a third or half its weight of fixed alkali . . . as already remarked by M. Macquer' (Marggraf). It is probable that alums could be formed with soda, magnesia (?), lime, and perhaps ammonia.

Fourcroy[8] still spoke of alum as 'sulfate d'alumine', but the presence of alkali in it was established by Vauquelin (1797) (see p. 553). In 1773 Lavoisier noticed the evolution of heat in the crystallisation of what must have been a supersaturated solution of Glauber's salt.[9]

Destruction of Diamond by Fire

Cosmo III, Grand Duke of Tuscany, in 1694–5 caused experiments to be made by Averani and Targioni with a large burning mirror, when diamonds disappeared in a few minutes.[10] The combustibility of diamond was foreshadowed by Newton.[11] The German Emperor Francis I in 1751 caused

[1] McKie, (2), 66.   [2] AdS, 1772 (1776), m 555; VIII, ii, 29; iii, 145.
[3] VIII, iii, 145, 206, 457, 707, 711.   [4] AdS, 1767, h 14.
[5] VIII, iii, 427; iv, 12, 17; Smeaton, Ann. Sci., 1957 (1959), xiii, 219 (225); Meldrum, (3), says the first memoir as printed is 'known to have been altered' from the state in which it was submitted; see Lavoisier, VII, 337; VIII, i, 254.
[6] (1), ii, 107.   [7] AdS, 1777 (1780), m 92; VIII, ii, 153.
[8] (4), 1793, ii, 209.   [9] Obs. Phys., 1774, i, 10; VIII, v, 243.
[10] Poggendorff, (2), 270, 419.   [11] Opticks, 1704, Bk. ii, prop. 10; 1730, 249.

diamonds and rubies worth 6000 florins to be exposed in crucibles in a reverberatory furnace for 24 hours, when the diamonds disappeared but the rubies
were not altered. The experiments were repeated at great expense, when it
was found that the diamond lost its polish, scaled off, and disappeared.[1] John
Hill[2] said that 'very many years ago' he put a small diamond in a wind furnace,
in the presence of Lord Granard and Mr. Charles Stanhope in his house in
Bloomsbury, when it 'appeared like a burning coal', then cracked into pieces
which finally 'entirely vanished'.

D'Arcet (in Rouelle's laboratory) heated diamonds enclosed in balls of clay
in crucibles and found they 'volatilised' even at moderate temperatures.[3]
D'Arcet and Rouelle,[4] in the presence of a crowd of named notabilities (including Lavoisier), found that diamonds disappeared when heated in a muffle,
in open crucibles, or in a paste of chalk and charcoal in a crucible. The *Histoire*
of the Academy[5] refers to 'Expériences faites au feu, sur un Diamant, des
Pierres précieuse & des Métaux: par M. d'Arcet' as being worthy of publication but this does not seem to have been done. It was, apparently, published
separately in 1771:

Second Mémoire sur l'action d'un feu égal, violent et continué pendant plusieurs
jours sur un grand nombre de terres, de pierres et de chaux métalliques . . . lu à
l'Academie . . . des Sciences les 7 et 11 mai 1768, 8°, Paris, 1771 (BN R. 32940; the first
memoir, with the same title was read on 16 and 28 May 1766 and publ., 8°, Paris,
1766; BN R. 32939). Lavoisier, VIII, ii, 44, refers to a third memoir by D'Arcet read to
the Academy on 19 August 1770, containing the experiments mentioned above.

Mitouard, 'Demonstrateur en Chymie, Apothecaire, et Maître en Pharmacie à Paris', had been heating diamonds and rubies early in 1772,[6] finding
that diamonds do not 'evaporate' if protected from the air, just as antimony
and zinc, also containing phlogiston, do not burn if enveloped in charcoal
powder. In his memoir with the curious title 'Sur la déstruction du diamant
par le feu'[7] Lavoisier refers at length to Mitouard's experiments and says
Cadet had published before him. 'Mm. Macquer, Cadet et moi . . . annon-
çames à la séance publique de cette Académie, du 29 Avril 1772, quelques
observations singulières que nous avons faites sur le diamant.'[8]

The publication of these experiments had 'given rise to an excellent work of
MM. Rouelle and Darcet on the same subject'.[9] Lavoisier gives a table of part
of the results contained in the 1773 publication of D'Arcet and Rouelle, saying
that they are, 'faut de bien peu', exactly the same as those which Macquer,
Cadet, and he had read in the public session of the Academy on 29 April 1772.

[1] D'Holbach in tr. of Henckel, *Pyritologie*, Paris, 1760, ii, 413.
[2] *Theophrastus's History of Stones*, 2 ed., London, 1774, 79; not in 1746 ed.
[3] *Intr. Obs. Phys.*, 1771 (1777), i, 108–23.   [4] *Ib.*, 1772 (1777), i, 484–8.
[5] AdS, 1770 (1773), h 119.   [6] *Intr. Obs. Phys.*, 1772 (1777), ii, 112, 197.
[7] AdS, 1772 (1776), m 564; VIII, ii, 38.
[8] Macquer, Cadet, and Lavoisier, *Intr. Obs. Phys.*, 1772 (1777), ii, 108, Cadet, *ib.*, 112;
Lavoisier, AdS, 1772 (1776), m 564; VIII, ii, 38; Brougham, 1872, 300, says the experiments
were not made until late in 1773 and the memoir was probably read in 1774; see also De la
Metherie, *Obs. Phys.*, 1785, xxvii, 144 (burning diamond by Lavoisier's method of a jet of
oxygen directed on burning charcoal); a full account of all the experiments by D'Arcet,
Rouelle, Mitouard, Cadet, Lavoisier and himself is given by Macqeur, *Dictionnaire*, 1778, i,
491–513.
[9] D'Arcet and Rouelle, *Obs. Phys.*, 1772 (1777), i, 484–8; 1773, i, 17.

He had 'always honoured the talents of the MM. Rouelle', and it grieved him to use harsh words about men from whom 'jusqu'à ce moment je n'avais éprouvé que des procédés honnêtes'.

The main results in Lavoisier's first memoir are: (i) diamonds heated in retorts in a confined volume of air are partly consumed, (ii) Maillard (a jeweller) during the course of the work showed that diamonds embedded in charcoal powder are not consumed, which was confirmed, (iii) a diamond heated with charcoal powder and iron was 'dissolved' where it was in contact with molten iron, 'either by evaporation or scorification by the iron', (iv) diamonds enclosed in balls of unglazed porcelain disappeared, but so did charcoal, since the porcelain was porous, and (v) Mitouard found that a diamond embedded in charcoal powder in a tobacco pipe lost neither in weight nor polish, but embedded in clay or in an empty pipe lost a fifth of its weight and became brown or black.

A second memoir[1] is undated but describes an experiment of 14 August 1773, and another experiment in Lavoisier's note-book is dated 22 October 1773.[2] The memoir was probably composed as late as 1776, when Lavoisier had made considerable progress in his theory of combustion, although the style suggests that part at least belongs to an earlier period. It gives details of nineteen experiments in which Macquer, Cadet, Brisson, Baumé, and Fourni de Villiers collaborated, although much of it is written in the first person.

Lavoisier says there was some 'carbonaceous effervescence' (and this may have come from surrounding bodies) when a diamond was exposed to a not very strong heat, but at a high temperature it was dissipated if exposed to air. The partly dissipated diamond became black and sooty. The air in which it evaporated acquired the properties of the fixed air evolved from the effervescence of alkalis or fermentation and given out by metallic calces on their reduction to the reguline state. The observations, and particularly Macquer's experiment (see below), suggest that diamond is combustible. If so, it should not burn or evaporate in a vacuum or in fixed air. A diamond surrounded by fixed air evaporated only very slowly on heating. Similar results were obtained with charcoal. Lavoisier says Macquer had shown that diamond on heating 'est susceptible de se réduire en charbon dans quelques circonstances', but he did not notice that the black matter is not charcoal but graphite.

Since Lavoisier did not know that diamond or charcoal heated in fixed air forms carbon monoxide, he naturally thought the diminution was due to evaporation. He hesitated to decide whether diamond simply evaporates in atmospheric air to form fixed air or whether its vapour converts atmospheric air into fixed air. He says:

It would never have been suspected that there could be any relation between charcoal and diamond, and it would be unreasonable to push this analogy too far; it exists only because both substances seem to be properly ranged in the class of combustible bodies, and because they are, of all these bodies, the most fixed when kept from the contact of air.

[1] AdS, 1772 (1776), m 591; VIII, ii, 64.   [2] Berthelot, (4), 270.

Lavoisier emphasises that Macquer 'pour la première fois' had observed that a red-hot diamond is enveloped by a flame. This capital discovery (which shows that diamond burns first to carbon monoxide, which gas then burns to carbon dioxide) was made in 1771. Macquer,[1] who summarises previous work, reports an experiment made in his own laboratory on 26 July 1771, in presence of 'several persons', in which he heated, not very intensely, a diamond on a cupel. This was taken out of the furnace and all observed that the diamond was redder and more luminous than the cupel, but:

je vis très distinctement qu'il étoit tout enveloppé d'une petite flamme légère & comme phosphorique, que je me hâtai de faire voir à ceux qui étoit le plus à portée, & singu-liérement à MM. d'Arcet & Rouelle.

Macquer rightly stresses that he was the first to make this observation, 'capable of throwing new light on the nature of the diamond and on the cause of its destructibility.'

Early Experiments on Combustion

In 1772 Lavoisier began the experiments on combustion which, as he says himself,[2] were the origin of all his later work, although it would be too optimistic to believe with him that: 'j'avois conçu, dès [a characteristic word] 1772, tout l'ensemble du système que j'ai publié depuis sur la combustion.' In September and October 1772 Lavoisier recorded in his note-book some experiments on the combustion of phosphorus:[3]

(i) On 10 September the glowing and fuming of phosphorus in air and its combustion in a medicine bottle, saying: 'I wanted to verify in the same apparatus whether phosphorus absorbed air in its combustion', but the entry breaks off.

(ii) On 20 October a 'Memoire sur l'acide du Phosphore' records the luminous smoke rising from phosphorus and surmises that 'if it could be col-lected' it would give 'a volatile acid spirit of phosphorus'. By burning phos-phorus in 'a closed vessel' a white sublimate is formed, which is 'the acid of phosphorus in an absolute degree of concentration nearly like glacial oil of vitriol'. This is resolved in a few hours solely by the humidity of the air into a very strong odourless acid with nearly the same appearance as oil of vitriol. 'A singular phenomenon is that the quantity of acid collected from the phosphorus by this last operation is much larger in weight than the quantity of phosphorus which produced it. This increase in weight, which is not easy to determine exactly, comes from the combination of the air which is fixed in this operation.'

Lavoisier does not say whether the 'acid' is the dry sublimate or (as it would seem) the deliquesced liquid, and he gives no figures for the increase in weight, although trivial details of some other experiments are given in full. Lavoisier[4] in dealing later with the combustion of phosphorus in air, says: 'the experiments reported in this memoir were made in 1772, and "paraphées" by the Secretary of the Academy on 20 October of the same year. They were repeated in 1773 . . . and published in ch. 9 of my *Opuscules physiques et chimiques* at the end of the year 1773.' This work was actually published in

[1] *Dictionnaire*, 1778, i, 494.   [2] IV, ii, 86.   [3] Meldrum, (2).   [4] IV, ii, 88.

1774 (see p. 388) and the experiments in it[1] were probably mostly made late in 1773. The 'paraphée' of 20 October, according to Meldrum,[2] 'is not available.'

(iii) On 1 November 1772 Lavoisier deposited a sealed note with the Academy, which was opened on 5 May 1773.[3] In this he says he had found about eight days before that 'sulphur on burning' increases in weight, 'that is to say, from a pound of sulphur one can obtain (retirer) much more than a pound of vitriolic acid, not counting the humidity of the air, and it is the same with phosphorus. This increase in weight comes from a prodigious quantity of air which is fixed during the combustion and combines with the vapours.'

Lavoisier gives no figures and did not then, or at any time later, say how the experiment was made. Sulphur on burning does not form vitriolic (sulphuric) acid but gaseous sulphur dioxide, and no one has ever explained what Lavoisier did. An entry in Lavoisier's note-book of 18 May 1785[4] reads: 'Combustion du soufre. Soufre 38·98 Air vital 61·02' (sum 100·0), which Berthelot remarks would agree approximately with the calculated value for sulphur trioxide (59 instead of 61·02), but sulphur trioxide is not directly formed by burning sulphur in oxygen, although Lavoisier always seems to have thought it was,[5] and in describing the combustion of phosphorus he says:[6]

I can assert from my own experiments that sulphur in burning absorbs air; that the acid formed is much heavier than the sulphur; that its weight is equal to the weight of the sulphur and of the oxygen absorbed; and finally that this acid is dense (pesant), incombustible, and capable of combining with water in all proportions.

If he had weighed the pure liquid sulphuric acid he would have made an error of 20 p.c. in assuming that its weight was the sum of the weights of sulphur and oxygen. The sealed note continues:

This discovery, which I have established (constatée) by experiments which I regard as decisive, made me think that what is observed in the combustion of sulphur and phosphorus might well take place in the case of all bodies which gain weight by combustion and calcination, and I am persuaded that the increase in weight of metallic calces (chaux) is due to the same cause. Experiment has completely confirmed my conjectures. I have made the reduction of litharge in closed vessels with Hales's apparatus and I have observed that at the moment the calx passes into metal a considerable quantity of air, at least a thousand times greater than the quantity of litharge used, is disengaged. This discovery seeming to me one of the most interesting made since the time of Stahl (depuis Staalh), I thought it my duty to assure myself of priority by depositing this note (j'ai cru devoir m'en assurer la propriété, en faisant le présent dépôt entre les mains du secrétaire de l'Académie).

The draft found among Lavoisier's papers ends differently:[7]

Comme il est difficile de ne pas laisser entrevoir a Ses amis dans la Conversation quelque chose qui puisse les mettre Sur la voye de la verité j'ay Cru devoir faire le present depost entre les mains de M. le Secretaire de l'academie en attendant que je rende mes experiences publiques.

[1] V, 1801, 337 f.   [2] (1), 2.
[3] Lavoisier, IV, ii, 85; VIII, ii, 103 (written about 1792).   [4] Berthelot, (4), 301.
[5] VII, 244: l'acide sulfureux [SO$_2$] est formé, comme l'acide sulfurique [SO$_3$], de la combinaison du soufre avec l'oxygène. See p. 464.
[6] VII, 66.   [7] IX, ii, 389.

Apart from the confusion of air with carbon dioxide, it does not seem that Lavoisier had actually made out if absorption of air is *necessary* for calcination, or only a concomitant of it, and he does not seem to have got much further than Rey in 1630.[1] Guerlac[2] pointed out Lavoisier's early interest in the evolution of 'air' in reductions of calces as shown in a memorandum of 8 August 1772 (over a month before the work on phosphorus),[3] in which he speaks of 'l'air fixe, ou plutôt sur l'air contenu dans les corps', and suggests measuring the quantity of air produced or absorbed in each operation by applying a burning glass to Hales's apparatus.[4] The idea may have come from a remark in Cramer's *Elementa Artis Docimasticæ*, the second Latin edition (1744) of which was in Lavoisier's library. This speaks of the foaming and bubbling when lead oxide is reduced by carbon:[5] 'Litharge . . . as soon as the Phlogiston gets into it, rises into a foamy Mass, consisting of a Multitude of small Bubbles . . . unless the Litharge [is] reduced to Lead, which sometimes rises above the Border of the Vessel.' This effect is referred to in Lavoisier's *Opuscules* (see p. 390), and in some of his memoirs not noticed by Guerlac.

Mitouard, on 12 December 1772, read a paper to the Academy on the residue in the retort in the preparation of phosphorus, which was reported on by Macquer and Lavoisier on 16 December.[6] When it was received is not stated. It was recommended for publication in the *Mémoires . . . divers Savants*, but as far as I can find it was not published, and all we know of it is contained in the report. The material was rich in phosphorus, since it inflamed in air, and when burnt in an apparatus which Mitouard described, and 'with precautions which he describes', it gave more than its weight of phosphoric acid, even when this was concentrated by evaporation. He had described (as Lavoisier was later to do) a simple preparation of phosphoric acid from phosphorus 'by combining it with the base of nitre' (presumably nitric acid). He also discovered what must have been red phosphorus, regarding it as 'phosphorus itself combined with a portion of white earth'. The increase in weight Mitouard attributed to 'the humidity of the air or to the air itself contained in the vessels in which the combustion was made'.

Mitouard, 'Membre du College de Pharmacie, & très-avantageusement connu par les Cours de Chymie qu'il fait tous les ans dans son laboratoire, rue de Baune, Fauxbourg St. Germain', is mentioned by Sigaud de la Fond[7] as having modified an apparatus used by Lavoisier. Speter[8] thought Mitouard's paper was *received* in October or even September, and suggested Lavoisier's experiments; Meldrum[9] pointed out (with unnecessary heat) that it was not *read* until December, but it must have been received in time for Macquer and Lavoisier to report on it by 16 December, and Guerlac[10] thought Mitouard should not be ignored. Meldrum thought Lavoisier had read the observation of Sage,[11] reported in a review of his book,[12] that 6 drachms of phosphorus

[1] Thomson, (1), ii, 101; Kopp, (1), iii, 145, 314.   [2] *Archives*, 1959, xii, 113.
[3] Speter, (1), sep. 33; Guerlac, *Isis*, 1959, l, 125–9.   [4] See V, 1801, 264; see p. 392.
[5] Cramer, *Elements of the Art of Assaying Metals*, 1741, 250.
[6] *Obs. Phys.*, 1774, iii, 421; Lavoisier, VIII, ii, 141–3.
[7] *Essai sur Différentes Especes d'Air*, Paris, 1779, 102.   [8] (2); (5).   [9] (2).   [10] Ref. 2, 132.
[11] *Élémens de Minéralogie Docimastique*, 1772.   [12] *Intr. Obs. Phys.*, 1772 (1777), ii, 43 (49).

deliquesced in two months to 18 drachms of phosphoric acid by taking up twice their weight of water. Cigna also[1] found that burning phosphorus decreases the 'elasticity' of air, 2 grains of phosphorus absorbing, according to circumstances, 28 or 13 inches of air; and Lavoisier had 'probably read Cigna's memoir soon after it appeared' — in fact (as Meldrum did not notice) he may have read it in the original publication of 1760 (see p. 402). He had also probably read Sage, since in 1772[2] he seems to be criticising him without mentioning his name, saying that the [Sage's] suggestion that phosphoric acid is a peculiar acid is in need of proof, and asserting that there are probably only two mineral acids, sulphuric and hydrochloric, the nature of nitric acid being unknown.

Meldrum (whose knowledge was rather specialised) fails to mention that Hanckewitz[3] had obtained 10 drs. of 'flowers' (P_2O_5) from 1 oz. (8 drs.) of phosphorus, Marggraf[4] obtained $11\frac{1}{2}$ drs.; and Hales[5] had proved that the volume of air is decreased by burning sulphur and phosphorus in it.

A document drawn up by Lavoisier and dated 20 February 1772 occurs in his note-book in a part containing entries of 1773,[6] and since Priestley (who had published nothing on gases until late in 1772) is mentioned in it, the date must be a mistake for 1773.[7] It seems to have been a sketch of material published in the *Opuscules physiques et chimiques* written in 1773. In it Lavoisier says: 'Before commencing the long series of experiments I propose to make on the elastic fluid disengaged from substances. . . . I feel that I must set down here some reflexions in writing.' He goes on to mention Hales, Black, Macbride, Jacquin, Cranz, Priestley, and de Smeth, whose work he reviewed in the *Opuscules* (Smeth also published only in 1772). In his characteristic way, Lavoisier says that everything done before him was 'merely suggestive', and that his own projected work (of the results of which he could know nothing then) would 'bring about a revolution in physics and chemistry'.

Fourcroy[8] says Priestley in 1772 had begun the rapid and copious publication of his experiments, and Lavoisier felt that: 'it was necessary in some way to check this experimental torrent' — a hopeless task where Priestley was concerned. It was time to turn back and examine each of Priestley's experiments and 'confirm it with care and accuracy'. Fourcroy[9] also says Lavoisier's work arose directly out of that of Black and Priestley:

Lavoisier . . . conçut le vaste projet de répéter & de varier toutes les expériences des deux célèbres physiciens anglois, & de poursuivre avec une ardeur infatigable une carrière nouvelle, dont il prévoyoit dès-lors l'entendue.

The first-fruits of this 'vast project' are gathered in Lavoisier's *Opuscules Physiques et Chimiques* (1774).

[1] *Intr. Obs. Phys.*, 1772 (1777), ii, 84.   [2] VIII, ii, 32.
[3] *Phil. Trans.*, 1733, xxxviii, 58.
[4] *Miscell. Berolin.*, 1740, vi, 58; *Chymische Schriften*, Berlin, 1761, i, 42; *Opuscules Chimiques*, Paris, 1762, i, 1.
[5] *Vegetable Staticks*, 1727, 169, 226.   [6] Berthelot, (4), 46, 225, 231.
[7] Grimaux, 1888, 104: 'le 20 février 1773'; 'rediscovered' by Speter, (2), 581; Meldrum, (1), 10; Winderlich, *A. Nat.*, 1931, xiii, 221; and others.
[8] (2), iii, 414.   [9] *Ib.*, 692.

Opuscules Physiques et Chimiques

The *Opuscules Physiques et Chimiques* (V, p. 372) was published in January 1774. Lavoisier,[1] it is true, says it 'a paru' in December 1773,[2] and in other places speaks of what he said in it 'in 1773'.

An analysis of the *Opuscules* in the *Histoire* of the Academy,[3] which Dumas[4] said was 'impartial and contemporary', was actually written by Lavoisier and exists in his handwriting.[5] It concludes by saying that Lavoisier:

applique à la chimie, non seulement les appareils et la méthode de la physique expérimentale, mais cet esprit d'exactitude et de calcul qui caractérise cette science. L'union
qui paraît prête à se faire entre ces deux branches de nos connaissances sera une
époque brillante pour les progrès de toutes deux, et M. Lavoisier est un de ceux qui,
jusqu'ici, ont le plus contribué à cette réunion vainment désirée depuis longtemps.

The long report on the book, dated 7 December 1773 and signed by de Trudaine, Macquer, Le Roy, and Cadet,[6] was also written by Lavoisier himself.[7] It speaks of 'la précision et la scrupuleuse exactitute' of all his experiments, made 'avec toute l'exactitude dont elles sont susceptibles', with 'plusieurs instruments de physique ingénieusement imaginés ou perfec-
tionnés', a 'méthode rigoureuse, qui, heureusement pour l'avancement de la chimie, commence à devenir indispensable dans la pratique de cette science'.

The first part of the book[8] gives a history of previous opinions and experiments on the nature of air and gases. It deals with Paracelsus and Van Helmont (who is highly praised: On est étonné, en lisant ce traité, d'y trouver une infinité de vérités, qu'on a coutume de regarder comme plus modernes) (ch. i), Boyle (ch. ii), Hales (ch. iii), Boerhaave (ch. iv), Stahl ('Stalh': ch. v — half a page), Venel (ch. vi), Black (ch. vii, 7 pp.), Saluces (ch. viii), Macbride (ch. ix), Cavendish (ch. x, 3 pp.), Meyer (ch. xi, 6 pp.), Jacquin (ch. xii, 7 pp.), 'Crans' (Cranz) (ch. xiii, 15 pp.), Smeth (ch. xiv, 23 pp.), Priestley (ch. xv, 43 pp.; full summary of 1772 paper), Duhamel (ch. xvi), Rouelle (ch. xvii), Bucquet (ch. xviii), and Baumé (ch. xix). The last four seem to have been added to provide some French work to eke out Venel's. The summaries are reasonably good but there are some mistakes in the section on Priestley, and the relative amounts of space (e.g. Black as compared with Venel, Cranz, and Smeth) show poor judgment. The account of Cavendish's work is defective, and when Lavoisier distributed copies of the book, with appropriate letters, he did not send one to Cavendish.[9] Rozier's journal for 1774 contains translations of several publications either used in the *Opuscules* or related to them.[10] The

---

[1] AdS, 1783 (1786), m 505; VIII, ii, 629.
[2] The report on it to the Academy is dated 7 December 1773; VIII, i, 657.
[3] AdS, 1774 (1778), h 71; VIII, ii, 89.   [4] In Lavoisier, VIII, ii, 89.
[5] Grimaux, in Lavoisier, VIII, v, 320.
[6] Extrait des Registres de l'Académie des Sciences, 7 December 1773; Lavoisier, V, 1801, 364; VIII, i, 657–66.
[7] Meldrum, (1), 17.   [8] V, 1801, 1–188.
[9] Grimaux, 1888, 105–6; Meldrum, (1), 17; Lavoisier, IX, ii, 398–455.
[10] *Obs. Phys.*, 1774, i, 123 (Jacquin on Meyer's *acidum pingue*), 210, 261 (Black's dissertation), 292, 394 (Priestley's 1772 paper), 197 (de Fourcy on *acidum pingue*, and affinity tables), 450 (Rutherford's dissertation); 1774, ii, 30 (Meyer on *acidum pingue*), 85 (Rutherford), 123 (Cranz), 218 (de Fourcy, reply to summary of Jacquin), 281 (summary of de Morveau's *Dissert. Académ.*); 1774, iii, 185 (Anon., Discours sur le Phlogistique), 408 (De Machy's criticism of Macbride), 418 (de Morveau on the parallelism of phlogiston and *acidum pingue*); etc.

summary of Meyer's theory,[1] the translation of Black's paper,[2] and Jacquin's defence of it,[3] may have been prompted by Lavoisier.

The account of Cavendish omits to mention that he had determined the densities of fixed and inflammable airs. The account of Black,[4] as Kopp[5] said, is 'sehr trocken, kurz und unbefriedigend', whilst a long and appreciative account of Meyer is given. In the index[6] under 'Black' Lavoisier adds, so that it will not be missed: 'Opinion contraire à la sienne établi [sic] par M. Meyer', and under Meyer: 'il établit une opinion contraire à celle de M. Black.' At the end of the summary of Black's work Lavoisier says:

On croit devoir prévenir le lecteur que la théorie de l'air fixe n'avoit pas acquis au sortir des mains de M. Black tout l'ensemble et toute la consistence qu'on lui a donné dans cet article; elle ne l'a acquise que d'après l'ouvrage de M. Jacquin, dont on rendra compte incessament,

whereas all that he says about fixed air is to be found in Black. Hoefer, who is otherwise very favourable to Lavoisier but was an unbiased author, says:[7]

Le reproche que l'on a fait à Lavoisier de ne pas avoir rendu à Black la justice qu'il méritait ne manque pas d'une certaine apparence de raison . . . L'ouvrage de Meyer, ouvertement dirigé contre Black, ne méritait pas un pareil éloge. . . . Lavoisier, après avoir consacré seulement cinq pages et demie à l'analyse du beau travail de Black . . . consacre quinze pages à l'analyse du méchant pamphlet de Crans [sic], et vingt-deux pages à celle de la thèse de Smeth, qui renferme plus d'erreurs que de faits; et encore ces derniers, loin d'être nouveaux, ne sont-ils qu'empruntés à Priestley et à des chimistes plus anciens.

No doubt following Lavoisier's guidance, Guyton de Morveau,[8] in a long article on *acidum pingue*, said that Meyer's book was 'filled with curious experiments, directed with sagacity and adapted to profound views and wise reasoning', but Fourcroy,[9] who was generally independent, gave a very unfavourable account of Meyer's theory.

Lavoisier begins his 23 pages on Smeth (to whom he sent a copy of his book) by saying that Cranz 'attacked the doctrine of Black on the air fixed in calcareous earths and the alkalis', and 'shook the foundations on which this doctrine was established'. He concludes by saying that Smeth's 'system does not always agree with his own experiments', but his treatise is clear and 'his experiments are well made, and the greater part are exact and true, at least those I have had occasion to repeat, which are the greatest part of them'. Since nearly all Smeth's experiments are incorrect (those which are correct being, as he says, repetitions of Macbride's), this does not speak very highly for Lavoisier's experimental skill.

The second part of the book[10] deals with Lavoisier's own experiments and is divided into eleven chapters. The first three deal with the existence of fixed air in chalk and mild alkalis and add very little to Black's researches. He says

---

[1] *Obs. Phys.*, 1773, ii, 30.   [2] *Ib.*, 1774, i, 210, 261.
[3] *Ib.*, 1774, i, 123.   [4] V, 1801, 37.
[5] (1), iii, 41; Meldrum, (1), 27, thought 'Lavoisier stated the doctrine of each in a satisfactory way'.
[6] V, 1801, 400, 415.   [7] (1), ii, 355, 357; (2), ii, 363, 365.
[8] *Ency. Méthod., Chymie*, 1786, i, 418–20.   [9] (2), 1796, iii, 371–3.
[10] V, 1801, 191–363; summary in Fourcroy, (2), iii, 427 f.; Meldrum, (1), 21–34.

100 lb. of chalk contain 31 lb. 15 oz. of fixed air, 15 lb. 7 oz. of water (pure chalk contains no water) and 52 lb. 10 oz. of alkaline earth; and quicklime contains a large amount of pure matter of fire, to which the heat evolved on slaking is due, although slaked lime still contains some, which it evolves on dissolving in acid. In the fourth chapter he shows that metals (mercury and iron) on precipitation from solutions in acids by chalk and lime increase in weight; the precipitate with lime weighs less than that with chalk but still probably contains some residual elastic fluid from the lime not driven out by burning. The fifth chapter deals with 'the existence of an elastic fluid fixed in metallic calces', especially the elastic fluid evolved by reducing minium with carbon; in it Lavoisier says he suspected that 'atmospheric air or some elastic fluid contained in the air was capable in a number of circumstances of fixing itself and combining with metals, and it was to the addition of this substance that the phenomena of calcination, the increase in weight of metals converted into calces, and perhaps many other phenomena', were due.[1] In no case does he say anything of the nature of the elastic fluid disengaged, except that it is analogous to fixed air. He says (see p. 386):

It is a fact known to all metallurgists and observed by all those who have worked in the operations of assaying, that in every reduction there is effervescence at the moment when the metallic substance passes from the state of calx to that of metal. But an effervescence is commonly nothing more than a disengagement of elastic fluid in a fixed form, which regains its elasticity at the moment of reduction (un dégagement de fluide élastique sous forme fixe, qui reprend son élasticité au moment de la réduction).

He first describes an experiment in which 2 gros of minium (red lead) was heated with 12 grains of dry powdered charcoal in a capsule supported in a bell-jar over water covered with a layer of oil, the powder being heated by a large burning glass. He found that some litharge sublimed, lead was formed, and about 14 cu. in. of elastic fluid were evolved.[2] He then describes an experiment in which a large volume (560 cu. in.) of 'air' is evolved when 6 oz. of red lead is reduced by heating with 6 gros of charcoal in an iron retort. This air was shown to be fixed air.[3]

The apparatus (Fig. 36) was very elaborate and only part of it is reproduced here. The iron retort was heated in a furnace and was connected by a luted joint with a wide tube passing through the wall of a wood or metal trough filled with water. This tube ended in a sphere, from which a vertical tube passed inside a tall bell-jar filled with water, the surface of which was covered with oil. Lavoisier says this apparatus is adapted from Hales's by Rouelle, with some changes and additions made by himself (he could have seen it in Rouelle's lectures).

From this experiment Lavoisier concluded that 'the calx of lead contains a quantity of elastic fluid equal to 747 times the volume of lead used to form it'. The weight of lead left was 5 oz. 7 gros 66 grains. The estimated weight of the elastic fluid was 4 gros 34 grains, and as the loss in weight of the minium and carbon was 6 gros 6 grains there was a deficit of 1 gros 44 grains. This might be water, but in an experiment in which this was collected it was found to be insufficient. Lavoisier concluded that the greater part of the elastic fluid came from the red lead: c'est . . . aux dépens du minium, que la plus grande partie

[1] V, 1801, 261.   [2] V, 1801, 264; plate II, fig. 8.   [3] V, 1801, 267; plate II, fig. 10.

du fluide élastique a été fournie. This is correct. He showed[1] that the elastic fluid was fatal to sparrows, rats, and mice, that it precipitated lime water and extinguished flames, and he concluded that it was fixed air. Only the second test is valid, and he did not determine the density of the gas, as Cavendish had done in 1766 (see p. 314).

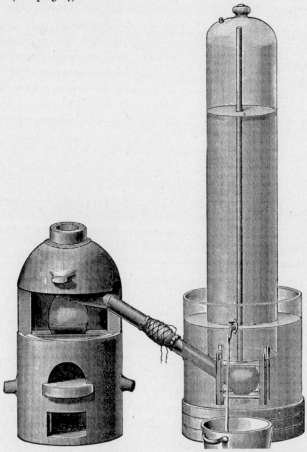

FIG. 36. LAVOISIER'S APPARATUS FOR COLLECTING THE GAS EVOLVED ON HEATING RED-LEAD AND CHARCOAL IN AN IRON RETORT.

The air could be removed from the bell-jar through the small aperture shown at the top or through a tube in the jar by an air-pump, not reproduced in the figure.

(From Lowry, *Historical Introduction to Chemistry*)

Lavoisier says[2] that from some experiments not yet completed he believed that:

'every elastic fluid results from the combination of some solid or fluid body with an inflammable principle, or perhaps even with the pure matter of fire, and the state of elasticity depends on this combination. [The substance fixed in metallic calces is] the fixed part of an elastic fluid which has been deprived of its inflammable principle. Carbon and all carbonaceous substances used in reduction . . . give to the fixed elastic fluid phlogiston, the matter of fire, and restore to it at the same time the elasticity which depends upon this.'

[1] V, 312 f.   [2] *Ib.*, 288. See p. 421.

In chapter six he studies the calcination of metals (tin, lead, and an alloy of the two) in air in a bell-jar over water or mercury, the metal being heated by a burning glass (Fig. 37).[1] He found a maximum diminution of the volume of the air of $\frac{1}{20}$ (instead of $\frac{1}{5}$) and in an experiment with lead, 3 gros of metal gave 3 gros $1\frac{3}{4}$ gr. of calx (with $\frac{1}{4}$ gr. estimated for the fumes); 2 gros of tin increased by $\frac{1}{8}$ gr. but the volume of air had not sensibly diminished. Lavoisier used too powerful a burning glass and volatilised some of the metals. Over two pages of conclusions are drawn from these inconclusive experiments, e.g. that 'a particular elastic fluid mixed with the air' enters into the composition of the calx.

FIG. 37. LAVOISIER'S APPARATUS FOR CALCINING LEAD OR TIN IN AIR.

Priestley[2] had correctly found a contraction of $\frac{1}{5}$, or $\frac{1}{4}$ as a maximum. In a footnote Lavoisier says that when he made his experiments he did not know that Priestley before him (avant moi) had found this contraction. Although Lavoisier mentions Priestley in his memorandum of 20 February 1773, this part of Priestley's work was then unavailable (see p. 249). Priestley, he says, attributed the diminution of the air to the phlogiston disengaged from the metal 'and he seems not to have suspected that the calcination itself was an absorption, a fixation of elastic fluid'. Lavoisier is on the right track here.

Meldrum[3] says the five conclusions drawn by Lavoisier from his experiments, 'usually regarded as unexceptionable', are, except the first that calcination proceeds with greater difficulty in a vessel than in free air (which was then well known), all open to objection, and Lavoisier had not really proved any satisfactorily. He supposed that fixed air was absorbed and his results were inferior to Priestley's. Lavoisier says he had proved that 'in the calcination of metals there is a combination of elastic fluid with them, which is fixed, and to this fixation their increase in weight is due', and that there is 'a diminution in the volume of the air, and this diminution is approximately (à-peu-près) proportional to the increase in weight of the metal', but he had not done this at all. His further conclusion he had not then proved:

the air we breathe is not suited for entry in its entirety into the combination of metallic calces, but there exists in the atmosphere a particular elastic fluid mixed with air, and as soon as the quantity of this fluid contained in the receiver is exhausted the calcination cannot occur.

In 1775, as will be seen (p. 404), Lavoisier was assuming that it was 'the whole air' which was fixed in the calx, but he deserves credit for having reached the conclusion just quoted, however imperfect, in 1773. It is practically what Mayow had said in 1674 (see Vol. II, p. 590).

The seventh chapter describes the collection of the elastic fluid evolved in

[1] Ib., 302.   [2] Phil. Trans., 1772, lxii, 228; E & O (see p. 255), 1774, i, 133.   [3] (1), 24.

effervescence (chalk and acid) and reductions; there is nothing to decide if this elastic fluid is different from air, or if it is air which has had something added or subtracted. The gas, being soluble in water, cannot expand the lungs of animals, and hence they die in it[1] — a purely physical theory of respiration. The eighth chapter deals with some properties of this elastic fluid (carbon dioxide), mentioning Cavendish, Priestley, and Rouelle.[2] The ninth chapter describes experiments which show that in the combustion of phosphorus in air about one-fifth of the air is removed, 3 cu. in. per grain of phosphorus, and 8 grains of phosphorus gave 14 grains of 'acide phosphorique concret' (i.e. 1 gr. gave 1·8 gr. of phosphorus pentoxide); but after conjectural corrections Lavoisier concluded that 6·5 gr. gave 17·5 gr. (or 1 part gave 2·69 parts).[3] The greater part of the substance absorbed, which increases the weight of the phosphorus, is not water but comes from the air, the diminution in volume of which is, in greater part, due to its extraction. It is 'either the air itself or some other elastic fluid contained in a certain proportion in the air we respire'.[4]

The tenth chapter describes the absence of explosion of gunpowder when heated in a vacuum and its explosion when air is admitted;[4] Lavoisier did not know that this had been described by Boyle (see Vol. II, p. 527). The eleventh chapter[5] says a bird can live in air in which phosphorus had burnt, although this extinguished a lighted candle. Lavoisier seems to have thought the phosphorus had combined with fixed air (carbon dioxide), which he knew extinguished a candle. He says an addition of one-third of the fixed air evolved in effervescence to the air left after the combustion of phosphorus should 'correct [corriger]' this and make it support combustion, but a lighted candle was at once extinguished in the mixture.

The *Opuscules* does Lavoisier great credit and established his reputation as a chemist. It contains many quantitative experiments, and although it necessarily involves omissions and some errors (excusable for the time) it is an advance over anything which had gone before.

His quantitative experiments are often inaccurate. If he wished to find how much 'elastic fluid' (impure carbon dioxide) was absorbed by lime water, instead of opening the mouth of an inverted bottle of the gas over lime water, he used an elaborate apparatus with pumps and wash-bottles, not troubling about the common air in the apparatus,[6] and finding only two-thirds absorbed. Priestley, he says, had found four-fifths. He seems to have thought (erroneously) that Priestley (he does not mention Cavendish) had found fixed air and common air of the same density; his own experiments showed that fixed air is heavier than common air, but since he thought that the air absorbed in the calcination of metals was fixed air, he concluded from these experiments that it has the same density as air.[7] On 15 January 1774, Lavoisier sent a copy of the *Opuscules* to the Royal Society to be given to Priestley with a letter, and the same day he sent one to the Royal Society of Edinburgh to be given to Black.[8] A draft[9] of a projected second volume, made about 1778, contains titles of chapters mostly contained in his *Traité* (VII, 1789).

---

[1] V, 314.   [2] *Ib.*, 331.   [3] *Ib.*, 337.   [4] *Ib.*, 358.   [5] *Ib.*, 361.   [6] *Ib.*, 318–22.
[7] *Ib.*, 199, 237–8, 242, 276.   [8] IX, ii, 398, 401; drafts of other letters also.   [9] VIII, v, 267.

In the same year, 1774, in which Lavoisier's *Opuscules* appeared some interesting papers were published by Bayen which had a bearing on it.

BAYEN

Pierre Bayen (Châlons-sur-Marne, 1725–Paris, 15 February 1798), a pharmacist in the French army (Apothicaire-Major des Camps et Armées du Roi), friend of Rouelle and Venel and pupil of the former and of Pierron de Chamousset (1717–73), was a man of great modesty and in consequence was far from well off. During the Terror he burnt his manuscripts.[1]

Bayen's writings were collected by his nephew Malatret and published[2] with a 'discours preliminaire' and Parmentier's éloge of Bayen to the Royal Society of Medicine in Paris. Shortly before Bayen's death he and Parmentier were described in a pamphlet as 'old men, full of the prejudices of the old régime'.[3] On the reorganisation of the Academy of Sciences, Bayen became a member of the Institut Nationale.

Bayen's first publication, on the hepatic waters of Luchon, also describes the analyses of some rocks.[4] He then worked on tin. Henckel[5] had reported that tin ores contain arsenic, and Marggraf,[6] by dissolving commercial tin in aqua regia made with nitric acid and sal ammoniac, obtained a white residue which he thought was arsenic. J. H. Schulze (who worked on the action of light on silver compounds, see Vol. IV) had said that tin was innocuous when used as vessels for preparing food, although he pointed out the dangers of lead and copper,[7] and this was mentioned by Rouelle the elder in his lectures. A commission consisting of Rouelle the younger, Louis Martin Charlard (b. Peronne, d. 1798), and Bayen was appointed by the Paris College of Pharmacy to examine the alleged presence of arsenic in tin. Rouelle died before the work was begun, but Bayen and Charlard reported in 1781.[8] They found that commercial tin is either quite free from arsenic or contains only traces.

Bayen's analyses of stones and rocks[9] confirmed that serpentine contains magnesia, as Marggraf had found (see Vol. II, p. 728). Bayen objected to the name 'magnesia', speaking of 'la terre qui sert de base au sel cathartique amer' or 'base du sel de Sedlitz', and he says the bitter salt (magnesium sulphate) imported from England was adulterated in Paris with Glauber's salt, whilst the salt from Sedlitz in Bohemia was purer but more expensive than Epsom salt.[10]

---

[1] Cadet-Gassicourt, *Biogr. Univ.*, 1843, iii, 337; Cap, *Gazz. Méd. Paris*, 1865, xx, 1–13; Grimaux, *Rev. Scient.*, 1884, viii, 408; Hoefer, NBG, 1853, iv, 865; Jörgensen, 1909, 111–72; Lassus, *Mém. de l'Inst.*, An VII (1799), ii, h 144–52; *Ann. Chim.*, 1798, xxvi, 278; Neave, *Ann. Sci.*, 1951, vii, 144 (portr.); Parmentier, Crell's *Ann.*, 1784, II, 257, 350.

[2] *Opuscules Chimiques*, 2 vols. 8°, Paris, An VI (1797–8).   [3] Bayen, *Opusc.*, I, lxix.

[4] *Analyse des Eaux de Bagnères-de-Luchon*, 8°, Paris, 1765; *Opusc.*, i, 1–202.

[5] *Pyritologia*, 1757, 203.

[6] *Hist. Acad. Berlin*, 1747 (1749), 33; 1756 (1758), 122; *Opuscules Chymiques*, 1762, i, 177; ii, 204.

[7] Schulze, *Dissertatio medica, in qua metallicum contagium in ciborum, potuum et medicamentorum præparatione ac asservatione cavendum indicatur: seu Mors in Ollâ*, 4°, Altdorf, 1722.

[8] *Recherches Chimiques sur l'Étain, faites et publiées par ordre du Gouvernement; ou Réponse a cette Question: Peut-on sans danger employer les Vaisseaux d'Etain dans l'usage économique?*, 8°, Paris, 1781 (viii, 285 pp.); Bayen, *Opusc.*, ii, 213–460.

[9] *Examen de différentes Pierres*, publié en 1778, in *Opusc.*, ii, 41–183, 203–12.

[10] *Opusc.*, ii, 125.

Bayen reported that (the poisonous) salt of sorrel (potassium binoxalate), which was used to remove ink spots and to make 'acidulous drinks, very agreeable and healthy' (hence perhaps the name 'salts of lemon' still used for it in England), could be manufactured by peasants from cultivated sorrel (*Rumex acetosa*), as was done in Würtemberg.[1]

The most interesting of Bayen's publications were on the precipitates of mercury,[2] which overlapped those of Priestley and Lavoisier. Since Priestley was familiar with French scientific literature he may have read Bayen's papers in Rozier's *Observations* of 1774-5 (Lavoisier certainly had), although he never mentions him by name.[3]

Bayen's first memoir[4] describes the precipitates formed on adding salt of tartar (potassium carbonate), mild volatile alkali (ammonium carbonate), caustic potash, and lime water to solutions of mercury in nitric acid; these precipitates all contained some acid and some of the precipitating base. They detonated violently on heating with sulphur and on heating alone were reduced to mercury with loss of $\frac{1}{8}$ of their weight. Since the precipitate from corrosive sublimate (mercuric chloride) also detonated with sulphur, the effect was not due to the nitric acid, and this precipitate is also most easily reduced by heat. Bayen says he will not discuss the theory, since Lavoisier had just published a memoir[5] on the existence of an elastic fluid fixed in some substances. Bayen then thought the increase in weight of the precipitates 'is due in part to their union with a greater or less amount of the precipitant and solvent'.

In his second memoir[6] Bayen points out that the increase in weight contradicts Stahl's theory, unless phlogiston is assumed (with Venel) (see p. 614) to have a negative weight. Besides the increase in weight due to the adherence of part of the solvent and precipitant, there is part amounting to $\frac{1}{8}$ the weight of the metal due to its conversion into calx, and this is probably due to the fixation of an 'elastic fluid' by the metal (this was Lavoisier's theory). Bayen says Lemery had explained the increase in weight of metals on calcination as due to union with 'corpuscules ignés' (see p. 607); Charas (whose opinion was not generally accepted) to the 'acides du bois, du charbon et des autres matières alimentaires du feu' (see p. 618). The first theory is really due to Boyle, and the second to Tachenius (see Vol. II). Hales, without absolutely rejecting igneous corpuscles, thought that air contributed to the effect, and Black that fixed air was the cause of the increase in weight. The partisans of Meyer attributed the cause to *acidum pingue*, 'a double denomination which one may some day be forced to adopt.' Bayen says all these names are comprehended in the term, which he says he took from Lavoisier, of elastic fluid: j'ai

[1] *Opusc.*, ii, 183.   [2] *Opusc.*, i, 203-356.
[3] Jörgensen, 1909, 140, 145, says it is really curious that a whole series of publications like Bayen's on calx of mercury should have completely escaped Priestley's attention, yet this seems actually to have been the case; Cuvier's suggestion, 1828, 65, that Bayen's papers in 1774 'avait donné à Priestley l'idée . . . de découvrir l'air pur', is most improbable; the discovery was made by accident (see p. 256).
[4] *Obs. Phys.*, 1774, iii, 219 (February); *Opusc.*, i, 203.
[5] *Opuscules Physiques et Chimiques*, 1774.
[6] *Obs. Phys.*, 1774, iii, 280 (April); *Opusc.*, i, 243.

adopterai le terme de fluide élastique, et j'emploierai toutes les fois qu'il faudra nommer l'air fixe des chimistes anglais, l'*acidum pingue* de Meyer, etc.[1]

Bayen heated the substances in retorts and collected the gas over water, sometimes covered with a layer of oil to diminish the rate of solution (Lavoisier had done this). He detected the presence of fixed air in the water by the phosphoric smell, the acidulous taste, and the action on iron filings, giving a solution which produced a black colour with powdered galls. He did not use lime water. In one experiment, 2 gros 63 grains of mercury precipitate made with fixed alkali gave on heating with charcoal a volume of elastic fluid displacing 13 oz. 6 gros of water and left 2 gros 44 grains of mercury. The elastic fluid must have weighed at least 15 grains and hence is much heavier than air.[2] One oz. of precipitate and 24 grains of charcoal gave 7 gros 5 grains of mercury. Ten grains of charcoal remained, and 46 oz. measures of elastic fluid collected, which slowly diminished to 8 oz. after 17 days.[3] Six gros of the same precipitate heated alone gave 44 oz. of elastic fluid only very slowly absorbed by water not covered with oil; the solution had an acid taste and acted on iron.[4]

Bayen[5] says: 'cette eau empreint du fluid élastique dégagé de notre précipité sans addition de matière phlogistique, ne me paroissoit différer en rien de celle que j'avois obtenue dans les opérations où le phlogistique avoit été employé comme intermède.' Six gros of a different precipitate gave a sublimate containing a little nitric acid, mercury, and 42 oz. of elastic fluid, the weight of which he estimated as 58 grains, and which was apparently insoluble in water.[6] This is a new experiment, since Lavoisier had not heated minium alone, but only with charcoal. Bayen had now obtained oxygen but he did not sharply distinguish it from fixed air. Meldrum[7] says that Bayen obtained a gas soluble in water from red precipitate both mixed with charcoal and alone — 'In one experiment he did obtain from the oxide, heated alone, a gas that was insoluble in water. This result he explained away.' But Bayen got this result in more than one experiment and I do not find any 'explaining away' in his memoir. Jörgensen[8] calculated that 40 oz. measures was 1224 c.c. and the amount of oxygen from 1 oz. less 10 grains of red precipitate would be 1570 c.c. at S.T.P. Speter,[9] for a reason unknown to me, 'corrected' the 58 grains weight of the gas given by Bayen to 70 grains. Bayen[10] concluded that:

the mercury owes its calcined state not to loss of phlogiston, which it has never experienced (qu'il n'a point essuyée) but to its intimate combination with the elastic fluid, of which the weight added to that of the mercury is the second cause of the increase in weight observed in the precipitates I have examined.

In the obituary of Bayen[11] it is said that Lavoisier was present when Bayen's paper was read, and Thomson,[12] who quotes the passage, says: 'It was in consequence of hearing Bayen's paper read [in 1774] that Lavoisier was induced to turn his attention to the subject.' It seems, however, that it was

[1] *Opusc.*, i, 250–3.   [2] *Opusc.*, i, 256.   [3] *Opusc.*, i, 260.   [4] *Opusc.*, i, 265.
[5] *Opusc.*, i, 267.   [6] *Opusc.*, i, 271–82.   [7] (1), 48.   [8] 1909, 111 f.
[9] (1), 200.   [10] *Opusc.*, i, 282.   [11] *Mém. de l'Inst.*, 1799, ii, 144.
[12] (2), 1802, i, 83; 1807, i, 138.

really Priestley's work (see p. 402) which was the point of departure of Lavoisier's.

Bayen about this time published a long summary of the book by Jean Rey (see Vol. II, p. 631),[1] pointing out that Rey's theory, that the increase in weight of metals on calcination is due to the fixation of air, was very like his own theory; Berthelot[2] thought this was done to diminish the importance of Lavoisier's experiments, but this is improbable. When Rey's book was published by Gobet in 1777, Lavoisier thought it was a forgery.

In Bayen's third memoir[3] he says that $6\frac{1}{2}$ oz. of mercury by conversion into red precipitate by dissolving in nitric acid, evaporating, and heating to drive off the nitric acid (when some of the precipitate decomposed), gained 3 gros 24 grains, or $\frac{1}{16}$ of its weight. One oz. 8 gros of precipitate *per se*, made by Deyeux (a Paris apothecary) by heating mercury in air, gave on complete reduction by heat (when the glass retort was melting) 7 gros 18 grains of mercury and 54 grains of elastic fluid occupying the volume of 43 oz. of water.[4] Bayen concluded that:

the mercury calx is reduced without the concourse of any matter proper to furnish phlogiston, and in recovering its metallic form it allows a sufficiently large quantity of elastic fluid to escape, to which it owed its state.[5]

In this case the red precipitate had been made with nitric acid but had been completely freed from the acid by heating, when some of it sublimed. If Bayen had put a lighted taper into the gas he would have identified oxygen.

On calcination, mercury cannot have lost phlogiston since experiment shows that it has gained a new principle. How can the increase in weight be reconciled with the loss of one of the constituent principles?[6] The cause of the increase in weight on calcination is to be sought, with Jean Rey, in the atmosphere. Air is to be considered under two states, free and combined. In the first it is a simple body, an element. Which part of the atmosphere calcines metals, the elastic fluid pure and simple, or this combined so as to form an acid, or one of the other fluids found in the air? Experiment must decide.

Innumerable experiments show that the body which unites with metals during calcination is an elastic fluid, and some already prove that this fluid is furnished by the atmosphere. Above all, those which Lavoisier has just published are very proper to dissipate the doubts which it is natural to have on such an interesting fact, which had not in fact escaped the chemical speculations of Jean Rey, but which until recent times had been concealed from the researches of experimental chemistry.[7]

Bayen[8] found that 2 oz. of mercury dissolving in nitric acid produced 26–30 oz. measures of water of 'elastic fluid' (nitric oxide). This must 'have been furnished by the nitric acid, a portion of which has been decomposed and reduced to its principles'. But not all the elastic fluid has been exhaled:

the mercury has absorbed a quantity of it sufficient to reduce it to the state of calx, the state in which it is found even during its union with the nitric acid; and perhaps some

---

[1] *Obs. Phys.*, 1775, v, 47.   [2] (4), 31.
[3] *Obs. Phys.*, 1775, v, 147 (February); *Opusc.*, i, 283; Crell's *Beyträge*, 1786–7, ii, 317, 364.
[4] *Opusc.*, i, 302–3.   [5] *Opusc.*, i, 299.
[6] *Opusc.*, i, 305.   [7] *Ib.*, 311.   [8] *Ib.*, 313 f.

day one will find that metals only dissolve in acids by the aid of an elastic fluid with which they are combined during the effervescence, as some very common experiments seem already to prove.

In his fourth memoir[1] on turbith mineral (basic mercuric sulphate) Bayen says the conversion of mercury into calces:

'is not due to loss of phlogiston, as has been supposed, but to a new combination of the mercury with another body which the atmosphere furnishes to this mineral when it is calcined by itself, or which it takes from the acids when it is calcined by the way of dissolution.'

The elastic fluid (sulphur dioxide and oxygen) evolved on heating turbith mineral comes from the vitriolic acid and there is no loss of phlogiston. He passed the elastic fluid through water, obtaining a solution of sulphurous acid and an elastic fluid (oxygen) not absorbed. The mercury of the turbith was revived. The experiments were quantitative. Bayen says this paper completes a research of more than three years:

'it is shown that the mercury united to the vitriolic acid has not suffered any alteration and that it can be recovered in its liquid form without the addition of any carbonaceous matter proper to give phlogiston to the substances which are supposed to have lost it. . . . I will leave it there, leaving to the Stahlians the trouble of replying to all the difficulties which could be made against their doctrine.

'May those chemists who love the progress of the art deign to run with me (concourir avec moi) and I venture to give them my word that they will not fail to surpass me in the race. Criticism may perhaps be an excellent incentive to retain chemists in researches the object of which is to confirm facts announced by others, but it has no charms for me.'

It is truly remarkable that these *quantitative* experiments by Bayen are not mentioned by Lavoisier in a memoir covering almost the same ground published five years later[2] (see p. 419).

In a memoir on spathic iron ore (ferrous carbonate) read in June 1774, Bayen[3] showed that the mineral on heating or dissolving in acids lost 'what the English call fixed air'. He used Hales's apparatus, measuring the elastic fluid or gas (gaz) evolved, which he found was absorbed by fixed alkali (potassium carbonate) to form a crystalline salt (potassium bicarbonate). He concluded that the mineral is a compound of 1 part of fixed air or gas and 3 parts of metallic iron, but it is really a compound of 1 part of fixed air and 1·6 of ferrous oxide.

Delametherie[4] says: 'Lavoisier n'a cité Bayen, parce qu'il n'étoit pas de l'Academie, ce qui se pratique toujours.' He said later[5] that Lavoisier had never forgiven him for bringing Bayen to notice:

Lavoisier voulant s'approprier la découverte de Bayen sur la revivication du *précipité rouge*, ou oxide de mercure, sans addition de matière charbonneuse, et ce qu'il disoit contre la doctrine du phlogistique, celle de Cavendish sur la composition de l'eau, ne parle jamais de ces belles expériences. Je réclamai pour eux: il ne me l'a jamais pardonné. D'autres ne me pardonneront non plus d'avoir rendu justice à Gahn, à Berg-

---

[1] *Obs. Phys.*, 1775, vi, 487 (December); *Opusc.*, i, 315.

[2] AdS, 1777 (1780), h 28, m 324 (no date).

[3] AdS *Mém. div. Sav.*, 1780, IX, xiii, 689; *Opusc.*, ii, 1–40; report by Daubenton and Lavoisier, in Lavoisier, VIII, iv, 232.

[4] *J. de Phys.*, 1798, xlvi, 392.   [5] *J. de Phys.*, 1809, lxix, 63; Kopp, (3), 143.

man. . . . Il faut m'arrêter: j'en ai peut-être déjà trop dit; mais la vérité triomphe, et c'est tout ce que je recherche. Revenons à notre sujet.

In a long account of Bayen's memoirs Macquer[1] says the experiments and conclusions are similar to Lavoisier's, but the reduction of red precipitate is not really in contradiction with the phlogiston theory. The mercury may have lost only a very small amount of phlogiston on calcination, or else the phlogiston necessary for reduction passed through the vessels in the form of the matter of light. Macquer points out that Bayen had failed to examine the nature of the gas evolved. Fourcroy[2] says Bayen would have discovered oxygen if only he had put a lighted candle into the gas he collected, but he did not. Keir[3] described Bayen's experiment but thought that 'a conclusion from a single fact, subversive of a theory [Stahl's] founded on the general course of appearances, ought to be very cautiously admitted'.

Bayen went further than Lavoisier in showing that a calx can be reduced *without* addition of 'phlogistic' material and that a gas is simultaneously evolved. He published this in February 1775, but in October 1774 Lavoisier had learnt the fact from Priestley, who had also told him that the gas supported combustion much better than air. Lavoisier could not mention Bayen without mentioning Priestley's earlier discovery, and he mentioned neither.

Hoefer[4] rightly said that Bayen must not be allowed to take credit from Lavoisier, but Bayen's strong criticism of the phlogiston theory some years before Lavoisier ventured openly to attack it (even if he thought of this) is noteworthy. A long anonymous attack on the theory was published in March 1774,[5] saying of phlogiston that 'its presence, even if it exists at all, has never been clearly manifested', and referring to the reduction of calces of lead and mercury without phlogiston, 'even by the recent experiments made with the burning glass.' Speter[6] at first thought the author was Bayen, later[7] that it was Buffon; Berthelot[8] improbably supposed that it was Lavoisier. A year before[9] an anonymous critic had said that nothing is more convenient than this new (*sic* !) entity phlogiston; chemists call it to their aid whenever they have need of it, and by its help succeed in explaining the most contradictory facts; everything they put forward about phlogiston is totally destitute of foundation.

Berthelot,[10] although admitting that Bayen 'a touché à la découverte de l'oxygène', said: 'les contemporains n'ont pas accueilli ses réclamations et la posterité ne saurait le faire davantage'; this seems to me ungenerous.

Lavoisier's Experiments on Calcination

In 1774 Lavoisier repeated Boyle's experiments (see Vol. II) on the calcination of tin and lead in glass retorts, but he weighed the *sealed* retort before and

[1] *Dictionnaire*, 1778, i, 349 f.   [2] (2), iii, 457.
[3] *A Treatise on the Various Kinds of Permanently Elastic Fluids, or Gases*, 2 ed., London, 1779, 118 f.
[4] (1), ii, 533.
[5] Discours sur le Phlogistique, *Obs. Phys.*, 1774, iii, 185–200; Crell's *Ann.*, 1784, II, 67, 361.
[6] (1).   [7] (2).   [8] (4), 54; McKie, (1), 235.
[9] *Obs. Phys.*, 1773, ii, 281: De la Doctrine de M. de Morveau, sur le Phlogistique; & Observations sur cette Doctrine; the criticisms are mostly in the 'Suite', 285 f.; Partington and McKie, *Ann. Sci.*, 1937, ii, 361 (399).
[10] (4), 60.

after heating and found no change in weight (or only 0·27 grain), thus disproving Boyle's hypothesis of the fixation of ponderable igneous corpuscles. On opening the drawn-off neck of the retort, air rushed in and there was an increase in weight, which Lavoisier thought was almost exactly equal to the weight of air 'destroyed or absorbed by the metal in forming the calx'. This is not strictly true, since after the calcination the retort is filled with nitrogen, which is lighter than air. Lavoisier later said this. Lavoisier says he used several retorts but most of them burst. He gives only two experiments with 8 oz. of tin, which was partly converted into a black powder, which in one experiment weighed over 2 oz. In order to prevent the bursting of the retort he heated it before sealing to drive out some air (as Boyle had done) and weighed again after sealing to find the weight of air driven out. In the first experiment the capacity of the retort was 43 cu. in. and the increase in weight of the tin was 3·12 gr. The calculated weight of 43 cu. in. of air (1 cu. in. 0·48 gr.) was 21 gr., of which $5\frac{2}{3}$ gr. was driven out in the preliminary heating, leaving $15\frac{1}{3}$ gr. The proportion of air absorbed by the tin was $3·12/15\frac{1}{3}$ or nearly $\frac{1}{5}$. In the second experiment the capacity of the retort was 250 cu. in. The increase in weight of 8 oz. of tin was 10·00 gr. (black powder — tin) or 10·06 gr. (increase in wt. of retort), and the calculated proportion of air absorbed $\frac{1}{8}$ to $\frac{1}{9}$ (a poor result). With lead only one experiment was made, the result being too uncertain to be worth giving. The increase in weight was very small (3 gr. on a total weight of 13 oz. and 10 gr. on nearly 21 oz.).[1]

Priestley[2] independently said: 'I had likewise found, that no weight is either gained or lost by the calcination of tin in a close glass vessel.' Alexander von Humboldt in 1796–7 found that when turbith mineral (basic mercuric sulphate) is reduced in a sealed vessel by the action of light there is no change in weight.[3]

Lavoisier's memoir was read on 12 November 1774 and a preliminary account of it was published in December.[4] Lavoisier gives as a reason for this publication his desire to warn experimenters of the great danger of injury owing to the bursting of the retorts, but this had been emphasised by Boyle. A much altered version was presented on 10 May 1777 and printed in 1778.[5] The historian of the Academy quotes from Rey and Beraut (see p. 607), who are not mentioned in the memoir.

In his publication of December 1774 Lavoisier says his paper had been 'paraphé' (initialled) by Fouchy, the Secretary of the Academy, on 14 April 1774, although it was not read until 12 November, and at that time (presumably April) he did not know of Boyle's experiments on the calcination of metals in sealed vessels, nor that Priestley had announced that the calcination in sealed vessels was limited (je ne connais pas que ... M. Priestley ... eût annoncé que la calcination dans les vaisseaux fermés avoit un terme au delà

---

[1] These figures are from the 1778 version.   [2] E & O, 1774, i, 192.
[3] Speter, *Chem. Ztg.*, 1909, xxxiii, 1353.
[4] Sur la Calcination des Métaux dans les vaisseaux fermés, & sur la cause de l'augmentation de poids qu'ils acquièrent pendant cette opération: *Obs. Phys.*, 1774, iv, 448–52 (dated 12 December); in some copies 446–51, since the two vols. for 1774 were reprinted.
[5] AdS, 1774 (1778), h 20, m 351; VIII, ii, 97, 105.

duquel elle ne pouvoit plus avoir lieu). Since sending his note to Rozier for publication in the *Observations* he received a letter from Beccaria, dated 12 November 1774 in Turin, stating that he had announced this last fact more than fifteen years before in the Turin *Memoirs*. Lavoisier asked for the publication of Beccaria's letter and the passage from the Turin *Memoirs* (& la lettre du Pere Beccaria & le Passage rapporté dans le tome II des Mémoires de Turin), and this was done.[1] Beccaria's letter was probably sent after he had read the experiments on calcination in Lavoisier's *Opuscules*, published in January 1774.

Beccaria after referring to what he said in 1760, goes on:

Je fonds de la raclure d'étain dans une bouteille de verre très forte, scellé hermétiquement; il s'y forme une pellicule de chaux très mince; mais elle n'y augmente pas davantage. Si à cette bouteille je soude hermétiquement des flacons, la portion de chaux qui se forme, croît en proportion de leur capacité, la somme totale du poids (en prenant garde d'ôter de la bouteille le léger enduit qu'y forme la flamme de l'esprit de vin dont je me suis sers pour cette opération), reste le même; mais les flacons adjoutés, qui avant la calcination se trouvoient en équilibre sur un certain point, cessent d'y être après l'opération, & se trouvent plus légers. écrite à Turin le 12 Novembre 1774.

Black[2] gives some quantitative data which are not in Beccaria's letter:

'Two small glass matrasses were joined hermetically by the necks. One of them contained a small quantity of an inflammable body which emitted no vapour on burning. The rest of the space . . . was filled with vital air [oxygen]; and the vessels were then sealed up . . . and this apparatus was accurately poised on an axis . . . like a common balance. . . . A burning-glass was now employed to kindle the body . . . when the burning could be maintained no longer by the action of the burning glass, the balance remained in a very oblique position, shewing a great addition of weight on the side of the burning body . . . the whole was allowed to grow as cold as at the first. It required about 13 grains to be laid on the other end to restore the equilibrium.'

The paper to which Beccaria refers is a memoir by Cigna. Giovanni Francesco Cigna (Mondovi, 2 July 1734–Turin, 16 July 1790) was professor of anatomy in Turin, and a nephew of Beccaria. His papers deal with the cause of the extinction of flame and animal life in an enclosed volume of air.[3] He mentions Boyle, Hales, and Saluce frequently, and in 1760 he says:

Cl. Beccaria expertus est (ut ipse mihi narrabat) cum limaturum stamni [*sic*], aut plumbi in vitris hermetice clausis calcinationi subjicerit, portionem tantum limatura ex subjecto igne in calcem redigi potuisse, ut eo majorem, quo vacui in vase vitreo spatii amplitudo major erat.

Cigna's memoir was published in French[4] next to one of Lavoisier's papers, and may have suggested Lavoisier's experiments[5] — if this was not Lomonosov's memoir (see p. 204).

The passage in the 1772 translation[6] is: 'M. Beccaria a prouvé qu'ayant voulu calciner de la limaille d'étain ou de plomb dans les vaisseaux de verre

[1] *Obs. Phys.*, 1774, iv, 452–3.
[2] *Lectures on the Elements of Chemistry*, Edinburgh, 1803, ii, 210.
[3] De caussa extinctionis flammæ in clauso aere, *Miscell. Taurinensia*, 1759, i, 22–51 (*Comment.*); De caussa extinctionis flammæ & animalium in aëre inclusorum, *ib.*, 1760, ii, 168–203 (176); long summary in J. C. Fischer, 1804, v, 128–52.
[4] *Intr. Obs. Phys.*, 1772 (1777), ii, 84–105 ('Cygna'; on Beccaria's expt., 89); also in *Collection Academique . . . de la Partie Etrangère*, Paris, 1789, xiii, 14, 158 (Beccaria's expt., 164).
[5] Meldrum, (1), 3, 36 f., 42 f.   [6] *Ib.*, 89.

bouchés hermétiquement, il n'avoit pu en calciner qu'une partie seulement; & cette partie étoit relative au plus ou moins grand espace vuide du vaisseau', whilst that at the end of Lavoisier's paper of 1774 reads: 'cette portion s'étoit trouvée d'autant plus grande que les vaisseaux avoit plus de capacité', which is less literal than the 1772 translation. Lavoisier could have seen the original, since in his *Opuscules Physiques et Chimiques* (written in 1773) he gives a detailed account of 'le mémoire de M. le comte de Saluces'[1] which is in the same volume of the *Miscellanea Taurinensia* as Cigna's memoir. In mentioning Beccaria's work Lavoisier says: j'ai été très-charmé de voir adopter & confirmer par un Physicien célebre la théorie de l'augmentation de poids des choses métallique que je crois avoir développée le premier', and in his final memoir (1778),[2] that Beccaria's experiment, 'communiqué . . . depuis la communication de ce mémoire, est une nouvelle démonstration du fait que j'ai établi.' We now know[3] that Saluces wrote on 29 March 1774 to Lavoisier especially drawing his attention to Cigna's memoir and giving the page.

Cigna also published on the cold produced by evaporation (based on Cullen's work),[4] on the colour of blood (confirming Lower's discovery that the clot is red where exposed to air),[5] and on respiration,[6] all subjects of interest to Lavoisier.

The Rediscovery of Oxygen

In October 1774 Priestley visited Paris with Lord Shelburne and told Lavoisier at dinner of his discovery of dephlogisticated air (see p. 256). Priestley, who was 'a person of the most scrupulous veracity, and wholly incapable of giving any false colouring to the facts which he related respecting his discoveries',[7] says:[8]

'Now that I am on the subject of the *right to discoveries*, I will, as the Spaniards say, leave no ink of this kind in my inkhorn; hoping that it will be the last time that I shall have any occasion to trouble the public about it. The case was this. Having made the discovery [of oxygen] some time before I was in Paris, in [October] the year 1774, I mentioned it at the table of M. Lavoisier, when most of the philosophical people of the city were present, saying, that it was a kind of air in which a candle burnt much better than in common air, but I had not then given it a name. At this all the company, and Mr. and Mrs. Lavoisier as much as any, expressed great surprise. I told them I had gotten it from *precipitate per se*, and also from *red lead*. Speaking French very imperfectly, and being little acquainted with the terms of chemistry, I said *plombe rouge*, which was not understood till Mr. Macquer said I must mean *minium*. Mr. Scheele's discovery was certainly independent of mine, though, I believe, not made quite so early.'

The name 'plomb rouge', however, had been used for red lead by de Morveau in 1772.[9]

Experiments on heating red precipitate of mercury appear in Lavoisier's note-book in March 1775:[10] and he speaks of 'air du precipité per se, air du mercure precipité per se . . . qui est l'air lui-même, celui que nous respirons';

[1] V, 44 f.   [2] VIII, ii, 105 (121).   [3] X, ii, 431.
[4] *Miscell. Taurenensia*, 1760-1, ii, 143–67: De frigore ex evaporatione & affinibus phoenominis *nonnullis*; *Intr. Obs. Phys.*, 1772 (1777), ii, 232.
[5] *Miscell. Taurenensia*, 1759, i, 68.   [6] *Ib.*, 1770–73, v, 109.
[7] Brougham, 1872, 307.
[8] *The Doctrine of Phlogiston Established*, 1800, 88; 2 ed., 1803, 116.
[9] *Digressions Académiques*, Dijon, 1772, 109.   [10] Berthelot, (4), 254, 264–5.

and near this place he speaks of 'appareil ordinaire de M. Priestley' and experiments with a candle: 'la flamme est beaucoup plus grande, beaucoup plus claire . . . que dans l'air commun.' An entry of 13 February 1776 records heating 'précipité per se de chez M. Baumé' and obtaining first red vapours (hence the precipitate was not 'per se'), then colourless 'air déphlogistiqué de M. Prisley [sic]'.[1]

Before Priestley's visit Lavoisier knew from Bayen's paper[2] that red precipitate on heating alone evolves a gas and forms mercury, and that phlogiston does not play any part. Priestley's information of his discovery that this gas supported combustion much better than common air 'surprised' Lavoisier, and this discovery belongs to Priestley 'unreservedly', as Berthelot said in a letter to Thorpe,[3] adding: 'it is certain that the discovery of oxygen is due to Priestley.' In a report presented to the Academy on 19 November 1774, Sage, Brisson, and Lavoisier say that 3 gros 64 gr. of red precipitate per se gave on heating 3 gros 42½ gr. of mercury, but no mention is made of any gas evolved.[4] This was after Priestley's visit. On 18 March 1775 Lavoisier wrote:[5] 'tout air non absorbable [by water] est un composé dun acide en vapeurs Combine avec le phlogistique', and:

'lair de latmosphere Celui que nous respirons est Composé de la même maniere. . . . il est bien prouve par les experiences que j'ay publiees precedemment que les metaux qui Se calcinent emprumptent de lair la Substance qui augmente leur poids mais est ce a lair meme ou bien a un acide a un principe quelconque Contenu dans lair que cet effet est du Cest Surquoi on na pas encore pu prononcer.

When calces are reduced by carbon fixed air is evolved. The reduction of mercury precipitate without addition of carbon or phlogiston would seem likely to throw light on this question. He found that the air disengaged was not fixed air, did not precipitate lime water, was more proper to support the combustion of candles, and:

il etoit diminué par lair nitreux en un mot il etoit [precisement dans letat de] ne differoit de l'air de latmosphere, que par la propriete dentretenir un peu mieux la combustion . . . il Suit de ses deux experiences que le fluide elastique fixé dans le mercure precipite per se est de lair Commun.

It may be concluded that if other metallic calces could be reduced without addition of carbon they would also give 'lair commun'. In a sealed note deposited on 24 March 1775[6] Lavoisier gives the substance of the draft, concluding:

S'il etoit possible de les reduire Sans addition; elles ne donnent de l'air fixe que parceque l'air commun qu'elles contiennent est converti en air fixe par la combustion du charbon comme il arrive au mercure.

A communication read to the Academy on 26 April 1775 and published in May 1775[7] describes the preparation of an 'air' by heating red precipitate in a retort, and also by Priestley's method of heating it by a burning glass. In a

---

[1] Ib., 270-1.　　　　　　　　[2] Obs. Phys., 1774, iii, 280 (April).
[3] Nature, 1890, xliii, 1, referring to his book (4), 61-2.
[4] Lavoisier, VIII, iv, 190.　　　[5] IX, ii, 472-4.　　　[6] IX, ii, 475-6.
[7] Obs. Phys., 1775, v, 429-33: Sur la nature du principe qui se combine avec les métaux pendant leur calcination, & qui en augmente le poids; Lu à la rentrée de l'Academie le 26 April; at the bottom of the last page is 'Mai 1775', apparently added by the editor, Rozier; VD, 1776, 407-19.

footnote Lavoisier refers to de Morveau's article in the *Encyclopédie*, 'qui portent par-tout l'empriente du génie.' A footnote also says the experiments with *a burning glass* were 'first tried' in November 1774, and afterwards made with all the necessary precautions and care 'dans le laboratoire de Montigny, conjointement avec M. de Trudaine, les 28 février, 1er & 2 mars de cette année [1775]; enfin, elles ont été répétées de nouveau le 31 mars dernier en presenca [*sic*] de M. le Duc de la Rochefoucault, de M. de Trudaine, de M. de Montigny, de M. Macquer, & de M. Cadet'. The Trudaine who assisted in the first experiments was probably Jean Charles Philibert de Montigny (1733–77); Priestley met him and his brother Étienne Mignot de Montigny (1714–82).[1] Lavoisier starts by saying that he proves that:

le principe qui s'unit aux métaux pendant leur calcination, qui en augmente le poids & qui les constitue dans l'état de chaux, n'est ni une des parties constituantes de l'air, ni un acide particulier répandu dans l'athmosphere, qui c'est l'air lui-même entier, sans altération, sans décomposition, au point même que, si après avoir été engagé dans cette combinaison, on le rendre libre, il en sort plus pur, plus respirable, s'il est permis de se servir de cette expression, que l'air de l'athmosphere est plus propre à entretenir l'inflammation & la combustion des corps.

He shows that red precipitate is a true calx (chaux) of mercury by heating it with charcoal and finding that fixed air is evolved. He then describes an experiment of heating 1 oz. of red precipitate in a retort, when 7 gros 18 gr. of mercury was formed and 78 cu. in. of 'air' collected over water, 'd'ou il suit qu'en supposant que toute la perte de poids dût être attribué à l'air', one cu. in. of this air weighs a little less than $\frac{2}{3}$ gr., 'ce qui ne s'écarte pas beaucoup de la pesanteur de l'air commun.' The air is reduced by a third with nitrous air, and some other properties resemble those of common air, including its suitability for respiration. In saying it supports combustion Lavoisier does not emphasise that it does so more brilliantly than common air. Thus:

cette air étoit non-seulement de l'air commun, mais encore qu'il étoit plus respirable, plus combustible, & par consequent qu'il étoit plus pur même que l'air dans lequel nous vivons. . . . ce principe qui se combine avec les métaux . . . n'est autre chose que la portion la plus pur de l'air même qui nous environne . . . & qui passe dans cette operation [calcination of metals] de l'état d'expansibilité à celui de solidité.

Lavoisier's mistake that the gas is contracted by $\frac{1}{3}$ with nitric oxide, which he regarded as a proof that it is common air (Priestley had obtained a correct result in this experiment) disappeared when the paper was republished[2] in 1778. In 1778, too, the gas which combines with metals is no longer 'l'air lui-même, entier, sans altération', but 'la portion de l'air la plus salubre et la plus pur'. The fixed air evolved in the detonation of nitre with charcoal in 1775 resulted from a change 'de l'air commun en air fixe', but in 1778 'l'air fixe est le résultat de la combinaison de la partie éminemment respirable de l'air avec le charbon'. The 'entire air' which combines with mercury to form the calx and is evolved again in 'its purest form' has become in 1778 'part of the air', or 'the eminently respirable part of the air'. Macquer[3] reproduced Lavoisier's words when he said in 1778:

[1] E & O, 1775, ii, 2–3.   [2] AdS, 1775 (1778), m 520; VIII, ii, 122.
[3] *Dictionnaire*, 1778, ii, 259.

ce gas retiré de la réduction du mercure sans addition, non seulement est véritablement de l'air & de l'air très pur, mais encore il est beaucoup plus pur que celui de l'athmosphere que nous respirons.

After mentioning experiments on the detonation of nitre with charcoal, Lavoisier says in 1775: 'l'air combiné dans le nitre . . . est de l'air commun, de l'air athmospherique privé de son expansibilité.' Lavoisier nowhere mentions Priestley's visit and gives him no credit at all, merely mentioning at the end what he calls 'Dr. Priestley's opinion' that fixed air is a compound of common air and phlogiston. Henry in his translation says: 'Dr. Priestley has, certainly, never delivered such an opinion as M. Lavoisier here ascribes to him.'[1] Priestley, referring to Lavoisier's paper[2] said[3] in 1775:

it appears by it, that after I left Paris, where I procured the *mercurius calcinatus* above mentioned, and had spoken of the experiments that I had made, and that I intended to make with it, he began his experiments upon the same substance, and presently found what I have called *dephlogisticated air*, but without investigating the nature of it, and indeed without being fully appraised of the degree of its purity. For he had only tried it with one-third of nitrous air, and observed that a candle burned in it with more vigour than in common air; and though he says it *seems to be* more fit for respiration than common air, he does not say that he had made any trial how long an animal could live in it.

He therefore inferred, as I have said that I myself had once done, that this substance had, during the process of calcination, imbibed atmospherical air, not in part, but in whole. But then he extends his conclusion, and, as it appears to me, without any evidence, to all the metallic calces; saying that, very probably, they would all of them yield only common air, if, like *mercurius calcinatus*, they could be reduced without addition.

This was Lavoisier's first experience of Priestley's unencumbered style, and thereafter he always treated him with careful respect.

It seems that in 1775 Lavoisier expected to obtain fixed air (carbon dioxide) on heating red precipitate, since in his note-book for March (?) 1775 he says:

Air du mercure précipité *per se*. On était bien persuadé que cet air ainsy dégagé d'une espèce de chaux métallique était de l'air fixe et on lui a fait subir l'épreuve de l'eau de chaux. Il l'a rendue un peu opale, sans en occasionner la précipitation. On a essayé d'y introduire une lumière; mais, loin qu'elle s'y éteignêt, sa flamme au contraire a été considérablement augmentée; comme il arrive à l'air nitreux, lorsqu'il a eu pendant longtemps le contact d'une grande surface de fer [nitrous oxide]. Ces différentes expériences ont démontré que l'air qui se dégage du mercure précipité est dans l'état d'air commun, et qu'il tient seulement un peu de la nature de l'air inflammable.[4]

Lavoisier in the 1778 memoir[5] says 'le mercure precipité *per se* . . . n'est autre chose qu'une chaux de mercure, comme l'ont déjà avancé quelques auteurs', perhaps Bayen.

Lavoisier in 1778, published[6] a completely revised version of his paper of 1774 on the calcination of tin and lead (see p. 400), which had been

[1] VD, 1776, Appendix, 407–19 (419), 420–8 (on Priestley's opinions).
[2] *Obs. Phys.*, 1775, v, 429.　　　　[3] E & O, 1775, ii, 320.
[4] Berthelot, (4), 264–5: 'interpretation curieuse.'　　[5] VIII, ii, 124.
[6] Mémoire sur la Calcination de l'Étain dans les Vaisseaux fermés et sur la Cause de l'Augmentation du Poids qu'acquiert ce Métal pendant cette Opération; Mémoire lu à la rentrée publique de la Saint-Martin 1774. Remis le 10 mai 1777; AdS, 1774 (1778), m 351; VIII, ii, 105, giving the date as 1774.

re-submitted to the Academy on 10 May 1777. Kopp[1] emphasised that the two forms of Lavoisier's publication are quite different, and also[2] that in April 1775 he was still talking about *the whole* of the air as concerned in calcination, combustion, and *respiration*. In 1778 Lavoisier says:[3]

> It is seen that a part of the air is suceptible of combining with metallic substances to form calces, whilst another part of the same air constantly refuses this combination; this circumstance made me suspect that the air of the atmosphere is not a simple being, that it is composed of very different substances. . . . I think I am able to announce that the whole of the air of the atmosphere is not in a respirable state, that it is the salubrious part which combines with metals during their calcination, and that what remains after the calcination is a species of mofette, incapable of sustaining the respiration of animals or the inflammation of bodies. Not only does atmospheric air seem to me evidently composed of two elastic fluids of very different nature, but I suspect in addition that the injurious and mephitic part is itself very complex (fort composée).[4]

Lavoisier says he had concluded from experiments not yet published that 'the part of the air which combines with metals is a little heavier than atmospheric air and that which remains, on the contrary, is a little lighter', the specific gravity of atmospheric air being a mean of those of the 'two airs'; but more direct tests are necessary, 'especially as the differences are inconsiderable.' Scheele had proved by direct weighing that the part of the air which does not support combustion is 'somewhat lighter' than common air, and that 20 oz. measures of fire air (oxygen) weighed 2 grains more than the same bulk of common air, and he had published this in 1777.[5]

Meldrum[6] pointed out that Lavoisier in his analysis of the *Opuscules* published in 1778,[7] said:

> M. Lavoisier s'est assuré, par des expériences directes, que l'air qui a ainsi servi à la combustion du phosphore n'est pas plus dense que l'air de l'atmosphère; sa pesanteur spécifique même se trouve plutot diminué qu'augmentée.

Thus, says Meldrum, Lavoisier 'conveyed the suggestion . . . that the *Opuscules* contains direct experiments on the specific gravity of gases. But what the *Opuscules* says is that the necessary apparatus was not ready in time'.[8] The clue to these mysterious 'considerations' and 'experiments' is found in a memoir of 1784 where Lavoisier remarked: 'the observation has been made that pure air [oxygen] is a little heavier than atmospheric air, in about the ratio of 187 to 185.'[9] Meldrum says: 'These data are Priestley's (see p. 263) though Lavoisier did not say so. Moreover, he misunderstood the data. . . . He was indebted to Priestley and would not admit his indebtedness.' Lavoisier in 1784 does give a figure for the density of carbon dioxide which he says he determined himself,[9] in 1784 he and Meusnier determined the densities of oxygen and hydrogen,[10] and in 1785 Lavoisier reports the densities of air, oxygen, and nitrogen.[11] Meldrum's stricture refers to 1778.

[1] (3), 1873, 163; 'rediscovered' by Jörgensen (1909), Speter ((1), 1910), Meldrum ((1), 1930, 46 f.; incorrectly said by Hartog, 1941, 32, to be 'first'), and McKie, 1935, 206 f.
[2] *Ib.*, 167.　　　　　[3] VIII, ii, 120.
[4] VIII, ii, 120; Lavoisier had announced two years before, in 1776, that air contains two gases, one supporting combustion and respiration and the other not, see p. 413.
[5] *On Air and Fire*, §§ 16, 49.　　　[6] (1), 41.　　　[7] VIII, ii, 95.
[8] VIII, i, 607.　　　　　[9] VIII, ii, 323.　　　[10] *Ib.*, 360.　　　[11] *Ib.*, 676.

Lavoisier in the autumn of 1774 had not only a visit by Priestley but also a letter from Scheele.[1] In this, written in French and dated 30 September 1774, Scheele told Lavoisier that the gift of his book (*Opuscules*) gave him great pleasure, and that Lavoisier had, by his new experiments, 'given to philosophers the finest opportunity of better examining, in the future, fire and the calcination of metals.' Scheele refers to Lavoisier's use of a burning glass, as described in this book, and informs him that he could not obtain ordinary air from fixed air in contact with moist iron filings and sulphur, as Priestley had said. He asks Lavoisier to try the experiment of heating silver carbonate (the preparation of which he describes) with a burning glass over lime water:

It is in this way that I hope you will see how much air is produced during this operation and if a lighted candle will burn, and animals live, in it. I shall be infinitely obliged if you will let me know the result of this experiment.

Scheele then knew that ordinary heating would give oxygen. Grimaux, who had examined the correspondence of Lavoisier, says this is the only letter from Scheele to Lavoisier, 'qui malheureusement ne donna pas suite à cette correspondance.'[1] The letter was written a month before Priestley's visit and could have been in Lavoisier's hands when Priestley visited him in Paris. Lavoisier had sent his book to Wargentin, Secretary of the Swedish Academy, with a request to pass it on to Scheele.[2] A draft of Scheele's letter (perhaps written by Bergman) exists among Scheele's papers, but no reply from Lavoisier is known.[3]

In the *Histoire* of the Academy,[4] in the volume containing the revised memoir on calcination, there is a long analysis of the *Opuscules* (1774) which exists in Lavoisier's handwriting.[5] This says:

Aussi M. Lavoisier a fait voir dans des Mémoires lûs depuis à l'Académie, qu'on pouvoit avoir à volonté le fluide élastique dégagé des chaux métalliques, ou dans l'état d'air fixe, ou dans celui d'air respirable, suivant qu'on employait ou qu'on n'employait pas de poudre de charbon pour la réduction. . . . Ces expériences sur la calcination des métaux, ont conduit M. Lavoisier à d'autres expériences de même genre sur la combustion.

This is based on a longer review of the *Opuscules* presented to the Academy in December 1773,[6] and also written by Lavoisier.

In the revised 'memoir (1778) on the nature of the principle which combines with metals during their calcination and which increases the weight'[7] read in Easter 1775 Lavoisier said:

'the first experiments relative to this memoir were made more than a year ago [i.e. in Easter 1774 or earlier]; those on mercury precipitate *per se* were first tried (ont d'abord été tentées) with the burning glass in the month of November 1774, and made (faites) with all precautions and the necessary care (les soins nécessaires) in the laboratory of Montigny, conjointly with M. Trudaine, on the 28 February, 1st and 2nd March of this year (de cette année); finally, they were repeated anew on the 31st March' [1775].

---

[1] Grimaux, *Rev. gén. Sci.*, 1890, i, 1–2; Dobbin, *Collected Papers of Scheele*, 1931, 350 (tr.).
[2] IX, ii, 436 (12 April 1774).
[3] U. Boklund, *Lychnos*, 1957, 39–62; *id.*, *Carl Wilhelm Scheele Bruna Boken*, Stockholm, 1961, 84; facsim., 42.
[4] AdS, 1774 (1778), h 77–8.   [5] Grimaux, in VIII, v, 320.   [6] VIII, i, 657–66.
[7] AdS, 1775 (1778), m 520 (lu à la rentrée publique de Pâques 1775, relu le 8 août 1778); VIII, ii, 122.

He says mercury precipitate *per se* is a true calx, since when heated with charcoal or 'according to the received expression, with addition of phlogiston', it is reduced to the metal, and 1 oz. of it with 48 grains of charcoal gave 64 cu. in. of fixed air collected over water, the same air as was obtained by heating calx of lead (minium) with charcoal. 1 oz. of precipitate heated alone in a retort gave 7 gros 18 gr. of mercury and 78 cu. in. of air, 1 cu. in. of which should thus weigh a little less than ⅔ grain, 'nearly the same as common air.' This supported combustion and respiration better than common air, a taper burning with a brilliance like phosphorus, and combustible bodies with astonishing rapidity.

Lavoisier says he recognised 'with much surprise' six properties of the air obtained on heating mercuric oxide:[1] (1) it does not dissolve in water, (2) it does not precipitate lime water, at most rendering it only slightly opalescent, (3) it does not combine with alkalis, (4) it does not decrease the causticity of alkalis, (5) it can serve anew for the calcination of metals, (6) it has none of the properties of fixed air, combustibles burn in it with great brilliance and 'it seems more proper to support respiration'.

This 'most pure part of the air' is probably contained in all metallic calces, and is fixed in nitre, in which it is one of the constituents of nitric acid, fixed air being a compound of this 'eminently respirable part of the air' with charcoal. Priestley is not once mentioned, the reference to his 'opinion' at the end of the 1775 publication being omitted. The intention is clearly to convey the impression that in February and March 1775 Lavoisier had discovered the gas formed by heating red precipitate, and had discovered 'with much surprise' that it supported combustion much better than common air, whilst in fact Priestley had told him this in October 1774 (see p. 402).

Lavoisier in 1782 said:[2]

'It will be remembered that in the meeting of Easter 1775 I announced to the public the discovery I had made several months previously with M. Trudaine in the laboratory of Montigny of a new kind of air, previously entirely unknown (alors entièrement inconnue), which we obtained by the reduction of mercury *precipité per se*: this air, which M. Priestley discovered about the same time as I (que moi), and I believe even before me (et je crois même avant moi), which he mainly extracted by the combination of minium and many other substances with nitric acid, was called by him *dephlogisticated air*; but later experiments having proved that it alone is able to maintain the life of animals which breathe, the historian of the Academy [Condorcet], and after him the majority of chemists, have given it the name of *vital air*.'

The words 'mainly extracted' are misleading, since Lavoisier knew perfectly well that it was not 'previously entirely unknown', and that Priestley had also obtained it by heating red precipitate. In 1776 Lavoisier had said[3] that on heating red precipitate he had obtained:

un air beaucoup plus pur que l'air commun, dans lequel les lumières brulaient avec une flamme beaucoup plus grande, beaucoup plus large, et beaucoup plus vive, et qu'à tous ses caractères je n'ai pu méconnaître pour être le même que j'avais retiré de la chaux de mercure, connue sous le nom de *mercure précipité per se*, et que M. Prisley [*sic*] a retiré d'un grand nombre de substances, en les traitant par l'esprit de nitre.

---

[1] VIII, ii, 126.   [2] AdS, 1782 (1785), m 457; VIII, ii, 423 (424).
[3] AdS, 1776 (1779), m 671; VIII, ii, 129 (132); for the publication in 1776 see p. 411.

Speter[1] pointed out that Lavoisier asserts that *he* obtained oxygen by heating red precipitate whilst Priestley had obtained it by *other* methods, whereas Priestley's book, published in 1775, had made it quite clear that he, in 1774, had first obtained it from red precipitate. He had told this to Lavoisier in October 1774 in the presence of other French chemists (see p. 402). Speter says: 'Lavoisier had always been silent on this fact, and here he presented the true relations falsely, and with intent.'

But Lavoisier's statement is literally correct, since he *had* obtained oxygen by heating red precipitate, although he knew that Priestley had done this before him. Lavoisier took great pains in choosing his wording. It seems certain[2] that until Priestley gave him an account of his experiment of August 1774, Lavoisier:

'never had the least idea of the air absorbed in calcination possessing any qualities like those of oxygen gas, or had supposed that the air evolved in the reduction of calcined metals was of that nature. Until he heard of Dr. Priestley's great experiment he had never thought of obtaining oxygen gas from those bodies, nor ever knew of the exisence of oxygen gas.'

In his *Traité de Chimie* (1789), intended for the use of students, which Lavoisier knew would be widely read and quoted, he omitted the words 'et je crois même avant moi' and said simply:[3] 'Cet air que nous avons découverte presque en même temps, M. Priestley, M. Scheele & moi, a été nommé par le premier, air déphlogistiqué; par le second, air empiréal.' In the French translation of Scheele's book his name 'Feuerluft' is correctly rendered 'Air du Feu',[4] the name 'empyreal air' ($\pi \hat{v} \rho$ = fire) being used only in the earlier English translation,[5] from which Lavoisier must have taken it. Lavoisier afterwards[6] excused himself by saying that he was young at the time (he was 31), had just entered upon a scientific career, and was anxious for fame (avide de gloire). In 1788 (in Lavoisier's lifetime), Le Fèvre de Gineau, 'Lecteur et Professeur Royale de Physique expérimentale', spoke of:[7] 'la découverte du gaz oxygène (air vital), faite par M. Priestley en 1774.' Fourcroy in 1796[8] said: 'on doit lui faire partager l'honneur de cette belle découverte avec Priestley', but in 1801[9] he says oxygen was 'découvert en août 1774 sous la forme de gaz, par Priestley'.[10]

It has been said[11] that:

'it was not until 1800, after Lavoisier's death, and when Priestley's memory was failing him, that he made Lavoisier's claims a matter of public complaint . . . I find it difficult to believe that a man of Lavoisier's noble character . . . would have made claims to which he had no right.'

This is incorrect. Priestley had referred publicly and privately to the circumstances in 1775, when the matter was fresh in his memory. He says:[12]

[1] (1), 135.   [2] Brougham, 1855, 303.   [3] VII, 1789, 38.
[4] *Traité Chimique de l'Air et du Feu*, 1781, 84.
[5] *Chemical Observations and Experiments on Air and Fire*, tr. J. R. Forster, 1780, 35.
[6] IV, ii, 84; VIII, ii, 102; written about 1792.   [7] *Obs. Phys.*, 1788, xxxiii, 457 (10 May).
[8] (2), iii, 447.   [9] (1), i, 140.   [10] See also Brande, 1848, I, lxxxix–xci; Muir, 1883, 86.
[11] Hartog, *Proc. Roy. Inst.*, 1931, xxvi, 395–430; reprint, 25. See also Rodwell, *Nature*, 1882, xxvii, 8; B. H. Paul, in Watts, *Dictionary of Chemistry*, 1872, ii, 778; Foster, 1901, 244–5; Mellor, *Treatise on Chemistry*, 1922, i, 345.
[12] E & O, 1775, ii, 36; repeated in E & O, 1790, ii, 108–9.

'I frequently mentioned my surprize at the kind of air which I had got from this preparation [red precipitate] to Mr. Lavoisier, Mr. le Roy, and several other philosophers, who honoured me with their notice in that city [Paris, in October 1774]; and who, I dare say, cannot fail to recollect the circumstance.'

In the same volume[1] he speaks of 'Mr. Lavoisier, my excellent fellow-labourer in these inquiries, and to whom, in a variety of respects, the philosophical part of the world has very great obligations'. Priestley was experimenting again in England on 19 November 1774.[2] In a letter dated Calne, 31 Dec. 1775 to Thomas Henry, Priestley said:[3]

He [Lavoisier] is an Intendant of the Finances, and has much public business, but finds leisure for various philosophical pursuits, for which he is exceedingly well qualified. He ought to have acknowledged that my giving him an account of the air I had got from *Mercurius Calcinatus*, and buying a quantity of M. Cadet while I was in Paris, led him to try what air it yielded, which he did presently after I left. I have, however, barely hinted at this in my second volume.

French[4] suggested that Priestley was not sure he had used genuine precipitate *per se* in August 1774, that he was not sure of this when he told Lavoisier of the experiment (although Priestley says in his account of the experiment that he used genuine red precipitate given him by Warltire, see p. 258), still thinking that the gas was nitrous oxide. Lavoisier, says French, did not obtain oxygen in his experiment in November 1774 (he says 'ont d'abord été *tentées* au verre ardente') and this experiment was first successfully made ('faites') in February and March 1775, when he tested the gas with nitric oxide but still thought that it was pure atmospheric air. But Priestley had also told Lavoisier that he had obtained the same gas by heating red lead, which is made by heating lead monoxide in air and never by the action of nitric acid;[5] he had obtained 'air' from red lead by heating it with a candle before,[6] and later said,[7] he 'had found it to be very pure'.

In 1776[8] Lavoisier mentions Priestley nine times by name, saying there is no one of his experiments to which Priestley could not, 'strictly speaking' claim to have had 'the first idea', but since the same experiments had led him to diametrically opposite ideas, if he were reproached with 'having borrowed proofs from the works of this celebrated physicist (ce celèbre physicien)' the propriety of his conclusions could at least not be contested. This only serves to emphasise Lavoisier's claim that *he* obtained oxygen by heating red precipitate, and his studied ambiguity is intended to reinforce this. It has often been said that when he obtained it in 1774 Priestley was not clear that oxygen was a new gas, but Lavoisier's words refer to the method of preparation.

The Composition of Nitric Acid

One of the most important of Lavoisier's earlier memoirs is that on the composition of nitric acid. It has often been said[9] that this was first published

[1] E & O, 1775, ii, 121.   [2] E & O, 1775, ii, 39.
[3] W. Henry, *An Estimate of the Philosophical Character of Dr. Priestley*, York, 1832, 15.
[4] *J. Chem. Educ.*, 1950, xxvii, 83–9.   [5] Priestley, E & O, 1775, ii, 37.
[6] E & O, 1774, i, 193.   [7] E & O, 1775, ii, 37.   [8] VIII, ii, 130.
[9] Kopp, (3), 168; Grimaux, 1888, 341; Berthelot, (4), 73; McKie, (1), 214; Hartog, 33.

in 1779,[1] and since it contains two important statements: (i) air is a mixture of oxygen and nitrogen, (ii) all acids contain oxygen, it is important to show that in all essentials it was published in 1776. In the preface to the third volume of his *Experiments and Observations on Air*,[2] the dedication of which is dated 3 February 1777, and in a part of the preface which was added after the first part was printed, Priestley refers to a memoir by Lavoisier printed in a 'Recueil des Memoires sur la formation et fabrication de Salpêtre' of 1776.[3] Jörgensen[4] pointed out that, except 'auf einige jetzt recht unwesentliche Zahlenangaben', the 1776 memoir is identical with that printed again in 1779.[5]

An anonymous announcement in 1775 of the prize offered by the Academy for an essay on the formation of saltpetre[6] gives a long account of different theories of nitrification, saying:[7] 'il est possible que l'air entre lui-même, comme partie constituante, dans la composition de cet acide [nitric acid], ou qu'il fournisse quelque substance *gazeuse* [italics in original], ou autre, qui, sans être de l'acide nitreux, se trouveroit cependant un des ingrédiens nécessaires à sa mixtion.' This is printed in the works of Lavoisier[8] as by him. The prize was ultimately awarded to the brothers Thouvenel, who had the same idea, which, it is true, had been expressed over a century earlier by Thomas Henshaw (1617–1699).[9]

Lavoisier dissolved 2 oz. 1 gros of mercury in 2 oz. of slightly fuming nitric acid of sp. gr. 1·31607 (about 50 per cent) and collected the gas (nitric oxide) over water. The liquid was evaporated to dryness and a white salt (mercuric nitrate) remained. He collected 190 (1779) or 'soixante-douze' (1776) cu. in. of nitrous air (nitric oxide). On heating, the salt gave 10 to 12 cu. in. of common air (d'air commun), although a candle burnt in it rather better, and the salt was converted into red precipitate. On heating this, he obtained 224 (1779) or 234 (1776) cu. in. of 'an air much purer than common air' or 'more air than common air (plus air que l'air commun)', and the mercury was recovered unchanged ('sensiblement' 1776, omitted 1779) in weight. Thus he obtained 190 cu. in. of nitrous air, 12 cu. in. of common air, and 224 cu. in. of air better than common air (1779). The 12 cu. in. of common air, he supposed, resulted from the mixture of 36 (1779) or 24 (1776) cu. in. of nitrous air and 14 (1779) or 24 (1776) cu. in. of 'air better than common air', 'd'après les expériences de M. Priestley', and thus for the 2 oz. of nitric acid, or calculated for 1 lb., he gives, in cu. in.:

	1776		1779	
	2 oz.	1 lb.	2 oz.	1 lb.
nitrous air	196	1568	226	1808
purest air	246	1968	238	1904
	442	3536	464	3712

[1] AdS, 1776 (1779), m 671; VIII, ii, 129.   [2] E & O, 1777, iii, pref. xxvii f.
[3] *Recueil de Memoires et d'Observations Sur la Formation & sur la fabrication du Salpêtre. Par les Commissaires nommes par l'Academie pour le jugement du Prix du Salpêtre*. A Paris, Chez Lacombe, Libraire, rue Christine, M.DCC.LXXVI (622 pp.), 601–17 (BM 62.a.17).
[4] 1909, 163; complete list of variants in Partington, *Ann. Sci.*, 1953, ix, 96–8.
[5] AdS, 1776 (1779), m 671; VIII, ii, 129: lu 20 Avril 1776. Remis Decembre 1777.
[6] *Obs. Phys.*, 1775 (1785), vi, 339–46: October 1775.   [7] *Ib.*, 345.   [8] VIII, v, 471.
[9] In T. Sprat, *The History of the Royal Society*, 1667, 260–76.

Priestley's experiments seem to be those[1] in which he mixed over water equal vols. of nitrous air and dephlogisticated air and the latter was 'diminished to almost one half of its original quantity'. This gives the 24 and 24 vols. of 1776, leaving 12 vols. (Priestley does not say the residue was common air), but it is not clear why Lavoisier added only 6 of nitrous air and 22 of pure air to the uncorrected volumes. The figures 36 and 12, which in 1779 were added directly to the uncorrected volumes, seem to be due to a manipulation of Priestley's alternative figure that five half-volumes ($5 \times 7 = 35$) of nitrous air could be added without appreciably altering the original volume (14) of pure air; but then the residue would be expected to be 14, not 12. Lavoisier may have increased 35 to 36 because Priestley says air from red lead took six half volumes, and he may have used 12 instead of 14 because of Priestley's use of the word 'appreciably'.

By mixing $7\frac{1}{3}$ vols. of nitrous air with 4 vols. of purest air (oxygen) over water Lavoisier obtained a residue of $\frac{1}{3}$ vol. and dilute nitric acid was formed. By mixing the gases over mercury covered with a thin layer of water, they formed 'very fuming spirit of nitre, as strong as it is possible to obtain', or with more water a weaker acid like that used originally. It is surprising, Lavoisier says, that here $7\frac{1}{3}$ of nitrous air and 4 of purest air were used, while in the decomposition experiment a little more purest air than nitrous air was obtained. He gives no explanation in 1776, but in 1779 he says (correctly) that the ordinary nitric acid made from saltpetre and clay contains 'a considerable superabundance of purest air', whilst that made by synthesis 'contains an excess of nitrous air'. He says quite correctly that the property of forming red fumes is not a proof of the concentration of the acid, and it is possible to have a very strong acid not evolving them: 'ces deux circonstances tienne uniquement à la proportion des deux airs dont est composé l'acide.' He thus recognised the existence of nitrous and nitric acids, which Scheele also did (see p. 226).

Lavoisier did not then know the composition of nitrous air but the equation $2NO = N_2 + O_2$ gives for his results:

1776	1779
196 nitrous air $= 98N_2 + 98O_2$	226 nitrous air $= 113N_2 + 113O_2$
oxygen $= \underline{\quad 246 \quad}$	oxygen $= \underline{\quad 238 \quad}$
344	351
$\therefore$ N/O by vol. $= 1/3 \cdot 35$	$\therefore$ N/O by vol. $= 1/3 \cdot 07$

instead of the correct ratio $1/2 \cdot 50$. Cavendish found $1/2 \cdot 33$. The correct ratio was first given by Berzelius.[2] Lavoisier's synthesis experiment gives $7\frac{1}{3}$NO $+ 4O_2$ or N/O $= 1/2 \cdot 09$, and Dalton and others used the formula NO_2 for the anhydride of nitric acid.

In 1783[3] Lavoisier said that: 'on sait que l'air nitreux et l'air vital, au moment où ils sont en contact l'un avec l'autre, perdent subitement leur élasticité, et se résolvent en une liqueur qui est l'acide nitreux', which is incorrect — they do this only in presence of water. After many experiments he found that 69 parts of nitrous air, obtained by the action of nitric acid on mercury, united with 40 of vital air, 'mais je suis au moins en état d'assurer

[1] E & O, 1775, ii, 45–9. [2] Ann. Phys., 1814, xlvi, 131–75.
[3] AdS, 1782 (1785), m 486 (Mémoire sur la combinaison de l'Air nitreux avec les Airs respirables; presenté 20 Dec., 1783); VIII, ii, 503.

que les proportions exacte sont entre 69 et 66 parties d'air nitreux contre 40 parties d'air vital, ces deux airs étant supposés parfaitement purs.' If μ is the ratio of nitrous air to the vital air absorbed in the formation of nitric acid (acide nitreux), a the quantity of air to be tested, b that of the nitrous air mixed with it, c the residue of the two airs, then:

the quantity of vital air absorbed in the mixture $= (a+b-c)/(1+\mu)$,
the quantity of nitrous air absorbed in the mixture $= \mu(a+b-c)/(1+\mu)$.

In one experiment $a = 100$, $b = 300$, $c = 131$. Since $\mu = 69/40$, the first formula gives 0·9872, hence the vital air used contained 98·72 per cent of 'real vital air' and 1·28 of mephitic air (nitrogen).

In 1776 Lavoisier found that 16 vols. of common air were required instead of 4 vols. of purest air to combine with $7\frac{1}{3}$ vols. of nitrous air, and concluded that 'the air which we breathe contains only a quarter of true air, and this true air is mixed (mêlé) in our atmosphere with three or four parts of a deleterious air, a kind of mofette, which kills most animals if the quantity of it is a little larger'.

The proportion of oxygen in atmospheric air is actually $\frac{1}{5}$ by vol. and this was found by Priestley in 1772 (see p. 253). Lavoisier gave different figures at different times, the earliest result being nearly correct:

> 1774,[1] combustion of phosphorus, $\frac{1}{5}$ to $\frac{1}{6}$.
> 1775,[2] mixing air and nitric oxide over water, $\frac{1}{4}$.
> 1777,[3] calcination of mercury, $\frac{1}{6}$.
> 1780,[4] oxidation of pyrites, $\frac{1}{5}$.
> 1783,[5] various methods, $\frac{1}{4}$.
> 1785–9,[6] various processes, $\frac{1}{4}$.

In 1774[7] air 'ought to be placed in the class of mixtures at least and perhaps even in that of compounds'. In 1789[8] air is said to be a compound (un composé) of vital air and azote (nitrogen), but in the same year[9] it is said to be formed from oxygen gas mixed (mêlé) with 'two-thirds of its weight of azotic gas', which Kerr[10] erroneously translated as 'about twice its weight of azotic gas'. In an undated memoir on an alkaline sulphide eudiometer[11] the composition of air at different times was found to be variable, the vital air varying from 24·0 to 30·0 per cent by vol.

For the densities of the two gases, Priestley's 'tentatifs' (see p. 406) were far from satisfactory and Lavoisier in 1776 had 'obtained only quite uncertain approximations', but he assumes (je supposerai) that 1 cu. in. of nitrous air weighs 0·4 grains and 1 cu. in. of purest air 0·55 grains. He thence calculated for 1 lb. of ordinary nitric acid:

---

[1] V, 1801, 339; VIII, i, 641.   [2] VIII, ii, 137.   [3] *Ib.*, 176.
[4] *Ib.*, 211.   [5] *Ib.*, 503.   [6] *Ib.*, 677, 688.
[7] *Obs. Phys.*, 1774, iv, 448.   [8] AdS, 1789 (1793), m 566.
[9] VII, 203.   [10] VII F, 1796, 255.   [11] IV, ii, 154; VIII, ii, 715.

	1776			1779		
	oz.	gros	grains	oz.	gros	grains
nitrous air	1	—	$51\frac{1}{2}$	1	2	$3\frac{1}{5}$
purest air	1	7	$2\frac{1}{2}$	1	6	$32\frac{1}{5}$
phlegm or common water	13	—	18	13	7	$36\frac{31}{5}$

Lavoisier claims[2] in this memoir of 1776 to have proved that:

' acids are all (tous) composed in great part of air, that this substance is common to all and they are differentiated one from another by the addition of different principles particular for each acid. . . . Not only air but the purest part of air (la portion la plus pure de l'air) enters into the composition of all acids without exception, and it is this substance which constitutes their acidity (qui constitue leur acidité).

'when mercury is dissolved in nitric acid, this metallic substance removes the portion of pure air contained in the nitric acid which constitutes its acidity; on the one side this metal combines with [the purest, omitted in 1776] air and forms a calx, and on the other the acid deprived of its [this same, 1779] air enters into expansion and forms nitrous air . . . and if, after having separated the two airs which enter into the composition of nitric acid, they are recombined anew, pure nitric acid is formed. . . . Since the mercury is recovered perfectly unchanged, there is no sign that it has lost or gained phlogiston, at least if it is not assumed that the phlogiston which served for the reduction of the metal passed through the vessels.' (See Bayen, p. 397.)

This is the first announcement of Lavoisier's theory of acids.

Priestley in the earlier part of his preface[3] says the Abbé Fontana (see p. 323) had 'converted a given quantity of mercury into red precipitate, and then expelled from it all the pure air that it could yield', and had 'found the very some [sic] weight of mercury that he had used to make the precipitate'.[4] In an addition to the preface[5] Priestley says he had repeated Lavoisier's experiment with 11 dwt. 10 grains of 'pure quicksilver' and 'I found there was a clear loss of 1 dwt. 2 grs. of the quicksilver' (over 7 per cent). A Mr. Winch had found from $\frac{1}{2}$ oz. of the purest mercury a loss of 88 grains, and from another $\frac{1}{2}$ oz. there was a considerable loss but not so much. Lavoisier's experiment, Priestley says, is the same as Fontana's, 'and which of them made it the first does not appear.'

Losses could arise from experimental errors but 'it is very possible that there may be less earth and more nitric acid in air than I supposed . . . the purest air is procured by distilling to dryness a mixture of earth and spirit of nitre'. He may have been mistaken in the opinion that air consists of earth and spirit of nitre: 'let others reason better from the facts with which I supply them if they can . . . speculation is a cheap commodity,' and 'new and important facts are most wanted'. One opinion in the modern doctrine concerning air which must be taken as the best founded is that: 'nitrous air is highly charged with phlogiston . . . this quality only . . . renders pure air noxious: affecting it in the

---

[1] As Fourcroy, (2), iii, 430, said, the last figure should be 12 oz. instead of 13 oz.
[2] VIII, ii, 129, 137.
[3] E & O, 1777, iii, pp.xiv f.
[4] Fontana, *Recherches physiques sur la Nature de l'Air Nitreux et de l'Air Déphlogistiqué*, Paris, 1776, 117–21.
[5] *Op. cit.*, xxvii f.

same manner as all other phlogistic processes, especially that most simple one the calcination of metals. If I have completely ascertained any thing at all relative to air, it is this.'[1]

In the text[2] Priestley describes a complicated experiment which, he thought, showed that 42 vols. of dephlogisticated air contain 4 parts of nitric acid. He does not mention Lavoisier in this part (which was probably printed before he wrote the preface), and these experiments must have been made before he saw Lavoisier's work.

In Lavoisier's memoir of 1776 Priestley's experiments, and the second volume of his book, are often mentioned with great respect, but Priestley's erroneous hypothesis is rejected: 'it is not air which is composed of nitrous acid . . . but nitrous acid which is composed of air.' Besides these references to Priestley, there are several others in Lavoisier's memoirs. In the memoir on the combustion of phosphorus[3] the 'eminently respirable air' is 'by Dr. Priestley very improperly named dephlogisticated air'; in the memoir on respiration[4] the 'expériences de Dr. Priestley et les miennes' on precipitate *per se* show that it is composed of mercury with $\frac{1}{12}$ its weight of 'un air beaucoup meilleure et plus respirable . . . que l'air commun'. The memoir on the pyrophorus[5] mentions twice 'l'air déphlogistiqué de M. Priestley'; that on combustion[6] refers to 'une . . . espèce d'air que M. Priestley a nommé *air déphlogistiqué*'; in that on elastic fluids[7] vital air is said to be the same as Priestley's dephlogisticated air; and in a discussion of the French translation of Scheele's book[8] his fire air (air du feu) is 'l'air déphlogistiqué de M. Priestley . . . que j'appelerait *air vital*'. Thus, in at least five papers concerned with oxygen, Lavoisier mentions Priestley only as having given it a name, and in not one of these does Lavoisier claim in clear words that he himself discovered it, although he once at least is so ambiguous that this could be inferred. It is interesting that the last experiment recorded in Lavoisier's laboratory journal which is mentioned by Berthelot[9] is one of 23 October 1788 (almost exactly 14 years after he first heard of it from Priestley), on the preparation of oxygen by heating red precipitate.

Kirwan[10] refers to 'the celebrated experiment of Mr. Lavoisier, which first gave rise to the antiphlogistic hypothesis, and on which it is still chiefly founded'. This is the one on the action of nitric acid on mercury, although most modern writers on Lavoisier barely mention it. The name 'antiphlogistic hypothesis' was then proposed by Kirwan[11] for 'the new opinion (which I shall take the liberty of calling the *Antiphlogistic* hypothesis, and its supporters *Antiphlogistians*, not by way of obloquy, but to avoid circumlocution)'. Fourcroy[12] called it the 'pneumatic doctrine', and said it was created in 1777 by the presentation of eight memoirs by Lavoisier, which are considered later. It seems, however, that it should be dated a year earlier.

[1] *Ib.*, xxx.   [2] *Ib.*, 41–5.   [3] AdS, 1777 (1780), m 195; VIII, ii, 184.
[4] AdS, 1777 (1780), m 185; VIII, ii, 174.   [5] AdS, 1777 (1780), m 363; VIII, ii, 199.
[6] AdS, 1777 (1780), m 592; VIII, ii, 225.   [7] AdS, 1780 (1784), m 334; VIII, ii, 261.
[8] AdS, 1781 (1784), m 396; VIII, ii, 391.   [9] (4), 310.
[10] *Essay on Phlogiston*, 1789, 104.   [11] *Ib.*, 7.   [12] (1), i, 38.

A memoir 'parafées' by the Secretary of the Academy on 28 February 1776[1] is little more than an account of a repetition of Priestley's experiments with hydrochloric acid gas, ammonia gas, and sulphur dioxide. Lavoisier says: 'Les expériences dont je vais rendre compte appartient presque toutes au docteur Priestley', but he thought it would be useful if his memoir was published. This was not done.

Combustion and Respiration

In 1777 nine important memoirs were presented to the Academy. Eight were published in 1780 and one in 1781.

(1) *On the combustion of phosphorus*.[2] The combustion of 1 grain of phosphorus gives $2\frac{1}{2}$ grains of 'concrete acid of phosphorus' (P_2O_5), by absorbing 3 cu. in. or $1\frac{1}{2}$ grains of 'air' and leaving $\frac{4}{5}$ or $\frac{5}{6}$ of the volume of what Lavoisier proposed to call a *mofette atmosphérique*, rather less dense than air; if to 4 vols. of this, 1 vol. of 'dephlogisticated or eminently respirable air' is added, common air is formed. He says later in the memoir that different experiments had shown that common air contains 'about a quarter' of dephlogisticated air absorbable by the combustion of phosphorus, which never removes all the 'eminently respirable air' from common air. The rest of the memoir deals with phosphoric acid and its salts, and shows that the precipitate of calcium phosphate differs from the carbonate. Lavoisier made the phosphoric acid by burning phosphorus under a bell jar with the sides wetted with water. He mentions that it is less easy to burn sulphur, since it is extinguished when only $\frac{1}{10}$ or $\frac{1}{8}$ of the eminently respirable air has been removed, yet he says he found by burning it in a bell-jar over mercury a diminution of the air proportional to the quantity of sulphur burnt, and there is deposited 'un acide vitriolique très-concentré' which weighs two or three times as much as the sulphur. Since the main product is gaseous sulphur dioxide, without change of volume, it is hard to understand Lavoisier's result. He says he will return to this matter later. In June 1787[3] he gave the correct composition of sulphuric acid (sulphur trioxide) as sulphur combined with $1\frac{1}{2}$ times its weight of oxygen, but he does not say how this result had been obtained. In a later account of the combustion of phosphorus (1789),[4] it is said that 100 parts of phosphorus require 154 parts of oxygen, making the percentage composition of 'concrete phosphoric acid' 39·4 phosphorus and 60·6 oxygen. The correct values for P_2O_5 are 43·3 and 56·7, so that the result is not good. By oxidising phosphorus with nitric acid, Valentin Rose[5] found 100 phosphorus to 114·75 oxygen, which is nearer the correct value of 100 to 129. An almost exact result (43·97 : 56·03) was found indirectly by Berzelius.[6]

(2) *On respiration*.[7] Respiration is compared with the calcination of mercury. Priestley is mentioned five times as having taught that respiration consists

---

[1] De Quelques Substances qui sont constamment dans l'état de Fluides Aériformes, au degré de chaleur et de pression habituel de l'Atmosphère, VIII, ii, 783, from a MS. deposited with the Academy on 5 September 1777.
[2] AdS, 1777 (1780), h 25, m 65; VIII, ii, 139; presented 21 March read 16 April 1777.
[3] VIII, v, 374.   [4] VII, 60.   [5] *J. Chem. Phys.* (Gehlen), 1806, ii, 309.
[6] *Théorie des Proportions Chimiques*, 1819, 126.
[7] AdS, 1777 (1780), h 30, m 185; VIII, ii, 174; read 3 May 1777.

in a phlogistication of air, as in the calcination of metals, etc., and air becomes irrespirable when saturated with phlogiston. Lavoisier's famous mercury experiment is described without detail of the apparatus; in the following description this is supplied from the later account in the *Traité*.[1]

He heated 4 oz. of mercury in a retort which communicated with a measured volume of air in a bell-jar over mercury (Fig. 38). The volume of air in the bell and in the retort was 50 cu. in. After a time he noticed the formation of red specks and scales of calx on the surface of the mercury. After twelve days the scales no longer increased; the fire was removed, and the experiment stopped. The air had contracted to 42 cu. in., and the gas left was mephitic air (*mofette*). The scales, or mercury calx (*mercurius calcinatus per se*), were collected and found to weigh 45 grains. They were transferred to a small retort and heated; 8 to 9 cu. in.

FIG. 38. LAVOISIER'S APPARATUS FOR HEATING MERCURY IN A CONFINED VOLUME OF AIR.

of 'the salubrious part of the air', or respirable air, were obtained, together with $41\frac{1}{2}$ grains of mercury. When this respirable air was added to the atmospheric mofette, ordinary air was formed.

This is an ideal experiment, which could hardly have been carried out as it is described. The results were made up by the combination of those of several separate experiments:[2]

J'ai été obligé de répéter plusieurs fois cette calcination du mercure en vaisseaux clos, parce qu'il est difficile, dans une seule et même expérience, de conserver l'air dans lequel on a opéré, et les molécules rouges . . . il m'arrivera souvent de confondre ainsi, dans un même récit le résultat de deux ou trois expériences de même genre.

The experiment was repeated by Bryan Higgins[3] with an improved apparatus, and also repeated and modified by V. V. Petrov (1761–1834) in St. Petersburg;[4] it was successfully repeated by Klaproth in the Berlin Academy of Sciences on 16 September 1792.[5]

Lavoisier found that the residual air after the respiration of a sparrow extinguished a candle and turned lime water milky. The decrease in volume, when the original temperature was restored after the death of the bird, was not more than $\frac{1}{60}$ of the original volume. Addition of caustic alkali decreased the volume by $\frac{1}{6}$ and the alkali became mild, hence fixed air was present, 'which I shall in future call chalky acid gas (acide crayeux aériforme; acide de la craie).' This name was proposed by Bucquet, as Lavoisier says later.[6] The gas

[1] VII, 35; VIII, i, 36; IV, i, 1; II, 3; the experiment appears in Lavoisier's note-book in April 1776; Berthelot, (4), 271.
[2] VII, 37.   [3] *Minutes of the Society*, etc. (see p. 729), 1795, 97 f.
[4] Menschutkin, *Isis*, 1935, xxv, 291 (no date given).
[5] Hermbstädt, *J. der Phys.* (Gren), 1792, vi, 422.
[6] AdS, 1777 (1780), h 29, m 195; VIII, ii, 184 (à l'imitation de M. Bucquet); Keir, *A Treatise on the Various Kinds of Permanently Elastic Fluids, or Gases*, 2 ed., 1779, 31, called it 'calcareous

remaining after treatment with caustic alkali was the same mephitic air as is produced in the calcination of mercury, and became ordinary air when $\frac{1}{4}$ of its volume of eminently respirable air was mixed (combiné) with it. In respiration, as in combustion, respirable or 'true air' (véritable air) is removed; the mephitic air is a purely passive medium (un milieu purement passif) and enters and leaves the lung without change or alteration, whilst the respirable air is converted into chalky acid.

Two opinions are possible: (i) that the respirable part of the air combines with the blood, or (ii) that it changes into chalky acid in passing through the lungs. Lavoisier was inclined to think that both processes occur. He also says that the respirable air (or rather, as he will show later, its basis) combines with the blood, and perhaps with a metallic substance in the blood, since the blood assumes a bright red colour like that of red precipitate, red lead, and colcothar (ferric oxide), formed by the calcination of metals. It could be supposed that the eminently respirable air which enters the lung comes out (en ressort) as chalky acid, but it is more likely that a portion of it remains in the lung and there combines with the blood. (Lavoisier soon abandoned this comparison with metallic calces.)

(3) *On the combustion of candles in ordinary air and in eminently respirable air*.[1] In the case of ordinary air there is no sensible diminution in volume but a tenth changes into acide crayeux (carbon dioxide). In the combustion of phosphorus one-fourth of the air is removed, leaving only 0·05 of respirable air, which is removed by the pyrophorus (see no. 5).

Lavoisier points out that experiments made in a bell-jar over water are inconclusive, since heated air bubbles out from the mouth of the jar (see Tabor, Vol. II, p. 624), and also the chalky acid formed dissolves in the water. Hence he covered a burning candle with a jar which he at once put into mercury in an inclined position, so that when vertical the mercury level was above that in the trough. When the vessel had cooled the mercury rose. He then added caustic potash solution, when there was a further contraction. He also used a siphon, then removed, to raise the mercury level, and a bit of phosphorus on the candle wick, ignited by a hot wire passed through the mercury. The decrease in volume by the combustion of the candle 'peut être regardé comme absolument nul'. In presence of water, lime water, or caustic alkali, a ninth or a tenth of the air was absorbed, corresponding with the chalky acid formed. A candle burning in 'pure air' (Priestley is mentioned) absorbs 66 parts, and by removing the chalky acid and repeating the combustion only $\frac{1}{8}$ of 'mofette' (probably an impurity in the pure air) remained. On Priestley's theory, there should have been a large residue of phlogisticated air. Lavoisier says the nature of the mofette is unknown, but it is probably very complex (très-composée). He announces that he is on the point of combating Stahl's theory of phlogiston and that of Priestley on the phlogistication

gas'; Fourcroy, (1), iv, 5, says: le nom d'acide crayeux que j'avais adopté dès 1778, avec Bucquet; the salts were called 'craies'.

[1] AdS, 1777 (1780), h 29, m 195; VIII, ii, 184; Fourcroy, (2), 1796, iii, 430, says that although Lavoisier now felt strong enough to oppose the phlogiston theory openly, he did not do this because 'il marchoit encore presque seul dans la carrière'.

of air, by a series of experiments. This, it should be noticed, is in 1777, published in 1780.

Lavoisier also says he could prove that the chalky acid formed in the combustion of a candle or taper 'is nothing but the inflammable air given off by the candle or taper, together with (plus) eminently respirable air (which Priestley had, improperly, called dephlogisticated air), less a considerable portion of the matter of fire which entered into the composition of the two primitive airs'; but he will postpone this till he has proved 'the existence of the matter of fire in elastic fluids and how chalky acid can be formed by the combination of inflammable air with the base of eminently respirable air'. It is clear that Lavoisier regarded the presence of the 'matter of fire in elastic fluids' as an essential part of his new theory before it was announced categorically, and that he called the gas rising from a candle wick 'inflammable air', as Priestley did. Cavendish in 1766 had used the name 'inflammable air from metals' for hydrogen.

(4) *On the dissolution of mercury in vitriolic acid and the decomposition of this into sulphurous acid air and eminently respirable air.*[1] Lavoisier shows that sulphurous acid is vitriolic acid deprived of part of its air. Six oz. of vitriolic acid heated in a small retort with 4 oz. of mercury gave off abundance of the 'volatile sulphurous air', otherwise called 'sulphurous acid air' (acide sulfureux aériforme) observed by Priestley. On strongly heating 2 oz. of the white residue of mercury vitriol (vitriol mercuriel) it gave off a little sulphurous acid air, absorbed by water, and 91 cu. in. of very pure eminently respirable air, the purest (by the nitrous air test) he had yet obtained, and mercury was revived, with the formation of some white and some grey sublimate. The loss in weight of 2 gros 5 grains was ascribed to sulphurous acid and respirable air. 'It is a consequence impossible to deny that volatile sulphurous acid is vitriolic acid partly deprived of eminently respirable air.'

Lavoisier fails to mention that Bayen in 1775[2] had published a *quantitative* experiment in which he heated turpeth mineral (basic mercuric sulphate) and obtained sulphurous acid air (sulphur dioxide) and a gas (oxygen) which he did not investigate (see p. 398).

(5) *On the combination of alum with carbonaceous matters and on the formation of pyrophorus.*[3] Lavoisier says that Homberg in 1718 (see p. 43) and de Suvigny[4] had shown that on heating alum with organic matter, a spontaneously inflammable powder (Homberg's pyrophorus) is formed. He found that on combustion in air or in pure air (oxygen) — in the second of which it burnt with great heat and brilliance — chalky acid is formed. On its combustion, 100 vols. of common air were reduced to $72\frac{1}{2}$, i.e. by more than a quarter, but in 'nearly all other experiments of this kind [the diminution] hardly amounts to $\frac{1}{5}$'. He speaks again of 'the base of the eminently respirable air'. (Black had shown in 1756 (see p. 141) that fixed air is formed when charcoal burns in air, but did not publish this experiment, although he described it in his lectures.)

[1] AdS, 1777 (1780), h 28, m 324 (no date); VIII, ii, 194.　　[2] *Obs. Phys.*, 1775, vi, 487.
[3] AdS, 1777 (1780), h 26, m 363; VIII, ii, 199.　　[4] AdS, *Mém. div. Sav.*, 1760, iii, 180.

Lavoisier found that the air (carbon monoxide) evolved in the calcination of alum with charcoal is inflammable, but less so than that evolved by the dissolution of metals in acids, from which it is quite different: it burns with much greater difficulty and hardly detonates when mixed with two-thirds of common air. A remarkable property is its conversion into chalky acid air on combustion; none of the other inflammable airs from metals and acids behave like this, and 'these appear to give acids analogous to those from which they were derived' (ils paraissent donner des acides analogues à ceux dont ils ont été tirés). This air he was 'very inclined to believe is the carbonaceous substance in the state of vapour and in the form of air'. He thought the other two inflammable airs were 'a species of vitriolic sulphur' (obtained from metals and dilute sulphuric acid) and 'a species of marine sulphur in the vaporous or aëriform state' (from metals and hydrochloric acid); this idea was afterwards adopted by Gren (p. 671).

In 1780, therefore, Lavoisier was wrong as to the nature of hydrogen, but he distinguished it from carbon monoxide, which Priestley never did, even in 1803 (see p. 276). The conversion of carbon monoxide into dioxide on combustion, established by Lavoisier, he lost sight of in his later work.

(6) *On the vitriolisation of martial pyrites.*[1] The efflorescence of some kinds of martial (iron) pyrites (FeS_2, when ferrous sulphate is formed) is shown to depend on the absorption of 'the base of respirable air', the 'matter of fire which holds it in dissolution' (a hypothesis) being liberated in combustion, flame and heat being due to the matter of fire disengaged by the respirable air when it is fixed by combustible bodies. This theory was held by Lavoisier to the end of his life. One-fifth of the air, the 'eminently respirable' part, is absorbed, leaving the atmospheric mofette. 'Vitriolisation is nothing but an addition of . . . the base of eminently respirable air, which converts the sulphur into vitriolic acid' which, as it is formed, 'attacks and dissolves the iron in a very finely divided state and converts it into vitriol of Mars' (ferrous sulphate). This is not quite correct, since the iron is oxidised as well:

$$FeS_2 + 7O + H_2O = FeO + 2SO_3 + H_2O = FeSO_4 + H_2SO_4.$$

(7) *On the combination of the matter of fire with evaporable fluids and on the formation of elastic aëriform fluids.*[2] Lavoisier supposes that 'the igneous fluid, matter of fire, heat, and light', is a very subtle fluid which penetrates all bodies and tends to come into equilibrium in them. It does not penetrate them with equal facility. It can exist in a free state or in a fixed state in combination with bodies. He does not mention Black (whose work was unpublished) but only Richmann, de Mairan, Cullen, and Baumé; Fourcroy[3] says 'il oublit' Black and did not then know of his work (but see p. 427).

Lavoisier compares this combined heat with 'water of composition' (water of crystallisation), and 'free matter of heat' with 'water of dissolution or more exactly water of solution' (he used the name 'dissolution' for a case when there

[1] AdS, 1777 (1780), h 27, m 398; VIII, ii, 209; see Valmont de Bomare, AdS, *Mém. div. Sav.*, 1768, v, 617.
[2] AdS, 1777 (1780), h 31, m 420; VIII, ii, 212.   [3] (2), iii, 435.

is a chemical reaction). He describes some experiments on the cooling of ether and alcohol when evaporated in vacuum (which he could have said Cullen had observed), which he says were part of a large research carried out together with Laplace (see p. 426). He found that the heat evolved on neutralising a caustic alkali with acid is greater than with mild alkali, when fixed air is evolved.

An elastic fluid is a solution of a volatile body in the matter of fire. Lavoisier did not adopt Van Helmont's name *gas* (long before used in France by Macquer) in the form *gaz* for an elastic fluid until 1787.[1] In the same year Guyton de Morveau[2] introduced the name *calorique* (in English *caloric*) for 'matière de la chaleur'; in 1785[3] he had called it 'le calorifique'.

Lavoisier's theory is an extension of Black's theory of latent heat:

$$\text{ice} + \text{latent heat} = \text{water}, \quad \text{and} \quad \text{water} + \text{latent heat} = \text{steam},$$

and now for any gas (and in particular oxygen gas):

$$\text{oxygen base} + \text{caloric} = \text{oxygen gas}.$$

This is an essential part of Lavoisier's theory of combustion, as is explained in the next memoir, the chemical process being combined with it.[4] A year before Lavoisier's memoir was presented, Herckenroth[5] regarded cold as a distinct substance of an alkaline nature, and not a mere deprivation of heat.

(8) *Memoir on combustion in general.*[6] Lavoisier says he will now propose a new theory, or (to speak with the reserve which he had imposed upon himself) a new hypothesis, which explains very satisfactorily all the phenomena of combustion and calcination, and even those accompanying the respiration of animals. In all cases of combustion there are four observable 'phenomena':

(i) there is disengagement of the matter of fire or of light;
(ii) combustion occurs only in one species of air, called by Priestley 'dephlogisticated air', and here 'pure air' (air pur), in which alone 'combustibles' will burn;[7]
(iii) there is 'destruction or decomposition of pure air ... in which the burnt body increases in weight exactly in proportion to the quantity of air destroyed or decomposed';
(iv) 'in every combustion the burnt body changes into an acid by addition of the substance which increases its weight', e.g. phosphorus into phosphoric acid, sulphur into vitriolic acid, carbon into fixed air or chalky acid, etc.

Guyton de Morveau[8] also suggested that vital air is 'a constituent of all acids', may be essential to their state of aqueous combination, 'and is the true

---

[1] VI, 30, 79, 83, table opposite 100; VII, 1789, 53 (nous avons conservé à l'exemple de M. Macquer, le nom de *gaz* employé par Vanhelmont); Macquer used the name 'gas' not 'gaz'.
[2] VI, 31.   [3] *Nouv. Mém. Acad. Dijon*, 1785, i, 90 (98).
[4] Cajori, *Isis*, 1922, iv, 483 (history of caloric); Seguin, *Ann. Chim.*, 1789, iii, 148 (227), says Lavoisier was proposing to measure the *light* evolved in combustion.
[5] *Obs. Phys.*, 1776, vii, 536.
[6] AdS, 1777 (1780), h 32, m 592 (dated 5 September 1777); VIII, ii, 225.
[7] He has overlooked Priestley's dephlogisticated nitrous air, nitrous oxide.
[8] *Élémens de Chymie*, Dijon, 1777, i, 325; ii, 2, 20 f.

universal acid, the acid element.' This had been published by Lavoisier in 1776 (see p. 414).

In June 1787[1] Lavoisier, who was a stickler for exact wording, says of his oxygen theory of acids: 'si toutefois on peut donner le nom de théorie à une vérité de fait et d'observation qui, par sa généralité, peut être regardée comme une loi constante de la nature.'

Lavoisier (1777) said that Macquer[2] had suggested that calcination is only a slow combustion, hence it follows that:

(i) in every metallic calcination there is a disengagement of the matter of fire,

(ii) true calcination can occur only in pure air,

(iii) there is combination of air with a body calcined, but instead of an acid there is formed a particular combination (une combinaison particulière) called a metallic calx (chaux métallique).

Lavoisier repeats his views on the matter of fire, now mentioning Franklin, Boerhaave, and 'some ancient philosophers' — who can hardly include Black. Pure air, Priestley's dephlogisticated air, is:

'an igneous combination in which the matter of fire or of light enters as a solvent (dissolvant) and in which another substance enters as a base; . . . if to the base a substance with which it has a greater affinity is presented, it at once unites with it, and the dissolvant which quits it becomes free; [the burning body] robs the air of its base and the matter of fire which served as solvent becomes free with all its known properties, viz. flame, heat, and light.'

Most of the fire fixed in the bodies is in the pure air, which 'is the true combustible body, perhaps the only one in nature'. The different phenomena of combustion and calcination are explained in a 'very happy [très heureuse]' manner by Stahl's hypothesis but there is no need to assume with Stahl that bodies which increase in weight lose part of their substance (the main difficulty in the phlogiston theory). Lavoisier does not claim to substitute for Stahl's doctrine a rigorously demonstrated theory but only 'a hypothesis which seems more probable, more conformable to the laws of nature, and contains less forced explanations and fewer contradictions'.

This 'new hypothesis' explains the production of fire in combustion by locating the matter of fire mainly in the oxygen gas, whilst Stahl located it in the combustible body. The matter of fire was called phlogiston by Stahl (see Vol. II, p. 668), whilst Lavoisier called it caloric. In his later 'Reflexions on Phlogiston' (see p. 426) it is again this aspect of his theory which predominates over the chemical aspect.

Kirwan[3] said: 'Mr. Lavoisier was undoubtedly the first who proved, by direct and exact experiments, that the weight which metals gain by calcination corresponds with that of the air which they absorb; he was also the first who published that the atmosphere consists of two distinct fluids . . . he also proved after Dr. Crawford, that pure air [oxygen] (a substance which Dr. Priestley first discovered and called dephlogisticated air) contained more fire than any

[1] VIII, v, 374.   [2] Dictionnaire de Chymie, 1778, i, 287, 344, 389; see Mayow, Vol. II.
[3] Essay on Phlogiston, 1789, 3–4.

other air' and gave it out as heat and light in combustion. Lavoisier in commenting on this[1] passes Priestley over in silence and says:

'We do not therefore affirm, that vital air [oxygen] combines with metals to form metallic calces [oxides], because this manner of enunciating would not be sufficiently accurate: but we say, when a metal is heated to a certain temperature, and when its particles are separated from each other to a certain distance by heat, and their attraction to each other is sufficiently diminished, it becomes capable of decomposing vital air, from which it seizes the base, namely *oxigene*, and sets the other principle, namely the *caloric*, at liberty. This . . . is not an hypothesis, but the result of facts. . . . No supposition enters into these explanations; the whole is proved by weight and measure . . . the property of burning is nothing else but the property which certain substances possess of decomposing vital air by the great affinity they have for the oxigenous principle. . . . An inflammable body is nothing else but a body which has the property of decomposing vital air, and taking the base from the caloric and light, that is to say the oxigene which was united to them . . . it is principally and almost entirely from this substance [vital air] that the caloric and light are disengaged.'

We are, therefore, happily in a position to know exactly what Lavoisier's theory was. As Parkes[2] said: 'Combustion is a process by which certain substances decompose oxygen gas, absorb its base, and suffer its caloric to escape in the state of sensible heat.'

In his memoir of 1777 Lavoisier[3] says he had shown (fait voir; in memoir no. 2) that in respiration 'the pure air passing through the lung [par le poumon] undergoes a decomposition similar to that occurring in the combustion of carbon', fixed air being formed; there is a 'disengagement of the matter of fire in the lung in the interval between inspiration and expiration', and this matter of fire, 'distributing itself with the blood to all the animal economy', maintains the heat of the body.

The 'fact' which was 'proved' that 'the matter of fire' is disengaged *in the lung* is incorrect. The blood absorbs oxygen gas in the lung, but this does not *necessarily* involve evolution of heat there as Lavoisier thought; the heat may be evolved in the viscera, as Mayow (1674) had supposed (Vol. II, p. 603).

(9) *General considerations on the nature of acids and on the principles of which they are composed.*[4] Lavoisier now proposed to name the base of vital air (oxygen gas) the 'acidifying principle' (principe acidifiant), or if a Greek word is preferred the 'oxiginous principle' (principe oxigine), which is dephlogisticated air or eminently respirable air in the state of fixity or combination. Fourcroy[5] says: 'de concert avec lui [Lavoisier] nous avons changés quelques années en celle *d'oxygène*', and this name (instead of oxigine) appears in part of the *Nomenclature Chimique*[6] written by Fourcroy.

Lavoisier says the oxygenous principle combined with the matter of fire, of heat and of light, forms the purest air. This is very probable but not rigorously demonstrated — it may not be susceptible of this. Combined with carbon it forms chalky acid (acide crayeux) or fixed air, with sulphur vitriolic acid, with nitrous air nitric acid, and with phosphorus phosphoric acid. 'It is

---

[1] *Ib.*, 13 f.   [2] *Chemical Catechism*, 5 ed., 1812, 375.   [3] VIII, ii, 232.
[4] AdS, 1778 (1781), m 535; VIII, ii, 248; presented 5 September 1777 but not read until 23 November 1779. Scheele had *published* the statement that 'all acids derive their origin from fire air [oxygen]' in the summer of 1777 (*Chemische Abhandlung von der Luft und dem Feuer*, 1777, § 93), but Lavoisier had *published* it in 1776 (see p. 413).
[5] (2), iii, 838.   [6] VI, 78.

the constituent principle of acidity and is common to all acids.' These are 'truths which I regard as very solidly established'.

Lavoisier later[1] said the name *oxygène* 'is derived from two Greek words ὀξύς, *acid*, and γείνομαι, *I produce*', but Hoefer,[2] says: 'Lavoisier is mistaken here: γείνομαι or rather γίνομαι, means *I become*; it is γεννάω which means *I produce*, and the term so formed should be *oxygénète* and not *oxygène*. But a great chemist may be pardoned for not knowing Greek.'

Lavoisier did not give a new name to 'phlogisticated air' or 'mephitic air'; Guyton de Morveau[3] says 'nous l'avons nommé *azote*, de l'α privatif des grecs & de ζωή *vie*'. In the table[4] 'Azote ou Radical nitrique' is combined with 'calorique' to form 'Gaz azotique', azote itself being the 'Base de l'air phlogistiqué ou de la mofète atmosphérique'. The awkward distinction between 'azote' and 'radical nitrique' was removed by Chaptal by calling the former 'nitrogène', but the French still use 'azote' and the Germans 'Stickstoff' with the same meaning.

In the memoir on the nature of acids Lavoisier distinguishes neutral salts from acids and bases (which had often been called 'salts'), and says chemical analysis must be taken a stage further in ascertaining the nature of the latter. His experiments had shown that the oxygen principle enters into the composition of phosphoric, vitriolic and nitric acids, and he supposed that it is the common constituent of all acids, with the possible exception of the acid of sea-salt (si ce n'est peut-être celui du sel marin) — hydrochloric acid. The theory is applied to the formation of the acid of sugar (oxalic acid), which Bergman had obtained from sugar and nitric acid (see p. 198). Lavoisier proposed to extend the experiment to the union of oxygen to animal horn, silk, lymph, wax, essential oils, expressed oils, manna, starch, arsenic, iron, and probably a great number of animal, vegetable, and mineral substances. The acid of sugar is 'nothing else than sugar in its entirety combined with the acidifying principle or oxygen'. This is not really true, since sugar is $C_{12}H_{22}O_{11}$ and must lose hydrogen to form oxalic acid $6\text{-}(C_2H_2O_4)$, but Lavoisier's theory is good for its time.

Nitric acid (acide nitreux) had been shown to be a compound of oxygen and nitrous air (nitric oxide), but the fuming acid contains a superabundance of nitrous air, whilst the acid which evolves white vapours contains an excess of dephlogisticated air. The acid he now used contained 48 parts of nitrous air to 60 of oxygen. On heating it with sugar, nitrous air was evolved (it is really a mixture of this and nitrogen dioxide) and acid of sugar is formed. On distillation of oxalic acid some fixed air and inflammable air (carbon monoxide) were evolved. Lavoisier found from quantitative experiments that oxalic acid is composed of sugar with about a third of its weight of oxygen, 4 gros of sugar combining with 1 gros 30 grains of oxygen. This could be used to find the composition of many vegetable and animal acids, many more of which could probably be discovered. Carbon appears to be present in vegetables and is not formed from them by the action of fire, as some chemists supposed. Sugar is composed of a little inflammable air and much carbonaceous principle (he did

[1] VII, 1789, 55.　　　[2] NBG, 1859, xxx, 13.　　　[3] VI, 1787, 36.　　　[4] *Ib.*, 100.

not know that it contains oxygen). Oxygen combines with most substances which it does not decompose to form acids, but with metals to form calces.

Landriani[1] believed that *all* acids were convertible into carbonic acid, but he was misled by the use of carbonaceous materials which were oxidised,[2] and Lavoisier was much in advance of this.

Memoirs published in 1784. I

The *Mémoires* of the Academy 'for 1780', published in 1784, contain two memoirs on phosphoric acid read in 1780, one on the conversion of liquids into vapours, read in 1777 but not previously printed (see p. 391), and a long memoir on heat, with Laplace, read in June 1783. The *Mémoires* 'for 1781' were also published in 1784 and will be dealt with later.

(1) *On different combinations of phosphoric acid.*[3] This describes several salts of phosphoric acid which had been made by the combustion of phosphorus, glacial phosphoric acid, the formation of an ethereal odour with the acid and alcohol; also a purple colloidal solution of gold formed by grinding gold-leaf with sugar in a mortar and then adding water. Copper is insoluble in phosphoric acid. The oxygen principle or vital air has more affinity with phosphorus than with metals. Lavoisier explained in a footnote in another memoir (see (3) below),[4] regarding the name 'vital air': 'the historian of the Academy [Condorcet] had so named Priestley's dephlogisticated air, and which I thought it my duty to adopt after him.'[5]

(2) *On a particular process for converting phosphorus into phosphoric acid without combustion.*[6] This consists in heating successive pieces of phosphorus with nitric acid of sp. gr. 1·29895 in a retort, and evaporating. The greater attraction of the phosphorus takes 'the acidifying principle or *oxygine*' from the nitrous gas combined with it in nitric acid. The phlogiston theory would say phlogiston was transferred from the phosphorus to the nitric acid, but Lavoisier says he will show later that Stahl's assumption of a principle of phlogiston is unnecessary (peut se dispenser). The wording suggests that this was written before the memoir no. 7, p. 420, dated 1777. A memoir printed in the volume for 1780 was really presented only in 1783 (see below) and the dating is uncertain.

(3) *On several liquids which may be converted into the aëriform state at a temperature only a little greater than the mean temperature of the earth.*[7] Ether can form an inflammable gas which can be collected over hot water but condenses to a liquid again on cooling. A mixture of ether vapour with vital air detonates violently when kindled. The product of combustion of a mixture of ether vapour and air in a bottle turned lime water milky, so that chalky acid

---

[1] Sur la conversion de tous les acides en un seul; *Obs. Phys.*, 1782, xx, 106.
[2] Chaptal, *Elements of Chemistry*, 1791, i, 208.
[3] AdS, 1780 (1784), h 32, m 343; VIII, ii, 271.
[4] AdS, 1780 (1784), h 26, m 334; VIII, ii, 261.
[5] Condorcet, AdS, 1777 (1780), h 23: nom auquel nous avons cru devoir substituer celle d'*air vital*.
[6] AdS, 1780 (1784), h 32, m 349; VIII, ii, 277; the name *oxygine* is frequently used as an alternative to 'acidifying principle'.
[7] AdS, 1780 (1784), h 26, m 334; VIII, ii, 261; cf. IV, i, 338; VIII, ii, 804; VII, 12.

was formed. Alcohol and water can also give vapours at a higher temperature than ether, water vapour being collected over mercury. If the earth were nearer the sun, alcohol and ether would form part of the atmosphere, but if it were further away, water and mercury would be solids. At a low temperature air, or at least some of its constituents, would become liquid, and there would result 'new liquids of which we have no idea'. The three states of matter are

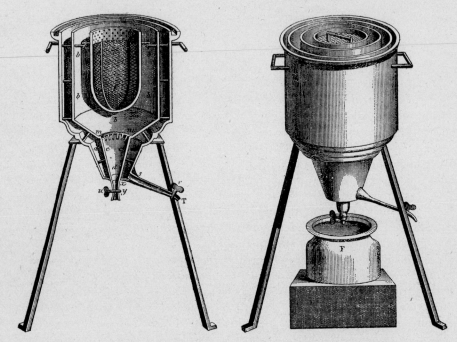

FIG. 39. ICE-CALORIMETER OF LAVOISIER AND LAPLACE.

due to different proportions of fire in the bodies; elastic fluids may be arranged in the order of density; the upper regions of the atmosphere contain inflammable elastic fluids, which are the cause of luminous and combustible meteors. Lavoisier does not sharply distinguish gases from vapours. That air would condense to liquid or solid if strongly cooled had been suggested before Lavoisier by Amontons (see p. 771), Black,[1] Watson,[2] and William Cleghorn.[3]

(4) *Memoir on Heat* (with Laplace).[4] This famous memoir, which laid the foundations of thermochemistry, describes what is called a 'machine', which was later named the 'ice calorimeter'.[5] Black[6] said: 'I am told it was contrived by Laplace.' It consisted (Fig. 39) of an inner vessel *bb* containing crushed ice,

---

[1] *Enquiry into the General Effects of Heat and Mixture*, 1770, 58.
[2] *Essay on the Subjects of Chemistry*, Cambridge, 1771, 3.
[3] *Disputatio Physica Inauguralis, Theoriam Ignis complectans*, Edinburgh, 1779, 22, 45: Aër est vapor, qui, calore minuto, densior usque fit; quem eo multum imminuto, fas est credere, elatere amisso, in solidum abiturum.
[4] AdS, 1780 (1784), h 3, m 355 (read 18 June 1783); VIII, ii, 283; IV, i, 29; Ostwald's *Klassiker*, 1892, xl.
[5] VII, 389: auquel je donnerai le nom de calorimètre.
[6] Letter to Watt, May, 1784 in Muirhead, *Correspondence of James Watt*, 1846, 66.

the melting of which measured the heat given off, surrounded by an outer jacket and lid containing ice to prevent the ingress of external heat. The water formed was allowed to drain out into a jam-pot and weighed to the nearest grain. The heat of fusion of ice was determined as 60° R. or 75° C. (instead of the modern 79). The ice used must not have a temperature below its melting-point, and many hours are required for the body in the calorimeter to reach the ice-temperature.

Wedgwood[1] was unable to obtain satisfactory results with a modified apparatus because of the retention of water by the ice, and the ice melting and water freezing at the same time. T. Thomson[2] says the method used by Lavoisier and Laplace 'has failed in the hands of every one who has attempted it since the publication of their experiments'. But Lavoisier and Laplace had emphasised that satisfactory results are obtained only when the air temperature is not more than 4° R. above freezing point.

They mention 'Vilke'[3] as having 'before us' proposed the idea of using the melting of snow in calorimetry. Black is not mentioned, although in 1772[4] some of Black's experiments on the latent heat of fusion of ice were published, and Lavoisier[5] hastened to establish his 'priority' in a short trival note on a similar matter, which had been 'paraphé' by the Secretary of the Academy, de Fouchy. Lavoisier in 1789 wrote in flattering terms to Black (accoutomé à vous regarder comme mon maître),[6] but in his *Traité de Chimie* and in a memoir[7] written in the same year he expounds the theory of latent heat as the cause of fluidity without mentioning Black, except as (with Boyle, Hales, and Priestley) having shown that the atmosphere is altered by the respiration of animals. The memoir on heat otherwise mentions Crawford, Kirwan, and 'les physiciens', and the wording[8] might suggest that the theory of latent heat originated with Lavoisier.

A table of heat capacities or specific heats (capacités de chaleur ou chaleurs spécifiques) is given (water = 1); it is pointed out that specific heat may depend on temperature:

sheet iron	0·109985	(0·105)
glass (free from lead)	0·1929	(0·16)
mercury	0·029	(0·033)
quicklime	0·21689	(0·177)
9 water + 16 quicklime	0·439116	
oil of vitriol s.g. 1·87058	0·334597	
oil of vitriol diluted (4 : 3)	0·603162	
oil of vitriol diluted (4 : 5)	0·663102	
nitric acid s.g. 1·29895	0·661391	
9⅓ nitric acid + 1 quicklime	0·61895	
1 nitre + 8 water	0·8167	

[1] *Phil. Trans.*, 1784, lxxiv, 358.   [2] *Heat and Electricity*, 1840, 60.
[3] Wilcke, KAH, 1781, ii, 49–78.   [4] *Intr. Obs. Phys.*, 1772 (1777), ii, 428.
[5] *Ib.*, 510.   [6] Andrews, *B.A. Rep.*, 1871, 59, 189; Brougham, 1855, 318.
[7] AdS, 1789 (1793), m 566.
[8] E.g. VIII, ii, 314 (on peut présumer), 324 (dans les Mémoirs de l'Académie pour 1777 . . . M. Lavoisier a été conduit à un resultat semblable par sa théorie générale de la formation des airs et des vapeurs).

The correct values are given in brackets. A comparison with density and coefficient of expansion was promised.

Experiments made with Laplace in 1781–2 on the expansion of solids by heat were published only many years later.[1] The specific gravities of liquids at different temperatures, giving the coefficients of expansion, were determined by an immersion method resembling Nicholson's hydrometer.[2] In a memoir on heats of fusion[3] Lavoisier concluded that the difference in solubility of a salt in boiling water and in cold water is greater if the melting point is lower. This is due to the different affinities of the salt for water and for caloric. Salts with water of crystallisation lower the temperature on solution, anhydrous salts raise the temperature. The water of crystallisation is in the form of ice (dans l'état de glace), and the combination of a salt with water involves the solidification of the water, with evolution of heat, and this exceeds the absorption of heat due to the liquefaction of the salt on solution. This idea was held for a very long time and still appears in the literature.

Lavoisier and Laplace (1784) say that heat may be regarded as a fluid penetrating all bodies, either free or combined, or alternatively as 'the result of insensible movements of the molecules of matter', oscillating in small voids in the body, and in both hypotheses the amount of heat is constant. This follows in the second hypothesis from the law of conservation of vis viva (mv^2 i.e. of kinetic energy $\frac{1}{2}mv^2$). The second hypothesis (which is almost certainly that held by Laplace) is favoured by many phenomena such as the production of heat by friction. Lavoisier and Laplace do not decide in favour of either hypothesis, since both lead to the 'conservation of free heat', which states that 'the quantity of free heat always remains the same in the simple mixture of bodies', and is the fundamental principle of calorimetry, and both hypotheses lead to the very general principle that:

'If in any combination or change of state there is a diminution of free heat (chaleur libre) this heat will reappear in totality (tout entière) when the substances return to their first state; and conversely, if in the combination or change of state there is an increase of free heat, this new heat will disappear in the return of the substances to their initial state. All the variations of heat, either real or apparent, which a system of bodies undergoes (éprouve) in changing its state, are reproduced in an inverse order when the system returns to its former state.'

More concisely: *as much heat is absorbed in the decomposition of a chemical compound as is evolved in its formation*. This is the fundamental law of thermochemistry.

It is pointed out that radiation should exert a pressure, which should be greater when it is reflected than when it is absorbed by a black body. The direct impulse of the solar rays, however, is inappreciable because the mass is so small even if the velocity is very large, but the heating effect, proportional to the vis viva, is very appreciable because it is proportional to the square of the velocity. (This part is certainly by Laplace.)

[1] IV, i, 246; VIII, ii, 739; Biot, *Traité de Physique*, 1816, i, 159 f., giving figures of the apparatus; the original engraved plates prepared for Lavoisier are reproduced in VIII, vi, 811 f.
[2] IV, i, 295; VIII, ii, 773.　　　　　　　　[3] IV, i, 281; VIII, ii, 765.

Experiments were made on the heat evolved by the detonation of nitre with carbon and sulphur, by the combustion of phosphorus, ether, and carbon, and by the respiration of a guinea pig.

The weights of ice melted were found to be, for the:

	lb.	oz.	gros	gr.
detonation of 1 oz. of nitre with $\frac{1}{3}$ oz. of charcoal	0	12	0	0
detonation of 1 oz. of nitre with 1 oz. of flowers of sulphur	2	0	0	0
combustion of 1 oz. of phosphorus	6	4	0	48
combustion of 1 oz. of ether	4	10	2	36
combustion of 1 oz. of charcoal	6	2	0	0
respiration of a guinea pig in 10 hours	0	13	1	$13\frac{1}{2}$

The heat of combustion of charcoal found by Lavoisier and Laplace is much too low. It corresponds with 7350 kcal. for 12 g. of charcoal, the correct value being 9765.[1]

Calculations of the 'absolute amount of heat' in 1 lb. of water in terms of the amount of heat required to raise its temperature 1° R., by several different methods, gave results in complete disagreement, including a negative quantity. These were thought to be due to errors in the values of the specific heats used, but such calculations are really meaningless.

It is supposed that combustion and respiration are due to absorption of pure air (oxygen) and the heat and light evolved are in large part due to changes which this air undergoes. Crawford[2] thought the matter of heat was free in the pure air, which lost a large part of its specific heat on combination, but Lavoisier thought the pure air contained the matter of heat in a combined state. Crawford[3] says:

'animal heat depends upon a process resembling a chemical elective attraction. The pure air is received into the lungs containing a great quantity of elementary fire; the blood is returned from the extremities impregnated with the inflammable principle; the attraction of pure air to the latter is greater than that of the blood. This principle will therefore leave the blood to combine with the air; by this combination the air is obliged to deposit a part of its elementary fire; and as the capacity of the blood is at the same moment increased, it will instantly absorb that portion of fire which had been detached from the air. The arterial blood, in its passage through the capillary vessels, is again impregnated with the inflammable principle, in consequence of which its capacity for heat is diminished . . . It will, therefore, in the course of the circulation, gradually give out the heat which it had received in the lungs, and diffuse it over the whole system.'

Crawford[4] had found the specific heats of venous and arterial blood 0·9708 and 1·12, or in the ratio 10 : $11\frac{1}{2}$. He[5] also (after Lavoisier and Laplace) made calorimetric experiments on the evolution of heat in respiration.

By burning charcoal in oxygen over mercury and absorbing the fixed air

[1] Ostwald, *Lehrbuch*, 1910, II, i, 171.
[2] *Experiments and Observations on Animal Heat and the Inflammation of Combustible Bodies*, 1779, 66 f., 76 f.; 2 ed. 1788, 284 f., 305 f., 361 f., 369 f.; the first account is tr. in Amoretti and Soave, *Opuscoli Scelti sulle Scienze e sulle Arti*, Milan, 1780, iii, 39–98; see Partington and McKie, *Ann. Sci.*, 1938, iii, 346 f.
[3] 1788, 361–2.   [4] 1788, 277.
[5] *Ib.*, 1788, 315, Plate IV (not in 1779 ed.); E. Farber, *Isis*, 1954, xlv, 3.

(carbon dioxide) with caustic potash, Lavoisier and Laplace[1] found that 202·35 cu. in. of dephlogisticated air after the combustion was reduced to 170·59 cu. in., and after absorption to 73·93 cu. in., 18 grains of charcoal being consumed. The dephlogisticated air used contained $\frac{1}{57}$ of its volume of fixed air (this must have been nitrogen) which had not been removed after standing over water for several months, and it was assumed that the residual gas in the present experiment contained $\frac{1}{57}$ of its volume of fixed air after treatment with caustic alkali. Thus $\frac{1}{57}$ was subtracted from 'the difference between the volume before combustion and that remaining after absorption by caustic alkali' (202·35–73·93) and 'by taking the same quantity from the volume of air absorbed by the caustic alkali, one will have the volume of fixed air formed by the combustion', viz. $\frac{1}{57}$ from (170·59–73·93). These calculations give 126·16 and 94·96 cu. in. The volumes for 1 oz. (576 gr.) of charcoal are 4037·1 and 3038·7 cu. in. (Lavoisier and Laplace give 4037·5 and 3021·7).

To find the weights it is assumed that the densities of oxygen and common air are in the ratio 187 : 185 (a misinterpretation of Priestley's old results, see p. 263), when De Luc's determination of the density of air gives the weight of 1 cu. in. of oxygen at 10° R. and 28 in. mercury as 0·47317 gr. 'M. Lavoisier has observed that at the same temperature and pressure 1 cu. in. of fixed air weighs very nearly $\frac{7}{10}$ gr.' Hence it is calculated that 1 oz. of charcoal in burning consumes 3·3167 oz. of pure air and forms 3·6715 oz. of fixed air. The figures 3·3167 and 3·6715 survive in the *Oeuvres* and Ostwald's *Klassiker* without comment, but 1 + 3·3167 is 4·3167 and not 3·6715. Later,[2] Lavoisier gave 1 lb. of charcoal combining with 2·5714 lb. of oxygen, to form 3·5714 lb. of carbonic acid gas weighing 0·695 gr. per cu. in., and said 1 lb. of charcoal formed 34242 cu. in. of carbonic acid gas, which Kerr[3] pointed out is a mistake for 47358·3 cu. in. In 1784 Lavoisier and Laplace (an eminent mathematician) concluded that 10 parts of fixed air contain about 9 parts of pure air and 1 part of 'a principle furnished by the charcoal, which is the basis of fixed air'. The figures 3·3167 and 3·6715 give 9·03, but the calculation is meaningless.

The calorimetric experiment (see p. 429) showed that 1 oz. of pure air, when carbon is burnt in it, evolves heat which melts 29·547 oz. of ice; whilst if phosphorus is burnt in it the heat evolved melts 68·634 oz. of ice; the two numbers are nearly in the ratio of 1 to $2\frac{1}{3}$.

Nitrous air (nitric oxide) absorbs pure air to form nitrous (nitric) acid with the evolution of very little heat, about enough to melt $3\frac{1}{4}$ oz. of ice per oz. of pure air. Hence in saltpetre most of the heat of the pure air (oxygen gas) is retained and can be evolved in the deflagration of saltpetre with charcoal, when most of its acid forms fixed air. Calculation gave $13\frac{1}{2}$ oz. ice melted per 1 oz. saltpetre and 12 oz. was observed.

In discussing respiration, Lavoisier and Laplace say that Priestley and Scheele had found mostly phlogisticated air (nitrogen) produced, and very little fixed air, whilst they themselves had found in the respiration of birds and guinea pigs in pure air that fixed air is the sole product; they regard the change

[1] Lavoisier, VIII, ii, 320 f.   [2] VII, 68.   [3] VIIF, 1796, 114.

of pure air into fixed air as the main source of animal heat. By measuring the heat of combustion of carbon and the amount of carbon dioxide formed in a given time in the respiration of a guinea-pig, they were able to calculate how much heat would be given out by the animal in 10 hours if the animal heat was produced by the combustion of carbon.

From the result (p. 430) that 1 oz. of charcoal forms 3·6715 oz. of fixed air and on combustion evolves heat which melts 6 lb. 2 oz. of ice, the heat evolved in the formation of 1 oz. of fixed air would melt 26·692 oz. of ice. The 224 grains of fixed air which they found produced in the respiration of the guinea-pig in 10 hours, therefore, corresponds with the production of heat which would melt 10·38 oz. of ice. By putting the animal in the calorimeter it was found that 13 oz. were melted.

The observed results really showed that 18 grains of charcoal formed 96·6 cu. in. of fixed air or 96·6 × 0·7 gr.; hence 224 gr. were formed from 18 × 224/96·6 × 0·7 gr. of charcoal. But 1 oz. or 576 gr. of charcoal evolve heat which melts 98 oz. of ice. Hence for 18 × 224/96·6 × 0·7 gr. the weight of ice melted is 98 × 18 × 224/576 × 96·6 × 0·7 = 10·14 oz., instead of 10·38 oz. Since the heat of combustion of charcoal found by Lavoisier and Laplace is quite wrong (see p. 429) the agreement is purely accidental.

In a later memoir[1] Lavoisier recalculated the results by using for the weights of 1 cu. in. in grains: vital air 0·47317, 'air inflammable aqueux' (hydrogen) 0·03745, and carbonic acid gas 0·6950, correcting for the water formed (determined by difference), and finding 23·4503 p.c. carbon and 76·5497 oxygen in carbonic acid. He now found that by the combustion of carbon, 105·06 cu. in. of oxygen gave 91·791 cu. in. of fixed air in one experiment, but in another, 'which merited most confidence', 114 cu. in. of oxygen was diminished to 109 cu. in., i.e. a decrease in volume of 5 p.c. (This was probably due to hydrogen in the charcoal.) The fact that oxygen does not change in volume when carbon burns in it to form carbon dioxide was established by Allen and Pepys,[2] who also made experiments on respiration.[3]

Although Lavoisier and Laplace's theory of animal heat is incorrect in points of detail it was a great advance over the prevailing views (Mayow's work of 1674 had been forgotten), and laid the foundations of the correct theory of respiration. They say:

'Respiration is thus a combustion, very slow it is true, but perfectly similar to that of carbon; it occurs in the interior of the lungs, without disengagement of visible light since the matter of fire which becomes free is at once absorbed by the humidity of these organs. The heat developed in this combustion communicates itself to the blood which traverses the lungs and from there it is spread over all the animal system.'

The pure air draws from the blood the basis of fixed air and heat is developed in the lungs. The animal heat is nearly the same in the different parts of the body, partly because of the rapid circulation of the blood, 'which promptly transmits even to the extremities of the body the heat which it receives in the lungs', partly to the cooling by evaporation in the lungs, and partly to the

[1] AdS, 1781 (1784), m 448; VIII, ii, 403.   [2] Phil. Trans., 1807, xcvii, 267.
[3] Phil. Trans., 1808, xcviii, 249; 1809, xcix, 404; 1829, cxix, 279.

increase in specific heat of the blood when it is deprived of the base of fixed air which it contains, in contact with pure air, this causing absorption of heat which is developed again in all parts of the body when the specific heat decreases as the blood takes up the base of fixed air. (This is Crawford's theory, see p. 429.) It is pointed out that the result is independent of whether the heat is combined in the pure air or the bodies which combine with it; it is an indisputable fact that in the combination of pure air with the basis of fixed air an appreciable amount of heat is developed. The most serious error in the theory (Lavoisier and Laplace were not physiologists) is the assumption that the heat produced by oxidation is developed in the *lungs*; Mayow had clearly said that it is developed in the muscles in all parts of the body, although he supposed that some is also generated in the blood (see Vol. II, p. 603).

A second memoir on heat by Lavoisier and Laplace, describing experiments said to have been made in the winter of 1783–4 (as the title states)[1] was written up in 1793 (as it says), but published much later.[2] It uses the name calorimeter (calorimètre) for the ice apparatus, with the remark that it might be considered objectionable as a mixture of Latin and Greek. Several new specific heats are given, including those of metals and oxides, atmospheric air and oxygen, sulphur, oil, etc., and heats of combustion of carbon, wax, oil, and hydrogen. In the last case, hydrogen and oxygen gases were burnt inside a closed glass globe, initially vacuous, in the calorimeter, the hydrogen jet being kindled by an electric spark; some heat was lost by conduction along the gas tubes. In measuring the specific heats of air and oxygen, these were passed through a copper spiral in hot water and then through another copper spiral in the ice calorimeter, the inlet and outlet temperatures being measured by thermometers.

Some specific heats (water = 1) found were as follows ('made in the winters of 1782 to 1784'). Figures in the preceding table (p. 427) are repeated, but 0·603162 is now said to belong to 4 : 5 sulphuric acid, and 0·818700 is given for the solution of 1 pt. of saltpetre in 8 of water. Modern values are in brackets:

Red oxide of mercury	0·050112 (0·0485)
lead	0·028189 (0·0306)
red oxide of lead	0·062270 (0·06)
tin	0·047535 (0·0536)
antimony sulphide	0·053180 (0·0829)
white oxide of antimony	0·147090 (0·093)
sulphur	0·208500 (0·176)
olive oil	0·309607 (0·471)
rectified alcohol	0·678786 (0·54)
quicklime	0·216890 (0·177)
vital air (oxygen)	0·65 (*sic*) (0·218)
air	0·33031 (0·248)

[1] Daumas, *Chymia*, 1950, iii, 45 (54), says the work appears as part of a laboratory register written in 1786.
[2] IV, i, 121; VIII, ii, 724; parts of it are contained in VII, 1789.

Heats of combustion as determined by the weights of ice melted by the combustion of 1 lb. of each substance were found:

phosphorus	100 lb.
wood charcoal (1783)	96 lb. 4 oz.[1]
wood charcoal (1784)	96 lb. 7 oz. 2 gros
olive oil	148 lb. 14 oz. 1 gros
white wax	140 lb.
tallow	95 lb. 13 oz.
ether	74 lb. 5 oz.
1 lb. saltpetre + 5 oz. charcoal	12 lb.
1 lb. saltpetre + 1 lb. sulphur	32 lb.

Since phosphoric acid (P_2O_5) is a solid it probably contains little caloric and the heat of combustion of phosphorus gives very nearly the amount of caloric contained in the oxygen gas. 1 lb. of phosphorus absorbs 1 lb. 8 oz. of vital air, the caloric in which melts 100 lb. of ice, hence 1 lb. of vital air contains at least enough caloric to melt 66 lb. 11 oz. 5 gros 24 grains. The experiment with phosphorus, and the specific heat of oxygen, show that: 'the caloric contained in vital air [oxygen] cannot be separated by cooling, that part is in a state of combination and cannot reappear unless it is set free by an affinity stronger than that exerted on the oxygen, as happens in combustions and analogous operations.' Vital air in becoming solid retains more or less caloric according to the nature of the substances with which it combines.

1 lb. of saltpetre contains 7 oz. 6 gros 51·84 grains of potash and 8 oz. 1 gros 20·16 grains of dry acid, the latter containing 6 oz. 3 gros 66·34 gr. of oxygen and 1 oz. 5 gros 25·82 gr. of azote.[2] When 1 lb. of saltpetre is detonated with charcoal, 145⅔ gr. of pure carbon are burnt by the 6 oz. 3 gros 66·34 gr. = 3738·34 gr. of oxygen, and since the ice melted is 12 lb. it follows that 1 lb. of vital air will melt 29·5832 lb. But 1 lb. of charcoal burning in 2 lb. 9 oz. 1 gros 10 gr. of oxygen gas melts 96 lb. 8 oz. of ice, whilst phosphorus burning in this weight of oxygen gas would melt 171 lb. 6 oz. 5 gros. Hence the caloric which remains in the carbonic acid gas would melt 74 lb. 14 oz. 5 gros of ice, or per lb. of oxygen gas 29·13844 lb. of ice. Hence the caloric in 1 lb. of oxygen as it is contained in nitric acid is 29·5832 + 29·13844 = 58·72164. But 1 lb. of oxygen gas contains at least 66·66667 (from the combustion of phosphorus experiment) and the difference is only 7·94503 lb. Hence 'nitric acid contains more than seven-eighths of the caloric which exists in the vital air which has served to form it'. The evolution of heat on the detonation of charcoal with saltpetre, when a gas is formed from two solids, is thus explained.[3]

These calculations removed the objections made by Leopold Vacca Berlinghieri[4] and De la Metherie[5] that more heat is evolved by the combustion of sulphur and phosphorus than of carbon in the same quantity of oxygen gas, although the heat is supposed to come from the gas.

An experiment on the heat of combustion of hydrogen in oxygen, lasting 11½ hours, forming 4 gros 2 grains of water and melting 6 lb. 1 oz. 2 gros

---

[1] In the table in VIII, ii, 730, this is 4 oz.; in the text, p. 725, it is 4 gros, on p. 734 it is 8 oz. In the first memoir, VIII, ii, 305, it is said 1 oz. of charcoal in burning melts 6 lb. 2 oz. of ice, and hence 1 lb. melts 98 lb., not 96 lb. 4 oz. (or 4 gros).

[2] Cavendish's result of 1785, see p. 341, must have been known.

[3] The calculation is reproduced in VII, 1789, 68, 103 f.; VIIF, 1796, 113, 150 f., 158; cf. Murray, 1806, ii, 136.

[4] Obs. Phys., 1789, xxxv, 113.   [5] Ib., 1790, xxxvi, 54.

18 grains of ice, gave 295 lb. 2 oz. 3 gros of ice per 1 lb. of hydrogen, which is less than was expected. The result of Crawford,[1] found by exploding the gases, Lavoisier says corresponded with 524⅔ lb. of ice, and Rosenthal[2] says this is more accurate than Lavoisier and Laplace's result. Lavoisier says that experiments on the heats of combustion of oil, candles, alcohol, ether, etc. were made, but the results were not worth reporting (n'avaient pas encore de bases assez certaines . . . il faut donc attendre de nouvelles expériences).

Memoirs published in 1784. II

The memoirs of the Academy for 1781, published in 1784, contain seven by Lavoisier, all but possibly one communicated after 1781, and two of the most important in their final form in 1784.

(1) Lavoisier and Laplace, on *the generation of electricity by evaporation*,[3] including also the evolution of hydrogen from iron and dilute sulphuric acid, of carbon dioxide from chalk and dilute sulphuric acid (weak effect), of nitric oxide from iron and dilute nitric acid (very feeble), and the combustion of charcoal. The experiments were really planned by Volta in 1782,[4] who was about when they were done and 'made himself useful' (et nous y être utile).

(2) *Reflections on Calcination and Combustion*,[5] a criticism of the French translation of Scheele's book: *Traité chimique de l'Air et du Feu* (1781). Lavoisier says he had previously 'published' many of the results contained in this book. Scheele's theory that heat is a compound of fire air (vital air) and phlogiston is contrary to facts and would not have been proposed if he had paid attention to the weights of the materials causing diminution or absorption of vital air. His experiments on the effects of vegetation on air are new but do not agree with those of Ingen Housz and Senebier. His theory of caustification is the same as Meyer's of *acidum pingue*, 'but all this doctrine has been destroyed and overturned by those of Black, Macquer, and others.' He praises Scheele's use of simple apparatus, and treats him with respect.

(3) *On the formation of fixed air or chalky acid, now* [first] *called acid of charcoal* (acide du charbon),[6] evidently written after (4) below, since it assumes the composition of water. It distinguishes charcoal (charbon) from pure carbon (substance charbonneuse), which combines with vital air or the oxygen principle (principe oxigine) to form *carbonous acid* (acide charbonneux) with liberation of matter of fire and heat from the vital air. Lavoisier now takes for the weights in grains of 1 cu. in. under a pressure of 28 in. of mercury at 10° R.: vital air 0·47317, inflammable air of water 0·03745, carbonic acid 0·6950. He later[7] corrected these to 0·50000, 0·03745, and 0·46950. By burning charcoal in a capsule in oxygen over mercury he found, after correcting for the water also formed, that 1 part of carbonous acid contains 0·234503 of matter of carbon and 0·765497 of oxygen principle. Other results, including the

---

[1] *Animal Heat*, 1788, 254.   [2] Ostwald's *Klassiker*, 1892, xl, 73.
[3] AdS, 1781 (1784), h 6, m 292; IV, i, 329.
[4] Volta, *Opere*, Milan, 1918 f., iii, 301; Arago, *Oeuvres*, 1854, i, 209.
[5] AdS, 1781 (1784), m 396; VIII, ii, 391; apparently written in 1781–2; see report by Berthollet and Lavoisier in August 1781 in VIII, iv, 376.
[6] AdS, 1781 (1784), h 25, m 448; VIII, ii, 403.   [7] IV, ii, 179.

combustion of wax and oil and the reduction of lead and mercury oxides by carbon, gave somewhat different values. He later[1] adopted 28 carbon and 72 oxygen as the percentage composition of carbonic acid gas, the modern figures for CO_2 being 27·3 and 72·7. This is one of the best of Lavoisier's quantitative results.

Wax was found to consist of 86·667 per cent of carbonaceous principle and 13·333 of aqueous inflammable air (it actually also contains oxygen), and the existence of compounds of carbon and hydrogen is so recognised.

In an experiment 4 gros $15\frac{4}{10}$ gr. of charcoal were heated in an iron tube lined with copper and water added drop by drop, when 6 gr. of ash remained in the tube and some water was collected on cooling the gas evolved. It was found that 2 oz. 3 gros 18 gr. of water were decomposed, and inflammable air and fixed air were collected, the latter being absorbed by caustic alkali, leaving 'heavy inflammable air' (air inflammable lourd, really a mixture of hydrogen and carbon monoxide) weighing 0·128 gr. per cu. in. This result gave the composition of carbonous acid as 78 oxygen and 22 carbon, a proportion 'evidently too low in carbon'. In the combustion of charcoal in oxygen over mercury some water was formed, and it was concluded that 17·2000 parts of charcoal contain 15·7537 of carbonaceous matter and 1·4463 of aqueous inflammable air (hydrogen).

(4) *Memoir to prove that water is not a simple substance but is susceptible of decomposition and recomposition.*[2] This celebrated memoir is said in a note added to it to have been 'read in the public meeting of Saint-Martin 1783, but several additions were made to it relative to the work in common with Meusnier on the same subject' (see no. 5). Fourcroy[3] says it was originally read on 12 November 1783, but details were added not contained in the memoir as read, also somewhat extended views (des vues un peu plus étendues) and some historical details (quelques traits historiques) not given in the reading. Daumas[4] says in relation to 'lu à la rentrée de la Saint-Martin de 1783': 'en realité, le 6 décembre de cette année Lavoisier n'a lu qu'une note sur la préparation de l'hydrogène par la limaille de fer et l'eau. Le mémoire . . . a été déposé en partie le 20 mars 1784 et lu un mois plus tard par Meusnier à l'Académie.' A full account of the memoir is given later (p. 436).

(5) Lavoisier and Meusnier, *Memoir to prove by decomposition that water is not a simple substance.*[5] A full account of this memoir is given later (p. 446).

(6) *Experiments on the Comparative Effect of different Combustibles.*[6] Lavoisier examined the calorific values of coal, coke, charcoal, and wood by comparing the weights and prices of each required to evaporate 2800 lb. of water.

(7) *On the Lighting of Theatres*;[7] of no chemical interest.

---

[1] VII, 1789, 68, 91.   [2] AdS, 1781 (1784), m 468; VIII, ii, 334.
[3] *Mémoires et Observations de Chimie*, 1784, 223; *id.*, (2), iii, 444.
[4] *Archives*, 1955, viii (old xxxiv), 411.
[5] AdS, 1781 (1784), h 21, m 269; VIII, ii, 360.
[6] AdS, 1781 (1784), h 5, m 379; VIII, ii, 377.
[7] AdS, 1781 (1784), m 409; VIII, iii, 91.

The Synthesis of Water

The famous memoir (4) on the composition of water begins with an historical summary. Macquer and Sigaud de la Fond, Lavoisier says, noticed 'in 1776 or 1777' the deposition of drops of water (the purity of which was not tested) on a porcelain saucer. Lavoisier says 'I had no knowledge then of the experiment of M. Macquer and was of the opinion that inflammable air on burning would give vitriolic or sulphurous acid. M. Bucquet, on the contrary thought it should result in fixed air'.

Macquer[1] says that he and 'Sigaud de Lafond' who assisted him had disproved an assertion of Priestley and others that addition of fixed air did not remove the inflammability of inflammable air; they found that the mixture in a wine bottle would not burn unless it contained some common air. Macquer then says:

'Je me suis assuré aussi, en interposant une sous-coupe de porcelaine blanche dans la flamme du gas inflammable, brûlant tranquillement à l'orifice du'une bouteille, que cette flamme n'est accompagnée d'aucune fumée fuligineuse; car l'endroit de la sous-coupe que léchoit la flamme, est resté parfaitement blanc; il s'est trouvé seulement mouillé de guettelettes assez sensibles d'une liqueur blanche comme de l'eau, & qui ne nous a paru en effet n'être que de l'eau pure.'

De la Metherie[2] afterward said: 'De l'air inflammable brûlé avec de l'air pur donne beaucoup d'eau, comme M. Macquer & mois nous étions apperçus des premiers'; he had[3] found that inflammable air procured by heating dry steel filings in a small glass bulb (when, it is true, some water always condensed on the neck),[4] burnt 'contre une glace' formed 'des guettes d'eau. M. Macquer avoit eu les mêmes résultats; mais il ne dit pas s'il avoit fait passer son air inflammable par l'eau, au lieu que dans mon procédé, il n'a aucun contact avec elle'.

Lavoisier goes on to mention an experiment made in September 1777 by Bucquet and himself in which the formation of fixed air was disproved by the absence of action on lime water. In 1781–2 he and 'Gingembre' (Gengembre) burnt a large quantity of vital air in a bottle of inflammable air, but again no acid was produced:

'We took a six pint bottle, which we filled with inflammable air; we kindled it quickly and poured into it at the same time two ounces of lime water; then we closed the bottle with a cork traversed by a copper tube terminating in a point, connected by a flexible tube with a reservoir filled with vital air. . . . There formed at the extremity of the copper tube, in the interior of the bottle, a beautiful point of very brilliant flame (un beau dard de flamme tres-brillant), and we saw with much pleasure the vital air burn in the inflammable air, in the same manner and with the same circumstances as inflammable air burns in vital air. We continued this combustion for a fairly considerable time, agitating the lime water and moving it about in the bottle without producing in it any appearance of precipitation.'

This case of 'reversed combustion' shows, as Wilson[5] said, 'how broad was the view he [Lavoisier] took of combustion as a phenomenon, in which each of the opposite bodies essential to its occurrence is equally concerned,

[1] *Dictionnaire de Chymie*, 1778, ii, 313–14.
[2] *Obs. Phys.*, 1786, xxviii, 3 (9).   [3] *Obs. Phys.*, 1782, xix, 16.
[4] *Obs. Phys.*, 1781, xviii, 156.   [5] *Life of Cavendish*, 1851, 339.

and may with equal propriety be termed the combustible, or the supporter of combustion.' The experiment (with similar ones) is described by Waldie.[1] If the lime water was replaced by distilled water or weak alkali, Lavoisier and Bucquet detected no trace of acid.

On 24 June 1783, Lavoisier and Laplace, in the presence of le Roi, Vandermonde and several other academicians, 'and of M. Blagden, at present (aujourd'hui) Secretary of the Royal Society of London', carried out an experiment of burning hydrogen and oxygen from a blowpipe in a closed glass vessel and collecting the water formed. Lavoisier says Blagden: 'told us that M. Cavendish had already tried, in London, to burn inflammable air in closed vessels, and that he had obtained a very sensible amount of water.' This is the sole mention of Cavendish:

Ce fut le 24 juin 1783 que nous fîmes cette expérience, M. de Laplace et moi, en présence de MM. le Roi, de Vandermonde, de plusieurs autres academiciens, et de M. Blagden, aujourd'hui secrétaire de la Société royale de Londres; ce dernier nous apprit que M. Cavendish avait déjà essayé, à Londres, de brûler de l'air inflammable dans des vaisseaux fermés, et qu'il avait obtenu une quantité d'eau très-sensible.

Blagden did not become Secretary of the Royal Society until May 1784, and the above must have been written after this. Lavoisier says that in his experiment water formed on the walls of the bell-jar in which the gases were burnt, and ran down on the surface of the mercury below. He collected 'a little less than 5 gros of water which, submitted to all the tests we could think of, appeared as pure as distilled water; it did not redden tincture of litmus, did not turn green syrup of violets, did not precipitate lime water; finally, with all the known reagents no trace of admixture could be discovered in it'. It was not possible to find the weights of the gases, 'but it is true no less in physics as in geometry that the whole is equal to its parts, and since we obtained nothing but pure water in this experiment, without any other residue, we thought we had the right to conclude that the weight of this water was equal to those of the two airs which had served to form it . . . One cannot make any reasonable objection against this conclusion . . . that water is not a simple substance and that it is composed, weight for weight, of inflammable air and vital air.' An account of the experiment was sent to the Academy next day. The register of the sittings of the Academy reads:[2]

Meeting of Wednesday, 25 June 1783.

MM. Lavoisier and De Laplace announced that they had lately repeated the combustion of Combustible Air with Dephlogisticated Air; they worked with about 60 pints of the airs, and the combustion was made in a closed vessel: the result was very pure water (le résultat a été de l'eau très pure).

Nothing is said of weights and Thorpe[3] says: 'The cautious scribe who penned that minute did not commit himself too far.'

The two gases were drawn from separate holders through leather tubes which, as Lavoisier says, would undoubtedly leak, and brought to a Y-tube of

---

[1] *Phil. Mag.*, 1838, xiii, 86; David Waldie (1813–89) was chemist to the Apothecaries' Society of Liverpool; he directed Simpson's attention to chloroform as an anaesthetic (October 1847); Duncom, *The Development of Inhalation Anaesthesia*, London, 1947, 172 f.

[2] Berthelot, (3).   [3] (1), 1902, 171.

copper, where they mixed, and were allowed to burn at the tail of the Y. This tube was fitted by grinding into the top of a bell-jar over mercury. The gases were not measured, but the rates were adjusted by trial so as to give the most luminous point of flame. When the gases had been burnt, the bell-jar was lifted by a saucer placed under the mercury, and its contents transferred to a funnel, from which the mercury could be run off and the water remaining collected. It weighed a little less than five drachms (*gros*).

It must be assumed, says Lavoisier, that the matter of heat produced in great abundance in the experiment, and passing through the pores of the vessels, is without weight, and the imponderability of heat and light, he says, had been proved in a memoir deposited with the Academy some months before, but not yet published. This was presumably the 'Nouvelles Réflexions sur l'augmentation de poids qu'acquièrent, en brûlant, le Soufre & le Phosphore; & sur la cause à laquelle on doit l'attribuer',[1] in which it is said that when phosphorus is kindled by a burning glass in a strong closed glass flask, the vessel after the combustion has 'exactly the same weight as before'.[2]

The historian of the Academy (Condorcet) says[3] the weight of water was 'sensibly' equal to the combined weights of the two gases, and that Lavoisier had heard at the same time (il apprit alors) that Cavendish had obtained water by the same operation.

A summary of the experiment and the conclusion was published in December 1783,[4] entitled:

Extrait d'un mémoire Lu par M. Lavoisier, à la Séance publique de l'Académie Royale des Sciences du 12 Novembre, sur la nature de l'Eau, & sur des expériences qui paroissent prouver que cette substance n'est point un élément proprement dit, mais qu'elle est susceptible de décomposition & de recomposition.

After mentioning Lavoisier and Bucquet's experiment in 1777 it says:

'Mr. Cavendish has . . . further observed, by using dry closed vessels, that a sensible quantity of moisture (une portion d'humidité sensible) deposits on the walls. Since the verification of this fact would be of extreme importance for chemical theory, M. La- voisier and M. de la Place proposed to confirm it by a large experiment (constater par une expérience en grande). . . . Finally [i.e., *after* this experiment], it has just been learnt from a letter written in London by M. Blagden to M. Berthollet,[5] that M. Cavendish had lately repeated (avoit repété dernièrement) the same experiment in a different way, and that, when the quantity of the two airs was well proportioned, he had constantly obtained the same result.'

This was probably the origin of the first note in Crell's *Annalen* (see p. 440) which was controverted by Blagden (who had ignored the French note). Nothing is said of Blagden's verbal communication of Cavendish's results.

[1] AdS, 1783 (1786), m 416; VIII, ii, 616.
[2] In IV, ii, 121, Lavoisier gives this paper a new title: 'Troisième Mémoire, Dans lequel on prouve que le calorique, qui se dégage de l'air vital pendant sa décomposition par le phosphore, n'a pas de pesanteur qu'on puisse apprécier', showing that he believed to the end of his life that the heat of combustion comes from the oxygen gas.
[3] AdS, 1781 (1784), h 21; Kahlbaum and Hoffmann, 1897, i, 158, plausibly suggest that the abstract was written by Lavoisier.
[4] *Obs. Phys.*, 1783, xxiii, 452–5 (December); Kopp, (2), iii, 272 ('wenig beachtet').
[5] In Duveen and Klickstein, *Ann. Sci.*, 1954, x, 58.

Blagden told De Luc[1] of his visit to Paris in June 1783, when he informed Lavoisier and others of Cavendish's experiments:

'en y ajoutant les idées de Mon. Cavendish & Watt [the mention of Watt is note-worthy] sur leurs Causes; mais il les avoit trouvés d'abord peu disposés à en admettre les conséquences sur la nature de l'eau, pensant toujours, que l'Eau recueillée après la combustion des deux Airs, y étoit contenue auparavant comme Substance étrangère.'

An experiment, however, was made on 24 June, Lavoisier being appointed to make it. In Lavoisier's note-book under the date 24 June 1783[2] it is said that the weight of the water was estimated at 3 gros (not 5 gros, as Lavoisier said, see p. 438) whilst 'on aurait dû retirer 1 oz. 1 gros 12 grains', so that there was a loss of $\frac{2}{3}$ of the air or else a loss in weight. Entries of 30 December 1784, to 1788 (mentioning experiments made in February 1785) record experiments on the composition and decomposition of water, and an entry of 1 May 1784 gives a calculation of the weights of water and the gases.[3]

On 28 June 1783 Laplace wrote to De Luc[4] that $2\frac{1}{2}$ gros (instead of 3 or 5) of pure water was obtained, but at that date: nous ne savons pas encore, si cette quantité d'eau représent le poids des airs consumés; c'est une expérience à recommencer avec toute l'attention possible.

Lavoisier[5] says later experiments made with Meusnier showed that the two gases 'in their greatest degree of purity' combined in the ratio of 12 vols. of vital air and 22·924345 of inflammable air, 'but it cannot be denied that some uncertainty still remains on the exactitude of this proportion' (given to six places of decimals; it should be 24·0). From the densities at 28 in. mercury pressure and 10° R., viz. 0·47317 grains per cu. in. for vital air and 0·037449 grains per cu. in. for inflammable air, as found in experiments with Meusnier,[6] it follows that the composition of water is:

	lb.
Vital air, or rather oxygen principle	0,86866273
Inflammable air, or rather inflammable principle of water	0,13133727
	1,00000000

or expressed in vulgar fractions of a pound, and in cubic inches:

	oz.	gros	gr.		cu. in.
oxygen principle	13	7	13,6	vital air	16919,07
inflammable principle	2	0	58,4	inflammable air	32321,29
	16	„	„		49240,36

[1] De Luc, Idées sur la Météorologie, London, 1787, ii, 223-4.
[2] Berthelot, (4), 293.   [3] Berthelot, (4), 119, 230, 299-310.
[4] Muirhead, Correspondence of James Watt, 1846, 41.
[5] AdS, 1781 (1784), m 468; VIII, ii, 340.   [6] In February 1785, see p. 447.

The ratio of the weights is 1 to 6·617 and of volumes 1·99628 to 1. The first is inaccurate (it should be 1 to 7·94) but the second is nearly correct (it should be 2·00288 to 1). Westrumb[1] complained about Lavoisier's 'mile-long decimals [meilenlange Dezimalbrüche]' and assumed accuracy, but since he weighed to a fraction of a grain his decimals have some justification. Lavoisier says water is 'composed, as is shown by the combustion of the two airs, by the union of the oxygen principle with the inflammable aqueous principle'. The latter un-ambiguously means hydrogen.

The notice in Rozier's journal (see p. 438) was probably the source of two statements published by Crell. The first[2] said that 'Lavoisier and Landriani have converted inflammable and dephlogisticated air into water [Wenn die Nachrichten sich bestätigen . . . sollen Hr. Lavoisier und Hr. Ritter Landriani die entzündbare und dephlogistierte Luft in Wasser verwandelt haben]'. The second, in May 1784,[3] said that:

'Mr. Cavendish, in London, has repeated the experiment of Lavoisier to generate water by the combustion of dephlogisticated and inflammable air. He presented the result of his experiment to the Royal Society of Science, which confirms that con-version of air or the generation de novo of water. His lecture was much applauded and also obtained the agreement of such a judicious chemist as Mr. R. Kirwan.'

'Hr. Cavendish in London hat die Versuche des Hrn. Lavoisier, aus der dephlogis-tierten und brennbaren Luft durch des Verbrennen Wasser zu erzeugen, nachge-macht. Er hat das Resultat seiner Versuch der Kön. Gesellschaft der Wissenschaft vorgelegt, die jene Verwandlung der Luft oder die neue Erzeugung des Wassers bestätigen. Seine Vorlesung hat vielen Beyfall, und auch die Beystimmung eines so einsichtsvollen Scheidekünstlers, als Hr. R. Kirwan gefunden.'

A translation by Blagden was given to Cavendish (who did not read German), and Blagden pointed out that Crell in the next number[4] had pub-lished a letter from Kirwan, 'mentioning your paper in proper terms, without any notice of Lavoisier's name or pretensions.'[5] Since the postscript to Blagden's memorandum is dated 'Thursday morning Mar. 10' it could not have been written in 1784, and he speaks of 'the number of Crell's Annals which I happened not to have looked over before (May 1784)': it must have been written in 1785. Cavendish was aware of what was going on in Paris, since a French translation of his paper (see p. 329) was published in London in 1785.[6] Inserted in Cavendish's paper as printed,[7] after it was read in January 1784, is the statement (in Blagden's handwriting in the MS.):

'During the last summer also, a friend of mine [Blagden] gave some account of them to M. Lavoisier, as well as of the conclusion drawn from them, that dephlogisticated air is only water deprived of phlogiston,' but 'till he [Lavoisier] was prevailed upon to repeat the experiment himself, he found some difficulty in believing that nearly the whole of the two airs could be converted into water'.

This agrees with what Blagden told de Luc (p. 439).

[1] Crell's Ann., 1793, I, 165.   [2] Crell's Ann., 1784, I, 95.
[3] Ib., 1784, I, 479.   [4] Ib., 1784, I, 523.
[5] Cavendish, Scientific Papers, 1921, ii, 32.
[6] Expériences Sur l'Air. Mémoire, Lû à la Société Royale, le 15 Janvier, 1784. A Londres, De l'Imprimerie du Sieur Edouard Cox, Great Queen-Street, Lincoln's-Inn Fields, 8°, 1785 (pp. viii, 68; Bolton, (1), 358; Duveen, 128).
[7] Phil. Trans., 1784, lxxiv, 119 (134).

In consequence of the information published by Crell, Blagden wrote to him a letter published early in 1786:[1]

'In the Spring of 1783, Mr. Cavendish communicated to me and other members of the Royal Society, his particular friends, the result of some experiments with which he had for a long time been occupied. He showed us that, from them, he must conclude that dephlogisticated air was nothing else than water deprived of its phlogiston; and *vice versa* that water was dephlogisticated air united to phlogiston. About the same time the news was brought to London that Mr. Watt of Birmingham had been induced by some experiments to hold a similar view. Soon after this I went to Paris, and in the company of Mr. Lavoisier and some other members of the Royal Academy of Sciences I gave some account of these experiments, and of the opinions founded upon them. They replied that they had already heard something of these experiments, and particularly that Dr. Priestley had repeated them. They did not doubt that in such manner a considerable quantity of water might be obtained, but they felt convinced that it did not come near the weight of the two kinds of air used, on which account it was not to be regarded as water formed or produced out of the two kinds of air, but was already contained in, and united with, the airs. This opinion was held by Mr. Lavoisier as well as the rest . . . but . . . they unanimously requested Mr. Lavoisier, who had all the necessary apparatus, to repeat the experiment on a somewhat larger scale, as soon as possible. This desire he complied with on the 24th June, 1783. . . . Mr. Lavoisier cannot in any way be charged with having advanced anything untrue, but it can still less be denied that he was silent on a part of the truth. (Ueberhaupt kann man auch Hrn. L. nicht überführen, irgend etwas der Wahrheit zuwider vorgebracht zu haben; ob er aber nicht einen Theil der Wahrheit verschwiegen habe, das mögte weniger zu leugnen stehen). For he should have acknowledged that I had, some days before, apprised him of Mr. Cavendish's experiments. . . . Mr. Lavoisier has also passed over a very noteworthy circumstance, viz. that the experiment was made in consequence of what I had told him. He should also have stated in his publication, not only that Mr. Cavendish had obtained "une quantité d'eau très sensible" but that the water was equal in weight to the two airs added together, and he might have added that I had told him Messrs Cavendish and Watt's conclusions, viz. that water, and not an acid or other substance, arose from the combustion of the inflammable and dephlogisticated airs. . . . Mr. Lavoisier was induced to institute again such experiments solely by reason of the account he had from me, and of our English experiments, and he really discovered nothing beyond what had been pointed out to him as having previously been done and demonstrated in England.'

Berthelot[2] spoke of 'the unjustifiable imputations of Blagden, who, impelled by passion, went so far as to interpolate and falsify, with his own hand, the manuscript memoirs of Cavendish, in order to gain arguments in support of his accusations'. These 'interpolations and falsifications' were added with authorisation by Cavendish and have been considered previously (p. 357). Berthelot's ill-tempered accusations are entirely baseless.[3]

Blagden must have felt perfectly sure of his facts before using such wording. He was, and continued to be, on excellent terms with the leading French chemists and was often in Paris, where he was apparently very welcome after his letter appeared.

When Priestley told him of his discovery of oxygen, Lavoisier was 'surprised', but when Blagden told him of Cavendish's synthesis of water he was incredulous. It will be noticed that Blagden also mentioned Watt's conclusions

[1] Crell's *Ann.*, 1786, I, pt. 1, 58–61; tr. in Muirhead, *Correspondence of the late James Watt*, 1846, 71–4; and in Cavendish, *Scientific Papers*, Cambridge, 1921, ii, 41–2; see Fourcroy, (2), iii, 444; Wilson, *Life of Cavendish*, 1851, 124, 142, 394, 432; for a summary of Lavoisier's work (incl. the compos. of water), see De la Metherie, *Obs. Phys.*, 1786, xxv, 3.
[2] (1), 1890.   [3] Thorpe, (1), 178.

to Lavoisier, as the same as those of Cavendish. Kirwan in December 1783 told Watt that Blagden had 'explained the whole minutely to Mr. Lavoisier last July. This he authorized me to tell you'. ('July' is a mistake for 'June'.) Lavoisier must, therefore, have been told that 'water is composed of dephlogisticated air and phlogiston', and he knew that in England inflammable air was by some regarded as phlogiston. He knew both the experiment and the explanation. Long before Blagden's letter appeared, Beddoes,[1] referring to Cavendish's experiments, said:

'Other chemists, both at home and abroad, have now amply confirmed this unexpected observation, as Dr. Priestley, S. Landriani at Milan, and Mr. Lavoisier at Paris, who has used very large quantities in his experiments, but has shamefully attempted to appropriate the discovery to himself; and he is accordingly mentioned in many foreign journals as the first discoverer.'

Lavoisier[2] says his paper was inserted 'par erreur' after that with Meusnier[3] on the decomposition of water, and in the *Oeuvres* the two have been transposed without comment. Muirhead[4] remarked that: 'although M. Lavoisier's paper was in part read before that by him and M. Meusnier, yet much of it contains express allusions to that other, and was therefore written later in order of time'; and Wilson[5] that 'Lavoisier was anxious to have his experiments on the synthesis considered as anterior in time to those on the analysis of water', as in fact, the earliest one was, but not the one for which numerical results are given.

Lavoisier does not claim that the early experiment was *quantitative*; he merely says he and Laplace 'avaient les premiers obtenu ainsi une quantité d'eau assez considérable pour la soumettre à quelques épreuves chimiques':[6] 'les premiers' must refer to the French experimenters, since Priestley had *published* his and Warltire's experiments in 1781,[7] but the words could also imply that Laplace and Lavoisier had 'les premiers' discovered this fact, and Daumas[8] was so misled.

In a paper printed in 1788[9] Lavoisier says:

j'ai cherché à établir dans de précédents mémoires . . . que l'eau est le résultat de la combinaison de quinze parties de base de gaz inflammable ou hydrogène, et de quatre-vingt-cinq d'oxygène . . . comme nous croyons l'avoir précédemment démontré.

It is said that this memoir was 'lu et deposé' before the *Nomenclature Chimique*, published in 1787, was begun, and it may go back to the first part of 1786 (see p. 469). In 1789[10] Lavoisier says the discovery of the composition of water is 'très-moderne' and its history 'est encore contestée'; for this the 'Mémoires de l'Académie des Sciences, année 1781' could be consulted.

It has been said that Lavoisier did not take notice of Blagden's letter, but

[1] Tr. (anon.) of Bergman, *Dissertation on Elective Attractions*, 1785, 344; the reference to Priestley is to Watt, *Phil. Trans.*, 1784, lxxiv, 329.

[2] AdS, 1781 (1784), iii 468.   [3] AdS, 1781 (1784), iii 269; see p. 446.
[4] *Correspondence*, 1846, 152.   [5] *Life of Cavendish*, 1851, 338.
[6] VIII, ii, 360.   [7] E & O, *Nat. Phil.*, 1781, ii, *395.
[8] *Chymia*, 1950, iii, 45 (53).   [9] AdS, 1786 (1788), iii 590; VIII, ii, 656.
[10] VII, 87.

this is incorrect. It could not be ignored. In a report by Lavoisier, Brisson, Meusnier, and Laplace[1] it is said:

Cavendish paroît avoir remarqué le premier que l'eau produit dans cette combustion est le résultat de la combinaison des deux fluides aëriformes et qu'elle est d'un poid égal au leur. Plusieurs expériences faites en grand et d'un manière très-précise, par Lavoisier, la Place, Monge, Meusnier, et Lefebvre de Gineau, ont confirmé cette découverte important.

This statement is almost identical with that in a report made on 28 August 1789 by Lavoisier, Brisson, Meusnier, and Laplace (not approved by d'Arcet and Baumé) on a memoir by Seguin,[2] in which, however, *gaz* appears instead of *fluides aëriformes*. The weightiest name here is Laplace, who had collaborated with Lavoisier in the first experiment, and he probably felt that, after Blagden's letter, the truth had better be told. Berthollet, who reproduced the passage in his *Statique Chimique*, printed the whole of it in italics. This disposes completely and finally of any claim that Lavoisier is entitled to the discovery stated.

Arago[3] simply ignored Lavoisier. Kopp,[4] who emphasised that Blagden told Lavoisier of the *conclusions* of Cavendish and Watt, which were 'similar', summed up by saying that: (i) Cavendish was the first to establish the fact that water is the sole and quantitative product of the combination of oxygen and 'inflammable air from metals' (hydrogen), as Lavoisier later publicly admitted (see above); (ii) Watt in April 1783 had concluded that water is a compound body (see p. 349), formed from oxygen and 'phlogiston', and *if* phlogiston means a particular kind of inflammable air, viz. hydrogen, this is correct, but Watt did not make this important point clear, and since he says phlogiston sometimes forms fixed air, he did not distinguish hydrogen from carbon monoxide; (iii) Lavoisier first recognised, and published in December 1783, that water is formed by the combination of oxygen and hydrogen (principe inflammable aqueux, obtained from iron or zinc and dilute sulphuric acid): water 'is composed, as is shown by the combustion of the two airs, by the union of the oxygen principle with the inflammable aqueous principle' (see p. 487). This conclusion is Lavoisier's own (war eine ihm eigenthümliche). Cavendish had recognised that this was a consequence of the antiphlogistic system (see p. 335) but Lavoisier had already published it.

Guyton de Morveau[5] restated Lavoisier's conclusion in the form: 'water is only oxygenated hydrogen, or the immediate product of the combustion of hydrogen gas with oxygen gas, deprived of the light and caloric which are disengaged.'

A metal such as zinc dissolves in dilute sulphuric acid to form a salt of the

---

[1] Lavoisier, IV, ii, 307 (309); see also VIII, v, 605; 'Extrait des registres de l'Académie des Sciences, du 28 août, 1790'; the passage is reproduced by Berthollet, *Statique Chimique*, 1803, ii, 25 (from IV); Kopp, (2), iii, 298 (from *Ann. Chim.*, 1790, vii, 257); and Wilson, *Proc. Roy. Soc. Edin.*, 1859, iv, 205.

[2] Lavoisier, VIII, iv, 515.

[3] Éloge of Watt, AdS, 1840, lxi, h lxi–clxxxvi; *Oeuvres*, 1854, i, 371 f.; Brougham's previous short account is added at the end.

[4] (2), iii, 271 f., 293 f., 305.   [5] In VI, 1787, 33.

metal and inflammable air is evolved, but when the oxide of the metal dissolves in the acid to form the salt, no inflammable air is formed. Whence comes the inflammable air in the first experiment? Cavendish in 1766 (see p. 314) had explained its formation by assuming that a metal is composed of its calx and phlogiston, and that inflammable air is phlogiston:

$$\text{metal} + \text{acid} = \quad \text{salt} \quad + \text{inflammable air.}$$
$$(\text{calx} + \phi) + \text{acid} = (\text{calx} + \text{acid}) + \quad \phi$$

whilst in the second case (calx + acid) = salt. Lavoisier was now able, from a suggestion by Laplace, to say that a metal such as zinc, dissolving in dilute acid, takes oxygen from water to form oxide of zinc, which dissolves in the acid to form a salt, and the hydrogen of the water is set free:

$$\text{zinc} + (\text{hydrogen} + \text{oxygen}) = \text{zinc oxide} + \text{hydrogen,}$$
$$\text{zinc oxide} + \text{sulphuric acid} = \text{sulphate of zinc.}$$

Lavoisier regarded the acid as an oxide; at present it is regarded as (oxide + water), so that the hydrogen really comes from the acid. He says[1] that Laplace, who had assisted in the experiments (avait partagées souvent), in a letter of September 1783 explained the evolution of inflammable air as due to the decomposition of water: the metal removes the vital air (oxygen) to form a calx, which then dissolves in the acid to form a salt, and at the same time 'the inflammable principle [of the water] is evolved in the form of air', which inflammable air on combustion in vital air reproduces water. Lavoisier says that Laplace's letter contained 'idées simples autant que profondes qu'il avoit conçues d'apres les expériences qu'il avoit faites en commun avec lui'. The metals dissolved in the acid in the form of calces (oxides) (Scheele knew this in 1776, see p. 230), and as this occurred in closed vessels the vital air did not come from the atmosphere. It did not come from the vitriolic acid (sulphur trioxide), as there was no formation of sulphur or sulphurous acid; the acid, as Lavoisier had shown, required the same amount of alkali for saturation before and after the dissolution of the metal, and thus only the water could have furnished the vital air to the metal, and its other principle was evolved as inflammable air. The latter could not have come from the metal, as it was not formed with nitric acid.

This note from Laplace induced Lavoisier to make experiments on the decomposition of water by iron. Lavoisier says Blagden had made known 'à cette époque' Priestley's experiments on the reduction of calces by inflammable air (see p. 268), and Magellan and other English physicists had communicated them to several members of the Academy. Fourcroy[2] says Lavoisier made further experiments 'pendant les vacances de l'académie en 1783', to which he was led by experiments of Bergman, Fontana, Hassenfratz, Stoultz and Lefèvre. Lavoisier knew that minium (lead oxide) loses $\frac{1}{12}$ of its weight on reduction and water is formed, hence the inflammable air does not unite with the calx but takes oxygen from it to form water.

[1] AdS, 1781 (1784), m 468; VIII, ii, 341–2.   [2] (2), iii, 445.

Lavoisier and Meusnier in the winter of 1783–4 made experiments on the decomposition of water by heated iron.[1]

Jean Baptiste Marie Charles Meusnier de la Place (Tours, 19 June 1754–Mainz, 17 June 1793) was a Lieut.-Col. in the Corps de Génie who became a General of Division and was killed in action. Besides this work he published a description of a gasometer[2] and a method of ensuring the complete combustion of oil and increasing the luminosity of lamps for use in the laboratory for distillations (see p. 533).[3] Meusnier was then engaged in perfecting Montgolfier balloons and was interested in the production of light inflammable air from water, hence Lavoisier chose him as a collaborator.

Lavoisier said:[4]

'I then [in 1783] observed that if water is really composed, as announced, by the combustion of the two airs, the union of the oxygen principle with the inflammable aqueous principle, it could not be decomposed so as to obtain one of its principles separately without presenting to the other a substance with which it has more affinity. The inflammable aqueous principle having more affinity with the principle of oxygen than with any other body . . . it is the oxygen principle which must be attacked. . . . M. Bergman has informed us, in his analysis of iron, that the filings of this metal are converted, in distilled water alone, into the martial ethiops [Fe_3O_4 hydrate], whilst at the same time a large quantity of inflammable air is disengaged.'[5]

In Lavoisier's first form of publication[6] Bergman is not mentioned, as Kopp[7] noticed; Lavoisier probably got to know of Bergman's observation from the French translation, *Analyse du Fer*, 1783, and his own discovery was perhaps independent. Lavoisier says that Fontana had obtained a notable quantity of inflammable air by extinguishing 'des charbons ardents' in water under a bell-jar filled with water, and Sage had told him of an observation sent from Germany by Hassenfratz, Stoultz, and d'Hellancourt, pupils in the School of Mines, that a red-hot iron plunged into water under a bell-jar produced inflammable air. Laplace had often told him (m'avait répété bien des fois) that he supposed that the inflammable air evolved in the dissolution of iron and zinc in acids was due only to the decomposition of water (see p. 444). 'All these considerations together could leave me in no doubt that the metals exert a marked action on water.'

Lavoisier then gives an account of Priestley's experiments on the revivification of metallic calces in inflammable air (see p. 268), when water 'must have been' formed (Priestley says it was).[8] He thus had plenty of prior information:

Tel était l'état de nos connaissances sur la décomposition et la recomposition de l'eau, lorsque nous nous trouvâmes insensiblement engagés, M. Meusnier et moi, à reprendre cette question sous un autre point de vue, pendant l'hiver de 1783 à 1784.

The use of inflammable air in 'machines aérostatiques' made it essential to find some cheap process for making it on the large scale and it was 'natural' to attempt to obtain it from water. The experiments would be found in another

---

[1] Lavoisier, AdS, 1781(1784), m 334; Meusnier and Lavoisier, *ib.*, 269 (read 21 April 1784); VIII, ii, 360.
[2] AdS, 1782 (1785), m 466.   [3] AdS, 1784, m 390–8.
[4] AdS, 1781 (1784), m 468; VIII, ii, 341.
[5] Bergman, *Opuscula*, Uppsala, 1783, iii, 82, 93, 95 (limaturi martis sub aqua aëris inflammabilis portionem promat, in pulverem nigrum sensim fatiscens); publ. in 1781; the discovery was really made by Scheele, see p. 229.
[6] *Obs. Phys.*, 1783, xxiii, 452.   [7] (2), iii, 272, 296.   [8] VIII, ii, 344–50.

memoir, read in Easter (Pâques) 1784 (see p. 435). Lavoisier[1] then describes
the method he and Meusnier used to decompose water by heated iron. An iron
gun-barrel coated outside with clay, sand, and charcoal powder was placed in a
furnace in a slightly inclined position, and water allowed to drip slowly into
the hot tube from a tin funnel attached to the upper end. The lower end was
attached to a spiral tube luted to a tubulated bottle to collect the liquid coming
over. From this a tube luted into the neck led the gaseous products to the
'pneumato-chemical apparatus' (Fig. 40). The iron tube was rapidly corroded,

FIG. 40. APPARATUS OF LAVOISIER AND MEUSNIER.

and since steam was found not to act on red-hot copper, a copper tube was
substituted. This was packed with iron in the form of thin rolled leaves or in
small bars turned into spirals:

'and having heated the tube to redness, we passed in the water. We continued some of
the experiments until the iron was perfectly saturated and there was no more production of air. When the experiment was finished we found 1st that the iron was reduced
to a friable black substance attracted by a magnet, which when reduced to powder did
not differ in any way from the martial ethiops obtained from cold water; 2nd that the
iron in this operation had acquired an increase in weight of about 25 pounds per
quintal; 3rd that the quantity of inflammable air disengaged was, per quintal of iron,
930198 cubic inches or 538⅓ cubic feet, which comes in weight to 3,77986075 pounds.
It is, however, difficult to bring the iron to this degree of complete saturation.'

The second memoir 'par MM. Meusnier et Lavoisier',[2] written by Meusnier
in the first person so as to make Lavoisier's contributions clear, mentions the
work of Monge (see p. 453) and says Berthollet acted as a 'witness and co-
operator'. It is said that the experiments consisted in passing through a red-
hot iron tube a current of steam or dropping in liquid water. The inflammable
air obtained was identical with that formed by the action of some metals on
sulphuric acid. It was inflammable, detonated with dephlogisticated air, and
had a strong empyreumatic odour (pure hydrogen is odourless).

[1] Ib., 351.
[2] Obs. Phys., 1784, xxiv, 368–80, and plate (Par M. Meusnier, Lieutenant en premier au
Corps du Génie, Membre de l'Academie, en commun avec M. Lavoisier; May 1784); AdS, 1781
(1784), m 269; VIII, ii, 360–73.

By interposing a cooling worm after the iron tube it was found that 125 pints of inflammable air collected and 3 oz. 1 gros of water disappeared. The inflammable air was 'weighed with the most scrupulous attention' and found to be nine times lighter than atmospheric air and hence the volume collected weighed 4 gros and some grains, or a sixth of the water used, which 'agrees precisely with the result of the capital experiment in which water is formed by the combustion of the two airs'. Another experiment gave 61 pints of inflammable air with a loss of 1 oz. 7 gros of water, 'of which the sixth part was, to a few grains, equal to the total of the disengaged gas.' With an iron tube lined with sheet copper, 2 oz. 5 gros 47 gr. of sheet iron increased in weight 2 gros 54 gr. 'as our theory requires', 1 oz. 5 gros 54 gr. of water was consumed, and 53 pints of inflammable air collected.

They then used 4 gros 15 gr. of previously ignited charcoal, used up 2 oz. 3 gros of water, found 6 gr. of ash, and collected 118 pints of gas which contained a little more than $\frac{1}{4}$ of its volume of fixed air and weighing about half that of atmospheric air, which 'agrees perfectly with that indicated by theory for a mixture of fixed air and the inflammable air of water' in these proportions. (The gas actually was a mixture of hydrogen and carbon monoxide, but Lavoisier and Meusnier's results were so inaccurate that they could easily find 'perfect' or 'exact' agreement.) The weight of inflammable gas was estimated as 9 gros 22 gr. 'This experiment gives the first example of a complete combustion operated without the concourse of the air.' More exact calculations (which they do not give) showed, it is said, that 'the inflammable air of water in its state of greatest purity, will be about thirteen times lighter than atmospheric air, and that water contains about the seventh part of its weight of it'. (These figures are quite good; the correct values are 14·4, and one-ninth.) It is suggested that the decomposition of water by iron or charcoal could be used on the large scale to produce inflammable gas; or other combustibles such as spirit of wine or oils could be used to give vapours decomposable by steam.

In 1785[1] Lavoisier mentions numerous experiments (des expériences nombreuses) which he will describe elsewhere (he does not seem to have done so) giving the weights of 1 cu. ft. at 28 in. barometer and 10° R. of the following gases (presumably dry ?), which Nicholson[2] recalculated in grains per 100 cu. in. as in the last column:

	oz.	gros	gr.	
Atmospheric air	1	3	3	46
Vital air (O_2)	1	4	—	50
Mofette (N_2)	1	2	48	44

In the altered version, vital air is 1 oz. 4 gros 12 gr. Hassenfratz[3] says Lavoisier later tried to correct for the nitrogen contained in the oxygen as impurity and gave 51 grains per 100 cu. in. as the density of pure oxygen. In his

[1] *Mémoires de Médecine et de Physique Medicale. Tirés des Registres de la Société Royale de Médecine*, 1787, v, 569–82 (lecture read in 1785); altered version, from IV, iii, 13, in VIII, ii, 676.
[2] In Kirwan, *An Essay on Phlogiston*, 1789, 37.　　　[3] In Kirwan, *op. cit.*, 37.

book[1] Lavoisier gives as the results of his own experiments: air 0·46005, azote 0·44444, oxygen 0·50694, hydrogen 0·03539, and carbonic acid 0·68985, and Kirwan's for nitrous gas (NO) 0·54690, ammonia 0·27488, and sulphurous acid (SO_2) 1·03820, in grains per cu. in. at 10° R. and 28 in. of mercury.

In May 1784, Dr. John Grieve wrote from Paris to Black: 'The chemical experiments made by Lavoisier and Meunier [sic] on water, & the conclusion drawn from them, viz. that water is composed of dephlogisticated and inflammable air, does not meet with general credit in this place.'[2]

Lavoisier[3] later described an 'ideal' experiment in which 274 grains of iron are placed in a glass tube, which is heated to redness and steam from water boiled in a small retort passed over (Fig. 41). A volume of 416 cubic inches of

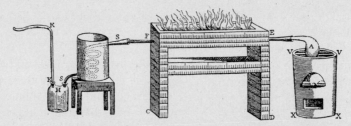

FIG. 41. APPARATUS OF LAVOISIER FOR THE DECOMPOSITION OF
STEAM BY RED-HOT IRON.

inflammable air is obtained, weighing 15 grains, and 100 grains of water were evaporated. The 274 grains of iron in the tube increased in weight by 85 grains. The result shows that:

'100 grains of water have been decomposed; 85 of oxygen have united with the iron to constitute it in the state of black oxide and 15 grains of a particular inflammable gas are disengaged: thus water is composed of oxygen and of the base of an inflammable gas, in the proportion of 85 parts to 15. Hence water, independently of the oxygen which is one of its principles, and which is common to many other substances, contains another which is peculiar to it and is its constituent radical, and for which we have been compelled to find a name. Nothing seems better than that of hydrogen (hydrogène), that is to say, generative principle of water, from υδορ [a mistake for ὕδωρ], water, and γείνομαι [a mistake for γέννάω], I produce. We call hydrogen gas the compound of this principle with caloric, and the word hydrogen alone expresses the base of this same gas, the radical of water.'

This name was introduced by Guyton de Morveau:[4] Hidrogène, c'est à dire engendrant l'eau.

A successful repetition of Lavoisier and Meusnier's experiment by Fontana[5] left him unconvinced of the correctness of their interpretation; it was still doubtful if water was a compound. Scopoli,[6] reporting experiments by Volta in which 'an astonishing amount of inflammable air' had been obtained by passing steam over red-hot iron or charcoal (and on the action of muriatic acid on pyrolusite), refused to accept Lavoisier's theory, but he also rejected the theory of Kirwan, Priestley and Wiegleb that inflammable air is phlogiston,

[1] VII, 572.   [2] Ramsay, Life and Letters of Joseph Black, 1918, 85.
[3] VII, 1789, 92.   [4] VI, 1787, 33.   [5] Obs. Phys., 1785, xvii, 228.
[6] Crell's Ann., 1785, II, 339, 433; Crell's Beyträge, 1786, I, Stück iv, 3.

since metals produce no inflammable air on calcination, inflammable air does not produce sulphur with vitriolic acid, etc., and there are different kinds of inflammable air (including marsh gas) but only one phlogiston. Giorgi and Cioni[1] in Florence, however, obtained a mixture of common air and dephlogisticated air on passing steam over red-hot iron. This was disproved, and Lavoisier and Meusnier's result confirmed, by Klaproth.[2]

Lavoisier and Meusnier's experiment did not convince Priestley (see p. 270), who gave a different explanation of it, and De la Metherie[3] thought the pure air combining with the iron had passed in through the red-hot tube in combination with the matter of heat. De la Metherie[4] after remarking that 'Cavendish's opinion' that inflammable and dephlogisticated airs are 'really in water' had been adopted by Monge, Laplace, and Lavoisier, gave as his own view that water is contained in the two airs: 'in fact we know that there is no air which does not contain water.' It could be supposed that the iron gave out phlogiston, which appeared as inflammable air, and at the same time the water united with the iron. The weights of hydrogen and iron calx would then be equal to the weights of iron and water. Thus the experiment was not conclusive and Cavendish's synthetic experiment, although less ambiguous, was explained by him on the basis of the phlogiston theory (see p. 334).

De Luc[5] in several letters to De la Metherie and Fourcroy on vapours, air, rain, and modern chemistry, refused to accept Lavoisier's theory of the composition of water; he first believed in this when he was told of the experiments by Watt, Laplace, etc., but Priestley's experiments had convinced him that it was incorrect. It also fails to explain the formation of rain, and 'what is the use of a few ounces of water made artificially' if this is the case ? De Luc repeated his criticisms in his book,[6] saying that clouds form on high mountains where the hygrometer indicates no dissolved or suspended water, and where there is no inflammable air. Whence comes this water if it is not an integral part of the gases which compose the atmosphere?

After describing the experiments made with Meusnier (see p. 447) on the action of steam on iron and on charcoal, Lavoisier said later[7] that in January–February 1785 the composition of water (85 oxygen and 15 hydrogen) was demonstrated in the presence of the 'Commissaires de l'Académie', and 'nous rendrons compte à l'Académie, dans un très-grand detail, des résultats que nous avons obtenus'. This was never done.

An account of the experiments is contained in MS. laboratory records.[8] The experiments were made on 27 (Sunday) and 28 February 1785 in the Arsenal. Lavoisier invited a crowd of notabilities to witness them and more than thirty attended on and off. There was an accident in an experiment on the decomposition of water by heated iron, when some of the water spirted on the wall of

[1] Obs. Phys., 1785, xxvii, 56.   [2] Crell's Ann., 1786, I, 202.
[3] Obs. Phys., 1786, xxviii, 3 (8).
[4] Obs. Phys., 1784, xxiv, 45; 1787, xxxi, 200 (Sur la prétendue décomposition de l'eau).
[5] Obs. Phys., 1790, xxxvi, 144, 193, 276, 363; 1791, xxxviii, 460; 1791, xxxix, 11.
[6] Introduction à la physique terrestre par les fluides expansible, précédée de deux Mémoires sur la nouvelle théorie chimique considerée sur différents points de vue, 2 vols., Paris, 1803.
[7] VII, 507, 511.   [8] Daumas and Duveen, Chymia, 1959, v, 113–29.

the room, but a correction was made by matching the wet patch with known weights of water. The complicated calculations of the synthesis experiments (perhaps by Meusnier) showed that 4 oz. 6 gros 60·62 gr. of oxygen and 6 gros 39·30 gr. of hydrogen formed 5 oz. 4 gros 51 gr. of water (corrected by 1 gros 7·5 gr. for the moisture in the gases). Thus 1 quintal (100 lb.) of water contains 86 lb. of oxygen. (The old figure was 85.) The water was weighed on 1 March and found to be acid. The residual gases were analysed on 7 March and found to contain fixed air, oxygen, hydrogen, and nitrogen, and the calculated results were signed by most of the commissioners on 12 March. Meusnier was given the task of writing up the memoir, which he does not seem to have completed. Two experiments on the decomposition of water by heated iron gave 82 and 81·5 lb. of oxygen per quintal.

Chaptal,[1] who says he was present at the experiment made in February 1785 'at the house of Lavoisier', gives $2364\frac{66}{100}$ grains of oxygen and $471\frac{125}{1000}$ of hydrogen, leaving a gaseous residue of 456 gr. and 35·25 gr. of moisture in the hydrogen to be deducted; thus a total weight of 3188·4 gr. of gas was used. The weight of the water (which was acid) was 3219 gr., which is 31 gr. more than the weight of the gases. 'It was ascertained by this experiment that 100 parts of water were formed of 85 of oxygen and 15 of hydrogen.'

Berthollet says in a letter to Blagden of 19 March 1785:[2] L'on s'est beaucoup occupé ici ces derniers tems de la belle découverte de Mr. Cavendish sur la Composition de Leau [sic]. Mr. Lavoisier a tâché de porter sur cet objet toute L'exactitude dont il est susceptible. . . . Il s'est formé cinq onces et demi d'eau qui contenait environ quarante grains d'acide nitreux: il n'y a eu que très peu de residu. La quantité d'air déphlogistiqué qui est entrée dans la composition de l'eau a été en poids à cette du gas inflammable à peu près comme 81 à 19 et cette de l'air déphlogistiqué qui s'est fixé dans le fer dans la décomposition de l'eau a été la même proportion avec le gas inflammable qui s'est dégagé.

Mr. Lavoisier veut répéter l'expérience en faisant brûler l'air déphlogistiqué dans le gas inflammable, et il y a apparence qu'alors on n'aura point d'acide nitreux, selon les belles observations de Mr. Cavendish. Mr. de Laplace a pensé d'après tout ce qu'en sait deja que Lacide nitreux était un composé de gas inflammable et d'une beaucoup plus grande quantité d'air dephlogistiqué qu'il y en a dans l'eau et que Le gas nitreux tent le milieu entre L'acide nitreux et Leau.

Some of the apparatus used in Lavoisier's experiments, including the gas-holders and the combustion globe, still exists in Paris.[3] Some large figures of the complete apparatus appeared in the *Journal Polytype des Sciences et des Arts*, which was published only (with the patronage of Lavoisier) in 1786.[4] The gasometer is shown in the plate accompanying the paper on blowpipes by Hassenfratz.[5] Guyton de Morveau[6] quotes 'le Journal polytipe, tom. I, n°. II, pag. 40' for the capacity of the globe as 961·92 cu. in. He was told about the apparatus by de Virly, who had seen it, and it was similar to Monge's (see p. 453). The apparatus used in February 1785 included two 'machines' (gasholders) for vital air and for hydrogen gas. It seems to be modified from that described by Meusnier[7] as concerns the gasholders; the gasholders and

[1] *Chemistry Applied to Arts and Manufactures*, 1801, iii, 436–9.
[2] Wilson, 1851, 345–6 (in full); Thorpe, (2), 1890, xliii, 3; *id.*, (1), 1902, 182; Duveen and Klickstein, *Ann. Sci.*, 1954, x, 58.
[3] Daumas, *Chymia*, 1950, iii, 45, and plates.
[4] Berthelot, (4), 287; Daumas and Duveen, 117.
[5] *Obs. Phys.*, 1786, xxviii, 345.   [6] *Ency. Méthod.*, *Chymie*, 1789, i, 731, 733 f.
[7] AdS, 1782 (1785), m 466; Lavoisier, VIII, ii, 432.

the combustion part are described by Lavoisier.[1] The apparatus (gasholders) for weighing the gases consisted of copper tanks open at the bottom, immersed in tanks of water, and counterpoised on an enormous balance, to the beam of which they were attached by chains. It is very elaborate and complicated, and Brande[2] said Lavoisier 'shines as the inventor of costly and complicated apparatus, the greater part of which might, however, have been superseded by simpler and cheaper utensils'. Girtanner[3] describes the various pieces of expensive apparatus for the synthesis of water made by Fortin in Paris (where Girtanner was then living). He says the experiments were 'made before the Academy' with the old apparatus used by Lavoisier in his house, and no experiments had then (1791) been made with the new apparatus described in the *Traité*. The experiments with the old apparatus were difficult and the calculations complicated. The apparatus used by Lavoisier and Meusnier was constructed to Meusnier's design by Mégnié.

Arthur Young, who visited Lavoisier at the Arsenal in October, 1787, says[4] he saw Lavoisier's apparatus for burning inflammable and vital air, 'a noble machine,' as Lavoisier said: 'et même par un artiste François.' This was to weigh the two 'airs' and 'the formation or deposition of the water, it not yet being ascertained whether the water be actually made or deposited'. Lavoisier's mercury trough contained 250 lb. of metal, 'but his furnaces did not seem so well calculated for the higher degrees of heat as some others I have seen.' Another 'engine' seen was 'an electrical apparatus enclosed in a balloon, for trying electrical experiments in any sort of air'. This was probably the glass globe described by Lavoisier.[5]

It consisted of a large balloon (about 30 pints) of crystal glass, to the wide mouth of which was cemented a copper plate BC (Fig. 42), with four holes to which abut four tubes. The first *Hh* could be adapted by its extremity *h* to an air pump to evacuate the balloon. The second *gg* communicated by its extremity *MM* with a reservoir of oxygen gas. The third *Dd* communicated by its extremity *dNN* with a reservoir of hydrogen gas: the extremity *d'* of this pipe terminated in a very small opening through which a very fine needle could barely pass. Through this small opening the hydrogen passed from the reservoir, in which it was under a pressure of one or two inches of water. To the fourth hole was cemented a glass tube through which passed a metal wire *GL*, with a small ball at *L* so that an electric spark could be taken from *L* to *d'* to ignite the hydrogen. The metal wire

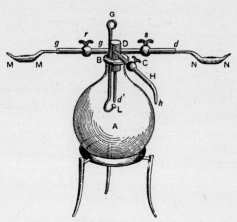

FIG. 42. LAVOISIER'S APPARATUS FOR THE SYNTHESIS OF WATER FROM HYDROGEN AND OXYGEN.

---

[1] VII, 96, 508; Partington, *The Composition of Water*, 1928, 42.   [2] 1848, I, lxxxix.
[3] *Neue chemische Nomenklatur für die deutsche Sprache*, Berlin, 1791, 5 f.
[4] *Travels in France*, ed. C. Maxwell, Cambridge, 1929, 81 f.
[5] VII, 96, 508; Kahlbaum and Hoffmann, 1897, i, 165, and Speter, (1), 147, 197, wrongly thought the experiment was never made.

GL was movable in the glass tube, so that the ball *L* could be moved from *d'* when the gas was kindled. Each of the pipes *dDd'*, *gg*, and *Hh* was provided with a tap.

The hydrogen and oxygen were dried by passing through the tubes *MM*, *NN*, about a foot long and an inch in diameter, filled with broken caustic potash, acetate of potash, or muriate or nitrate of lime. The oxygen gas, made by heating red precipitate, was left a long time over caustic potash solution, the hydrogen was made by the decomposition of water by very pure iron.

One or other of the gases was allowed to enter the exhausted balloon by the tube *gg*, then the other gas was forced by pressure through the tube *dDd'* and kindled by an electric spark. By supplying the two gases the combustion could go on for a long time. It was, however, enfeebled by the accumulation in the globe of azotic gas contained as an impurity in the hydrogen and oxygen, so that at a certain point the hydrogen and oxygen were shut off and the azotic gas pumped out of the globe. The process was so repeated two, three, etc., times. The water deposited on the inside of the balloon ran down and collected at the bottom. By weighing the balloon before and after the experiment the weight of water was found, and should be equal to the sum of the weights of the gases.

'It is by an experiment of this kind that M. Meusnier and I have recognised that 85 parts by weight of oxygen and 15 parts by weight of hydrogen are necessary to compose 100 parts of water. This experiment, which has not yet been published, was made in the presence of a numerous commission of the Academy. We brought to it the most scrupulous attentions and we have reason to believe it exact to a two-hundredth at least.'[1]

It was not so accurate as this, the true figures being 89 of oxygen and 11 of hydrogen, but Lavoisier used his result in many later important calculations.[2] During the winter of 1786–7 Lavoisier and Laplace repeated the synthesis of water in connexion with the heat of combustion of hydrogen (see p. 432), and later experiments were made by several chemists.

Le Fèvre de Gineau in an experiment made at the Collège de France from 23 May to 7 June 1788, 'in presence of almost all the chemists of Paris',[3] combined 35085·1 cu. in. of oxygen and 77267·4 cu. in. of hydrogen, at 10° R. and 28 in. mercury, of total weight 20323·8 gr. forming 20293 gr. of water, a deficit of 30·8 gr. The oxygen weighed 18298·5 gr. and the hydrogen 4756·3 gr. The residual gas turned lime water milky unless the oxygen (obtained from manganese dioxide) had been washed with milk of lime. The water had a sp. gr. of 1·001025 (Lavoisier's was 1·0051) and contained 23·63 gr. of nitric acid.[4] Chaptal gave the result as 84·8 oxygen and 15·2 hydrogen. Guyton de Morveau[5] says he saw in 1787 the apparatus made for Lavoisier by 'Sr Meignié' (Mégnié) but had constructed one at Dijon which was much cheaper.

Fourcroy, Vauquelin, and Seguin[6] found that 25582 cu. in. of hydrogen, weighing 1039·358 gr., combined with 12457·342 cu. in. of oxygen (from potassium chlorate) weighing 6209·869 gr. (both volumes reduced to 10° R. and 28 in. pressure), or in total 7249·227 gr., to give 7245 gr. of neutral water, giving a deficit of 4·227 gr. The oxygen contained 415·256 cu. in. of nitrogen

[1] VII, 100.   [2] Kopp, (3), 192.

[3] *Obs. Phys.*, 1788, xxxiii, 457 (read 10 November); Chaptal, *Elements of Chemistry*, 1791, i, 165; *id.*, *Chemistry Applied to Arts and Manufactures*, 1805, iii, 436 f.; Guyton de Morveau, *Ency. Méthod.*, *Chymie*, 1789, i, 721.

[4] In Chaptal, 1791, the weight of water is given as 2 lb. 3 oz., containing 27½ gr. of acid.

[5] *Op. cit.*

[6] AdS, 1790 (1797), m 485 (read 21 May 1790); Seguin, *Ann. Chim.*, 1791, viii, 230; 1791, ix, 30; Fourcroy, (2), iii, 574; Lavoisier, IV, ii, 307, 313 (397); for a report by Lavoisier, Brisson, Meusnier, and Laplace (not approved by d'Arcet and Baumé) see Lavoisier, VIII, iv, 515.

and at the end of the experiment, which lasted 185 hours (a very tiny flame being used), 467 cu. in. of gas remained, an increase of 51·744 cu. in. This gives 2·052 hydrogen to 1 oxygen by volume (instead of 2·00) and by weight, for 100 parts of water, 85·662 of oxygen and 14·338 of hydrogen were calculated (5·974 parts of oxygen combining with 1 of hydrogen).

Bryan Higgins,[1] with a simple apparatus, combined 416·5 gr. of oxygen and 72·5 gr. of hydrogen to form 487 gr. of pure non-acid water; this gives 5·745 parts of oxygen combining with 1 of hydrogen. The apparatus described by Cuthbertson[2] gave only crude values of the combining volumes. Adam Wilhelm von Hauch (Copenhagen; 1755–1838) described another simplified apparatus.[3]

Lavoisier says:

'We did not know that M. Monge was occupied with the same subject, and we were not informed till some days later by a letter he addressed to M. Vandermonde, which the latter read to the Academy; . . . his experiment is much more conclusive than ours and leaves nothing to be desired: the result he obtained was pure water, the weight of which was found to be very nearly equal to that of the two airs.'[4]

MONGE

Gaspard Monge (Beaune, 10 May 1746–Paris, 28 July 1818), the son of a knife-grinder, studied in Lyon and Mézières, became a member of the Academy in 1780, and was one of the founders of the École Polytechnique, where he became professor of mathematics. He accompanied Napoleon to Egypt and was made Count of Pelusium.[5]

The work of Monge[6] was carried out at Mézières in June to July, and repeated in October, 1783, without (as Monge says) knowledge of Cavendish's experiments (published in 1784). The title of the memoir is: 'On the result of the inflammation of inflammable gas and dephlogisticated air in closed vessels.' Blagden[7] says Monge's work was carried out 'I believe at least two months later than Lavoisier's', but[8] this refers to Monge's experiments of October 1783 and Blagden missed those of June and July. Monge's experiments were independent of and perhaps just prior to Lavoisier's.

The method used was suggested by Volta's work (p. 326), to which Monge refers, in which a mixture of the two gases was fired by an electric spark in a glass vessel. The matter of heat set free 'hurls itself against the walls of the vessel', passing through the glass. The dephlogisticated air was prepared by heating red precipitate of mercury previously heated in a retort to free it from

---

[1] *Minutes of a Society*, 1795, 175 f., 194; *Phil. Mag.*, 1798, ii, 148.

[2] *Phil. Mag.*, 1798, ii, 317; *Nicholson's J.*, 1799, ii, 235.

[3] *Skrifter Videns. Selsk. Nye Saml.*, Copenhagen, 1799, v, 18–27, and plate.

[4] Lavoisier, AdS, 1781 (1784), m 468; VIII, ii, 339; Fourcroy, *Philosophie Chimique*, 1806, 151, names Monge along with Lavoisier in making 'cette belle découverte, publiée en 1784'.

[5] Arago, Éloge (1846), AdS, 1854, xxiv, j–clvij; *Oeuvres*, 1854, ii, 427–592 (says Monge d. 18 July 1818); C. Dupin, *Essai historique sur les services et les travaux scientifiques de Gaspard Monge*, Paris, 1819 (chemical work, pp. 288 f.); Brocard, *L'Intermédiaire des Mathématiciens*, 1906, xiii, 118–19; Aubry, q. in *Isis*, 1956, xlvii, 81.

[6] Monge, AdS, 1783 (1786), m 78; repr. in Muirhead, *Correspondence of James Watt*, 1846, 205 f.; tr. of part in Partington, *The Composition of Water*, 1928, 49.

[7] *Crell's Ann.*, 1786, I, 58.   [8] Wilson, *Life of Cavendish*, 1851, 347.

nitrate, and the inflammable air by dissolving clean iron wire in dilute sulphuric acid. The gases were contained in two glass cylinders (Fig. 43), previously calibrated by admitting successive equal volumes of air measured at atmospheric pressure and marking the water levels on vertical scales alongside the cylinders. The densities of the moist gases were determined by

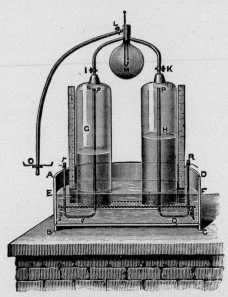

FIG. 43. MONGE'S EXPERIMENT ON THE COMBINATION OF
HYDROGEN AND OXYGEN GASES.

THE GASES WERE COLLECTED THROUGH SYPHON-TUBES, pr PR, IN THE CYLINDERS G AND H; THEY
PASSED THROUGH THE STOPCOCKS I AND K TO THE GLOBE, M, PREVIOUSLY EXHAUSTED THROUGH THE TAP
L, LEADING TO AN AIR-PUMP AT O. THE MIXED GAS WAS THEN EXPLODED BY AN ELECTRIC SPARK AT M,
AND THE PROCESS REPEATED.

weighing in a glass globe of 14 pints capacity, previously weighed evacuated: the weights of 1 cu. ft. at 15° R. and 27 in. 5 lines barometer were: dephlogisticated air 1 oz. 3 gros 67·36 gr., atmospheric air 1 oz. 2 gros 44·03 gr., inflammable air 1 gros 36·86 gr.

'In a hydropneumatic cistern, of which the section is represented by ABCD and in which the level EF of the surface of the water was held constantly at the same height, I fixed two large jars G and H, similar to those which had been used to determine the weights of the gases and graduated separately by the same method . . . open below and at the top communicated by the metal tubes provided with stopcocks I and K with a balloon M . . . in which was an exciter to produce an electric spark after the manner of M. Volta. This exciter was of silver.'

Guyton de Morveau[1] emphasised this use of a non-oxidisable metal in place of copper, and suggested that for work over mercury platinum (which does not amalgamate) should be used. This was universally adopted in later apparatus.

'A third metal tube with a stopcock L connected the globe with an excellent air pump O to form a vacuum in the globe and to extract elastic fluids from it. . . . To introduce the dephlogisticated air in the jar H, I opened the stopcocks L and K, then

[1] Ency. Méthod., Chymie, i, 738.

by pumping with the air pump I raised the water in the jar until its surface was just hidden by the upper metallic cap . . . then closed the stopcock K.'

To remove air between the surface of the water and the stopcock Monge passed the end of a siphon tube PQR into the metal tube till it touched the stopcock and sucked at the end R, provided with a valve of bladder, till all the air was removed and the jar completely filled with water. The gas was then introduced from below, and in a similar way the jar G was filled with inflammable air.

'When everything was thus prepared, the two stopcocks I and K being closed and the stopcock L alone open, I produced as perfect a vacuum as I could in the globe M and closed the stopcock L. Then, by opening K, I allowed one-twelfth of its volume of dephlogisticated air to enter the globe, measured with great precision by the alteration of the water surface in the jar H; then by opening the stopcock I, I allowed inflammable air to enter as far as it would, and, all the stopcocks being closed, I drew a spark which produced the first explosion.'

Another twelfth of dephlogisticated air was then added and a second explosion made, and so on for six explosions. Then another twelfth of dephlogisticated air was added and inflammable air allowed to enter again as far as it would. This time, owing to the heat of the globe and the accumulation of impurities, only five explosions could be made. In all, 137 explosions were made; the globe was allowed to cool, and the gas extracted for subsequent examination by a special pneumatic apparatus adapted to the pump. The operation was then begun anew.

'In this way, and in three series of a total of 372 explosions, I consumed $145\frac{91}{144}$ pints of inflammable air and $74\frac{9}{16}$ pints of dephlogisticated air. . . . During the explosions the weight of the atmosphere had diminished and its mean height was not more than 26 in. 11 lines, the temperature of the apartment being still the same. It is, therefore, necessary to diminish the total weights of the two airs in the ratio of 27 in. 5 lines to 26 in. 11 lines, since, although the different elastic fluids are not equally dilatable by heat, it is very probable that they are all compressible according to the same law, at least in the mean state, that is to say in the ratio of the compressing weights. In this way the total of the airs used is found to be 3 oz. 6 dr. 27·56 gr.'

The later explosions were accompanied by a hissing noise, probably due to the great compression of the gas in the globe owing to the high temperature.

'When these operations were finished I unluted the globe, weighed it with the liquid which it contained, transferred this product, and after having well dried the globe I weighed it again. I found by difference 3 oz. 2 gros 45·1 gr. This weight is that of the liquid product of the inflammation of the two gases.'

The gases extracted from the globe measured 7 pints and weighed 2 gros 27·91 gr., and hence the total weight of products was 3 oz. 5 gros 1·01 gr., differing from the weight of the gases used by only 1 gros 26·55 gr. The difference was ascribed to changes in barometric pressure and of the temperature of the reservoirs during the experiment, and to loss by evaporation in each exhaustion of the globe. The 7 pints of residual gas turned lime water milky and contracted by $\frac{1}{15}$. When sparked in a Volta's eudiometer it contracted by $\frac{1}{5}$ and the residue on mixing with nitric oxide behaved like atmospheric air, which it was assumed to be, and that it contained $\frac{1}{4}$ its volume of oxygen. The residual nitrogen was an impurity. The liquid product reddened litmus only imperceptibly (Monge exploded gases containing an excess of hydrogen), had no action on lime water, and gave only a slight opalescence with silver nitrate solution. He supposed that it contained a trace of sulphuric acid carried over with the hydrogen, but he did not test for this, nor for nitric acid, which it probably was.

'It follows from this experiment that when inflammable gas and dephlogisticated gas, both considered pure, are exploded, there is no other result than pure water, the matter of heat and that of light. . . . It remains to determine actually if the two gases being solutions of different substances in the fluid of fire (fluide du feu), considered as a common solvent, these substances on inflammation abandon the solvent and combine to form water, which would then be no longer a simple substance, or whether the two gases being solutions of water in different elastic fluids (dans des fluides élastiques differens), these abandon the water which they dissolved in order to combine and form the fluid of fire and light, which escapes through the walls of the vessels, in which case fire will be a compound substance.'[1]

The assumption that water is a compound of the bases of dephlogisticated and inflammable airs would explain many phenomena, but these two gases require heat to induce combination, i.e. to separate their combined fire, and if fire were the solvent of their bases it is hard to see why the introduction of more fire should decrease the adherence it has for the bases, which is totally opposed to all that is observed in analogous chemical operations. 'We lack still much light on this subject, but we have the right to expect it with time and the cooperation of the works of physicists.'

The volumes of hydrogen and oxygen (uncorrected for the small pressure change) were in the ratio 1·953 : 1 (less accurate than Cavendish's result), and the ratio of the weights (uncorrected) 1 : 4·042 (instead of 1 : 8).

The Dutch Chemists

Another apparatus for the synthesis of water was described by Van Marum.[2] This consisted of two glass gas-holders and a combustion globe similar to Monge's. In this the process of combination was slow, 1000 cu. in. of hydrogen being burnt in $3\frac{1}{3}$ hours, and water quite free from acid was obtained.

Paets van Troostweyk (sic) and Deiman, in a long criticism of Lavoisier's theory,[3] particularly of the composition of water, affirmed that water is deposited during the combination of dephlogisticated air with other gases besides inflammable air, and that if Cavendish's theory (see p. 334) is adopted, water should cease to be water by increase or diminution of its phlogiston. They found difficulty in understanding why the two gases should not combine without heating (this had been explained by Cavendish's theory), and why the resulting water should be acid. The supposed decomposition of water by

[1] On this, see Humboldt and Gay-Lussac, J. de Phys., 1805, lx, 129 (144).
[2] Description de quelques Appereils Chimiques, in Verhandelingen uitgegeeven door Teyler's Tweede Genootschap, Haarlem, 1798, Stuk 10, 1 f.; communicated to Berthollet on 31 December 1791, and printed in abstract in Ann. Chim., 1792, xii, 113; J. der Physik, 1792, v, 154–76, and plates; Phil. Mag., 1798, ii, 85 (plates); the apparatus was modified by Thenard, Traité de Chimie, 1834, i, 256; Atlas, pl. 14, fig. 1.
[3] Crell's Beyträge, 1788, iii, 3–111: Uber die verschiedenen Arten von Luft.

heated iron is not a valid proof, since the inflammable air could have come from the metal, and there seems to be no reason, if Lavoisier's theory is true, why other metals than iron and zinc should not decompose water. (It is hard to see why this is not also an objection to the phlogiston theory, if all metals contain phlogiston.)

After quoting some erroneous experiments in which calces of metals were supposed to have been formed in nitrogen, etc., the authors put forward the unreasonable objection that Lavoisier had found the weight of calx equal to that of the metal and oxygen *gas*, whilst he assumed the latter to consist of (oxygen basis + matter of heat). (Lavoisier had proved experimentally that heat is imponderable.) They were also unable to understand why oxygen, the acidifying principle, should form calces with metals, which calces did not contain an acid. They thought that all acids contain the same combustible principle, but the dephlogisticated air is different according to the acid from which it is obtained.

In 1785 Van Marum, investigating the action of the electric spark on various substances with the great frictional machine in the Teyler Institute in Haarlem, found that metal calces were reduced, which indicated that 'the electric matter is either phlogiston itself or at least contains much of this principle';[1] but in 1787[2] he adopted Lavoisier's theory and supposed that the electric spark can both produce and decompose metallic calces. He also decomposed water by electric sparks[3] but thought he obtained only hydrogen, perhaps because the latter had a greater affinity for heat than oxygen (actually because the oxygen combined with the metal wire). Van Troostwijk and Deiman, assisted by Cuthbertson (who had constructed the electrical machine in Haarlem) showed[4] that both oxygen and hydrogen are evolved, and admitted Lavoisier's views on the composition of water, although speaking with reserve of the general application of the antiphlogistic theory.

Lavoisier's Memoirs published in 1785

The results of the experiments on the composition of water were very important. They enabled Lavoisier to explain the source of the inflammable gas evolved when many metals dissolve in acids (which had previously caused him difficulty, see p. 444) and during the fermentation of vegetable matters, and also why and in what cases water 'burns' combustible bodies or augments their combustion when it has begun. He also explained how water operates in the calcination of metals and how it is decomposed and formed in a large number of chemical operations. The further applications of this discovery were later made to the abundant formation of water in the combustion of spirit of wine and oils, the production of carbonic acid in the action of water on red-hot carbon, the formation of water in the combustion of charcoal

---

[1] Van Marum, Description d'une très grande Machine Electrique, in *Verhandelingen*, etc., 1785, Stuk 3, p. 190; 1795, Stuk 9, pp. 176, 258.
[2] *Verhandelingen*, 1787, Stuk 4, p. 110.
[3] *Verhandelingen*, 1787, Stuk 4, p. 144.
[4] *Obs. Phys.*, 1789, xxxv, 369 (376–80); *J. der Physik* (Gren), 1790, ii, 131; Crell's *Ann.*, 1796, II, 291; confirmed by Pearson (with Cuthbertson), *Nicholson's J.*, 1797, i, 241.

containing hydrogen, and the decomposition of water when vegetable matter is exposed to a high temperature.

In 1785 several memoirs on the applications of the new theory were printed, most of them presented in 1783.[1]

(1) *On a method of augmenting the action of fire.*[2] This describes the fusion of platinum in a hollow in a piece of charcoal heated by a blowpipe flame, and then blowing on it a jet of oxygen from a bladder or a special gas-holder which is described in detail. Lavoisier disingenuously says: 'Cette idée a dû se présenter sans doute a beaucoup de personnes avant moi, et on m'a même assuré que M. Achard, célèbre chimiste de Berlin, en avait fait des applications.' Lavoisier had probably read Achard's memoir (in French)[3] even if he had not seen or been told of the very detailed papers (in Swedish) by B. R. Geijer, published a year before Lavoisier's memoir.[4] Lavoisier mentions that 'M. le président de Saron' had communicated to him a very ingenious idea of using two blowpipes, one supplied with inflammable air and one with vital air, apparently side by side, when one obtained 'un dard de flamme très-blanc, très-lumineux [probably the hydrogen was impure] et très-chaud, avec lequel on fond aisément le fer, mais avec lequel, cependent, il ne m'a pas été possible de fondre le platine' (see p. 699). Lavoisier says one can 'imagine' an apparatus in which, if the vital air 'could be made to surround the inflammable air on all sides, so that the latter in some way burns in an atmosphere of vital air, perhaps a more considerable effect will be obtained', but he did not construct the double-tube oxyhydrogen blowpipe first described by Daniell,[5] in which the oxygen is supplied to the inside of the flame.

(2) *On the effect of a very violent fire on precious stones,*[6] describing the effect of the above apparatus on various gems; it is stated that only diamond 'burns in the manner of combustible bodies and is entirely dissipated by a moderate degree of heat'; other gems soften, or melt, or change colour. Baryta (la terre pesante) 'is probably a metallic substance, as Bergman suspected, although it has not yet been reduced to the state of regulus'.

(3) *On the union of the oxygen principle with iron.*[7] Some thin iron shavings, covered with 'a morsel of tinder and an atom of phosphorus' in a porcelain dish and ignited in oxygen over mercury in a bell-jar, burnt rapidly and furnished 'a very beautiful spectacle' (un très-beau spectacle): 145·6 grains became 192·0 grains, the increase of 46·4 grains corresponding with the absorption of 97 cu. in. of oxygen weighing 45·9 grains, and the black oxide (aethiops martial) was formed. On heating this in air a brown oxide (ochre) is formed by absorption of more oxygen. Iron may also be oxidised by standing in water (Bergman), by moistening with vinegar (Rouelle), or dilute nitric acid (Croharé),[8] or by dissolving in more concentrated nitric acid and preci-

---

[1] Fourcroy, (2), iii, 446.   [2] AdS, 1782 (1785), h 28, m 457; VIII, ii, 423.
[3] *Hist. Acad. Berlin*, 1779 (1781), m 20–6.
[4] Geijer, KAH, 1784, v, 122, 193, 283; the first in April 1784.
[5] *Phil. Mag.*, 1833, ii, 57–60; Winderlich, *A. Nat.*, 1928, x, 427–31.
[6] AdS, 1782 (1785), m 476 (Nov. 1782); VIII, ii, 441–50.
[7] AdS, 1782 (1785), h 37, m 541 (20 Dec. 1783); VIII, ii, 556.
[8] Croharé, apothecary to the Comte d'Artois, *Mém. Soc. Roy. de Méd.*, 1776 (1779), 324 (326).

pitating with alkali. When a solution of iron in vitriolic acid is precipitated with potash, the same weight of vitriolated tartar (potassium sulphate) is formed as would have been obtained from the acid alone,[1] hence the oxygen taken by the metal in this case came from the water, whilst with nitric acid it came from the acid. In dissolving iron in dilute vitriolic acid, the metal robs the water of oxygen and is covered with a film of oxide which is at once dissolved by the acid, whilst the hydrogen of the water escapes, as had been suggested by Laplace (see p. 444). Iron oxide in mass does not dissolve in the acid, since 'the attraction which the molecules exert on one another [in the aggregate] is an obstacle which the acid can hardly overcome'. (This refers to ignited ferric oxide, which is insoluble in acids.) Iron will not dissolve in concentrated sulphuric acid, in which the water is combined with the acid up to a certain point (acide de saturation), only free water being decomposable. The quantity of inflammable air evolved permits of an accurate calculation of the amount of oxygen combining with the metal. Lavoisier in this memoir recognised, before Proust (p. 646), that some metals can form more than one oxide.[2]

The combustion of a spiral of iron or steel wire in oxygen is described in a MS.[3] as 'la belle expérience de M. Ingen-Housz', who had not examined what happens to the iron and oxygen, which Lavoisier did in quantitative experiments. Ingen Housz made the experiment about 1780.[4] Lavoisier showed that commercial iron contains carbon by heating iron filings with mercuric oxide, when fixed air was produced. Metals are combustible bodies, which can combine with other combustible bodies such as sulphur, phosphorus, and carbon.

(4) *On the combination of nitrous air with respirable airs.*[5] Priestley's method of measuring the 'goodness' of air by mixing with nitric oxide over water and observing the contraction was modified, and a formula given. Let μ be the ratio of nitrous air to vital air absorbed 'dans la formation d'acide nitreux', a the quantity of pure air tested, b that of nitrous air mixed with it, c the residue. The quantities absorbed on mixing are:

$$\text{vital air} = (a + b - c)/(1 + \mu), \quad \text{nitrous air} = \mu(a + b - c)/(1 + \mu).$$

If excess of nitrous air is used the first formula gives the quantity of vital air contained in a. If less nitrous air is used than is required to absorb all the vital air, the second formula gives the real quantity of nitrous air in b. Examples are given. It was found that 66 to 69 vols. of nitrous air combine (in presence of water) with 40 of vital air, and that atmospheric air contains 25 per cent of oxygen (which is too large).

---

[1] Fordyce, *Phil. Trans.*, 1792, lxxxii, 374, proved this also with zinc.
[2] Kopp, (1), iii, 166.   [3] VIII, ii, 575; *Ann. Chim.*, 1789, i, 19; VII, 1789, 41.
[4] Amoretti and Soave, *Opuscoli Scelti sulle Scienze e sulle Arti*, Milan, 1783, vi, 325; Ingen Housz, *Nouvelles Expériences et Observations sur divers Objets de Physique*, 2 vols., Paris, 1785–9, i, 400, 446; Lippmann, (1), i, 252; Speter, *Draeger-Hefte*, Lübeck, 1935, 2884, points out that Lichtenberg burnt iron in oxygen in 1782, but Lippmann, and Cohen, *Janus*, 1909, xiv, 21–32, think he had heard of the experiment from Ingen Housz; M. Garthshore, *Ann. Phil.*, 1817, x, 161, says Ingen Housz was fond of showing this experiment to his lady friends. It was shown to German chemists by Göttling in the summer of 1793 and was regarded as very convincing evidence of the truth of Lavoisier's new theory: Scherer, *Grundzüge der neuern chemischen Theorie*, Jena, 1795, 50.
[5] AdS, 1782 (1785), m 486; VIII, ii, 503; presented 20 December 1783.

(5) *General considerations on the dissolution of metals in acids.*[1] In his previous memoirs, Lavoisier says, he:

'has not one single time used the word phlogiston . . . the existence of this principle seems to be absolutely hypothetical. . . . It had made a science obscure and unintelligible, . . . it is a being which explains everything and explains nothing, and is supposed in turn to have opposed qualities.'

He summarises his previous work (giving, as usual, the dates of the *Mémoires*, not the years of publication), and describes experiments on the dissolution of mercury in nitric acid showing that the acid free from water contains equal weights of nitrous air and oxygen (should be 60NO : 48O); 16 oz. contain 8 oz. of water, 4 oz. of nitrous air and 4 of principe oxygène. He uses chemical equations with Bergman's symbols, 'which could be taken for algebraic formulæ, but they have not the same object and are not derived from the same principles', although they are quantitative. Iron takes up more oxygen from hot than from cold nitric acid. In the solution of a metal in an acid, eight different forces are supposed to act, four depending on the action of heat, and four on affinities, and the nature of the gases evolved is discussed.

The forces acting in the dissolution of a metal in an acid are: the action of heat, which (1) tends to separate the molecules (molécules) of water and reduce it to vapour, (2) tends to disunite the principles of nitric acid and convert it into gaseous substances, (3) acts on the constituent principles of water, (4) diminishes the affinity of aggregation of a metal and tends to separate its parts; (5) the reciprocal action of nitrous gas and the oxygen principle, (6) their combined action on water, (7) the action of the metal on the oxygen principle of the acid and on that of the water, and (8) the action of the acid on the metal, or rather on the metallic calx.
'To know the energy (énergie) of all these forces, to succeed in giving them a numerical value, to calculate them, is the end which chemistry proposes; it marches in slow steps but it is not impossible that it will reach it. In awaiting this we are compelled to limit ourselves to general views.'

A few of these are given. Here, as elsewhere,[2] Lavoisier correctly distinguished between 'solution' when no chemical change occurs (solution of salts in water) and 'dissolution' when it does (metals in acids).

(6) *On the precipitation of metallic substances by one another.*[3] Bergman's experiments (see p. 196) are interpreted on the oxygen theory. The metal dissolving takes up oxygen whilst the metal precipitated loses it, and the quantities of oxygen combined with the metals are inversely proportional to the weights of the metals. From his own analysis of oxide of mercury, and Bergman's results, Lavoisier calculated the compositions of the oxides of 16 metals, in the case of iron two oxides (in the state of martial ethiops and saffron of Mars). For 100 parts by weight of metal the following weights of oxygen (among others) were calculated by the precipitation method (the correct figures are given in brackets):

iron	27 (29·5)	tin	14 (13·6)
iron	37 (39·3)	silver	10·8 (7·4)
copper	36 (25·3)	bismuth	9·622 (11·3)

---

[1] AdS, 1782 (1785), h 33, m 492; VIII, ii, 509.   [2] VII, 423.
[3] AdS, 1782 (1785), h 36, m 512 (20 Dec. 1783); VIII, ii, 528; see the extension in the tr. of Kirwan's *Essay on Phlogiston* (1789, 250 f.; VIII, ii, 671).

manganese	21·176 (29)	mercury	8 (7·7)
zinc	19·637 (24·8)	lead	4·47 (7·7)

Lavoisier recognised (before Proust, see p. 644) that some metals have two stages of oxidation but the inaccurate results prevented him from seeing the whole-number ratio. He says the oxygen principle has more affinity to the principle of heat than to gold, silver, or platinum. Guyton de Morveau's quantitative results on the calcination of metals are quoted (from his *Digressions Académiques*, 1772). Lavoisier concluded that: 'the metals both in precipitating one another and on calcination in air, saturate one another with a nearly equal quantity of oxygen and each metal requires a quantity which is peculiar to it. Copper and lead only seem to form an exception but judgment should be suspended on these differences.' He quotes such old results as those of Boyle and Geoffroy.

Memoirs published in 1786

The *Mémoires* of the Academy for 1783, published in 1786, contain three by Lavoisier.

(1) *On the action of fire animated by vital air on the most refractory minerals*,[1] in which it is shown that all metals except platinum volatilise, gold and silver much more slowly than others, that some metals are incombustible, whilst others burn with a very marked flame, and that iron burns rapidly, throwing out a shower of sparks; the use of oxygen in cupellation is advised.

Friedrich Ludwig Ehrmann (Strasbourg; 1741–17 February 1800), professor of physics in Strasbourg, published on fusion with the aid of oxygen.[2]

(2) *Affinity of the oxygen principle for different substances*,[3] containing a table of affinities of substances for oxygen, beginning with 'the unknown principle of the marine acid, which I will in future call the muriatic principle', and ending with 'calx of manganese', on the basis of results with 25 compounds. No numbers are given. Lavoisier also gives tables of affinities in his book but explains in the preface[4] that he refrained from explaining the subject of affinity because Guyton de Morveau was on the point of publishing on it in the *Encyclopédie* (see Vol. IV). A large part of Kirwan's objections to the antiphlogistic theory[5] turned on the question of affinities, on which he was an expert.

In his memoir Lavoisier emphasises that the order of affinity depends on the temperature, and although Bergman had provided two tables, for the wet and dry way, it would be necessary to form one for every degree of the thermometer. It is also necessary to take into account the effects of attraction of water, which had been regarded as 'a simply passive agent', and of the degree of saturation modifying 'the attractive force of the molecules of bodies',

---

[1] AdS, 1783 (1786), m 563; VIII, ii, 451–502.

[2] *Versuch einer Schmelzkunst mit Beihülfe der Feuerluft*, Strasbourg, 1786; tr. in 1787 with papers by Lavoisier and Laplace added as an appendix: Ehrmann, *Essai d'un Art de Fusion à l'Aide de l'Air du Feu, ou Air Vital. Traduit de l'Allemand par M. de Fontallard & revu par l'Auteur. Suivi des Mémoires de Mr. Lavoisier . . . sur le même sujet*, 8°, Strasbourg & Paris, 1787 (xxxii, 366 pp., i l., 3 fold. plates).

[3] AdS, 1783 (1786), m 530; VIII, ii, 546.

[4] VII, xiv.   [5] *Essay on Phlogiston*, 1786, 44 f., 53, etc.

vitriolic and sulphurous acids, between which there is no intermediate compound, having quite specific and different affinities; and similarly the two acids of phosphorus obtained *per deliquium* (phosphorous acid) and by combustion, and the marine acid and dephlogisticated marine acid (chlorine).

The views of Laplace, and the experiments he and Lavoisier projected (presumably those on heats of combustion), he says, made the possibility of expressing the forces of affinity by numbers not absolutely chimerical. This foreshadows the principle proposed by Thomsen in 1853 and Berthelot in 1864 (see Vol. IV).

(3) *New reflexions on the increase in weight of sulphur and phosphorus on burning*:[1] a criticism of Bergman's and Scheele's theories of combustion (pp. 194, 228) in which it is shown that when 92 grains of phosphorus are burnt in air in a closed phial or 1 lb. of water freezes in a glass flask, there is no change in weight greater than $\frac{1}{10}$ grain (it would actually be very difficult to achieve such accuracy); hence: 'caloric can be considered as having no sensible weight in chemical experiments.' This disproves Bergman's theory that the increase in weight of phosphorus and sulphur on combustion is due to an increase of specific heat. Since, however, Bergman and Scheele assumed that vital air is a constituent of caloric and is fixed in combustion, their theory was the same as Lavoisier's, except that it assumed that vital air combined with phlogiston forms caloric, the latter having an appreciable and sensible weight.

(4) *Reflexions on phlogiston.*[2] The object is to prove that 'phlogiston is a hypothetical being, a gratuitous supposition'. At the time when Stahl wrote 'the principal phenomena of combustion were yet unknown' (Lavoisier ignores Boyle, Hooke and Mayow). For Stahl (at least as presented by Macquer) phlogiston was an earthy principle having weight, which escapes in burning or calcination, but this does not explain the increase in weight in these processes. Baumé[3] assumed an inflammable principle composed of the matter of fire combined with an earthy principle in continuously varying proportions. Metals on calcination lose phlogiston which is replaced by pure fire, or fire less charged with the earthy element. But Lavoisier had proved that the matter of fire and of heat disengaged from 92 grains of phosphorus on burning has no appreciable weight. He had also demonstrated that the increase in weight of metals on calcination is a condition of every metallic calcination and combustion, and is due to combination and fixation of air.

Macquer[4] supposed that metals and combustibles contain a large amount of the matter of light in a combined state, which he called phlogiston, identical in all bodies. The air, or rather its purest part, combines with metals and combustibles and increases their weight, phlogiston at the same time separating as

[1] AdS, 1783 (1786), m 416; IV, ii, 121; VIII, ii, 616.
[2] AdS, 1783 (1786), m 505 (a footnote says: 'Quelques-uns de ces Mémoires ne sont point encore imprimés'); VIII, ii, 623; sub-title: 'pour servir de suite à la théorie de la combustion et de la calcination, publiée en 1777' (the comma is typical). Daumas, *Archives*, 1955, viii (old xxxiv), 411, says it was read on 28 June 1785. Parts of it are reproduced in the report of 27 June 1787 on the *Nomenclature* (VIII, v, 365) although it is not named and no ref. is given. Hartog, 1941, 43, called it 'the knock-out blow' to the phlogiston theory.
[3] *Chymie expérimentale et raisonné*, 1777, i, 145.
[4] *Dictionnaire de Chymie*, 1779, i, 344; iii, 99.

the matter of light. Macquer rejects the element of fire and the matter of heat, supposing that heat consists in a very rapid motion impressed on the molecules of bodies. But if phlogiston is the pure matter of light it should still have weight, which light has not, and *all* metallic calces should be reduced on exposure to light, whereas most of them fuse to glasses (when exposed to a burning glass), even in absence of air. Lavoisier's essay is mainly directed against Macquer's hybrid theory, and he does not make it clear that he himself was entangled in a theory not unlike Macquer's, his caloric or *material* fluid of 'light and heat' (which he carefully avoids distinguishing) should also have some weight. He evades the question why some calces are not reduced by heat. He says:

'chemists have made of phlogiston a vague principle which is not at all rigorously defined, and which, in consequence, adapts itself to all explanations in which it is wished it shall enter; sometimes this principle is ponderable and sometimes it is not; sometimes it is free fire, sometimes it is fire combined with the earthy element; sometimes it passes through the pores of vessels, sometimes they are impenetrable to it; it explains both causticity and non-causticity, transparency and opacity, colours and absence of colours. It is a veritable Proteus which changes its form every instant. It is time to conduct chemistry to a more rigorous mode of reasoning . . . to distinguish fact and observation from what is systematic and hypothetical.'

Lavoisier says he had deduced all his own explanations from a single 'principle', viz. that there is a matter of heat which exists as a fluid among the particles of bodies and is expelled when they are compressed, like water from a sponge. Pure or vital air is composed of a peculiar principle or base, called *principe oxigine*, combined with the matter of fire and heat, or the igneous fluid. This fluid is to some extent hypothetical, but it is assumed also by the phlogistians. It is clear, independently of any hypothesis, that the more the molecules of a body are separated from one another, the more they allow among them the capacity of receiving the matter of heat, so that the specific heat of a liquid is less than that of the same body in the gaseous state, and it is less still in the solid state.

Lavoisier says he had proved that the matter of heat (caloric) has no weight by burning phosphorus in air in a sealed flask, and by freezing water in a sealed flask; in neither case was there any change in weight (see 3). In his memoir with Laplace (see p. 428) it was said that heat might consist in the movements of the molecules of matter, but now this is one of the mistaken ideas of Macquer, who thought there was no proper matter of heat, and that: 'la chaleur consiste dans un mouvement très-rapide imprimé aux molécules élémentaires des corps.' If metals contain more matter of heat than their calces (Macquer had really said matter of *light*), then the metals should have higher specific heats than their calces, whereas the experiments of Crawford, Wilcke, and Lavoisier and Laplace all showed that the opposite is true (this is correct).

In combustions in which oxygen forms a solid compound (e.g. phosphorus forming the oxide) the evolution of heat and light comes from the loss of matter of heat by the oxygen gas, the particles of which come close together and squeeze out the matter of heat. In the combustion of sulphur the product is very dense liquid sulphuric acid. It is actually *gaseous* sulphur dioxide and Guy-Lussac[1] said:

'Depuis Lavoisier, qui avoit pensé que la combustion du soufre dans l'oxigène donnoit de l'acide sulphurique, tous les chimistes avoient partagé la même opinion; mais M. Chaptal a prouvé qu'elle n'étoit pas fondée.'

Lavoisier says the maximum evolution of heat should occur when the two combining substances are gases, the product of combustion a solid, and the change occurs instantaneously; such a case is not known but the formation of water from inflammable and vital airs approaches it.

When the product is gaseous (e.g. carbon forming carbon dioxide), the effect is due to the displacement of the matter of heat from the interstices between the oxygen particles by particles of carbon; this is proved by the 'facts' that the oxygen gas contracts by a tenth when carbon burns in it (in fact it does not contract at all), and that the heat capacity of gaseous fixed air (carbon dioxide) is less than that of an equal volume of oxygen gas (it is actually considerably greater).

A combustible body is one having the capacity of decomposing vital air and for which the oxygen principle has more affinity than for the matter of heat. Combustion takes place at the moment when the oxygen principle abandons the matter of heat to enter into a new combination. In detonations with saltpetre the matter of heat is provided almost exclusively by the saltpetre, as 'a multitude of reasons' show, principally the combination of nitrous air (NO) with the oxygen principle, when nitric acid is formed. Lavoisier later[2] said he and Laplace had found that 1 lb. of oxygen in burning phosphorus and charcoal, respectively, melted 66·7 and 37·5 lb. of ice, hence, assuming that all the caloric is disengaged in the case of phosphorus, 29·2 lb. were retained in the gaseous carbonic acid. In the detonation of nitre with charcoal, 1 lb. of combined oxygen melted 29·6 lb. of ice. Assuming that the solids contain comparable amounts of caloric, this gave $29·6 + 29·2 = 58·8$ parts out of 66·7 parts of caloric retained by the oxygen in passing into nitric acid, and only $66·7 - 58·8 = 7·9$ parts were lost. The enormous amount of retained caloric, tending to gasify the oxygen, accounted for the detonating properites of nitric acid and nitrates (and also oxygenated muriates, i.e. chlorates).

The cold produced when salts dissolve in water is due to a change of state of aggregation; the evolution of heat when sulphuric acid is mixed with water is accompanied by a decrease in volume, and the maximum effects coincide with the same mixture. The main conclusion is that:

'Since the specific heat of air, and that which is combined with it, is infinitely more abundant than that of any combustible body whatever, except perhaps inflammable air, it results that it is the air which furnishes much the greater part of the matter of heat which disengages during the combustion.'

This is Lavoisier's theory of combustion, destined to replace the phlogiston theory, and which he was pleased to see young chemists without prejudice, as

---

[1] *Mém. Soc. Arcueil*, 1807, i, 215 (247).
[2] VII, 103–12; Partington and McKie, *Ann. Sci.*, 1938, iii, 342.

well as geometers and physicists, adopting. Lavoisier did not distinguish the matters of heat and of light, speaking as if both were substantially the same.[1] Guyton de Morveau[2] said:

'Light and caloric seem in some circumstances to produce the same effects, but as our knowledge is too little advanced to allow us to affirm their identity or their differ-ence we have retained for each its proper denomination; we have only thought it necessary to distinguish heat, which ordinarily means a sensation, from the material principle which is its cause, which we have designated by the word *caloric* (calor-ique). . . . This seems as clear and less embarrassing than . . . *matter of heat* . . . introduced some years previously.'

By analogy with 'caloric' Chaptal[3] proposed to call the fluid of light 'lumic', but this was not adopted. Fourcroy[4] remarked that Lavoisier's caloric in some ways resembled the old phlogiston, only it was transferred from the com-bustible to the oxygen gas. Lavoisier clearly realised that a new theory must explain the production of fire in combustion, which had been a central part of the phlogiston theory, and the history of the last phases of this theory centres around this important problem. Text-books on chemistry in the first half of the nineteenth century devoted a good deal of space to the 'imponderable ele-ments' heat, light, magnetism and electricity, these subjects being presented to physics after Joule's experiments on energy about 1850. The electric and magnetic fluids were regarded by Lavoisier[5] as similar to but less subtle than caloric. Berzelius adopted as imponderable elements caloric, light, and the electric and magnetic fluids.[6]

The view of the constitution of a gas or elastic fluid held by Lavoisier[7] is like that subsequently adopted by Dalton (see p. 767). The elasticity is due to the 'tendency of the molecules to separate from one another', and there is some pressure even when they are very rarefied, hence this repulsion is exerted at very great distances. Parts of the memoir are reproduced in a report on the *Nomenclature Chimique* read by Lavoisier to the Academy on 27 June 1787.[8] For his oxygen theory of acids he refers to the *Opuscules* (1774, ch. ix), and says of the caloric theory of combustion: 'Rien n'est supposé dans ces expli-cations, tout est prouvé, le poids et la mésure à la main . . . Quant à nous, qui nous sommes fait une loi de ne rien conclure au delà des faits', etc. etc.[9]

'There is thus a true repulsion between the molecules of elastic fluids, or at least things happen in the same way as if this repulsion exists, and there is some reason to conclude that the molecules of caloric repel one another . . . it must be admitted, how-ever, that it is difficult to conceive of a repulsive force between very small molecules which acts at great distances. It would perhaps seem simpler to suppose that the mole-cules of caloric attract one another more than the molecules of the body attract one another, and that they cannot be separated from one another without obeying the force of attraction which compels them to reunite. . . . It is probable that the separation of the molecules of a body by caloric is a combination of different attractive forces . . .

[1] Partington and McKie, *Ann. Sci.*, 1938, iii, 337.
[2] VI, 30; the table opp. p. 100, begins with 'Lumière' but it looks as if it had been squeezed in later outside the bracket enclosing 'Calorique, Oxigène, Hydrogène'.
[3] *Chemistry Applied to Arts and Manufactures*, London, 1807, i, 28.
[4] (4), 1793, i, 141.   [5] IV, i, 338; VIII, ii, 804.
[6] *Lehrbuch der Chemie*, Dresden, 1825, i, 70 (electricum), 136 (magnetische Stoff).
[7] VII, 17 f., 24 f.   [8] VIII, v, 365-75.
[9] See also IV, i, 1 f.: Vues générales sous la Calorique, ou principe de la Chaleur.

which we seek to express in a more concise way and more comformably to the state of imperfection of our knowledge when we say that caloric communicates a repulsive force to the molecules of bodies.'

Lavoisier[1] and Hassenfratz[2] proposed that the names combustion, inflammation, calcination, and burning should not be used indiscriminately, but De la Metherie[3] objected to this 'change of language'.

A serious objection to Lavoisier's theory of combustion was raised by the Dutch chemists Deiman, Van Troostwyk, Nieuwland, and Bondt,[4] viz. that the combustion of metals occurs in heated sulphur in the absence of oxygen. (Scheele had noticed the incandescence on heating iron or lead filings and sulphur.)[5] They explained it as due to a change in heat capacity, the sulphide having a specific heat smaller than the sum of the specific heat of the mixture and the heat of fusion of the sulphur. Richter[6] explained it by the incorrect hypothesis that the sulphur contains water, which is decomposed by heat to furnish oxygen to the metal. The Dutch chemists also supposed that in the explosion of a mixture of hydrogen and oxygen, part of the caloric evolved comes from the hydrogen. Since modern writers overlook the fact that Lavoisier's theory was intended to give an explanation of the heat and light evolved in combustion as an alternative to the phlogiston theory (most of the *Reflexions on Phlogiston* turns on this), they usually find it difficult to understand why it was not enthusiastically adopted. This matter is dealt with later (ch. XIII).

Saltpetre

The Régie des Poudres et Salpêtres had the monopoly of refining saltpetre from 1775 until it was suppressed during the Revolution. Until his retirement in 1791 the leading light in it was Lavoisier, who seems to have written its publications.[7]

In 1775 the Academy offered a prize of 4000 livres for a process for procuring an abundant supply of saltpetre,[8] the announcement being written by Lavoisier. Altogether 66 papers were received and the prize was finally awarded in 1782 to the brothers Thouvenel, who gave a full account of nitre plantations.[9] The material was published in 1786 in one volume by the Academy.[10]

---

[1] AdS, 1783 (1786), m 503; VIII, ii, 641.   [2] *Obs. Phys.*, 1788, xxxiii, 384   [3] *Ib.*, 384.
[4] Expériences sur l'inflammation du mélange du Soufre et des Metaux sans la Présence de l'Oxygine, in *Recherches Physico-Chymiques*, 4°, Amsterdam, 1794, Cahier iii, 71–96; Crell's *Ann.*, 1793, II, 383–98; Lowitz, *ib.*, 1796, I, 239.
[5] *On Air and Fire*, § 81; see Vol. II, 367, 614.   [6] Crell's *Ann.*, 1794, II, 291.
[7] W. A. Smeaton, *Ann. Sci.*, 1956 (1957), xii, 157, quoting: *Instruction sur l'établissement des Nitrières et sur la Fabrication du Salpêtre* (1777); *Observations sur le travail des Eaux-Mères de Salpêtre, et sur celui des Eaux d'Atelier* (1778); *L'Art de Fabriquer le Salin et la Potasse* (1779); *Instructions sur les moyens que l'on peut employer pour connoître la qualité des Salpêtres* . . . , 1787 (28 pp.); *Instruction sur la manière dont on doit procéder à l'épreuve du Salpêtre*, 1789. See H. Lenoir, *Historique et legislation du salpêtre* (1793–5), Paris, 1922 (*Isis*, 1924–5, vi, 215; 1925, vii, 223); Partington, (4), 320 f.
[8] *Obs. Phys.*, 1775, vi, 339.
[9] *Obs. Phys.*, 1786, xxix, 264–72, and criticism by De la Metherie; Pierre Thouvenel: *Precis chimique sur les principes de la formation de l'acide nitreux, ouvrage qui a remporté le prix par la Société Royale des Sciences de Copenhague en 1776*, 4°, Copenhagen, 1784: BM B. 729. (19.).
[10] *Recueil des Mémoires sur la Formation & la Fabrication du Salpêtre* (which is quite different from the volume of 1776 mentioned on p. 411) in AdS, *Mém. div. Sav.*, 1786, xi: the *Histoire*

In it[1] Lavoisier describes 'Expériences sur la décomposition du nitre par le charbon' said to have been made in 1784. A mixture of $1\frac{1}{2}$ oz. of saltpetre with 1 gros 42 grains of charcoal in a brass tube was kindled by a fuse and the gas collected over water or mercury. The fixed air was absorbed by caustic alkali and the residual mofette (nitrogen) measured. The white fixed alkali (potassium carbonate) left in the tube was decomposed by acid and the fixed air measured. The average result is given as:

	cu. in.	oz.	gros	grains
Fixed air or carbonic acid	585·82	0	5	47·143
Mofette (nitrogen)	161·76	0	1	3·419
Caustic alkali		0	6	63·438
		1	5	42·000

The alkali was found by difference. Carbonic acid contains 28 of carbon and 72 of oxygen and the following densities, the weights in grains of 1 cu. in. at $10°$ R. and 28 in. mercury pressure, were used:

vital air	0·47317	fixed air	0·69500
common air	0·46811	mofette	0·46624

He thus calculated:

	cu. in.	oz.	gros	grains
carbon		0	1	42·000
vital air	619·53	0	4	5·143
mofette	161·73	0	1	3·419
caustic alkali		0	6	63·438
		1	5	42·000

Thus 5 gros 8·562 grains of nitric acid (acide nitreux) contain 4 gros 5·143 grains of vital air and 1 gros 3·419 grains of mofette. These figures give at once the ratio of the weights of nitrogen and oxygen in nitric acid as $1 : 3·89$ and the percentages as 20·45 and 79·55, instead of 25·9 and 74·1 for N_2O_5. Lavoisier, by a most complicated calculation involving the composition of nitric oxide, finds the same figures (20·5 and 79·5). The result is wrong and he probably used too little charcoal.

Lavoisier gives for saltpetre (the approximately correct figures are given in brackets):

contains papers by Macquer, Darcy (*sic*), Lavoisier, Sage, and Baumé, on saltpetre (p. 11), de la Rochefoucauld, Clouet, and Lavoisier, on saltpetre earth (p. 192), and an anonymous report on experiments made in England (Cavendish's) on the composition of nitric acid (p. 197). The *Mémoirs* contain papers by Cornette (p. 1), Thouvenel and Thouvenel (p. 55), Le Lorgna (p. 167), Gavinet and Chevrand (p. 268), de Beunie (p. 371), Romme (p. 421), Clouet and Lavoisier (pp. 503, 571), de Rochefoucauld, (p. 610), and Lavoisier (p. 625).
[1] *Op. cit.*, 625; VIII, v, 605; Kirwan, *Essay on Phlogiston*, 1789, 97 f.

vital air	4 gros	5·143 gr.	= 293·14 gr. =	33·9 (40)
mofette	1 gros	3·419 gr. =	75·42 gr. =	8·7 (14)
caustic alkali	6 gros	63·438 gr.	= 495·44 gr. =	57·4 (47)

$$100·0$$

He says the truths established in his work 'viennent de recevoir un très-grand degré d'evidence par les superbes expériences de M. Cavendish dont M. Blackden [*sic*] Sécretaire de la Société Royale de Londres vient de nous donner connoissance', which showed that 7 parts (vols.) of vital air require 3 parts of mofette.[1] Although Cavendish's result was published a year before Lavoisier's, the wording implies that Lavoisier was an independent discoverer of the elementary composition of nitric acid, and he says his work was done in 1784.

Davy[2] found 29·50 nitrogen and 70·50 oxygen, which he says agree with Cavendish's results, and Lavoisier's proportion of oxygen was too high. In an article on 'Detonation' written in 1793[3] Lavoisier says 76 grains of charcoal are necessary to detonate 1 oz. of saltpetre and the results are:

	cu. in.	grains
Fixed air or carbonic acid	390⅔	271·5
Mophete or azotic gas	114	50·2
Caustic alkali		330·3

These figures give 20·44 per cent. of nitrogen and 79·56 of oxygen in nitric anhydride, which are the same as those reported above.

A report on the processes for making soda from common salt submitted for a prize offered by the Academy in 1783 was drawn up by Lavoisier about 1788.[4] The Leblanc process came later (see p. 562).

Organic Chemistry

Lavoisier was the founder of modern organic chemistry by (i) his recognition of the qualitative composition of vegetable and animal substances, (ii) his recognition that these contain compound radicals which can combine with oxygen to form oxides such as sugar or alcohol and acids such as oxalic and acetic acids, and (iii) his introduction of a method of combustion analysis. He did not, unlike Scheele, discover any new organic compounds, since his interest lay in quantitative investigations.

In his memoir with Meusnier[5] Lavoisier says plants decompose water by taking from it the base of inflammable air and setting free vital air, and this is the mechanism of the formation of vegetable oils. By burning spirit of wine and condensing the gaseous product in a cooling worm, they obtained more than 18 oz. of water from 16 oz. of spirit, hence air must combine with the inflammable air in the spirit of wine.

[1] Cavendish, *Phil. Trans.*, 1785, lxxv, 372.
[2] *Researches concerning Nitrous Oxide*, 1800, 38, 43.   [3] VIII, v, 311.
[4] VIII, vi, 16   [5] AdS, 1781 (1784), m 468; VIII, ii, 334 (355).

This line of thought is carried further in Lavoisier's *Reflexions on the Decomposition of Water by Vegetable and Animal Substances.*[1] He showed that the inflammable air obtained by heating moist charcoal is nearly twice as dense as pure inflammable air (hydrogen), and thought it was hydrogen holding carbon in solution. (It was mostly carbon monoxide.) Fixed air is not a component of vegetables. Organic acids (acides végetaux et animaux) are not, as some thought, compounds of carbonic acid and hydrogen, which are formed on dry distillation of them. Sugar contains a large quantity of oxygen combined with hydrogen and carbon in a triple compound (une combinaison triple), the oxygen and hydrogen being approximately in the proportions to form water, with a slight excess of oxygen. Water, 'regardée jusqu'ici comme un élément, est un composé de 85 parties d'oxygène et de 15 parties d'hydrogène, comme nous croyons l'avoir précédemment démontré, M. Meusnier et moi.'[2] The above theory agrees with the decomposition of sugar by heat. Many animal and vegetable substances when oxidised form (like sugar) oxalic acid, since they contain the correct amounts of carbon and hydrogen. They contain radicals (les radicaux) composed of carbon and hydrogen,[3] which on oxidation form acids. Animal matters contain triple compounds of oxygen, hydrogen, and carbon, and sometimes, as Berthollet had shown (see p. 514), azote as a fourth element.

Alcohol on oxidation forms ether, then oxalic acid, acetic acid, etc. Combustion is an oxidation, and oxidation by water and acids is a sort of combustion. In vegetation, carbonic acid and water are necessary; the hydrogen leaves the oxygen of water to join to the carbon to form oils and resins, and to constitute the vegetable, and at the same time the oxygen of the water and of the carbonic acid is abundantly evolved, as shown by the experiments of Priestley, Ingen Housz, and Senebier, and combines with light to form oxygen gas (se combine avec la lumière pour former du gaz oxygène).[4]

The name 'acidifiable base', or concisely the *radical* (used here by Lavoisier) was proposed by de Morveau[5] for the substance which unites with oxygen to form an acid (les bases acidifiables ou principes radicaux des acides), and probably many acids have 'compound bases' (bases composées), which may differ only in the different proportions of the same principles. 'Nous sommes contentés de désigner l'être simple qui y modifie l'oxigène, par l'expression de *base acidifiable*, ou, pour abréger, de *radical* de tel acide.' Lavoisier[6] says: 'Il faut donc distinguer dans tout acide, la base acidifiable à laquelle M. de Morveau a donné le nom de radical, & le principe acidifiant, c'est à dire, l'oxigène', so admitting that the name was due to Guyton de Morveau. In an earlier paper de Morveau[7] mentions 'radicaux' once in a different, if allied, sense. The part of the *Nomenclature* (VI) concerned is a memoir read to the Academy by de Morveau on 2 May 1787. The theory of compound radicals so proposed by Guyton de Morveau and Lavoisier was later to have far-reaching

[1] AdS, 1786 (1788), m 590; VIII, ii, 656.   [2] VIII, ii, 659.
[3] *Ib.*, 665.   [4] *Ib.*, 670.
[5] Lavoisier, etc., VI, 1787, 38–9.
[6] VII, i, 69.   [7] *Obs. Phys.*, 1782, xix, 370.

consequences in theoretical organic chemistry (see Vol. IV), and is still an integral part of that science.

The gas evolved from fecal matter (night-soil) when fresh was found to be mainly fixed air, but in putrefaction inflammable air is evolved.[1] Fixed air is regarded as poisonous; in 1789[2] carbonic acid gas is 'a deadly poison' (un poison mortel), which cannot be respired by animals, even in the smallest quantity, without the most deadly consequences (des accidents funestes). It is, in fact, non-poisonous and suffocates by depriving the organism of oxygen.

Organic Analysis

In an undated memoir published in 1787[3] Lavoisier describes the combustion of alcohol and olive oil in a small weighed lamp, and of a wax candle, in air in a large bell-jar over mercury, oxygen being added from time to time from a second bell-jar. The volume of carbon dioxide formed was absorbed by caustic potash solution (Fig. 44). Alcohol could not be burnt in pure oxygen,

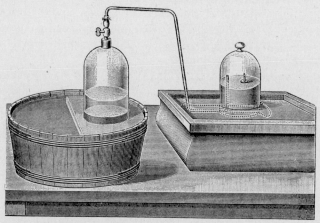

FIG. 44. LAVOISIER'S APPARATUS FOR THE COMBUSTION OF SPIRIT OF WINE CONTAINED IN A SMALL LAMP FLOATING ON MERCURY IN THE BELL-JAR, OXYGEN BEING SUPPLIED FROM A SECOND BELL-JAR.

as this gave rise to dangerous explosions and Lavoisier found later[4] that ether also causes dangerous explosions when burnt in the same way as alcohol.

In the combustion of spirit of wine the weight of water was determined by difference (he noticed that it was slightly acid); the composition calculated for 100 lb. was:

	lb.	oz.	gros	gr.	per cent	
carbon	28	8	4	6	29·779	carbon
hydrogen	7	13	7	46	17·205	hydrogen
water	63	9	4	20	53·016	oxygen
	100					

[1] AdS, 1782 (1785), m 560; VIII, ii, 601.
[2] Lavoisier and Seguin, AdS, 1789 (1793), m 566; VIII, ii, 693.
[3] AdS, 1784 (1787), m 593; VIII, ii, 586.   [4] AdS, 1786 (1788), m 590; VIII, ii, 667.

Lavoisier did not allow any oxygen in the composition of the alcohol and regarded the water as present as such in the spirit. The last column of percentages is given by Klaproth and Wolff.[1]

The results of an analysis of wax (which Lavoisier thought contained only carbon and hydrogen) are:[2]

	cu. in.
Volume of oxygen before combustion	194·80
Volume of gas after combustion	150·30
Residual oxygen after treatment with alkali	53·51
Volume of oxygen consumed	141·29

The density of oxygen at 10° R. and 28 in. mercury is 0·5 gr. per cu. in., hence the weight of oxygen consumed is 70·64 gr. The weight of wax consumed was 21·75 gr., total 92·39 gr. The carbonic acid gas measured 96·438 cu. in. and its density, he found, is 0·695 gr. per cu. in., hence its weight is 67·08 gr. The weight of water formed is found by difference as 92·39 − 67·08 = 25·31 gr. (The volume of carbonic acid gas is 150·30 − 53·51 = 96·79 cu. in., not 96·438 which Lavoisier gives.) The weight of hydrogen in the water is 25·31 × 0·150 = 3·80 gr., and the weight of oxygen 21·51 gr. The weight of oxygen which combined with the carbon is 70·64 − 21·51 = 49·13 gr. To find the weight of carbon, Lavoisier simply subtracted the weight of hydrogen from the weight of the wax, 21·75 − 3·80 = 17·95, and thence calculated for 1 lb. of wax:

	oz.	gros	gr.
Substance charbonneuse	13	1	64
Principe inflammable de l'eau	2	6	26

Lavoisier had found that carbonic acid contains 28 per cent of carbon and the weight of carbon in 67·08 gr. is, therefore, 18·78 gr. The sum 18·78 + 3·80 = 22·58 gr., instead of 21·51. In addition, wax contains about 5 per cent of oxygen. Lavoisier also concluded that olive oil (which contains oxygen) is a compound of carbon and hydrogen only, in this case finding the hydrogen by difference.

Some entries in Lavoisier's note-book from March 1788[3] show that he analysed oxide of mercury by heat, finding 92 mercury (instead of 100) and 8 oxygen, and then heated sugar with the oxide, collecting the carbon dioxide in weighed flasks of caustic potash solution. This gave 22 to 23 (instead of 42) per cent of carbon in sugar. The same method was used with other organic substances. Manganese dioxide, and potassium chlorate, were then used as oxidising agents. The density of pure carbon dioxide was determined by weighing in a glass globe.

Respiration

Mayow, Scheele, Priestley and Lavoisier were all aware of the great similarity between combustion and respiration. Lavoisier's first theory of respiration

---

[1] *Chemisches Wörterbuch*, Berlin, 1807, i, 60.   [2] VIII, ii, 598.   [3] VIII, iii, 773.

(1774) was purely physical.[1] The lungs must be distended by atmospheric air (enflés presque à chaque instant par le fluide élastique qui compose notre atmosphère). If an animal breathes fixed air, which is very soluble in water, this dissolves in the liquid in the lungs and loses its elasticity at once; hence the lungs collapse and the animal dies (le jeu du poumon doit être donc suspendu par le défaut de fluide élastique; il doit s'affaisser et devenir flasque). Priestley had done better than this (see p. 284).

Lavoisier's first memoir on respiration (1777) has been dealt with (p. 416); in it he hesitates to decide whether oxygen is converted into carbonic acid in passing into and out of the lung, or whether the oxygen is absorbed by the blood and carbonic acid emitted from it in passing through the lungs; he inclined to the second opinion.[2] Lavoisier and Laplace in 1784[3] said: 'Respiration is a combustion, very slow it is true, but otherwise perfectly similar to that of charcoal (La respiration est donc une combustion, à la verité fort lente, mais d'ailleurs parfaitment semblable à celle du charbon).' They reported that a guinea-pig confined for $1\frac{1}{4}$ hr. in 248 cu. in. of 'pure air' diminished it to $240\frac{1}{4}$ cu. in., of which nearly 40 cu. in. were absorbed by caustic potash. The result calculated on 100 vols. gives a diminution of 3·5 cu. in. and of the remainder 16·5 cu. in. were absorbed by potash.

In a paper on the changes produced in air by respiration, read on 15 February 1785 to the Société Royale de Médecine,[4] Lavoisier assumes that atmospheric air contains 25 of oxygen and 75 of nitrogen by volume, and says some analyses of air in public buildings, which must have passed several times through the lungs of each person in them, showed that the oxygen fell to 22 per cent (it is actually only 20 per cent in fresh air!) and the carbonic acid rose to 3 per cent, especially in the upper portions. He repeats the results of the guinea-pig experiment and says he had found by 'numerous experiments' (which he never published) that 1 cu. ft. at 28 in. Hg and 10° R. of the gases weighed:

	oz.	gros	grains
atmospheric air	1	3	3
vital air	1	4	12*
gaz azote	1	2	48

* In the altered version; 12 gr. is omitted in original.

The result calculated on 100 vols. gives a diminution of 3·18 cu. in. and 19 cu. in. were absorbed by caustic potash. Lavoisier calculated that the weight of oxygen consumed was greater than the residue plus that in the carbonic acid, and concluded that the missing part 'combined with a portion

[1] V, 1801, 314; VIII, i, 626.
[2] For Lavoisier's work on respiration see Fourcroy, *Ency. Method., Médicale*, 1787, i, 492–592; Bostock, *An Essay on Respiration*, Liverpool, 1804, 79–81; Murray, 1807, iv, 547–78; Underwood, *Proc. Roy. Soc. Med.* (*Hist. Med.*), 1944, xxxvii, 247.
[3] AdS, 1780 (1784), h 3, m 355; VIII, ii, 331.
[4] *Mémoires de Médecine et de Physique Médicale, Tirés des Registres de la Société Royale de Médecine*, 1787, v, 569–82: Sur les altérations qui arrive à l'air dans plusieurs circonstances où se trouvent les hommes réunis en société; reprinted with 'quelques changements' in IV, iii, 13; VIII, ii, 676; Seguin, *Ann. Chim.*, 1790, v, 191 (261).

of hydrogen to form water' in the lung (dans le poumon), where the carbon is also burnt: 'l'air, par l'acte de la respiration, extrait donc du poumon une matière véritablement charbonneuse.' He says that in crowded rooms (such as in operatic performances) the air is probably charged with 'exhalations more or less putrid' which may cause disease.

Lavoisier and Seguin[1] said:

'Respiration is a true combustion, brought about by the combination of the carbon and of the hydrogen contained in the blood with the oxygen of the atmospheric air, a combustion entirely similar to that of a burning candle.... Thence, again, comes the permanence of the animal heat sustained by the caloric disengaged from the vital air.

La respiration est une véritable combustion, opérée par la combinaison du carbone et de l'hydrogène contenus dans le sang, avec l'oxygène de l'air athmosphérique, combustion entièrement semblable à celle d'une bougie allumée.... De-là, encore, la permanence de la chaleur animale entretenue par le calorique dégagé de l'air vital.'

At the beginning of the memoir it is said that atmospheric air is a 'compound (composé)' of vital air and azotic gas. The air supplies the oxygen and caloric, the blood supplies the combustible (carbon and hydrogen) and must be constantly replenished by food: 'the flame of life is kindled at birth and extinguished at death.' Some discussion of diet is given, with moral and political (democratic) observations, perhaps by Seguin, an army contractor who later amassed a fortune.

The quantity of oxygen consumed is almost exactly the same whether respiration occurs in pure vital air or in vital air mixed with a considerable

FIG. 45. LAVOISIER'S EXPERIMENTS ON RESPIRATION.
SEGUIN IS BREATHING AIR OR OXYGEN FROM A JAR STANDING IN A TROUGH THROUGH A TUBE FITTED IN A MASK. MADAME LAVOISIER IS SEATED AT THE DESK.
(From a Drawing by Mme. Lavoisier.)

amount of azote, and there is no evolution or absorption of azote in respiration. A mixture of vital air and hydrogen gas may be used for respiration equally with atmospheric air. The quantity of vital air consumed increases with the

[1] AdS, 1789 (1793), h xxi, m 566–84 (on Seguin see p. 106); VIII, ii, 688; Daumas, *Archives*, 1955, viii (old xxxiv), 411, says the memoir was read to the Academy on 17 November 1791, and not in 1789.

temperature, and during digestion. Movement and exercise cause a large increase. In all cases the temperature of the blood remains sensibly constant. (The body temperature is given as $32°$ R. or $104°$ F.!) In 24 hours, respiration consumes 24 cu. ft. or 2 lb. 1 oz. 1 gros of oxygen and forms 2 lb. 5 oz. 4 gros of carbonic acid and 5 gros 51 gr. of water. This is equivalent to the removal from the blood of 10 oz. 4 gros of carbon and 1 oz. 5 gros 51 gr. of hydrogen (*sic*). Lavoisier seems to have thought that the change of composition of *each* part of the inspired air occurs completely in the lungs before it is expired. The weights of oxygen and carbonic acid correspond with 913·43 grams and 1146·97 grams, respectively, and with volumes of 639·7 and 584·24 lit. at S.T.P., respectively, or 100 oxygen and 91·32 carbon dioxide.

Bostock[1] pointed out that Lavoisier's theory that some hydrogen is burnt rested only on some inaccurate experiments, that the weights of hydrogen and water just given are obviously absurd, and that a similar method of estimating the amount of water formed in the lungs had been used by Crawford.[2] Bostock said that Lavoisier's theory of the combustion of hydrogen of the blood had been admitted without sufficient evidence and that 'at present we have no proof of the emission of any substance from this fluid, depending upon the effects of respiration, except carbone'.[3]

Lavoisier and Seguin say[4] that the carbonic acid is formed 'dans le poumon', although it is admitted[5] that:

'there is no decisive proof that it is formed immediately in the lung or in the course of the circulation . . . it is possible that part . . . is formed by digestion, that it is introduced into the circulation with the chyle, and at last, reaching the lung, it is disengaged from the blood in proportion as the oxygen combines with it by a superior affinity.'

Seguin and Lavoisier[6] said that in cold regions more heat is produced, possibly because the air is denser and more oxygen is breathed.

Seguin and Lavoisier proposed the theory that oxidation occurs in the tubes of the lungs, in which a 'humour' composed of carbon and hydrogen is continually secreted from the blood:

'Il faut savoir d'abord qu'il suinte continuellement dans les bronches une humeur qui se sépare du sang, qui se filtre à travers les membranes du poumon, et qui est principalement composée d'hydrogène et de carbone. C'est cette humeur qui, se trouvant très-divisée au moment où elle sort des extremités déliées des vaissaux exhalant du poumon, se brûle en partie, en décomposant l'air vital avec lequel elle était en contact, et forme, pendant cette combustion, de l'eau et du gaz acide carbonique.[7]

The water formed in this combustion, and that transpiring in the lungs with the carbonated hydrogen (hydrogène carboné), were calculated from the oxygen used up, the carbonic acid formed, and the water exhaled by the lungs, and comparison with the water evolved by cutaneous transpiration. The loss by transpiration in 24 hrs. was found to be 1 lb. 14 oz. and by respiration 15 oz.

[1] *An Essay on Respiration*, 1804, 128, 207, 227 f.   [2] *On Animal Heat*, 1788, 154, 347.
[3] Bostock, 129; analysis of Lavoisier and Seguin's two papers, 229–41.
[4] VIII, ii, 697.   [5] *Ib.*, 702.
[6] AdS, 1790 (1797), m 601–12; VIII, ii, 704: first memoir on the transpiration of animals: 'Lu à la rentrée publique, le 14 avril 1790', but Daumas, *Archives*, 1955, viii (old xxxiv), 411, says it was read on 10 June 1791.
[7] VIII, ii, 708.

Of the little more than 22 cu. ft. of vital air absorbed in respiration in 24 hrs., weighing 33 oz. 1 gros 10 grains, 13 cu. ft. are used to form water and 9 cu. ft. to form carbonic acid. The volume of carbonic acid exhaled is 8 cu. ft. 6 cu. in. and the weight 1 lb. 1 oz. 7 gros 4 grains, and the weight of water 1 lb. 7 oz. 5 gros 20 grains. 100 vols. of oxygen now give only about 41 vols. of carbonic acid. Although the 24 cu. ft. of oxygen in the 1789 experiments are said to weigh 2 lb. 1 oz. 1 gros, or 33 oz. 1 gros, the 22 cu. ft. in 1790 weigh 33 oz. 1 gros 10 grains, practically the same weight for very different volumes. Bostock,[1] taking 100 cu. in. to weigh 50·5 Paris grains, calculated 20943·36 grs. and 19198·08 grs., respectively, the last being 15661·66 English Troy grains.

A second memoir on respiration by Lavoisier and Seguin was not published until 1814,[2] and the second memoir on transpiration in the same year.[3] Both were based on work done in 1792.

Laplace[4] said Lavoisier assembled apparatus for work on respiration costing over £500. His experiments were interrupted by his death, but he had found that in 24 hours a man consumes 32·48437 Troy oz. of oxygen gas and gives out 15·73 oz. of carbonic acid gas and 28·55 oz. of water vapour. Assuming that the carbonic acid contains 10·486 oz. of oxygen and 5·243 oz. of carbon, and the water 24·2675 oz. of oxygen and 4·2825 oz. of hydrogen, the excess of oxygen emitted over oxygen absorbed is 34·75416 − 32·48437 = 2·3697916 oz. (*sic*).

There is something wrong with these figures; Bostock,[5] from the same source, calculated the oxygen consumed in 24 hrs. as 15592·5 Troy grains; 1 Troy oz. = 480 grains, and this corresponds with 32·48437 oz. This is in reasonable agreement with the 1790 figure (15661·66 gr.), but the carbonic acid and water figures are different. Bostock[6] calculated the carbonic acid of 1789 as 17720·89 Troy gr., of 1790 as 8450·24 gr., and in Laplace's account as 7550·40 gr. He calculated that Davy[7] found 17811·38 gr. The amounts of water emitted, calculated by Bostock[8] are in 1789, 337·18 gr.; in 1790, 11180·57 gr.; Laplace's account gives 13704 gr., and 'from such very discordant calculations it is impossible to draw any conclusions'.

In a separate publication read to the Société de Médecine in May 1790, Seguin gave a more satisfactory account of previous work on respiration, particularly Crawford's.[9] Lavoisier and Seguin assumed that no carbonic acid is emitted in transpiration (which is nearly true), whilst Jurine[10] found that a considerable amount is emitted in this way. Seguin[11] gave a good historical account of the theory of heat, calorimetry, and animal heat, which supplied the deficiencies in Lavoisier's memoirs.

The difficulty that, if the combustion occurs in the lungs, the animal heat should be concentrated there and not spread over the body, was got over by Lavoisier and Laplace by saying that the rapidity of the circulation, the evaporation in the lungs, and the increased capacity for heat of arterial blood (Crawford's theory) could explain the phenomena. Hassenfratz (1791)

---

[1] *Essay*, 1804, 204.   [2] Seguin, *Ann. Chim.*, 1814, xci, 318.
[3] Seguin, *Ann. Chim.*, 1814, xc, 5.
[4] Q. by T. Thomson, *Ency. Brit. Suppl.*, 1801, ii, 594.   [5] *Essay*, 83.
[6] *Essay*, 86.   [7] *Researches on Nitrous Oxide*, 1800, 434.   [8] *Essay*, 94–5.
[9] Seguin, *Obs. Phys.*, 1790, xxxvii, 467; repr. in *Ann. Chim.*, 1797, xxi, 225.
[10] Q. by Fourcroy, *Ency. Méthod., Méd.*, 1797, iii, 679.
[11] *Ann. Chim.*, 1789, iii, 148–242 (Mémoire sur le calorique et la théorie de Black, Crawford, Lavoisier et Laplace sur la chaleur animale); 1790 ,v, 191–271 (Second Mémoire sur le calorique).

published[1] a very interesting discussion of the opinions of Crawford, Lavoisier, Girtanner, 'la Place' and 'la Grange' on respiration, saying that Lagrange was of the opinion that: 'the lungs are not the place where all the caloric necessary to support the animal heat is disengaged'; this heat 'is disengaged during the circulation of the blood, by the combination of the hydrogen and of the carbon of the blood with the oxygen which is mingled with it'. Hassenfratz spoke of oxygen being 'dissolved' by the blood, and says the theory of Lagrange that oxygen 'mixed' with the blood combined with the carbon and hydrogen in it had been rejected by Lavoisier. Hassenfratz also described experiments (similar to Priestley's, see p. 285) in which blood was exposed to oxygen and carbon dioxide and the colour changes observed.

Crawford[2] found that in the respiration of a guinea-pig 40·86 cu. in. or 20·1 grains of carbonic acid gas were exhaled while 56·86 cu. in. or 18·9 grains of oxygen were absorbed, not very different from Lavoisier's result, 26 grains and 23·2 grains, respectively. Robert Menzies[3] discussed the work of Goodwyn, Black, Crawford, and Lavoisier, and described his own experiments, showing that the volume of oxygen absorbed was equal to that of the carbon dioxide expired, a result also found by Davy[4] and by Dalton in 1806.[5]

The problem was finally cleared up by a very accurate investigation by H. V. Regnault and J. Reiset,[6] who showed that the *respiratory quotient*: (vol. of CO_2 exhaled) ÷ (vol. of O_2 inhaled), with various animals, birds, reptiles and insects is mostly less than unity, say 0·8, but in some circumstances may exceed unity. Vauquelin[7] found that worms and snails absorb oxygen *completely* from air in which they die. L. Spallanzani (1729–1799)[8] pointed out two theories:

(i) part of the oxygen of the inspired air is absorbed by the blood in the lung and part combines with carbon 'emitted by the blood' so that the oxygen is diminished and the air at the same time infected with carbonic acid;

(ii) the oxygen is not totally absorbed by the blood but part forms carbonic acid 'with the carbon of the lung', and the other part forms water with the hydrogen of the lung.

He experimented with six classes of the animal kingdom, including snails, insects, worms, fish and hibernating animals. Snails absorb all the oxygen detectable by burning phosphorus, but there is a small residue detectable by nitric oxide. The nitrogen mostly 'remains intact, or if it suffers a diminution this is always small in comparison with the oxygen.[9]

---

[1] *Ann. Chim.*, 1791, xi, 261: Sur la combinaison de l'oxigène avec le carbone et l'hydrogène du sang, sur la dissolution de l'oxigène dans le sang, & sur la manière dont le calorique se dégage.

[2] *On Animal Heat*, 1788, 346 f.; Murray, 1807, iv, 547.

[3] *Tentamen physiologicum inaugurale de Respiratione*, Edinburgh, 1790 (4 ll., 59 pp., fold. pl.); abstr. in *Ann. Chim.*, 1791, viii, 211–23; *J. der Physik*, 1792, vi, 109–20.

[4] *Researches on Nitrous Oxide*, 1800, 429.

[5] Thomson, (2), 1817, iv, 619; Thomson, *ib.*, found a little more oxygen absorbed but attributed this to abstraction 'by some other way than respiration'.

[6] *Ann. Chim.*, 1849, xxvi, 299–519.   [7] *Ann. Chim.*, 1792, xii, 273.

[8] *Mémoires sur la Respiration*, tr. J. Senebier, 8°, Geneva, An XI (1803), 102; also in Italian, 2 vols., Milan, 1803.

[9] *Ib.*, 62, 87 f., 141, 145 f., 155 f., 162 f., 230, 251.

In pure oxygen, snails absorb more oxygen than in air and also form more carbonic acid; in air they absorbed 20 oxygen and 4 nitrogen and formed 6 carbonic acid; in oxygen they absorbed 38 and formed 14 carbonic acid.[1] Dead snails, etc., also absorb oxygen, more rapidly than live ones, and produce carbonic acid.[2]

Snails in an atmosphere of pure hydrogen continue for some time to evolve carbon dioxide but Spallanzani thought that this came from food in the stomach, entered the blood, and then passed out through the skin and lungs. Even dead animals, worms, and insects evolved carbon dioxide in pure nitrogen, and hence it could not be formed by combination with oxygen.[3] 'There are reasons for thinking that the carbonic acid gas which appears in the experiments with snails is the product of this acid pre-existing in these animals rather than of the combination of oxygen with their carbon.'[4] The oxygen absorbed by the blood in the lungs combines with the muscle of the heart and this produces the movement of the heart.[5]

'In this astonishing function of the animal economy, part of the oxygen of the common air combines with the hydrogen of the blood and forms water which is exhaled in expiration; another part seems at the same moment to combine in the pulmonary blood, which acquires a bright red colour; a third part combines with the carbon of the blood and produces carbonic acid, or rather according to the opinion of a celebrated physicist the carbonic acid pre-exists in the blood and escapes from it in the gaseous state, as if precipitated or disengaged by the oxygen gas.'[6]

Priestley[7] showed that oxygen is necessary for the life of fish. Provençal and Humboldt[8] found that in the respiration of fish more oxygen is absorbed than is converted into carbon dioxide, and some nitrogen is absorbed.

H. Davy[9] was able to obtain a little carbonic acid from venous blood and a very small quantity of oxygen from arterial blood, by heating. He then regarded oxygen gas (phosoxygen) as a compound of light and oxygen, and said: 'phosoxygen is not decomposed by the lungs', it 'combines with venous blood in the lungs . . . carbonic acid and water are both liberated from the lungs during this process, either by the increase of temperature, or from the superior affinity of phosoxygen for the venous blood'. A year later, Davy[10] found that some nitrogen is absorbed, amounting to 5·1 cu. in. per min., 23·9 cu. in. of oxygen being also absorbed and 12 cu. in. of carbonic acid produced. Priestley[11] had found some absorption of nitrogen in the respiration of air enriched with oxygen, but his result was not generally accepted. Jurine[12] found that some nitrogen is *evolved*, but his experiments were misinterpreted.[13] Davy in 1800 adopted Lavoisier's views; experiments on the respiration of hydrogen and nitrous oxide led him to believe that some at least of the carbonic acid in expired air was not formed directly by combustion in the lungs, but

[1] *Ib.*, 65 f., 165.   [2] *Ib.*, 63 f., 285, etc.   [3] *Ib.*, 66 f., 78 f.   [4] *Ib.*, 259.
[5] *Ib.*, 327.   [6] *Ib.*, 187, 217 f.; the 'physicist' is Lavoisier in his experiments on digestion.
[7] E & O, 1790, iii, 382.   [8] *Mém. Soc. Arcueil*, 1809, ii, 359–404.
[9] *Theory of Respiration*, in Beddoes, *Contributions to Medical and Physical Knowledge, Principally from the West of England*, Bristol, 1799, 128–47; Davy, *Works*, 1839, ii, 75–86.
[10] *Researches on Nitrous Oxide*, 1800, 435 f., 447; *Works*, 1839, iii, 257, 263; Henderson, *Nicholson's J.*, 1804, viii, 40.
[11] E & O, 1790, iii, 379.
[12] Q. by Fourcroy, *Ency. Méthod., Méd.*, i, 493 f.   [13] Bostock, *Essay*, 97.

pre-existed in venous blood and transpired from it through the coats of the minute blood vessels. Davy[1] also made experiments with fish and zoophytes.

Allen and Pepys[2] found that in respiration no water is produced by oxidation and no nitrogen is absorbed. More carbon dioxide is formed in the respiration of oxygen than of air. The carbon dioxide in expired air amounts to 8 to 10 per cent and 10 to 11 oz. of carbon are oxidised in 24 hours. Prout[3] found about 3·45 per cent of carbon dioxide in expired air. William Frederic Edwards (Jamaica, 14 April 1777–Versailles, 23 June 1842),[4] brother of Milne-Edwards, found that more oxygen is absorbed than corresponds with the carbonic acid exhaled. He mentions Spallanzani and found that frogs, fish, and infant mammals on respiration in hydrogen evolve much more carbonic acid than corresponds with the oxygen remaining in their lungs when they are removed from the air.

The view that the evolution of heat does not occur only in the lungs but in all parts of the body in which the blood circulates goes back to Mayow (see Vol. II, p. 603), although he supposed that it also occurred in the circulating blood. This view was not generally adopted, and early in the nineteenth century three other theories were generally held:

(i) The modified 'combustion theory' of Lavoisier, held in England, that the hydrocarbonous material undergoing combustion in the lungs is not secreted as such in the air-vesicles but is oxidised while still in the venous blood by oxygen passing through the coats of these vessels.

(ii) The air as a whole or the oxygen in it passes through the coats of the air vessels and combines with the blood, and at the same time the hydrocarbonous material in the venous blood develops or secretes carbonic acid. This 'secretion' theory was developed to explain the results of W. F. Edwards,[5] and was held by only a few.

(iii) The 'diffusion' theory of Lagrange, that oxygen passing into solution in the blood is consumed in the capillaries, giving rise to carbonic acid which escapes in the lungs. This theory was mostly rejected because it was found difficult to demonstrate the presence of free carbonic acid in venous blood and free oxygen in arterial blood. H. Davy[6] claimed to have obtained these in small amounts, but others failed to do so.[7]

L. Gmelin and F. Tiedemann with the collaboration of Mitscherlich[8] found that neither arterial nor venous blood evolved any gas in a vacuum. Gustav Magnus,[9] using the high vacuum of a mercury pump, first showed that both arterial and venous blood give off both oxygen and carbon dioxide, as well as

[1] In Beddoes, 1799, 128; Researches, 1800, 366.
[2] Phil. Trans., 1808, xcviii, 249; 1809, xcix, 404; 1829, cxix, 279.
[3] Ann. Phil., 1813, ii, 328; 1814, iv, 331.
[4] De l'Influence des Agens Physiques sur la Vie, 1824; tr. Hodgkin and Fisher, On the Influence of Physical Agents on Life, 1832, 212, 220 f., 226, 232–41.
[5] On the Influence of Physical Agents on Life, 1832, ch. xvi, 212–44 (On the alterations in the Air from Respiration).
[6] In Beddoes, Contributions to Physical and Medical Knowledge, Bristol, 1799, 132; Davy, Works, 1839, ii, 78.
[7] M. Foster, in Watts, Dictionary of Chemistry, 1874, v, 85.
[8] Ann. Phys., 1834, xxxi, 289; Ann., 1834, xii, 346–54; Mitscherlich, Gesammelte Schriften, 1896, 350.
[9] Ann. Phys., 1837, xl, 583–606; 1845, lxvi, 177–206.

some nitrogen, arterial blood giving more oxygen. Blood shaken in oxygen absorbed 10 to 12 per cent of its volume. Thus, Lagrange's theory that arterial blood contains only oxygen and venous blood only carbon dioxide was disproved, but his 'diffusion' theory was favoured and was then generally adopted.[1] Magnus supposed that the gases were simply dissolved in the blood, but Liebig[2] suggested that the greater part of the oxygen is in a loose state of chemical combination, like nitric oxide in ferrous sulphate solution, and Lothar Meyer,[3] in Bunsen's laboratory, showed that part of the oxygen and also the carbon dioxide in blood do not obey the law of partial pressures and are chemically combined. Later experimenters pointed out the role played by the hæmoglobin,[4] and Stokes[5] definitely said that this exists in two states of oxidation. Further developments of the theory of respiration are considered in Vol. IV.

A. Crawford[6] found that animals (including frogs) in a space at a temperature above blood heat do not become hotter and the venous blood assumes the character of arterial blood. G. Fordyce[7] confirmed this with a dog. C. Blagden[8] found that the temperature of the human body does not rise more than 2° F. above the normal in a space containing dry air at 260° F. (hotter than boiling water). Crawford said that Alexander Wilson (professor of astronomy in Glasgow, 1760–84), to explain this 'power of producing cold', had suggested that 'if the sensible heat of animals depends on the separation of absolute heat from the blood by means of its union with the phlogistic principle in the minute vessels', there may be 'a temperature at which that fluid is no longer capable of combining with phlogiston, and at which point it must of course cease to give off heat'. Lord Kelvin,[9] drawing attention to these observations, suggested that in this case there might be an excess of oxygen and even an absence of carbon dioxide in the expired air, animal cold being due to a deoxidation of matter within the body.

Fermentation

In his explanation of vinous fermentation, Lavoisier at first assumed that water is decomposed, the oxygen combining with the carbon of the sugar to form carbonic acid which is evolved, and the hydrogen combining with another portion of the carbon to form alcohol, as is proved by the formation of water on the combustion of alcohol.[10] In the chapter on 'the decomposition of vegetable oxides by the vinous fermentation' in his *Traité*[11] Lavoisier says that sugar is converted into carbonic acid gas and spirit of wine, more appropriately called by the Arabic word alcohol (alcool) since it is formed from cider or

[1] Foster, *op. cit.*; *id., History of Physiology*, Cambridge, 1901, 252–3.
[2] *Familiar Letters on Chemistry*, tr. Gregory, 3 ed., 1851, 332–4.
[3] *Phil. Mag.*, 1857, xiv, 263–8.
[4] Hoppe-Seyler, *Virchow's Archiv*, 1862, xxiii, 464; 1864, xxix, 233, 597.
[5] *Proc. Roy. Soc.*, 1864, xiii, 355.   [6] *Phil. Trans.*, 1781, lxxi, 479.
[7] *Phil. Trans.*, 1787, lxxvii, 310.   [8] *Phil. Trans.*, 1775, lxv, 111, 484.
[9] *Phil. Mag.*, 1903, v, 198: Animal Thermodynamics.
[10] AdS, 1781 (1784), m 468; VIII, ii, 356.
[11] VII, 139 f.; VIII, i, 100; for a draft made in 1788 see VIII, iii, 777; the weights in the original are reduced to decimals of the pound (as in the text here) in Kerr's tr., VIIF, 1799, 185.

fermented sugar as well as wine (a typical Lavoisierian touch). The 'axiom' already quoted (see p. 377) shows that:

$$\text{must of grapes} = \text{carbonic acid} + \text{alcohol},$$

'une véritable égalité ou équation entre les principes du corps qu'on examine et ceux qu'on en retire par l'analyse.' (The first use of the name chemical equation.) Experiments had shown that the 'true vegetable oxide' sugar, composed of carbon, hydrogen, and oxygen combined in such a way that a very slight force is sufficient to destroy their equilibrium, contains in 100 parts 8 of hydrogen, 64 of oxygen and 28 of carbon. This equilibrium is disturbed when about a tenth of its weight of yeast paste is added to sugar dissolved in about 4 parts of water, at 15° to 18° R. A description of the apparatus for absorbing the carbonic acid in weighed potash bulbs[1] is given. The newer apparatus made for Lavoisier's experiments on fermentation and putrefaction still exists in Paris; he probably never had the opportunity to use it.[2]

From results with a few lb. of sugar Lavoisier calculated the proportions of the elements in the mixture of 100 lb. sugar, 400 lb. of water, and 10 lb. of yeast paste (including the azote in the yeast, an analysis of which is given), and those in the products. Omitting the yeast and taking account of 4·1 lb. of undecomposed sugar in the products, the approximate figures (Lavoisier gives the results to 0·01 gr., or seven decimal places) are:

```
     95·9 lb. crystalline sugar = 26·8 carbon + 7·7 hydrogen + 61·4 oxygen
 ⎧  57·7 lb. alcohol           = 16·7    „      + 9·6    „      + 31·4   „
 ⎨  35·3 lb. carbonic acid     =  9·9    „                      + 25·4   „
 ⎩   2·5 lb. acetic acid       =  0·6    „      + 0·2 hydrogen +  1·7   „
     total products 95·5 lb.   = 27·2    „      + 9·8    „      + 58·5   „
```

All the quantitative data of this 'travail très-pénible' are erroneous, but the general conclusion is correct.

It is not necessary to suppose that any water is decomposed, unless it is assumed that the oxygen and hydrogen exist in the sugar combined in that form (as he had assumed previously), since the three elements in the sugar are really in a state of equilibrium:

'The effects of vinous fermentation are thus reduced to the separation of the sugar, which is an oxide, into two parts, the oxygenation of one at the expense of the other to form carbonic acid, and the deoxidation of the other in favour of the first to form a combustible substance, alcohol, in such a way that, if it were possible to recombine these two substances, alcohol and carbonic acid, sugar would be re-formed.'[3]

The carbon and hydrogen in alcohol are not in the form of oil but are combined with a portion of oxygen which renders them miscible with water, all three elements being in a state of equilibrium. Lavoisier seems here to abandon his earlier radical or dualistic theory (p. 469) in favour of a unitary theory of the alcohol molecule. His theory of fermentation is very interesting and has some relation to modern views.

Lavoisier differed from Boerhaave and agreed with Stahl (see Vol. II) in regarding putrefaction as a variety of fermentation. In 'la fermentation

---

[1] VII, 461.   [2] Daumas, *Chymia*, 1950, iii, 45 (60) and plates.   [3] VII, 149–50.

putride'[1] the whole of the hydrogen appears as hydrogen gas and the oxygen and carbon as carbonic acid. (He says nothing of methane, which Volta had proved to exist in marsh gas.) If azote (which disposes to putrefaction) is present it combines with part of the hydrogen to form ammonia; sulphur and phosphorus form sulphuretted hydrogen gas (gaz hydrogène sulfuré) and phosphoretted hydrogen (gaz hydrogène phosphoré), respectively.

Acetous fermentation[2] involves the oxidation of alcohol; air is necessary, the volume of which is reduced by absorption of oxygen, and 'wine may be changed into vinegar by other means of oxidation'. By hydrogenation, carbonic acid could be changed into all the vegetable acids. Further experiments are necessary to find the constituents in vegetable acids and oxides, 'but it is easily seen that this part of chemistry, like all others, makes rapid progress to perfection, and is much simpler than was formerly believed.' Lavoisier's very promising entry into the field of organic chemistry was arrested by his untimely death.

The Nomenclature Chimique

The *Méthode de Nomenclature Chimique* was the result of eight months of intensive work by Guyton de Morveau, Lavoisier, Berthollet, and Fourcroy, who met almost daily from the middle of 1786 until its publication in 1787 (see VI in list of p. 372). It is based on the earlier work of Guyton de Morveau (see p. 526).[3] The preliminary discourse by Lavoisier (Sur la nécessité de réformer et de perfectionner la nomenclature de la chimie) was read to the Academy on 17 April 1787.[4] After mentioning de Morveau's table of 1782 and the '*Logique* de l'Abbé de Condillac' (1780), Lavoisier explains that:

'Nous aurons . . . trois choses à distinguer dans toute science physique; la série des faits qui constituent la science; les idées qui rappellent les faits; les mots qui les expriment. Le mot doit faire naître l'idée; l'idée doit piendre le fait: ce sont trois empreints d'un même cachet.'[5]

Fourcroy[6] said: 'the trial of the nomenclature which has already been made in 1787 and 1788 in the courses in the Jardin du roi and the Lycée' indicated that the new system would be very favourable to the progress of chemistry. He points out that in the old system the same substance might have 8, 10 or 12 different names, mostly having no relation to the thing. The main object of the *Nomenclature* was really to present a systematic view of the new system of chemistry and, if the names proposed were adopted, to make it impossible to speak or write in terms of any other. The book had only a small number of editions (see p. 372), since its contents were incorporated into Lavoisier's *Traité de Chimie* (1789). In 1794 Pearson (whose book is not simply a 'translation') proposed the name nitrogen instead of azote ('I believe not now used for the first time'; see Chaptal, p. 560), and he emphasised (from a conversation with Cullen in 1773) that it was discovered by Rutherford in 1772.[7] 'Gaz' used in 1794[8] is altered to 'gas' in 1799.[9] In 1794 'sulfit' and 'sulfat' but

[1] VII, 153.   [2] *Ib.*, 159.   [3] *Obs. Phys.*, 1782, xix, 370.
[4] VIII, v, 354–64; VI, 1787, 1–25 (says 18 April).
[5] VI, 1787, 13; Fourcroy, (2), iii, 563; summary of VI, *ib.*, 562–5 (24 sections); Hartog, 1941, 49.
[6] (4), 1793, v, 220.   [7] VIC, 19, 26.   [8] VIC, 26.   [9] VIC', 2.

'sulphures or sulphurets' are used, but in 1799 'ph' replaces 'f' throughout, 'sulphite' and 'sulphate'[1] 'Nitrous oxyd gas'[2] became 'oxide'.[3] In 1799 the prefix 'oxy-', e.g. in 'oxymuriatic acid' replaces 'oxygenated', at the suggestion of Kirwan.[4] Pearson translated 'silice' as 'silica' to conform with the names of other 'earths' (magnesia, baryta), and this was adopted by Thomson,[5] but Murray[6] preferred the old name 'silex'.

Chenevix uses the terminations '-eous' or '-ous', '-ite', and '-ic', 'ate'; instead of the modern '-ide' he uses '-uret' (from the French '-ure'), e.g. 'sulphuret, phosphuret, carburet', etc. He uses 'hydro-oxide' or 'hydroxide' instead of Proust's 'hydrate'.[7] The names 'barytes', 'strontia',[8] and 'ammonia' instead of 'ammoniac' (following Mrs. Fulhame)[9] are used. Other names used by Chenevix are 'thermogen' (instead of Gadolin's 'gasogen')[10] for Pearson's 'calorific' (caloric), and 'photogen' for light,[11] 'sulphuretted hydrogen' and 'phosphuretted hydrogen',[12] 'hydrogenized sulphuret of potash' (instead of hydrosulphuret),[13] 'gaseous nitrous oxide' and 'gaseous nitric oxide' for N_2O and NO,[14] 'gaseous carbonic oxide' (CO),[15] 'oxygenizement',[16] 'dissolution',[17] and 'gas' (for gaz).[18] There are symbols for *liquid* oxygen, hydrogen and nitrogen.[19]

Proposals to change names always arouse opposition. After giving a good summary of the *Nomenclature*[20] De la Metherie turned on it[21] as barbaric, misleading, and in conflict with well-established names (all favourite criticisms in this field); he also published critical letters from abroad.[22] De Luc[23] thought it was based on unproved hypotheses. It was also criticised by de Marivetz,[24] Sage,[25] and Opoix.[26] A letter from a professor in Pisa to De la Metherie[27] said:

'Je me souviens d'avoir entendu dire par un des Messieurs les réformateurs: "Messieurs, dans deux ans d'ici il n'y aura plus de phlogistique en France." Les Messieurs ont tenu parole. Voilà la France, quant à eux, bien dephlogistiquée.'

James Watt junr. reported to Crell[28] that most English chemists (except Priestley and Keir) were using the new theory, but De la Metherie[29] reported that it was uniformly rejected in England: the anonymous English professor who said that Lavoisier's theory had been adopted by a small number but then abandoned,[30] was perhaps Beddoes. Kirwan[31] proposed to retain the old names, since every chemist knew what they meant. Adet and Hassenfratz defended the new nomenclature[32] against the criticism by De la Metherie,[33] they denied Lavoisier's statements that pure air (oxygen) contained most matter of heat (which had not been proved experimentally), and that it always formed acids

[1] VIC', 35.   [2] VIC, 30.   [3] VIC', 44; oxide is sometimes called 'half-acid'.
[4] VIC', 5; see Chenevix, VIE, 56.   [5] (2), 1807, ii, 77.   [6] 1807, iii, 542.
[7] VIE, 34, 77.   [8] *Ib.*, 20.   [9] *Ib.*, 55.   [10] *Ib.*, 43.
[11] *Ib.*, 65–6.   [12] *Ib.*, 75–6.   [13] *Ib.*, 78.   [14] *Ib.*, 93.
[15] *Ib.*, 94.   [16] *Ib.*, 159.   [17] *Ib.*, 168.   [18] *Ib.*, 187.
[19] *Ib.*, 214 f.   [20] *Obs. Phys.*, 1787, xxxi, 210–19.
[21] *Ib.*, 1787, xxxi, 270–85; 1788, xxxii, 12; Crell's *Ann.*, 1787, I, 532.
[22] *Obs. Phys.*, 1789, xxxv, 75–6.   [23] *Ib.*, 1790, xxxvi, 144–54, 193–207.
[24] *Ib.*, 1788, xxxii, 61.   [25] *Ib.*, 1788, xxxiii, 478.
[26] *Ib.*, 1789, xxxiv, 76.   [27] *Ib.*, 1789, xxxv, 76.
[28] *Ib.*, 1793, xliii, 394.   [29] Crell's *Ann.*, 1788, II, 139 (140).
[30] *Obs. Phys.*, 1789, xxxv, 75–6.   [31] Crell's *Ann.*, 1791, I, 425.
[32] *Obs. Phys.*, 1787, xxx, 215.   [33] *Ib.*, Discours préliminaire, 27 f., 33.

when in combination: the formation of water and of dephlogisticated marine acid (chlorine) disproved this.

The new nomenclature was explained in W. Lewis's (see Vol. II, p. 762) *Pharmacopoeia*[1] but it was attacked as late as 1870 in a French work.[2] Hassenfratz and Adet devised a shorthand set of symbols (nouveax caractères chimiques) to accompany the new nomenclature, a report on which by Lavoisier, Berthollet, and Fourcroy was read by the first to the Academy on 27 June 1787,[3] and this, with the symbols, was included in the *Nomenclature Chimique*;[4] they said they did not disapprove of the new signs nor did they examine to what point they would be useful, but they thought they were better than the old symbols, since they represented facts, and were worthy of publication. The report (certainly written by Lavoisier) 'profits by the occasion' to reply at great length to criticisms of the antiphlogistic system and to expound Lavoisier's doctrine of caloric.

The first account in German of the new nomenclature was an alphabetical list of the old and new names published by Göttling.[5] A fuller account was given by Girtanner.[6] J. B. A. von Scherer[7] proposed the name Schwefelwasserstoffgas for sulphuretted hydrogen, and other German names. G. Eimbke gave the old and new names in various languages.[8] Wiegleb[9] said the French nomenclature of 1787 had not found general acceptance even in France and was almost unanimously rejected abroad, but this is not correct.[10]

Trommsdorff[11] says some objected to the name 'oxyd' as too foreign and used the name 'half-acid (Halbsäure)', which he thought objectionable. A. N. Scherer[12] calls nitrous oxide (N_2O) 'oxydirtes Stickstoffgas.' Crell[13] calls oxymuriatic acid 'die entbrennbarte Kochsalzsäure', and translated Kirwan's name for sulphuretted hydrogen 'hepatischer Luft'.[14] Other remarks on nomenclature were made by Roloff.[15] Gren[16] gave a list of Latin names with German equivalents, criticised by Wiegleb,[17] who gave some specimens of his own proposals.

In Russia a beginning of a new nomenclature was made about 1800 but

[1] *The Edinburgh New Dispensatory with additions: and account of the new chemical doctrines published by Mr. Lavoisier*, 5 ed., 8°, 1797 (BM 777. h. 37); recommended to his students by Black.
[2] C. E. Jullien, *La Chimie nouvelle; ou le Crassier de la nomenclature chimique de Lavoisier deblayé*, 8°, Paris, 1870 (BM).
[3] VIII, v, 365–75.   [4] 1787, 253–312.
[5] In *Almanach oder Taschenbuch für Scheidekünstler und Apotheker*, 1790, 147–55 (Kahlbaum and Hoffmann give 171); *J. der Physik* (Gren), 1790, ii, 295; Crell's *Ann.*, 1791, I, 225, 327; Kahlbaum and Hoffmann, 1897, 83; Duveen and Klickstein, *Isis*, 1954, xlv, 278 (287).
[6] *Neue chemische Nomenklatur für die deutsche Sprache*, Berlin, 1791; Kahlbaum and Hoffmann, 84.
[7] *Versuch einer neuen Nomenclatur für deutsche Chemiker*, Vienna, 1792.
[8] *Versuch einer systematischen Nomenklatur für die phlogistische und antiphlogistische Chemie*, Kiel, 1793.
[9] (2), 1791, i, 413.   [10] Kopp, (1), ii, 418.
[11] *Systematisches Handbuch der gesammten Chemie*, 2 ed., Erfurt, 1805 f., i, 137.
[12] *Kurze Darstellung der chemischen Untersuchungen der Gasarten*, 3 ed., Berlin, 1808, 26 (1 ed. Weimar. 1799).
[13] *Ann.*, 1790, II, 444 f.; tr. of Berthollet.   [14] *Ann.*, 1787, I, 26; tr. of Kirwan.
[15] *N. allgem. J. Chem.*, 1805, iv, 554.
[16] 1796, iv, 1–140.   [17] Crell's *Ann.*, 1796, II, 233.

nomenclature first assumed its modern form with Hess's *Fundamentals of Pure Chemistry* (in Russian, 1831–3).[1]

The Traité Élémentaire de Chimie

The acceptance of the new theory was greatly promoted by the appearance in 1789 of Lavoisier's text-book, the *Traité Élémentaire de Chimie*, which grew out of his own attempt to draw up a reformed nomenclature of chemistry, announced in a memoir read to the Academy in April 1787 (his part of the *Nomenclature*). The editions are given on p. 373. Daumas[2] says the book was on sale in March 1789, and was printed by Chardon before the 'approbation' (dated 4 February) was received from the Academy. A supposed early 'first edition' without approbation was probably only a few copies of the page-proofs or printed pages sumptuously bound up for Lavoisier for presentation to important persons.[3] The English translation by Robert Kerr, made hastily and published in Edinburgh in 1790 (see p. 373), is rather inaccurate and was corrected in later editions, some notes being added.[4] The German translation by Hermbstädt, with additions and notes, was published in 1792 (see p. 373). A review was published by De la Metherie,[5] and there were some English criticisms.[6] A detailed analysis was given by Fourcroy.[7]

The book is divided into three parts dealing respectively with (i) the formation and decomposition of aëriform fluids, the combustion of simple bodies and the formation of acids, (ii) the combination of acids with salifiable bases and the formation of neutral salts, and (iii) the description of the apparatus and the manual operations of chemistry. The third part forms the second volume: Thomson[8] said it 'contains the description of various expensive and useless pieces of machinery'.

The *Traité* was a model for later text-books; earlier books are now largely unintelligible without a knowledge of the history of chemistry, but Lavoisier's reads rather like an old edition of a modern work. It appealed to students by its clarity, logical order and method, and delusive comprehensiveness. Berzelius said:[9] 'the scientific study of chemistry was then easy enough, since the antiphlogistic theory at first rejected everything which it was not able to explain, and what it explained it not infrequently held to be simpler than it was.' Liebig, who attended the lecture courses in Paris, said:[10] 'die französische Chemie hatte zwar die Geschichte der Chemie vor Lavoisier unter die Guillotine gebracht', and he recognised from his own reading that much of what he heard had come from Priestley, Cavendish, Watt, Kirwan, etc., who were not mentioned. In making 'modern' chemistry begin with Lavoisier undue empha-

[1] Leicester, *Chymia*, 1959, v, 138.   [2] *Archives*, 1955, viii (old xxxiv), 413.
[3] Smeaton, *The Library*, 1956, xi, 132.
[4] On the interest taken in Lavoisier in Edinburgh see Lord Cockburn, *Memorials of his Time*, Edinburgh, 1856, 45; for American ed., Philadelphia, 1799, Lusk and le Goff, *Bull. Soc. Chim.*, 1920, xxvii, 667; Duveen, *Isis*, 1950, xli, 168; *id.* and Klickstein, *Ann. Sci.*, 1954, x, 321.
[5] *Obs. Phys.*, 1789, xxxiv, 304.
[6] E.g. Anon., *A Critical Examination of the first part of Lavoisier's Elements of Chemistry*, 8°, London, 1797; BM T. 99. (3.).
[7] (2), iii, 691 f.   [8] (3), 480.
[9] *Selbstbiographische Aufzeichnungen*, ed. Söderbaum, Leipzig, 1903, 17.
[10] *Ber.*, 1890, xxiii, III, 817 (824).

sis has been laid on the theory of combustion. There are other parts of the science, and Davy had correctly said that if the theory of combustion had to be modified, 'the great doctrines of chemistry, the doctrine of definite proportions, and the specific attractions of bodies must remain immutable.'[1]

When the *Traité* appeared the antiphlogistic theory was widely accepted. In a memoir on fermentation, apparently written about 1788 but not published, Lavoisier said[2] he learned from correspondence that 'the modern theory of chemistry, which I venture to call mine [*la mienne*, italics in original]', was gaining converts among the majority of the most celebrated physicists and chemists of Europe.

Lavoisier's definition of an 'element or principle' as 'the last point which analysis is capable of reaching', is essentially that of Boyle: it is tentative, 'since we have not hitherto discovered the means of separating them, they act with regard to us as simple substances, and we ought never to suppose them compounded until experiment and observation have proved them to be so':[3]

'Nous attachons au nom d'élémens ou de principes des corps l'idée du dernier terme auquel parvient l'analyse, toutes les substances que nous n'avons encore pu décomposer par aucun moyen, sont pour nous des élémens; . . . puisque nous n'avons aucun moyen de les séparer, ils agissent à notre égard à la manière des corps simples, & nous ne devons les supposer composés qu'au moment où l'expérience & l'observation nous en auront fourni la preuve.'

Lavoisier's table of the elements[4] is shown in Fig. 46 (*acidifiables* in the third class should obviously read *salifiables*, although it remained uncorrected in the later editions).[5] Lavoisier's non-metallic elements are the 'bases' of the existing substances (e.g. oxygen gas), in which they are combined with the imponderable element caloric and hence really compounds which can be 'decomposed' (see p. 421). We still distinguish between the 'element' oxygen and oxygen gas. The metals are regarded as elements, after being so long considered to be compounds of their calces and phlogiston.[6] Lavoisier (see p. 444) thought[7] that metals dissolve in acids in the form of their oxides, formed from the metal and oxygen of water in the solution of the acid:

'Oxygen is the bond (*moyen*) of union between metals and acids, and this . . . may lead us to suppose that all substances which have a great affinity for acids contain oxygen. It is thus quite probable that the four alkaline earths . . . contain oxygen, and that this is the bond (*latus*) which unites them with acids . . . These substances may be nothing but oxidised metals, with which oxygen has more affinity than for carbon, and by this circumstance are irreducible. This is only a conjecture which later experiments alone can confirm or destroy.'

Silica (la terre siliceuse) and the fixed alkalis may be compound bodies the nature of which is not known.[8]

'The salts are not simple bodies but are composed of an acid and a base, and

---

[1] *Elements of Chemical Philosophy*, 1812, 488; *Works*, 1840, iv, 364.
[2] VIII, iii, 785.   [3] VI, 1787, 17; VII, 1789, pref. xvij, 192.
[4] VII, 192.   [5] The correct form is given in VII, 182.
[6] VII, 179, 194: il est à présumer que les terres cesseront bientôt d'être comptées au nombre des substances simples . . . peut-être des oxides métalliques oxygénées jusqu'à un certain point.
[7] *Ib.*, 176, 179.
[8] VI, 17; in the table, Fig. 46, silica, 'silice', is classed with the alkaline earths.

	Noms nouveaux.	Noms anciens correſpondans.
Subſtances ſimples qui appartiennent aux trois règnes & qu'on peut regarder comme les élémens des corps.	Lumière.........	Lumière.
	Calorique........	Chaleur. Principe de la chaleur. Fluide igné. Feu. Matière du feu & de la chaleur.
	Oxygène.........	Air déphlogiſtiqué. Air empiréal. Air vital. Baſe de l'air vital.
	Azote...........	Gaz phlogiſtiqué. Mofete. Baſe de la mofete.
	Hydrogène.......	Gaz inflammable. Baſe du gaz inflammable.
Subſtances ſimples non métalliques oxidables & acidifiables.	Soufre..........	Soufre.
	Phoſphore.......	Phoſphore.
	Carbone.........	Charbon pur.
	Radical muriatique.	Inconnu.
	Radical fluorique .	Inconnu.
	Radical boracique..	Inconnu.
Subſtances ſimples métalliques oxidables & acidifiables.	Antimoine........	Antimoine.
	Argent..........	Argent.
	Arſenic..........	Arſenic.
	Biſmuth.........	Biſmuth.
	Cobolt..........	Cobolt.
	Cuivre..........	Cuivre.
	Etain...........	Etain.
	Fer.	Fer.
	Manganèſe.	Manganèſe.
	Mercure.........	Mercure.
	Molybdène.......	Molybdène.
	Nickel..........	Nickel.
	Or.	Or.
	Platine..........	Platine.
	Plomb..........	Plomb.
	Tungſtène.......	Tungſtene.
	Zinc...........	Zinc.
Subſtances ſimples ſalifiables terreuſes.	Chaux..........	Terre calcaire, chaux.
	Magnéſie........	Magnéſie, baſe du ſel d'Epſom.
	Baryte..........	Barote, terre peſante.
	Alumine........	Argile , terre de l'alun, baſe de l'alun.
	Silice..........	Terre ſiliceuſe, terre vitrifiable.

FIG. 46. LAVOISIER'S LIST OF THE ELEMENTS (1789).

it is this union which gives them their state of neutrality.'[1] Acids and bases (i.e. the modern acidic and basic oxides) are 'binary compounds of simple substances with oxygen';[2] acids are compounds of non-metals or of compound radicals (in organic acids) with oxygen, and bases compounds of metals with oxygen.[3] It is possible that azote is one constituent of the alkalis potash and soda (which do not appear in the table of elements), since Berthollet had

[1] VII, 193; by 'acid' he means acid anhydride. [2] Ib., 207. [3] Ib., 197, 209 f., etc.

proved that the base ammonia is a compound of about 80·7 per cent of azote and 19·3 per cent of hydrogen; but this is 'a mere presumption which no decisive experiment has yet confirmed'.[1] De Morveau[2] says Berthollet had proved that azote (so called from α and ζωή, life) exists in the volatile alkali, in animal substances, and probably in the fixed alkalis; it had been called *alkaligène* by Fourcroy (see p. 539). The analysis of these compounds (composés) was not sufficiently advanced to enable the mode of existence of this principle in them to be determined with certainty, and it would be improper to use one name to express its property of forming the radical of an acid (nitric acid, as proved by Cavendish) and of concurring in the production of an alkali, hence the non-commital name azote was preferred.

Lavoisier[3] was still uncertain if the potash formed by the combustion of vegetables pre-exists in them, since 'one has not yet succeeded in separating this substance from vegetables without using processes or intermediates which could furnish oxygen or azote, such as combustion or combination with nitric acid; in such a way that it is in no way proved that this substance may not be a product of these operations'. The old problem was still open!

Acids and bases (our acidic and basic oxides) 'enter as such (purement et simplement) into the composition of neutral salts without any intermediary which serves to unite them, whilst metals, on the contrary, cannot combine with acids unless they have first been more or less oxidised. It can be said rigorously that metals are not soluble in acids, but only metallic oxides', the oxygen being taken from water or from the acid, and then this oxygen must have a greater affinity for the metal than for hydrogen or the acid radical, respectively.[4] This was the basis of the later Dualistic Theory of Berzelius (see Vol. IV).

A table of binary compounds of oxygen with metals and with oxidable and acidifiable non-metals (non métalliques)[5] distinguishes the first, second, third, and fourth degrees of oxidation (degrés d'oxygenation), some of which are unknown, e.g.

azote	{ oxide nitreux (nitric oxide)	acide nitreux (fuming nitric acid)	acide nitrique (nitric acid)	—
arsenic	oxide gris	oxide blanc (As_2O_3)	acide arsenique (As_2O_5)	—
radical muriatique	oxide muriatique (unknown)	acide muriateux (unknown)	acide muriatique (hydrochloric acid)	acide muriatique oxygéné (chlorine)
tin	oxide gris (SnO)	oxide blanc (SnO_2)	acide stannique	—

The salts are arranged in tabular form under the acids, 'in the order of affinity of the bases for the acid.' Organic acids,[6] the decomposition of vegetable and animal matter by heat,[7] fermentation,[8] and putrefaction[9] come before the inorganic part of the book.

---

[1] *Ib.*, 170; he does not say the alkalis contain oxygen.   [2] VI, 1787, 35; see also VII, 55.
[3] VII, 168.   [4] VII, 176.   [5] VII, 203.   [6] *Ib.*, 129 f.
[7] *Ib.*, 132.   [8] *Ib.*, 139.   [9] *Ib.*, 153: la Fermentation putride.

The Reception of the Antiphlogistic Theory

Lavoisier's first publications proposing his new theory began to appear in 1776 (see p. 410) and in ten years it began to make converts. Fourcroy[1] said the discovery of the composition of water removed the doubts and uncertainties of most chemists, and[2] they accepted the theory in some form or other from 1787: Berthollet accepted it in 1785 (see p. 506) and was followed by the mathematicians Condorcet, Laplace, Cousin, Monge, Coulomb, and Dionys de Séjour. Guyton de Morveau accepted the theory in 1787; Fourcroy began to teach it in 1786–7,[3] saying: 'et alors se forme l'école française que les étrangers nomment antiphlogistique.' He also said[4] in 1797:

'De 1777 à 1785, malgré les grands efforts & les nombreux mémoires de Lavoisier, il étoit bien véritablement seul dans son opinion' . . . for the 'bon esprits' there was 'une sorte de neutralité qui résistoit non aux découvertes, mais au renversement total de l'ancien ordre d'idées'.

Fourcroy[5] usually speaks of 'la chimie pneumatique', only rarely of 'la chimie Française', the latter name being apparently first used by Bonjour in his translation of Bergman.[6] It was used by Fourcroy[7] as a rare alternative to 'la chimie pneumatique'[8] but in the *Encyclopédie* Fourcroy gives Lavoisier full credit. In his book[9] Lavoisier says:

If at any time I have adopted, without acknowledgement, the experiments or the opinions of Berthollet, Fourcroy, de la Place, Monge, or in general of any of those whose principles are the same as my own, it is due to the circumstance that frequent intercourse and the habit of communicating our ideas, observations, and ways of thinking to each other has established among us a sort of community of opinions, in which it is often difficult for every one to know his own.

Later,[10] about 1792, he said:

This theory is not, as I have heard it said, the theory of the French chemists, it is mine (elle est *la mienne*) and it is a property which I claim (réclame) from my contemporaries and from posterity.

Cuvier,[11] however, thought that the other French chemists, for their noble support of Lavoisier, rather than by their own discoveries, might merit some share in the glory of 'la science française'.

Wurtz[12] announced that 'La chimie est une science française. Elle fut constituée par Lavoisier d'immortelle mémoire'. This called forth protests from German chemists, Fittig,[13] Kolbe,[14] and especially J. Volhard,[15] who said,

---

[1] (2), iii, 541.   [2] *Id.*, (2), iii, 450 f., 561 f.; (1), i, 44 f.
[3] Fourcroy, (1), i, 47.   [4] (2), iii, 541.   [5] (1), i, Discours Préliminaire.
[6] *Traité des Affinités Chimiques*, Paris, 1788, pref.; Smeaton, *Ambix*, 1959, vii, 47 (50).
[7] *Élémens d'Histoire Naturelle et de Chimie*, 1793, i, pref. x.
[8] *Ann. Chim.*, 1800, xxxii, 80 (116).   [9] VII, 1789, xxviij.
[10] IV, ii, 87; VIII, ii, 104.
[11] 1828, 69. For Grimaux, 1888, 128, 'toute la science moderne' (not only chemistry) stems from Lavoisier.
[12] Discours Préliminaire. Histoire des Doctrines Chimiques depuis Lavoisier jusqu'à nos jours (1868), in his *Dictionnaire de Chimie* (t.p. dated 1869), i, first page; tr. H. Watts, *A History of Chemical Theory from the Age of Lavoisier to the Present Time*, 1869, who says (p. 210) the statement 'requires some qualification'.
[13] *Bull. Soc. Chim.*, 1869, xi, 276; Wurtz, *ib.*, 277.
[14] *J. prakt. Chem.*, 1870, ii, 173: Über den Zustand der Chemie in Frankreich.
[15] Die Begründung der Chemie durch Lavoisier, *J. prakt. Chem.*, 1870, ii, 1–47, see especially pp. 9, 17, 38; Guichard, *Essai historique sur les Mesures en Chimie*, 1937, ii, 64.

among other things, that Lavoisier was a physicist rather than a chemist: Macquer had said that Stahl was 'un grand chimiste' and Lavoisier 'un bon physicien'. Volhard's article was the object of protest at a meeting of the Russian Chemical Society[1] and he[2] made some 'corrections'. Kopp[3] showed that Lavoisier himself admitted that some sort of chemistry existed before his time.

One of the earliest of the leading chemists to adopt Lavoisier's views must have been Black, who was teaching them in Edinburgh before 1784. His pupil Richard Lubbock (Norwich; 1759–1808)[4] in his Edinburgh M.D. dissertation of 1784 openly accepted Lavoisier's theory. He says Black had incidentally and without confidence taught the phlogiston theory in his lectures for many years, but had lately (in ultimis) abandoned it.[5] Lubbock called the 'base' of oxygen *principium sorbile*:[6] quod principium ex modo quo hisce substantiis adficitur, absorptione scilicet, posthac SORBILE nuncupatibur. In a dramatic farewell to the phlogiston theory, using expressions like those in Lavoisier's later *Reflexions on Phlogiston*,[7] he says:[8]

Sequentem, maximi in chemia momenti conclusionem, stabilire nunc liceat; quod nullum a corpore combustibili, comburendo, aufugiat principium; quod nullum, quale perhibitum fuerit phlogiston, in natura existat; quod phlogiston mera sit contemplatio, mera qualitas; quae, si nunquam vixisset Stahlius, ipsa, vitam fortasse nunquam, nunquam corporis dotes et honores fuerit assecuta. Sed, quamvis hoc principium, hoc instrumentum, quod chemiae et chemicis, ob universum suum imperium, adeo commodum fuerit, falsum, et mera contemplatio esse, demonstretur, quamvis eadem haec contemplatio, omnia in chemia confuderit, et rebus aliter satis perspicuis multum obscuri intulerit; tamen eandem, quae tam distinctis, tam apte ementitis fuco coloribus, veritatis ipsius speciem potis fuerit aemulari, sero nunc demum morti cedere, sine admiratione, nedum dolore, quis possit? Pace dulci quiescat; et quamvis, et gloria et honoribus, corpori formossisimo secunda, tamen talis corporis simulacro etiam formoso debitis potita, longa et aeterna oblivionis nocte decenter et silenter reponatur.

Lavoisier in October 1789 and July 1790 wrote to Black in flattering terms, professing himself to be 'zélé admirateur de la profondeur de votre génie' and 'accoutomé à vous regarder comme mon maître . . . et de me ranger au nombre de vos disciples',[9] and Black in a letter to Lavoisier[10] said he had begun to teach the new system. Lord Brougham[11] says Black mentioned Lavoisier with great respect in his lectures (as he also did Stahl, see p. 135) and Fourcroy[12] calls Black 'le chef et le Nestor de cette grande révolution chimique'; but Lavoisier and Seguin[13] mention Black with 'Boile', Hales, and Priestley only as having shown that air is 'markedly altered by the respiration of animals'.

[1] *Ber.*, 1870, ii, 87.   [2] *J. prakt. Chem.*, 1870, ii, 381–4; see also Grimaux, 1888, 363.
[3] (3), 86–8.   [4] Partington and McKie, *Ann. Sci.*, 1938, iii, 337 (portr.).
[5] Lubbock, *Dissertatio Physico-Chemica, Inauguralis, de Principio Sorbili . . . Quaestionem, an Phlogiston sit Substantia, an Qualitas, agitans . . .*, Edinburgh, 1784, 12 f.
[6] *Ib.*, 21.
[7] Lubbock is mentioned by Fourcroy in VI, 1787, 133: Principe sorbile de M. Ludbock (sic), Oxigène.
[8] *Ib.*, 79–80; Girtanner, *Anfangsgründe der antiphlogistischen Chemie*, Berlin, 1792, 462; 2 ed., 1795, 460; Kopp, (1), iii, 164.
[9] Andrews, *B.A. Rep.*, 1871, 59, 189: three letters from Lavoisier to Black, examined 'through the kindness of Dr. Black's representatives'.
[10] First publ. in French in *Journal de Paris*, Suppl. Feb. 1791 (Duveen and Hahn, *Isis*, 1960, li, 64–6); then in *Ann. Chim.*, 1791, viii, 225; Fourcroy, (4), 1793, I, xi; *id.*, (2), 1796, iii, 560; Kahlbaum and Hoffmann, 56, 133.
[11] 1872, 318.   [12] (1), i, 28, 49; (2), iii, 692.   [13] AdS, 1789 (1793), m 568.

William Higgins[1] claimed that he had adopted the antiphlogistic theory in 1785. William Nicholson[2] thought the existence of phlogiston was 'very far from being well ascertained', but there are difficulties in explaining many facts without it; 'the antiphlogistic hypothesis' is equally as probable as the modified system of Stahl, and he explained both. Kirwan in 1786[3] could say that the number of opponents to the phlogiston theory in England was continually increasing (nimmt immer noch zu), but there were some die-hards. Priestley never abandoned it (see p. 292) and although Cavendish is said to have done so in later life,[4] he had then ceased to publish on chemistry. Priestley's friends Watt and Keir remained phlogistians, and some cranks wrote on the subject.

Robert Harrington[5] assumed that fire is material and capable of chemical attraction, the strongest attractions being to acids, earths, and water, and the union of these constitutes oxygen (empyreal air). Fire chemically united with other bodies is phlogiston, as in oils, spirits, bitumens, etc. Different acids contain different proportions of fire with the earths; in nitric and sulphuric acids the proportion of fire is that to form oxygen. Phosphoric and marine acids attract a higher concentration of fire and form inflammable air. Oxygen gas 'exposed to different bodies, will have its concentrated fire or phlogiston attracted, and become an acid, the phlogiston which neutralized the acid having left it'. Phlogiston is dormant, neutralised, and concentrated fire. Air concentrates the light of the sun and conveys it to animal and vegetable life. Vegetables contain a large quantity of neutralised fire or phlogiston, which they received from the fire of the sun; in animals this is discharged as animal heat. The book discusses these theories and is not experimental.

Edward Peart[6] assumed two principles, 'fixed matter' and 'active matter', the latter of two kinds, ether and phlogiston. A fixed particle in an atmosphere of ether forms earth; in an atmosphere of phlogiston it forms an acid-producing substance; the two active principles attract one another.

These authors had counterparts in France in addition to genuine chemists who opposed the antiphlogistic theory.

Lamarck, the biologist, assumed as elements a vitrifiable earth, water, air, fire, and light, which have no attraction for one another but tend to separate unless constrained by force; he developed his views in great detail; coal-fire is the radical of all combustibles and on combustion separates as heat-fire.[7] He proposed a new 'pyrotic theory'.[8]

The Abbé Para du Phanjas (1724–97) published a course of physics[9] in which he still maintained the oscillatory theory of combustion proposed by Boerhaave (Vol. II,

[1] A Comparative View of the Phlogistic and Antiphlogistic Theories, London, 1789, xi.
[2] First Principles of Chemistry, London, 1790, pp. vii, 89.
[3] Crell's Ann., 1786, II, 142. [4] Fourcroy, (2), 1797, iii, 711.
[5] Thoughts on the Properties and Formation of the Different Kinds of Air; with remarks on Vegetation, Pyrophori, Heat, Caustic Salts, Mercury, and on the different Theories upon Air, (Anon.), London, 1785 (x, 330 pp.), pref.; Harrington also published The Death-Warrant of the French Theory of Chemistry, signed by Truth, Reason, Common Sense, Honour and Science . . . Likewise, Remarks upon Mr. Dalton's late Theory . . . , London, Printed for the Author, 1804.
[6] The Generation of Animal Heat investigated . . . , Gainsborough, 1788; On the Elementary Principles of Nature and the Simple Laws by which they are governed, Gainsborough, 1789 (not in BM); On the Properties of Matter, the Principles of Chemistry, and the Nature and Construction of aëriform Fluids and Gases, Gainsborough, 1792; The Anti-phlogistic Doctrine of Lavoisier critically examined and demonstratively confuted, 1795; On the Composition and Properties of Water, 1796.
[7] Recherches sur les Causes des principaux Faits physiques, et particulièrement sur celles de la Combustion . . . , 2 vols., Paris, An II (1794); Refutation de la Théorie pneumatique, ou de la Nouvelle Doctrine des Chimistes Modernes . . . , Paris, An IV (1796).
[8] J. de Phys., 1799, xlviii, 345; Kahlbaum and Hoffmann, Monographien, 1897, i, 131.
[9] Théorie des Êtres sensibles, ou Cours Complet de Physique, Spéculative, Experimentale, Systématique et Géometrique, mis a la Portée de Tout le Monde, 4 vols. 8°, Paris, 1774; new ed. 1788.

p. 751), but considered that phlogiston escaped during the process.[1] He explained, following Stahl (Vol. II, p. 671), that sulphur is a compound of vitriolic acid and phlogiston.[2] In a supplement[3] he protests against the 'antiphilosophical dreams' of modern savants.

A story about the burning of the works of Stahl in the Arsenal by Mme. Lavoisier dressed up as a priestess is reported in a letter from Paris by Herr von E** to Crell,[4] which says there was an:

Auto-da-fé über das Phlogiston, worinn seine Gattin (die wirklich viele Kenntnisse in der Chemie hat, und verschiedene chemische Schriften übersetzte) die Ober-priesterin machte, Stahl zur Vertheidigung desselben, als *Advocatus diaboli* erschien; wo bey allem dem aber doch das arme Phlogiston, auf Anklage des Oxygens, zuletzt verbrannt wurde . . . alles is buchstäblich war.

Lichtenberg[5] said: 'Wäre Newton im Stande gewesen durch seine Frau, wenn er eine gehabt hätte, die Cartesianischen Wirbel verbrennen zu lassen, so hätte er unmöglich seine Principia schreiben können.' Hoefer[6] reported that phlogistic fanatics burnt Lavoisier in effigy in Berlin.

Lavoisier's theory was taught in Belgium by Jean Baptiste Van Mons (Brussels, 11 November 1765–Louvain, 6 September 1842), who wrote a defence of it in 1785.[7] He became friendly with the French chemists after the annexation of Belgium, in 1795 was professor at Brussels and from 1817 at Louvain, and was one of the editors of the *Annales de Chimie*.[8] He defended Lavoisier's theory of calcination,[9] showed that red precipitate of mercury evolves oxygen on heating (contrary to some statements by German chemists),[10] and investigated detonating mixtures[11] and the preparation of potassium chlorate.[12] He contributed to the *Annales de Chimie* translations from Brugna-telli's *Giornale fisico-medico* (from 1790).[13]

Lavoisier's views were first adopted in Italy by Giovanni Antonio Giobert (Mongardino, nr. Asti, 28 October 1761–Millefiore, nr. Turin, 4 (or 14) September 1834), professor of agriculture (1800) and of chemistry and mineralogy (1802) in the University of Turin and important in industry.[14] He published papers on agriculture, on vitriolated tartar,[15] 'sur le phosphorisme du tartre vitriolé' (evolution of light on the crystallisation of potassium sulphate),[16] the preparation of phosphoric and prussic acids and phlogisticated alkali (potassium ferrocyanide),[17] the supposed oxidation of sulphuric acid by distillation over manganese dioxide,[18] a chemical examination of the doctrine of

---

[1] *Ib.*, 1788, ii, 473.   [2] *Ib.*, 1788, ii, 230.
[3] *Théorie des Nouvelles Découvertes en genre de Physique et de Chymie*, 8°, 1786, 23, 35 f.
[4] *Ann.*, 1789, I, 519; Wiegleb, (2), 1791, ii, 478.
[5] Pref. to his (6) ed. of Erxleben, *Anfangsgründen der Naturlehre*, Göttingen, 1794, xxii.
[6] (1), ii, 507.
[7] *Essai sur les principes de la Chimie antiphlogistique*, Brussels, 1785; he wrote many other books and published many papers on a variety of subjects; Poggendorff, (1), ii, 189–90; Stas, *Oeuvres Complètes*, 1894, ii, 1.
[8] Cap, ii, 272 (bibl.); portr. in *Allgem. J. Chem.* (Scherer), 1799, iii.
[9] Crell's *Ann.*, 1792, I, 131; 1794, I, 116.   [10] *Ann Chim.*, 1793, xviii, 1–6.
[11] *Ann. Chim.*, 1798, xxvii, 72, 78; 1799, xxix, 91, 170.
[12] *Bull. Acad. Bruxelles*, 1835, ii, 275.   [13] *Ann. Chim.*, 1798, xxvii–xxix, *passim*.
[14] E.G., NBG, 1857, xx, 584; Poggendorff, (1), i, 900.
[15] *Mém. Acad. Turin*, 1788–9 (1790), v, 38, 73.
[16] *Ib.*, 1789 (1790), ix, 73.   [17] *Ib.*, 1788 (1790), ix, 38.   [18] *Ib.*, 1791 (1793), x, 123.

phlogiston (accepting Lavoisier's theory but pointing out difficulties),[1] an analysis of native magnesia,[2] and the action exerted by the galvanic fluid on different aeriform fluids,[3] in which he showed that gaseous carbon dioxide confined over water is reduced to carbon monoxide by the nascent hydrogen evolved from the negative wire in the water in a separate tube. He also published on sulphurous mineral waters.[4]

Another early convert was Count Carlo Lodovico Morozzo (Mouroux) (Turin; 5 August 1744–2 July 1804), general in the army of Piedmont, who published on the purification of air by plants,[5] the composition of air,[6] the colours of flowers and other vegetables,[7] eudiometry of pure air and air vitiated by animal respiration,[8] the gases obtained from dew,[9] animal colours,[10] the absorption of air by charcoal,[11] and the respiration of oxygen.[12]

Luigi Valentino Brugnatelli (Pavia; 1761–24 October 1818), professor of chemistry at Pavia (1796), published a text-book based on the new views: *Elementi di Chimica, appogiati alle più recenti scoperti . . .* , 2 vols., Pavia, 1795–7, 3 vols., Venice, 1800; 2 ed., Pavia, 1803,[13] and edited journals.[14] He published many papers in these and other journals. He modified Lavoisier's theory by supposing that oxygen gas on entering into combination could sometimes retain most of the caloric and light it contained, and he called this condensed form *thermoxygen*.[15] He discovered suberic acid by oxidising cork with nitric acid,[16] investigated the glow of phosphorus and the solubility of phosphorus in ether,[17] and described a method of distilling spirit of wine.[18] His son Gaspard Brugnatelli also published a text-book: *Guida allo Studio della Chimica Generale*, 3 vols., Pavia, 1819–19–20, and *Supplementa* (giving publications of 1820–23), Pavia, 1824.

Antonio Bucci (Faenza; 18 August 1723–*c*. 1793), teacher of philosophy in the gymnasium in Faenza, defended the phlogiston theory on the basis of Priestley's experiments.[19]

The reception of antiphlogistic chemistry in Germany, the birthplace of the phlogiston theory, is interesting.[20] Kopp[21] thought the reception of the new

---

[1] *Ib.*, 1791 (1793), x, 299.   [2] *Ib.*, 1803, xii, 293, 313.   [3] *Ib.*, 1805, xv, 196.

[4] *Des Eaux Sulphureuses et Thermales de Vaudier, avec des Observations physiques, économiques et chimiques sur la Vallée de Gesse et des Remarques sur l'Analyse des Eaux sulphureuses en général*, Turin, 1793.

[5] *Commentarii Bononiensi*, 1791, vii, 215.   [6] *Mem. Soc. Ital.*, 1792, vi, 221.

[7] *Miscell. Taurin.*, 1770–3, v, 11.   [8] *Mém. Acad. Turin*, 1786, i, 313.

[9] *Ib.*, 1786, i, 305.   [10] *Ib.*, 1786–7 (1788), iii, 275.

[11] *Obs. Phys.*, 1783, xxii, 294; 1783, xxiii, 362.   [12] *Ib.*, 1784, xxv, 102.

[13] Bolton, (1), 341; Poggendorff, (1), i, 316, 1544; NBU, 1855, vii, 582 (d. 24 August 1815).

[14] *Annali di Chimica* (21 vols., Pavia, 1790–1802); *Giornale di Fisica, Chimica, e Storia Naturale* (10 vols., Pavia, 1808–17), contd. as *Giornale di Fisica, Chimica, Storia Naturale, Medicina ed Arti del Regno Italico* by G. Brugnatelli (10 vols., Pavia, 1818–27).

[15] *Ann. Chim.*, 1799, xxix, 182; from *Annali di Chimica*, 1798, xv; Thomson, (2), 1802, i, 354; Partington and McKie, *Ann. Sci.*, 1938, iii, 341.

[16] Crell's *Ann.*, 1787, I, 145.   [17] *Ann. Chim.*, 1797, xxiv, 57–77.

[18] Crell's *Ann.*, 1798, II, 267.

[19] *Saggio sopra il Flogisto le Differenti Specie d'Aria e il Calore*, 8°, Florence, 1783 (84 pp.); *Osservazione circa il flogisto e le differenti specie d'aria secondo le moderne scoperte*, 8°, Pavia, [1784]; Gmelin, (1), iii, 317; Bolton, (1), 343; Duveen, 107; Poggendorff, (1), i, 324.

[20] A long list of contemporary chemists who accepted or opposed Lavoisier's views is given by Gmelin, (1), 1799, iii, 283–98.

[21] (1), i, 341.

theory was slower in Germany than elsewhere, but this is not correct. From 1785 it was adopted by several important chemists (Klaproth, Richter, Bucholz, Girtanner, Hermbstädt, Trommsdorf, A. N. Scherer, and Gren; see ch.XIII), a few (Abich and Wiegleb) refusing to accept it, like Priestley and De la Metherie in other countries.[1] The new theory was defended in a dissertation of Friedrich Ludwig Schurer (dates unknown), who became professor of chemistry and physics in the Artillery School in Strasbourg.[2] Girtanner's new chemical nomenclature was published in 1791[3] and his text-book in 1792,[4] in which year Hermbstädt's translation of Lavoisier's *Traité* appeared (see p. 373). The second edition of Gren's text-book[5] attempted to combine the phlogistic and antiphlogistic theories (see ch. XIII). By 1795 the new theory was very generally accepted in Germany. Wiegleb's excellent text-book[6] is based on the phlogiston theory, but the English translation by Hopson[7] used a combination of the phlogistic and antiphlogistic theories proposed by Gadolin.[8]

Fourcroy[9] distinguished the German chemists who accepted Lavoisier's theory completely (Hermbstädt, Klaproth, Girtanner, Scherer, Hildebrandt, and Humboldt) from those who adopted special combinations of the old theory of phlogiston and the new theory (Crell, Westrumb, Richter, Göttling, and Gren; see ch. XIII). Girtanner in a letter in 1796 to Van Mons[10] said:

'As for our Germany, the chemical revolution has taken effect. There are only Gren, a distinguished but obstinate scientist, Westrumb, Gmelin and Crell who still defend the existence of phlogiston. These . . . chemists will never yield; they have declared a war to the death on the antiphlogistic doctrine. Trommsdorff, who has yielded to the new doctrine, holds still by some chains to the old. Göttling defends the new hypothesis. Among our young chemists, Scherer of Jena promises great things; he is a zealous sectary of French chemistry, a good experimenter and endowed with much knowledge. Professor Mayer of Erlangen is an excellent mind, who unites profound knowledge of mathematics, physics and chemistry, like Monge in Paris, although I think Monge has more genius. Hermbstädt does all he can for the advancement of the new doctrine.'

Van Mons, who passed on this letter to Fourcroy, said:

'I must undeceive my French comrades on this subject, since the war does not allow one to become familiar with the progress of the new chemical doctrine in Germany. This country counts no more among its chemical authors any partisan of the traditional phlogistic system, since I have convinced them of the presence of oxygen in oxide of mercury heated to redness by fire. They have all adopted the new doctrine without restriction or with restrictions of little importance. Crell, Westrumb, Wiegleb,

[1] Kahlbaum and Hoffmann, 1897, i, 111.
[2] *Synthesis oxygenii experimentis confirmata*, 4°, Argentorati, 1789 (J. C. Fischer, 1808, viii, 22; Poggendorff, (1), ii, 869); Gmelin, (1), iii, 286, gives 1790, as Pt. II of Schurer's M.D. dissertation, Pt. I being *Historia praecipuorum experimentorum circa analysis chemicam aëris atmospherici usumque principiorum ejus in componendis diversis naturæ corporibus*, 4°, Argentorati, 1784.
[3] *Neue chemische Nomenclatur für die deutsche Sprache*, Berlin, 1791.
[4] *Anfangsgründe der antiphlogistischen Chemie*, Berlin, 1792, 2 ed. 1795.
[5] *Systematisches Handbuch der gesammten Chemie*, 4 pts., Halle, 1794–6.
[6] *Handbuch der allgemeinen Chemie*, 2 vols., Berlin and Stettin, 1781, i, 134 f.
[7] *A General System of Chemistry, Theoretical and Practical . . . Taken chiefly from the German of M. Wiegleb*, 4°, London, 1789.
[8] Crell's *Ann.*, 1788, I, 15, 417; see ch. XIII.
[9] (2), 1797, iii, 712.   [10] Fourcroy, (2), iii, 617; Hoefer, (1), ii, 564.

Trommsdorff, Gmelin, Richter, Leonhardi, etc., although all trying to ally the new theory with the existence of phlogiston in combustible bodies, admit it in its entirety and in its consequences.'

In Russia, the new theory was adopted by Vasiliĭ Vladimirovich Petrov (1761–1834), professor of physics in St. Petersburg, who published (in Russian) *A Collection of New Physico-chemical Experiments and Discoveries* (1801). A. N. Scherer (see p. 598), Severgin (1765–1826) and Zakharov (1775–1836) also supported it.[1] Girtanner's *Anfangsgründe* was translated into Russian in 1801.[2]

The new theory was taught at Harvard, U.S.A., by Aaron Dexter, who was elected professor of chemistry and materia medica in 1783, from Fourcroy's text-book,[3] in which both the phlogistic and antiphlogistic theories are explained.[4]

De la Metherie

We have reserved a special place for an inveterate opponent of Lavoisier's views in France, Jean Claude Delametherie or De la Metherie (Clayette, nr. Mâcon, 4 September 1743–Paris, 1 July 1817), a non-practising doctor of medicine, editor from 1785 of the *Observations sur la Physique*, later the *Journal de Physique* (in the earlier volumes of which Lavoisier published many papers before publishing them in full in the *Mémoires* of the Academy), and from 1801 professor of natural history in the Collège de France.[5] De la Metherie also published some scientific[6] and many political works. He was obviously a very able man.

The *Journal de Physique* was a continuation (from vol. 44, 1794, publication ceased with vol. 96, 1823) of the *Observations sur la Physique, sur l'Histoire Naturelle et sur les Arts*, edited for a long time by the Abbé François Rozier (Lyon; 24 January 1734–29 September 1793), Dr. Theol., director of the Veterinary School at Lyon (1765), later prior of Nanteuil-le-Haudouin and finally priest in Lyon; his publications are mostly on agriculture.[7] He was later assisted in editing the *Observations* by Mongez and De la Metherie.

Many of De la Metherie's views were based on inaccurate experiments of Priestley (to which he added some of his own) or on misinterpretations of experimental results. He thought that all combustibles (including perhaps diamond) contain inflammable air,[8] which he identified with phlogiston and thought it is contained in metals. Iron precipitates copper from a solution of copper sulphate because the phlogiston is transferred from the iron, whilst

[1] Leicester, *Chymia*, 1959, v, 138.   [2] Bolton, (1), 481.
[3] *Leçons élémentaires d'histoire naturelle et de chimie*, 2 vols., Paris, 1782; tr. T. Elliot, *Elementary Lectures on Chemistry and Natural History*, 2 vols., Edinburgh, 1785.
[4] Cohen, *Chymia*, 1950, iii, 17 (39).
[5] Blainville, *J. de Phys.*, 1817, lxxv, 78; Thomson, *Ann. Phil.*, 1818, xi, 1; portr. in *Phil. Mag.*, 1804, xix.
[6] *Essai Analytique sur l'Air Pur, et les différentes Espèces d'Air*, 1785 (iii ll. 474 pp., i l.), 2 ed. 2 vols., 1788; tr. *Ueber die reine Luft und verwandte Luftarten und Stoffe*, 2 pts. 8°, Leipzig, 1791; *Principes de la Philosophie Naturelle*, 1787; *Leçons de Minéralogie, données au Collège de France*, 2 vols., 1811–12. A *Mémoire sur la Platine ou Or Blanc, lu à l'Académie Royale des Sciences en Juin 1785, par M.L.*, is attributed to him in the BM Cat.
[7] Neave, *Ann. Sci.*, 1950, vi, 416; 1951, vii, 101, 144, 284, 393; 1952, viii, 28; McKie, *ib.*, 1957 (1958), xiii, 73.
[8] *Essai*, 1785, 68 f

iron dissolving in an acid parts with its phlogiston in the form of inflammable air.[1] He called oxygen 'pure air' and nitrogen (phlogisticated air) 'impure air'.[2] Pure air consists of vesicles inflated by the principle of heat.[3] Nitrous air (nitric oxide) is a compound of nitric acid and inflammable air or phlogiston.[4] Fixed air, which he called 'acid air', can be converted into phlogisticated air or into pure air.[5] Inflammable air is formed from pure air and the principle of fire or light, i.e. phlogiston; silver oxide (chaux d'argent) when exposed to sunlight forms silver and gives pure air.[6] Phlogisticated alkali (potassium ferrocyanide) is a compound of alkali and inflammable air.[7]

De la Metherie[8] says that he had obtained much water from a hydrogen flame in contact with a glass (contre une glace), but thought it came from water in the two gases.[9] He stated (correctly) that oxygen is not a necessary constituent of acids.[10] Among many miscellaneous observations he showed that nitric acid converts olive oil into a waxy solid (i.e. elaïdic acid).[11] He[12] regarded hydrogen and oxygen as devoid of gravity, owing all their weight to the water with which they are combined. During combustion the water of the two gases is deposited and the gases themselves escape through the vessel and are lost. Thomson[13] says De la Metherie 'complains bitterly that this theory had never been noticed by his antagonists', adding 'as if it were necessary' to refute it.

De la Metherie, who criticised Lavoisier's theory in a letter to Crell,[14] reported[15] that Beddoes in Oxford at first thought Lavoisier's theory advantageous, but later gave it up on account of Priestley's experiments[16] in which an acid was formed from the union of dephlogisticated and inflammable airs.

Since the *Journal de Physique* was opposed to the new doctrines, Lavoisier participated in founding in 1789 the *Annales de Chimie* at the suggestion of Adet,[17] in which papers on the antiphlogistic chemistry were published.

The first title was: *Annales de Chimie; ou, Recueil de Mémoires Concernant la Chimie et les Arts qui en dépendent*; from 1799 (An VIII) *et spécialement la Pharmacie* was added. In 1816 (at first ed. by Gay-Lussac, till 1850), it was called *Annales de Chimie et de Physique*; in 1914 it was divided into *Annales de Chimie* and *Annales de Physique*. The first volume (only) was translated as *The Annals of Chemistry, or a Collection of Memoirs relative to Chemistry and the Arts with which it is connected*, London, 1791.

The phlogiston theory was also supported by Senebier in Geneva (see p. 280).

[1] *Ib.*, 78, 82.   [2] *Ib.*, 117, 128.   [3] *Ib.*, 94.   [4] *Ib.*, 142.
[5] *Ib.*, 111, 115.   [6] *Ib.*, 86, 91.   [7] *Ib.*, 400.   [8] *Ib.*, 435, 465.
[9] *Ib.*, 457.   [10] *Ib.*, 391 (see Berthollet, p. 498).
[11] Crell's *Ann.*, 1786, I, 331.   [12] Crell's *Ann.*, 1786, II, 92.
[13] *Ency. Brit. Suppl.*, 1801, I, i, 293.   [14] Crell's *Ann.*, 1787, I, 532.
[15] *Ib.*, 1789, II, 45.   [16] *Phil. Trans.*, 1788, lxxviii, 313.
[17] Grimaux, *Revue Scient.*, 1887, xiv, 839–41.

CHAPTER X

BERTHOLLET AND GUYTON DE MORVEAU

BERTHOLLET

Claude Louis Berthollet (Tailloire, nr. Anneci (Annecey), Savoy, 9 December 1748–Arcueil, nr. Paris, 6 November 1822) was of French ancestry in Savoy. He studied medicine at the University of Turin, becoming M.D. in 1768. In 1772 he was befriended by his countryman Tronchin, physician to the Duke of Orléans and the latter made Berthollet physician to Mme. de Montesson. He studied chemistry under Macquer and Bucquet in Paris. He graduated M.D. in Paris in 1778 with a dissertation on wines.[1] In 1780 he became a member of the Academy of Sciences. In 1784 he was an unsuccessful candidate for Macquer's chair at the Jardin du Roi, Fourcroy (who was a much better lecturer than Berthollet) being chosen: it was said that Berthollet was unsuccessful because the Duke of Orléans would not pay court to Buffon. He became F.R.S. in 1789.[2]

'Berthollet was a tall muscular man, with a hooked nose and chin, a wide smiling mouth, and a high broad forehead';[3] he was 'a most amiable man; when the friend of Napoleon even, always good, conciliatory, and modest, frank and candid'.[4] He was in private life a plain, homely man, dressing and looking like a farmer. He was a man of high moral courage. During the reign of terror, he was told to analyse some brandy which, it was alleged, had poisoned some soldiers, and the vendors were awaiting execution when Berthollet's report was received. This said that it had merely been diluted with water holding particles of slate, which could be removed by filtration. Robespierre

---

[1] *De variorum liquorum vinosorum diaeteticis proprietatibus*, 4°, s.l., 29 May 1778 (8 pp.; BN S. 5905).

[2] Anon., *The Chemist*, 1825, ii, 250, 258, 329, 345, 362, 380, 393; *id.*, *Nature*, 1948, clxii, 882; H. Colquhoun, *Ann. Phil.*, 1825, ix, 1, 81, 161 (tr. Müller, *Berthollets Leben nach der Beschreibung von Hugh Colquhoun*, Erlangen, 1828); Cuvier, *Éloge*, AdS, 1829, viii, clxxix–ccx; *id.* in *Recueil de Discours dans la Séance publique de l'Acad. Roy. des Sciences*, Paris, 1824, 1 f.; *id.*, *Éloges historiques* (in *Bibliothèque Classiques des Célébrités Contemporaines*), Paris, 1860, 285; *id.*, *Recueil des Éloges lus dans les Séances Publiques de l'Institut Royale de France*, 3 vols., Paris, 1819-19-27, iii, 177; Gmelin, (1), iii, 427; Hoefer, (1), ii, 549–55; E. F. Jomard, *Notice sur la Vie et les Ouvrages de Cl. L. Berthollet*, Anneci, 1844, with a *Notice sur l'erection à Anneci du Monument Berthollet* [in 1843], with list of subscribers; the *Notice sur la Vie* . . . ends with a bibliography of 88 publications by Berthollet (pp. 55–63; a contemporary MS. note in the BM copy of Jomard's book says: 'Cet écrit déjà imprimé en 1825 pour l'ouvrage sur l'Egypte fut supprimé par ordre du Gouvernement de Charles X; la Ville d'Anneci l'a publié en 1844, in 8°, à l'occasion de l'inauguration du Monument Berthollet'); Lemay and Oesper, *J. Chem. Educ.*, 1946, xxiii, 230; NBU, 1853, v, 716; E. Pariset, *Histoire des Membres de l'Académie Royale de Médecine*, 2 vols., Paris, 1845, i, 164; Partington, *Chymia*, 1959, v, 130; Patterson, *Chem. and Ind.*, 1944, 99; Smith, *Nature*, 1948, clxi, 11; Thomson, (1), ii, 141; Vibert, *Ann. Chim. Anal.*, 1943, xxv, 84; portr. in *N. allgem. J. Chem.* (Gehlen), 1806, i (frontisp.).

[3] *Life of Sir R. Christison, by his Sons*, 1885, i, 242.   [4] Davy, *Works*, 1839, i, 167.

sent for Berthollet and tried to persuade him that the liquor was poisonous, whereupon the chemist filtered a glass of it and drank it. 'Thou art daring, sir, to drink that liquor', said Robespierre, and there is little doubt that Berthollet would have been executed if his services had not been too valuable. As Thomson says, 'it was in all probability his zeal, activity, sagacity and honesty, which saved France from being overrun by foreign troops.'

FIG. 47. C. L. BERTHOLLET, 1748–1822.

In 1784 Berthollet succeeded Macquer as inspector of dyeworks and director of the Gobelins. He took a keen practical interest in dyeing and bleaching and became notable by his introduction of chlorine in bleaching. After the Revolution he was charged with the organisation of the French industries, and with other French chemists such as Monge, Fourcroy, and Chaptal, introduced the manufacture of saltpetre, steel, etc., and made France largely independent of foreign imports.

Early in 1794 the Convention decided to institute a new college in which young men could be taught the basic principles of science before entering more specialised institutions. It was planned by a commission including Monge, Berthollet, Guyton de Morveau, and Chaptal, and opened in December 1794 as the École Centrale des Travaux Publiques, which in 1795 changed its name to the École Polytechnique. There were no fees and the students received maintenance grants from the State. The courses in chemistry included systematic practical work, and Berthollet, Fourcroy, and Guyton de Morveau participated in them. In 1797 the practical work was reduced owing to economic difficulties but it still continued, and although the generous time allotted to chemistry was reduced between 1799 and 1806, a new practical course was planned in 1806. By 1811, Berthollet and Guyton had retired and Fourcroy was dead, but chemistry continued to be taught by Gay-Lussac and Thenard.[1] Berthollet, whose main interest was in research, was not very successful as a teacher, his lectures being too difficult for the pupils. Cuvier says: 'toujours maître de sa matière . . . il supposait dans ses auditeurs la même capacité; et c'est toujours de la supposition contraire qu'un professeur doit partir.'

Eleven of Berthollet's lectures summarised by Fourcroy[2] dealt with (1) chemical attractions (simple, elective, complex), (2) anomalies of attractions ('dont il fournit un assez grand nombre d'exemples importans'), (3) heat (which is identified with light), (4) chemical effects of light, (5) water, (6) carbonic acid, (7) vegetable and animal substances as compounds of carbon and hydrogen, including respiration, (8) nitric acid, (9) muriatic acid and oxymuriatic acid (including much of his own work), (10) atmospheric air and eudiometry (air a mixture and not a compound, as shown by its density), (11) on acids in general, in which he controverts Lavoisier's oxygen theory of acids: water and metallic oxides contain oxygen and are not acid, sulphur behaves as an acid, muriatic, fluoric and boracic acids are not proved to contain oxygen and oxymuriatic acid is not really an acid but becomes one when further oxidised, prussic acid is free from oxygen: thus, although oxygen on its accession increases the solvent power, it cannot be considered as an element inseparable from acidity. A report by Lavoisier and Macquer to the Academy on 'a work on chemistry' (un ouvrage de chimie)[3] shows that it dealt with stones and earths, gems, metals (in which he adopted Macquer's modification of the phlogiston theory), and mineral salts (divided into acids, alkalis, and neutral salts) in which he supports Rouelle's doctrine of acid salts.

In 1796 Berthollet was sent by Napoleon with Monge to Italy to collect the looted art treasures for transmission to France, a disagreeable duty which he carried out with tact and courtesy. He became a friend of Napoleon, who had a high opinion of his talents, attended his lectures, asked his advice, and shared his conviction of the great utility of applied science.

In 1798 Berthollet and Monge, with other scientists, accompanied the expedition of Napoleon to Egypt, and were often exposed to considerable danger. An 'Institute of Egypt' was founded at Cairo, on the lines of the National Institute of France,[4] the first paper being read in August 1798. Berthollet read his memoir on mass action and affinity at one of its last meetings (1799). The work of the Institut d'Égypte was published in the Memoirs on Egypt edited by E. F. Jomard,[5] containing some papers by Berthollet,[6] but the

---

[1] Smeaton, *Ann. Sci.*, 1954, x, 224; *J. Roy. Inst. Chem.*, 1958, lxxxii, 650; L. P. Williams, *Isis*, 1956, xlvii, 369 (376).
[2] (2), iii, 707–11.   [3] Lavoisier, *Œuvres*, 1868, iv, 379.   [4] *Isis*, 1937, xxvi, 466.
[5] *Mémoires sur l'Égypte, publiés pendant les campagnes du Général Bonapartes dans les années VI et VII [+ VIII et IX]*, 4 vols., Paris, 1800–3 (BM 280. d. 7–10).
[6] On dyeing, i, 162, on natron, i, 271, on eudiometry, i, 284.

memoir on affinity was first published in the *Memoirs* of the Paris Institut,[1] and separately as a book.[2] In his memoir on natron, Berthollet[3] suggests that this is formed from common salt by interaction with limestone, and says he had given 'l'explication de cette production dans un mémoire que je présenterai incessament à l'institut'. A footnote explains that it was read 'dans les dernieres séances' but read again in Paris to the Institut National. The explanation was confirmed by experiments in which an efflorescence of soda was formed from limestone moistened with a solution of common salt;[4] the formation of carbonate is 'further aided by efflorescence', which acts as 'a new force which removes this compound'. Berthollet's researches on affinity are considered in Vol. IV.

In 1804 Berthollet was made a Senator and became an officer of the Legion of Honour, but he continued his scientific research in a private laboratory in his house (decorated in the Egyptian style) at Arcueil, a suburb of Paris, where Laplace also lived. In 1807 the two founded the Société d'Arcueil, which had as members also Gay-Lussac, Thenard, Humboldt, Biot, De Candolle, Collet-Descotils, Malus, and Berthollet's son Amédée, who committed suicide in 1811 by breathing carbon monoxide.[5] The Société d'Arcueil published three volumes of *Mémoires* in 1807–17 (the last rarely found complete); it met fortnightly and was visited by Davy, Wollaston, Berzelius and other famous chemists. In this period Berthollet interested himself in lighting by coal gas, the use of charcoal in keeping water fresh on board ship, and other practical applications of chemistry. He also made analyses of vegetable and animal products. The loss of his son affected Berthollet deeply; he tempered his grief by his kindness to the young chemists he gathered around him, treating them as his adopted children and giving them all the encouragement and advice in his power.

In 1814 Berthollet voted for the downfall of Napoleon, his former friend. This must be regarded as evidence of the high political integrity of Berthollet, who realised that a prolongation of war could only bring misery and ruin to France. On the Bourbon restoration he was created a Count by Louis XVIII. The loss of his friends Guyton de Morveau and Monge depressed him and after a long period of poor health he contracted and died of anthrax in 1822.

Berthollet was a man of simple habits with a love for his garden. He read with enjoyment the classics of French literature, and was an authority on sculpture and painting.[6] He took an objective view of affairs, recognising when foreign products were superior to French. In the laboratory he was a careful and conscientious worker, but not a very good manipulator — in later life he employed assistants[7] — and in the field of theory his writings show that he was actuated with a serious purpose based on sincere convictions. He was the first prominent French chemist (April 1785) to adopt Lavoisier's views. He

[1] *Mémoires de l'Institut Nationale des Sciences et Arts, Classe math. et phys.*, 4°, 1801, iii, m 1–96.
[2] *Recherches sur les Lois de l'Affinité*, sm. 8°, Paris, An IX (1801), 105 pp.
[3] *Mém. sur l'Égypte*, i, 271 (276).   [4] *Recherches*, 1801, 54 f.
[5] Jomard says 'gaz acide carbonique', which cannot be breathed.
[6] Jomard, 37 f.   [7] Jomard, 53.

was one of the outstanding founders of physical chemistry; his broad sweep of view, his critical power, and his full realisation of the interplay of chemical and physical forces mark him as a master mind in this science. His idea that chemical attraction was of the same nature as gravitation was probably incorrect, but it was an advance on the supposition that it is some occult force, a view held by chemists before his time and since. The title of his book, *Chemical Statics*, is significant.

In his first memoir, on tartaric acid,[1] Berthollet criticised some chemists (e.g. Demachy) severely, and the editor (Rozier) added some notes calling into question some statements and saying the chemists criticised 'ne meritent pas d'être traité si crûment d'erreurs'. Berthollet obtained tartaric acid and nitre by the action of nitric acid on tartar, prepared sodium tartrate (tartre minéral), ammonium tartrate, and the double tartrates of ammonium with sodium and potassium.

Berthollet next published a small brochure on gases[2] in which he mentions Priestley's discovery of dephlogisticated air. He describes the gases formed by distilling tartaric acid and nitric acid (largely fixed air), and potassium acetate (both fixed and inflammable airs). He concluded that tartaric and acetic acids owe their acid properties to fixed air combined with oil, and with oil and inflammable air, in the two acids. He gives the quantitative composition of potassium acetate as 147 grains of alkali and 429 of acetous acid (containing 131 grains of fixed air, 130 grains of inflammable air and 168 grains of oil and phlegm) in 1 oz. Alcohol was a compound of inflammable air and phlegm united by fixed air. Berthollet ascribes important functions to fixed air in nature, and seems to regard it almost as a universal acid. Nitrous air he recognised as nitrous acid deprived of air. He refutes Priestley's idea that dephlogisticated air is nitrous (nitric) acid united with an earth, and says vital air forms part of metallic calces, but defends the phlogiston theory against Buffon and tries to give it precision.

In a paper on phosphoric acid in urine[3] he describes its determination by precipitating with lime water and weighing the calcium phosphate.

In 1780–83 Berthollet defended the phlogiston theory and criticised Lavoisier.[4] In the memoir on the decomposition of nitric acid[5] he attacked Lavoisier's theory[6] that 'fire' is the cause of fluidity, vaporisation, and elasticity, saying that it did not explain the great heat evolved in the detonation of carbon, sulphur, and metals with nitre, since none of these substances occurs in the liquid, vapour, or gaseous state, and he found it difficult to understand the 'matter of heat' postulated by Lavoisier. He regarded phlogiston and matter of heat as modifications of the same principle, since heat and light reduce calces of the noble metals and phlogisticate nitric acid; he thought

---

[1] Sur l'acide tartareux, *Obs. Phys.*, 1776, vii, 130–48.

[2] *Observations sur l'Air. Par Mr. Berthollet, Docteur en Médecine*, 12°, Paris, 1776, 59 pp.; Sotheran *Cat.* 852 (1938) No. 1121; not in BM or BN; summary in Fourcroy, (2), iii, 482.

[3] AdS, 1780, m 10.

[4] (a) Sur la causticité des sels métalliques, AdS, 1780, m 448 (causticity is due to privation of phlogiston); (b) Sur la décomposition de l'acide nitrique (3e mémoire), AdS, 1781, m 234; reports by Macquer and Lavoisier, Lavoisier, *Œuvres*, iv, 343.

[5] AdS, 1781, m 234.   [6] Lavoisier, AdS, 1777 (1780), m 592.

fixed air was produced on detonating nitre with metals, and that when zinc dissolves in nitric acid practically nothing but heat is evolved.[1]

In a memoir 'on the causticity of the alkalis and lime'[2] Berthollet described the action of alkalis and earths on animal substances (silk, wool, etc.), noting the odours produced and the changes of colour, and finding that the solution was neither acid nor alkaline; acids gave with it a jelly with no effervescence of fixed air. Silver nitrate gave a white precipitate rapidly turning black, hence calx of silver exercises its causticity on animal substances, but calcareous earth (lime) gave no precipitate, hence it reacted only by its affinity for water. Alum gave an abundant white precipitate, and a study of this might lead to an explanation of the action of alum as a mordant for silk and wool. There are two types of combination between animal substances and alkali, that described in this memoir, and that in which Prussian blue is formed, in which the animal substance seems to act with acidic properties.

In his memoir on the causticity of metallic salts[3] Berthollet criticised the theory of 'a savant of the Academy' (Lavoisier) that acidity is due to combination with vital air (oxygen); the causticity of the metallic calces cannot be due to the air, since then the causticity would be relative to the quantity of this principle and almost equal in all the calces. 'Can one imagine that the causticity of ten or twelve grains of red precipitate is due to the grain of air combined with it?'

In 1782, he admitted[4] that his experiments on the oxidation of phosphorus were 'in perfect accord with those of M. Lavoisier', making the increase in weight of phosphorus as $\frac{1}{2} - \frac{2}{3}$, due to the air. He describes experiments on the composition of sulphuric acid (SO_3), finding 69·3 sulphur (and 30·7 oxygen), a poor result. Berthollet then admitted the fixation of vital air in the formation of acids, but thought phlogiston was also evolved.

In 1785, however, he announced his adoption of Lavoisier's theory and considered phlogiston a useless hypothesis:[5] 'le phlogistique me parassoit enfin être devenu une hypothèse inutile, lorsque je crus devoir soumettre à de nouvelles expériences l'acide marin déphlogistiqué, dont les propriétés pouvoient détruire ou confirmer l'opinion que j'ai adoptois.'

In 1778[6] he showed that nitre on heating evolves dephlogisticated air and leaves 'fixed alkali' (he missed the nitrite but on strong heating it forms the oxide); hence the nitric acid had been converted into dephlogisticated air. In a memoir on arsenic (1780)[7] he described the preparation of arsenic acid by evaporating white arsenic with nitric acid, nitrous air (NO) being evolved, and showed that it precipitated metallic arsenates from solutions of salts of metals, but formed soluble lime and alumina salts. He suggested that other metals besides arsenic might be compounds of acids and phlogiston. In 1782 he

---

[1] AdS, 1781, m 241; Fourcroy, (2), iii, 542 f. [2] AdS, 1782 (1785), h 27, m 616–19.
[3] AdS, 1780, m 448.
[4] AdS, 1782 (1785), h 25, m 602–7 (dated 1782): Sur l'augmentation de Poids qu'éprouvent le Soufre, le Phosphore & l'Arsenic lorsqu'ils sont changés en Acide.
[5] AdS, 1785, m 276; first reading, 6 April 1785; Partington, *Chymia*, 1959, v, 130.
[6] Report by Cadet and Lavoisier, Lavoisier, *Œuvres*, 1868, iv, 298.
[7] Report by Macquer and Lavoisier, Lavoisier, *Œuvres*, 1868, iv, 350.

found that arsenious oxide increases by one-ninth of its weight when converted into arsenic oxide.[1]

Priestley in 1775–7[2] found that when electric sparks are passed through ammonia gas its volume was trebled and an inflammable gas was produced; in later experiments, by the action of heat in presence of iron, the volume was nearly doubled but some ammonia was left. In 1785 Berthollet repeated this experiment and analysed the gas formed by sparking by exploding it with oxygen, finding it to contain 2·9 vols. of inflammable gas and 1·1 vols. of azote.[3]

Berthollet attempted to find the composition of ammonia by decomposing ammonium nitrate by heat, collecting the water in receivers cooled in ice and the gas evolved at the pneumatic trough. The gas was soluble in water to form a neutral solution, supported a taper flame almost as effectively as vital air, and could be regarded as 'a nitrous gas which contains a little more of vital air than the ordinary', and was apparently the same as Priestley's dephlogisticated nitrous air (p. 289). This was nitrous oxide. Its composition is given incorrectly, since it contains less oxygen than nitrous air.

The formation of nitrous oxide on heating ammonium nitrate had apparently been noticed by Bryan Higgins about 1775:[4] he speaks of 'the curious decomposition of nitrous ammoniac . . . effected by distilling . . . and passing the vapour thereof thro' water into an inverted vessel void of air'; he showed that the 'air' supported the combustion of many substances 'as when common air acts on them, in like circumstances'. Black, also, had noticed it (see p. 142).

A consideration of the quantities of the products obtained[5] by decomposing ammonium nitrate by heat showed that ammonia contained hydrogen; in collaboration with Laplace Berthollet then showed that the action of dephlogisticated marine acid (chlorine) on ammonia gave phlogisticated air (nitrogen). Berthollet also showed that nitrogen is evolved in the explosion of fulminating gold prepared by the action of ammonia on calx of gold, and proved the nature of the gas by sparking it with vital air as Cavendish did (p. 339). Some experiments with fulminating silver prepared from silver oxide and ammonia were described in 1788.[6]

In 1787 William Austin, in Oxford, sparked ammonia gas and fired the gaseous product with oxygen by an electric spark, obtaining a residue of nitrogen; he concluded that ammonia is composed of 'phlogisticated and light inflammable airs'.[7] Austin showed that ammonia is formed when copper nitrate solution is reduced with zinc, when moist iron filings or moist iron filings and sulphur stand in phlogisticated air (N_2), common air, or (especially) nitrous air (NO), and by mixing hepatic air (H_2S) and nitrous air

[1] AdS, 1782, h 25, m 602; it should be nearly a quarter.
[2] E & O, 1775, ii, 239; 1786, vi, 189.
[3] Analyse de l'alcali volatil, AdS, 1785 (1788), m 316–26; read 11 June 1785; Obs. Phys., 1786, xxviii, 273; 1786, xxix, 175; Crell's Ann., 1791, II, 169; Thomson, Life of Cullen, 1859, i, 647 (letter of 5 July 1785, from Blagden to Cullen, saying Berthollet 'makes the proportions of the two airs to be, six parts of phlogisticated, and one of inflammable'; Berthollet says this, also that the inflammable gas is ⅔ the volume of the decomposed ammonia).
[4] Essay on Light, 1776, 83–4.
[5] Confirmed by Guyton de Morveau, Crell's Ann., 1788, I, 124.
[6] Obs. Phys., 1788, xxxii, 474; AdS, 1788, m 728–41.   [7] Phil. Trans., 1788, lxxviii, 379.

(as had been shown by Kirwan).[1] From the densities of hydrogen, nitrogen, and ammonia gas as determined by Kirwan, and Berthollet's observation that 1·7 vols. of ammonia expand to 3·3 on sparking, Austin calculated that the ratio of the weights of nitrogen and hydrogen in ammonia is 121 : 32, whilst Berthollet had found 121 : 29. His experiments were made without knowledge of Berthollet's.[2] In 1789[3] Austin found that ammonium nitrate (nitrous ammoniac) when heated in closed vessels 'yields dephlogisticated nitrous air [nitrous oxide] in great abundance', with a little fixed air (carbon dioxide).

Jean Michel Hausmann of Colmar (Colmar, 4 February 1749–Strasbourg, 16 December 1824), owner of dyeworks,[4] found[5] that purified nitric oxide in contact with precipitated ferrous hydroxide suspended in pure water or alkali solution is reduced to ammonia, the ferrous hydroxide forming ferric hydroxide; he also found reduction on absorption in ferrous sulphate solution. On standing over an alkaline solution of arsenic sulphide nitric oxide is reduced to nitrous oxide.

Berthollet's experiments on the composition of ammonia were confirmed by his son, A. B. Berthollet,[6] who found 18·87 hydrogen and 81·13 nitrogen. He also noticed that iron heated in ammonia gas becomes brittle.

Berthollet's masterly research on chlorine was read to the Academy on 6 April 1785, and the announcement of his conversion to Lavoisier's theory must have been made then, since the whole memoir depends on it and it is assumed in the preliminary publication in 1785,[7] in which it is said that its formation 'is due to the dephlogisticated air of the manganese, which combines with the marine acid'. Berthollet certainly had doubts about Lavoisier's oxygen theory of acidity, since he emphasises that dephlogisticated marine acid (chlorine) 'does not exhibit the characteristics of other acids and, strictly speaking, it should not be included among them'. It dissolves iron and zinc without effervescence (unlike other acids) and bleaches vegetable colours without first reddening them, itself becoming marine acid. Its use in bleaching is suggested. In 1786 Berthollet showed that a solution of dephlogisticated marine acid exposed to sunlight evolved bubbles of vital air (oxygen), which could be collected from the solution contained in a flask fitted with a delivery tube, whilst the effect of heat is simply to expel the gas,[8] and he then says 'les progrès de la Physique ayant rendu l'hypothèse du phlogistique insuffisante & inutile . . .', etc.

In 1786 he thought that silver muriate under water is decomposed by light with evolution of bubbles of oxygen, but in 1803[9] he says the bubbles were only air adhering to the solid, although the water contained muriatic acid. The

[1] Phil. Trans., 1786, lxxvi, 118; Obs. Phys., 1787, xxx, 133 (144).
[2] W. Higgins, Comparative View of the Phlogistic and Antiphlogistic Theories, 1789, 313.
[3] Phil. Trans., 1790, lxxx, II, 51: read December, 1789.
[4] Poggendorff, (1), i, 1037.   [5] Obs. Phys., 1787, xxx, 461.
[6] C. L. Berthollet, Introd. to tr. of T. Thomson, Système de Chimie, 1809, i, 149; A. B. Berthollet, Mém. Soc. Arcueil, 1809, ii, 268 (read to the Institut 24 March 1808).
[7] Obs. Phys., 1785, xxvi, 321–5: Sur l'Acide Marin Déphlogistiqué; the name 'acide marin' for hydrochloric acid had been used by Demachy in his tr. of Pott's Dissertations, 1759 (see Vol. II, p. 720); Lavoisier called it 'acide muriatique' (see p. 461).
[8] Obs. Phys., 1786, xxix, 81–5 (August); presented to the Faculty of Medicine in July 1786.
[9] Statique Chimique, 1803, i, 195 f.

blackened muriate was completely soluble in ammonia. 'It was, therefore, without foundation that I supposed that in this case the oxygen was determined by the action of light to resume the elastic state and abandon the metal.' Lavoisier[1] said 'en 1785 Berthollet écrivait encore dans le système phlogistique', which misled Duveen and Klickstein into thinking that Berthollet had not abandoned the theory in 1785. From April 1785 all his work is explained on the antiphlogistic theory, using the old names since the new nomenclature was not introduced until 1787.[2] The title of the paper is 'Mémoire sur l'Acide Marin Déphlogistiqué'.[3]

There is a certain irony in this, since the supposed compositions of muriatic and oxymuriatic acids, which convinced Berthollet of the correctness of the antiphlogistic theory, were later shown by Davy (see Vol. IV) to be incorrect, neither gas containing any oxygen. Berthollet's arguments are summarised later (see p. 505). Berthollet emphasised that dephlogisticated marine acid (chlorine) is 'almost entirely destitute of acidity (presque entièrement dépourvu d'acidité)'[4] since it does not effervesce with mild alkali, although the muriatic acid was supposed to have taken vital air (oxygen) from the manganese dioxide to produce dephlogisticated marine acid. On Lavoisier's theory this should have been a stronger acid. He does not say this, but Giobert[5] pointed out that although oxymuriatic acid is supposed to contain more oxygen, the acidifying principle, than muriatic acid, it is not so acid as this.

To Guyton de Morveau's objection[6] that gaseous muriatic acid did not combine with vital air, Berthollet replied[7] that: 'The elastic state of a substance is an obstacle to combination.' Berthollet failed to notice the union of chlorine and hydrogen on exposure to light or on sparking, and said: 'I am compelled to believe that dephlogisticated marine acid has no action at all on inflammable gas while it is in the gaseous state.'[8] Curiously, he did not examine the combustion of phosphorus in the *gas*, but he found that it formed phosphoric acid in a solution of dephlogisticated marine acid exposed to light.[9] He describes crystalline chlorine hydrate,[10] independently discovered in 1785 by Bertrand Pelletier,[11] who also noticed that the gas was explosive with hydrogen.[12] Pelletier's paper was sent to the Academy on 5 April, and read 9 April 1785. He thought chlorine hydrate was solid oxygenated muriatic acid (le gaz prend une forme concrète). Chlorine hydrate is also mentioned (as solid chlorine) by W. J. G. Karsten.[13]

Berthollet opens the 1788 publication by saying that experiments on the nature of water and de la Place's explanation of the origin of the inflammable

[1] *Mémoires*, ii, 87; Duveen and Klickstein, *Osiris*, 1956, xii, 342–67 (351), say this was written in 1792.

[2] Partington, *Chymia*, 1959, v, 130.

[3] AdS, 1785 (1788), m 276–95 (no notice in *Histoire*, no date of reading); Crell's *Ann.*, 1790, II, 444; ACR, xiii.

[4] AdS, 1785, m 279.   [5] *Mém. Acad. Turin*, 1792 (1793), x, 299.

[6] *Ency. Méthod.*, *Chymie*, 1786, i, 250–60.   [7] AdS, 1785 (1788), m 281.

[8] *Ib.*, 289.   [9] *Ib.*, 290.   [10] *Ib.*, 278; *Ann. Chim.*, 1789, ii, 155.

[11] *Obs. Phys.*, 1785, xxvi, 389, 452; *Mémoires et Observations de Chimie*, Paris, 1798, i, 111.

[12] *Ib.*, 126.

[13] *Physisch-chymische Abhandlungen durch neuere Schriften von hermetischen Arbeiten und andere neuere Untersuchungen veranlasset*, 2 pts., 8°, Halle, 1786–7.

air evolved in the dissolution of metals have thrown much light (grand jour) on chemistry. He will enter into more detail than in 1785, adding some new experiments, and answering some objections (by de Morveau) to the theory he had established (que j'avois établie). He gives Scheele's theory (see p. 213). The solution of the dephlogisticated marine acid has a harsh taste unlike that of acids, and the solution bleaches litmus without any trace of preliminary red colour. The dephlogisticated marine acid is 'presque entièrement dépourvu d'acidité'; it makes no effervescence with fixed alkali (potassium carbonate), but on boiling with soda solution, fixed air is disengaged and common salt is formed. 'C'est donc l'air vital de la manganèse, qui se combine avec l'acide marin, qu'est dûe la formation de l'acide marin déphlogistiqué', as Lavoisier and later Fourcroy had asserted (but for Fourcroy's view see p. 541).

The solution in cold alkali and in lime lost its colour and smell, but on adding acetic acid there is effervescence 'as if the alkali were simply dissolved in water' and the smell recovers all its vigour. (He seems to think the efferves-cence is due to carbon dioxide.) A solution of chalk in it is precipitated by lime water, showing that 'lime combines more strongly with this liquor than effervescent calcareous earth'.

Metals dissolve in a solution of dephlogisticated marine acid without evolv-ing any gas; they take vital air from it and hence do not need to decompose water, forming inflammable gas. The solution dissolves mercury to form cor-rosive sublimate, in which mercury is combined with a larger proportion of vital air and marine acid than in calomel. It converts hepatic gas (hydrogen sulphide) into vitriolic acid. On mixing with nitrous air (nitric oxide) red fumes were produced.

'It is not by a simple affinity that the marine acid takes vital air from manganese calx. It is only because part of this acid dissolves the manganese, expelling the part of the vital air which is superfluous to the new combination, that the other part can unite with this vital air, deprived in part of its principle of elasticity, since the acid has only a feeble affinity for it.'

He says de Morveau had also asserted that in its reactions with alkalis, earths, or metals there is no proof that it has not received in exchange some phlogiston or inflammable gas, 'since this fluid, according to M. de Morveau, is nothing but phlogiston put into the state of gas by the matter of heat.' But at ordinary temperature vital air does not combine with inflammable gas, and it is better to regard vital air as a compound of light or heat with a base, and the marine acid has only a very feeble affinity with vital air, another substance being required to decompose it by double affinity. Bonjour admitted the justice of Berthollet's criticisms.[1]

François Joseph Bonjour (Onglières, nr. Nozeret, Jura, 12 December 1754–Dieuze, Lorraine, 24 February 1811) was (1784) 'préparateur' to Berthollet and assisted him in work on bleaching by chlorine (see p. 507). He was later professor in the École poly-technique (1794), then a commissioner for the production of salt and chemicals in the east of France (1797).[2]

[1] Tr. of Bergman, Traité des Affinités Chymiques, 1788, 340 f.
[2] NBU, 1853, vi, 606; Fourcroy, (2), iii, 758; Notice biographique sur J. F. Bonjour, chimiste . . . par son nevue, Jacques Bonjour [Conservateur du Musée de Lons-le-Saunier], 8°, Lons-le-Saunier, 1853 (8 pp.; BN Ln²⁷. 2346); Smeaton, Ambix, 1959, vii, 47.

The name 'oxygenated muriatic acid' was contracted to 'oxymuriatic acid' by Pearson at the suggestion of Kirwan,[1] Chenevix calling it 'oxygenized muriatic acid'.[2] The theory of the process of preparation of chlorine was more fully explained by Vauquelin[3] in the same way as by Berthollet (see p. 505). Lavoisier[4] said that muriatic acid is not fully saturated with oxygen but can 'take a new dose if it is distilled over metallic oxides, such as oxide of manganese, oxide of lead or that of mercury', forming oxygenated muriatic acid. The statement is true only for the *higher* oxides of manganese and lead, and not true for oxide of mercury.

Berthollet[5] found that 51·1 cu. in. of solution of oxygenated muriatic acid gave 15·27 cu. in. of oxygen at 17° on exposure to sunlight; the remaining liquid gave 383 grains of muriate of silver. He does not calculate the composition of oxymuriatic acid from these figures, but Murray[6] deduced from them the percentage composition: muriatic acid 89, oxygen 11. There is other evidence that Berthollet accepted the antiphlogistic theory in 1785. The memoir on dephlogisticated marine acid is followed by one on aqua regia[7] and one on the oxidation of alcohol and ether by dephlogisticated marine acid.[8] In the first (read 19 April 1785) he mentions that new discoveries show that metals decompose water, uniting with its vital air, and inflammable air is 'par-là' disengaged. In aqua regia, part of the marine acid unites with part of the vital air in the nitric acid, and is evolved as dephlogisticated marine acid, the nitrous gas being retained in the aqua regia. The liquid does not contain ready-formed dephlogisticated marine acid. The marine acid takes vital air from nitric acid by a double affinity. Berthollet also showed that hydrochloric acid decomposes sodium sulphate only incompletely, some sulphate being left unchanged. Kirwan's views are criticised. The second memoir (read 27 April 1785) is also conceived entirely on the basis of the antiphlogistic theory. Berthollet examined the action of chlorine on alcohol and ether. From the nature of the products he concluded that alcohol is a compound of sugar, oil and inflammable gas, and ether of a light oil and inflammable gas.

Memoirs on 'the combination of vital air with oils'[9] and on the nature of animal substances[10] are also wholly based on the antiphlogistic theory. When Lavoisier[11] said about 1792 that 'en 1785, Berthollet écrivoit encore dans le système du phlogistique' he might have been thinking of Berthollet's use of names such as 'dephlogisticated marine acid', but the new names were not introduced until 1787 (see p. 481) and Lavoisier's words are both ungenerous and misleading. He never shone in historical discussions.

[1] Pearson, *A Translation of a Table of Chemical Nomenclature*, 4°, 1799, 5; T. Thomson, *Ency. Brit. Suppl.*, 1801, I, i, 315; Murray, 1806, ii, 546.
[2] Chenevix, *Remarks upon Chemical Nomenclature*, 1802, 91.
[3] *J. de l'École polytechn.*, An IV (1796), cahier iii, 386.
[4] *Traité de Chimie*, 1789, 257.
[5] AdS, 1785, m 282–4.   [6] 1806, ii, 546–52.
[7] Observations sur l'eau régale et sur quelques affinités de l'acide marin, AdS, 1785 (1788), m 296–307.
[8] Mémoire sur la décomposition de l'esprit-de-vin et de l'éther, par le moyen de l'air vital, AdS, 1785 (1788), m 308–15.
[9] AdS, 1785 (1788), m 327–30; read November 1785.
[10] AdS, 1785 (1788), m 331–49; read December 1785.   [11] *Mémoires*, ii, 86–7.

Berthollet soon turned the bleaching action of chlorine water to practical use.[1] 6 oz. of pyrolusite and 16 oz. of salt were put into a glass bolt-head or a stoneware or lead retort and 12 oz. of sulphuric acid (sp. gr. 1·848) diluted with 8 to 12 oz. of water poured on. The retort was heated in boiling water and the gas collected in 100 quarts of water for every 1 lb. of salt used, to form the bleaching solution. The cloth was boiled with dilute caustic potash solution, washed, and put into the bleaching solution in wooden troughs for 3–4 hours. The processes were repeated 4–8 times. The cloth was washed with soft soap and then soaked in very dilute sulphuric acid. The alternate action of chlorine and alkali was considered necessary. In his book[2] the proportions are 5 pyrolusite + 13·5 salt and 10 acid diluted with an equal weight of water.

Berthollet suggested that a solution of indigo in sulphuric acid might be used to indicate the strength of a bleaching solution, and this was worked up into a practical volumetric method by François Antoine Henri Descroizilles (Dieppe, 11 June 1751–Paris, 14 April 1825), professor of chemistry at Rouen and director of a bleach works at Lescure, near Rouen.[3] The process was speedily made known in England.[4] Pajot des Charmes (see below)[5] used 4 lb. of salt, 20 oz. of manganese, 44 oz. of sulphuric acid 'of 60° Mossy' diluted with 3¼ lb. of water.

The exposure of the workmen to the chlorine emitted from the chlorine water used in bleaching caused unpleasant and even dangerous effects. C. Pajot des Charmes, formerly an inspector of manufactures, added potash or soda (carbonates), or these and quicklime, to the chlorine water, and recommended that the workmen should wear masks and chew liquorice.[6] Bonjour (see p. 505), who had been assistant to Berthollet, joined Constant, a cloth finisher of Valenciennes, in establishing a bleach works in 1788, but they encountered so much opposition from the old-fashioned bleachers that, in spite of the interest of the Count de Bellaing, Bonjour was obliged to appeal to the National Bureau of Commerce.

Soon after, some manufacturers at Javelle (now Javel), near Paris, announced in the press that they had discovered a bleaching liquor which they called 'lye de Javelle', which Berthollet found to be a solution of chlorine in

[1] Description du blanchîment des toiles & des fils par l'acide muriatique oxygéné; *Ann. Chim.*, 1789, ii, 151–90; 1790, vi, 204, 210; separ., Paris, 1795; the preparation from salt, manganese dioxide and somewhat diluted sulphuric acid is described, *Ann. Chim.*, 1789, ii, 165 f.: the account is written in terms of antiphlogistic chemistry, which thus became familiar in chemical technology.

[2] *Elements of the Art of Dyeing*, tr. Ure, London, 1824, i, 199.

[3] *Description et Usage du Berthollimètre*, 1802; *Notices sur l'Alcalimètre et autres tubes chimico-métriques ou sur le Polymètre Chimique*, 1810 and later eds. (5 ed. 1839) — volumetric apparatus (burette); a different burette was devised by Gay-Lussac (see Vol. IV); Poggendorff, (1), i, 559, says Descroizilles was the first to absorb chlorine in milk of lime for bleaching liquor.

[4] *Essay on the New Method of Bleaching by means of Oxygenated Muriatic Acid . . . from the French of Mr. Berthollet* . . . By Robert Kerr, Dublin, Published by Order of the Trustees of the Linen and Hempen Manufacture, n.d. [? 1790], a tr. of *Ann. Chim.*, 1789, ii, 151, with notes, and the paper of Lavoisier and Berthollet from Chaptal, *Ann. Chim.*, 1789, i, 69, also tr. (see p. 508).

[5] *Essay on the New Method . . .*, 47.

[6] Pajot des Charmes, *L'Art du Blanchiment des Toiles, Fils et Cotons de tout Genre*, Paris, An VI (1798) (282 pp., BN V. 48729); tr. W. Nicholson, *The Art of Bleaching Piece-Goods, Cottons and Threads, by means of the Oxygenated Muriatic Acid*, London, 1799, with Appendix and 9 plates, 64 f., 176; the preface says the book should have been published in 1791.

potash solution, but, disappointed in their commercial prospects at home, these manufacturers set up in Liverpool and applied to Parliament for the exclusive right to make and supply in bottles their 'liquor de Javelle' for 28 years. Parliament was informed that the process was not new, and this, with a petition from Manchester, led to their petition being refused. They continued, however, to make and sell the solution. A Mr. Foy, one of their workmen, offered for a considerable premium to erect the necessary apparatus for several manufacturers.[1]

Berthollet[2] says: 'One of the original establishers (anciens entrepreneurs) of the Javelle process had gone to England to demand an exclusive privilege for this invention, which he claimed as his own.'[3] The Javelle manufacturer seems to have introduced the method of dissolving the chlorine in alkali solution, since Berthollet criticises this by saying the alkali would partly neutralise the chlorine and make it useless, which is not, in fact, true.

Berthollet was careful (in the year of the Revolution) to point out the social and economic advantages of his process; the products of the power-looms then coming into use could not be bleached at the necessary rate by the old process of grass-bleaching, which could be used only at the proper season, the workers at other times being exposed to an unjust commercial exploitation of their poverty. In 1787 the Montpellier Academy sent some observations by Chaptal, of Rouen, on chlorine for publication by the Paris Academy, which were reported upon by Lavoisier and Berthollet.[4] Chaptal used chlorine water for bleaching paper and cleaning engravings, but chlorine gas for bleaching fabrics, for which purpose, however, Lavoisier and Berthollet said chlorine water was better.

Early in 1787 Copeland, professor of Natural Philosophy in Marischal College, Aberdeen, visited Geneva with the Duke of Gordon, and was shown some experiments on bleaching with chlorine *gas* by de Saussure; and in July 1787, chlorine *water* was used by Gordon, Barron and Co. at Aberdeen. In the same year James Watt was shown experiments by Berthollet in Paris and the process was used in 1787 by Watt, and in Glasgow in 1788 by MacGregor, Watt's father-in-law.[5] Kerr,[6] however, said he was informed that MacGregor and Watt had since given up the use of chlorine and reverted to the old method of bleaching. Chlorine was also used by Thomas Henry in Manchester in 1788; he was in relation with Watt.[7] The petition by French industrial chemists for exclusive rights was rejected by Parliament on account of prior use by Watt and Henry, and a large works was established in Lancashire at Raikes, near Bolton (it was still there in my youth), by Thomas Cooper (London, 22 October 1759–South Carolina, 11 May 1840), afterwards president of Columbia College, South Carolina.

Charles Tennant (Ochiltree, Ayrshire, 3 May 1768–Glasgow, 10 October

[1] Parkes, *Chemical Essays*, 2 ed., London, 1823, ii, 288.   [2] *Ann. Chim.*, 1789, ii, 180.
[3] The English tr. by Kerr, Dublin, 1790 (?), 86, embellishes this by saying the Javellois 'had the effrontery' to do this.
[4] *Ann. Chim.*, 1789, i, 69; tr. in Kerr, *op. cit.*, 117 f.
[5] Smiles, 1904, 353.   [6] *Op. cit.*, 1790 (?), 32.
[7] Henry, *Manchester Mem.*, 1790, iii, 361; Rupp, *ib.*, 1798, v, 298.

1838)[1] a pupil of Black, was in 1798 granted a patent for the use of milk of lime, but when he tried to stop Lancashire bleachers from infringing this it was shown that the process had been in use in secret in Northampton. In 1799 he obtained a patent for absorbing chlorine in solid slaked lime (the process is said to have been invented by Charles Macintosh, his partner), and in 1800 founded the famous factory in St. Rollox, Glasgow, for making bleaching powder.[2]

Tennant's patent of 23 January 1798 specifies the absorption of oxymuriatic acid (chlorine) in calcareous earths, strontites, or barytes in their carbonated or calcined forms instead of by alkaline substances such as pot or pearl ashes, kelp or barilla. In the subsequent litigation the use of magnesia was mentioned.[3] Davy[4] proposed the absorption in a suspension of magnesia, and says this was used at his suggestion by Duffy, a calico-printer in Dublin, Davy having found that it 'bleaches without injuring the vegetable fibre' and it did not destroy reds and yellows fixed by mordants.

Tennant took out two patents, (I) BP 2209/1798 and (II) 2313/1799. I covered the absorption of chlorine in a suspension of lime and II the use of dry lime. I was the subject of Tennant's infringement action in 1802 and he was non-suited, since the process had been used six years previously, and the evidence showed that the process had been communicated to Tennant. Tennant in 1800 brought an infringement action for II against eleven Lancashire bleachers. This was dismissed when it was shown that in 1791 a Robert Roper had absorbed chlorine for bleaching purposes in slaked lime. The dismissal of the infringement suit did not necessarily invalidate the patent.[5]

Antoine Germain Labarraque (Oléron, Dép. Basses-Pyrénées, 29 May 1777–Paris, 9 December 1850), a Paris apothecary and pupil of Chaptal,[6] introduced the use of alkali hypochlorite as a disinfectant, using sodium hypochlorite solution ('Labarraque's liquid') in 1822:

Manière de se servir du chlorure d'oxyde de sodium, soit pour panser les plaies de mauvaise nature, soit comme moyen d'assainissement des lieux insalubres et de désinfection des matières animales, 4°, Paris, printed by Mme. Huzard, [1825], 4 pp. (BN 4° Tc⁵³. 28 (1); also in Italian, 4°, Paris (Mme. Huzard), 1825, 3 pp. (BN 4° Tc⁵³. 28 (2)); Ordonnance du préfet de police, en date du 19 octobre 1823, prescrivant l'emploi du chlorure de chaux, suivi d'observations sur l'emploi des chlorures, par A. G. Labarraques, 4°, Paris (Mme. Huzard), s.a. [1825 ?] (BN 4° Tc⁵³. 26); Sur la préparation des chlorures désinfectants, 1826; On the Disinfecting Properties of Labarraque's Preparations of Chlorine . . . with an Appendix by the Translator, 3 ed. 1828 (40 pp.).

[1] Fourcroy, (2), 1796, iii, 586; Walker, 1862, 186; Harden, DNB, 1898, lvi, 60; S. H. Higgins, A History of Bleaching, 1924, 73 f.; W. Alexander, Chem. and Ind., 1943, 411–16.
[2] Parkes, Chemical Essays, 5 ed., 1812, 276 f.; W. Henry, Ann. Phil., 1815, vi, 421; Schofield, Chem. and Ind., 1947, 506; Tennant, Chem. and Ind., 1947, 667, 967; Mond, J. Soc. Chem. Ind., 1896, xv, 713; Hardie, Chem. and Ind., 1952, 606; Chem. Age, 1957, lxxvii, 468; G. Macintosh, Biographical Memoirs of the Late Charles Macintosh, Glasgow, 1847 (privately printed, BM 1453. h. 3), 37 f., 40, 58 (letter of 30.6.1831 by C. Macintosh, speaking of 'Mr. Tennant's manufactury of dry chloride of lime (at first established by myself, and who invented the substance)'), Appendix, 1, p. 121.
[3] A full account of the proceedings in the Court of Chancery is given by Higgins, 1924, 82–8; portr. of Tennant.
[4] Elements of Chemical Philosophy, 1812, 243.
[5] Letter of 3.4.1957 from Dr. D. W. F. Hardie.   [6] NBG, 1859, xxviii, 323; Cap, i, 284.

Another investigation with an important technical bearing was that on steel made by Berthollet, Monge and Vandermonde,[1] which had the object of making France independent of England in obtaining supplies of steel. The relation between the properties of different kinds of iron and steel and the carbon content was established. The effect of temperature on the proportion of carbon dissolved by molten iron, and the separation of part of this carbon on cooling, were established experimentally. This work and that of Rinman (see p. 178) were discussed by Wilhelm Albrecht Tiemann.[2]

Charles Auguste Vandermonde (Paris; 1735–1 January 1796), director (1782) of the Conservatoire pour les arts-et-métiers, was also an eminent mathematician ('Vandermonde's theorem', etc.) and wrote on the theory of music. He published on the cold of 1776 with Bézout and Lavoisier,[3] and on the manufacture of bayonets and sword blades at Klingental, department of the Lower Rhine.[4]

In July 1787 Berthollet[5] reported that when 'acide marin dephlogistiqué ou acide muriatique oxygéné' (chlorine) is passed into concentrated caustic potash solution a liquid with bleaching properties is obtained (containing hypochlorite), but when the solution is saturated with the gas it loses its bleaching properties and on standing deposits two crystalline salts. One of these is muriate of potash (KCl), formed in large amount, the other a salt much less soluble in cold water, which detonates with carbon, forming muriate of potash; hence it is formed from muriatic acid combined with oxygen and potash, and he called it 'muriate oxygéné de potasse', the acid being 'acide muriatique suroxygéné'. This salt was potassium chlorate, the crystalline form being described. This (when pure) gives no precipitate with silver nitrate. When strongly heated it evolved oxygen, 'pour que la lumière rend l'état élastique à l'oxygène',[6] and this is a convenient method for the preparation of very pure oxygen. The salt (potassium chlorate) deflagrated with carbon much more vividly than nitre, for which it was proposed as a substitute in gunpowder (see p. 511). 100 grains of salt gave 75 cu. in. of oxygen at 12° R. The sodium salt, also prepared, was much more soluble.

Some further experiments by Berthollet[7] showed, contrary to Chenevix's results,[8] that chlorate is formed only in the later stages of the action of chlorine on alkali, which is perfectly correct, although the reaction is still mis-described in many text-books.

The chlorate was investigated by Thomas Hoyle in 1797,[9] who showed that it evolves a yellow explosive gas with concentrated sulphuric acid (Chenevix thought this gas was a mixture of oxymuriatic acid (chlorine) and hyperoxy-

[1] Obs. Phys., 1786, xxix, 210, 281; AdS, 1786, m 132–200; Ann. Chim., 1797, xix, 13.
[2] Bemerkungen und Versuche über das Eisen, Brunswick, 1799 (xiv, 130 pp.).
[3] AdS, 1777, h 1, m 505.   [4] Ann. Chim., 1797, xix, 45–57.
[5] Mém. Acad. Turin, 1786–7 (1788), iii, 385; Obs. Phys., 1788, xxxiii, 217; Hassenfratz, Crell's Ann., 1787, II, 57; Lavoisier, Traité, 1789, i, 254.
[6] Obs. Phys., 1788, xxxiii, 222.
[7] Statique Chimique, 1803, ii, 194 f.
[8] Chenevix, Phil. Trans., 1802, xcii, 126: Observations and Experiments on oxygenised and hyperoxygenised muriatic acid; Chenevix prepared other chlorates.
[9] Manchester Mem., 1798, v, 222.

muriatic (chloric) acid), and also independently by Fourcroy and Vauquelin (see p. 541).

Potassium chlorate had been obtained by Bryan Higgins in 1786[1] but he thought it was nitre. Attention was drawn to Higgins by Dollfuss.[2] Sodium chlorate (dephlogistisch-salzsäuren Soda) was rediscovered by Ferdinand Wurzer (Brüel, 22 June 1765–Marburg, 30 July 1844), professor of chemistry in Bonn and Marburg.[3] He also wrote on the manufacture of nitric acid,[4] supposed that he had converted steam into nitrogen by passing it through heated tubes,[5] obtained some corrosive sublimate in making spirit of salt from common salt and sulphuric acid,[6] detected manganese in blood;[7] and experimented on mineral waters, making sea water drinkable, on calculi, etc.

In 1788 Berthollet tried to increase the power of French gunpowder by using potassium chlorate instead of saltpetre. The mill at Essones making this powder exploded and two persons were killed.[8] Fourcroy[9] said the chlorate gunpowder was twice as strong as that made with saltpetre, and Parkes[10] said he was assured that the French used chlorate gunpowder in later campaigns. Black[11] says it was tried at Woolwich Arsenal, and chlorate gunpowders, although dangerous, were used during the nineteenth century.[12]

In 1787 Berthollet in a careful study of prussic acid concluded that it is a compound of hydrogen, carbon and nitrogen and free from oxygen. By the action of chlorine upon it he obtained a white solid (cyanogen chloride), which he thought contained oxygen.[13] He says:[14] 'It seems that no doubt remains as to the composition of prussic acid, other than the proportion of its principles, which I have not yet been able to determine. It is a combination of azote, hydrogen and pure charcoal or carbon.' The existence of acids free from oxygen was again emphasised by him in 1789,[15] when he also points out that it had not yet been shown that boric, fluoric, lithic (uric), and muriatic acids contain oxygen, and the state of combination and the capacity to form series of salts determine the acidity rather than the nature of the constituent elements, although Lavoisier's theory was true in the majority of cases. Another experimental proof of an acid free from oxygen was given by his investigation of sulphuretted hydrogen (prepared from ferrous sulphide and dilute sulphuric acid)[16] which he showed has all the properties of a weak acid, resembling carbonic

[1] *Experiments and Observations relating to Acetous Acid . . . and other subjects of Chemical Philosophy*, London, 1786, 180.
[2] Crell's *Ann.*, 1788, I, 319.
[3] Crell's *Ann.*, 1792, II, 402; for Wurzer's numerous other publications, see Poggendorff, (1), ii, 1378–9.
[4] Crell's *Ann.*, 1792, II, 511. [5] Crell's *Ann.*, 1798, I, 179, 273 (see p. 345).
[6] *J. f. Chemie*, 1823, xxxvii, 83; see H. M. Rouelle, p. 77 and Proust, p. 641.
[7] *J. f. Chemie*, 1830, lviii, 481.
[8] Jagnaux, 1891, ii, 91; Hoefer, (1), 1869, ii, 555, from an account in the *Journal de Paris*, 31 October 1788, written by Lavoisier; Lavoisier, *Oeuvres*, 1892, v, 741.
[9] *Philosophie Chimique*, 1806, 243. [10] *Chemical Catechism*, 5 ed., 1812, 222.
[11] *Lectures on Chemistry*, 1803, ii, 452.
[12] Romocki, *Geschichte der Explosivstoffe*, Berlin, 1896, ii, 40 f.; T. L. Davis, *Chymia*, 1948, i, 75.
[13] Sur l'acide prussique; AdS, 1787 (1789), m 148–62; *Ann. chim.*, 1789, i, 30–9.
[14] AdS, 1787, m 159. [15] Sur l'acide sulfureux; *Ann. chim.*, 1789, ii, 68.
[16] Sur l'hydrogène sulphuré; *Ann. chim.*, 1798, xxv, 233, read in An IV (1796); *Statique Chimique*, 1803, ii, 8.

acid, which contains oxygen; it reddened the colour of litmus, combined directly or by double decomposition with alkalis forming 'hydrosulfures', and decomposed soaps. Thus:[1] 'If several other common properties did not demand a separate class of hydrogen compounds, it would undoubtedly be ranged among the acids', and this is sufficient evidence in 'opposing the opinion of those who pretend that acidity is an attribute that occurs only with oxygen'. Berthollet gives a comprehensive table of the reactions of sulphuretted hydrogen and alkali hydrosulphides with various metals, thus recognising their utility as reagents.[2] He also investigated hydrogen persulphide, discovered by Scheele (1777; see p. 229).[3]

In a criticism of the new nomenclature G. D'Arejula[4] especially emphasised the weakness of the assumption that all acids contain oxygen. From his results with prussic acid and sulphuretted hydrogen, Berthollet felt compelled to admit that, although 'oxygen may be regarded as the most usual acidifying principle', yet 'to conclude that all acidity is caused by it, even that of the muriatic, fluoric and boracic acids, is to press the limits of analogy too far'.[5]

Berthollet recognised in 1788 that in several cases 'if metals when oxygenated function in the manner of alkalis with acids, they will behave as acids towards alkalis'.[6] He obtained solid calcium plumbite by boiling litharge with lime water, discovered fulminating silver from silver oxide and ammonia,[7] obtained 'triple salts' of mercury, and found that mercury oxide combined with lime, and he says that Lavoisier had obtained crystals from a solution of mercuric oxide in ammonia.[8] Berthollet prepared pure caustic potash by solution in alcohol and evaporation.[9]

Berthollet's analyses of sulphuric acid were made by two different methods.[10] In one method, sulphur was heated with nitre and the amount of sulphate of potash formed ascertained; in another, sulphur was boiled with nitric acid and the sulphuric acid formed precipitated as sulphate of baryta. The compositions of the two sulphates were assumed known.

By oxidising sulphur with nitric acid and precipitating with barium chloride, he obtained 948 grains of barium sulphate, which lost 28 grains when calcined, from 1 gros 17 grains of sulphur. From Bergman's analysis of barium sulphate (84 baryta + 16 sulphuric acid) he calculated that 86 grains of sulphur form 124 grains of vitriolic acid (sulphur trioxide). By heating sulphur with saltpetre to form vitriolated tartar (potassium sulphate) and using Bergman's analysis of this he calculated that 60 grains of sulphur form 87 grains of vitriolic acid, in good agreement with the first result. The correct calculation of the first result gives 113·5 parts of sulphur trioxide from 32 of sulphur, instead of 80.

In the first process he found that 60 of sulphur gave 87 of acid, and in the second 89 of sulphur gave 124 of acid. Lavoisier calculated from Berthollet's

[1] *Ann. chim.*, 1798, xxv, 237.   [2] *Ib.*, 272.   [3] *Ib.*, 248.
[4] *Obs'. Phys.*, 1788, xxxiii, 262; he suggests 'debrûlé' for 'reduced'.
[5] *Statique Chimique*, ii, 8 f.
[6] Sur les Combinaisons des oxides métalliques avec les alkalis & la chaux. *Ann. chim.*, 1789, i, 52–64.
[7] *Ib.*, 55.   [8] *Ib.*, 61.   [9] *Obs. Phys.*, 1786, xxviii, 401.
[10] AdS, 1782 (1785), h 24, m 597 (sur l'acide sulfureux), m 602.

results that 69 or 72 parts of sulphur were combined with 31 or 28 parts of oxygen;[1] these results are very inaccurate. Chenevix[2] gave 61·5 sulphur and 38·5 oxygen. The correct result is 40 sulphur and 60 oxygen, and Lavoisier had given this (see p. 416), although he does not say how it was found. In the same research Berthollet found that 72 grains of phosphorus give 158 grains of 'dry phosphoric acid'; the correct result for P_2O_5 is 165.

In 1789 Berthollet prepared and examined a number of sulphites,[3] which had not been much investigated since Stahl's work (see Vol. II, p. 679). He had supposed that sulphurous acid is a solution of sulphur (which he still supposed contained phlogiston) in vitriolic acid, possibly in variable proportions.[4] In 1798[5] Berthollet examined the liquid hydrogen persulphide discovered by Scheele (see p. 229); he prepared it by pouring a polysulphide solution into acid, showed that it contained more sulphur than sulphuretted hydrogen and called it *soufre hydrogèné*. Compounds of sulphuretted hydrogen Berthollet called 'hydrosulfures' (hydrosulphides), those of hydrogen persulphide 'sulphures hydrogènés' (polysulphides); Chenevix[6] called these 'hydrogenized sulphurets' or 'sulphuretted hydrogurets', and 'hydroguretted sulphurets' (derived from 'hydroguretted sulphur'), respectively; Kirwan[7] called them 'hydrosulphurets' and 'super-sulphuretted hydrosulphurets'; Murray[8] altered the last into 'sulphuretted hydrosulphurets', retaining the name 'super-sulphuretted hydrogen' for hydrogen persulphide. In 1796[9] Berthollet showed that phosphorus does not glow in oxygen, but does so in mixtures of oxygen and nitrogen; he does *not* mention the effect of pressure on the glow in oxygen.

In his *Observations sur l'Air* (1776) he described the production of an ammonia soap from lime soap and mild volatile alkali, and explained the precipitation of soap by hard water as due to the formation of a lime soap by double decomposition; the same explanation was given by Thouvenel.[10]

Pierre Thouvenel (Lorraine, 1747–Paris, 28 February 1815), General Inspector of Mineral Waters in France, fugitive to Italy in the Revolution, physician to Louis XVIII on the Restoration, published on animal nutrition,[11] on mucous bodies[12] and on medical chemistry,[13] and was the first French author to write on galvanism.[14] He made analyses of cantharides and woodlice[15] and with his brother wrote a prize essay on saltpetre (see p. 466); Pierre Thouvenel also gained a prize on this subject.[16] He wrote on the phlogistic and antiphlogistic theories.[17]

[1] *Traité*, 1789, 241.   [2] *Nicholson's J.*, 1802, v, 344.
[3] *Ann. chim.*, 1789, ii, 54; Sur l'acide sulfureux.
[4] AdS, 1782 (1785), m 597–601.   [5] *Ann. chim.*, 1798, xxv, 247.
[6] *Remarks upon Chemical Nomenclature*, 1802, 78, 201.
[7] *Trans. Roy. Irish Acad.*, 1802, viii, 53.   [8] 1806, ii, 453.
[9] *J. de l'École Polytechnique*, An IV, 3 cahier, 274.
[10] *Mémoire Chymique et Médicinal sur les principes et les vertus des Eaux minerales de Contrexeville*, Paris, 1774.
[11] *De corpore nutritivo et nutritione tentamen chymico-medicum*, 4°, Piscenis, 1770; BM T. 15.(2.).
[12] *Mémoire sur les corps muqueux*, Montpellier, 1770.
[13] *Mémoires de Chimie Médicale couronnés dans différentes Académies*, Paris, 1780.
[14] Poggendorff, (1), i, 1101–2.   [15] Chaptal, *Elements of Chemistry*, 1791, iii, 381–3.
[16] *Précis chimique sur les principes de la formation de l'acide nitreux, ouvrage qui a remporté le prix par la Société Royale des Sciences de Copenhague en 1776*, 4°, Copenhagen, 1784; BM B. 729. (19.).
[17] *Trasunto di confabulazione e scritti del Signor Touvenel relativo alle questioni presenti fra gli Stahliani, e i Neochimici*, 8° [Padua, 1790] (BM 8808. aa. 49).

Berthollet[1] later investigated metallic soaps prepared similarly. Berthollet[2] tried to connect vegetable and animal chemistry by the production of oxalic acid from both vegetable and animal substances by the action of nitric acid, the amount of acid being related to the nutritive value (propriété nutritive) of vegetables. Animal substances also gave nitrogen, phosphoric acid, and carbon; they are more complex than vegetable, consisting of a substance resembling sugar, a particular oil, phosphoric acid combined with a little lime, phlogisticated air or mofette (nitrogen), and probably some fixed air. He showed that oxalic acid (similarly obtained from sugar) is formed by heating silk with nitric acid.[3] He[4] concluded that animal materials contain nitrogen (azote) as an essential constituent, readily evolved by nitric acid in the cold.

'All the substances that are characteristic of animal substances contain azote, which is readily evolved by the action of nitric acid in the cold. . . . When the volatile alkali (ammonia) is formed by distillation, the azote of the animal substances combines with the inflammable gas from the oil, or more probably that which arises from the decomposition of water, while the vital air combines with the carbon to form fixed air. In putrefaction the inflammable gas combines with the azote, as in the case of vegetable fermentation, where this inflammable gas combines with a vegetable oil and sugar to produce spirit of wine.'[5]

In the analysis of the charcoal of animal products a phosphate was found, hence 'another principle that probably exists in all animal substances, and does not appear in many vegetable substances, is phosphoric acid'.[6]

A so-called zoonic acid (acide zoonique)[7] obtained by the dry distillation of animal and nitrogenous vegetable matter (gluten, yeast) and formed on roasting meat, was shown by Thenard[8] to be impure acetic acid.

Berthollet in 1784 succeeded Macquer as inspector of dyeworks and director of the Gobelins. He laboured to place the operations of dyeing and bleaching on a scientific basis and published a treatise on these subjects:

I.   Éléments de l'art de la teinture, 2 vols., Paris, 1791;
II.   Elements of the Art of Dyeing, tr. by Wm. Hamilton (Physician to London Hospital and Lecturer on Chemistry), 2 vols., London, 1791;
III. 2 French ed., Éléments de l'Art de la Teinture, Avec une description du blanchîment par l'acide muriatique oxigéné, by C. L. and A[médée]. B. Berthollet, 2 vols., Paris, 1804 (reviewed by Thenard, J. de Phys., 1804, lix, 300);
IV.   tr. by Alexander Ure, Elements of the Art of Dyeing, with a description of the art of bleaching by oxymuriatic acid, 2 vols., London, 1824; 1841.

Berthollet's theory of dyeing was a chemical one.[9] After criticising Macquer

[1] AdS, 1780 (1784), m 1; Crell's Ann., 1786, I, 532; Nicholson's J., 1797, i, 170; report by Bucquet and Lavoisier, Lavoisier, Oeuvres, iv, 301.
[2] Obs. Phys., 1785, xxvii, 88; 1786, xxviii, 272; 1786, xxix, 389.
[3] AdS, 1780, m 120; 1785, m 331.
[4] AdS, 1785, m 331 (read December, 1785, publ. 1788); Fourcroy, Ann. Chim., 1789, i, 40; id., (3), 1790, iii, 159 f.
[5] Obs. Phys., 1786, xxviii, 272.
[6] AdS, 1785 (1788), m 331 (348); Obs. Phys., 1786, xxviii, 272.
[7] Berthollet, Bull. Soc. Philomath., An VI (1797), No. 14, p. 109; Ann. chim., 1798, xxvi, 86; J. de Phys., 1798, xlvi, 385.
[8] Ann. chim., An X (1801), xliii, 176.
[9] IV, i, 56 f.; see E. Knecht, C. Rawson, and R. Loewenthal, Manual of Dyeing, 2 vols. and book of patterns, London, 1893; 2 ed. 1910; P. J. King, J. Soc. Dyers and Colourists, 1919, xxxv, 171, 190 (hist. of theories of dyeing in 18-19 cents.); J. J. Beer, Isis, 1960, li, 21-30

for adopting Hellot's physical theory (see p. 67) he remarks that Du Fay[1] had perceived that dye particles were disposed by their nature to contract a greater or less adhesion to textiles, since the latter can sometimes rob the dye-bath of its colour, 'which seems to indicate that the ingredients have less adherence to water than to wool'; Du Fay was willing to abandon this theory if a better one could be produced. Bergman[2] had referred the dyeing of wool and silk by a solution of indigo in sulphuric acid diluted with much water to the greater affinity between the indigo and the textile than between the indigo and the acidulated water. According to Berthollet the coloured particles unite with the textile by chemical affinity, much more firmly when they combine with the mordants which unite them to wool, silk, cotton, etc.[3] In combining with a substance the original colour of the dye may be modified. Berthollet showed that salts such as alum, used as mordants, precipitate animal substance dissolved in alkali; alum alone sometimes precipitates a solution of a dye and always when an alkali is added, which precipitates alumina, 'then the colouring particles are precipitated in combination with the alumina and the liquid becomes clear.'[4]

Walter Crum in a paper read to the Glasgow Philosophical Society in 1843,[5] mentions Hellot, etc., and Le Pileur d'Apligny[6] as teaching a physical theory, whilst Bergman and Berthollet held a chemical one. Crum proposed what is really a physical theory of adsorption, comparing the adhesion of the dye to a porous fabric with the adhesion of dissolved substances to charcoal.

Many ideas in Berthollet's book on dyeing, e.g. that there exist 'reciprocal affinities', viz. (i) that of the colouring particle, that of the stuff, and that of the principles of the mordants; and (ii) many circumstances can produce variations in the result of these affinities which merit some explanation,[7] were developed later in his *Statique Chimique* (1803).

Berthollet's explanation of the different colours produced by mordants was less correct. He supposed that the colour was changed by a combustion produced by the mordant and by atmospheric oxygen, which removed hydrogen from the colour, the predominating carbon then giving rise to a darkening of colour.[8] This 'combustion theory' was criticised by Edward Nathaniel Bancroft, F.R.S. (Westfield, Massachusetts 1744–? 1821),[9] in 1794.[10] Bancroft says he used the antiphlogistic nomenclature in his book because it was 'according

[1] AdS, 1737 (1740), m 253.
[2] Analysis Chemica Pigmenti Indici (see p. 199); *Opusc.*, 1788, v, 54 f.; *id.*, *Scheffers Föreläsningar*, Upsala, 1775, § 339 f., § 379 f.
[3] *Ann. chim.*, 1789, i, 239; I, 1791, i, 20 f.   [4] I, 1791, i, 35 f.; IV, 1824, i, 36 f.
[5] *Phil. Mag.*, 1844, xxiv, 241 (April); *J. prakt. Chem.*, 1844, xxxii, 164.
[6] *L'Art de la Teinture des Fils et Étoffes de Coton*, 12°, Paris, 1776; 8°, 1798; he also wrote *Essai sur les Moyens de Perfectionner l'Art de la Teinture*, 8°, Paris, 1770; *Traité des Couleurs matérielles et de la manière de Colorer*, 8°, Paris, 1779; and other books.
[7] I, 1791, i, 41.   [8] I, 1791, 117 f.; IV, 1824, i, 114 f.
[9] Bettany, DNB, 1885, iii, 105 (no details of life).
[10] *Experimental Researches concerning the Philosophy of Permanent Colours and the Best Means of producing them, by Dying* [sic], *Calico Printing, &c.*, London, 1794, vol. I (all publ.), 32, 47 f., 195: the pref. says most was printed by 1792; 2 ed., complete (vol. I remodelled), 2 vols., 1813. He also wrote: *An Essay on the Natural History of Guiana in South America. Containing a Description of many Curious Productions in the Animal and Vegetable Systems of that Country . . .*, London, 1769.

much better with facts than the old'.[1] He introduced the important distinction between 'substantive' (in Francis Bacon's sense) dyes and 'adjective' dyes, according as 'they do not depend upon any basis or mordant, either for their permanency or their lustre', or 'are capable of being enlivened and fixed only by being adjected or applied upon a suitable basis'.[2] Bancroft[3] relates how he carried a cambric handkerchief dyed with animal purple for nine months in America to test its fastness to washing, but on his arrival in London his pocket was picked and the experiment terminated.

Berthollet's work on affinity, involving his theory of indefinite proportions (see under Proust, p. 645) and the law of mass action, is considered in Vol. IV. Berthollet[4] found that the production of light, which is ordinarily a result of combustion in oxygen gas, can result from other combinations (such as sulphur with metals) and even from compression: 'it is sufficient if there has been a change, under certain conditions, of the proportion of caloric of a body or of a system of bodies.' He found that air or pure oxygen emits light when suddenly compressed, but not hydrogen, nitrogen or carbon dioxide. Cuvier[5] reported that a workman of Saint-Étienne noticed the production of light on compressing air. 'L.B.'[6] used compression of air to ignite tinder, and Biot[7] exploded a mixture of hydrogen and oxygen, which burst the apparatus.

Thenard[8] showed that the light evolved on compressing air or oxygen was due to the combustion of oil lubricating the piston in the apparatus. Davy in his youth[9] thought oxygen gas is 'a chemical combination of the simple substance light, with the simple substance oxygen', or *phos*-oxygen, and in his last work[10] he maintained that oxygen is the only gas (except those into which oxygen has entered without undergoing combustion) which gives out light on compression.

GUYTON DE MORVEAU

Louis Bernard Guyton de Morveau (Dijon, 4 January 1737–Paris, 2 January 1816) studied and practised law. His father purchased for him in 1760 the post of Avocat Général in the Parliament of Dijon. The family name was Guyton. On taking this office he added de Morveau from the name of a family fief and he later signed himself De Morveau. He spent a time in Paris studying law and literature, visited Voltaire at Ferney in 1756, and wrote some descriptive and satirical poetry, ridiculing the Jesuits. In 1764 he was admitted an honorary member of the Dijon Academy and once criticised a chemical lecture by Chardenon before that body; as a result Chardenon advised him to confine himself to subjects with which he was familiar. This had the effect of leading de Morveau to study chemistry from Macquer's and Baumé's works, and to

[1] 1794, I, pref. ix.
[2] Ib., I, vi, 78; Delaval, Manchester Mem., 1785, ii, 131–256; T. Henry, ib., 1790, v, 343–408 (read 1786).
[3] 1794, I, 96.   [4] Statique Chimique, 1803, i, 190, 205 f., 254.
[5] Rapport, 1828, 41.   [6] Bulletin des Sciences, An XII (1803–4), no. 87, p. 209.
[7] Ib., An XIII (1804–5), no. 93, p. 259.   [8] Ann. Chim., 1830, xliv, 181.
[9] An Essay on Heat, Light, and the Combinations of Light, 1799; Works, 1839, ii, 5, 21 f.
[10] Consolations in Travel, 1830; Works, 1840, ix, 331.

make experiments with apparatus purchased from Baumé; thus equipped he returned to the charge with such success that he was complimented and encouraged by Chardenon. Jean Pierre Chardenon (Dijon; July 1714–16 March 1769)[1] published a memoir[2] on calcination which is considered later (see p. 610). Still practising law and literature, Guyton gave with two collaborators, Maret and Durande (see p. 534), a course of lectures on chemistry at the Dijon Academy from 1776 to 1789, and these were published in 1777–8 (see p. 521).

In 1772 Guyton became a Correspondent of the Paris Academy of Sciences, being attached to Macquer, whom he repeatedly consulted on his work. As permanent Secretary of the Dijon Academy from 1786 he became acquainted with the Paris chemists. He became F.R.S.

in 1788 but failed to enter the Paris Academy in 1789. In 1778 he became a director of saltpetre works and in 1783 established the first French soda factory, using a process (due to Scheele, see p. 218) in which a paste of slaked lime and salt brine was allowed to effloresce on exposure to the atmosphere; he later sold the soda factory to Courtois. From 1784–9 he ran a successful glass factory, which (in other hands) was closed only in 1816. In 1779 he was asked to contribute the chemical part of the *Encyclopédie Méthodique*, which began to appear in 1786; he gave up his legal practice in 1783.

FIG. 48. LOUIS BERNARD GUYTON DE MORVEAU (1737–1816).

In the Revolution he became Citoyen Guyton-Morveau, Guyton, and finally Guyton-Morveau again. He adopted revolutionary principles, was a member of the National Assembly in Paris in 1791, and was one of those who decreed the death of the King in 1793. He served in public offices and in the army. He developed the use of military balloons, himself ascending during the battle of Fleurus in 1794. In 1794 he became professor of chemistry at the École Centrale des Travaux Publiques, which in 1795 became the École Polytechnique, and was acting Director in 1798–9 during Monge's absence in Egypt; he became Director in 1800. He participated in a course of instruction on the manufacture of saltpetre, gunpowder, and cannon, given to citizens in 1794:

Programmes des Cours Révolutionnaires sur la fabrication des Salpêtres, des Poudres et des Canons. Faits à Paris, par ordre du Comité du Salut public, dans l'amphithéatre du Museum d'histoire naturelle, et dans la salle des Électeurs, maison du ci-devant Évêché, les 1, 11 et 21 Ventôse, deuxième année de la République Française une et indivisible; par les citoyens Guyton, Fourcroy, Dufourny, Berthollet,

[1] Partington and McKie, *Ann. Sci.*, 1937, ii, 361 (373); 1938, iii, 1 (58).
[2] *Mém. Acad. Dijon*, 1769, i, 303.

Carny, Pluvinet, Monge, Hassenfratz et Perrier, la. 4°, Paris, 1794 (50 pp., 5 blank); Duveen, (1), 486.

He was one of the first members of the Institut in 1796. He ceased to lecture in 1811, when he was created a baron.

Although de Morveau did, and probably could do, nothing to prevent the execution of Lavoisier, there is no evidence that he was in any way responsible for it. In a letter to Crell[1] de Morveau says he received his passport to Meulan, where he joined the army, on 29 April 1794, and Lavoisier's trial was on 5–8 May 1794, so that he was probably not in Paris then (Lavoisier, however, had been imprisoned since December 1793). He gives dates where he was between 5 May–17 July 1794, and says he had heard of Lavoisier's death only long after 27 July, when he found that he himself was on the list, although he never belonged to the Jacobins. The letter refuted an unfounded charge by Robison,[2] to which Crell had drawn attention in his German translation of the book.

Arthur Young visited De Morveau in Dijon in August 1789[3] and was much impressed by his personality; he found him unaffected, lively and conversational, 'who in any station of life would be sought as an agreeable companion.' He was then writing the article 'Air' in the *Encyclopédie*, which was being printed at Dijon. His thoughts were 'entirely occupied by the non-existence of phlogiston, except a little on the means of establishing and enforcing the new nomenclature'. His laboratory consisted of two large rooms well stocked with apparatus, with many eudiometrical experiments in progress, particularly with Fontana's and Volta's eudiometers and one of De Morveau's using burning phosphorus. The balance, holding 3000 grains, turned with $\frac{1}{20}$ grain. Mme. Picardet (who in 1798 became Mme. de Morveau) was also present: 'a treasure to M. de Morveau, for she is able and willing to converse with him on chemical subjects, and on any others that tend either to instruct or please', and was learned but unaffected and pleasing. (She translated Scheele's *Mémoires de Chymie*, 2 vols., Dijon, 1785, learning German and Swedish for the task, and may have assisted de Morveau in translating the first two volumes of Bergman's *Opuscula*, 1780–5, with notes.)

In many ways Guyton de Morveau resembled Kirwan. Both practised law and later turned to experimental chemistry. Both abandoned the phlogiston theory from conviction at the opportune time; both published extensively but many of their papers were unimportant (or even incorrect); both enjoyed a great reputation and authority; and both are now almost forgotten.[4]

In 1772 he published a notable essay on phlogiston (together with two other essays) in which he took up and developed the subject started by Chardenon (see p. 517) on the increase in weight of metals on calcination; this topic is dealt with in the chapter (p. 611) on the later phlogiston theory:

---

[1] Berichtigung wegen der angeblichen Miturheber von Lavoisier's Tode, in *Journal für Chemie und Physik* (Gehlen), 1806, ii, after p. 740 at end, 4 pp. without pagination or date but printed on the same sheet as p. 729 in signature 47 and making up 8 leaves; Nierenstein, *J. Soc. Chem. Ind.*, 1932, li, 438.

[2] In Black, *Elements of Chemistry*, Edinburgh, 1803, ii, 218, 220.

[3] *Travels in France*, ed. C. Maxwell, Cambridge, 1929, 195 f.

[4] G. Bouchard, *Guyton-Morveau, Chimiste et Conventionelle (1737–1816)*, Paris, 1938 (367 pp.); Gmelin, (1), iii, 430 (list of publs.); A. B. Granville, An Account of the Life and Writings of Baron Guyton de Morveau, *Quart. J. Sci. Arts*, 1817, iii, 249–96, and separately, 1817 (48 pp.; BM B 596. (2.); says de Morveau d. 21 December 1815); Hoefer, (1), 1869, ii, 545; Kopp, (1), i, 317; Louvet, NBG, xxii, 968; Partington and McKie, *Ann. Sci.*, 1937, ii, 361 (portr.); W. A. Smeaton, *M.Sc. Dissert.*, London, 1953; *id.*, *Ambix*, 1957, vi, 18; Thomson, *Ann. Phil.*, 1818, xi, 401; *id.*, (1), ii, 130, 174 (Thomson says he first studied chemistry in de Morveau's articles in the *Encyclopédie*); for lists of Guyton de Morveau's papers, Poggendorff, (1), i, 981–2; *Roy. Soc. Cat. of Sci. Papers*, 1869, iii, 99.

I. Digressions académiques ou Essais sur quelques sujets de Physique, de Chimie & d'Histoire naturelle, 12°, Dijon, M.DCC.LXII (sic; the Approbation at the end by Macquer is dated 'A Paris, ce 19 Mars 1772'; pp. xvj, 417 (index 385–417), Patent Office Library). Contains:

(a) Digression sur le phlogistique, Consideré comme Corps grave, & par rapport aux changemens de pesanteur qu'il produit dans les corps auxquelles il est uni (pp. 1–267; p. 268 blank),

(b) Essai physico-chimique sur la Dissolution et la Crystallisation, Pour parvenir à l'explication des affinités par la figure des parties constituantes des Corps (pp. 269–377; p. 270 blank),

(c) Observations sur une nouvelle espece de Guhr (pp. 378–384; it is a colloidal form of silica).

Review and summary by Rozier, Obs. Phys., 1773, ii, 281. A short continuation of (a) was published as:

IA. Défense de la Volatilité du Phlogistique ou Lettre de l'Auteur des Digressions Académiques ... , s.l.e.a (at the end: 'Je suis, &c. A Dijon, ce 27 Novembre, 1772); BN R. 33120 (Roy.), old T 3934 pré.

A work by Guyton de Morveau:

Discours publics et éloges, par M. *** Avocat Général, 3 vols. 12°, Paris, 1775–74–82 (BM 12301. aaa. 2) deals with legal and political matters only.

In 1774[1] de Morveau drew attention to the parallel between the *acidum pingue* of Meyer (see p. 145) and phlogiston and says Lavoisier was induced to repeat the experiments of Black and his opponents (Lavoisier's *Opuscules*, see p. 389). In 1776 de Morveau published a 'Conciliation of the principles of Stahl with the modern experiments on fixed air',[2] written, as Fourcroy says,[3] with such finesse of reasoning that it contributed to the prolongation of the phlogiston theory, although based on such errors as a confusion of fixed air with oxygen, metallic calces being supposed to contain fixed air. He admits that the new discoveries have shaken Stahl's theory, since it is proved that metals on calcination absorb air of a particular kind, and the state of calx is not solely due to absence of phlogiston. He had convinced himself that calcination is a true precipitation. There are two elastic fluids, phlogiston or the matter of fire, and fixed air, with different orders of affinity. On calcining a metal, fixed air unites with metallic earth and simultaneously phlogiston separates. The fixed air unites with the earth as the acid in horn silver (silver chloride) by an affinity superior to that which holds them in solution, and the new compound is precipitated without regular form because its passage to the solid state is too rapid.

The affinity of fixed air for the different metallic earths is variable and it separates very easily from mercury. The metallic earths are always united with phlogiston, or fixed air, or an acid, and are never pure. Calces are compared with alkalis and chalk; fixed air is contained in acids (which Newton said 'attract strongly and are strongly attracted'; see Vol. II, p. 482) since acids calcine metals, and hence acids are not elements. Fixed fire (phlogiston) and fixed air mutually exchange the metallic earths by their attraction. These views had little influence.

Guyton de Morveau contributed some articles to the supplement of the first *Encyclopédie*. In the article 'Phlogistique',[4] he says phlogiston is the

[1] Obs. Phys., 1774, iii, 416 (or 418): extrait des Registers de l'Acad. de Dijon, Art. III.
[2] Obs. Phys., 1776, vii, 389; id., Élémens de Chymie, 1777, i, 225.
[3] (2), 1796, iii, 484.   [4] Ency. Suppl., Amsterdam, 1777, iv, 336.

principle of inflammability, although authors differ as to its real nature; some regard it as the pure matter of fire, others as a compound of fire and vitrifiable earth; in metals it acts as a solvent for the calces and is dissipated by calcination. Calx of mercury is revived by heat alone, which would be expected if phlogiston is pure fire; its identity with the matter of light and the pure element of fire cannot be doubted. It is the same in all substances. The necessity for air in the calcination of a metal is explained by the assumption that, as in combustion, an oscillation is necessary which favours the displacement of the particles, and in closed vessels the rarefaction of the air arrests this motion. A fundamental question is whether there is addition or subtraction of matter in forming a calx. The first alternative is favoured by Black, Meyer, Priestley, and particularly Lavoisier (who had just published experiments on the elastic fluid which, according to him, is fixed in the earths of metals on calcination). Phlogiston is essentially volatile, the volatility of fire is explained by the greater specific gravity of air: it is on this hydrostatic ratio that the increase in weight of metals by removal of phlogiston to form calces depends. Buffon's theory[1] that phlogiston is a compound of fire and air fixed in bodies (p. 616) and its consequences are summarised; de Morveau never missed an opportunity of praising Buffon.

In his article on 'Air',[2] de Morveau mentions Black's and Macbride's work and Black's theory that quicklime is limestone deprived of fixed air; but in the article on 'Causticité and Causticum'[3] he explains Meyer's theory of *acidum pingue* (see p. 145) and says those cannot be blamed who refuse to admit the complete truth of Black's theory; it seems that alkalis become more caustic the more they are deprived of phlogiston. The hypothesis of *causticum* encounters difficulties, since limestone loses rather than gains weight on conversion into quicklime. The article on 'Calcination'[4] refers to the increase in weight: 100 lb. of lead form 110 lb. of calx; it is explained by his hypothesis that phlogiston is a matter less dense than all the media, consequently essentially volatile, and the volatility of which can equilibrate the gravitation of part of the metallic earth to which it is united.

The article on 'Combustion'[5] explains that this differs from calcination in that the escaping phlogiston carries away part of the burning body in the form of a flame or a thick fume. Liver of sulphur when gently heated is calcined, but when exposed to a violent fire the phlogiston carries off many saline parts, and it burns with fume and flame. Air is necessary for combustion to maintain the oscillatory movement, and if it becomes too rare or too dense it ceases to favour combustion, since this requires a fluid which yields and reacts continually. This simple mechanical principle explains why charcoal strongly heated in a closed vessel does not burn, since the effort of dilatation in a closed vessel is equivalent to density and is uninterrupted: its tension has a power equal to a great density or the action of an equivalent weight. An ignited coal is extinguished in spirit of wine, although this is inflammable, because the

[1] *Histoire naturelle, Supplément*, Paris, 1774, i, 44, 58, 72 f., 109.
[2] *Ency. Suppl.*, 1776, i, 234.   [3] *Ib.*, 1776, ii, 275.
[4] *Ib.*, 1776, ii, 114.   [5] *Ib.*, 1776, ii, 515.

medium is too dense; it slowly consumes in a vessel with a long narrow neck which permits the expansion of the air but does not allow air to enter. The amount of calcination of a metal in a closed vessel is in proportion to the volume of the vessel, etc. The theory of oscillations was proposed in Guyton's first scientific paper, 'Mémoire sur les phénomènes de l'air dans la combustion',[1] adopting the theory of Boerhaave (see Vol. II, p. 751) that flame is supported when the surrounding medium is in a state of oscillating compression and rarefaction, without ever becoming too dense or too rare. In a confined volume, the heated air is too dense, in a vacuum the medium is too rare.[2]

De Morveau explained some of his other peculiar views in articles in the *Encyclopédie Supplement*: on 'Dissolution',[3] 'Crystallisation',[4] 'Affinity',[5] and 'Hépar':[6] a 'hépar' is a compound like liver of sulphur, of an acid, alkali, and phlogiston; carbon is a compound of vegetable acid, a peculiar earth, and fixed fire; pyrites is a compound of vitriolic acid, calx of iron, and fixed fire; phlogisticated alkali (potassium ferrocyanide) is a compound of animal acid, alkali, and fixed fire; and Prussian blue is formed by replacing the alkali by the ferruginous base; and even vegetable matters are true hépars.

Lord Brougham[7] pointed out that de Morveau in these articles (1777) does not mention Cavendish's work on hydrogen (1766), Rutherford's on nitrogen (1772), Priestley's on oxygen (1775), or Scheele's on chlorine (1774), nor the theory of combustion in Lavoisier's *Opuscules* (1774).

The lectures in the 'public course' of chemistry in the Dijon Academy from 1776 by Guyton de Morveau, Maret, and Durande were published. The arrangement of the material is very unusual:

II. Élémens de Chymie, théorique et pratique, rédigés dans un nouvel ordre, d'après les découvertes modernes, pour servir aux Cours publics de l'Académie de Dijon, 3 vols. 12°, Dijon, 1777–77–78; the dedication to the Prince de Condé signed by de Morveau, Maret and Durande.

IIA. German tr., with notes, by C. E. Weigel, Anfangsgründe der theoretischen und praktischen Chemie, zum Gebrauch der öffentl. Vorlesungen auf der Acad. zu Dijon ... von den Herrn de Morveau, Maret und Durande, 2 vols. Leipzig, 1779–80 (BM 8905. c. 11). A collection of experiments in the lectures, supplementing the book, was publ. in Crell's *Ann.*, 1788, II, 118–31.

The introduction says: 'all the theory of chemistry is in the two words *attraction, equiponderance*, and all the practice in the two other words *dissolution, crystallisation*.'[8] De Morveau believed in the possibility of the transformation of silver into gold on the basis of erroneous experiments by means of arsenic,[9] and in a primary matter the modifications of which constitute all bodies, even the elements, which are 'simple bodies which we cannot decompose'.[10] The same body is sometimes presented as solvent (*dissolvans*) and solute (*dissous*). A distinction is made between *natural elements* (fire, air, water,

---

[1] *Mém. Acad. Dijon*, 1769, i, 416 (read 11 December 1768).
[2] A similar theory is given in the *Nouveau Cours de Chymie, suivant les Principes de Newton & de Sthall*, Paris, 1723, i, 18; see p. 58.
[3] *Ency. Suppl.*, 1776, ii, 724. [4] *Ib.*, 1776, ii, 662. [5] *Ib.*, 1776, i, 182–4.
[6] *Ib.*, 1777, iii, 347. [7] 1872, 10.
[8] II, i, 2. [9] Crell's *Ann.*, 1786, II, 427. [10] II, i, 10 f.

and earth) and *chemical elements* (acids, metallic earths, vitrifiable earths, cal-careous earths, alkalis, oils, etc.). Sulphur is a compound of fire and acid, a metal is a compound of a particular metallic earth and fixed fire or phlogiston.[1] Distinction is made between a mixture and a compound (the latter includes solutions, e.g. of aqua fortis and water), between *specific* and *absolute weight* (*pesanteur*) and *attraction* or *gravitation*. *Affinity* or *rapport* unites parts of two bodies, the most subtle parts being *integrant parts*, the smallest atoms. *Constituents* are parts such as water and spirit of wine in brandy. *Equiponderance* is equality of weight or attraction to the centre of the earth; a body is equi-ponderant in water when it floats in it indifferently.[2] Homogeneous and hetero-geneous bodies are defined (an early use of this idea in chemistry).[3] Apparatus described[4] includes that for manipulating gases. The section on attraction follows Buffon and criticises Newton,[5] and describes Guyton de Morveau's experiments on the adhesion of metal plates to mercury, which are said to be in the order of the affinities (see Vol. IV).

The section on dissolution[6] makes use of the second part of the *Digressions*,[7] which criticises Spielmann and puts forward a theory that dissolution is due to a kind of adherence between solvent and solute particles, 'as by a kind of glue', the particles being 'en rapport exact de pesanteur', depending on division into imperceptible parts and equiponderance. In crystallisation similar particles attract one another and the solvent between them is squeezed out.[8] Metals can also crystallise. The particles of a crystal must have the same shape as the latter.

The section on affinity[9] gives Geoffroy's table (see p. 52) as modified by Rouelle and a large table of 'chemical solvents' and 'simplest bases', arranged as mineral, vegetable, and animal. The dissolvents are simple elementaries (fire, air, water), acids of the three kingdoms, alkalis, oils, and mercury; the bases are fluid elements (fire, air, water), four earths, three alkalis, eight metals, six semi-metals (antimony, bismuth, zinc, arsenic, 'cobolt', and nickel), and six oily substances (including spirit of wine). Fire is the only simple solvent, since water contains it, but this would lead to confusion in practical chemistry. The salts are separated from the acids and alkalis, and metals,[10] and include vitriols. The rest of the book follows the lines of the table. For theory it follows mostly Buffon and for facts it relies mainly on Baumé, and both are often wrong.

Diamond is pure vitrifiable earth but evaporates in a violent fire.[11] Metals are 'metallic earths'.[12] Phlogiston is fixed fire and in metals behaves like water of crystallisation in salts.[13] In calcination metals lose phlogiston but the pre-sence of air is necessary;[14] a metal is a compound of earth and fire, a calx is a compound of earth and fixed air.[15] A vapour is a compound of a liquid with a more volatile fluid serving as dissolvent, viz. a mixture of fire and air, made equiponderable with air.[16] Combustion differs from distillation in being made

[1] II, i, 12–13.   [2] II, i, 20–1.   [3] II, i, 21.   [4] II, i, 29–42.
[5] II, i, 50–68.   [6] II, i, 68 f.   [7] I, (b), 269 f.   [8] II, i, 73 f.
[9] II, i, 78–97.   [10] II, i, 127.   [11] II, i, 101.   [12] II, i, 108.
[13] II, i, 164.   [14] II, i, 207.   [15] II, i, 225.   [16] II, i, 277.

in free air; charcoal is 'a veritable hepar, in which heavy black oil and acid are intimately combined with earth', whilst ash is a compound of the same with air, which expels phlogiston and most of the oil.[1] Metals are calcined by air uniting with their earths and expelling phlogiston, fire acting as a dissolvent; mercury calx is revivified by fire alone since it has little affinity with 'the air which constitutes the metallic calx'.[2] In the combustion of sulphur, fixed air replaces phlogiston which it expels and 'unites with the acid at the moment when the actual fire brings the sulphur in dissolution'.[3] Sulphur on combustion unites with air and becomes 'a sort of hepar' (sulphur dioxide).[4] Guyton repeated Cadet's experiments on fuming arsenical liquor by distilling white arsenic and potassium acetate[5]; it is 'a true liquid phosphorus which inflames spontaneously in air'. He describes the preparation of phosphorus from urine;[6] in its combustion, air is fixed and increases its weight.[7]

Alkali from all plants is the same.[8] The mineral alkali (soda) is really contained in some plants, from which it is obtained on combustion.[9] Although the volatile alkali (ammonia) may be obtained from some plants by dry distillation or from mushrooms, it is possible that it may have come from animal débris, and its source must (apart from volcanic sal ammoniac) be sought in the animal kingdom,[10] in which it exists 'tout formé', or is formed by putrefaction, which (in spite of Boerhaave's distinction) is a species of fermentation,[11] an internal spontaneous movement giving different products. Volatile alkali is rich in phlogiston and precipitates metals;[12] it liberates inflammable air from zinc.[13]

Vinous fermentation depends on the presence of a mucous body (corps muqueux), containing an oily and a saline principle, a true hepar formed of oil, acid, and earth. In fermentation air and phlogiston (having dangerous effects) are formed by the motion, attractions, and collisions of molecules, which are in equiponderance with gravity and acted on by affinities, and heat is evolved.[14] The appendix[15] on 'the vegetable astringent principle' is important:[16] by experiments on galls it was shown that it rises in distillation like essential oils, is soluble in water like gums, in alcohol like soaps, in oils like extractive matters, and in ether like pure resins; it reddens litmus, unites with acids and alkalis, reduces gold and silver in solution, dissolves iron directly to form an ink, and with metallic salts gives precipitates of various colours. The section on amalgams gives precise directions for producing a silver tree (arbor Dianae).[17]

Guyton de Morveau agreed with Lavoisier that only part of the air is combined in combustion or calcination but he still thought that phlogiston was released, and since air has weight it would follow (though he does not say this) that some at least of the increase in weight was due to combined air, although perhaps some of it was due to the cause he had given in his Digressions

---

[1] II, i, 291.   [2] II, i, 329.   [3] II, ii, 23.   [4] II, ii, 46.
[5] II, iii, 41.   [6] II, iii, 101.   [7] II, iii, 108.   [8] II, iii, 151.
[9] II, iii, 204.   [10] II, iii, 229 f.   [11] II, iii, 234 f.   [12] II, iii, 248.
[13] II, iii, 257.   [14] II, iii, 266–7.   [15] II, iii, 403.
[16] Nierenstein, Incunabula of Tannin Chemistry, 1932, no. 4.   [17] II, iii, 434.

Académiques (see p. 519).[1] This might appeal to those who refused to believe that 10 lb. of air could be fixed in the calcination of 100 lb. of lead. He now distinguished (i) 'air in the greatest state of purity' or dephlogisticated air, which combines with metallic earths on calcination, from (ii) fixed air which is formed by the combination of carbonaceous matter and dephlogisticated air, and differs from other phlogisticated airs (common air, hydrogen, nitrogen, putrid effluvia) by its affinity for water.[2] The article on chemistry in the new *Encyclopédie* was begun by Guyton de Morveau in 1780 and was published in parts beginning in 1786. He wrote only the first volume, others being written by Fourcroy and the last (1815) by Vauquelin:

III. Encyclopédie Methodique. Chymie (later Chimie), Pharmacie et Metallurgie, Vol. I, pt. i, 1786; pt. ii, 1789 (date in colophon) parts (e.g. 'Acier') completed in 1786. Arthur Young's statement (see p. 518) shows that Guyton was still working on it in August 1789.

In the first part Guyton de Morveau follows the phlogiston theory but several conferences with Lavoisier (beginning in 1775), who realised his importance and influence,[3] convinced him early in 1787 of the truth of the antiphlogistic theory. In the second half-volume (pp. 417–774) the article 'Affinité' (pp. 535–613) is masterly; extracts from it were published by Seguin.[4] In pp. 625–64 there is a second preface (Second Advertissement, Pour servir d'introduction aux articles qui suivent, & pour indiquer quelques corrections à faire à ceux qui précèdent) announcing that de Morveau had accepted Lavoisier's views and the new nomenclature is used. The theory is followed in the article 'Air' (pp. 665–72), which refers to Lubbock (pp. 708–9, 712, 715, etc.), Crawford, Priestley, Cavendish, and Lavoisier. He says:[5]

'L'eau est un composé! Il est difficile de se défendre d'une impression de surprise la première fois qu'on entend un proposition aussi contraire à la tradition de tous les siècles, aux principes enseignés jusqu'à ce jour dans toutes les Écoles; . . . une autre génération s'approche, qui, n'ayant pas été deçue par l'autorité d'une tradition uniforme, n'aura besoin, pour se décider, qu'une simple exposition.'

In the earlier part[6] he still supposed that phlogiston is evolved when vital air (oxygen) combines with sulphur. Dollfuss had found that sulphuric acid does not form sulphurous acid when boiled with sulphur, hence sulphurous acid does not simply contain more sulphur than sulphuric acid, as Lavoisier had assumed. Metals are compounds of an earth and phlogiston with vital air;[7] if all the phlogiston could be removed they might be acids. In the later part[8] he abandoned the idea that phlogiston played any part; the discovery of the composition of water and Cavendish's proof that phlogisticated air (nitrogen) was an entirely separate substance had removed the difficulties in the new theory.

In speaking of Lavoisier's hypothesis to explain the increase in weight of etals on calcination he[9] says:

'je crois avoir contribué à en établir la réalité par les expériences nombreuses que je publiai en 1772 (*Digressions académiques*, &c.), expériences qui, par la conformité des

[1] II, i, 170, 328.   [2] *Ib.*, i, 312–24.   [3] Kirwan, *Essay on Phlogiston*, 1789, p. xvi.
[4] *Ann. Chim.*, 1790, vii, 46; see Vol. IV.   [5] III, 1789, I, ii, 727.
[6] III, 1786, i, 399.   [7] *Ib.*, 115.   [8] *Ib.*, 1789, i, 631 f.   [9] *Ib.*, 1789, I, ii, 699.

résultats obtenus des divers procédés de calcination & par les proportions déterminées de cet accroissement de poids suivant la nature de chaque métal, ne permettoient plus de l'attribuer à quelqu'accident.'

He explains how the process of calcining tin in air was carried out 'dans les Cours de l'Académie de Dijon, dans lequel il n'y a point d'explosion à craindre'. The neck of the retort containing the tin (which is heated over an Argand lamp) is prolonged by a curved tube passing into air contained in a large receiver over water (as in Lavoisier's experiment with mercury). If lime water is used the result is the same and there is no turbidity. He then regarded atmospheric air as a compound (un surcomposé homogène) formed from oxygen, azote and caloric 'by reason of the affinity which renders in it the parts equiponderable or soluble in all proportions'.[1] This theory, also held by Berthollet, was refuted by Dalton (see p. 773).

De Morveau says[2] those who examine the facts impartially and submit the consequences to the rules of exact logic 'cannot hesitate to recognise that this doctrine [Stahl's], which has reigned so long in the chemical schools of Europe, is only an hypothesis which cannot be sustained. In this respect the revolution is achieved'. The old theory was more useful than harmful, since it established a relation among a multitude of isolated observations, and provided an aim for research (a favourite later judgment of the phlogiston theory).

After saying that he felt 'plus à honneur d'être le dernier dans le chemin de la verité, que le premier dans la route de l'erreur', de Morveau[3] gives a succinct account of the new theory and replies to some objections made against it. He quotes several publications of 1787, including the *Méthode de Nomenclature Chimique*.[4]

The detailed article 'Acide',[5] probably based on Leonhardi's translation of Macquer's *Dictionnaire* (see p. 82), says Guyton[6] and the other authors of the *Élémens de Chymie*:

'assured by the beautiful experiments of Lavoisier on the presence of vital air in nitric acid, and having also observed that sulphur and phosphorus absorb a quantity of air in passing to the state of acid, began to suspect that this fluid enters as a constituent part *into the composition of all acids*, that it may be essential to their state of aqueous combination — in a word that it might well be the true *universal acid*, the acid element, instead of the acid of sulphur [assumed by Stahl, see Vol. II, p. 679] which does not exist of itself, completely formed, in sulphur.'

Lavoisier had developed this idea in 1778 (see p. 421) when he 'concluded that this air is the true *principe oxigine ou acidifiant*', but 'we are far from adopting completely the explanation in which this learned chemist believes he is able to become absolutely free from phlogiston (croit pouvoir se passer absolument du phlogistique)'. Guyton[7] thought that the presence in sulphur of phlogiston, which is lost during combination with vital air, seemed to have been proved by his own experiments and by other considerations; he also gives the view of Scheele that it is the water contained in vital air which combines with substances, whilst its saline principle combined with the phlogiston of the

---

[1] *Ib.*, 747.   [2] *Ib.*, 626.   [3] *Ib.*, 630 f.   [4] *Ib.*, 635.   [5] III, 1786, i, 27 f.
[6] II, 1777, i, 325; ii, 2, 20 f.   [7] III, i, 369 f.

combustible or metal to form heat. He did not accept phlogiston in the form understood by Stahl[1] but as an intermediary of the union of the matter of fire which confers volatility and can even bind a portion of sulphur, as in hepatic gas (hydrogen sulphide). There is little doubt that sulphur as such (tout formé) exists in sulphurous acid, 'but whether it exists or not, it is sufficiently proved that phlogiston is an essential part of this acid, or rather of the gas which composes it by its absorption in water.'

In 1782 de Morveau published an important memoir on nomenclature.[2] In this, the names of salts are derived from those of their acids: *vitriol de cuivre, nitre de mercure, oxalt de calce*, etc., the acid being the distinctive part of the name. He used the name 'acide' for all acids, adding muriatique, vitriolique, nitreux, arsénical, boracin, citronien, oxalin, etc. Fixed air was acide méphitique, and its salts méphites. Alcohol was regarded as a base. He uses the name *barote* for Scheele's *terra ponderosa*, which he had proposed in 1782.[3] He also has the classes of *hépars* (sulphides), e.g. hépar de soude, and *pyrites*, e.g. pyrite d'argent (silver sulphide). Practically nothing is said of phlogiston. The name *radicaux* is used once in a way related to the definition of 1785 (see below). In 1782[4] de Morveau gives the following table of names:

Acids	Salts	Bases
I. *Mineral*		
méphitique	méphites	phlogistique
vitriolique	vitriols	alumine
nitreux	nitres	calce
muriatique	muriates	magnésie
arsénical	arseniates	barote
boracin	boraxs	potasse
fluorique	fluors	soude
[molybdique	molybdes	ammoniac
stannique	stannes]	metals
		esprit de vin
II. *Vegetable*		
aceteux	acètes	
tartareux	tartres	
oxalin	oxaltes	
saccharin	sacchartes	
citronien	citrates	
lignique	lignites	
III. *Animal*		
phosphorique	phosphates	
formicin	formiates	
sébacé	sébates	
galactique	galactes	

The genius of a language is a kind of 'convenance de matérial' of sounds, of the metaphysics of style, together with the opinions and habits of a nation. The ear is no less exacting than the intelligence (esprit). French is more con-

---

[1] *Ib.*, 399.

[2] Mémoire sur les dénominations chimiques, la nécessité d'en perfectionner le système, les règles pour y parvenir, suivi d'un tableau d'une nomenclature chimique, Dijon, 1782; *Obs. Phys.*, 1782, xix, 370.

[3] *Nouv. Mém. Acad. Dijon*, 1782, i, 159.   [4] *Obs. Phys.*, 1782, xix, 382.

servative (than English and German) in the use of compound words and, even in the sciences, will only accept words so arranged that they agree with a gentle articulation. For example, the adjective derived from *suif* is not *suifacé* but *sébacé*.[1]

In the *Encyclopédie* (1786) the article 'Acide'[2] gave twenty general properties and[3] a list of 28 acids; succinic acid (acide karabique) is included among mineral acids (amber, following Bergman, being regarded as a mineral, see p. 191) and phosphoric acid among the animal acids.

In 1785[4] de Morveau said Lavoisier had supposed that sugar when treated with nitric acid becomes acid of sugar (*acide saccharin*) (oxalic acid) by taking up vital air, as sulphur forms vitriolic acid and phosphorus phosphoric acid (see p. 424). But if sugar enters undecomposed into acid of sugar it must exist in all other substances from which this acid is extracted by the same means, which cannot be accepted. The acid is really formed by the combination of vital air with a particular radical (radical particulier ou base acidifiable)[5] found in numerous bodies of different kinds, in this case the *radical saccharin*. Thus de Morveau introduced the name *radical* into organic chemistry.

After his 'conversion', de Morveau joined Lavoisier, Berthollet, and Fourcroy in founding the new *Annales de Chimie* in 1789, since the *Observations sur la Physique*, edited by de la Metherie, supported the phlogistic theory (see p. 495). In 1787 he took a share and probably a major share (as Thomson says) in devising the new chemical nomenclature, published in that year. His name comes before Lavoisier's on the title-page.[6] He must have been converted before April 1787; he visited Paris in January or early February 1787 (not 1786 as is sometimes said) and stayed eight months.[7]

The long 'Tableau de la Nomenclature' in the later *Encyclopédie*, 'Second Avertissement',[8] includes the radicals of the organic acids among 'substances non décomposées'. The spelling 'gas' (not Lavoisier's 'gaz') is used and 'fluate d'argent' under (11); under (12) de Morveau's 'acide karabique' for succinic acid has become a 'nom ancien'. Nos. 48–55 are headed 'Suite des Substances non décomposées', and after No. 55 come 'divers substances plus composées' but 11 of them instead of only 2 in the *Nomenclature*: the additions are gluten, sucre, amidon, huile fixe, huile volatile, l'arome, résine, extractif, extracto-résineux and résino-extractif.

De Morveau[9] introduced the name *acide prussique*; he called uric acid *acide lithiasique* or *acide lithique*,[10] and succinic acid (which he obtained crystalline by distilling amber) *acide karabique*.[11] At first he thought prussic acid was a compound of a radical, containing the volatile alkali and phlogiston, with

[1] *Obs. Phys.*, 1782, xix, 370 (376).   [2] III, i, 30.   [3] *Ib.*, 32.
[4] *Nouv. Mém. Acad. Dijon*, 1785, i, 90–102; *Obs. Phys.*, 1786, xxviii, 205 (and note by De la Metherie); III, 1786, i, 142, 280, 404.
[5] *Ib.*, 1785, 102.
[6] *Méthode de Nomenclature Chimique, proposée par MM. de Morveau, Lavoisier, Bertholet (sic) et de Fourcroy*, Paris, 1787; in it, p. 27, his previous essay of 1782 is mentioned, but, p. 4, Lavoisier characteristically says: 'il a offert la sacrifice de ses propres idées.'
[7] Smeaton, *Ann. Sci.*, 1954, x, 102; Duveen and Klickstein, *Osiris*, 1956, xii, 342.
[8] III, 1789, I, ii, 654–64.   [9] III, i, 225, 658.   [10] *Ib.*, i, 407, 658.
[11] *Nouv. Mém. Acad. Dijon*, 1783, ii, 1; *Obs. Phys.*, 1785, xxvi, 463.

oxygen;[1] later, it was a compound of the 'radicale prussicum' with oxygen.[2] He calls the acid obtained by oxidising milk sugar with nitric acid '*acide saclactique* ou *sach-lactique*, pour mieux conserver l'étymologie, c'est à dire, *acide du sucre de lait*'.[3] De Morveau[4] by the distillation of tartaric acid or cream of tartar obtained what he called 'acide empyreumatique de tartre' or 'acid tartareux par distillation', which differed from tartaric acid in not crystallising and in forming a soluble salt with lime. The name was soon changed to 'acide pyrotartareux'.[5] Fourcroy and Vauquelin[6] supposed that it was impure acetic acid but this was disproved by Valentin Rose.[7]

In a long discussion of the nature of tartar[8] he says it was regarded by Boerhaave, Neumann, Montet, and others as the essential salt of wine which separated on fermentation, but Rouelle junr. had obtained it from fresh grape juice, in which it existed ready formed. Corvinus in a dissertation[9] under Spielmann showed that it separated free from sugar from evaporated must and is not produced by fermentation, as Scopoli maintained. De Morveau thought that although tartar might be separated from grapes or other fruits without fermentation,

'there must always be a decomposition of the vegetable to separate it from its other constituent parts, and we have no proof that the methods used in this separation acted only on the substance dissolving the tartar already formed, instead of procuring at the same time, as so often happens, an intermediate and more intimate union of some of the principles of the super-compound body (corps surcomposé).'

In 1787[10] he gave a table expressing various views¯of the compositions of substances in terms of Bergman's symbols (see p. 192).

The so-called 'law of neutrality' of Richter (1797, see p. 676) was anticipated by de Morveau in 1787 in a criticism of Kirwan's figures for the combining proportions of acids and bases (see p. 667).[11] He dissolved 100 grains of sodium sulphate (vitriol de soude) and 48 grains of potassium nitrate (nitre de potasse) in water and evaporated to crystallisation.

'These proportions were combined according to the evaluations of M. Kirwan, so that there would be in the mixture the quantity of potash necessary for the saturation of all the real vitriolic acid in 100 gr. of vitriol of soda. In fact, 48 gr. of nitre of potash contain, according to him, 30·71 of potash and there is necessary 30·68 to saturate completely the 13·19 of vitriolic acid which exist in 100 of crystalline vitriol of soda. In this manner, there should remain in the case of exchange of base between the two acids, 1·77 of free nitric acid; for the 21·87 of soda taken by the vitriol would not be able to take more than 12·57 of the 14·34 gr. of real acid contained in the 48 gr. of nitre.'

[1] III, 1786, i, 233.   [2] III, 1789, i, 658.
[3] *Ib.*, i, 283, 288, discussing Hermbstädt's views.   [4] III, 1786, i, 316.
[5] *Nomenclature Chimique*, 1787, 151.   [6] *Ann. Chim.*, 1800, xxxv, 161.
[7] *J. Chem. Phys.*, 1807, iii, 598.   [8] III, 1786, i, 311.
[9] *Analecta de tartaro*, 1780.   [10] *Obs. Phys.*, 1787, xxx, 45.
[11] De Morveau, art. 'Affinité' in III, 1786 (7), i, 582 f., 595 f.; *Mém. Acad. Turin*, 1788–9 (1790), ix (v in N.S.), 18 (12 April 1788); *Ann. Chim.*, 1798, xxv, 292; *Mém. de l'Inst.*, 1799, ii, 326; *Nicholson's J.*, 1799, ii, 340; Davy, *Phil. Trans.*, 1811, ci, 1 (17), read Nov., 1810; *Works*, v, 328, speaks of 'Richter and Guyton de Morveau' as discoverers of the 'mutual decomposition of the neutral salts'; Gilbert, *Ann. Phys.*, 1811, xxxix, 361 (394); Löwig, *J. B. Richter*, Breslau, 1874, 14; and finally, Speter, 'Ein unbekannte [!] Entdecker [de Morveau] der Grundtatsache des J. B. Richterschen Neutralisationsgesetzes', in *Chem. Ztg.*, 1930, liv, 1005; Partington, *Ann. Sci.*, 1951, vii, 173; the *Encyclopédie* article was tr. with notes by Hermbstädt, *Allgemeine theoretische und praktische Grundsätze der chemischen Affinität oder Wahlanziehung*, Berlin, 1794.

In the same way he mixed 100 gr. of nitrate of soda and 96 gr. of sulphate of potash, when there should have remained 6·8 gr. of free soda.

'Neither of these mixtures manifested, by test papers, the presence of a free acid or alkali. . . . Thus the numbers of M. Kirwan do not at all accord here with observation.'[1]

By considering the various results for the separate combining proportions of acids and bases, de Morveau arrived at the following generalisations:[2]

(1) 'a weak base takes more of the same acid than a strong base, (2) the quantities of bases necessary for the saturation of an acid are in the direct ratio of their affinities with this acid, or (what is the same) an acid takes more of a base for saturation the greater the affinity it has for it, (3) the quantities of acids taken by the same base are in the ratio of the powers (puissances) of the acids in the order of affinities, or a base takes more of an acid according as it is stronger.

'Tout ce qui vient d'être exposé . . . peut être resumé dans ces deux propositions: 1° Un acide prend d'autant moins d'une base quelconque, qu'il est plus puissant. 2° Un acide prend d'autant plus de divers bases, qu'il a plus d'affinité avec elles.'

He uses the results of Homberg, Plummer, Kirwan, Bergman, and Wenzel, which he discusses in detail. A detailed account of Guyton de Morveau's views and experiments on affinity will be given in Vol. IV.

In 1782[3] he described a volumetric titration of a chloride solution with a standard lead nitrate solution. The mother liquor of saltpetre contains calcium nitrate and chloride; he added an acid solution of lead nitrate which precipitated the chloride, then neutralised with potash. By subtracting the potash needed to neutralise the acid in the lead solution from the total amount, the rest is the amount of potash required to decompose only the calcium nitrate, and the potassium nitrate can be crystallised from the solution containing the calcium chloride originally present. He devised a method suitable for the saltpetre workers, based on the compositions of the salts given by Wenzel.

In 1773 the cathedral of Dijon became so infected by putrid exhalations from bodies buried in it that it was deserted. De Morveau, suspecting that the miasma were rich in ammonia gas, purified it by fumigation with hydrochloric acid gas generated from salt and sulphuric acid.[4]

Before Guyton de Morveau the use of muriatic acid gas in disinfection had been recommended by James Johnstone,[5] and later by James Johnstone junr.[6] Sir James Carmichael Smyth used nitric acid vapour from 1780 in preventing contagion in ships, hospitals, and prisons, publishing the process in 1795 and 1796 (he was awarded £5000 by Parliament):

A Description of the Jail Distemper, as it appeared among the Spanish Prisoners, at Winchester, in the Year 1780, with an account of the means employed for curing that fever, and for destroying the contagion, which gave rise to it, 8°, London, 1795 (iv ll., 248 pp.); id. An Account of the Experiment made at the desire of the Lords Commissioners of the Admiralty, on board the Union Hospital Ship, to determine the effect of

[1] III, 1786 (7), i, 595–6.   [2] *Ib.*, 598 f., 600.
[3] *Nouv. Mém. Acad. Dijon*, 1782, ii, 1–16, 16–26; III, 1786, i, 146; Crell's *Ann.*, 1788, ii, 149.
[4] *Obs. Phys.*, 1773, i, 436; 1774 (1785), iii, 73; III, 1786, i, 132; Partington, *Isis*, 1932, xviii, 191; report on prisons by du Hamel, etc., and Lavoisier, AdS, 1780 (1784), m 409 (421).
[5] *An historical Dissertation concerning the malignant Epidemical Fever of 1756*, London, 1758.
[6] *Treatise on Malignant Angina*, Worcester, 1779.

Nitrous Acid in Destroying Contagion, and the safety with which it may be employed, 8°, London, 1796 (3 ll., 75 pp. with folding diagram).

James Johnstone's claims were pressed by John Johnstone[1] but Smyth's claim to the use of an acid vapour was upheld by the College of Physicians.

Guyton de Morveau afterwards used chlorine,[2] which had previously been introduced in Woolwich Military Hospital by William Cruickshank in 1795.[3] 2 pts. of common salt were mixed with 1 pt. of powdered crystalline manganese; 2 oz. of the powder and 1 oz. water were put in a small basin and $1\frac{1}{2}$ oz. of concentrated sulphuric acid gradually added 'so as to preserve a gradual discharge of the oxygenated muriatic acid gas'; the apparatus for generating the gas is described.[4] De Morveau's 'portable bottle' or 'preservative phial'[5] was a bottle containing 46 grains of manganese dioxide, 2 fl. drachms of nitric acid (sp. gr. 1·400) and 2 fl. drachms of hydrochloric acid (sp. gr. 1·130). The phial was enclosed in a wooden case with a screw cap to keep the stopper in place, and was opened until the smell of chlorine was perceived.[6] Guyton found that a mixture of dephlogisticated marine acid (chlorine) and inflammable air (hydrogen) is explosive (détonant) even if no air is present.[7] He showed by quantitative experiments that ammonia is formed when tin dissolves in nitric acid.[8] Fourcroy[9] confirmed this with tin, manganese, zinc, and iron.

Guyton observed that alloys of silver and iron are heterogeneous owing to limited miscibility of the solids.[10] He was one of the first to mention crystallisation in iron[11] and other metals.[12] In his article 'Acier'[13] he pointed out that the three kinds of iron differ in their content of plumbago (carbon), wrought iron being pure metal, cast iron contained most plumbago (plombagine ou soufre méphitique), and steel a smaller amount. Berthollet, Vandermonde, and Monge published the same result in 1786[14] after Guyton had written the article but before it was published. He wrote to Berthollet, who published the letter.[15] Guyton suggested that wrought iron takes up plumbago (carbon) on conversion into steel in the cementation process. He showed that wrought iron could be converted into steel by heating in contact with diamond. Vauquelin[16] concluded from analyses that steel contains on an average $\frac{1}{140}$ part of carbon (0·00631 to 0·00789 p.c.); he used the method of dissolving the iron in sulphurous acid, the carbon remaining undissolved, and Higgins claimed this

[1] *An Account of the Discovery of the Power of Mineral Acid Vapours to Destroy Contagion,* 1803; id., *Reply to Dr. James Carmichael Smyth . . . and a further Account of the Discovery of the Power of Mineral Acids in a State of Gas to destroy Contagion,* 1805.

[2] Guyton de Morveau, *Traité des Moyens de Désinfecter l'Air, de prévenir la Contagion, et d'en arrêter les progrès,* Paris, 1801 (pp. xxxii, 306; list of works at end, giving *Digressions Académiques . . .* , Dijon, 1772); enlarged 2 ed., 1802 (ii ll., xlviii, 429 pp.).

[3] John Rollo, *An Account of Two Cases of the Diabetes Mellitus. With some observations on the nature of sugar,* &c. by William Cruickshank, 2 vols. 8°, London, 1797, ii, 283.

[4] *Ib.,* i, 61 f. and plate. See de Morveau, *Moyens,* etc., 1801, 58, 132 f., 171, 202 f., 280.

[5] *Moyens,* 294.   [6] S. Parkes, *Chemical Catechism,* 5 ed., 1812, 424.

[7] III, 1786, i, 251: Berthollet had failed to find this, see p. 504.

[8] Crell's *Ann.,* 1788, II, 118 (127) mentioning Pott and W. Higgins; III, 1789, i, 756; W. Higgins claimed this discovery in 1789, see p. 746.

[9] (2), 1796, iii, 575.   [10] *Obs. Phys.,* 1777, xii, 135–6.

[11] AdS, *Mém. div. Sav.,* 1780 (presented in 1775), ix, 513; *Obs. Phys.,* 1776, viii, 348.

[12] *Obs. Phys.,* 1779, xiii, 90.   [13] III, 1786, i, 420–51, 443, 447.

[14] AdS, 1786, 132; *Ann. Chim.,* 1797, xix, 1.

[15] *Obs. Phys.,* 1786, xxix, 308.   [16] *Ann. Chim.,* 1797, xxii, 3–25.

also (see p. 746). Clouet[1] said carbon unites with iron in different proportions to form different products. The proportion varies with the unequal intensity of the fire and the porosity of the crucibles; increasing amounts of carbon up to 'un sixième de poids' improve the quality of the steel, but it becomes increasingly difficult to forge and more easily softened by fire.[2]

In 1785 Guyton tried heating a diamond in fused nitre but the crucible was attacked. He said it would be necessary to use a gold crucible, which he did not then possess.[3] The experiment was first made by Tennant in 1796.[4] Guyton[5] found that a diamond burnt without leaving any residue when dropped into fused nitre (il éprouvait une vraie combustion . . . il disparoissoit en totalité; he mentions that fused nitre attacks platinum). He described a twin crystal of diamond.[6]

That charcoal was an oxide of carbon was first suggested by Edward Nathaniel Bancroft:[7] it is 'a kind of vegetable *oxyd*, consisting of the carbonaceous basis, united to a certain proportion of oxygene, enough to render this basis black' (as in manganese dioxide).

De Morveau regarded diamond as the only pure form of carbon, charcoal being 'carbonous oxide'. By burning diamond in oxygen with a burning glass he found that 1 part of diamond combines with 4·55 parts of oxygen.[8] Since it had been found that 1 part of charcoal combined with 2·86 parts of oxygen, this would indicate that 1 part of charcoal consists of 0·688 of carbon and 0·312 of oxygen.[9] De Morveau's consumption of oxygen with diamond is much too high, and disagrees with Tennant's value of 1 of diamond to 2·6 of oxygen. De Morveau summarised his experiments, which were very crude, in 1813.[10] He found that 28 of charcoal combined with 72 of oxygen to form 100 of carbonic acid, which is formed from 17·88 of diamond and 82·12 of oxygen. Thus $28 - 18 = 10$ of charcoal must be oxygen, or charcoal consists of 64 of carbon and 36 of oxygen. Berthollet[11] considered that charcoal is a compound of carbon and hydrogen, with a little oxygen, and graphite also contained a little hydrogen.[12]

Allen and Pepys[13] showed that there is no change in volume when carbon burns in oxygen (Lavoisier had found a considerable contraction), and that there is practically no difference between the weights of diamond, charcoal, and plumbago combining with oxygen to form carbon dioxide. The amounts forming 100 pts. of carbon dioxide found from the weight of the latter (I) and from the amount of oxygen used (II) were (the correct value is 27·27):

[1] *J. Mines*, An VII (1798), no. xlix, 3–12.
[2] Thomson, (2), 1817, i, 378–9, gives $\frac{1}{60}$ for steel and $\frac{1}{6}$ for cast iron, from Clouet.
[3] Bergman, *Opuscules*, French tr., 1785, ii, 124.
[4] *Phil. Trans.*, 1797, lxxxvii, 123; read 15 December 1796.
[5] III, i, 742.   [6] *Ann. Chim.*, 1809, lxx, 60–3.
[7] *Philosophy of Permanent Colours*, London, 1794, 48; Bostock, *Essay on Respiration*, Liverpool, 1804, 224.
[8] *Ann. Chim.*, 1799, xxxi, 72 (99).
[9] Thomson, (2), 1807, i, 46–8.
[10] *Correspondance sur l'École Polytechnique*, 1813, ii, 457.
[11] AdS, *Mém. de l'Inst.*, 1803–4, iv, 269 (315).
[12] *Statique Chimique*, 1803, ii, 55.
[13] *Phil. Trans.*, 1807, xcvii, 267 (On the element Carbon); T. A. Wertime, *Osiris*, 1954, xi, 211–20 (a poor article).

	I	II
Wood charcoal	28·92	28·77
Diamond	28·95	28·81
	28·82	28·72
Mineral carbon (anthracite)	28·20	28·27
Plumbago	28·46	28·46
Mean	28·67	28·46

They found the weight of 100 cu. in. of carbon dioxide at 30 in. mercury and 60° F. to be 47·26 grains. Their average result, 28·6 of carbon, gives $C = 12·82$ if $O = 16$, which is too high.

Guyton de Morveau found that dry charcoal when strongly heated evolves only a trace of gas, and when burnt in excess of oxygen the residual gas, after absorption of carbon dioxide in alkali, is pure oxygen.[1] He found[2] that in Stahl's experiment (Vol. II, p. 671) in which potassium sulphate is heated with charcoal, carbonic acid gas is evolved. Since some hydrogen is also evolved (from the water in the materials), he used in his course at Dijon barium sulphate and charcoal, both previously heated to redness, when carbonic acid almost free from hydrogen was evolved: '& j'ose dire que cette expérience simple n'a pas peu contribué à de siller les yeux par son opposition frappante aux résultats annoncés par l'éthiologie de Stahl' (the 'hydrogen' was probably CO).

De Morveau's investigations on barytes, which he at first called *barote*, were important.[3] He converted heavy spar (barium sulphate) into barium sulphide by heating it with charcoal and dissolved the sulphide in acids. De Morveau changed the name *barote* to *baryte* in 1787[4] and Kirwan[5] changed this into *barytes*. De Morveau also investigated the freezing of sulphuric acid,[6] recognising sulphuric anhydride, and the manufacture of saltpetre[7] and devised a quantitative method for the determination of dissolved carbon dioxide (acide méphitique) in water.[8] His article on carbonic acid (acide méphitique) in the *Encyclopédie*[9] is very detailed and describes many new discoveries; that on nitric acid (acide nitreux)[10] describes the manufacture of saltpetre. A memoir on 'a cold effervescence'[11] deals with the solution of mineral alkali (sodium carbonate) in nitric acid. De Morveau used the name permanent gas (gas proprement dit ou permanens);[12] he liquefied ammonia gas by cooling at − 40° C. in a mixture of crystalline calcium chloride and ice.[13]

[1] Crell's *Ann.*, 1788, I, 118.   [2] III, 1789, i, 749.

[3] *Nouv. Mém. Acad. Dijon*, 1782, i, 159–75 (Observations minéralogiques & chymiques sur le spat pesant & sur la manière d'en retirer le barote ou terre barotique).

[4] *Nomenclature Chimique*, 1787, 64.

[5] *Elements of Mineralogy*, 1794, i, 134 (preface dated 1 January 1795).

[6] *Nouv. Mém. Acad. Dijon*, 1782, i, 68 (Observations sur la congelation de l'acide vitriolique concentré).

[7] *Nouv. Mém. Acad. Dijon*, 1782, ii, 1, 16 (Sur les moyens de saturer les eaux-mères du nitre, sans perte de l'alcali).

[8] *Ib.*, 1784, i, 85.   [9] III, 1786, i, 74–115.   [10] III, 1786, i, 141–9.

[11] *Mém. Acad. Dijon*, 1772, ii, 183.   [12] III, 1789, i, 759.   [13] *Ann. Chim.*, 1799, xxix, 290.

De Morveau paid much attention to pigments;[1] he proposed the use of zinc oxide instead of white lead in paint.[2] A report[3] by de Morveau and others describes analyses of pigments and experiments on the causes of their alteration by age and the means of preventing these changes. He examined a very ancient dish (the Holy Grail) in Genoa Cathedral, the Catino de Smeraldo, supposed to be emerald, and showed that it is really of green glass, since it contains air bubbles and could be scratched by rock crystal.[4] It may be of Phoenician origin.[5]

De Morveau described a small laboratory furnace which would melt steel and even platinum.[6] He investigated and improved the Wedgwood pyrometer (see p. 297).[7] The Argand oil lamp, with air supplied inside and outside a flame burning on a circular wick, was shown in London in 1783 by Aimé Argand (Geneva, 1755–London (?), 24 October 1803). It was patented in 1784 and Boulton undertook its manufacture, but it was pirated; Argand lost a lawsuit and his patent was declared invalid in France in 1787. He then turned to alchemy and died in poverty.[8]

Lavoisier's collaborator Meusnier (see p. 445) showed to the Paris Academy on 19 March 1783 a new kind of smokeless lamp used for heating in distillations, with flat wicks, a chimney with a tap at the top for regulating the air current and an arrangement of tubes for bringing air to the flame; he mentions that Argand's lamp had been brought to Paris at the end of the previous year (? 1783).[9]

The Argand lamp was used by Guyton[10] with a glass chimney and supported by a clamp on a retort stand; when it was in use for illuminating a room it could at the same time be making distilled water by boiling water in a retort. Robison[11] had used in Glasgow in 1767–8 an Argand-type lamp with two concentric circles of rush-pith wicks stuck on pins, with air coming up in the centre between the two circles, and it 'stood on the laboratory table of Glasgow College for two years'. Girtanner[12] used a copper chimney from 1786. Guyton de Morveau[13] also reported on the Carcel lamp (1780).

Guyton de Morveau used a platinum crucible weighing $122\frac{1}{4}$ grains.[14] His investigation on the tenacities of metals was important.[15] He described a small chemical chest of apparatus and reagents (nécessaire chymique), including blowpipe tests,[16] and a hydrometer (pese-liqueur) for sugar solutions.[17] He was

---

[1] *Nouv. Mém. Acad. Dijon*, 1782, i, 1 (Recherches pour perfectionner la préparation des couleurs employée dans la peinture).

[2] Chaptal, *Chemistry Applied to Arts*, etc., 1805, iii, 366, who says it is deficient in covering power.

[3] *Rapport sur la restauration du tableau de Raphaël connu sur le nom de la Vierge de Foligno*, 4°, Paris, Ventose An X (1803), 16 pp. (BN).

[4] *Ann. Chim.*, 1807, lxi, 260.   [5] Partington, *Origins of Applied Chemistry*, 1935, 454.

[6] *Obs. Phys.*, 1776, viii, 117, and plate opp. 188.

[7] Guyton de Morveau, *Ann. Chim.*, 1803, xlvi, 276; 1810, lxxiii, 254; 1810, lxxiv, 18, 129; 1811, lxxviii, 73; 1814, xc, 113, 225.

[8] Gilbert, *Ann. Phys.*, 1817, lvi, 391–426; Leybold, *Gas- und Wasserfach*, 1928, lxxi, 745.

[9] AdS, 1784 (1787), m 390–8.

[10] *Ann. Chim.*, 1797, xxiv, 310, and plate; *Nicholson's J.*, 1799, ii, 209, and plate.

[11] In Black, *Lectures on Chemistry*, 1803, i, 539; Thomson, *Ency. Brit. Suppl.*, 1801, II, i, 64.

[12] *Allgem. J. Chem.*, 1800, iv, 417.   [13] *Ann. Chim.*, 1801, xxxviii, 135.

[14] III, 1789, i, 725.   [15] *Mém. de l'Inst.*, 1809, x, 267.

[16] *Nouv. Mém. Acad. Dijon*, 1783, i, 159, and plate.   [17] *Ib.*, 1783, ii, 52.

much interested in mineralogy and supervised the translation by Mme. Picardet of Werner's *Von den äusserlichen Kennzeichen der Fossilien* (Leipzig, 1774) as *Traité des Caractères extérieurs des Fossiles* (1790). He made a large number of mineral analyses;[1] a paper of modern interest is on an incombustible coal.[2] He prepared bismuth acetate,[3] investigated whether gold is dissolved by boiling nitric acid in parting gold and silver,[4] investigated the solubility of quartz,[5] and prepared artificial blende by heating sulphur with zinc and zinc oxide.[6] He determined the solubilities of salts in alcohol.[7] Guyton de Morveau, Maret, and Durande obtained a crude solution of pyrogallic acid by subliming gall nuts, and showed that it blackened iron salts. They definitely identified the astringent principle (tannin, or tannic acid) of galls.[8]

It is seen from the above account that Guyton de Morveau had an excellent knowledge of all branches of chemistry, acquired by assiduous study and by his own very numerous researches. His writings served to instruct the younger generation of chemists and always contain ingenious ideas. In his day he enjoyed a great reputation but from about 1820 his name dropped, undeservedly, into oblivion. The two collaborators with de Morveau in the *Élémens de Chymie* were Maret and Durande. Hugues Maret (Dijon; 6 October 1726–11 June 1785), M.D., demonstrator in chemistry in the Jardin des Plantes and Secretary of the Academy in Dijon,[9] published some chemical papers.[10] He examined the precipitation of a solution of iron in nitric acid by ammonia, extracted phosphoric acid from ox-flesh, found that an acid is formed by the combustion of camphor, examined a number of mineral waters, confirming the presence of boric acid in that of Tuscany, discovered by Francis Hoefer,[11] and described the preparation of artificial mineral waters charged with carbon dioxide; he drew up a chart of over forty mineral waters for his lectures.[12] Jean François Durande (Dijon; ?–23 January (or February) 1794) was professor of botany in Dijon.

---

[1] *Nouv. Mém. Acad. Dijon*, 1782, i, 100 (Examen des mines de cuivre, appellées verd de montagne, etc.); 1782, ii, 41 (lead ore); 1783, ii, 90 (limestone of Brion); 1785, i, 102 (fossil tooth); and many others.

[2] *Ib.*, 1783, i, 76; it was probably anthracite.   [3] *Ib.*, 1783, i, 187.   [4] *Ib.*, 1784, ii, 133.

[5] *Ib.*, 1785, i, 46, 60.   [6] *Ib.*, 1783, i, 37.   [7] *Obs. Phys.*, 1785, xxvii, 64.

[8] II, 1778, iii, 403 (Appendice sur le principe astringent végétal); Nierenstein, *Incunabula of Tannin Chemistry*, 1932, 13 f., 160.

[9] Vicq D'Azyr, 1805, iii, 95, 107, 131 f. (list of chemical publ.).

[10] *Nouv. Mém. Acad. Dijon*, 1782, i, 106 (sur l'air dégagé de la crême de chaux & du minium); 1783, i, 10 (on the combination of mercury and muriatic acid by simple affinity).

[11] *Sopra il sale sedativo della Toscana*, 12°, Florence, 1778; Hoefer, (1), ii, 384.

[12] Vicq D'Azyr, iii, 131–4.

CHAPTER XI

FOURCROY. VAUQUELIN. CHAPTAL

FOURCROY

Antoine François de Fourcroy (Paris; 15 June 1755–16 December 1809) came of a noble family which had fallen on bad times and he grew up in poverty. His mother died when he was seven and he was cared for by an elder sister. At school he had a brutal master and he left at the age of 14. At first he had ambitions to be an actor, then became a clerk. Vicq D'Azyr persuaded his father, who had been an apothecary, to allow him to study medicine, which he began about 1773, apparently in poor circumstances. He received much encouragement and some financial support from members of the Société Royale de Médecine, of which Vicq D'Azyr was secretary. A grant left to poor students which would have enabled Fourcroy to take his doctorate was withheld because his patron Vicq D'Azyr had quarrelled with the medical faculty. Fourcroy's richly deserved degree was conferred in 1780 as a result of the endeavours of several persons who had noticed his talents. The highest award (doctor régent) was denied him by the faculty.

A pupil of Roux, Macquer, and especially Bucquet, the professor of chemistry in the medical faculty (some of whose lectures he gave), Fourcroy was well grounded in chemistry and began to give an annual course in 1778 (before he graduated), but his first work, which gained him the entry to the Academy in 1785, was on natural history and anatomy. His fortunate marriage enabled him to purchase the apparatus of Bucquet. He took lectures for Macquer and on the death of the latter in 1784 he was made professor of chemistry at the Jardin du Roi (later Jardin des Plantes), with the influence of Buffon, the superintendent, although Berthollet was a candidate for the chair. Fourcroy was a splendid lecturer to large audiences; his eloquence is reflected in his books. He also lectured in the Lycée, a private institution in the Rue de Valois, from 1787 till 1807. With the coming of the Revolution Fourcroy placed his talents at the disposal of the State. In 1793 he succeeded Marat as a member of the National Convention, in which he played a part in the foundation of the metric system of weights and measures.

In 1793 he was a member of a commission charged with the establishment of a national medical school and he presented the report to the Convention. As a result the École de Santé, later the École de Médecine, was opened in Paris in January 1795, two smaller colleges being opened in Strasbourg and Montpellier. In 1794 he participated in planning the École Centrale des Travaux Publiques, which in 1795 became the École Polytechnique, and he was one of the professors. He remained professor at the Muséum d'Histoire Naturelle, formerly the Jardin du Roi, and was also professor of chemistry in the École de Médecine, lecturing on the chemistry of animal substances, and the school was also a centre of research.

In 1801 (when he was made Consul by Napoleon) he organised public instruction in chemistry and was Minister of Public Instruction in 1802–8.

During the blockade of France he played a part in organising national industries, especially of saltpetre, which later rendered the country largely independent of imports. He was greatly disappointed when he was not made head of the new university, and this is said to have hastened his death. His part in the development and propagation of Lavoisier's ideas has already been described (p. 488). He denied the accusation that he was partly responsible for Lavoisier's execution, and the most that can be said against him is that, in this time of terror and danger, he did not openly exert himself in what he probably realised would be useless efforts to save his colleague; he was responsible for saving the life of D'Arcet. Cuvier, after a careful investigation, acquitted

FIG. 49. ANTOINE FRANÇOIS DE FOURCROY (1755–1809).

him of implication in the sentence on Lavoisier; in any case at the time Fourcroy had little influence in the Convention. Cuvier says: 'si dans les sévères recherches que nous avons faites, nous avions trouvé la moindre preuve d'une si horrible atrocité, aucune puissance humaine ne nous aurait contraint de souiller notre bouche de son éloge.'[1]

In 1796 Fourcroy[2] was not afraid of denouncing Lavoisier's execution as 'l'irréparable outrage, que la tyrannie a fait à la philosophie', and 'un crime atroce'. The accusation made against Fourcroy (like that made against Guyton de Morveau) was repeated by Berthelot[3] but is now regarded as baseless.[4] On 16 December 1809 Napoleon created him Count de Fourcroy, but on that day, at the age of 45, Fourcroy cried out 'Je suis mort' and fell dead.[5]

[1] Cuvier, Éloge (1811), AdS, Mém. de l'Inst., 1814, phys. math., ii, II (xi), pp. xcvij–cxxviij (cxx); Recueil des Éloges historiques, 1819, ii, 1–55; id., Éloges historiques (Bibliothèque Classique des Célébrités Contemporaines), Paris, 1860, 101; Grimaux, Lavoisier, 1888, 309, also acquits him.
[2] Notice sur la Vie et les Travaux de Lavoisier, 1796, 26, 44; (2), iii, 415.
[3] AdS, s.a., XLV, m xix (lxx).
[4] Guerlac, Isis, 1954, xlv, 51; G. Kersaint, q. in Nature, 1959, clxxxiv, 1452.
[5] Crell, Ann., 1796, II, 632; Cuvier, op. cit.; Gmelin, (1), iii, 436, 654; Hoefer, (1), ii, 555; Kopp, (1), i, 325 (index has 66 refs.); NBG, 1856, xviii, 338 (b. 15 Jan.); Palissot de Beauvois, Éloge historique de M. Fourcroy, 4°, Paris, [1810], 39 pp.; Smeaton, Endeavour, 1959, xviii, 70 (portr.); Thomson, (1), ii, 165; id., Ann. Phil., 1813, i, 321; portrs. in Allgem. J. Chem. (Scherer), 1802, viii; Ann. Sci., 1939, iv, 113; Phil. Mag., 1801, xi.

Thomson, his contemporary, says of Fourcroy that 'the prodigious reputation which he enjoyed during his lifetime was more owing to his eloquence than to his eminence as a chemist — though even as a chemist he was far above mediocrity'. The papers of which he was author or joint author number over 160; many are with Vauquelin (see p. 553) and Thomson says 'the general opinion is, that the experiments were all made by Vauquelin; but that the papers themselves were drawn up by Fourcroy'. Vauquelin was ignorant of languages and could not write up his work. His steady friendship for Vauquelin must be counted high in Fourcroy's favour. Fourcroy says of himself:[1] 'the natural bent of my genius, no less than my particular situation, leads me to cultivate both sciences [chemistry and medicine] with the most earnest wishes to promote their improvement.'

His large library included works in all branches of learning and literature as well as medicine and chemistry.[2] At the end of his article 'Chimie' in the *Encyclopédie Méthodique*[3] he gives an 'Essai de Bibliothèque chimique', the authors being divided into six classes. He gives practically all the titles of German works in French and some authors' names are disfigured, but the list is good and useful. Fourcroy published a book based on his lectures:

I. Leçons élémentaires d'histoire naturelle et de chimie, 2 vols. 8°, Paris, 1782 (I, lxxxviii, 584, II, (4), 848, 1 l., 5 pl.)

2 ed. revised and enlarged, Élémens d'histoire naturelle et de chimie, 4 vols. 8°, Paris, 1786; Supplementary vol. written by Adet by comparison with 3 ed., 1789; 3 ed., 5 vols. 1789; 4 ed., 5 vols. 1791; 5 ed. (exact copy of 3 ed.), 5 vols. 1793 (the one quoted). Summary in Fourcroy, (2), iii, 687 f.

IA. Elementary Lectures on Chemistry and Natural History . . . With many additions, notes, and illustrations by the Translator (Thomas Elliot), 2 vols. 8°, Edinburgh, 1785 (tr. of I, 1782);

2 ed. Elements of Natural History and Chemistry, tr. W. Nicholson, 4 vols. 8°, London, 1788, and Supplement, 1789 (with histor. pref. by translator);

3 ed., 3 vols., 1790 (wholly rewritten), the ed. quoted;

4 ed., tr. R. Heron, 4 vols., 1796;

5 ed. with notes by J. Thomson [W. Nicholson, and W. Allen], 3 vols., Edinburgh, 1800. The translator, Robert Heron, wrote Elements of Chemistry: comprehending a Variety of Facts and Views which have never before been communicated to the World . . . with the Addition of the more recent chemical discoveries . . . in Britain and the Continent, London, 1800 (628 pp. and folding table).

IB. Rearranged resumé of I, 2 ed., for the use of ladies and the students in the Veterinary School (I, 1793, pref. viii): Principes de Chimie, 2 vols. 12°, in Bibliothèque Universelle des Dames, Classe 9, Chimie, t. III–IV, Paris, 1787 (III, xxiii, 212 pp.; IV, 214 pp.); this uses the antiphlogistic theory.

II. Supplement to I: Mémoires et Observations de Chimie . . . Pour servir de suite aux Élémens de Chimie, publié en 1782, 8°, Paris, 1784 (xvj, 448 pp., 3 pls.); tr., Chemische Beobachtungen und Versuche, Leipzig, 1785; summary in Crell's *Ann.*, 1786, I, 285, 364.

Fourcroy[4] says he approved the antiphlogistic theory in 1777 but a footnote in 1784 announces that he then approved fully 'the ingenious theory of Macquer' (see p. 462). In the preface to the first edition of I Fourcroy says he had compared the phlogistic and antiphlogistic theories, neither rejecting the first nor adopting the second, which nevertheless seemed then to be more convincing,

---

[1] (3), 1790, i, 17.
[2] *Catalogue des livres de la bibliothèque de feu M. A. F. de Fourcroy*, Paris, June 1810, 338 pp.
[3] 1797, iii, 739–81.   [4] II, 1784, 31.

since it was based on confirmed facts. Lavoisier, in a report of May 1785,[1] referred to this 'impartialité' and evidently regarded Fourcroy's book as influential. In 1784 Fourcroy asked for an 'approbation' from the Société de Médecine for the second edition of I. Lavoisier and Geoffroy were appointed to examine it, but it was not until July 1786 that Lavoisier and Poulletier de la Salle reported. Fourcroy also asked the Académie des Sciences in July 1784 for a report, but Lavoisier and Sage did not report until July 1786. Smeaton[2] suggests that in the interval Fourcroy 'was gradually being converted to the new theory'; he was 'conditioned' as we might say. When the book appeared, the preliminary discourse announced the acceptance of the new theory but in the text the phlogistic and antiphlogistic theories are still presented as alternatives.[3] Fourcroy published:

III. Système des Connaissances Chimiques, et leurs Applications aux Phénomènes de la Nature et de l'Art, with (vol. xi) Table alphabétique et analytique des Matières, redigée par Mme. Dupiery; 11 vols. 8° (the ed. quoted) or 6 vols. 4°, Paris, An IX–X (1801–2); crit. by Proust, *Ann. Chim.*, 1802, xlii, 225; *J. de Phys.*, 1802, lvi, 97;
IIIA. tr. W. Nicholson, A General System of Chemical Knowledge, and its Application to the Phenomena of Nature and Art, 11 vols., London, 1804 (with long pref. by Nicholson on the history of the antiphlogistic theory).

This large work was begun in 1793 and continued in times of very great difficulty.[4] Fourcroy is said to have received 25,000 francs for the manuscript, which was prepared for the press in sixteen months.[5] It was intended to be followed by three treatises on the history, practice, and applications of chemistry, which never appeared. After an eloquent and interesting *Discours Préliminaire* of 176 pages, giving a plan of the whole work, it is divided into eight parts: (1) generalities and introduction, (2) simple or undecompounded bodies, (3) burnt bodies, oxides or acids, (4) salifiable bases, earthy or alkaline, (5) acids united to salifiable bases, or earthy or alkaline salts, (6) the metals in particular, (7) organic vegetable compounds (des composés organiques végétaux), (8) organic animal compounds (Fourcroy believed in the existence of a 'vital force'). Special stress is laid on classification and method; the section on salts is very systematic and was regarded by the author as a great advance on previous treatments.[6] Fourcroy's article on *Chimie* in the *Encyclopédie Méthodique*[7] gives a masterly and detailed historical survey of the subject. His article *Air* in the medical section[8] gives a full account of respiration. A very good concise summary of the new system of chemistry is given in Fourcroy's:

IV. Philosophie Chimique ou vérités fondamentales de la Chimie moderne disposées dans un nouvel ordre, 12°, Paris, 1792; 2 ed. 1795; 3 ed., 8°, 1806 (three printings) entitled: Philosophie Chimique, ou Vérités fondamentales de la Chimie Moderne, Destinées à servir d'élémens pour l'étude de cette Science (with a new *Introduction* of 86 pp.); Nouvelle édition augmentée de notes et d'axiomes tirés des dernières découvertes, 8°, Brussels, 1795 (with notes by Van Mons). The Philosophy of Chemistry, or Fundamental Truths of modern Chemical Science. Arranged in a new order, tr. from

[1] *Oeuvres*, iv, 419.   [2] *Ann. Sci.*, 1956 (1957), xii, 236–7.
[3] See the Avertissement to the 3 ed., 1789, I, viii.
[4] See the 'Discours Préliminaire', I, clxxiij f.
[5] *Allgem. J. der Chem.* (Scherer), 1799, iii, 287.   [6] III, i, pp. xciv f., xcv; iii, iv.
[7] 1796–7, iii, 303–781.   [8] *Ency. Méthod., Méd.*, 1787, i, 492–592.

2 French ed. 'signed by the author', 8°, London, 1795, another ed. (tr. by W. Nicholson), 1795; 3 ed., Chemical Philosophy; or, the established base of Modern Chemistry, considerably enlarged and amended, tr. W. Desmond, 8°, London, 1807 (xxiii, 291 pp., i l. advt.).

This work is based on the art. 'Axioms' in Ency. Méthod., 1792, ii, 455–89 (see *ib.*, iii, 691). The book was tr. into Italian (1794), Swedish (1795), German (1796), Danish (1797), Russian (1799), Spanish (1801 ?), Greek (Vienna, 1802), and Polish (1808).

V. Tableaux synoptique de Chimie pour servir de résumé aux leçons données sur cette science dans les écoles de Paris, Paris, 1800 (f°, 11 pp., 12 folding tables); tr. W. Nicholson, Synoptic Tables of Chemistry, intended to serve as a Summary of the Lectures delivered on that Science, in the Public Schools at Paris, la. f°, London, 1801 (2 ll., 12 double-page tables). This atlas was intended to accompany III; very few copies have survived.

Only the more important of the numerous publications of Fourcroy can be mentioned; many are on medical subjects and he was the originator of modern pathological chemistry. He analysed many drugs and mineral waters[1] and laid stress on the value of chemistry in medicine and pharmacy, but avoided a one-sided enthusiasm in this region. He gave a chemical classification of mineral waters into acidulous, saline, sulphurous and ferruginous, each class being subdivided so as to make nine orders, and describes their chemical analysis.[2]

Fourcroy introduced some names which were long in use, e.g. *acide arsenieux* for white arsenic (1800), *gaz oléfiant* for ethylene, and *acide muqueux* (mucic acid) for Scheele's *acidum sacchari lactis* (*acide saccho-lactique* or *saclactique* in French), but his name *alcaligène* for nitrogen (forming ammonia) was not adopted. In 1789[3] he adopted the suggestion of the Spanish chemist Arejula[4] and changed the name 'gaz azotique' to 'gaz azote'.

Fourcroy gave a sketch of the history of chemistry in his elementary book,[5] mentioning Boyle, Hales and Priestley but not Hooke, Mayow, Black or Cavendish (he mentions Bayen, 'si justement célèbre par l'exactitude de ses travaux'), but a longer account in the *System*[6] refers to all but Hooke. He opposed alchemy.[7]

Fourcroy at first[8] thought light and caloric (the matter of heat) were different, later[9] that heat and light are probably modifications of caloric.[10] At first[11] vital air is oxygen base dissolved in two solvents, caloric and light, later[12] in caloric only, and the same views were held of hydrogen gas.[13] This is the orthodox Lavoisierian theory.

Priestley's confusion between different kinds of 'inflammable air' was at first shared by Fourcroy (1780–82), who thought the inflammable constituent of the gases from metals and acids (hydrogen), from heated Prussian blue (cyanogen), from heated carbon and zinc oxide (carbon monoxide), marsh gas

[1] Fourcroy and Delaporte, *Analyse chimique de l'Eau Sulfureuse d'Enghein, pour servir à l'Histoire des Eaux Sulfureuses en général*, Paris, 1788 (9 ll., 385 pp.).
[2] IA, 1790, iii, 366 f.   [3] Suppl. vol. to 2 ed. of I, 1789; (2), iii, 687.
[4] *Obs. Phys.*, 1788, xxxiii, 262.   [5] I, 1793, i, 26–44.
[6] III, i, *Discours prélim.*, and 10–49.   [7] III, v, 5.   [8] IV, 1795, 17.
[9] IV, 1806, 99.   [10] Partington and McKie, *Ann. Sci.*, 1939, iv, 113.
[11] IV, 1795, 25.   [12] IV, 1806, 109.
[13] IV, 1795, 34; 1806, 150; but he says, 1806, 155, both or *ib.*, 267, vital air, contain caloric and light.

and the gas obtained by distilling organic materials (impure methane) were, as Macquer also thought in 1782 (p. 84), only impure hydrogen:

'en un mot, qu'il n'existe dans ce genre que le gaz hydrogène présentant plus ou moins d'inflammabilité et des couleurs diverses dans sa combustion, suivant qu'il est mêlé ou combiné avec différens autres corps.'[1]

The later editions (from 1789) of I contain a 'Discours sur les principes et l'ensemble de la Chimie moderne'[2] and a table of nomenclature.[3] The first gives a clear and brief account of the antiphlogistic system. It classifies gases into (1) those capable of maintaining combustion and respiration (vital air, atmospheric air), (2) those unfit for maintaining combustion and respiration and neither saline nor soluble in water (azotic gas, nitrous gas), (3) those unfit for maintaining combustion and respiration but 'saline' and soluble in water (carbonic acid, sulphurous acid, fluoric acid, muriatic acid, oxygenated muriatic acid, ammonia); (4) those unfit for maintaining combustion and respiration but inflammable (hydrogenous gas, sulphurated hydrogenous gas, phosphorated hydrogenous gas, hydrogenous gas mixed with azote (Volta's inflammable air of marshes, really methane), hydrogenous gas mixed with carbonic acid gas from the dry distillation of vegetable matter, and carbonaceous hydrogenous gas from the solution of cast iron in acid). Atmospheric air is 'a compound of vital air with azotic gas'.[4] In spite of its inclusion in (3) as a non-supporter of combustion, it is said[5] that oxigenated muriatic acid gas (chlorine) 'weakens and reddens the flame of a taper, but does not extinguish it'.

Fourcroy divides combustible mineral matters into five genera: diamond, hydrogen gas, sulphur, metals and bitumens.[6] Even in 1806[7] 'the basis of the different species and denominations of inflammable gases which are admitted is always hydrogen gas'. He included azote and diamond among simple combustibles,[8] regarded graphite as a 'coal formed in the interior parts of the globe, or buried in the earth',[9] and charcoal as the lowest oxide of carbon,[10] following de Morveau (p. 531).

Fourcroy suggested that the alkalis and quicklime 'contain pure air [oxygen] united to an inflammable matter'.[11] At first[12] baryta was supposed to be a metallic oxide; later[13] it was classed with the alkalis and this suggestion omitted. Before they can form salts metals must first unite with oxygen.[14] All acids (including muriatic, fluoric, and boric) contain oxygen,[15] but regarding muriatic acid he says[16] he arrived at the suspicion in 1780 that 'the existence of oxigene in the muriatic acid has not yet been fully evinced; it is only from analogy that it has been admitted', and later[17] he said the presence of oxygen is 'a pure hypothesis':

[1] II, 1784, 151, 167; I, 1793, i, 327.   [2] I, 1793, v, 135–200.
[3] Ib., v, 201–368; IA, 1790, iii, 452–68, and appendix, 1–91.
[4] I, 1793, v, 145.   [5] I, 1793, v, 155.   [6] I, 1793, ii, 301.   [7] IV, 1806, 153.
[8] IV, 1806, 120–22.   [9] IA, 1790, ii, 467: in the section on iron it is described as iron carbide.
[10] IV, 1806, 165.   [11] II, 1784, 355.   [12] IV, 1795, 44.   [13] IV, 1806, 222.
[14] IV, 1795, 109, 116; 1806, 265, 273.   [15] IV, 1806, 161, 168, 181–2.
[16] I, 1782, i, 168, 183; Cadet, D'Arcet, and Lavoisier, in Lavoisier, Oeuvres, 1868, iv, 419 (report of 1785 on Fourcroy, I); Fourcroy, IA, 1790, i, 357.
[17] III, ii, 108; cf. III, i, p. lxxij: 'on peut donc conclure . . . que la nature de l'acide muriatique n'est pas encore connue, et qu'il est encore dans la classe des composés dont l'analyse n'est pas faite.' Berthollet's results 'ne sont pas suffisantes pour décider la nature de cet acide'.

'On ne connoît pas bien la nature intime de l'acide marin. On n'a pas encore pu le decomposer. . . . On soupçonne seulement qu'il est formé d'un corps combustible, inconnu, combiné avec l'air pur qu'on peut retirer de quelques matières alterées par cet acide.'

The marine acid contained in aqua regia is only: 'l'acide marin chargé d'air pur & qui à raison de ce principe surabondant auquel il est peu adhèrent, devient capable de calciner les métaux les plus parfaits.' In his section on manganese, Fourcroy[1] in discussing the action of the marine acid on pyrolusite says the calx becomes white (manganous oxide), 'soit en donnant une partie de son air à l'acide marin, soit en lui enlevant le phlogistique que M. Schéele admet dans cette substance saline [HCl].' In 1796[2] he repeated that: 'ce n'est encore que d'après l'analogie, dont la lueur, quelque foible qu'elle soit, est préférable à une obscurité parfaite, qu'on le regarde [l'acide muriatique] comme un composé d'un radical inconnu avec d'oxigène.' Lavoisier would not care for these views, afterwards established by Davy.

Fourcroy found[3] that oxymuriatic acid (chlorine) inflames phosphorus and supports the combustion of a taper 'with much more activity than atmospheric air'. The flame is dull but the taper consumes faster than in atmospheric air. Westrumb in 1786, he says, had discovered the inflammation of metals in the gas (see p. 572). Fourcroy found that chlorine decomposes ammonia gas with a white brilliant flame. He recommended the action of chlorine gas on ammonia solution for the preparation of nitrogen, but said later that if the chlorine is used in excess there is an explosion (from the formation of nitrogen chloride).[4]

Fourcroy[5] says he and Vauquelin first used potassium chlorate for preparing pure oxygen gas, but Berthollet (1788) had done this, and that he and Vauquelin experimented on the detonation of the chlorate with combustible materials[6] in 1796. Fourcroy and Vauquelin[7] and Thomas Hoyle junr.[8] independently observed the explosion of potassium chlorate when triturated with sulphur, the ignition of a mixture of chlorate and sugar by a drop of concentrated sulphuric acid, and the evolution of a yellow explosive gas (chlorine dioxide) from chlorate and concentrated sulphuric acid. From its smell, the gas was thought to contain 'nitrous fumes'. Its composition was first determined by H. Davy (see Vol. IV).

Fourcroy[9] thought the swimming-bladder of the carp contained nitrogen, but Accum found that it was ordinary air when the fish was fresh.[10] Fourcroy's observation that muscular flesh evolves nitrogen on heating with dilute nitric acid[11] had been anticipated by Berthollet.[12] Fourcroy and Vauquelin obtained crystalline hydrate of ammonia in 'longs faisceaux de prismes ou d'aiguilles brillantes et satinées à six pans' by cooling concentrated ammonia solution to $-28°$ to $-30°$ R.[13]

[1] I, 1782, i, 525.   [2] (2), iii, 587.
[3] AdS, 1788, m 365; Ann. Chim., 1789, iv, 249; (2), iii, 586.
[4] Ann. Chim., 1789, i, 47; (2), 1796–7, iii, 575, 658.   [5] (2), 1796–7, iii, 607.
[6] Ib., 608.   [7] Ann. Chim., 1797, xxi, 235.   [8] Manchester Mem., 1798, v, 221.
[9] Ann. Chim., 1789, i, 47; Priestley, E & O, 1790, ii, 462, also said the air-bladders in fish contain 'perfectly or not quite noxious air'.
[10] Nicholson, in Fourcroy, IIIA, 1804, I, xi.   [11] Ann. Chim., 1789, i, 40.
[12] AdS, 1785 (1788), m 331.   [13] Fourcroy, III, 1801, I, lxxxviij.

Fourcroy[1] at first classed acids, alkalis, and alkaline earths as *sels purs* or *sels primitifs*; true salts (formed from alkalis and earths with acids) are called *sels composés*. In 1795[2] he reserved the name *sel* for true salts, 'combinaisons des acides ou salifians avec les bases salifiables alcalines ou terreuse.'[3] Silica and alumina are called earths (*terres*); lime, magnesia, and baryta are saline earths (*substances salino-terreuses*).[4] All salts except nitrate of ammonia are incombustible.[5]

Fourcroy's studies on salts were very extensive. The new systematic nomenclature indicated the possible existence of great numbers of combinations of acids and bases which had not been prepared and Fourcroy filled in a large number of the gaps. In the *Système* he describes 134 species. He distinguishes (following Rouelle, see p. 74) neutral from acid and basic salts (*acidule* or *avec excès d'acide; avec excès de base* or *sursaturées de base*).[6] The salts are classified according to the acids, and under each is given: synonymy and history, physical properties, preparation, action of heat, action of air, action of water, decomposition and proportions of principles (analysis), and uses. He describes many new salts, especially of ammonia, obtained potassium disulphate ($K_2S_2O_7$) by heating the acid sulphate ($KHSO_4$),[7] and prepared crystalline calcium chloride.[8] Fourcroy and Vauquelin prepared and examined a number of sulphites.[9]

In his memoirs on iron precipitates, partly read to the Academy in 1777–8 but not published,[10] Fourcroy[11] showed that the precipitate (*craie de fer*) obtained with mild alkali or chalk, as well as iron rust, contain fixed air. Fourcroy was apparently the first to suggest and show experimentally that the green patina formed on copper is the basic carbonate;[12] in most cases the patina is now the basic sulphate or near the sea the basic chloride.[13]

Fourcroy[14] rejected the division of metals into true malleable metals and non-malleable semi-metals (mercury, antimony, bismuth, cobalt, arsenic, and zinc) proposed by Brandt (1735; see p. 168), since the division is not sharp. The metallic salts are described separately under the metals; there are good descriptions of mercury salts, which Fourcroy investigated in 1791–1804, and of compounds of these with ammonia.[15] In 1790[16] he found that magnesia is not completely precipitated by ammonia from its salts, the solution containing a soluble salt of magnesia and ammonia with the acid; he called such salts 'triple salts' (*sels triples* or *sels trisules*),[17] following Bergman.[18] The more appropriate name 'double salts' was introduced by Berzelius.[19] Fourcroy and Vauquelin[20] obtained the soluble 'superphosphate of lime' (phosphate acidule de chaux)

---

[1] I, 1793, i, 383 f., 401.   [2] VI, 1795, 93.   [3] III, iii, 1.
[4] I, 1793, i, 238, 403.   [5] II, 1784, 349.   [6] III, iii, 1 f.
[7] I, 1793, ii, 11.   [8] *Ib.*, ii, 135.
[9] *Ann. Chim.*, 1797, xxiv, 229; *Nicholson's J.*, 1797, i, 313; Crell's *Ann.*, 1800, II, 299.
[10] See the report by Cadet and Lavoisier, in Lavoisier, *Oeuvres*, 1868, iv, 283.
[11] II, 1784, 28, 73, 96, 118.   [12] IA, 1788, iii, 367.
[13] Vernon, *J. Chem. Soc.*, 1934, 1853.   [14] I, 1793, ii, 379.
[15] *Ann. Chim.*, 1791, x, 293; 1792, xiv, 34.   [16] *Ann. Chim.*, 1790, iv, 210.
[17] IV, 1795, 107.   [18] De Magnesia, *Opuscula*, 1779, i, 378, with the same example.
[19] *An Attempt to Establish a pure Scientific System of Mineralogy*, 1814, 26; T. Thomson, *An Attempt to Establish the First Principles of Chemistry by Experiment*, 1825, ii, 236.
[20] AdS, *Mém. de l'Inst.*, 1799–1801, ii, 274.

by the action of phosphoric or sulphuric acid on phosphate of lime; they showed that acids remove two-thirds of the lime from the latter, which correctly corresponds with the modern equation:

$$5Ca_3(PO_4)_2 + 11H_2SO_4 = 4CaH_4(PO_4)_2 + 2H_3PO_4 + 11CaSO_4.$$

Fourcroy regarded fuming sulphuric acid as a compound of sulphuric and sulphurous acids.[1]

Berthollet[2] and W. Higgins[3] found that iron dissolves in sulphurous acid without evolution of gas (Stahl had noticed this in 1718; see Vol. II, p. 680) and Fourcroy and Vauquelin[4] found the same result with zinc and tin. Schönbein[5] showed that a peculiar acid, hyposulphurous acid, is formed, also by electrolytic reduction of sulphurous acid; its salts were investigated by Schützenberger,[6] who thought the sodium salt was $NaHSO_2$; the correct formula $Na_2S_2O_4$ was found by Bernthsen.[7]

In his *Élémens* Fourcroy dealt with organic substances in close relation with natural history, but in the *Système* a more chemical treatment is followed, since chemistry has its own methods. The division into vegetable and animal chemistry is used, and Fourcroy's book contributed largely to the form which organic chemistry bore for some decades.[8] He says vegetable matters cannot be prepared artificially.[9] He[10] supposed that many vegetable acids, such as tartaric, since they are converted into oxalic acid by oxidation with nitric acid, 'have the same radical, and differ only by the proportion of oxygen' (see Lavoisier, p. 424). Analyses by Fourcroy and Vauquelin[11] are inaccurate and at that time no good method of organic analysis was known (see Vol. IV):

	Carbon	Hydrogen	Oxygen
Gum	23·08	11·54	65·38
Oxalic acid	13	10	77
Tartaric acid	19	10·5	70·5

Stahl (Vol. II, p. 685) obtained very concentrated acetic acid by distilling copper acetate. This was known as *radical vinegar* or *vinegar of Venus*. Berthollet[12] and Fourcroy concluded that there were two different acids, Fourcroy saying of radical vinegar: 'this acid appears to bear the same relation to common vinegar which the oxigenated muriatic acid bears to the pure muriatic acid', i.e. it contains more oxygen than the acid obtained from vinegar; he called the two acids acetic acid and acetous acid respectively.[13] Chaptal[14] thought acetous acid was oxidised to acetic by distilling with manganese dioxide, when it dissolved copper to form a crystalline acetate instead of corroding it to verdigris.

[1] AdS, 1785 (1788), m 373; IA, 1790, i, 386; III, vi, 199.   [2] *Ann. Chim.*, 1789, ii, 54.
[3] *Comparative View of the Phlogistic and Antiphlogistic Theories*, 1789, 49.
[4] Fourcroy, III, vi, 199.   [5] *Wien Ber.*, 1854, xi, 464; *J. prakt. Chem.*, 1854, lxi, 193.
[6] *Compt. Rend.*, 1869, lxix, 196; *Ann. Chim.*, 1870, xx, 351.   [7] *Ber.*, 1881, xiv, 438.
[8] Hjelt, *Geschichte der organischen Chemie*, 1916, 22; see Vol. IV.
[9] IV, 1795, 126; 1806, 303.   [10] I, 1793, iv, 103.
[11] Fourcroy, III, vii, 153 (gum), 224 (oxalic acid), 261 (tartaric acid).
[12] AdS, 1783 (1786), m 403.
[13] IA, 1790, iii, 145; IV, 1795, 69; the distinction is abandoned in IV, 1806, 164.
[14] (1), 1791, ii, 290.

The identity of acetous and acetic acids, asserted by Adet in 1798,[1] was still doubted by Dabit, of Nantes,[2] and Chaptal[3] but was confirmed by Proust[4] and Darracq.[5] Fourcroy[6] incorrectly supposed that prussic acid contains oxygen (which he doubted in the case of muriatic acid), because it is obtained by the action of nitric acid on many nitrogenous organic compounds, such as blood serum.

Fourcroy and Vauquelin[7] obtained benzoic acid by the action of hydrochloric acid on cow's or horse's urine or the drainage of manure, and proposed its use in pharmacy. Liebig[8] showed that it is really formed from another acid containing nitrogen, which he called 'hippuric acid', and he afterwards determined its formula as $C_9H_{10}NO_3$ (the correct formula is $C_9H_9NO_3$).[9] Liebig's statement that Fourcroy and Vauquelin mistook it for benzoic acid is incorrect.[10] Dessaignes[11] showed that the other product of the hydrolysis of hippuric acid is glycocoll (glycine):

$$C_6H_5 \cdot CO \cdot NH \cdot CH_2 \cdot COOH + H_2O = C_6H_5COOH + NH_2 \cdot CH_2 \cdot COOH$$

Fourcroy and Vauquelin investigated the acid of ants (formic acid),[12] incorrectly concluding that it is a mixture of acetic acid and malic acid, and date pollen,[13] in which they found malic acid, calcium and magnesium phosphates, and organic substances resembling albumin and gelatin. The individuality of formic acid was established by Suersen,[14] and Döbereiner[15] obtained formic acid by distilling tartaric acid solution with pyrolusite.

Fourcroy at first supposed that water is decomposed in fermentation, most of the oxygen burning the carbon of the sugar to carbonic acid, and the hydrogen combining with the decarbonised residue of the sugar to form alcohol, which is sugar plus hydrogen and minus some carbon.[16] He later thought that the oxygen came from the sugar to burn the carbon, whilst at the same time the hydrogen of the decarbonised sugar combined with more sugar to form alcohol, which is sugar minus some carbon and oxygen and plus hydrogen.[17]

Thenard[18] modified Lavoisier's theory of fermentation (see p. 480) by supposing that some carbon dioxide is first formed by the carbon of the yeast (ferment) combining with the oxygen of the sugar. The equilibrium is thus broken and the parts of the sugar combine to form carbon dioxide and alcohol. Part of the hydrogen of the ferment also combines with some oxygen of the sugar and its nitrogen probably enters, with the remaining elements of the sugar, into the composition of the alcohol. The rest of the elements of the ferment not so used form acetic acid and an insoluble precipitate.

[1] Ann. Chim., 1798, xxvii, 299.   [2] Ann. Chim., 1801, xxxviii, 66.
[3] Ann. Chim., 1799, xxviii, 113.   [4] J. de Phys., 1802, lvi, 200 (205, 211).
[5] Ann. Chim., 1802, xli, 264; Phil. Mag., 1802, xiii, 12.
[6] Ann. Chim., 1790, vi, 180; III, ix, 91.   [7] Ann. Chim., 1799, xxxi, 48 (62).
[8] Ann. Phys., 1829, xvii, 389.   [9] Ann., 1834, xii, 20.
[10] Volhard, Liebig, 1909, i, 204.   [11] Ann., 1846, lvii, 322.
[12] Fourcroy, Ann. Muséum d'Hist. Nat., 1802, i, 333.   [13] Ib., 1802, i, 417.
[14] N. allgem. J. Chem. (Gehlen), 1805, iv, 3, 553.
[15] J. Chem. Phys. (Schweigger), 1822, xxxv, 113.
[16] IV, 1795, 164.   [17] IV, 1806, 559.
[18] Ann. Chim., 1803, xlvi, 294 (308); Nicholson's J., 1804, vii, 33.

Brande[1] and Gay-Lussac[2] proved that alcohol is present as such in fermented liquors and is not produced on distillation, as had been stated by Fabroni,[3] since they separated alcohol by saturating the liquid with potassium carbonate.

The mechanism of the formation of ether by heating alcohol with sulphuric acid was not understood at the end of the eighteenth century. Macquer[4] regarded alcohol as a compound of an oil or phlogistic material and water. The sulphuric acid in converting alcohol into ether removes most of the water of the alcohol and 'brings it nearer in nature to the oils'. Later in the distillation, an 'oil of wine' passes over, since at the higher temperature the sulphuric acid removes more water. Bucquet regarded alcohol as a compound of oil, water, and an acid; when mixed with sulphuric acid it gave a sort of bituminous fluid which, on distillation, afforded the same principles as other bitumens, viz. a sort of naphtha (ether) and then a less volatile oil (oil of wine).[5]

Fourcroy[6] suggested tentatively that sulphuric acid in forming ether from alcohol oxidises part of the hydrogen of the alcohol to water, 'and the alcohol deprived of this portion of hydrogen forms ether.' In 1797,[7] however, Fourcroy and Vauquelin supposed that sulphuric acid, which remains unchanged, usually exerts a 'predisposing affinity' which causes hydrogen and oxygen to be removed from organic compounds in the form of water, whilst the parts remaining combine together. They thought that the 'ethers' (esters) formed by other acids were very similar to ordinary ether.

Fourcroy and Vauquelin found that a *small* quantity of ether, together with water, is formed from alcohol and sulphuric acid in the cold and they say that it must not be thought that ether is only alcohol minus oxygen and hydrogen (water), since carbon is also separated and relatively more than hydrogen. The oxygen which combines with hydrogen to form water saturates not only the hydrogen but the carbon of the alcohol, and since some carbon separates, and from the small amount of hydrogen in the water formed, it must be assumed that 'ether is alcohol plus hydrogen plus oxygen'. This corresponds with their analyses of alcohol and ether.[8]

Scheele[9] found that when alcohol is distilled with sulphuric acid and pyrolusite (manganese dioxide) there first passes over 'an ether which has a fine smell' (this would be aldehyde), and later in the distillation vinegar is formed. Laudet of Bordeaux (1800)[10] and Dabit[11] reported that ordinary ether is formed by this process, and that in the ordinary process ether is formed by oxidation of part of the hydrogen of the alcohol and not, as Fourcroy and Vauquelin supposed, by abstraction of the elements of water. Fourcroy and Vauquelin[12] found that the product in Scheele's process is not ordinary ether. It mixes in all proportions with water, has a different smell, a greater density, and a higher

[1] *Phil. Trans.*, 1811, ci, 337; 1813, ciii, 82.   [2] *Ann. Chim.*, 1813, lxxxvi, 175.
[3] *Ann. Chim.*, 1799, xxxi, 299 (303).   [4] *Dictionnaire*, 1766, i, 458.
[5] Fourcroy, I, 1793, iv, 245.   [6] I, 1793, iv, 246.
[7] *Ann. Chim.*, 1797, xxiii, 203 (De l'action de l'acide sulfurique sur l'alcool et la formation de l'éther); *Nicholson's J.*, 1797, i, 385; Crell's *Ann.*, 1798, I, 400.
[8] Volhard, *Liebig*, 1909, i, 273.
[9] KAH, 1782, iii, 35; *Collected Papers*, 1931, 230.   [10] Kopp, (1), iv, 326.
[11] *Ann. Chim.*, 1800, xxxiv, 289; *Allgem. J. Chem.*, 1801, vi, 444.
[12] *Ann. Chim.*, 1800, xxxiv, 318; *Allgem. J. Chem.*, 1801, vi, 453, 467.

boiling-point. It is, as Dabit discovered but did not carefully investigate, a new substance: 'by this operation the alcohol loses no carbon but a part of its hydrogen, which combines with the oxygen of the pyrolusite, and the liquid contains more carbon and oxygen and less hydrogen.' The substance was what was later called 'aldehyde' (i.e. alcohol dehydrogenatus), investigated by Döbereiner (1821–3) and Liebig (1831), and Fourcroy and Vauquelin's explanation is the correct one (see Vol. IV).

Fourcroy discovered an albuminous matter in vegetables[1] and showed that it contains nitrogen. Rouelle[2] had noticed the deposition from expressed vegetable juices of a green solid which he called *green fecula* and regarded as analogous to gluten of wheat, an opinion which was supported by experiments of Proust.[3] Thomson[4] pointed out that vegetable albumin was known to Scheele,[5] who calls it 'mucilaginous matter'. Fourcroy and Vauquelin also investigated gluten,[6] usually said to have been discovered in wheat flour by Jacopo Bartolomeo Beccaria,[7] but first prepared from wheat flour and named *glutin* by F. M. Grimaldi, a Jesuit of Bologna and the discoverer of the diffraction of light.[8] Gluten was partly separated into gliadin (soluble in alcohol) and zymome or glutenin (insoluble in alcohol) by Giovacchino Taddei, professor of organic chemistry, physics, and medicine in Florence,[9] and more fully by Ritthausen.[10] Fourcroy and Vauquelin[11] discovered sugar in onion juice, and investigated rubber latex from Mexico.[12] In his analysis of cinchona bark from San Domingo,[13] Fourcroy thought he had identified a proximate vegetable principle called 'extract' (*extractive*), which Vauquelin[14] found in the sap of trees. Hermbstädt[15] thought it was largely present in saffron, and Schrader[16] obtained it from cinchona bark. It was later recognised as a mixture of various substances, some of them products of decomposition.[17]

The *spiritus rector* of Boerhaave (Vol. II, p. 757) was retained by Fourcroy under the name aroma[18] but he later[19] said the odour of each essential oil is its

[1] Mémoire sur l'existence de la matière albumineuse dans les végétaux: *Ann. Chim.*, 1789, iii, 252.
[2] *J. de Médecine*, 1773, xxxix, 264; 1773, xl, 59; Crell's *Beyträge*, 1785, I, iii, 87; Murray, 1807, iv, 156, 164.
[3] *J. de Phys.*, 1802, lvi, 97; *Phil. Mag.*, 1803, xvii, 23.   [4] *Ency. Brit. Suppl.*, 1801, II, ii, 533.
[5] *Collected Papers*, 1931, 259.   [6] *Ann. Mus. d'Hist. Nat.*, 1806, vii, 1.
[7] *De Bononiensi Scientiarum et Artium Instituto atque Academia Commentaria*, 1745, ii, I, 122; J. and W. Thomson and D. Craigie, *Life of Cullen*, 1859, ii, 600, say Beccaria made the discovery in 1728; Beccaria (Bologna; 1682–1766) was professor of medicine, anatomy, and chemistry at the Bologna Institute.
[8] Grimaldi, *Physico-mathesis de Lvmine, Coloribvs, et Iride*, Bologna, 1665, 47, and index: remanet ipsum glutinum exsiccatum, durum ac inflexibile; R. Savelli, *VIIIe Congrès Internat. d'Hist. des Sciences*, Florence, 1956.
[9] *Ann. Phil.*, 1820, xv, 390; *J. Chem. Phys.* (Schweigger), 1820, xxix, 514.
[10] *J. prakt. Chem.*, 1864, xci, 296; see Thomson, (2) 1807, v, 32; Berzelius, *Lehrbuch der Chemie*, 1837, vi, 455; Lippmann, (7), 1921, 16, 43.   [12] *Ann. Chim.*, 1805, lv, 296.
[11] *Ann. Chim.*, 1808, lxv, 161.
[13] *Ann. Chim.*, 1791, viii, 113; 1791, ix, 7.
[14] *Ann. Chim.*, 1799, xxxi, 20; *Bull. Soc. Philomath.*, 1797, No. 10, 76.
[15] *Physikalisch-chemische Versuche und Beobachtungen*, Berlin, 1789, ii, 65; Crell's *Ann.*, 1793, II, 423, 493.
[16] *J. Chem. Phys.* (Gehlen), 1809, viii, 548: Extractivstoff.
[17] Turner, *Elements of Chemistry*, 6 ed. by Liebig and Gregory, 1847, 1158.
[18] I, 1793, iv, 139–46 (a whole chapter on it); IA, 1790, iii, 38; *Bull. Soc. Philomath.*, 1797, No. 7, 52; *Ann. Chim.*, 1798, xxvii, 232.
[19] III, 1802, vii, 361.

specific property. Fourcroy also at first thought that the colour of a dye was perhaps 'a very subtle body, perhaps not less so than the principle of smells',[1] but he also later abandoned this idea.[2]

Picric acid was obtained by Woulfe[3] by the action of nitric acid on indigo, and again by the same method by J. M. Hermann, of Colmar,[4] and by Fourcroy and Vauquelin.[5] Welter,[6] who says the work was done in An III (1794–5) under Guyton de Morveau, and called the substance *amer*, obtained it by the action of nitric acid on silk, along with oxalic acid, and mentioned that the potash salt is explosive 'like the report of a gun' (which is correct). It was also investigated by Chevreul.[7] Braconnot[8] obtained it by heating aloes with nitric acid. Fourcroy and Vauquelin (1806) called it 'hydro-carbure d'azote suroxigéné'.

Fourcroy mentions an opinion of Parmentier (see p. 102) that some bitumens (under which head he classes amber, asphalts, jet, coal and petroleum) are of animal origin, but he says some are of vegetable origin.[9] Fourcroy and Vauquelin[10] confirmed the observation of J. L. Macie (James Smithson)[11] that tabaschir is almost pure silica (containing only traces of potash and lime) and explained its production from a (colloidal) solution: it is 'portée dans le végétal à l'état de dissolution, et . . . deposée ensuite sous forme crystalline'.

When the bodies in the crowded cemetery of the Innocents in Paris were moved in 1786, Fourcroy and Thouret independently observed the presence of a waxy material in combination with ammonia, which Fourcroy named *adipocire*.[12] It had been observed long before by Sir Thomas Browne[13] in a body buried for ten years: 'large lumps of fat, in the consistence of the hardest castle [Castile] soap.' Fourcroy thought adipocire (a mixture of calcium and potassium palmitates, which has long disappeared from the text-books)[14] was the same as the material extracted from gall-stones by Conradi,[15] Gren in 1788,[16] and Fourcroy,[17] and called cholestérine by Chevreul,[18] but this identification is incorrect.[19]

[1] IA, 1790, iii, 76.   [2] III, 1802, viii, 51.
[3] Phil. Trans., 1771, lxi, 114.   [4] Obs. Phys., 1788, xxxii, 161.
[5] Ann. Chim., 1805, lv, 303; AdS, Mém. de l'Inst., 1806, vi, 531, 544.
[6] Ann. Chim., 1799 (An VII), xxix, 301.
[7] Ann. Chim., 1809, lxxii, 113.   [8] Ann. Chim., 1808, lxviii, 18 (28): chrysophanic acid.
[9] IA, 1790, ii, 570.   [10] AdS, Mém. de l'Inst., 1806, vi, 383.
[11] Phil. Trans., 1791, lxxxi, 368; Obs. Phys., 1792, xl, 122.
[12] Ann. Chim., 1790, v, 154; 1792, viii, 17; (2), 1796, iii, 662.
[13] Hydrotaphia; Urne Buriall, 1658 (probably written in 1656), 4 ed., London, 1736, 29; Barnes, Isis, 1934, xx, 337; letter of Oldenburg (1664), in Boyle, Works, ed. Birch, 1744, v, 323.
[14] See Chevreul, Ann. Chim., 1815, xcv, 5.
[15] Dissert. sistens experimenta nonnulla cum calculis vesiculæ felleæ humanæ instituta, 4°, Jena, 1775.
[16] Ann. Chim., 1790, v, 186; Crell's Beyträge, 1789, iv, 19.
[17] Ann. Chim., 1789, iii, 242.
[18] Mém. Muséum d'Hist. Nat., 1824, xi, 239; id., Recherches Chimiques sur les Corps gras d'Origine animale, Paris, 1823, 153; Ann. Chim., 1815, xcv, 5.
[19] T. Thomson, (6), 1843, 152, 574, who points out that Chevreul, Recherches, 159, says cholesterin was first obtained from biliary calculi by Poulletier de la Salle, and that this is also stated by Macquer, Dictionnaire, 1778, ii, 195: 'une espece de sel', deposited in glittering crystals from a hot solution in alcohol. François Paul Lyon Poulletier de la Salle (Lyon, 30 September 1719–Paris, 1787 or 1788) was president of the Société de la Médecine of Paris, and assisted Macquer in his Dictionnaire. Vicq D'Azyr, 1805, ii, 1–18.

According to Fourcroy[1] and Cuvier[2] the discovery of adipocire was turned to profit in England by converting the cadavers of horses into combustible substances by letting them stand in running water. This probably refers to the statements of G. Smith Gibbes,[3] who says a factory for working the process was established in Bristol.

Fourcroy and Vauquelin investigated milk, cheese, blood, bile, etc.,[4] tears and nasal mucus,[5] saliva and urine,[6] and the colouring matter of blood, which they thought was phosphate of iron with excess of oxygen and metal.[7]

Erasmus Darwin[8] said (probably from Crawford):

'When Air's pure essence joins the vital flood,
And with phosphoric Acid dyes the blood,

because when 'the pure part of the atmosphere' combines with 'the phlogistic part of the blood . . . the phosphoric acid is probably produced by this combination; by which acid the colour of the blood is changed in the lungs from a deep crimson to a bright scarlet'.

Vauquelin[9] afterwards gave up this fanciful theory and regarded the red colour as due to an organic substance; William Wells had suggested this in 1797,[10] although he thought the change of colour from purple to scarlet was due only to a finer state of division of the pigment. The name *haematosin* was given to the red colouring matter of blood by Le Canu.[11] Berzelius[12] proposed the present name *hæmatin*, suggesting that this name as then used (by Chevreul) for the vegetable colouring matter of logwood should be changed to hæmatoxylin, which was done.

Fourcroy and Vauquelin showed that fish-roe contains phosphorus,[13] and bones contain calcium and magnesium phosphates.[14] Calcium fluoride was discovered in the enamel of fossil elephant (mammal) teeth by Morichini.[15]

Domenico Pini Morichini (Civitantino, 23 September 1773–Rome, 19 November 1823), professor of chemistry in the Sapienza, Rome, reported that he had magnetised steel needles by exposure to ultraviolet light.[16] This was supposed to have been confirmed by Mrs. Mary Somerville[17] and by Zantedeschi,[18] but was disproved by Riess and Moser.[19]

[1] (2), 1797, iii, 684.　　　　　　　　　　[2] *Rapport historique*, 1828, 131.
[3] *Phil. Trans.*, 1794, lxxxiv, 169; 1795, lxxxv, 239; *id.*, *Observations on the Component Parts of Animal Matters; and on their conversion into a substance resembling Spermaceti*, Bath, 1796 (38 pp.); Thomson, (2), 1807, v, 775.
[4] Fourcroy, *Ann. Chim.*, 1790, vii, 146.
[5] Fourcroy and Vauquelin, *Ann. Chim.*, 1791, x, 113; 1808, lxvii, 26.
[6] Fourcroy and Vauquelin, AdS, *Mém. de l'Inst.*, 1799, ii, 431; 1804, iv, 112.
[7] Fourcroy, III, ix, 152.
[8] *The Economy of Vegetation*, pt. i of *The Botanic Garden*, 2 vols., Lichfield, 1789–91, 1789, i, canto I, lines 399–400, and note.
[9] *Ann. Chim.*, 1816, i, 9.　　　　　　　[10] *Phil. Trans.*, 1797, lxxxvii, 416.
[11] *Ann. Chim.*, 1830, xlv, 5; *Études Chimiques sur le sang humain*, Paris, 1838; Thomson, (6), 1843, 219, dates this 1837 and says the name was proposed by Chevreul, as does Gmelin, *Handbook*, 1871, xviii, 395, but I have found no correct reference to Chevreul on the matter.
[12] *Lehrbuch*, 1840, ix, 62.　　　　　[13] *Ann. Chim.*, 1807, lxiv, 5.
[14] *Ann. Muséum d'Hist. Nat.*, 1805, vi, 397.
[15] *Analisi di alcuni denti fossili di elefante trovati fuori della porta del popolo di Roma*, Rome, 1802; Poggendorff, (1), ii, 205.
[16] *Sopra la forza magnetizzante del lembo estremo del raggio violetto*, Rome, 1812, and *Memoria secondo sopra la forza magnetizzante*, etc., Rome, 1813; *Ann. Phys.*, 1813, xliii, 212.
[17] *Phil. Trans.*, 1826, cxvi, II, 132 (On the magnetizing power of the more refrangible solar rays); *Ann. Phys.*, 1826, vi, 493.
[18] *Ann. Phys.*, 1829, xvi, 187.　　　　　　[19] *Ann. Phys.*, 1829, xvi, 563.

Fluorine was discovered in normal teeth by Gay-Lussac,[1] and although Fourcroy and Vauquelin[2] failed to find it except in fossil teeth, its presence in bones and enamel of normal teeth was confirmed by Berzelius.[3]

Urea, obtained in an impure form by Rouelle junr. (p. 78), was prepared nearly pure in deliquescent yellowish-white quadrangular plates and named *urée* by Fourcroy and Vauquelin[4] (it is deliquescent only in very moist air when pure). Urea nitrate had been obtained by William Cruickshank in 1797[5] by adding concentrated nitric acid to evaporated urine, in 'shining slender scales, resembling the acid of borax'. He regarded it as 'some unknown animal acid, produced by the action of the nitrous acid on this urinous residuum' (i.e. the residue on evaporation of urine).

Thomson[6] says Fourcroy and Vauquelin do not mention Cruickshank in their paper of 1808 (see above), but 'Fourcroy added copious notes to the French translation of Rollo's work, and must therefore of necessity have been acquainted with that book'. Fourcroy repeatedly spoke of the 'long series of researches' made by himself and Vauquelin on urine. Fourcroy later[7] mentioned Cruickshank's discoveries (particularly of urea nitrate), but says he and Vauquelin made them 'bien avant le chimiste anglais'. Fourcroy and Vauquelin[8] say they had discovered urea before they got to know of Rollo's book from a long notice of it in the *Bibliothèque Britannique*.[9] Berzelius[10] was the first to obtain pure urea by way of the oxalate but the work was not known till the English translation of his book appeared.[11] Berzelius[12] later used nitric acid, saying that urea nitrate was first noticed by Cruickshank. Urea oxalate was investigated by Prout.[13]

Fourcroy[14] examined gall stones and calculi. In 1800 Fourcroy and Vauquelin[15] published an important memoir on the composition of urinary calculi, which somewhat extended the publications of Wollaston[16] — which they do not mention — and of Pearson,[17] who changed Scheele's name 'lithic acid' into 'uric oxide' or 'ouric oxide'; Fourcroy and Vauquelin[18] called it 'acide urique'. They analysed over 600 calculi and concluded that they are of twelve main species, consisting of the following substances, or mixtures of them: uric acid, urate of ammonia, phosphate of lime, phosphate of magnesia and ammonia,

[1] *Ann. Chim.*, 1805, lv, 258.   [2] *Ann. Chim.*, 1806, lvii, 37.
[3] *Lehrbuch der Chemie*, 1831, IV, i, 445, 451.
[4] AdS, *Mém. de l'Inst.*, 1799, ii, 431 (443); 1799–1800, iv, 402; *Ann. Chim.*, 1799, xxx, 66; *Ann. Mus. Hist. Nat.*, 1808, xi, 226–30.
[5] In J. Rollo, *An Account of Two Cases of the Diabetes Mellitus*, 1797, i, 113, 239.
[6] (6), 1843, 76.
[7] III, x, 114, 161 (déja remarqué par M. Cruicshanck).
[8] *Ann. Chim.*, 1800, xxxi, 48–71; 1800, xxxii, 80–162.
[9] *Bibl. Brit.*, 1798, vii, II, 307–49 (urea nitrate, p. 313); 1798, viii, II, 147–84.
[10] *Förelásningar i Djurkemien*, 1808, ii, 279.
[11] *View of the Progress and present State of Animal Chemistry*, tr. G. Brunnmark, 8°, London, 1813.
[12] *Traité de Chimie*, Paris, 1833, vii, 370, 372.
[13] *Med. Chirurg. Trans.*, 1817, viii, 526; 1818, ix, 472.
[14] *Ann. Chim.*, 1789, iii, 242; (2), 1793, ii, 671 f.
[15] *Ann. Chim.*, 1800, xxxii, 213; *Ann. Mus. Hist. Nat.*, 1802, i, 93–113 (with coloured plate); Fourcroy, *ib.*, 1803, ii, 201–9; Fourcroy, III, 1801, x, 204.
[16] *Phil. Trans.*, 1797, lxxxvii, 386; Thomson, (2), 1807, v, 690.
[17] *Phil. Trans.*, 1798, lxxxviii, 15 (37).   [18] *Ann. Chim.*, 1799, xxx, 57.

and oxalate of lime,[1] together with silica (very rare; 2 only) and animal matter. Uric acid was the commonest constituent. Fourcroy and Pouilletier de la Salle regarded biliary calculi as composed of adipocire (see p. 547) and resinous matter,[2] and Fourcroy and Vauquelin considered that bezoar stones (see Vol. II, p. 97) are composed of a kind of resin (probably ingested) in the case of those of the Persian wild goat; common bezoars consisted sometimes of phosphates of lime or magnesia, sometimes of concretions of resinous matter of bile.[3] Fourcroy[4] found that intestinal calculi (common in the horse) are composed of magnesium ammonium phosphate; human renal and urinary calculi were mostly uric acid (acide lithique).

A large collection of calculi was studied by Thomas Taylor,[5] who pointed out that Fourcroy and Vauquelin's 'résine animale bézoardique' in bezoar stones was really derived from the resinous parts of plants on which the wild goat feeds; it had been called Bezoarstoff by J. F. John,[6] Bezoarsäure by A. Lipowitz,[7] lithofellic acid by Göbel,[8] and resino-bezoardic acid by Taylor. Another kind examined by Taylor and by Merklein and Wöhler[9] consists of ellagic acid.[10]

Cuvier[11] says Fourcroy was the first to recognise the three main constituents of animal tissues and fluids: gelatin, fibrin, and albumin. Albumin and gelatin were clearly distinguished by Bostock[12] who found that albumin but not gelatin is precipitated by basic lead acetate. Bostock found that mucus is also precipitated by this reagent.[13] Fourcroy and Vauquelin[14] claimed to have shown that ox-blood contains bile and gelatin. By evaporating the serum they obtained a yellow liquid like bile. Parmentier and Deyeux[15] could not confirm this, but Deyeux[16] did later with 'le sang bilieux'. Fourcroy and Vauquelin[17] by heating blood or flesh with nitric acid obtained a yellow bitter solution giving a detonating solid product which they called 'hydro-carbure d'azote suroxigéné' (probably picric acid); the first observation had been made by William Higgins.[18] The presence of gelatin in blood was refuted by Bostock.

Fourcroy[19] introduced the name fibrin in its present meaning; the nature of the coagulation of the blood had been a subject of discussion and experiment

[1] Bergman had found oxalic acid in calculi in 1776: Opuscula, i, 254.
[2] Fourcroy, Mém. Soc. de Méd., 1789, x, p. xxii; id., (2), 1793, ii, 671 f.
[3] Fourcroy, Ann. du Muséum d'Hist. Nat., 1803, ii, 201.
[4] (2), 1793, ii, 671 f.
[5] Phil. Mag., 1838, xii, 337, 412; 1844, xxiv, 354; 1846, xxviii, 36, 192.
[6] Neue chemische Untersuchungen mineralischer, vegetabilischer und animalischer Substanzen, Berlin, 1811, iii, 37–40.
[7] In F. Simon, Beiträge zur physiologischen und pathologischen Chemie und Mikroskopie, Berlin, 1844, i, 463–7: Ueber eine neue organische Säure in den Bezoarsteinen.
[8] Ann., 1841, xxxix, 237; 1851, lxxix, 83; 1852, lxxxiii, 280; Wöhler, ib., 1842, xli, 150.
[9] Ann., 1845, lv, 129 (bezoardic acid).
[10] Guibourt, Compt. Rend., 1843, xvi, 130–4; Nierenstein, The Natural Organic Tannins, London, 1934, 131.
[11] Rapport historique, 1828, 113; see Fourcroy, Histoire des découvertes sur la chimie animale, in his III, ix, 25 f., and his paper in AdS, 1789, h x, m 297 (Nouv. expér. sur les matières animales).
[12] Nicholson's J., 1805, xi, 244.
[13] Ib., 1806, xiv, 140.
[14] Ann. Chim., 1790, vi, 177.
[15] J. de Phys., 1794, xliv, 372 (388).
[16] AdS, Mém. div. Sav., 1805, i, 136.
[17] AdS, Mém. de l'Inst., 1806, vi, 531, 544.
[18] Comparative View of the Phlogistic and Antiphlogistic Theories, 1789, 163.
[19] III, ix, 136, 157.

since Aristotle's time.[1] In his analysis of brain Fourcroy[2] found that it had no oily or soapy character but is albuminous, and also contains mucus, other animal matters, and phosphates, It was further examined by Vauquelin (see below).

The text-books of the early nineteenth century[3] are full of references to the pioneering work of Fourcroy and Vauquelin. Most of it soon became obsolete as the methods of chemical analysis improved. Chemical analysis, now regarded as a routine occupation, was in their day a necessary branch of chemical discovery, since the laws of chemical combination were still unknown. Methods for the isolation of organic compounds from vegetable and animal materials were also hardly known before their time. It is the destiny of pioneers to be forgotten and their work superseded in other walks of life besides chemistry.

VAUQUELIN

Louis Nicolas Vauquelin (Saint-Andrée d'Hébertat, nr. Pont l'Evêque, Normandy; 16 May 1763–14 November (or October) 1829), the son of a farm bailiff, was born in a Normandy village, where, after a brilliant career in Paris, he retired after a long illness to die. In 1776 he was apprenticed to an apothecary in Rouen: his master gave lessons in chemistry which Vauquelin heard in secret and made notes, which when discovered were impounded and his menial position explained to him. He left Rouen and wandered to Paris, where he arrived penniless and ill, but a friendly apothecary, Cheradame, got him a post as laboratory boy with Fourcroy in 1780. Fourcroy soon recognised Vauquelin's capacity and made him his assistant and colleague. Vauquelin was associated with Fourcroy for nine years. A member of the Paris Academy in 1791, Vauquelin became professor at the École des Mines in 1794, also teaching in the École Polytechnique. In 1801 he succeeded D'Arcet at the Collège de France, and in 1802 he became Assayer to the Mint. His *Manuel de l'essayeur* was published in 1799. Vauquelin was admitted to the Legion of Honour on its foundation by Napoleon. In 1803 he was made Director of the new École Spéciale de Pharmacie; in 1804 he succeeded Anton Louis Brongniart (d. 1804) as professor at the Jardin des Plantes. He succeeded Fourcroy in 1811 as professor in the Medical Faculty, gaining his doctorate of medicine by a thesis on the composition of the brain,[4] in which he established the existence of organic compounds of phosphorus (lecithins). He was dismissed in 1822 but pensioned in 1823. His lectures on salts at the École Polytechnique were published (with other lectures).[5]

Vauquelin's character was simple and honest and he did not participate in the politics of the troubled times in which he lived. Davy says his methods

[1] Detailed summary by Gulliver, in *The Works of William Hewson*, 1846, pp. xxv–xlviii.
[2] (2), iii, 155–67.
[3] Thomson, (2); W. B. Johnson, *History of the Progress and Present State of Animal Chemistry*, 3 vols., London, 1803.
[4] *Analyse de la matière cérébrale de l'homme et de quelques animaux*, 4°, Paris, Med. Fac., 1811, 26 pp.; *Ann. Chim.*, 1812, lxxxi, 37; *Ann. Phil.*, 1813, i, 332.
[5] *J. de l'École Polytechnique*, 1794, i, 145, 169, 349, 646.

were more those of a pharmacist than a chemist,[1] but Cuvier that: 'il était tout chimiste, chimiste chaque jour de sa vie et pendant la durée de chaque jour'; Gmelin calls him 'ein sehr geschickter Künstler', and Thomson says he 'was by far the most industrious of the French chemists, and has published more papers, consisting of mineral, vegetable and animal analyses, than any other chemist without exception, . . . he was respected and esteemed by every person.'[2]

FIG. 50. L. N. VAUQUELIN, 1763–1829.

Two of Fourcroy's sisters, Mme. Lebailly and Guedon, who kept a small perfume and toy shop, nursed Vauquelin when he was ill, and lent him a little money, saying: 'Acceptez; si quelque jour vous réussissez, vous nous rendrez ces légères avances.' When Fourcroy died in 1809, Vauquelin was able to offer the two ladies a home, and they lived with him until they died, keeping house for him.[3]

[1] *Works*, 1839, i, 166.
[2] *Allgem. J. Chem.*, 1802, viii (portr.); Arnault, *Biographie Nouvelle des Contemporaines*, 1825, xx, 455; J. B. A. Chevallier, *Inauguration d'un monument à la mémoire de Louis-Nicolas Vauquelin. Notice Biographique*, extr. from *J. Chim. Méd.*, 1850, xxvi, 249, 540–59; Cuvier, Éloge (1831), AdS, *Mém. de l'Inst.*, 1833, XII, xxxix–lvj; Gmelin, (1), iii, 439; Kopp, (1), i, 350; E. Pariset, *Histoire des Membres de l'Académie Royale de Médecine*, Paris, 1845, i, 316; Poggendorff, (1), i, 1182–90 (list of publs.); J. M. Quérard, *La France Littéraire*, 1839, x, 79 (list of publications); *Roy. Soc. Cat. Sci. Pap.*, 1872, vi, 114 (305 + 15 papers); Thomson, (1), ii, 211; A. Vauquelin, NBG, 1866, xlv, 1033.
[3] Chevallier, 10, 14; Davy, *loc. cit.*

We can picture Vauquelin, modest and industrious, working away in Fourcroy's laboratory and turning out results which the brilliant and eloquent Fourcroy, busy with so many other matters, worked up into joint (or sometimes singular) memoirs in his lucid and attractive style; but whether this picture has any relation to the facts we cannot stay to investigate. The experimental work in many of the joint researches was probably carried out by Vauquelin alone, but the two formed an excellent combination of talents, like Gay-Lussac and Thenard later on. In his large laboratory Vauquelin also taught pupils and made chemicals and reagents for sale.

Vauquelin made a large number of analyses of minerals. Thomson says the results were sometimes vitiated by a poor choice of the specimens given to him by Haüy. Nevertheless, in this work Vauquelin discovered two new elements, chromium and beryllium. Chromium oxide was discovered in 1797 (independently of Klaproth) in a specimen of a new mineral ('red lead spar', now called crocoïsite) from Siberia, described in 1762 by Lehmann (see p. 98), which Vauquelin and Marquardt had examined in 1789 without finding anything new in it. In 1797 Vauquelin[1] prepared a number of chromium compounds from it, including potassium dichromate, lead chromate, impure chromic anhydride (prepared in a purer condition by Count Apollo Mussin-Pushkin of St. Petersburg in 1798),[2] and green chromic oxide — the latter important in providing a green glaze for porcelain.[3] He obtained metallic chromium in 1798.[4]

In 1798 Vauquelin[5] examined beryl, which Haüy suspected was the same as the true emerald, and found in it a new 'earth' which he called 'la terre de béril', but, since its compounds have a sweet taste, the editors of the *Annales de Chimie* proposed to call it 'glucina', from the Greek γλυκύς, sweet. The name 'beryllia' was substituted for this by German chemists.[6] The metal beryllium was first isolated independently by Bussy[7] and Wöhler[8] by heating the anhydrous chloride with potassium.

Vauquelin[9] confirmed that alum is not simply sulphate of alumina but also contains potash or ammonia (see p. 381, Lavoisier). Soda alum was described as a product of the Whitby alum works by R. Winter.[10]

A convenient method of preparing baryta (the carbonate is very stable) found by Vauquelin in 1797 is by heating the nitrate.[11] Fourcroy and

[1] *Ann. Chim.*, 1798, xxv, 21, 194; 1809, lxx, 70 (Analyse du plomb rouge de Sibérie et expériences sur le nouveau métal qu'il contient); *Nicholson's J.*, 1799, ii, 387.

[2] Crell's *Ann.*, 1798, I, 355; 1798, II, 443; 1799, I, 3.   [3] Cuvier, *Rapport hist.*, 1828, 85.

[4] *Ann. Chim.*, 1798, xxv, 194.   [5] *Ann. Chim.*, 1798, xxvi, 155, 169 (editors).

[6] H. F. Link, *Allgem. J. Chem.* (Scherer), 1799, iii, 603; Klaproth, *Beiträge zur chemischen Kenntniss der Mineralkörper*, Posen and Berlin, 1802, iii, 79.

[7] *J. Chim. Médic.*, 1828, iv, 455.

[8] *Ann. Phys.*, 1828, xiii, 577; *Ann. Chim.*, 1828, xxxix, 77.

[9] *Ann. Chim.*, 1797, xxii, 258; 1804, l, 154.

[10] *Nicholson's J.*, 1810, xxv, 241–57 (254); Kopp, (1), iv, 64, thought it was first described by Zellner, of Plass, in 1816; *J. Chem. Phys.*, 1816, xviii, 344; Thomson, (4), 1831, ii, 766, says it 'was perhaps first formed about the year 1805 by Charles Macintosh, Esq., of Cross Basket. Mr. W. Wilson of Hurlet, near Glasgow, furnished me with beautiful specimens of it about the year 1823'.

[11] Fourcroy, AdS, *Mém. de l'Inst.*, 1799, ii, 57 (saying the discovery was made by Vauquelin alone); *Ann. Chim.*, 1797, xxi, 276.

T

Vauquelin[1] found that phosphorus does not glow in moist oxygen at room temperature. Vauquelin[2] showed (as had been found by Louis Lemery[3] with sea-salt and nitre) that more of a salt may dissolve in its saturated solution if a second salt is added. He described a method for the quantitative analysis of stones,[4] analysed gadolinite,[5] and found soda in cryolite ('chrysolith') from Greenland.[6] The mineral, brought from Greenland by Andrade, was first examined by Peter Christian Abilgaard (Copenhagen; 22 December 1740–11 January 1801), director of the Veterinary College in Copenhagen, who named it Kryolith or Iissteen (from κρύος, ice).[7]

Sodium thiosulphate was discovered by François Chaussier (see p. 95)[8] by the action of sulphur dioxide on sodium sulphide solution and in other ways. He called it hydrosulfure sulfuré de soude. Vauquelin[9] showed that the salt, 'sufite de soude sulfuré', is also formed by boiling sulphur with sodium sulphite solution. John Frederick William Herschel (Slough, 7 March 1792–London, 11 May 1871) prepared a number of thiosulphates, which he called 'hyposulphites' (a name still used). He determined correctly the composition of the acid (the anhydride is $2S + 2O$), found that the sodium salt is formed by the oxidation of a solution of sodium sulphide, noticed that the silver salt precipitated by silver nitrate dissolves in excess of sodium thiosulphate solution to give a liquid with a sweet taste, and that 'muriate of silver [AgCl], newly precipitated, dissolves in this salt [sodium thiosulphate], when in a somewhat concentrated solution, in large quantity and almost as readily as sugar in water'.[10] This was later applied in fixing photographs (see Vol. IV).

Vauquelin investigated cerium compounds and prepared metallic cerium,[11] tungstates,[12] and meteorites,[13] which Edward Howard[14] found to consist mainly of iron and nickel. Vauquelin showed that the minerals rutile and anatase are two varieties of titanium oxide,[15] prepared fairly pure lead dioxide by boiling red-lead with dilute nitric acid,[16] and determined the composition of carbon disulphide by passing the vapour over red-hot copper.[17]

Fourcroy and Vauquelin[18] investigated the properties of nitrous oxide, confirming many of Davy's results. In 1803–4 they described the residue from the action of aqua regia on native platinum as a new metal;[19] it was shown to con-

[1] *Ann. Chim.*, 1797, xxi, 189. [2] *Ann. Chim.*, 1792, xiii, 86.
[3] AdS, 1716 (1718), m 154.
[4] *Ann. Chim.*, 1799 (An VII), xxx, 66–106: Réflexions sur l'analyse des pierres en général, et resultats de plusieurs de ces analyses faites au laboratoire de l'école des mines depuis quelques mois.
[5] *Ann. Chim.*, 1801, xxxvi, 143.
[6] Vauquelin, *Ann. Chim.*, 1801, xxxvii, 89; Jameson, *Mem. Wernerian Nat. Hist. Soc.*, 1811, i, 465–8.
[7] *Dansk. Vidensk. Selskab. Skrivt.*, 1800, i, 305.
[8] *Bull. Soc. Philomath.*, 1799, no. 33, 70.
[9] *Bull. Soc. Philomath.*, 1799, no. 33, 71; *Ann. Chim.*, 1802, xli, 190.
[10] *Edin. N. Phil. J.*, 1819, i, 8, 396; 1820, ii, 154.   [11] *Ann. Chim.*, 1805, liv, 28.
[12] *J. des Mines*, 1795–6, iv, No. xix, p. 10 (with Hecht).
[13] *J. des Mines*, 1802–3, xiii, 308; *Ann. Chim.*, 1802, xlv, 225.
[14] *Phil. Trans.*, 1802, xcii, 168.
[15] *Ann. Chim.*, 1802, xlii, 72; *Nicholson's J.*, 1806, xv, 322; AdS, *Mém. de l'Inst.*, 1807, viii, I, 159.
[16] *Ann. Chim.*, 1807, lxii, 221.   [17] *Ann. Muséum Hist. Nat.*, 1812, xix, 396.
[18] AdS, *Mém. de l'Inst.*, 1806, vi, 312.   [19] *Ann. Chim.*, 1804, xlix, 188; 1804, l, 5.

tain two metals, osmium and iridium, by Smithson Tennant in 1804.[1]
Vauquelin[2] described a method for separating platinum, palladium, rhodium,
iridium, and osmium. He confirmed the existence of lithia,[3] discovered by
Arfvedson in Berzelius's laboratory whose paper was published later.[4]
Vauquelin received news of the discovery and a specimen of petalite from a
correspondent in Sweden. He showed that alkali sulphides should be regarded
as compounds of the *metals* with sulphur,[5] and analysed native silver iodide
from Mexico.[6]

Vauquelin, partly in collaboration with Fourcroy, discovered several important organic compounds. They distinguished a number of 'proximate
constituents' (Fourcroy's *principes immédiats*) in vegetables, such as acids, oils,
camphor, gum, resin, tannin, starch, fibre, cork, caoutchouc, and extractive (a
product of extraction with cold water and evaporation).[7] Several definite compounds which had previously been obtained but the existence of which was in
doubt were confirmed. Among these was malic acid and its salts. Sodium
malate (with other salts of organic acids) was obtained by Donald Monro in
1767[8] and the acid from apples by Scheele in 1785 (see p. 232). The acid and
its salts were studied by Fourcroy and Vauquelin.[9] Vauquelin[10] showed that
the 'sorbic acid' isolated from mountain-ash berries by Donovan[11] is malic acid
(the modern sorbic acid is a different substance); Vauquelin's elementary
analysis of malic acid was inaccurate.

Quinic acid, obtained by F. C. Hofmann[12] from the calcium salt discovered
by Hermbstädt,[13] was investigated by Vauquelin.[14] Henry and Plisson[15] found
for it the incorrect formula $C_2H_4O_3$. Liebig[16] found $C_{15}H_{24}O_{12}$, and S. Baup[17]
$C_{15}H_{20}O_{10}$, for the anhydride ($C=6$, $O=8$). The correct formula $C_7H_{12}O_6$ for
the acid ($C=12$, $O=16$) was first found by Woskresensky.[18]

Pyroligneous acid[19] was shown by Fourcroy and Vauquelin[20] to be impure
acetic acid, and Berthollet's zoonic acid (1798 (see p. 514)), obtained by the
distillation of gluten and animal matter, was shown by Thenard[21] to be also
mostly impure acetic acid. On the other hand, Fourcroy and Vauquelin mistakenly supposed that some definite organic acids such as formic and lactic
acids, which do not crystallise, and pyrotartaric acid, are acetic acid contaminated by impurities which are difficult to separate.[22] Some of their mistakes were
due to incorrect methods of treatment; e.g. they distilled lactic acid, although

[1] *Phil. Trans.*, 1804, xciv, 411.   [2] *Ann. Chim.*, 1814, lxxxix, 150, 225.
[3] *Ann. Chim.*, 1817, vii, 284.
[4] Arfvedson, KAH, 1818, 23 (he says it was named by Berzelius); *Ann. Chim.*, 1819, x, 82;
Berzelius, *ib.*, 103.
[5] *Ann. Chim.*, 1817, vi, 5; Gay-Lussac, *ib.*, 321.   [6] *Ann. Chim.*, 1825, xxix, 99.
[7] Vauquelin, *Bull. Soc. Philomath.*, 1798, No. 10, 76; Fourcroy, (1), vii, 125; Thomson, (2),
1807, v, 106.
[8] *Phil. Trans.*, 1767, lvii, 479.   [9] *Ann. Chim.*, 1800, xxxiv, 127; 1800, xxxv, 153.
[10] *Ann. Chim.*, 1817, vi, 337.   [11] *Ann. Chim.*, 1816, i, 281.
[12] Crell's *Ann.*, 1790, II, 314.   [13] Crell's *Ann.*, 1785, I, 115.
[14] *Ann. Chim.*, 1806, lix, 113 (162).
[15] *Ann. Chim.*, 1827, xxv, 165; *J. de Pharm.*, 1829, xv, 389: acide kinique.
[16] *Ann. Chim.*, 1831, xlvii, 147 (193); *Ann.*, 1833, vi, 14.
[17] *Ann. Chim.*, 1831, li, 56–72.   [18] *Ann.*, 1838, xxvii, 257.
[19] *Acide pyroligneux* in Lavoisier, *Traité de Chimie*, 1789, 286.
[20] *Ann. Chim.*, 1800, xxxv, 161.   [21] *Ann. Chim.*, 1802, xliii, 176.
[22] *Ann. Chim.*, 1800, xxxv, 161; 1807, lxiv, 42.

Scheele (see p. 233) had previously said that this converts it into acetic acid. Crell[1] thought he had shown that tartaric, oxalic, and acetic acids are all modifications of the same acid; Hermbstädt[2] thought that other vegetable acids could be converted into acetic acid, and Bouillon Lagrange at first adopted these views (see p. 108).

Vauquelin[3] suspected that an oxyacid of cyanogen (*acide cyanique*) is formed when cyanogen is dissolved in water or alkali: this is correct but the cyanates were first characterised by Wöhler in 1822 (see Vol. IV). Vauquelin[4] was the first to investigate vegetable jelly (pectin) in fruits. He examined 'vegetable albumin' in the juice of the *Carica papaya* of the Isle de France,[5] ulmin in excrescences from elm bark,[6] and salts of mellitic acid.[7] Buniva and Vauquelin[8] obtained a crystalline substance from what they supposed was the amniotic liquid of the fœtal calf and called it *acide amnique*, since they thought it was acid in reaction. Dzóndi[9] and Prout[10] were unable to find it in amniotic liquid and Lassaigne[11] showed that it is really contained in the allantoic liquid, hence calling it *acide allantoïque*. C. G. Gmelin[12] then found that it did not neutralise bases, and Liebig and Wöhler, who confirmed this (except for silver oxide) and found it to be a neutral substance, renamed it *allantoin*.[13] Wöhler[14] obtained it by oxidising uric acid with a suspension of lead dioxide, and established its formula.

Vauquelin discovered asparagine in asparagus in 1805;[15] the name is due to Thomson.[16] Aspartic acid (aminosuccinic acid) was discovered by Plisson[17] by boiling asparagus with water and lead oxide till evolution of ammonia ceased. Dessaignes[18] showed that it forms succinic acid on fermentation.

Vauquelin investigated cinchona bark[19] and belladonna,[20] but the alkaloid and glycoside, respectively, which are present were isolated only by later chemists (see Vol. IV). The alkaline substance which Vauquelin obtained by distilling *Daphne alpina* with magnesia[21] was called daphnin by Berzelius,[22] but its nature is doubtful. C. G. Gmelin and F. L. Baer[23] obtained true daphnin from mezerion bark (*Daphne mezerium*) and showed that it is a colourless neutral crystalline solid which they regarded as similar to asparagin, but it is really a glycoside.

Many other investigations of Vauquelin in animal chemistry include those

[1] *Obs. Phys.*, 1785, xxvii, 297.   [2] See p. 579; Chaptal, (1), 1791, iii, 120.
[3] *Ann. Chim.*, 1818, ix, 113; *Ann. Mus. d'Hist. Nat.*, 1819, v, 1–33.
[4] *Ann. Chim.*, 1790, v, 92 (101); 1790, vi, 275 (282).
[5] *Ann. Chim.*, 1802, xliii, 267; 1804, xlix, 295; Cadet, *ib.*, 1804, xlix, 250.
[6] *Ann. Chim.*, 1797, xxi, 39.
[7] *Ann. Chim.*, 1801, xxxvi, 203; *Nicholson's J.*, 1800, iv, 515.
[8] *Ann. Chim.*, 1800, xxxiii, 269; Michel François Buniva (1761–1834), professor of medicine in Turin (1790–1814).
[9] *N. Allgem. J. Chem.*, 1805, ii, 652.
[10] *Ann. Phil.*, 1815, v, 416.
[11] *Ann. Chim.*, 1821, xvii, 295.
[12] *Ann. Phys.*, 1820, lxiv, 347–53.
[13] *Ann.*, 1838, xxvi, 241.   [14] *Gött. Nachr.*, 1849, 61.
[15] *Ann. chim.*, 1806, lvii, 88; Robiquet, *ib.*, 1809, lxxii, 143; Liebig, *Ann.*, 1833, vii, 146.
[16] (2), 1807, v, 35.   [17] *Ann. Chim.*, 1829, xl, 309.
[18] *Compt. Rend.*, 1850, xxxi, 432.   [19] *Ann. Chim.*, 1806, lix, 113.
[20] *Ann. Chim.*, 1809, lxxii, 53.   [21] *Ann. Chim.*, 1812, lxxxiv, 173.
[22] *Lehrbuch der Chemie*, 1827, III, i, 291.   [23] *J. Chem. Phys.*, 1822, xxxv, 1–28.

on semen,[1] synovial fluid,[2] hair,[3] and suint;[4] he rediscovered uric acid in serpent excrement,[5] in which it had previously been found by Prout.[6]

CHAPTAL

Jean Antoine Claude Chaptal (Nogaret (Lozère), 9 May (or 4 June) 1756–Paris, 30 July 1832) was professor of chemistry and a practising physician in Montpellier. His lectures there were published in 1783.[7] In 1793 he was brought by Fourcroy to Paris to be director of a gunpowder factory, but he returned to his chair at Montpellier in 1794. In 1798 he followed Berthollet at the École des Arts; in 1800–4 as Minister of the Interior he was instrumental in developing chemical industry, and in directing large chemical factories which he owned at Rouen and Montpellier. Napoleon made him Count de Chanteloup and Louis XVIII in 1819 created him a peer of France.

Chaptal, a wealthy industrialist and man of the world, was independent of the small circle of academicians in Paris. He was very well informed and had wide interests. His books were much read, show originality, and are still pleasant to read; 'tous se font remarquer par l'élégance du style, par une méthode rigoureuse et une grande clarté.'[8] He adopted the ideas of the Revolution but so far disapproved of its excesses as to be imprisoned, but he was soon released.[9]

Chaptal was the author of two very good and popular text books:

I. Élémens de Chimie, 3 vols. 8°, Paris and Montpellier, 1790 (Duveen, 129; not in BM or BN); Paris, 1794, 1796 (the ed. used), 1804;
IA. tr. W. Nicholson, Elements of Chemistry, 3 vols. 8°, London, 1791 (the ed. used), 1795, 1800, 1803; American eds.
II. Chimie appliquée aux Arts, 4 vols. 8°, Paris, 1807, with 12 fold. copperplates (CUL Hh. 57. 43);
IIA. tr. by W. Nicholson, Chemistry Applied to Arts and Manufactures, 4 vols. 8°, London, 1807 (one of the best treatises on technical chemistry of its time, and the preface contains some economic and political considerations which are still true).

He also wrote a number of other works dealing with various branches of applied chemistry:

Mémoires de Chimie, vol. i, Montpellier, 1781 (BN); Essai sur le Perfectionnement des Arts Chimiques en France, Paris, 1800 (repr. in *Ann. Chim.*, 1800, xxxiii, 295; 1800, xxxiv, 112); Essai sur le Blanchîment, Paris, 1801 (see Lavoisier and Berthollet, *Ann. Chim.*, 1789, i, 69; Lavoisier, Oeuvres, 1868, iv, 484); Art de Faire, de Gouverner et de Perfectionner les Vins, Paris, 1801 (also in *Ann. Chim.*, 1800–1, xxxv, xxxvi, xxxvii), and 1819; Traité theorique et pratique de la Culture de la Vigne, avec l'Art de faire le Vin, with Rozier, Parmentier, and Dussieux, 2 vols., Paris, 1801, 1807, 1839 (BN); L'Art de la Teinteure du Coton en Rouge, Paris, 1807 (BN); L'Industrie

---

[1] *Ann. Chim.*, 1791, ix, 64.   [2] *Ann. Chim.*, 1817, vi, 399.
[3] *Ann. Chim.*, 1806, lviii, 41.   [4] *Ann. Chim.*, 1803, xlvii, 276.
[5] *Ann. Chim.*, 1822, xxi, 440.   [6] *Ann. Phil.*, 1815, v, 413; 1819, xiv, 363.
[7] *Tableau analytique du Cours de Chimie, fait à Montpellier*, 8°, Montpellier, 1783 (209 pp.) (Nourry-Thiébaud *Cat.*, Paris, 1938, No. 66, 862).
[8] Anon., NBU, 1854, ix, 706–9.
[9] E. V. Armstrong and H. S. Lukens, *J. Chem. Educ.*, 1936, xiii, 257; Brande, 1848, I, xci; Flourens, AdS, 1838, xv, h i–xxxix; J. Pigeire, *La Vie et l'Oeuvre de Chaptal*, Paris, 1932, 394 pp. (*Isis*, 1934, xx, 548); Vibert, *Ann. Chim. Anal.*, 1944, xxvi, 76; K. R. Webb, *Chem. and Ind.*, 1956, 1443–5.

Françoise, 2 vols., Paris, 1819; Chimie appliquée à l'Agriculture, 2 vols., Paris, 1823, 2 ed. 1829 (BN); Chemistry Applied to Agriculture, with Additions, 18°, New York, 1840.

Chaptal emphasised the close relation between physics and chemistry in an eloquent and interesting preliminary discourse.[1] He considered that historical treatment of a subject is out of place and only permissible when it affords

FIG. 51. JEAN ANTOINE CHAPTAL (1756–1832).

interesting facts or leads 'by uninterrupted degrees to the present state of our knowledge',[2] yet he has a long mention of Rey,[3] saying that in 1630 he 'attributed the increase in weight in calcined metals to the combination of air with the metal [sic]', and that Libavius was his friend whom he disliked to contradict; he also gives a short biography of Palissy[4] and frequently quotes Becher with approbation, including his claim for the reality of transmutation.[5] He showed that a volume of hydrogen could be breathed several times, and is not poisonous and not absorbed in the lungs.[6] The rise in pitch of the voice after breathing hydrogen was described by Maunoir.[7] Chaptal[8] mentions a flexible marble, and says he obtained quartz crystals by letting hydrofluoric acid stand for two years in a glass vessel.[9] He mentions colloidal silica (*guhr*)

[1] IA, 1791, I, p. lvi.   [2] IA, i, 56.   [3] IA, 1791, ii, 216.
[4] Ib., ii, 90.   [5] Ib., ii, 215, 456 f.; iii, 240, 246, 394, 396–7, 399.   [6] Ib., i, 108.
[7] Phil. Mag., 1799, iv, 214.   [8] IA, 1791, ii, 23.   [9] Ib., ii, 117.

found in the earth, on which quartz crystals were growing.[1] He thought the vitreous earth of Becher (see Vol. II, p. 644) was heavy spar,[2] but the quotation he gives (lapidis species quæ in igne fluant, et fluens vitrum exhibet) suits fluorspar. He thought, from their property of phosphorescence, that there was an analogy of fluorspar with diamond.[3]

Chaptal mentions the name *cendres gravelées* for burnt tartar.[4] He gives seven methods proposed for making soda from common salt:[5] (i) decomposing with nitric acid and detonating the nitrate of soda with charcoal, (ii) the action of potash (K_2CO_3) in the cold (as he says he found), (iii) forming sulphate of soda with sulphuric acid and heating with charcoal to form sulphide ('does not appear to be economical') or decomposing the sulphate with acetite of barytes and calcining the acetite of soda, (iv) Marggraf's process of throwing salt on fused lead, (v) Scheele's and Turner's process of decomposing salt mixed with litharge to a paste ('never complete'), (vi) Bergman's method of decomposition by barytes, (vii) salts of lead with vegetable acids precipitate muriate of lead, and the soluble soda salt is calcined. He supposed that soda was a compound of ammonia with magnesia, and potash of ammonia with lime, from experiments by himself, Thouvenel, De Luc, Deyeux, Lorgna and Osburg.[6] In 1790 he still thought that alum is sulphate of alumina, and that the function of the alkali added was only to neutralise the excess of acid which prevented crystallisation;[7] in 1807[8] he corrected this, with a reference to Marggraf; it had also been established by Lavoisier in 1777 (see p. 381).

The Epsom salt sold on the Continent and extracted from salt brine was very impure.[9] Chaptal pointed out that many antimonial preparations used in medicine are dangerous because of the varying antimony content, and recommended inspection to check fraudulent manufacture.[10] The fuming liquor of Libavius ($SnCl_4$) is 'a muriate of tin, in which the acid is in the state of the oxigenated muriatic acid'.[11]

Chaptal still believed that water could be converted into earth, on the basis of Van Helmont's experiment, and says fish grow in water alone.[12] He thought that salts and iron are formed in plants, and earth from mucilage in testaceous animals.[13] Atmospheric nitrogen, he thought, formed alkalis when plants were burned.[14] Monro[15] had considered that only those acids are identical which form exactly the same salts with the same base, but Chaptal quotes in detail experiments of Hermbstädt, Crell, Scheele, Westrumb, Berthollet, Lavoisier, etc., which show that 'the vegetable acids are merely modifications of one or two primitive acids'.[16] He thought Chinese ink was made from sepia (it is really a carbon black).[17] He gives a good account of the history and preparation of phosphorus (emphasising that Kunckel and Boyle discovered it independently of Brand) and of phosphoric acid, thinking that Becher's statement 'homo

[1] *Ib.*, ii, 119; see Guyton de Morveau, p. 519.   [2] *Ib.*, ii, 203.
[3] *Ib.*, ii, 45.   [4] *Ib.*, i, 172.
[5] *Ib.*, i, 260; he does not mention the Leblanc process.   [6] *Ib.*, i, 181.
[7] *Ib.*, ii, 64; this question had been investigated by Bergman in 1767: *Essays*, 1788, i, 377 f.
[8] IIA, 1807, iv, 39.   [9] IA., ii, 56.   [10] *Ib.*, ii, 260 f.   [11] *Ib.*, ii, 318.
[12] *Ib.*, iii, 22, 30.   [13] *Ib.*, iii, 139, 170, 172.   [14] *Ib.*, iii, 140.
[15] *Phil. Trans.*, 1767, lvii, 479.   [16] IA., iii, 119 f., 134.   [17] *Ib.*, iii, 378.

vitrum est' (see Vol. II, p. 649) meant that he knew of glacial phosphoric acid.[1] Chaptal's account of dyes and dyeing is detailed,[2] and he described improvements in apparatus for distilling alcohol[3] and the manufacture of Roquefort cheese.[4]

Chaptal in 1790 proposed the name nitrogen instead of azote,[5] but the latter is still used (with the symbol Az) in France. He gave an account of the manufacture of saltpetre.[6] He experimented on the manufacture of litmus (turnsole) but admits that he was not very successful until the Dutch process was revealed in the French invasion of Holland.[7] He noticed (independently of Keir, see p. 299) in 1784 the crystallisation of sulphuric acid on cooling,[8] saying that Kunckel, Bohn, and Boerhaave had mentioned the solidification of the *fuming* acid on cooling. He thought the degrees of oxidation of sulphur were: sulphurous acid, sulphuric acid, fuming sulphuric acid.[9] Fourcroy[10] reports that Chaptal had recently informed him that he had improved the manufacture of sulphuric acid on the basis of the new chemical theory (of Clement and Desormes, 1793), and was also supplying muriatic acid to Paris, Lyon, Spain and England at a much cheaper price than formerly. The improvements in Chaptal's sulphuric acid works are said to have been introduced by an Englishman, John Holker.[11] Chaptal later[12] gave precise details of the manufacture of sulphuric acid by the chamber process in his works.

Manufacture of Sulphuric Acid

Bergman in 1774[13] says oil of vitriol was made in England by burning sulphur and nitre, condensing the fumes in water, and distilling off water. He mentions that dark coloured acid is rendered white by heating with nitric acid or saltpetre, but is then not pure.[14] The English process was invented by Joshua Ward (1685–1761), 'Spot Ward', a quack of great reputation who made a fortune from his pills,[15] and worked at Twickenham and Richmond on the manufacture of saltpetre and porcelain. He made sulphuric acid, first at Twickenham and then at Richmond, using large glass globes of 40–50 gallons capacity containing a little water; a stoneware pot was put inside the globe and on it rested a red-hot iron saucer, into which was put a mixture of sulphur and saltpetre, the neck of the globe being closed by a wooden stopper. The charge was repeated. A hundred globes were used and the acid sold at 2s. per lb. Ward left his secrets to John Page, who published them.[16] This sulphuric acid process

[1] *Ib.*, iii, 350 f.   [2] *Ib.*, iii, 140–60.
[3] *Ib.*, iii, 251–6.   [4] *Ann. Chim.*, 1790, iv, 31–61.
[5] I; 1791, i, xlix (gaz nitrogène); IA, 1791, I, xxxv (nitrogen gas).
[6] *Ann. Chim.*, 1797, xx, 308–55; tr. McLachlan, *J. Soc. Chem. Ind.*, 1936, lv, 803R; Prieur, *Ann. Chim.*, 1797, xx, 298–307; anon. (Chaptal ?), 308–55 (on nitre beds); Chaptal, *Traité des Salpêtres et des Goudrons*, Montpellier and Paris, 1796, tr. F. Wolff, *Ueber künstliche Erzeugung und Läuterung des Salpeters*, Königsberg, 1805 (preface mentions the French wars).
[7] IIA, 1807, iii, 3.   [8] IA, 1791, i, 215*.
[9] IIA, iii, 48; cf. Fourcroy, p. 543.
[10] (2), 1796, iii, 586.   [11] Baud, *Compt. Rend.*, 1933, cxcvi, 1797.
[12] IIA, iii, 88 f.   [13] *Scheffers Chem. Föreläsningar*, 1775, § 11, n. 2.
[14] *Ib.*, § 13 n.   [15] A. C. Wooton, *Chronicles of Pharmacy*, 1910, i, 208.
[16] *Receipts for Preparing and Compounding the Principal Medicines made use of by the late Mr. Ward. Together with an Introduction etc. By John Page, Esq., to whom Mr. Ward left his Book of Secrets*, 8°, London, 1763, 33 pp. (Duveen, 445).

was really the same as that used by Lemery (see p. 35).[1] Ward's process is described in an anonymous work ascribed to Dossie (see Vol. II, p. 762),[2] the author of which says he could produce a model of an apparatus made a considerable time before 'the persons' took out a patent for the process 'a few years ago'.

A factory making sulphuric acid in lead chambers was established by John Roebuck, M.D. Leyden (Sheffield, 1718–Kinneil House, Firth of Forth, 17 July 1794), and Garbett in Birmingham (where Roebuck had a manufacturing laboratory in 1747) and Prestonpans, Scotland, in 1749.[3] They also established the famous Carron Ironworks in 1759–60, using coal to smelt the ore.[4] Roebuck was associated with James Watt and Black in experiments on making alkali by decomposing common salt by lime and took out a patent, but the process eventually proved a failure.[5] The sulphuric acid and alkali works at Prestonpans, and the Carron ironworks, were visited and described by Faujas Saint-Fond.[6]

Parkes[7] says that in 1756 a workman of Roebuck and Garbett's went to Bridgenorth and set up a works, then went to Dowles near Bewdley, where he was associated with Skey; the chambers were 10 ft. square. The first London sulphuric acid works was that of Kingscote and Walker at Battersea, begun in 1772; it had 71 circular lead chambers 6 ft. by 6 ft., also square chambers 12 ft. by 12 ft. A nephew of Walker set up a works in Eccles, Lancashire, with Baker and Singleton about 1783 with four chambers 12 ft. square, and four others 45 ft. long and 10 ft. wide. Soon after, a works was established in Leeds, and by degrees they spread to different parts of England, Scotland, and Ireland, there being eight large ones in and near Birmingham. Parkes gives a detailed account of a contemporary works, the chambers being 20, 40, or 60 ft. long and 16 or 18 ft. wide. The charge was 1 lb. of a mixture of 7 to 8 pts. of ground brimstone and 1 pt. of crude saltpetre for 300 cu. ft. of chamber space.

The use of a jet of steam in the chambers was introduced by La Follie;[8] pyrites was first used instead of sulphur by Thomas Hills of Bromley-by-Bow (BP 4263/1818) and copper pyrites in 1835 by Perret et Fils in Chessy in France, the burnt pyrites being smelted for copper. Chaptal[9] said the most advantageous chambers were 25 ft. long and 15 ft. high; although he had constructed a chamber 80 ft. long, 40 wide, and 50 high, it collapsed after eighteen months.

A sulphuric acid factory was set up by the firm of Bealey, bleachers in Radcliffe, Lancashire in 1791, and in 1799 they had six lead chambers, each

[1] Parkes, Chemical Essays, 1823, i, 463.
[2] The Elaboratory laid open, or, the Secrets of Modern Chemistry and Pharmacy revealed, 1758, Introd., 44, 158; 2 ed. 1768; the book was known in 1757.
[3] Jardine, Trans. Roy. Soc. Edin., 1798, iv, pt. I, no. iv, pp. (65)–(87).
[4] Ency. Brit. Suppl., 1801, II, ii, 466; A. Chalmers, Biographical Dictionary, 1816, xxvi, 319; O. Guttmann, J. Soc. Chem. Ind., 1901, xx, 5; S. Smiles, 1904, 102, 123, 150; Dickinson, Trans. Newcomen Soc., 1937–8, xviii, 43–58; Schofield, Chem. and Ind., 1946, 106.
[5] Smiles, 117.
[6] Voyage en Angleterre, etc., 1797, i, 202 f., also mentioning Dr. Swediaur, the manufacture of green vitriol by the weathering of pyrites at Newcastle, and coke manufacture, ib., i, 167 f., 175 f.
[7] Chemical Essays, 1823, i, 478 f.
[8] Obs. Phys., 1774, iv, 335; 1777, x, 139.   [9] IIA, 1807, iii, 40 f.

12 ft. × 10 ft. × 10 ft.[1] Thomson[2] reported that in 1831 the lead chambers were 70 ft. × 20 ft. × 20 ft., and the price of the acid had fallen from 9d. per lb. at the beginning of the century to less than 1½d. He says the Prestonpans plant was not dismantled till about 1820. The largest manufacturers were Tennant and Co., St. Rollox, Glasgow, who made 200,000 lb. of acid a week; the chamber acid was then concentrated by boiling in large cylindrical platinum stills, which had replaced glass retorts.[3]

The Leblanc Process

Until the beginning of the nineteenth century the soda required for the manufacture of hard soap was obtained either from kelp (seaweed ash) or barilla, a plant ash mostly imported from Spain or the South of France. The alkali content of barilla was very variable. Parkes[4] found that the best Spanish kinds contained from 10 to 20 p.c. of Na_2O (one, exceptionally, 30 p.c.); kelp contained only 1 to 8 p.c. Stahl knew that the base of common salt was soda (see Vol. II, p. 681), and during the eighteenth century many attempts were made to obtain soda from common salt. The most promising approach was to convert the salt into sodium sulphate by heating with sulphuric acid.

Father Joseph François Marie Malherbe (Rennes, 31 October 1733–Paris, 17 February 1827), teacher of philosophy in Saint-Germain-des-Prés, Paris, who left a French translation of Becher's *Physica Subterranea* in manuscript,[5] in 1777 obtained a prize for a process in which a mixture of sodium sulphate, carbon, and iron was heated and the product exposed to the atmosphere, and in 1792–3 he took part in improving the manufacture of soap in Paris. Emil Kopp (Wasselonne, nr. Strasbourg, 3 March 1817–Zürich, 27 November 1875), who was assistant to Persoz, professor in the École supérieure de Pharmacie in Paris (1847), expelled from France as a socialist, chemist in a dye factory in Manchester, and finally professor in Zürich (1871), modified the process by using ferric oxide instead of iron, and his process was worked for a time in England, producing some thousands of tons of soda annually.[6]

J. C. F. Meyer[7], Westrumb,[8] and Van Mons[9] treated a solution of common salt with potash (potassium carbonate) and evaporated, when potassium chloride crystallised, followed by sodium carbonate. The litharge process (see p. 218) was used in the works of Chaptal.[10] Meyer tried (1793) without success a process in which salt was heated with carbon, quicklime, litharge, and sugar.

De la Metherie in a visit to England in 1788[11] learned that Lord Dundonald ('Milord Dundonas') had separated common salt into hydrochloric acid, which he combined with ammonia from the distillation of animal matter to

---

[1] Carpenter, *J. Soc. Chem. Ind.*, 1901, xx, 7.   [2] (4), 1831, ii, 29.

[3] L. F. Haber, *The Chemical Industry during the Nineteenth Century*, Oxford, 1958.

[4] *Chemical Essays*, 1823, ii, 585.   [5] Levot, NBG, 1860, xxxiii, 58.

[6] E. Kopp, *Ann. Chim.*, 1856, xlviii, 81–99; Bertrand, *J. des Savants*, 1884, 549.

[7] Crell's *Ann.*, 1784, II, 126.   [8] *Ib.*, 1785, II, 365; 1793, II, 378.

[9] *Ib.*, 1794, I, 39.

[10] IIA, 1807, ii, 107 f.   [11] *Obs. Phys.*, 1789, xxxiv, 3 (43–5).

make sal ammoniac, and soda, which was used to make glass, soap, and washing lyes. De la Metherie proposed a method in which salt was decomposed by oil of vitriol and the 'vitriol of soda' (Na_2SO_4) heated with coal, when sulphurous acid (SO_2) was given off and the residue, after dissolving, filtering, and crystallising, gave soda. Unchanged hepar (Na_2S) was treated with acetic acid and the salt formed (sodium acetate) on heating gave alkali (see below). The first part of this process had been used by Lord Dundas and Lord Dundonald, who sent William Losh to Paris in 1791 to get to know of a French process,[1] which was that of Nicolas Leblanc (or Le Blanc) (Ivoy-le-Pré, Cher, 6 December 1742 or Issoudon, nr. Orleans, 1753–Paris, 16 January or February 1806).[2] Claims for the invention of this process have been made on behalf of Michel Jean Jacques Dizé (Aine, 1764–Paris, 1852), assistant to D'Arcet (1784–91) and later an apothecary and refiner in Paris.[3]

In the Leblanc process common salt is converted into sodium sulphate by heating with concentrated sulphuric acid, and the sulphate is then heated with carbon and chalk to form sodium carbonate and calcium sulphide:

$$Na_2SO_4 + 2C + CaCO_3 = Na_2CO_3 + CaS + 2CO_2.$$

Leblanc seems to have devised this process in 1787.[4] In 1791 he set up a works with a loan from Philippe Égalité (Louis Philippe Joseph, Duc d'Orléans, friend of the Prince of Wales who was afterwards George IV).[5] The process was published in 1794:

Description de divers Procédés pour extraire la Soude du Sel Marin, faite en Exécution d'un Arrêté du Comité de Salut Public du 8 Pluvoise, an 2 de la République Française. Imprimé par ordre du Comité du Salut Public, Paris, Imprimerie du Comité de Salut Public, An 3 (1794), 4°, pp. 80, 11 folding plates; Sotheran Cat. 839 (1934), no. 1034.

An extract was published by Lelièvre, Pelletier, D'Arcet, and Giroud[6] in which processes used or proposed by Athénas (associated with Malherbe), Guyton and Carny, Ribaucourt, Malherbe, Chaptal and Bérard, Souton, etc., are also described, but Leblanc's is said to be the best. A prize offered in 1783 by the Académie des Sciences was never awarded.[7]

Chaptal at Montpellier had since about 1788 been using Scheele's process of

[1] A. and N. Clow, The Chemical Revolution, 1952, 100 f.
[2] A. Anastasi (a grandson of Leblanc), Nicolas Leblanc, sa vie, ses travaux, et l'historie de la soude artificielle, Paris, 1884 (fully documented); Bertrand, J. des Savants, 1884, 546–56; Scheurer-Kestner, Revue Scientif., 1885, ix, 385; id., N. Leblanc et la soude artificielle, in Conférences faites à la Soc. Chim. de France, 1886; Flückiger, Archiv d. Pharmazie, 1885, xxiii, 865; T. S. Patterson, Proc. Roy. Phil. Soc. Glasgow, 1925, liii, 113; id., Chem. and Ind., 1944, 367; Bloch, in Bugge, Das Buch der grossen Chemiker, 1929, i, 291; Oesper, J. Chem. Educ., 1942, xix, 576; Reilly, Isis, 1951, xlii, 287.
[3] De la Metherie, J. de Phys., 1809, lxix, 421; Dizé, ib., 1810, lxx, 291; Schelenz, Chem. Ztg., 1906, xxx, 1191; 1907, xxxi, 29; Pillas and Balland, Le Chimiste Dizé, Paris, 1906; Lunge, Handbuch der Soda-Industrie, Brunswick, 1894, ii, 382 f.; Partington, The Alkali Industry, 1925, 81, 116.
[4] Dizé, Ann. Chim., 1810, lxx, 291; Gillespie, Isis, 1957, xlviii, 152 (159) says in 1789.
[5] Tournois, Histoire de Louis-Philippe-Joseph, Duc d'Orléans, 2 vols., Paris, 1842, has nothing to say on this.
[6] J. de Phys., 1794, xlv, 118–34, 191–9; Ann. Chim., 1797, xix, 58–156 (Extrait d'un Rapport sur les Divers Moyens d'extraire avec Avantage la Soude du Sel Marin).
[7] Baud, Compt. Rend., 1933, cxcvi, 701, 1498.

treating brine with litharge (which had been in use for some time in England for making lead oxychloride as a yellow pigment; see p. 219). In Guyton de Morveau's process, brine was treated with quicklime and the paste exposed to air in a humid place, when sodium carbonate effloresced (1783); Hollenweger, an artisan in a glass factory, reduced sodium sulphate to sulphide by heating with charcoal and then derived soda from this — how was not said (1783). Géraud de Fontmartin and Jean Antoine Carny claimed to have developed eleven processes, one of which was to precipitate a solution of lead acetate with brine and calcine the sodium acetate obtained (1789). At least seven processes had been tried on a large scale.[1]

On 27 March 1790, Leblanc deposited a document giving a complete description of his process with a notary in Paris, and this, discovered in 1856, gave him priority over Dizé, who first published his claim in 1810. This claim was repeated in 1819 but a jury in that year, and also a commission appointed by the Académie des Sciences (Dumas, Thenard, Chevreul, Pelouze, Regnault, and Balard), reported that Leblanc was the true inventor.[2]

Associated with Leblanc were J. J. Dizé and Henri Shée. Dizé was a young man of twenty in 1790, when work in the factory at St. Denis began; Shée was an agent for the Duke of Orléans and without any technical qualifications. In 1791 Leblanc was using a reverberatory furnace for the black-ash process, perhaps Dizé's invention. Leblanc left the factory in the care of Shée before the sequestration and went to Paris for a post in the Agence des poudres. The State took over the factory on 28 January 1794 — it was legally the property of the Duke of Orléans, who was executed on 6 November 1793, and hence became public property. Leblanc was never deprived of his patent although his process had been published, and it was confirmed in April 1794; it was, of course, useless to him. He is said to have acted in a 'dilatory and impractical' way. In 1801 the factory was restored to him but the process was apparently not worked. Leblanc shot himself in 1806. The process became economical only after a special remission of the salt tax in 1807; in 1810 it was quite largely worked.

De la Metherie[3] in describing Leblanc's process gave the charge for the black-ash furnace as 1000 lb. saltcake, 1000lb. washed Meudon chalk, and 550 lb. charcoal (the latter is larger than the amount 35·5, used later). The black-ash was exposed to the air till it effloresced, lixiviated in barrels, and the solution evaporated till the soda crystallised, the mother-liquor being evaporated to dryness and the calcined residue used for glass making. Leblanc also invented a process for making sal ammoniac by mixing hydrochloric acid gas and impure ammonia gas formed by burning organic matter.[4]

The Leblanc process was introduced into England by James Muspratt (Dublin, 12 August 1793–Liverpool, 4 May 1886), of an English family, who

[1] Gillespie, 1957.
[2] Dumas (reporter), Compt. Rend., 1856, xlii, 553–76; id., ib., 1883, xcvii, 209–14; Baud, ib., 1933, cxcvi, 701; C. C. Gillespie, Isis, 1957, xlviii, 152–70 (based on official documents).
[3] J. de Phys., 1794, xlv, 118, 191 (reporting Lelièvre, Pelletier, D'Arcet and Giroud); Chaptal, IIA, 1807, ii, 107.
[4] Ann. Chim., 1797, xix, 58; J. de Phys., 1794, xlv (or II), 118–34.

migrated to Merseyside in 1823. In that year he sold black-ash (to be used directly) at £12 a ton, in 1830 it was £8 a ton. From 1832 to 1850 (when he retired) Muspratt was almost continuously harassed as a result of the damage caused to surrounding vegetation by the hydrochloric acid gas escaping from his works, a nuisance only mitigated by its absorption in water trickling over coke in a tower, a process patented by Gossage in 1836.[1] In 1838 Muspratt tried an ammonia-soda process but it failed (see Vol. IV).

GENGEMBRE

Philippe Gengembre, of whom nothing seems to be known, described[2] the preparation of hydrogen phosphide (*gas phosphorique inflammable*), which was rediscovered by Kirwan (see p. 670), by heating phosphorus with concentrated caustic potash solution. He found that 100 vols. of the gas are burnt by about 300 vols. of oxygen (actually 200 vols.: $2PH_3 + 4O_2 = P_2O_5 + 3H_2O$) and its density is about twice that of oxygen (which is much too large). He also noticed that the phosphorous acid prepared by Sage[3] by putting small pieces of phosphorus on the sloping sides of a glass funnel and allowing the liquid formed to drop into a bottle, is still luminous in the dark, has a slight odour of phosphorus, and when heated in an open vessel gives intermittent flashes of light.

PELLETIER

Bertrand Pelletier (Bayonne, 30 July 1761–Paris, 21 July 1797 (after inhaling chlorine)) was first an assistant to D'Arcet, then an apothecary, finally from 1795 professor in the École Polytechnique, and a member of government commissions.[4] He worked on arsenic acid,[5] which he obtained by heating arsenious oxide with ammonium nitrate, the crystallisation of deliquescent salts,[6] chlorine,[7] discovering chlorine hydrate independently of Berthollet (see p. 504), ethers,[8] plumbago and molybdenite,[9] and the preparation of phosphorus and its compounds, including phosphorous acid, phosphoric acid, and hydrogen phosphide[10] (discovered by Gengembre); he was severely burned by an accident with phosphorus, which he showed would burn in air under water.[11] He also published on strontium compounds,[12] the analyses of

[1] S. H. Higgins, *History of Bleaching*, 1924, 67 (portr. of Muspratt); D. W. F. Hardie, *Chem. Age*, 1957, lxxvii, 715 (portr. of Muspratt); E. K. Muspratt, *My Life and Work*, London, 1917, 3.

[2] AdS, *Mém. div Sav.*, 1785, x, 651 (read 3 May 1783); Crell's *Ann.*, 1789, I, 450.

[3] AdS, 1777, m 435. In the *Méthode de Nomenclature Chimique*, 1787, it is called 'acide phosphoreux'.

[4] Lassus, AdS, An VII (1799), h 138–43.

[5] *Obs. Phys.*, 1782, xix, 127.   [6] *Ib.*, 1784, xxv, 205

[7] *Ib.*, 1785, xxvi, 389; see the report by Cadet, D'Arcet, and Lavoisier, Lavoisier, *Œuvres*, 1868, iv, 419.

[8] *Ib.*, 1785, xxvi, 455; 1786, xxviii, 138; 1787, xxxi, 178; *J. de Phys.*, 1801, liii, 158.

[9] *Obs. Phys.*, 1785, xxvii, 343, 434; 1789, xxxiv, 127.

[10] *Ib.*, 1785, xxvii, 26; 1789, xxxiv, 193; 1790, xxxv, 378; 1790, xxxvii, 161; 1792, xli, 284, 292; *Ann. Chim.*, 1792, xiv, 113.

[11] *Obs. Phys.*, 1785, xxvii, 26; Black, *Lectures on Chemistry*, 1803, ii, 255, says Pelletier used oxygen.

[12] *Mémoires et Obs. de Chimie*, 1798, ii, 433.

zeolites,[1] on chlorides of tin,[2] and several industrial products (mosaic gold, verditer, bell-metal, etc.). His papers were collected and published by his son Charles and Sédillot.[3] His son P. Josephe Pelletier (Paris; 22 March 1788–19 July 1842) made important researches on alkaloids with Jean Bienaimé Caventou (see Vol. IV).

[1] *Ib.*, i, 39–62.   [2] *Obs. Phys.*, 1792, xl, 307.
[3] *Mémoires et Observations de Chimie*, 2 vols., Paris, 1798, with portr., and life by Sédillot; Bouillon Lagrange, *Ann. Chim.*, 1798, xxvii, 195–217; Lassus, AdS, *Mém. de l'Inst.*, 1799, ii, 138; Gmelin, (1), iii, 434; Thomson, *Ency. Brit. Suppl.*, 1801, II, i, 339; Parkes, *Chemical Essays*, 1823, ii, 296.

CHAPTER XII

CHEMISTRY IN GERMANY

WIEGLEB

Johann Christian Wiegleb (Langensalza; 21 December 1732–16 January 1800) was a town-councillor and apothecary.[1] He gave practical instruction in his laboratory.[2] He supported Meyer's theory of acidum pingue (see p. 145). He opposed alchemy (IV). Wiegleb was to the end of his life a supporter of the phlogiston theory (see p. 636). He was a copious author both in journals and books.

I. Kleine chymische Abhandlungen von dem grossen Nutzen der Erkenntnis des Acidi pinguis bey der Erklärung vieler chymischen Erscheinungen. . . . Nebst einer Vorrede worinnen Herrn Meyer's Leben erzählt und von dessen Verdiensten gehandelt wird, von E. G. Baldinger, sm. 8°, Langensalza, 1767 (112 pp.) (BM 1032. a. 30); 2 ed. 1771 (182 pp.) (Duveen, 619); see p. 145.

I contains a disquisition on the red colour of cinnabar, reproduces an improved conception of the origin of glass and rock crystal by Meyer, gives another conception of glass and an explanation of the action of the Bologna vials (Springkölbchen), the reciprocal precipitation of copper by iron and of iron by copper according to Meyer, remarks on two places in Meyer's book, and describes the green flame of boric acid in alcohol.

IA. Fortgesetzte kleine chymische Abhandlungen, Langensalza, 1770 (also given as 1775).
II. Chymische Versuche über die alcalische Salze, 8°, Berlin and Stettin, 1774; 2 ed. 1781.
III. Neuer Begriff von der Gährung und den ihr unterwürfigen Körpern, 8°, Weimar, 1776.
IV. Historisch-kritische Untersuchung der Alchemie, oder der eingebildeten Goldmacherkunst, Weimar, 1777, and with new t.p. 1793; in this, pref. *3, he divided the periods of development of chemistry into three epochs: (1) metallurgical alchemy (which he begins with Geber); (2) Iatrochemistry (Basil Valentine and Paracelsus), and (3) Phlogistic chemistry (Becher and Stahl). All the names, except Geber's, are of Germans.
V. (a) Geschichte des Wachsthums und der Erfindung in der Chemie der neuern Zeit, 8°, Berlin and Stettin, I, i and ii, 1790; II, 1791; (b) Geschichte des Wachsthums und der Erfindung in der Chemie in der ältesten und mittlern Zeit (a tr. of Bergman's essays, see p. 183), Berlin and Stettin, 1792.
VI. Handbuch der allgemeinen Chemie, 2 vols. 8°, Berlin and Stettin, 1781 (BM 1034. i. 15), 2 ed. 1786, 3 ed., 3 vols., 1796 (published by F. Nicolai, the friend of Lessing); the first part is on 'physische Chemie'. Tr. as:
VIA. A General System of Chemistry Theoretical and Practical. Digested and

---

[1] Gmelin, (1), iii, 553, 616, 701; Poggendorff, (1), ii, 1320; Stöller, *Allgemeines Journal der Chemie* (Scherer), 1800, iv, 684 (partly autobiographical); Scherer, *ib.*, 701 (bibl.); portr. in *Berlinisches Jahrbuch der Pharmacie*, 1795.
[2] Haussler, *Schweiz. Apotheker Ztg.*, 1919, lvii, 319.

Arranged with a Particular View to its Application in the Arts. Taken chiefly from
the German of M. Wiegleb, by C. R. Hopson, 4°, London, 1789 (with additions by
Hopson); still based on the phlogiston theory, but clear and well-arranged.

VII. Die natürliche Magie, Berlin, 1779, 2 ed., 2 vols. 1782–6.

VIII. Onomatologia Curiosa Artificiosa et Magica. Oder natürliches Zauber-
Lexicon, in welchem vieles Nützliche und Angenehme aus der Naturgeschichte,
Naturlehre und natürliche Magie, Nürnberg, 3 ed. 1784.

IX. Teutsches Apothekerbuch (with J. C. T. Schlegel), 2 vols. 8°, Gotha, 1793,
3 ed. 1797.

His paper on chemical affinity is of some interest,[1] mentioning Wenzel (die
Verwandtschaft der Körper mit einem gemeinschaftlichen Auflösungsmittel
ist umgekehrt wie die Zeiten der Auflösung) and Guyton de Morveau, and
giving a classification of types of affinity. Wiegleb made quantitative analyses
of salts[2] and ancient bronze implements.[3] He at first (II, 1774) thought alkali
was present as such in plants before burning but that some more was generated during the combustion, but afterwards (II, 1781) that all was present
before burning. His opposition to Black's theory (p. 147) and his champion-
ship of the phlogiston theory (p. 636) are described elsewhere. He showed that
the 'earth' (formed by the action of silicon fluoride on water) produced on distilling fluorspar with sulphuric acid probably came from the glass retort
(1781),[4] and that silica cannot be changed into alumina by fusion with alkali as
Baumé thought (see p. 93).[5] Baumé's opinion was also disproved by Scheele
(see p. 230), but it was supported by Buffon[6] and G. K. C. Storr,[7] professor of
medicine, chemistry, and botany in Tübingen. It was disproved again by
J. C. F. Meyer.[8]

Wiegleb thought he had shown that Ceylon zircon (Hornschiefer) contained silica, lime, magnesia, and iron.[9] He discussed the formation of 'nitre'
('Saltpeterfrass') on walls.[10] He found (as Marggraf did) that heavy spar can be
decomposed by heating with potassium carbonate.[11] Besides publishing a large
number of analyses of minerals,[12] Wiegleb communicated papers on a refutation of Baumé's claim[13] to have produced borax from clay and fat,[14] on the green
flame from alcohol and boric acid,[15] on hydrofluoric acid and its solution of
silica,[16] glacial metaphosphoric acid (acid of bones),[17] experiments with platinum,[18] on fulminating silver,[19] on the amount of sulphuric acid in sulphur (from
the increase in weight of liver of sulphur heated in air),[20] on arsenic acid (con-

[1] Revision der Grundlehren von der chemischen Verwandtschaft der Körper, in *Acta
Academiae Electoralis Moguntinae Scientiarum quae Erfurti est*, 1778–9 (1780), iii, 9–24.
[2] VI, 1781, ii, 92 f.; Crell's *Ann.*, 1797, I, 482; Kopp, (1), ii, 73.
[3] *Acta Acad. Mogunt.*, 1777, ii, 50.   [4] Crell's *Neueste Entdeck.*, 1781, I, 3; see p. 214.
[5] Wiegleb, Disquis. chim. de silice, *Nova Acta Acad. Nat. Curios.*, 1778, vi, 397.
[6] *Histoire Naturelle des Minéraux*, 5 vols. 4°, Paris, 1783–8, i, 24, 150: l'argile doit son
origine à la décomposition des matières vitreuse, qui, par l'impression des élémens humides, se
sont divisées, atténuées & réduites en terre.
[7] Crell's *Ann.*, 1784, I, 5; II, 520.
[8] *Schriften Berlin. Ges. naturforsch. Freunde*, 1785, vi, 368.
[9] Crell's *Ann.*, 1787, I, 302.   [10] *Acta Acad. Mogunt.*, 1776, i, 41.
[11] VI, 1781, ii, 301.   [12] Refs. in Gmelin, (1), iii, 701; mostly in Crell's *Ann.*
[13] *Chymie Expérim.*, 1773, ii, 132.   [14] Wiegleb, Crell's *Chem. J.*, 1780, iv, 44.
[15] I, 1767.   [16] Crell's *Neueste Entdeck.*, 1781, i, 3.
[17] *Ib.*, 1781, ii, 5.   [18] *Ib.*, 1784, xii, 111, with history.
[19] Crell's *Ann.*, 1789, II, 426, in which he 'thanks God a thousand times' for sparing his eyes
in explosions.
[20] Ib., 1792, I, 400, phlogistic explanation.

cluding that phlogiston has a negative weight),[1] on the calcination of lead (increased weight due to absorption of water from the air),[2] the precipitation of copper by iron,[3] and the decomposition of sal ammoniac by iron.[4]

Wiegleb's determinations of the weights of 'dry acids' in salts were made by neutralisation, evaporation, and weighing, like Kirwan's (see p. 664).[5] He criticised Bergman's assertion[6] that a given alkali requires a greater weight of a strong and heavy acid for neutralisation (saturation) than a weak and light acid. By experiments with potash and soda Wiegleb[7] found that the weights of acids for a fixed weight of alkali increase in the order: muriatic, sulphuric, nitric.

He made a detailed investigation of salt of sorrel, which he supposd consisted of a peculiar acid;[8] Scheele afterwards proved that this was identical with the acid of sugar (oxalic acid) (see p. 232). Wiegleb[9] thought the acid of sugar (oxalic acid), which he obtained by the action of nitric acid on alcohol, was nitric acid modified by the inflammable principle and he criticised the experiments of Bergman and Scheele on it.

In his book on fermentation (III) he supposed that alcohol and vinegar are present as such in the fermentable substances in a state of firm combination and are separated by fermentation. This was disproved by Westrumb (see p. 572). He[10] assumed that alcohol consists of an ethereal oil combined with water, and[11] that in the preparation of ether, the sulphuric acid decomposes alcohol into water and ethereal oil, the latter then combining with the acid to form ether. He described the preparation of ethyl nitrite (?) from alcohol and nitric acid,[12] and improved the preparation of tartaric acid from tartar by precipitating the lime salt with milk of lime prepared from calcined oyster shells, instead of with chalk (the impurities in which gave a discoloured product).[13] Wiegleb's detailed views on phlogiston and his criticism of Lavoisier's theory[14] are mentioned later (p. 636).

WESTFELD

Christian Friedrich Gotthard Henning Westfeld (Apfelstädt, Gotha, 2 June 1746–?, 23 March 1823) was at first the Rector of the state school at Bückeburg (1766), then in civil service in Hannover (1773) and Westphalia, and Districtsrath at Wehnde near Göttingen (1796). He published on mineralogy.[15] He thought the action of pyrolusite (Braunstein) in decolorising glass (the colour caused by it being due to iron) was owing to its content of alumina; he described its solution in hydrochloric acid without noticing the chlorine evolved, and also mentioned the colours (but not green) formed on fusing it

[1] *Ib.*, 1792, I, 516. [2] *Ib.*, 1797, I, 213. [3] I, 1767, no. 4.
[4] IA, 1770 (?). [5] Crell's *Ann.*, 1797, I, 482.
[6] *Scheffers Chemiske Föreläsningar*, § 51, Anm. 3; Uppsala, 1775, 67.
[7] Crell's *Neueste Entdeck.*, 1782, vii, 7.
[8] Chemische Untersuchung des Sauerkleesalzes: Crell's *Chem. Journal*, 1779, ii, 6.
[9] Crell's *Ann.*, 1784, II, 12, 100. [10] VI, 1781, ii, 518.
[11] *Ib.*, 1781, ii, 548; IX, 1793. [12] Crell's *Neueste Entdeck.*, 1783, xi, 102.
[13] Crell's *Chem. J.*, 1780, iv, 42. [14] Crell's *Ann.*, 1784, I, 207; 1791, II, 387–464.
[15] *Mineralogische Abhandlungen, Erstes Stück* (all publ.), Göttingen and Gotha, 1767 (72 pp., BM).

with saltpetre.[1] Ilsemann[2] and Schmeisser[3] thought magnesia was the main constituent of pyrolusite. Westfeld confused manganous sulphate with alum. Pott[4] said calcined pyrolusite (Braunstein) extracted with sulphuric acid gave crystals tasting of alum and perhaps a kind of alum. Westfeld mentioned the solution of flints,[5] attempted to find the components of crystals (quartz, calcite, etc.),[6] and in a discussion of feathery limestones[7] put forward some obscure ideas on crystal forms. In his description of calc spar[8] he mentioned its different crystal forms and says the crust formed on lime water is due to the escape of *acidum pingue*. His accounts of graphite (Wasserbley),[9] pyritic nodules in chalk (kiesartigen Kalchnieren),[10] marl,[11] and a green diamond[12] are of little interest.

WESTRUMB

Johann Friedrich Westrumb (Noerten, near Göttingen, 2 December 1751–Hameln, 31 December 1819), an apothecary, commissioner of mines and Senator at Hameln, published a collection of his experiments[13] containing the following dissertations:

Vol. I, i: on oxalic acid (Zuckersäure) (establishing, against Wiegleb, that it is a peculiar acid) 1,[14] Saxon red arsenic 79, resin formed in preparation of ether 103, sulphur of some mineral waters 117, preparation of mineral alkali (from common salt and potassium carbonate) 133, rectification of oil of vitriol 149, precipitation of iron from salts of lime and magnesia (with caustic potash) 151, tartaric acid 154, Seignette's salt 155.

Vol. I, ii: sweetening of muriatic acid by alcohol 1 (Salzsäures Naphta = ethyl chloride, with full history of the subject), testing mineral water 71, Meinberg mineral water 135, Meinberg pyrites 167, the supposed presence of oxalic acid in vinegar 189, distilled water 207, potassium acetate (essiggesäurtes Weinsteinsalz) 209, purification of tartaric acid 212, action of electricity on the human body 214, an acid constituent of blood-ley (ferrocyanide) 217, the discoverer of tartaric acid 227 (Scheele, not Retzius), the discoverer of fulminating silver and mercury [oxalates] (Klaproth, 1779) 228, the change of tartaric acid into vinegar 229 (by fermentation).

Vol. II, i (1787): a contribution to the theories of fire and the generation of air and water 1, on water in metallic calces 119, tests for iron in phlogisticated alkali 149, Pyrmont 'Dunstköhle' 207, researches on plant acids 225, mineral water at Verden, Uhlmühle 259, greywacke of Harz 297, do alkalis contain muriatic acid? 304, does nitric acid contain phlogiston? 307, on phosphorus 328, decomposition of digestive salt (potassium chloride) by tartaric acid 337, constituents of pyroacids 350, cajeput oil 353, dry volatile alkali 355, nature of malic acid (Apfelsäure) 357.

[1] *Ib.*, 1767, 1–22.   [2] Crell's *Neueste Entdeck.*, 1781, iv, 24.   [3] Crell's *Ann.*, 1789, II, 39.
[4] *Fortsetzung . . . der Lithogeognosie*, 4°, Berlin and Potsdam, 1751, 76.
[5] *Min. Abhl.*, 1767, 23.   [6] *Ib.*, 27.   [7] *Ib.*, 32.   [8] *Ib.*, 41.
[9] *Ib.*, 51.   [10] *Ib.*, 57.   [11] *Ib.*, 59.   [12] *Ib.*, 70.
[13] *Kleine physikalisch-chemische Abhandlungen*: I, i, 1786; I, ii, 1786; II, i, 1787; II, ii, 1788; III, i, 1789 (all Leipzig); III, ii, 1793; IV, i, 1793 (both Hannover) (BM 1035. c. 23–6); reviewed (with contents) in Crell's *Ann.*; Gmelin, (1), iii, 488, 616; Poggendorff, (1), ii, 1307.
[14] *Obs. Phys.*, 1786, xxix, 8.

Vol. II, ii (1788): Driburg mineral water 1, Meinberg mineral spring 67, Meinberg sulphur spring 97, chemical analysis of Meinberg waters 139, Regensdorf so-called cobalt ore 181 (was pyrolusite), Ilefeld wacke 201, decomposition of stones and earths in the wet way 221, constituents of the colouring part of Prussian blue ley 255 (ferrocyanide; he thought it contained a combustible animal or vegetable substance and ammonium phosphate, 'phosphorsäurer Salmiak'), sweetened spirit of salt (ethyl chloride) 260, preparation of nitric ether (ethyl nitrite) 263, rectification of mercury 264, on fermentation 266, on the doctrine of air, phlogiston (Brennstoff) and metal calces in view of some new publications (Gren's) 278–98.

Vol. III, i: Pyrmont mineral water 1, sedative spar (calcium borate) of Lüneburg 165, wine vinegar 199, the supposed solubility of iron in pure water (mechanically suspended oxide) 247, magnesia and sal ammoniac (calcined or mild magnesia decomposes the latter) 275, decomposition of minerals 319, doubts and questions on phlogiston, metal calces and acids 343–70, white lead spar from Upper Harz 371, greywacke of Upper Harz 384, cubical formed lead ore from Kulf 401, ignition of magnesia by vitriolic acid (magnesium oxide becomes incandescent with the fuming acid) 405, a story of modern alchemy (on Wiegleb) 410, Gren's reply to Westrumb's article on air, phlogiston, and metallic calces 417–79.

Vol. III, ii (Hannover, 1793): a new German chemical nomenclature (some sections are on theory, e.g. of fermentation), xxxii, 335 pp., viii ll.

Vol. IV, i (Hannover, 1793): manufacture of brandy 1, cross-stone of St. Andreasberg 105, tough (derbe) heavy spar of Rammelsberg 135, preparation of mineral alkali (soda) from common salt (double decomposition of common salt or Glauber salt with potash, the best process) 163, preparation of pure baryta (also of barium chloride) from heavy spar 213, salt springs and panstone (calcium sulphate) 277, antimony preparations 329, a crystalline mineral 343, yellow sulphur and its arsenic content 357, Richter's new bone earth (it is phosphate of lime) 377, bleaching (with chlorine; requires expert workmen not available in Germany) 393, the action of alkali on green glass 414, arsenic in silver ores 420, mercury sublimate 423, Richter's decomposition of potassium sulphate by lime 427.

Westrumb's works on chemical technology (bleaching, distillation of brandy, vinegar, glass, etc.) also appeared separately.[1] Westrumb disproved[2] the supposed reduction of baryta, magnesia, etc., described in a letter to Baron Born by Ruprecht and Tondi (or Tondy) in 1790,[3] showing that the regulus contained iron from the crucible, and iron, manganese and phosphorus from the flux, and was not formed in porcelain or pipeclay crucibles. The same result was found by Klaproth[4] and Göttling.[5] In 1784 Westrumb

[1] Bolton, (1), 912–13.
[2] *Geschichte der neu entdeckten Metallisirung der einfachen Erden. Nebst Versuchen und Beobachtungen*, Hannover, 1791 (BM 987. a. 27); *J. der Physik* (Gren), 1791, iii, 44, 212.
[3] Crell's *Ann.*, 1790, II, 1, 91, 195, 291, 483 (Born); Lavoisier, *Elements of Chemistry*, tr. Kerr, Edinburgh, 1796, 220 (addition by Kerr).
[4] Ueber die vorgegebene Reduction der einfachen Erden, *J. der Physik* (Gren), 1791, iii, 197.
[5] *Ib.*, 1791, iii, 216.

showed that calcined magnesia becomes incandescent when mixed with fuming sulphuric acid, which was regarded as an objection to Lavoisier's theory of combustion.[1] He found arsenic in some specimens of sulphur (1793), and boric acid in boracite (1788).

Westrumb observed the spontaneous combustion in chlorine of bismuth, antimony, powdered zinc, etc. (1790), and some metallic sulphides (1789–90),[2] hence he called chlorine 'zündendes Salzgas'. The spontaneous inflammation of phosphorus in chlorine, the corrosion of metals by the gas, its absorption by mercury, and the explosion of its mixture with hydrogen when kindled by a taper, were described anonymously in 1785.[3] Bryan Higgins[4] said he had 'lately discovered . . . the sparkling combustion of the powder of regulus of antimony dropt into a narrow mouthed vessel filled with the acid vapour arising from four parts of dephlegmated nitrous acid with one part of strong marine acid'. Although Hermbstädt (1786, see p. 579) found that a taper was extinguished in chlorine, Westrumb found that it burnt with a dull red flame, which Hermbstädt[5] afterwards confirmed. Fourcroy's observation (p. 540) that it burnt more brightly than in air was, says Hermbstädt, due to the presence of oxygen.

Westrumb's observation that an oil is formed by the action of chlorine on ammonia[6] was disproved by Berthollet,[7] although the oil may have been nitrogen trichloride. The flashes of light produced when chlorine was bubbled through ammonia are mentioned by Simon.[8] Westrumb noticed (1790) that *concentrated* hydrochloric acid precipitates barium salts.[9] He opposed (1788) Wiegleb's theory of fermentation by experiments.[10]

He made experiments on esters (ethyl chloride from alcohol, pyrolusite and muriatic acid, etc.), and also tried (independently of Hermbstädt, see p. 580) to show that vegetable acids (tartaric acid) are converted into acetic acid by fermentation for three months, by oxidation, etc., e.g. (1785) that tartaric acid gives acetic acid with pyrolusite.[11] Döbereiner[12] showed that *formic* acid is so produced. Westrumb assumed that alcohol is present in must before fermentation as a very subtle oil (Pflanzenbrennstoff), which is separated from tartar, tartaric acid, mucus, resin, and air by the fermentation:[13] 'spirit of wine is present at least as parts if not in form in the bodies which produce it on fermentation.' In his paper on magnesia and sal ammoniac[14] he showed that calcined magnesia (oxide) will decompose sal ammoniac, whilst caustic ammonia precipitates magnesia incompletely from a solution of a salt of magnesia. Although magnesia has a greater affinity for the acid, the volatile alkali has an advantage in greater solubility, although perhaps an immense excess would be needed for complete precipitation.

[1] Crell's *Ann.*, 1784, II, 329, 432; *Kleine phys.-chem. Abh.*, 1789, III, i, 405.
[2] Crell's *Ann.*, 1790, I, 1 f., 109 f.; Hermbstädt, *ib.*, 1793, I, 237.
[3] Herr H., Crell's *Beyträge*, 1785, I, iii, 38: Ueber das Gas der dephlogistisirten Salzsäure; see Fourcroy, p 540.
[4] *Essay on Light*, 1776, 89.   [5] Crell's *Ann.*, 1793, I, 237.
[6] *J. der Physik* (Gren), 1791, iv, 195.   [7] Crell's *Ann.*, 1796, I, 33.
[8] Göttling, *Elementarbuch der chemischen Experimentirkunst*, Jena, 1809, ii, 270.
[9] *Kleine phys.-chem. Abh.*, IV, i, 241.   [10] *Ib.*, II, ii, 266.   [11] *Ib.*, I, i, 66.
[12] *J. Chem. Phys.*, 1822, xxxv, 113.   [13] *Abh.*, II, ii, 272.   [14] *Ib.*, III, i, 275 f., 311.

Westrumb made experiments on lead glazes.[1] He says his health had been poor for many years, attributing this to lead poisoning, and that all vessels in his house were of pure English tin.

He made many analyses of mineral waters and introduced some new reagents.[2] He detected 'extractive matter' in water by the brown precipitate with silver nitrate after chlorides and sulphates had been precipitated with lead nitrate,[3] and detected small amounts of petroleum (Erdharz, Harzstoff) in some waters.[4]

Westrumb believed that metallic calces, even after strong ignition, contain water;[5] he never accepted the antiphlogistic theory, opposing it as late as 1804,[6] and published a criticism of it in 1792,[7] saying that he was still a Stahlian. He explained[8] the evolution of oxygen on heating saltpetre by supposing that the salt contains water, from which the nitric acid attracts phlogiston, and the fire streaming in attracts the dephlogisticated part of the water and forms with it the first part of the dephlogisticated air (brennstoff-leerer Luft) coming off, which still contains some nitric acid. The next (purer) part of the gas is formed from the firmly bound water in the salt and that (Grundwasser) of the acid and alkali: ' the affinity of the acid for the phlogiston of the water increases, is made active by fire, and the fire streaming through forms a new quantity of vital air (Lebensluft) from the new dephlogisticated basis of the water.' This agrees with Cavendish's and Watt's theories, except that the former regarded vital air as dephlogisticated water without matter of heat. Westrumb thought the water of sulphuric and phosphoric acids formed by combustion in (moist) air came from the union of the phlogiston of the sulphur or phosphorus with pure air.

He thought that the oxygen evolved when steam is passed over red-hot pyrolusite comes from the dephlogistication of the water in the pyrolusite into pure air.[9] Combustion he explained[10] as a true decomposition beginning with ignition. The pure part of the air combines with the phlogiston of the combustible and forms air, heat, and fire, escaping into 'the general sea of creation'. The other part of the pure air is set free and becomes water (durch den Verlust des Phlogistons und durch die Beymischung des Feuers Luft ward, er zieht dieses ihm fehlende Phlogiston an, und wird Wasser). If another body is present this water combines with it; if not, as in the combustion of combustible air (hydrogen) with common or pure air (oxygen), the water assumes a visible form.

[1] Über die Bleiglasur unserer Töpferwaare und ihre Verbesserung, with t.p. Chemische Abhandlungen. Zweiter Band, Hannover, 1795 (189 pp. and index, BM 1042. b. 21); Ib., Erste Fortsetzung, Hannover, 1797 (159 pp., BM T. 824. (6.)).
[2] Abh., I, ii, 71; Kirwan, An Essay on the Analysis of Mineral Waters, London, 1799, 157, calls him 'the most experienced hydro-analyst in Europe'.
[3] Abh., III, i, 57.   [4] Ib., II, ii, 41 f., 56; III, i, 152.
[5] Crell's Beyträge, 1787, II, 165 (172).
[6] Handbuch der Apothekerkunst, 3 vols., Hannover, 1804, I, p. x.
[7] Crell's Ann., 1792, I, 3 f., 152.
[8] Crell's Beyträge, 1786, I, iv, 35; Abh., 1787, II, i, 53.
[9] Abh., II, i, 124.   [10] Crell's Beyträge, 1786-7, ii, 81, 165, 179.

Suckow

Lorenz Johann Daniel Suckow (or Succov) (Schwerin, 19 February 1722–Jena, 26 August 1801) was a teacher in the University of Jena, professor of mathematics in Hamburg for a year, then professor of mathematics and physics in Jena (1756), where he also taught chemistry (1759–87) from a physical standpoint.[1] His writings are mostly on physics, but he published a book on physical chemistry[2] and a paper on the effect of crystallisation on affinity.[3] His son, Georg Adolph Suckow (Jena, 28 January 1751–Heidelberg, 13 May 1813) was professor of physics, chemistry, natural history, and economics at Heidelberg from 1774, and published several books and papers on chemistry.[4] Gmelin (index) and Poggendorff quote his publications on the manufacture of mercury (1773–4), the use of gypsum as a fertiliser (1775), the manufacture of starch from horse-chestnuts (1780), the action of various gases on vegetation (1784), on chemical affinity,[5] the preparation of oxygen from saltpetre,[6] the synthesis of water,[7] phosphine,[8] and the production of mould (which he compared with fermentation).[9]

Weber

Jakob Andreas Weber (1742–12 January 1792), M.D. Tübingen, lived at first in Tübingen, then Vienna, and finally near Coburg, where he was active in a Prussian blue factory. He published many works, including one criticising Black and Meyer (see p. 152):

Neu entdeckte Natur und Eigenschaften des Kalkes und der äzenden Körper, nebst einer öconomisch-chemischen Untersuchung des Kochsalzes und dessen Mutterlauge, 8°, Berlin, 1778 (237 pp.); Völlstandige theoretische und praktische Abhandlung von dem Salpeter und der Zeugung desselben, 8°, Tübingen, 1779; Bekannte und unbekannte Fabriken und Künste, 8°, Tübingen, 1781; Entdeckte chemische Geheimnisse. Ein hinterlassenes Werk, 8°, Neuwied, 1793 (manufact. of sal ammoniac, Prussian blue); Z. Winzler, Anmerkungen über die Sammlungen von den Nachrichten und Beobachtungen über die Zeugung des Salpeters von A. J. Weber, 8°, Tübingen, 1793 (Duveen, 610); Poggendorff, (1), ii, 1271; Ferguson, ii, 531.

Wasserberg

Franz August Xaver von Wasserberg (Vienna; 27 November 1748–1791), a printer's reader in Vienna, translated many French and Latin works into German and wrote a good text-book:

[1] Chemnitius, *Die Chemie in Jena von Rolfinck bis Knorr*, Jena, 1929, 19.
[2] *Entwurf einer physischen Scheidekunst*, 8°, Jena and Leipzig, 1769.
[3] De affinitate, ut ajunt, corporum. *Acta Acad. Moguntinae*, 1776, i, 31.
[4] List in Poggendorff, (1), ii, 1046: *Vom Nutzen der Chemie zum Behuf des bürgerlichen Lebens und der Oekonomie*, Lautern, 1775; *Anfangsgründe der ökonomischen und technischen Chemie*, 8°, Leipzig, 1784 (BM 1035. l. 6); 2 ed. 1789, with *Zusätze zu der zweiten Auflage*, 8°, Leipzig, 1798 (BM 1035. l. 71.); *Anfangsgründe der Physik und Chemie nach den neuesten Entdeckungen*, 2 pts. Augsburg and Leipzig, 1786 (BM 537. b. 33); *Bemerkungen über einige chymische Gewerbe*, Mannheim, 1791.
[5] Crell's *Neueste Entdeck.*, 1783, ix, 83.   [6] Crell's *Ann.*, 1786, II, 429.
[7] Crell's *Ann.*, 1789, I, 483; 1790, I, 33.
[8] Crell's *Ann.*, 1789, II, 195.   [9] Crell's *Ann.*, 1789, I, 136.

Institutiones Chemicae in usum eorum qui scientiae huic operam dant, Tomus I:
Regnum Minerale: Metalla in genera: metalla perfecta; Tomus II: Semimetalla;
Tomus III: Inflammabilia; 3 vols. 8°, Vienna, 1778–80 (BM 44. d. 19); Institutiones
Chemicae. Regnum Animale. Sectio prior: Ovum, Lac, 8°, Vienna, 1773 (BM 1035. b.
21); Chemische Abhandlung von Schwefel, Zusätze, Vienna, 1788 (BM 1035. c. 21);
Bolton, (1), 904, gives Institutiones Chemicae as in 3 pts., Regnum animale 1773,
Regnum minerale 1778, Inflammabilia 1780, and adds: Von dem Nutzen die Luft
rein zu halten, Vienna, 1772, and Beiträge zur Chemie, Vienna, 1791.

MODEL

Johann Georg Model (Rothenburg on the Tauber, 8 February 1711–St.
Petersburg (Leningrad), 22 March 1775), professor of pharmacy and political
economy in St. Petersburg (Leningrad), published memoirs on borax,[1] common salt, Persian salt (native soda), sal ammoniac, turf, coal, mineral resin,
rhubarb, camphor, ergot, brandy, Dippel's oil, etc.[2] The dissertations on
borax[3] and sal ammoniac[4] are not without interest.

GREN

Friedrich Albert Carl Gren (Bernburg, 1 May 1760–Halle, 26 November
1798) was born in poor circumstances, the family being of Swedish extraction.
He was apprenticed in 1776 to an apothecary. In 1780 he became dispenser in
Trommsdorff's pharmacy at Erfurt, where he had facilities for research and
for study in the University. In 1782 he went to Helmstädt, where Crell
recommended him to Karsten, professor in the University of Halle, where
Gren went in 1783 as Karsten's assistant. He became M.D. in 1786 and D.Phil.
in 1787, his M.D. dissertation being on a chemical subject.[5] He had previously published a work on fermentation[6] under the initials G. F. J.[aspen] von
P.[irch]. In 1787 he became assistant and in 1788 full professor in the medical
and philosophical faculty at Halle, lecturing on medicine and natural history
and later on chemistry, pharmacology and physics. His courses were largely
attended. He had poor health in his later years and died young.[7]

Gren's text-books are clear and comprehensive and give extracts from original sources:

---

[1] *Dissertatio de borace nativa, a Persis borech dicta*, 4°, London, 1747; not in BM or BN.
[2] Gmelin, (1), ii, 577; Model, *Chymische Nebenstunden*, St. Petersburg, 1762, and *Fortsetzung*, 1768 (not in BM or BN but I have seen it); *Kleine Schriften*, St. Petersburg, 1773; French
tr. by Parmentier, *Récréations physiques, économiques et chimiques* (with notes and additions), 2
vols. 8°, Paris, 1774.
[3] *Récréations*, 1774, ii, 70–217.   [4] *Ib.*, ii, 218–65.
[5] *Dissertatio inavgvralis physico-medica sistens. Observationes et experimenta circa genesin
aëris fixi et phlogisticati*, Halle, n.d. [1786], pp. [iv], 100; tr. from § 12 as 'Versuche und Beobachtungen über die Entstehung der fixen und phlogistirten Luft', in Crell's *Beyträge*, 1787,
II, iii, 296; iv, 425; *ib.*, 1788, III, ii, 229 f.
[6] *Betrachtungen über die Gährung und die dadurch erhaltene Producte und Educte*, Halle,
1784.
[7] *Allgem. J. der Chemie* (Scherer), Leipzig, 1799, ii, 357, 615; 1800, iv, 720; P. H. Külb, in
Ersch and Gruber, *Allgemeine Encyclopädie der Wissenschaften und Künste*, Leipzig, 1871,
Sect. I, pt. 90, 138–9; J. C. P. Elwert, *Nachrichten von dem Leben und dem Schriften jetz-
lebender teutscher Aerzte, Wundärzte und Naturforscher*, vol. i (all publ.), Hildesheim, 1799,
171–85; Partington and McKie, *Ann. Sci.*, 1938, iii, 1 (portr.).

I. Systematisches Handbuch der gesammten Chemie zum Gebrauch seiner Vorlesungen entworfen, Halle, Erster Theil (1787), Zweiten Theiles erster Band (1789), Zweiten Theiles zweiter Band (1790); 2 (completely revised) ed.: Systematisches Handbuch der gesammten Chemie, Halle, Erster Theil (1794), Zweiter Theil (1794), Dritter Theil (1795), Vierter Theil (1796); new ed. by Klaproth, 3 vols., 1806–7.

IA. I abridged as Grundriss der Chemie nach den neuesten Entdeckungen entworfen und zum Gebrauch akademischer Vorlesungen eingerichtet, 2 pts., Halle, 1796–7. Tr. by Gruber, a pastor of the Austrian colony in London:

IB. Principles of Modern Chemistry systematically arranged, 2 vols., London, 1800 (with 7 plates engraved by Lowry added).

II. Grundriss zum Gebrauch akademischer Vorlesungen entworfen, Halle, 1788; new ed., Grundriss der Naturlehre in seinem mathematischen und chemischen Theile neu bearbeitet, Halle, 1793; later eds., 1801, 1808, etc., to 1820.

III. System der Pharmakologie, 2 vols. Halle, 1791–2, 2 ed. 1798–9, and later eds. Schelenz, 612, gives 1800, ed. Valentin Rose, as Handbuch der Pharmakologie oder die Lehre von der Arzneimittel.

Gren founded the *Journal der Physik* (8 vols., Leipzig, 1790–98), continued as *Neues Journal der Physik* (4 vols., Leipzig, 1795–8), which became the *Annalen der Physik*, edited at first (from 1799) by L. W. Gilbert, later (1824–78) by Poggendorff; it still continues.

A. N. Scherer, an early adherent to Lavoisier's views in Germany, says Gren, living in the birthplace of the phlogiston theory (Halle), strove to defend its principles at a time when other German philosophical chemists had ceased to believe in it. Gren proposed a modification of the antiphlogistic theory in 1794 (see ch. XIII), which assumed the presence of phlogiston in combustibles and caloric in oxygen gas, and phlogiston + caloric = fire. He retained the old classification of acids and bases as varieties of 'salts'.[1] He showed that the solid separating from a solution of mixed salts depends on the temperature.[2] In his long section on affinity,[3] distinguishing affinities in the 'wet and dry way',[4] Gren introduced the name *affinitas producta*[5] for the cause of combination of a body A (e.g. gold) with a compound BC (e.g. liver of sulphur) composed of two others B (sulphur) and C (potash), with neither of which the first body A reacts separately. He used the slow oxidation of phosphorus for the eudiometric analysis of air.[6] He distinguished between mechanical mixture and chemical compound by giving the example of iron filings and sulphur.[7] His earlier theoretical views were often inaccurate, e.g. he thought that ammonia was a compound of phosphoric acid and phlogiston.[8] He disbelieved in the transmutation of metals.[9] Constantini, a physician in Melle, near Hannover, reported in 1755 that a solution of mercuric chloride on heating with borax and tartar gave a glittering precipitate which on heating gave a smoke which formed a golden film on lead or silver. J. F. Meyer in his *Alchymistische Briefe* (1767, see p. 145) said, without careful examination, that this was gold. Gren showed that the film could not be gold, since it was soluble in nitric acid.[10]

[1] I, 1794, i, 197, 205.   [2] *J. der Physik*, 1791, iii, 33.   [3] I, 1794, §§ 41–63; i, 43 f.
[4] *Ib.*, § 63, i, 57.   [5] *Ib.*, § 55, i, 52.   [6] *N. J. der Physik*, 1797, iv, 363.
[7] I, 1794, § 28; i, 36.   [8] II, 1793, § 370, p. 268.
[9] I, 1795, § 2279, iii, 116.   [10] I, 1795, iii, 235; Kopp, (1), iv, 350; Schelenz, 258.

Gren regarded sugar as a compound of phlogiston, aërial acid (carbon dioxide) and water. On fermentation the aërial acid is mostly set free, the small part remaining combines with phlogiston and water to form alcohol, in which the ratio of phlogiston to aërial acid is greater than in sugar. Some constituents, however, are precipitated as mucus (Schleim) and tartar (Weinstein).[1] Vinegar contains less phlogiston than alcohol, and vegetable acids are converted into vinegar on dephlogistication with acids.[2] He found that gallstones consist mainly of a peculiar waxy-looking substance (cholesterol).[3]

HERMBSTÄDT

Sigismund Friedrich Hermbstädt (or Hermbstaedt) (Erfurt, 24 April 1760–Berlin, 22 October 1833) was first an assistant to Wiegleb, then a pharmacist, then professor in the Collegium Medico-Chirurgico, Berlin (1791), where he had a teaching laboratory, and professor of technology in the University of Berlin (1810).[4] He was the first in Germany to adopt the views of Lavoisier, whose *Traité* he translated in 1792 (see p. 373). He also translated Scheele's works (1793) (see p. 210).[5] His numerous publications were collected in two volumes (I). He wrote a good text-book (II) and an elementary book for engineer and artillery officers (III), as well as many technical works on bleaching, sugar manufacture (beet sugar, glucose from starch), the cultivation of tobacco and the manufacture of smoking tobacco and snuff, and the distillation of brandy (IV). Hermbstädt not only gave very good courses of lectures but he also furthered the interests of chemical industry by his researches and books.

I. Physikalisch-chemische Versuche und Beobachtungen, 2 vols. Berlin, 1786–9. (The parts marked * below are contained in C. G. Selle's Neue Beiträge zur Natur- und Arzenei-Wissenschaft, Berlin, 1786, iii, 3 f.; also on Proust's perlsalz, 182, see p. 642), that marked † in *Obs. Phys.*, 1789, xxxv, 181.)
Vol. I: on fermentation 3, the production of ether and sweetening of acids 45, action of acids on spirit of wine 116, nature of dephlogisticated muriatic acid 165, the fundamental acid (Grundsäure) of the vegetable kingdom 193, the nature and formation of vital air (Lebensluft; criticism of Lavoisier's theory) 253, the generation of aërial acid (Luftsäure, carbon dioxide) from oxygen and phlogisticated (brennstoffhaltigen) bodies 273, the nature of the acid earth (mucic acid) from milk sugar and nitric acid 291, observations on the newly discovered acid of apples (Apfelsäure), p. 304.
Vol. II: on formic acid (acid of ants) 3, preparation of oxygen from pyrolusite and its use in sickrooms 40,* on extracts 65,* the preparation of calomel 101,* tincture of antimony 117,* a crystalline gallstone 127, the acid nature of metallic earths (Grunderden) 133, the formation of acids 161 (criticising Lavoisier's theory),† benzoic acid (Benzoesalz) 199, oil of fennel 225, fermentation 241, sodium phosphate 267, ether 301.
II. Systematischer Grundriss der allgemeinen Experimentalchemie, 4 vols. Berlin, 1791–3; 2 ed., 2 vols., Berlin, i (1800, 392 pp.), ii (1801, 408 pp.); 3 ed., 5 vols., Basel and Leipzig, i (1812) ii (1813), iii (1819), iv (1823), v (1827); contains a general bibliography (1800, i, 9 f.) and literature references at the end of each section.

[1] II, 1793, § 496, p. 357.   [2] II, 1793, § 499, p. 360.
[3] Gren, in G. S. Dietrich, *Dissertat. continens duas observationes circa calculos in corpore humano inventos*, Halle, 1778, 62; Crell's *Beyträge*, 1790, iv, 19; *Ann. Chim.*, 1790, v, 186; Gren, I, 1794, § 1712, ii, 445.
[4] Haussler, *Schweiz. Apotheker Ztg.*, 1919, lvii, 319.
[5] Kopp, (1), ii, 136; Mensing, *J. B. Trommsdorff*, Erfurt, 1839, 35; portr. in *Berlinisches Jahrbuch der Pharmacie*, 1797; Poggendorff, (1), i, 1082.

III. Elemente der theoretischen und praktischen Chemie für Militärpersonen; besonders für Ingenieur- und Artillerie-Officiere zum Gebrauch bei Vorlesungen und zur Selbstbelehrung, 3 vols., Berlin, 1823 (explains Dalton's atomic theory, i, 103).

IV. Allgemeine Grundsätze der Bleichkunst oder theoretische und praktische Anleitung zum Bleichen . . . nach den neuesten Erfahrungen der Physik, Chemie und Technologie. . . . Mit Kupfern, Berlin, 1804 (pp. xxiv, 432; BM 7945. h. 23, uncut when I used it).

V. Bibliothek der neuesten physikalischen, chemischen, metallurgischen und pharmaceutischen Litteratur, 4 vols. 8°, Berlin, 1789–95.

VI. Miscellaneous technical works:

(a) Anleitung zur Fabrikation des Syrups und des Zuckers aus Stärke . . . , Berlin, 1814; (b) Anleitung zur praktisch-ökonomischen Fabrikation des Zuckers aus den Runkelrüben, Berlin, 1814.

(c) Gruendliche Anleitung zur Kultur der Tabakpflanzen und der Fabrikation des Rauch- und Schnupfstabaks, Berlin, 1822.

(d) Sammlung praktischer Erfahrungen für Branntweinbrenner, Berlin, 1800; (e) Chemische Grundsätze der Destillierkunst und Liqueurfabrikation, Berlin, 1819; (f) Chemische Grundsätze der Kunst Branntwein zu brennen, Berlin, 1817, 2 ed. 1823 (Bolton, (1), 526).

Hermbstädt criticised the old-fashioned theoretical views of his teacher, Wiegleb,[1] but his own theoretical ideas are very inexact. In his dissertation on fermentation he concluded that alcohol is already partly formed in the fermented body but is set free in the pure state.[2] In his second dissertation on this subject[3] he replies to French critics of his theory that the aërial acid (CO_2) is formed from the oxygen of the air acting upon the phlogiston from the fermenting matter. Westrumb[4] had disproved this by showing that fermentation occurs in an atmosphere of aërial acid, and Hermbstädt now said that the substrate of the fermenting matter is composed of a vegetable acid combined with gummy matter (Schleim), which is the basis of the aërial acid, and much absolute heat. Water attracts the vegetable acid which is surrounded by phlogiston and sets free the absolute heat, which combines with the basis of the aërial acid, setting it free as elastic aërial acid (Luftsäure), whilst some heat is set free.

He gives the theories of the formation of ether proposed by Macquer,[5] Wiegleb[6] and Scheele,[7] and concludes[8] that ether is a compound of sulphuric acid with the combustible part of the oil of wine which is combined with water to form alcohol. The oil is completely destroyed, its oily particles forming phlogiston and tartaric acid (Weinsäure). The phlogiston combines with the mineral acid, and part of the tartaric acid forms vinegar. This vinegar combines with the phlogisticated mineral acid to form ether. He later (in II) supposed that the sulphuric acid decomposed the alcohol, the oxygen of the acid forming carbonic acid and a vegetable acid with part of the alcohol, and the radical of the acid formed ether with the other part of the alcohol. Hence ordinary ether is a compound of sulphur and alcohol. He thought he had obtained sulphuric acid from ether and nitric acid.[9]

In his paper on dephlogisticated muriatic acid (dephlogistisirte Salzsäure, i.e. chlorine) he says it is formed by the action of muriatic acid on red lead and

[1] I, i, p. iv.   [2] I, i, 39; *Obs. Phys.*, 1788, xxxii, 248.   [3] I, ii, 241 f.
[4] *Phys.-chem. Abhandlungen*, 1788, II, ii, 275.   [5] I, i, 51.   [6] I, i, 55.
[7] I, i, 57.   [8] I, i, 162.   [9] I, i, 45; ii, 301.

mercuric oxide (Lavoisier's statement, see p. 506; it is incorrect) but not on zinc oxide, etc.[1] By the action of it on ammonia he obtained a gas (nitrogen) which was not absorbed by milk of lime and did not support combustion: 'ich halte sie phlogistischer Natur.'[2] He regarded oxygen (Lebensluft) as pure fire,[3] and dephlogisticated muriatic acid as a compound of muriatic acid, oxygen and fire.[4]

He thought all vegetable matter which produces vinegar on fermentation gave tartaric acid with nitric acid,[5] and that he had converted tartaric acid into vinegar by fermentation.[6] All vegetable acids were modifications of tartaric acid, and oxalic acid is tartaric acid free from phlogiston.[7] Hermbstädt's views on vegetable acids were criticised by Fourcroy.[8] Hermbstädt's experiments on the supposed transformation of vegetable acids, e.g. tartaric or oxalic into acetic by means of chlorine, etc.,[9] were made independently of Westrumb's (p. 572). Cuvier[10] gives Hermbstädt[11] credit for the discovery of malic acid, although he called it an 'imperfect vinegar'.

Hermbstädt's acceptance of the antiphlogistic theory was announced in 1789 in a review of Kirwan's Essay on Phlogiston with the answers of the French chemists (see p. 662),[12] in which he says his previous opposition to the theory was based on an imperfect knowledge of it. In his text-book[13] he used both the old and new theories, since it would be impertinent to suggest that the latter should form the basis of the book. In his translation of Lavoisier's Traité[14] he frequently opposed the phlogiston theory in notes and had quite abandoned it, but feared that it was too early to expect the new theory to be considered impartially. He complained[15] that he had been abused by his German colleagues for his adoption of Lavoisier's theory, but the principles he advocated had triumphed. Hermbstädt, who thought oxygen was mostly matter of fire, adopted Scheele's theory of combustion.[16] By mixing oxygen with nitrous air (NO) over lime-water he obtained a precipitate and thought aërial acid (CO_2) was formed. Hermbstädt discovered sodium bicarbonate (independently of V. Rose) (see p. 659),[17] and gave a detailed account of the quantitative analysis of plants into the 'proximate constituents'.[18]

He obtained mucic acid independently of Scheele,[19] but thought it was calcium oxalate (zuckersäuren Kalch): he then confirmed Scheele's observations, including the formation of impure pyromucic acid as a 'brownish salt'. Although he obtained calcium quinate[20] he thought it was calcium tartrate. In his essay on formic acid[21] he says he obtained $10\frac{1}{2}$ oz. of acid from 16 oz. of ants. He explains how the ants should be collected and refers to Arvidson

[1] I, i, 176.　　　[2] I, i, 180.　　　[3] I, i, 177.　　　[4] I, i, 177, 183 f.
[5] I, i, 225.　　　[6] I, i, 238; Obs. Phys., 1787, xxxi, 161.　　　[7] I, i, 249.
[8] (2), iii, 620.　　　[9] I, i, 193; ii, 161; summary in Nicholson, Dictionary, 1795, ii, 974 f.
[10] Rapport, 1828, 91.　　　[11] Obs. Phys., 1788, xxxii, 57: l'acide des pommes.
[12] Hermbstädt, V, 1789, ii, 257.
[13] II, 1791, pref. vi; Kahlbaum and Hoffmann, Monographien, 1897, i, 94.
[14] System der antiphlogistischen Chemie, Berlin and Stettin, 1792, 244.
[15] Crell's Ann., 1793, II, 479.　　　[16] I, i, 286 f.; ii, 41 f.
[17] II, 1801, ii, 68 (§ 449); mentd. by Rose.
[18] Abhl. K. Akad. Wiss. Berlin, 1824 (1826), 57; see Vol. IV.
[19] Crell's Neueste Entdeckungen, 1782, v, 31–50; I, 1786, i, 291.
[20] Crell's Ann., 1785, I, 115.　　　[21] Crell's Ann., 1784, II, 209; I, ii, 9.

(Afzelius, see p. 200) and W. H. S. Bucholz.[1] Hermbstädt concluded that formic acid, which he obtained in a concentrated form, sp. gr. 1·0934, by distilling the sodium salt (Richter used the potassium salt, see p. 687) with sulphuric acid of sp. gr. 1·5, was very like acetic acid (Essigsäure) yet different. He thought formic acid is converted into acetic by distilling with nitric acid and dephlogistication: it is 'ein wahrer Essig der nur einer gelinden Dephlogistikation bedarf, um alle Eigenschaften einer reinen Essigsäure anzunehmen'.[2]

Hermbstädt[3] thought that 4 oz. of pyrolusite gave 382 cu. in. of 'purest dephlogisticated air' on heating, without loss in weight, although it became brownish red ($3MnO_2 = Mn_3O_4 + O_2$). He claimed that he first obtained oxygen by heating pyrolusite with oil of vitriol:[4] 1 pt. gave 55 pts. of oxygen (by volume). Selle[5] experimented on the use of dephlogisticated air in medicine but thought it too expensive; Hermbstädt[6] claimed that it could be procured quite cheaply from pyrolusite.

J. C. F. MEYER

Johann Carl Friedrich Meyer (Stettin; 1733-20 February 1811), Court Apothecary in Stettin, besides his papers on colloidal silica (see p. 188), hydrofluoric acid (see p. 215), the non-convertibility of silica into alumina (see p. 568), and the preparation of sodium carbonate from common salt (see p. 562), investigated the solubility of lead in sulphuric acid[7] and the action of acids on strontia,[8] and analysed minerals.[9] He prepared artificial Seltzer water.[10] He found that Siberian native iron dissolves in dilute sulphuric acid to a green solution, which becomes blue with ammonium chloride.[11] Proust[12] later showed that native (Peruvian) and meteoric iron contain nickel. Meyer's supposed new metal, *hydrosiderum*, he showed himself was iron phosphide (see p. 194).

W. H. S. BUCHOLZ

Wilhelm Heinrich Sebastian Bucholz (Bernburg, 23 September 1734–Weimar, 16 December 1798), the teacher of Trommsdorff, physician and apothecary in Weimar, Hofmedicus and Bergrath,[13] published on Meyer's acidum pingue,[14] the antiseptic properties of fixed air,[15] the blue colour of some animal bones,[16] hydrofluoric acid (Flussspathsäure),[17] and formic ester.[18] He announced in 1788[19] that he did not accept Lavoisier's theory and that he agreed with Kirwan that inflammable air is phlogiston.

[1] Crell's *Neueste Entdeckungen*, 1783, vi, 55; Bucholz obtained formic ester.
[2] I, ii, 34.   [3] I, i, 171; ii, 48 f.   [4] Crell's *Ann.*, 1787, I, 152; I, i, 172, 275.
[5] *Neue Beiträge zur Natur- und Arzenei-Wissenschaft*, Berlin, 1783, ii, 1 f.
[6] I, ii, 44 f.   [7] Crell's *Ann.*, 1789, II, 116.
[8] *Ib.*, 1796, I, 204.   [9] Poggendorff, (1), ii, 134; Gmelin, (1), iii, 512, 717.
[10] *Schriften Berlin. Ges. naturforsch. Freunde*, 1783, iv, 313–20.
[11] *Beschäft. Berlin. Ges. naturforsch. Freunde*, 1776, ii, 542–5; 1777, iii, 385–414; *Schriften Berlin. Ges. naturforsch. Freunde*, 1780, i, 219–30.
[12] *J. de Phys.*, 1799, xlix, 148; An XII (1804–5), lx, 185.
[13] Poggendorff, (1), i, 328; Loth, in Diergart, 1909, 545.
[14] *Chymische Versuche über das Meyer'sche Acidum Pingue*, Weimar, 1771.
[15] *Acta Acad. Moguntinae*, 1776, i, 71.   [16] *Ib.*, 1778–9, iii, 3.
[17] Crell's *Neueste Entdeckungen*, 1781, iii, 50.   [18] *Ib.*, 1783, vi, 55.
[19] Crell's *Beyträge*, 1788, iii, 474.

C. F. BUCHOLZ

Christian Friedrich Bucholz (Buchholz or Bucholtz) (Eisleben, 19 September 1770–Erfurt, 9 June 1818), nephew of W. H. S. Bucholz, was an apothecary and professor in Erfurt, and published many papers on chemical subjects from 1799.[1] From about 1814 he became blind and his publications ceased. He was a very active chemist, often quoted and much respected in his time but now forgotten.[2] He made numerous good quantitative analyses of salts from about 1800[3] and investigated many minerals. In his book on pharmacy[4] he uses the name *chemische Masse* for active mass.[5] Bucholz's researches on mercuric sulphide[6] led him to think the black precipitated mercuric sulphide was the true sulphide, whilst the red was the hydrosulphide (Schwefelwasserstoff Mercur); Berthollet held the opposite view, but both materials are really of the same composition, mercuric sulphide.

The publications of C. F. Bucholz are numerous and some important. They are contained in Scherer's *Neues allgemeines Journal der Chemie* (NJC), Gehlen's *Journal für die Chemie und Physik* (later, from 1808, vol. v, with the addition *und Mineralogie*) (JCP), and Schweigger's *Journal für Chemie* (JC), which will be denoted as shown. He edited the *Almanach oder Taschenbuch für Scheidekünstler und Apotheker* in 1802–14. He and Gehlen made suggestions for improving the condition of poor apothecaries in old age.[7]

Bucholz obtained sulphur sesquioxide in a blue solution by boiling sulphur with concentrated sulphuric acid, the liquid dissolving indigo like fuming sulphuric acid;[8] the deep blue liquid formed by dissolving flowers of sulphur in fuming sulphuric acid or fused sulphur trioxide was described by F. C. Vogel.[9] Milk of sulphur was shown by Bucholz[10] not to be a hydrate of sulphur, as T. Thomson (see p. 718) supposed. Bucholz[11] established the existence of two chlorides of sulphur, the mono- and dichloride; the monochloride was obtained by Thomson in 1804 and called by him 'sulphuretted muriatic acid' (p. 718). Bucholz made analyses of mineral iron carbonate,[12] aragonite,[13] Thuringian 'rock-soap' (argilla saponiformis Wernerii),[14] granite,[15] calcspars

---

[1] *Beiträge zur Erweiterung und Berichtigung der Chemie*, 3 vols., Erfurt, 1799–1802; Poggendorff, (1), i, 329, gives 2 vols., 1799–1800.
[2] Scherer, *Allgem. J. Chem.*, 1799, ii, 591–615 (list of papers, 'Bucholtz'); Kopp, (1), ii, 118; Poggendorff, (1), i, 329.
[3] Kopp, (1), ii, 76; Thomson, (2), 1807, ii, 520 f.
[4] *Grundriss der Pharmacie mit vorzüglicher Hinsicht auf die pharmaceutische Chemie*, 1802; 2 ed. by Rudolph Brandes, Erfurt, 1819 (577 pp).
[5] *Ib.*, 1819, 40; Richter is mentioned and he still speaks of 'Phlogistisirung', 78.
[6] Versuche zur endlichen Berichtigung der Bereitung des Zinnobers auf dem sogenannten nassen Weg, with Trommsdorff's Chemische Untersuchungen einiger Fossilien, as Zwey chemische Abhandlungen, Erfurt, 1801; in *Nova Acta Academiae Moguntinae*, Erfurt, 1800–2, ii, and 1804, iii; with bibl. from G. Schulze (1687).
[7] JCP, 1810, ix, 189: Gedanken und Vorschläge über die Verbesserung der Lage armer Individuen aus der dienendern Klasse der Apotheker im Alter.
[8] NJC, 1804, iii, 3.   [9] JC, 1812, iv, 121.
[10] *Almanach für Scheidekünstler*, 1808, 135; G. Bischof, JC, 1825, xliii, 392.
[11] JCP, 1810, ix, 172: Versuche über Thomson's Schwefelhaltige Salzsäure (Verbindung von Schwefel, Sauerstoff, und Salzsäure).
[12] NJC, 1803, i, 231; 1807, iii, 114.   [13] NJC, 1804, iii, 72.
[14] NJC, 1804, iii, 324, 597.   [15] NJC, 1805, iv, 172.

and other carbonates of lime,[1] aluminous earth,[2] tripolitanian earth,[3] iron mica[4] and other iron ores,[5] siliceous schists,[6] rock crystal,[7] zoisite,[8] hyalith,[9] magnesite,[10] red schorl from Roschna,[11] and pycnite (a variety of topaz).[12]

He investigated the separation of copper from silver,[13] of iron and manganese with sodium succinate,[14] nickel and cobalt,[15] and magnesium and calcium (with potassium bicarbonate).[16] He analysed silver chloride (salzsäures Silber) and alkali chlorides,[17] and found copper in plant ashes (1816). He investigated the two oxides of iron (FeO, Fe_2O_3) and their reactions with some acids under different conditions,[18] and artificial pyrites and sulphides of iron,[19] differentiated between strontium oxide (infusible) and hydroxide (fusible),[20] obtained crystalline barium hydroxide and showed that (unlike barium oxide) it is fusible,[21] investigated the fusion of calcium carbonate[22] and determined the solubility of gypsum[23] and of arsenious oxide.[24] He described the preparation of barium compounds from heavy spar[25] by heating with charcoal and common salt, and by manganese dioxide (Dizé's process),[26] investigated the oxides and salts of nickel and cobalt,[27] described the analysis of litharge, lead sulphate etc.,[28] Swedish copper sulphate,[29] and the preparation of potassium cyanide free from iron.[30]

He described the reduction of fused caustic alkalis and of baryta by charcoal.[31] His extensive experiments on molybdenum[32] included the preparation of metallic molybdenum, molybdenum trioxide (from ammonium molybdate), the preparation of ammonium molybdate from molybdenite, and the blue lower oxide of molybdenum, and were partly published separately.[33] He also investigated tungsten compounds.[34] His experiments on uranium compounds[35] dealt with the extraction from pitchblende, reduction to the supposed metal, composition of the oxides, and preparation of the salts. He prepared green potassium ferrioxalate.[36] He thought the green solution of potassium manganate is converted into red permanganate by atmospheric oxygen.[37]

Bucholz observed the formation of crystals of tin when water is poured over a concentrated solution of stannous chloride containing some excess of metallic tin.[38] He supposed the water set free some tin oxide, which was

[1] NJC, 1805, iv, 410; JCP, 1806, ii, 18.
[2] NJC, 1805, iv, 445.
[3] JCP, 1806, ii, 21; 1809, viii, 171.
[4] JCP, 1807, iii, 104.
[5] JCP, 1807, iv, 155; 1808, vi, 147.
[6] JCP, 1806, ii, 28, 34.
[7] JCP, 1808, vi, 147.
[8] JCP, 1806, i, 197.
[9] JCP, 1806, i, 202; 1809, viii, 176.
[10] JCP, 1806, ii, 24; 1809, viii, 662, with Haberle.
[11] JCP, 1809, viii, 162.
[12] JC, 1811, i, 385.
[13] NJC, 1803, i, 149.
[14] NJC, 1804, ii, 515; Ann. Chim., 1811, lxxix, 310.
[15] NJC, 1804, iii, 201.
[16] JC, 1816, xvii, 56.
[17] JCP, 1807, iii, 328.
[18] JCP, 1807, iii, 696; 1808, vii, 681 (Thenard's white oxide of iron).
[19] JCP, 1807, iv, 291, with Gehlen.
[20] JCP, 1807, iv, 664.
[21] JCP, 1807, iv, 258, with Gehlen.
[22] JCP, 1806, i, 271.
[23] NJC, 1805, v, 153.
[24] JC, 1813, vii, 387.
[25] NJC, 1803, i, 310.
[26] NJC, 1804, iii, 188.
[27] NJC, 1804, ii, 282; 1804, iii, 201.
[28] NJC, 1805, v, 253.
[29] NJC, 1805, v, 153.
[30] NJC, 1803, i, 406; Richter, Neuern Gegenstände der Chymie, 1802, xi, 46.
[31] JCP, 1808, v, 696.
[32] NJC, 1805, iv, 598.
[33] Drei chemische Abhandlungen, Erfurt, 1818.
[34] JC, 1811, iii, 1.
[35] NJC, 1805, iv, 17, 134, 410.
[36] JCP, 1810, ix, 673.
[37] JC, 1810, viii, 162, 178.
[38] NJC, 1804, iii, 324, 423.

reduced to tin by the concentrated stannous chloride solution, but wished for a better explanation. This was an early concentration cell. The explanation was given by J. W. Ritter,[1] who used concentrated and dilute solutions of stannous chloride stratified in a tube with a rod of tin immersed in both. He found that crystals of tin were deposited from the concentrated solution, and explained that tin was dissolved by oxidation in the dilute solution (as he proved) and deposited by reduction with nascent hydrogen liberated on the metal in the concentrated solution. Bucholz[2] obtained similar results with copper, silver, lead, and zinc solutions, but not with iron; he says the liquid above the concentrated solution must be somewhat acid, water giving only a weak or no effect. Another paper dealt with the formation of brass in the wet way.[3]

Bucholz observed the formation of hydrocyanic acid from bitter almonds.[4] He investigated the formation of ethyl chloride[5] from salt, alcohol, and sulphuric acid, established the identity of camphoric acid,[6] analysed calcium acetate,[7] and lead tartrate and citrate,[8] and investigated ambergris (which he considered to be a peculiar substance) (1809),[9] Tibetan caoutchouc,[10] retinasphaltum from Halle,[11] and the capacity of pure milk sugar to undergo fermentation.[12] He prepared neutral and acid sodium tartrates,[13] determined the solubilities of benzoic and camphoric acids,[14] and investigated turf,[15] club moss,[16] hemp seeds,[17] and a calculus from a horse.[18] With Trommsdorff he investigated the so-called agust earth,[19] the purification of potash with alcohol,[20] and the preparation of acetic acid from sugar of lead.[21]

SCHILLER

Johann Michael Schiller (Windsheim, 27 May 1763– ?) was an apothecary at Rothenburg on the Tauber, where he had a teaching laboratory in 1789 and in 1823 built a pharmaceutical school.[22] He confirmed the luminescence on the crystallisation of potassium sulphate,[23] and published on the preparation of lead plaster[24] and sealing wax coloured blue with mountain blue.[25]

---

[1] NJC, 1805, iv, 253.
[2] JCP, 1808, v, 127: Ueber die chemische Wirksamkeit der einfachen galvanisch-elektrischen Ketten aus Metallauflösungen, Wasser oder Säuren, und Metallen; besonders im Hinsicht auf die dadurch bewurkte Desoxydation der Metalloxyde.
[3] JCP, 1808, vii, 736.   [4] NJC, 1801, iii, 83.
[5] Ueber die Gewinnungsart des leichten Salzäthers nach Basse's Vorschrift, Erfurt, 1804 (32 pp.).
[6] JCP, 1810, ix, 332: Die Kamphersäure wieder in ihre Rechte und auf ihren Platz als eine eigenthümliche Säure gesetzt.
[7] JCP, 1810, ix, 767.   [8] NJC, 1805, v, 253.
[9] Trommsdorff's Journal der Pharmacie, 1809, xviii, 28; Ann. Chim., 1810, lxxiii, 95.
[10] JC, 1811, i, 54.   [11] JC, 1811, i, 290.   [12] JC, 1811, ii, 259.
[13] NJC, 1805, v, 520.   [14] JCP, 1810, ix, 332.
[15] Allgem. J. Chem., 1802, viii, 579.
[16] NJC, 1806, vi, 593.   [17] NJC, 1806, vi, 615.   [18] JC, 1816, xvii, 1.
[19] Trommsdorff's Journal der Pharmacie, 1804, xii, II, 24–30.
[20] Ib., 1804, xii, II, 59.   [21] Ib., 1804, xii, II, 67.
[22] Haussler, Schweiz. Apotheker Ztg., 1919, lvii, 319; Schiller, Vermischte Aufsätze chemischen, pharmaceutischen und physikalischen Inhalts, Nürnberg, 1790.
[23] G. Pickel, Almanach für Scheidekünstler, Weimar, 1787, 55; Schiller, ib., 1791, 45.
[24] Crell's Ann., 1787, II, 163.   [25] Ib., 1789, I, 17.

THE DUTCH CHEMISTS

The Dutch chemists Johann Rudolph Deiman (Hage, East Friesland, 29 August 1743–Amsterdam, 15 January 1808),[1] Adrien Paets van Troostwijk (usually Troostwyk) (Utrecht, 1 March 1752–Breukelen, 3 April 1837), Anthoni Lauwerenburgh (Utrecht, 21 August 1758–Amsterdam, 21 July 1820), Nicolas Bondt (Wilsveen, 20 March 1765–Leyden, 17 August 1796), and Peter Nieuwland (Diemermeer, nr. Amsterdam, 5 November 1764–Leyden, 14 November 1794), published work in association and are often called 'the Dutch chemists'.[2] They obtained nitrous oxide by heating ammonium nitrate and showed that it contains less oxygen than nitric oxide (1793), and prepared ethylene from alcohol and sulphuric acid and discovered ethylene dichloride (Dutch liquid) (1794).[3]

Ethylene may have been obtained by Becher (see Vol. II, p. 652). Ingen Housz reported in March 1779[4] that in November 1777 he had seen Enée (or Æneæ) and Cuthbertson in Amsterdam prepare 'a very powerful inflammable air from equal quantities of oil of vitriol and spirit of wine, by applying heat to the phial containing these ingredients'; it formed a violently explosive mixture with common air or oxygen, and was much heavier than common air, the relative densities of hydrogen, marsh gas, and the new gas being 25, 92, and 150, common air being 138. Ingen Housz found that a mixture of ether vapour and oxygen was violently explosive.

Priestley[5] by passing alcohol vapour over red-hot copper obtained a large amount of inflammable gas and (also with silver) the deposition of a black powder which he called 'charcoal of metals'. Van Marum[6] by passing alcohol vapour over heated silver, copper, lead, and tin obtained an 'inflammable air', 'carburetted hydrogen', and hydrogen. He thought that carbides of the metals were formed. He obtained hydrogen by the action of alcohol vapour on heated zinc, bismuth, cobalt, antimony sulphide (Spiessglanz) and pyrolusite.

The Dutch chemists' discovery of ethylene by heating a mixture of alcohol and concentrated sulphuric acid, or by passing alcohol or ether vapour over heated silica, alumina, or pipe-clay in a glass tube, and the formation of an oily liquid by the action of chlorine on ethylene, were communicated to the Paris Institut in March 1796 in a letter from Van Mons. In August 1796 Fourcroy communicated the memoir, divided into 24 paragraphs.[7] They found its density 0·909 (air = 1), concluded from experiments that it consisted of carbon and hydrogen, and called it *gaz hydrogène carboné huileux*: the name *gaz oléfiant* is due to Fourcroy.[8] The gases formed by passing alcohol and ether vapours through red-hot *glass* tubes were different from olefiant gas; the

[1] Portr. in *Allgem. J. Chem.* (Scherer), 1801, vii; see *Ency. Brit. Suppl.*, 1801, II, i, 300.
[2] *Recherches physico-chimiques*, sm. 4°, Amsterdam, 3 Cahiers: i, 1792, ii, 1793, iii, 1794; the Leyden University copy was used.
[3] *J. de Phys.*, 1794, xlv, 178; Crell's *Ann.*, 1795, II, 430; *Ann. Chim.*, 1797, xxi, 48.
[4] Ingen Housz, *Phil. Trans.*, 1779, lxix, 376; Priestley, E & O *Nat. Phil.*, 1779, i, 474.
[5] E & O, 1790, iii, 425.　　　　　[6] *J. der Phys.* (Gren), 1796, iii, 369–82.
[7] Summary in Fourcroy, (2), 1796, iii, 580; *Nicholson's J.*, 1797, i, 44, 49; in full in AdS, *Mém. div. Sav.*, 1805, i, 101 (dated 1 Fructidor An 4, August 1796).
[8] (2), 1796, iii, 580.

Dutch chemists called them *gaz hydrogène carboné retiré de l'alcohol* (*de l'éther*). Olefiant gas was decomposed by passing through a red-hot tube or by electric sparks. By exploding with oxygen over mercury by an electric spark, they found all these three gases to contain 20–26 per cent of hydrogen and 80–74 of carbon, olefiant gas having most carbon. They did not discover the true nature of the oil formed with chlorine. The Dutch chemists thus discovered the modern process for manufacturing ethylene by passing alcohol vapour over a heated alumina catalyst.[1]

In their memoir on alkali sulphides[2] they found no sulphuretted hydrogen when hydrogen was passed over boiling sulphur, but Gengembre had obtained it by heating with a burning glass.[3] They found that water partially decomposes alkali sulphides with formation of hydrogen sulphide and alkali. Sulphuretted hydrogen gas dissolves in alkalis and when it is mixed with ammonia gas there is a contraction and a solid is formed.

In their memoir on 'gaseous oxide of azote' (nitrous oxide)[4] they proposed this new name for the gas. They showed that it is formed by the action of iron, alkali sulphides, stannous chloride, and copper and ammonia, on nitric oxide; also[5] by heating ammonium nitrate. The composition was found to be 75 vols. oxygen in 200 vols. of the gas (should be 100).

Their experiments on the incandescence resulting from the combination of metals and sulphur on heating[6] raised an objection to Lavoisier's theory of combustion (see p. 466).

LOWITZ

Johann Tobias Lowitz (Göttingen, 25 April 1757–St. Petersburg, 7 December 1804)[7] was the son of Georg Moritz Lowitz (Fürth, nr. Nürnberg, 1722–Ilovla on the Volga, 1774), professor of applied mathematics in Göttingen, then from 1767 professor in St. Petersburg (Leningrad). J. T. Lowitz was first a student (1776) in the Imperial Pharmacy in Leningrad, then in Göttingen (1780–83). He returned to St. Petersburg as Assistant in 1783, becoming Correspondent (1787), Adjunct (1790), and full member (1793) of the Academy of Sciences, the equivalent of professor. He is best known for his discovery (1785) of adsorption from solutions on wood charcoal, first with discoloured tartaric acid.[8] He had suspected that charcoal, with a strong attraction for phlogiston, would remove it from solution, and speaks of its 'dephlogisticating power'. He followed this up with several other memoirs on the subject including the use of charcoal with brandy etc., and drinking

---

[1] Passagez, *Bull. Soc. Chim.*, 1935, ii, 1000.

[2] Memoire sur la nature des sulfures alkalins, ou foies de soufre, *Recherches*, 1792, i, 1–40.

[3] Fourcroy, *Elements of Natural History and Chemistry*, 1790, ii, 141.

[4] Memoire sur la nature de l'oxyde gazeux d'Azote, nommé par M. Priestley Gas nitreux dephlogistiqué, *Recherches*, 1793, ii, 41–70.

[5] *Ib.*, 53, 67.

[6] Experiences sur l'inflammation du melange du soufre et de métaux sans la presence de l'oxygine, *Recherches*, 1794, iii, 71–96; Crell's *Ann.*, 1793, II, 383–98.

[7] Thomson, *Ann. Phil.*, 1814, iii, 161; A. N. Scherer, *Worte der Erinnerung an Leben . . . von Tobias Lowitz, gesprochen an 12 December, 1819*, St. Petersburg, 1820 (42 pp.; BN Mp 5861); Walden, in Diergart, 1909, 533–44.

[8] Crell's *Ann.*, 1786, I, 293.

water.[1] Lowitz prepared glacial acetic acid (which he called *Eisessig*) by distilling potassium acetate with concentrated sulphuric acid, and noted that the liquid supercools before freezing.[2]

Glacial acetic acid had been prepared by Stahl (see Vol. II, p. 685) by the same method; sodium acetate and sulphuric acid were used in 1772 by J. C. Westendorf,[3] but Lowitz's preparation was more concentrated.[4] Solid glacial acetic acid (*acide radicale glaciale*) was obtained from 'radical vinegar' (from verdigris) by Bonvoisin.[5]

Lowitz, who was one of the founders of physical chemistry, carried out excellent researches on supersaturated solutions,[6] discovering the dihydrate of sodium chloride (48 per cent of water)[7] and the hydrates of caustic soda and caustic potash.[8] Scheffer[9] reported that Dippel had found that Glauber's salt does not crystallise in closed vessels; Bergman, in a note, incorrectly suggested that this is due to exclusion of aërial acid (CO_2). Lowitz noticed the evolution of heat when liquids or solutions crystallise, and the fact that the presence of the solid phase always induces crystallisation.[10] He worked on freezing-mixtures, obtaining accurate values for what are now called eutectic temperatures,[11] and first used ice and crystalline calcium chloride as a freezing mixture.[12]

Lowitz established the identity of acid potassium sulphate[13] and potassium bicarbonate,[14] separated barium chloride from calcium and strontium chlorides by the action of absolute alcohol,[15] investigated the solubility of silica in concentrated caustic potash solution,[16] examined titanium compounds,[17] observed the spontaneous ignition of a finely-divided alloy of copper, tin, and zinc,[18] prepared tartaric acid from argol,[19] absolute alcohol ('alkoholisirten Alkohol') by standing, and then distilling, over a large excess of anhydrous potassium carbonate,[20] crystallised glucose from solution in alcohol,[21] and obtained a liquid (monochloracetic acid) and a solid (trichloracetic acid) acid by the action of chlorine on acetic acid.[22]

[1] *Ib.*, 1788, II, 36, 131; 1791, I, 308, 398, 494; 1792, II, 506; 1793, I, 31, 135; 1794, II, 514; 1800, I, 191.

[2] *Ib.*, 1790, I, 206, 300.

[3] *Disputatio inauguralis de optima acetum concentratum eiusdemque Naphtham conficiendi Ratione utriusque Affectionibus ac Usu Medico*, 4°, Göttingen, 1772 (pp. vi, 75); Sotheran *Cat.* 852 (1938) No. 1393.

[4] See the long abstract in Nicholson, *Dictionary of Chemistry*, 1795, ii, 997 f.

[5] *Mém. Acad. Turin*, 1778–9 (1790), v, 373; also on phlogisticated alkali, *ib.*, 382, and other papers; Poggendorff, (1), i, 342 (no dates): Benedetto Buonvicino (Bonvoisin), physician in Turin, published *Elementi de Chimica e d'Istoria Naturale*, 2 vols., Turin, 1810.

[6] Crell's *Ann.*, 1793, I, 220, 314, 352; 1794, I, 206; 1800, I, 291.

[7] *Ib.*, 1793, I, 314, 352.   [8] *Ib.*, 1796, I, 306, 530.

[9] *Scheffers Chemiske Föreläsningar*, ed. Bergman, Uppsala, 1775, 74.

[10] Bemerkungen über das Kristallisieren der Salze, und Anzeige eines sichern Mittels, regelmässige Kristallen zu erhalten, Crell's *Ann.*, 1795, I, 3; Lavoisier had noticed the evolution of heat in 1773, see p. 381; Ostwald, *Lehrbuch*, 1902, II, ii, 382, 705.

[11] Crell's *Ann.*, 1796, I, 529; 1802, I, 24.   [12] *Ib.*, 1793, I, 354.

[13] *Ib.*, 1794, I, 206.   [14] *Ib.*, 1800, I, 29, 96.   [15] *Ib.*, 1795, I, 109; 1796, I, 125.

[16] *Ib.*, 1799, II, 375.   [17] *Ib.*, 1799, I, 183.   [18] *Ib.*, 1801, II, 247.

[19] *Ib.*, 1799, I, 99.   [20] *Ib.*, 1796, I, 195.

[21] *Ib.*, 1792, I, 218, 345, *J. de Phys.*, 1793, xlii, 456.   [22] Crell's *Ann.*, 1793, I, 223.

HAHNEMANN

Christian Friedrich Samuel Hahnemann (Meissen, 10 April 1755–Paris, 2 July 1843),[1] the founder of Homœopathy, M.D. Erlangen, moved to Paris in 1835. He published some chemical work, and translations of Demachy's books.[2] Hahnemann wrote a book on arsenical poisoning,[3] and with van den Sande one on the testing of drugs.[4] Hahnemann found that sodium carbonate can be made from potassium carbonate and common salt, but the preparation is difficult,[5] and that baryta is formed by heating barium carbonate, but not barium sulphate, with charcoal.[6] He supposed that he had discovered a new acid in plumbago[7] and a new fixed alkali (pneum-alkali),[8] which Klaproth, Karsten, and Hermbstädt found was only borax.[9] Hahnemann's wine test[10] for lead in wine was hydrogen sulphide in acid solution, which does not precipitate iron in the wine. He supposed that zinc, copper, and mercury are insoluble in ammonia,[11] and that mercury has a strong attraction for carbonic acid,[12] mostly incorrect observations. The black precipitate (mercurous oxide) formed by ammonia and mercurous nitrate solution was called after him *mercurius solubilis Hahnemanni*; he found that it was soluble in acetic acid and formed globules of mercury when triturated with water.[13] He found that silver nitrate in dilute solution prevented putrefaction,[14] and investigated bile and gallstones.[15] At first he denied the decolorising property of charcoal discovered by Lowitz (see p. 585) but later partly confirmed it.[16]

Hahnemann[17] stated that two salts dissolved in water decompose one another by double affinity when one at least of the new salts is less soluble (and hence more coherent) than either of the original compounds, a proposition afterwards developed by Berthollet (see p. 645). Among his homœopathic remedies was a 'causticum' (Meyer's acidum pingue, see p. 145) prepared by distilling freshly-slaked lime with water and acid potassium sulphate (1830).[18] Hahnemann's book on fuels[19] deals with the proper use of coal, coke, briquettes, etc. He appears to have remained true to the phlogiston theory.

TROMMSDORFF

Johann Bartholomä Trommsdorff (Erfurt; 8 May 1770–8 March 1837), son of Wilhelm Bernhard Trommsdorff (1738–82) the professor of medicine at

[1] R. Haehl, *Samuel Hahnemann*, Leipzig, 1922; tr., 2 vols., London, n.d. (1927); Gmelin, (1), iii, 18, 392, 497, 779, 798, 800, 817, 915; Poggendorff, (1), i, 995; Lippmann, (3), ii, 291–8; Tischner, *Janus*, 1923, xxvii, 220–40.
[2] *L'Art du Distillateur d'Eaux-Fortes*, tr. as *Laborant im Grosse*, 2 vols., Leipzig, 1784, repr. 1801; *Art du Distillateur Liquorist* (1775), tr. as *Der Liquerfabrikant*, 2 vols., Leipzig, 1785.
[3] *Über die Arsenikvergiftung*, Leipzig, 1786.
[4] *Kennzeichen der Güte und Verfälschung der Arzneimittel*, Dresden, 1787.
[5] Crell's *Ann.*, 1787, II, 386.   [6] *Ib.*, 1789, II, 143.   [7] *Ib.*, 1789, II, 291.
[8] *Allgem. J. Chem.*, 1800, v, 380, *J. de Phys.*, 1801, liii, 84.   [9] Kopp, (1), iii, 24.
[10] Crell's *Ann.*, 1788, I, 291; 1794, I, 104.   [11] *Ib.*, 1791, II, 117.
[12] *Ib.*, 1790, I, 256.   [13] *Ib.*, 1790, II, 22, 52.   [14] *Ib.*, 1788, II, 485.
[15] *Ib.*, 1788, II, 296.   [16] *Ib.*, 1789, I, 202; 1790, I, 256.
[17] Tr. Demachy, *Laborant im Grosse*, 1784, pref. 2; Gmelin, *Handbook*, 1848, i, 123.
[18] Kopp, (1), iii, 42; Lippmann was unable to give a source for Kopp's statement.
[19] *Abhandlung über die Vorurteile gegen die Steinkohlen-Feuerung*, Dresden, 1787.

Erfurt, was first an apothecary and then professor of physics and chemistry in the university of Erfurt from 1795 till its dissolution in 1816. He also founded in 1796 a Chemico-Physical-Pharmaceutical Institute in Erfurt, which boarded the pupils and functioned for 33 years. Trommsdorff was a very highly esteemed man, well known in public life, becoming Director of the Academy of Applied Science at Erfurt. He was the author of many books and edited several journals, e.g. the *Journal der Pharmacie*, in which most of his papers were published.[1] His text-book:

Systematisches Handbuch der gesammten Chemie zur Erleichterung des Selbst-studiums dieser Wissenschaft, 8 vols. Gotha and Erfurt, 1800–7; 2 ed., Erfurt, i (1805), ii (1806), iii (1808), iv (1812), v (1808: on galvanism), vi (1815), vii (1818), viii (1820),

is on the lines of Fourcroy's *Système* in being elementary and yet very detailed: it is based on the antiphlogistic theory, which Trommsdorff accepted in 1796. Trommsdorff in 1794[2] had announced that he adopted a position of neutrality with respect to the antiphlogistic theory ('ich bin weder Phlogistiker noch Antiphlogistiker'). He taught both the phlogistic and antiphlogistic theories, but held neither for the pure truth. It was too early to construct a system without hundreds of new experiments.

Trommsdorff[3] was the first German chemist (1789) to separate acids and bases from the class of 'salts'. He called hydrogen sulphide 'Hydrothion-säure'.[4] The supposed new earth, Agust-Erde (from ἄγευστος, since its salts were tasteless) was extracted by Trommsdorff from Saxon beryl.[5] Richter[6] thought he had confirmed its individuality, but it was shown independently by Vauquelin, Klaproth, Bucholz[7] and Trommsdorff himself in 1803[8] to be basic calcium phosphate.

Trommsdorff also wrote on analysis,[9] gases,[10] pharmacy, manufactures (he first used iron retorts for making potassium), etc., and a history of chemistry.[11] He published a very large number of papers, mostly in his *Journal der Pharmacie* and of little interest.[12]

He investigated the solubility of metals and oxides in benzoic acid,[13] mer-

[1] J. W. G. Mensing ('Trommsdorff's son-in-law), *Des Geheimen Hofraths und Professor Dᵣ. Joh. B. Trommsdorff Lebensbeschreibung*, Erfurt, 1839 (list of publs., 74 f.); O. Rosenhainer and H. Trommsdorff, *Das Lebensbild eines der grössten Pharmaceuten und Chemiker an der Wende des 18 Jahrhunderts*, Jena, 1913 (portr., a reprint of Mensing and another life by L. F. Bley, and a detailed list of Trommsdorff's publications, also in *Roy. Soc. Cat. Sci. Papers*, 1872, vi, 45–52); Gmelin, (1), iii, 549; Poggendorff, (1), ii, 1136; Loth, in Diergart, 1909, 545–54; Lothmann, *Schweiz. Apotheker Ztg.*, 1937, lxxv, 130; Prandtl, *Deutsche Chemiker*, 1956, 74 (portr.).
[2] *J. der Pharm.*, 1794, i, II, 108.   [3] *J. der Pharm.*, 1789, v, 43.
[4] *Handbuch*, 1801.
[5] *J. der Pharm.*, 1800, viii, 138; *Allgem. J. Chem.*, 1800, iv, 312.
[6] *Ueber die neuern Gegenstände der Chymie*, 1802, xi, 18 f.: Agustit oder Agust-Erde.
[7] *N. Allgem. J. Chem.*, 1803, i, 457.
[8] *N. Allgem. J. Chem.*, 1803, i, 458; Karsten, *ib.*, 1803, i, 281.
[9] *Chemisches Probierkabinet oder Nachricht von den Gebrauch und den Eigenschaften der Reagentien*, Erfurt, 1801, 64 pp.
[10] *Tabelle über die bis jetz bekannten Gasarten*, 1 sheet roy. f°, Erfurt ? 1800 ?; Bolton includes this under 'Dictionaries'.
[11] *Versuch einer allgemeinen Geschichte der Chemie*, 3 pts. in 1 vol. 16°, Erfurt, 1806; Sotheran *Cat.* 851 (1937) no. 1318.
[12] *Roy. Soc. Cat. of Scient. Papers*, 1872, vi, 45–52.
[13] *J. der Pharm.*, 1790, i, Stück I, 162; Crell's *Ann.*, 1790, II, 303.

curic phosphate,[1] the ignition of metals and sulphur in absence of air,[2] chlorates,[3] the coloured flames of alcohol containing salts,[4] the presence of strontia in heavy spar,[5] bleaching powder[6] and the manufacture of white lead.[7]

Trommsdorff investigated cassia[8] and sumach.[9] With his stepfather, Planer, he showed (1778–9) that the blue dye from woad is identical with indigo.[10] He investigated the metallic benzoates,[11] and Richter's process for extracting gallic acid from galls by cold water, followed by evaporation and extraction with absolute alcohol.[12] He showed that acetic acid contains no nitrogen; by distilling potassium acetate he obtained a liquid (acetone) which he thought was intermediate between alcohol and ether.[13] He characterised saccharic acid.

Scheele[14] in oxidising sugar with nitric acid had obtained, before oxalic acid is formed, another acid which he thought was malic acid. Trommsdorff[15] showed that it is not malic acid. Guérin Varry[16] arrived at the same conclusion and called the acid 'acide oxalhydrique', regarding it as a compound of oxalic acid and hydrogen. Hess[17] determined its composition correctly and gave it the name saccharic acid, used by Scheele for oxalic acid.

Trommsdorff[18] found that mucic acid ('saccholactic acid'), discovered by Scheele (see p. 232), on distillation forms acetic and pyrotartaric acids, and succinic acid sublimes. The solid 'artificial camphor' obtained by Kind, a pharmacist of Eutin (Eutin; 16 August 1775–3 January 1837)[19] was investigated by Trommsdorff[20] and Gehlen,[21] who showed that it had many properties of camphor.

GIRTANNER

Christoph Girtanner (St. Gall, Switzerland, 7 December 1760–Göttingen, 10 or 17 May 1800) lived many years in Paris and was well acquainted with the leaders of the antiphlogistic chemistry.[22] He was a physician in Göttingen. He at first plagiarised the Brunonian system of medicine[23] by assuming that the combination of oxygen with animal fibres produced irritability, but he afterwards violently opposed Brown (see p. 130).[24] Scherer says Girtanner had little time for practical work and did hardly any. He introduces the work of others

[1] *J. der Pharm.*, 1794, i, II, 94; III, 113.   [2] *Ib.*, ii, II, 99.
[3] *Ib.*, 1796, iii, II, 106; Crell's *Ann.*, 1792, I, 422.   [4] *J. der Pharm.*, iii, II, 130.
[5] *Ib.*, iii, II, 281; 1798, v, II, 113.
[6] Om de oxygenerede Saltsyres Forbindelse med Kalkjorden, Talk-og Leerjorden, *Nye Saml. Kgl. Danske Videns. Selsk. Skrift.*, 1799, v, 391–401.
[7] *Neue Abhl. Acad. Erfurt*, 1827, i.   [8] *Acta Acad. Moguntinae*, 1776, i, 27.
[9] *Ib.*, 1778–9, iii, 25.
[10] *Ib.*, 1778–9, iii, 34.   [11] Crell's *Ann.*, 1790, II, 303.
[12] Trommsdorff, *Ueber die Darstellung der reinen Gallussäure aus den Galläpfeln mit Hinsicht auf die Richtersche Scheidungsmethode*, Erfurt, 1804 (19 pp.); Richter, *Ueber die neuern Gegenstände der Chymie*, 1802, xi, 67.
[13] *N. Allgem. J. Chem.*, 1805, v, 573.
[14] KAH, 1785, vi, 17; *Collected Papers*, 1931, 272.
[15] *N. J. der Pharm.*, 1830, xx, II, 1–14; *Ann.*, 1833, viii, 36.
[16] *Ann.*, 1833, viii, 24.   [17] *Ann.*, 1838, xxvi, 1; 1839, xxx, 302.
[18] *Ann. Chim.*, 1809, lxxi, 79.   [19] *J. der Pharm.*, 1803, xi, II, 132,
[20] Boullay, *Ann. Chim.*, 1804, li, 270.   [21] *N. Allgem. J. Chem.*, 1806, vi, 458.
[22] Meyer, *Allgem. J. Chem.*, 1800, iv, 535 (18 May, reporting his death); A. N. Scherer, *ib.*, 1801, vi, 79, 352; R. Wolf, *Biographien zur Kulturgeschichte der Schweiz*, Zürich, 1862, iv, 305; Kopp, (4), ii, 167 (says he believed in alchemy).
[23] *Obs. Phys.*, 1790, xxxvi, 422; 1790, xxxvii, 139.
[24] Puschmann, *Geschichte der Medizin*, Jena, 1903, ii, 107.

(unnamed) by saying: 'Wenn man . . .', but at the end says: 'Nach meinen Versuchen. . . .' His book (see below) is largely a collection of excerpts. Girtanner and 'the celebrated Swediauer' set up, it is said, some chemical factories in Scotland. Girtanner translated the new nomenclature into German[1] and was the author of a popular text-book[2] (used by Berzelius as a student). He says in the preface to the second edition that his book was the first based on the antiphlogistic system to be published in Germany, and that between the dates of the first and second editions the new ideas had gained such ground there that their only open opponents were Hermbstädt and [J. T.] Mayer of Erlangen. In the second edition he frequently refers to objections made to him by J. B. Richter (see p. 630). In the first edition he refers[3] to Lavoisier's *Traité* for the famous mercury experiment, but omits the reference in the second edition. He says[4] that boric acid and hydrofluoric acid (spathsäure) are of unknown composition, and in 1792 that muriatic acid also has an unknown base, but in 1795[5] that it is a compound of hydrogen and oxygen. Girtanner's experiments leading to the last conclusion[6] were refuted by Van Mons[7] and Fourcroy,[8] who explained the production of hydrogen from muriatic acid as due to decomposition of water. Girtanner also supposed that steam is converted into nitrogen by passage through a red-hot pottery tube,[9] which was refuted by Lagrange.[10] Girtanner measured the transmission of sound through gases.[11] In 1782[12] Girtanner thought he had proved the existence of fire matter in quicklime by finding that the loss of weight on treating chalk with an acid is less than the loss on heating. This theory was also supported by Scopoli in his Italian translation of Macquer's *Dictionnaire* (9 vols. 8°, Pavia, 1783–4).

Scopoli

Giovanni Antonio Scopoli (Cavellese, nr. Trent, Italy, 3 June 1721–Pavia, 8 May 1788), professor of chemistry and botany in Pavia (1777), besides the translation of Macquer, published a text-book, *Fundamenta Chemiae* (1777 and 1780), and many books and papers on mineralogy, botany, and zoology.[13] He had been professor of mineralogy in Chemnitz (1766). Many of Scopoli's papers were published in his *Annis Historico-Naturalibus*, 5 vols. 8°, Leipzig, 1769–72. He showed by using a gilt-silver retort that the 'earth' formed when the gas from fluorspar and concentrated sulphuric acid distilled in a glass

[1] *Neue chemische Nomenklatur für die Deutsche Sprache*, Berlin, 8°, 1791, giving, 7 f., an account of five experiments which had been made on the composition of water; see Göttling, p. 595.
[2] *Anfangsgründe der antiphlogistischen Chemie*, Berlin, 1792 (pp. x, 470, 1 p. errata, with portr. of Girtanner); 2 (enlarged) ed., Berlin, 1795; 3 ed., Berlin, 1801.
[3] 1792, 59.   [4] 1792, 394; 1795, 337.   [5] 1795, 154.
[6] *Göttingen Anzeigen*, 1795, St. lii, p. 526.
[7] *Mém. de l'Inst.*, 1799, i, 36, 44; read in 1795.   [8] (2), 1796, iii, 587.
[9] *Allgem. J. Chem.* (Scherer), 1800, iv, 203; *Nicholson's J.*, 1801, iv, 137, 167, 268.
[10] Q. by Berthollet, *Nicholson's J.*, 1801, iv, 371; Murray, 1806, ii, 29; several papers by other chemists on this subject are in *Allgem. J. Chem.*, 1801, vi.
[11] *Anfangsgründe*, 1795, 238.
[12] *Dissertatio inauguralis chemica de terra calcarea cruda et calcinata*, 4°, Göttingen [1782] (BM B. 379. (3.)); Poggendorff, (1), i, 906 (dated it 1783); Kopp, (1), iii, 40 (dated 1781).
[13] Gmelin, (1), ii, 478, 634–8 (list of publs.); Poggendorff, (1), ii, 880; NBG, 1864, xliii, 634–8 (long list of publs.).

retort comes in contact with water is formed from the glass.[1] He found that chlorine gas (dephlogistisiertes Salzsäuresgas) supports combustion, bleaches (including blood), acts on metals (including gold, hence it is present in aqua regia) and oxides, and forms an explosive mixture with hydrogen.[2] He investigated the supposed varying mercury content of corrosive sublimate,[3] and published 'thoughts on phlogiston',[4] and on the preparation of potassium ferrocyanide.[5] His publication on the manufacture of coke[6] was important. He assisted the Abbé Spallanzani in an analysis of gastric juice but was soon after violently and maliciously attacked by him on the basis of a faked anatomical preparation provided by Spallanzani, an account of which Scopoli had sent to the Royal Society. This and similar actions by Spallanzani caused great distress to Scopoli, who is described as a simple and good-natured man; he lost his sleep and his life was curtailed as a result.

ERXLEBEN

Johann Christian Polykarp Erxleben (Quedlinburg, 22 June 1744–Göttingen, 19 August 1777), professor of physics (extraordinary 1771, ordinary 1775) in the university of Göttingen,[7] who is not mentioned by Kopp or Hoefer, investigated fixed air, gold purple, and the red colour of alum from Brunswick (due to cobalt).[8] Erxleben's papers were collected:

Physikalisch-chemische Abhandlungen, Leipzig, 8°, 1776, vol. i (all publ.): I Ueber die fixe Luft und die fette Säure, 1–279, containing a defence of Black's theory and in particular a refutation of Cranz's criticisms (from *Nova Comment. Soc. Gott.*, 1777, vii, 81); II Bemerkungen über den Mineralischen Purpur, 280 (from *Nova Comment. Soc. Gott.*, 1774 (1775), v, 107); III Chemische Untersuchungen des rothen Alauns, den die Gebrüder Gravenhorst zu Braunschweig verfertigen, 304 (from *Nova Comment. Soc. Gott.*, 1775 (1776), vi, 90); IV Einige Anmerkungen über das plötzliche Gefrieren desjenigen Wassers, das ausser Berührung mit der Luft der Atmosphäre gesetzt worden ist, 330 (supercooling); V Ueber den Nutzen der Schwimmblase bey den Fischen, 343; VI Einige Bemerkungen zur Naturgeschichte, 348; VII Beschreibung eines neuen Werkzeuges, wodurch man das Wasser sehr bequem mit fixer Luft schwängern kann, 353.

His text-book[9] has a good bibliography, including alchemy.[10] He discussed Black's and Meyer's theories in detail, to the advantage of the former,[11] and refers to the increase in weight of 'some and perhaps all metals' on calcination,[12] attributing it to combination with fixed air and saying that Kunckel's theory (Vol. II) is 'zuferlässig falsch', whilst Vogel's (see p. 608) is 'gar keine Erklärung'.[13] His *Anfangsgründe der Naturlehre*[14] deals with air, light, heat, magnetism, electricity, etc.

[1] Crell's *Ann.*, 1784, I, 236–7.   [2] *Ib.*, 1785, II, 433–6.   [3] *Ib.*, 1784, I, 24.
[4] *Ib.*, 1785, II, 433.   [5] Crell's *Neueste Entdeck.*, 1783, viii, 3–6.
[6] *Abhl. ökonom. Ges. zu Bern*, 1771, ii; *Abhandlung von Kohlenbrennen*, 8°, Bern, 1773 (Gmelin, (1), ii, 636).
[7] Speter, *Isis*, 1937, xxvii, 11; obit. in *Nova Comment. Soc. Gott.*, 1778, viii, 74.
[8] *Nova Comment. Soc. Gott.*, 1775 (1776), vi, 90; Bergman, *Essays*, 1788, i, 371.
[9] *Anfangsgründe der Chemie*, Göttingen, 1775; 2 ed. *mit neuen Zusätze vermehrt von J. C. Wiegleb*, Göttingen, 1784.
[10] *Ib.*, 1784, 9–44.   [11] *Abhandlungen*, 1776, 1–279; *Anfangsgründe*, 1784, 165 f.
[12] *Abh.*, 1776, 257.   [13] *Anfangsgründe*, § 810, 484.
[14] Göttingen and Gotha, 1768; Göttingen, 1772; ed. Gmelin, 1782; ed. G. C. Lichtenberg, 1791, 1794.

ACHARD

Franz Carl Achard (Berlin, 28 April 1753–Cunern, 20 April 1821), of French extraction, son of a Protestant minister, pupil and successor of Marggraf as professor in the Berlin Academy, worked on chemical and physical subjects.[1] Achard published a very large number of papers on physical and chemical subjects, many of no importance. They are mostly collected in two books:

I. Chymisch-physische Schriften, Berlin, 1780, 367 pp. 10 tables.
II. Sammlung physikalischer und chymischer Abhandlungen. Erster Band (all publ.), Berlin, 1784, 480 pp., 2 folding plates.

He investigated the dilatability and thermal expansion of gases[2] and liquids,[3] the thermal conductivity of liquids,[4] the effects of insoluble and soluble substances on the freezing point of water,[5] the adhesion of solids to liquids,[6] the changes of volume of water by dissolved salts,[7] and the boiling points of salt solutions.[8] He made a large number of electrical experiments. He noticed the 'sulphureous' smell (ozone) of the electric discharge and supposed that the electric fluid contains, but is not wholly, phlogiston.[9] He investigated the hatching of eggs by electricity,[10] and found that seeds grow faster in electrified earth.[11] He found that thermal and electrical conductivities are parallel,[12] as had previously been shown by Franklin,[13] improved Volta's electrophorus[14] and described an electrometer.[15] He showed in 1775 by many careful experiments that ice at low temperatures is a non-conductor of electricity (anticipating Faraday) and that it becomes electric by friction.[16] He investigated the cold and heat produced by evaporation[17] and the electrification of mercury by friction.[18] He reported on Bertier's researches on weight.[19]

Achard described a eudiometer using burning phosphorus,[20] investigated the phlogistication of dephlogisticated air,[21] concluded from experiments similar to Priestley's (see p. 345) that nitrogen is a compound of water and the matter of fire,[22] and supposed[23] that fluorspar contains a volatile earth (as Marggraf,

[1] Allgem. J. Chem., 1800, iv (portr.); Dubois, in tr. of Achard, Analyse de quelques Pierres précieuse, 1783, pref.; Gmelin, (1), iii, 516, 716; Köhnke, Geschichte der Königl. Preussischen Akademie der Wissenschaften, Berlin, 1900, iv, 3–7, 389 f. (list of publs.); Lippmann, (1), i, 296; id., (3), i, 266–75; Poggendorff, (1), i, 7; Speter, Isis, 1939, xxx, 125; W. F. C. Stieda, F. C. Achard und die Frühzeit der deutschen Zuckerindustrie, Abhl. Sächs. Akad. Wiss., Phil.-hist. Kl., 1928, xxxix, no. 3 (218 pp.).
[2] Mém. Acad. Berlin, 1778, 27; 1786, 19.
[3] Ib., 1784, 3.   [4] Ib., 1786, 59.   [5] Ib., 1784, 58.
[6] Ib., 1776, 149; I, 354; Guyton de Morveau, Ency. Méthod., Chymie, 1787, i, 468 f.; J. C. Fischer, 1805, vi, 239–45; see Vol. IV (affinity).
[7] Mém. Acad. Berlin, 1785, 101.   [8] Ib., 1785, 67.
[9] Mém. Acad. Berlin, 1781, 9; II, 1784, 283.   [10] Mém. Acad. Berlin, 1778, 33; I, 241.
[11] Mém. Acad. Berlin, 1781, 9.   [12] Ib., 1779, 27; II, 1784, 141.
[13] Obs. Phys., 1773, ii, 276.   [14] Mém. Acad. Berlin, 1776, 122.
[15] Beschäft. Berlin. Ges. naturforsch. Freunde, 1775, i, 53.
[16] I, 1780, 34; J. C. Fischer, 1808, viii, 435; Achard, Vorlesungen über Experimentalphysik, 4 vols., Berlin, 1791–2.
[17] I, 1780, 283.   [18] Ib., 205.   [19] Ib., 197.
[20] Mém. Acad. Berlin, 1778, 91, plate V (II, 1784, 319).
[21] Ib., 1778, 8; (II, 1784, 307).   [22] Ib., 1783, 49; Crell's Ann., 1785, I, 304.
[23] Mém. Acad. Berlin, 1779, 64; Obs. Phys., 1783, xxiii, 37–40; (II, 1784, 332).

see p. 214, thought), which was disproved by Scheele[1] and others (see p. 215). By evaporating distilled water on a silver plate Achard obtained earth, which he thought was separated rather than formed.[2] Carl von Dalberg[3] allowed 50,000 drops of water to evaporate on a silver plate and obtained no more earth than that contained in the water.

Achard obtained malleable platinum by means of arsenic,[4] produced high temperatures with an oxygen blowpipe[5] and by burning carbon in oxygen,[6] investigated the gas from burning gunpowder,[7] arsenic compounds,[8] copper-iron alloys,[9] the fusion of boric acid with earths and metallic oxides,[10] the effect of perfumes on air,[11] and the decomposition of common salt with litharge to obtain alkali, criticising Turner's process (see p. 219).[12]

Achard's investigations on the composition of gems[13] were very inaccurate. He claimed to have obtained quartz crystals by the action of a solution of carbon dioxide in water on alumina and lime,[14] and analysed several gems,[15] finding that the hyacinth contains alumina, lime, silica, and fluoride, and missing the zirconia.[16] His investigations of high-temperature reactions[17] were probably useful in the porcelain industry. He experimented on the precipitation of lime compounds from water on boiling,[18] the solvent properties of a solution of carbon dioxide[19] and the acidity of this solution,[20] on elastic resin,[21] animal hair,[22] the colours of plants,[23] the growth of teeth,[24] the antiseptic properties of fixed air and nitric oxide,[25] vegetable and animal earth,[26] and the action of hydrochloric acid on oils and combustibles[27].

Achard is best known for his industrial development of Marggraf's discovery of sugar in beets (see Vol. II), beginning in 1786. In 1799 he had presented to Friederich Wilhelm III of Prussia a loaf of beet-sugar and a description of his process (the personal interview is apocryphal). The king appointed a committee (including Klaproth) to supervise further trials and Achard received financial aid, a factory being opened in Cunern, nr. Wohlau, Silesia in 1801 which began work in 1802. The beet-sugar industry was developed in France under the encouragement of Napoleon, Achard having

[1] Crell's *Ann.*, 1786, I, 3.
[2] *Journal littéraire*, Berlin, 1776, 185; I, 1780, 234; J. C. Fischer, viii, 91.
[3] *Acta Moguntinae*, 1782–3; *Neue chemische Versuche um die Aufgabe aufzulösen, ob sich das Wasser in Erde verwandeln lasse*, Erfurt, 1783 (4); q. by J. C. Fischer, viii, 92; On Dalberg and artificial steatite, see E. Stenger, *A. Nat.*, 1928, xi, 92–110.
[4] Crell's *Ann.*, 1784, I, 3.   [5] Crell's *Neueste Entdeckungen*, 1783, viii, 79.
[6] *Mém. Acad. Berlin*, 1779, 20.
[7] *Mém. Acad. Berlin*, 1782, 125; Crell's *Ann.*, 1784, II, 484.
[8] *Mém. Acad. Berlin*, 1781, 103, 112, 119; II, 1784, 232, 246, 255, 266.
[9] II, 1784, 223.   [10] II, 1784, 154.   [11] *Obs. Phys.*, 1785, xxvi, 81.
[12] *Mém. Acad. Berlin*, 1786 (1788), 26, 42; II, 1784, 93, 110.
[13] (1) *Bestimmung der Bestandtheile einiger Edelsteine*, Berlin, 1779 (128 pp., 2 plates); (2) *Analyse de Quelques Pierres Précieuse...*, *Traduit de l'Allemand, avec des Remarques*: Par M. J. B. Dubois, Paris, 1783 (with pref. and notes by Dubois, and Reports to Paris Academy by Brisson, Macquer, de Fontanieu, and Cadet); *Abhl. Bayerischen Akad. Wiss.*, 1778, i, 219–350.
[14] (1), 1779, Anhang; (2), 1783, Appendix.
[15] (1), 1779; ruby 10, sapphire 22, emerald 41, hyacinth 55, Bohemian garnet 67, Saxony chrysoprase 104.
[16] (1), 1779, 55; (2), 1783, 73, and Dubois' note.
[17] *Obs. Phys.*, 1783, xxiii, 49; II, 1784, 132; 199, 350, 371–480.   [18] I, 1780, 5.
[19] I, 34–156.   [20] I, 328.   [21] I, 211.   [22] II, 1784, 166.   [23] II, 189.
[24] I, 1780, 157.   [25] I, 162; see Priestley, p. 254.   [26] *Ib.*, 265.   [27] I, 305.

informed the Paris Institut of his results in 1799, and the process was started in 1811 as a reply to the English blockade of Continental ports. Achard is the real founder of the beet-sugar industry, although he did not live to see the success of his work. The accounts in the literature are confused and contradictory.[1]

Achard published several books and pamphlets on the beet and on the manufacture of sugar from it:

Der neueste deutsche Stellvertreter des indischen Zuckers oder Zucker aus Runkel-rüben, Berlin, 1799 (not seen); Ausführliche Beschreibung der Methode, nach welcher bei der Kultur der Runkelrübe verfahren werden muss . . . , Berlin, 1799 (viii, 63 pp.); Kurze Geschichte der Beweisen welche ich von der Ausführbarkeit der von mir angegebenen Zuckerfabrication aus Runkelrüben geführt habe . . . , Berlin, 1800 (BN S. 14844); Opuscules chymiques, mises aux pieds de Sa Majesté par son très respec-tueux et soumis serviteur et sujet F. C. Achard, s.l.e.a. (BN R. 26044); Ann. Chim., 1800, xxxii, 163; 1800, xxxiii, 67; Anleitung zum Anbau der zur Zuckerfabrication anwendbar Runkelrüben, Breslau, 1809 (and Ostwald's Klassiker, clix); Die europäi-schen Zuckerfabrication aus Runkelrüben, 4°, Leipzig, 1809; 2 ed. Breslau and Leip-zig, 1813; Traité complet sur le sucre Européen de Betteraves; Culture de cette plante considérée sous le rapport agronomique et manufacturier: Traduction abrégée de M. Achard; Par M. D. Anger; Précédé d'une Introduction et accompagné des Notes et Observations par M. CH. Derosne, Pharmacien de Paris, Raffineur de Sucre, Paris, Chez Derosne [and] D. Colas, 1812 (all copies signed by Anger) (xxxvj, 268 pp., 4 folding plates); Instruction sur la culture et la récolte des betteraves, sur la manière d'en extraire economiquement le sucre et le sirop . . . , tr. Copin, 2 ed. with report to the Emperor by Chaptal, Paris, 1812 (BN Sz. 1147).[2]

WEIGEL

Christian Ehrenfried Weigel (Stralsund, 24 May 1748 – Greifswald, 8 August 1831), ennobled 1806 as von Weigel, was professor of botany and chemistry in Greifswald from 1775.[3] Weigel translated Scheffer's lectures (1779, see p. 175), the text-book of Guyton de Morveau, Maret, and Durand (see p. 521)[4] and Lavoisier's Opuscules with an appendix on gases (see p. 372). He edited a Magazin für Freunde der Naturlehre etc. (4 vols. 8°, Berlin, Stralsund, and Greifswald, 1794–7). He supported Meyer's theory of acidum pingue against Black (see p. 148).[5]

Weigel was the author of a good text-book (I) and other works:

I. Grundriss der reinen und angewandten Chemie, zum Gebrauch academischer Vorlesungen entworfen, 2 vols. 8°, Greifswald, 1777 (BM 1035. d. 12–13; Bolton, (1), 34), bibliography, i, 5 f., full bilbiographies in text, and good indexes.

---

[1] N. Deerr, The History of Sugar, 1950, ii, 471–500; Légier, Histoire des Origines de la Fabrication du Sucre en France, Paris, 1901; Lippmann, opp. cit.; J. Scoffern, Stray Leaves of Science and Folk-lore, London, 1870; Speter, Deutsche Zuckerindustrie, 1932, 28; 1933, 31 (portr.); Stieda, op. cit.

[2] Other early publications on beet sugar are by Lampadius, Ann. Chim., 1801, xxxviii, 76; Deyeux (report of Institut), Ann. Chim., 1800, xxxv, 134; Göttling, Phil. Mag., 1801, ix, 184; and Hermbstädt, Nicholson's J., 1806, xiii, 267.

[3] Vom Nutzen der Chemie . . . Eine Eintrittsrede, 4°, Greifswald, 1774; Der Einfluss chemischer Kentnisse in die Oekonomie . . . zum Antritt der neu errichteten chemischen Lehrstelle, 21 Decem-ber 1775, 4°, Greifswald (Gmelin, (1), iii, 662); Einladungs-Schrift vom Vortrage der Chemie auf Academien. Nebst einer Anzeige seiner Wintervorlesungen, 4°, Greifswald, 1775 (BM 7306. h. 2. (4.)).

[4] Anfangsgründe der theoretischen und praktischen Chemie . . . , 3 vols. 8°, Leipzig, 1778–78– 80.

[5] Gmelin, (1), iii, 511, and index; Poggendorff, (1), ii, 1283.

II. Einleitung zur allgemeine Scheidekunst, 3 pts. Leipzig, 1788–94 (with good bibl.).
III. Observationes Chemicae et Mineralogicae, 2 pts. 4°; I Göttingen, 1771; II Greifswald, 1773 (BM 457. c. 32). German tr. by J. T. Pyl:
IV. Chemisch-Mineralogische Beobachtungen, 2 pts. 8°, Breslau, 1779 (BM 970. i. 5).

The contents of III are as follows. Vol. I: 1. Distillatio spiritus vini (p. 1: describing a 'Liebig's condenser'; descr. in text of IV, p. 9, and pictured in frontisp.); 2. Mercurii in pulverem conversio per solum ignem (p. 21; Weigel, p. 29, calls the flat-bottomed flask used for calcination of mercury *per se* a 'Boyle'; Lavoisier, *Traité*, 1789, 520, called it a 'Boyle's hell', 'enfer de Boyle'); 3. Solutio stanni (p. 44); 4. Terra fullonum Hiddesensis (p. 46); 5. De Salinis quibusdam (p. 49); 6. Oleum vini aquam continere posse (p. 51); 7. Auri et argenti in igne per sal mirabile Glauberi solutio (p. 52); 8. Cohobatio (p. 53); 9. Methodus gradum concentrationis determinandi (p. 55); 10. Arena ferrea rudensis (kaltbrüchig; rotbrüchig) (p. 58); 11. Aqua fortis viridis (p. 60); 12. Sal medium in cineribus clavellati (p. 61); 13. De Spathis (p. 64); 14. Aquam destillatam purissimam parare (p. 67); 15. De duobus novis salibus metallicis (cobalt chloride, Büttner; potassium thioantimoniate, Vogel) (p. 70).

Vol. II: 1. Responsio ad dubia Welliana explicationi nostrae obsers. Prior. II opposita (p. 1); 2. Methodus refrigerandi nova (p. 41); 3. Furnus retortae novus (p. 53); 4. Crystallisatio salis alcalici lixiviosi (p. 61); 5. Mercurius vivus in spiritu vini (p. 72); 6. Salis medii lixivioso-vitriolici e cineribus clavellatis crystallisatio (p. 74); 7. Furnus mineralium indagatoris (p. 77).

GÖTTLING

Johann Friedrich August Göttling (Derenberg, 5 June 1755–Jena, 1 September 1809) was assistant to Wiegleb in Langensalza and Bucholz in Weimar. In 1789, through the influence of Goethe, he became the first independent professor of chemistry in Jena, although he combined the subject with pharmacy and technology. He visited Holland and England.[1] He published a number of books, including:

I. Einleitung in die pharmaceutische Chemie für Lernende, 8°, Altenburg, 1778.
II. J. A. F. Göttlings Chemische Versuche über eine verbesserte Methode den Salmiak zu bereiten . . . , sm. 8°, Weimar, 1782.
III. Praktische Vortheile und Verbesserungen verschiedener pharmaceutisch-chemischer Operationen für Apotheker, Erste Sammlung, sm. 8°, Weimar, 1783, 3 ed. 1797.
IV. Vollständiges chemisches Probir-Cabinet, Jena, 1790; tr. Description of a Portable Chest of Chemistry or Complete Collection of Chemical Tests, 8°, London, 1791.
V. Versuch einer physischen Chemie für Jugendlehrer beym Unterricht, Jena, 1792.
VI. Beytrag zur Berichtigung der antiphlogistischen Chemie, auf Versuche gegrundet, 2 pts. Weimar, 1794–8.
VII. Handbuch der theoretischen und praktischen Chemie, 3 pts. Jena, 1798–1800.
VIII. Handbuch der Pharmacie, 1800.

[1] Chemnitius, *Die Chemie in Jena von Rolfinck bis Knorr*, Jena, 1929, 25; Gmelin, (1), iii, 535–40, 655, 754; Kopp, (1), iii, 158; iv, 45; Poggendorff, (1), i, 923.

IX. Praktische Einleitung zur prüfenden und zerlegenden Chemie, Jena, 1802.
X. Elementarbuch der chemischen Experimentirkunst, 2 vols. Jena, 1808–9.

Göttling gave the first account in German of the new nomenclature in the form of an alphabetical list of the old and new names (see p. 483). He was the first editor of the *Almanach oder Taschenbuch für Scheidekünstler und Apotheker* (Weimar, from 1780). He tried to prove that pyroligneous acid and acetic acid are different.[1] In his *Almanach*, Göttling published on succinic acid (1780) and formic acid (1781), and a great number of other subjects (see index to Gmelin). He investigated the production of soda from common salt (1781) by Scheele's litharge process (see p. 219) and the freezing of oil of vitriol.[2] He described the preparation of a pyrophorus without alkali[3] but Scheele[4] found that this could not be done. Göttling supposed (1797) that alcohol is a compound of the matter of light, inflammable air, a little carbon, and an incomplete vegetable acid; etherification involves the reduction of the sulphuric acid to sulphurous acid, an organic acid and water being formed, and the sulphurous acid combines with the elements of the alcohol to form ether.[5] He described the detonation of potassium chlorate and sulphur.[6] Göttling and others found that phosphorus glows in nitrogen gas,[7] and he supposed that nitrogen gas contains the matter of light. Brugnatelli adopted this theory.[8] Kopp refers to Göttling's supposed production of metallic globules from barium carbonate by the action of galvanism (June 1808).

LAMPADIUS

Wilhelm August Lampadius (Hehlen, Brunswick, 8 August 1772–Freiberg, 13 April 1842), pharmacist in Göttingen (1785–91) and professor (extraordinary 1794, ordinary 1795) of chemistry and mineralogy in the Mining Academy in Freiberg, is best known for his discovery of carbon disulphide (*Schwefelalcohol*), which he accidentally obtained in 1796 by distilling iron pyrites with moist charcoal, or fossil wood penetrated by pyrites.[9] In later experiments he concluded that the 'alcohol of sulphur' might be a compound of sulphur and hydrogen.[10] Berthollet[11] thought it contained hydrogen as well as sulphur and carbon; Vauquelin and Robiquet,[12] and Berthollet junr.,[13] that it contained only hydrogen and sulphur. The qualitative composition was established by Clement and Desormes,[14] who obtained it by passing sulphur vapour over heated charcoal, and called it carburetted sulphur. Vauquelin,[15] and Berthollet, Thenard, and Vauquelin,[16] who were appointed by the Institut to report on

---

[1] Crell's *Chem. Journal*, 1779, ii, 39, and other publications of 1779–96; they so appear in Lavoisier's *Traité*, 1789, 286, 294.
[2] Crell's *Ann.*, 1784, II, 42.   [3] Crell's *Ann.*, 1784, I, 341; *Beyträge*, 1786, i, 60.
[4] *Collected Papers*, 1931, 148, 304.   [5] *Almanach*, 1797, 66; Kopp, (1), iv, 284.
[6] *Almanach*, 1793; Gmelin, (1), iii, 538.   [7] *N. J. der Phys.* (Gren), 1795, i, 1.
[8] *Phil. Mag.*, 1819, liii, 321.
[9] *N. J. der Phys.* (Gren), 1796, iii, 304; Crell's *Ann.*, 1796, II, 136.
[10] *Ann. Chim.*, 1804, xlix, 243 (soufre liquide); *Phil. Mag.*, 1804, xx, 131.
[11] *Ann. Chim.*, 1802, xlii, 282.   [12] *Ann. Chim.*, 1807, lxi, 145.
[13] *Ann. Chim.*, 1807, lxi, 127; *Mém. Soc. Arcueil*, 1807, i, 305.
[14] *Ann. Chim.*, 1802, xlii, 135 f.; *Phil. Mag.*, 1802, xiii, 155.
[15] *Ann. Muséum d'Hist. Nat.*, 1812, xix, 396.   [16] *Ann. Chim.*, 1812, lxxxiii, 252.

the work of Cluzel, published later,[1] concluded that it was a compound of 15 of carbon and 85 of sulphur, and this was confirmed by Berzelius and Marcet.[2]

Lampadius published many examinations of minerals, and other works.[3] Lampadius (1800) observed a deflagration when charcoal was added to fused caustic alkali, which he ascribed to reduction and reoxidation; it must have been due to liberation of alkali metal.[4] He examined honeystone (aluminium mellitate) and found it to contain over 85 per cent of carbon, with alumina, silica and water.[5] He explained[6] that, although previously an opponent of the antiphlogistic system,[7] he now made it the basis of his lectures, although he inclined to De Luc's theory, which retained phlogiston.

GEHLEN

Adolph Ferdinand Gehlen (Bütow, Pomerania, 15 September 1775–Munich, 15 July 1815) was the son of an apothecary. He at first practised pharmacy with K. G. Hagen in Königsberg then with V. Rose in Berlin (where he studied with Klaproth). He became Dr.Chem. Halle (1806) and M.D. Königsberg. He was chemist in Reil's Institute in Halle, then (1807) a member of the Munich Academy of Science (equivalent to a professorship). Gehlen edited journals and worked on minerals, esters and organic substances.[8] He used sodium carbonate for mineral fusions, and barium carbonate in the determination of alkalis in minerals,[9] and suggested sodium succinate for the separation of iron and manganese,[10] a process which was put into use by Klaproth, with whom he worked in Berlin. He worked on palladium.[11] Gehlen first suggested that the poisonous water distilled from bitter almonds contained prussic acid.[12] His last work was on arsenic hydride,[13] which caused his death by poisoning. He published a work on saltpetre manufacture,[14] described ethyl fluoride (Flussspathäther),[15] tannin,[16] and artificial camphor,[17] established the identity of formic acid,[18] examined starch sugar,[19] and investigated the formation of indigo from woad.[20]

[1] Ann. Chim., 1812, lxxxiv, 72, 113.

[2] Phil. Trans., 1813, ciii, 171; Ann. Phil., 1814, iii, 185.

[3] Sammlung praktisch-chemischer Abhandlungen und vermischter Bemerkungen, 3 vols. 8°, Dresden, 1795–97–1800 (BM 1142. f. 1); for list of papers (many in this work) see Gmelin, (1), iii, 531, 704–7; for books see Bolton, (1), 599: Handbuch zur chemischen Analyse der Mineralkörper, 8°, Freiberg, 1801, and Nachtrag, 1818; Grundriss der Elektrochemie, 8°, Freiberg, 1817; Chemische Briefe für Frauenzimmer, Freiberg, 1818.

[4] Kopp, (1), iv, 11.

[5] Sammlung, 1797, ii, 51, 135.   [6] Ib., 1795, i, 131.

[7] Kurze Darstellung der vorzüglichsten Theorien des Feuers, Göttingen, 1793.

[8] Thomson, Ann. Phil., 1816, viii, 401; Prandtl, Chymia, 1949, ii, 81 (83); portr. in J. Chem. (Schweigger), 1815, xv.

[9] Kopp, (1), iv, 73.   [10] Ib., 87.   [11] N. Allgem. J. Chem., 1803, i, 529; 1805, iv, 234.

[12] Ib., 1803, i, 95.   [13] J. Chem. (Schweigger), 1815, xv, 501; Ann. Chim., 1816, iii, 135.

[14] Fassliche Anleitung zu der Erzeugung und Gewinnung des Salpeters; zunächst für Landleute, Nürnberg, 1812.

[15] N. Allgem. J. Chem., 1804, ii, 381.   [16] Ib., 1806, vi, 220.   [17] Ib., 1806, vi, 458.

[18] J. f. Chem. (Schweigger), 1812, iv, 1; Denkschr. Akad. Wiss. Munich, 1811–12, iii, 243–72.

[19] J. f. Chem., 1812, v, 32.   [20] Ib., 1812, vi, 1; 1813, viii, 136; 1814, x, 236.

A. N. SCHERER

Alexander Nicolaus von Scherer (St. Petersburg; 30 December (O.S.) 1771–16 October (O.S.) 1824), who studied in Jena (D.Phil. 1794) (where he lectured for a time on chemistry) and Weimar, visited England, became professor of physics in Halle (1800), and of chemistry and pharmacy in Dorpat (1803) and St. Petersburg (1804). He supported Lavoisier's views:[1]

I. Grundzüge der neuern chemischen Theorie, Jena, 1795 (very clearly written and with an excellent bibliography, including many French works, 297–384, and footnotes; portr. of Lavoisier).
II. Nachträge zu den Grundzügen der neuern chemischen Theorie ... Nebst einigen Nachrichten von Lavoisier's Leben (by Lalande), 2 pts., Jena, 1796 (BN R 50363; BM 956. i. 36).
III. Grundriss der Chemie, Tübingen, 1800.
IV. Kurze Darstellung der chemischen Untersuchungen der Gasarten, Weimar, 1799, 3 ed. Berlin, 1808 (78 pp.); tr. (with histor. intr.), A Short Introduction to the Knowledge of Gaseous Bodies, London, 1800 (Gmelin, (1), iii, 668, gives Progr. de primis chemiæ pneumaticæ originibus, 4°, Göttingen, 1797).

Scherer edited the *Allgemeines Journal der Chemie* (10 vols. 1798–1803), continued as *Neues allgemeines Journal der Chemie*. In II he rejected heat and light as substances: 'only what is ponderable is the object of chemical investigation.' This differed from Lavoisier's view (see p. 463).

A. N. Scherer must not be confused with Johann Baptist Andreas von Scherer (Prag, 24 June 1755–Vienna, 10 April 1844), who wrote *Versuch einer neuen Nomenclatur für deutsche Chemiker*, 8°, Vienna, 1792 (see p. 483), on eudiometry, and on Mayow (see Vol. II, p. 580).[2]

CRELL

Lorenz Florenz Friedrich von Crell (Helmstädt, 21 January 1744–Göttingen, 7 June 1816), a pupil of Black (with whom he regularly corresponded), was the first professor of chemistry and mineralogy in Brunswick (1771–3), then professor of philosophy and medicine in the university of Helmstädt (1773 to its dissolution in 1810), and finally professor of chemistry in Göttingen, F.R.S. 1788. He was most active in a literary capacity, editing several periodicals:

(1) *Chemisches Journal* (6 vols. Lemgo, 1778–81, translated as *Chemical Journal*, 3 vols. London, 1791–3); (2) *Chemische Annalen* (40 vols., Helmstädt and Leipzig, 2 vols. numbered I and II annually, 1784–1803–4; with index to 1791 in 1791, II; for 1792–99 in 1799, II, 412 f.; for 1800–03 in 1804, II, 407 f.); (3) *Beyträge zu den chemischen Annalen* (6 vols. Leipzig and Dessau, 1785–99); (4) *Chymisches Archiv* (Leipzig, I, i and ii, 1783; II, 1783); (5) *Neues chymisches Archiv* (Leipzig, i, ii, 1784; iii, iv, 1785; v, 1786; vi, 1787; vii, 1788; viii and index, 1791); (6) *Neuestes chemisches Archiv* (Weimar, I, 1798); (7) *Die neueste Entdeckungen in der Chemie*, 13 vols., 1781–6; (8) *Auswahl aller eigenthümlichen Abhandlungen aus den neuesten Entdeckungen der Chemie*, 5 vols., Helmstädt, 1785–6 (?); (9) *Auswahl vorzüglicher Abhandlungen aus der sämmtlichen Bänden der französischen Annalen der Chemie, Erster Band* (all publ.), Helmstädt, 1801.

---

[1] Ferguson, ii, 333; Gmelin, (1), iii, 542; Kahlbaum and Hoffmann, *Monographien*, 1897, i, 111; Poggendorff, (1), ii, 788.
[2] Poggendorff, (1), ii, 787.

These contain original communications, abstracts from other journals (including English, French and Italian), obituaries, and reviews of books. Crell was an active correspondent with many learned men of other countries, and his publications diffused a knowledge of British, Swedish and French discoveries in Germany. Many of Scheele's original papers were published in his *Annalen*.

Chemists long suspected that an acid could be obtained from tallow, on account of the acrid fumes evolved at high temperatures. The first particular treatment of it was in a dissertation on marrow by Francis Grützmacher,[1] and it was mentioned in a dissertation on blood[2] by J. J. Rhades. D. H. Knape published a dissertation on it (under J. A. Segner).[3] Crell[4] obtained the 'acid of fat' (acidum pinguedinis) by distilling suet, and prepared salts from it. It was said by Thenard[5] to be acetic acid contaminated by empyreumatic matter, and he claimed to have obtained a true sebacic acid (see Vol. IV). Gren[6] had previously suspected that Crell's acid was impure acetic acid.

Crell[7] investigated Gahn's preparation of phosphorus and prepared some phosphates; he wrote on the synthesis of water[8] and the new nomenclature.[9] His son, Carl Justus Ludwig von Crell (Brunswick, 12 December 1772–Helmstädt, 4 September 1793) published a work on extracts describing distillation apparatus.[10]

WINTERL

Jacob Joseph Winterl (Eisenerz, Steiermark, 15 April 1732–Buda Pest, 23 November 1809), professor of chemistry and botany in Buda Pest, held fantastic views on the chemical elements. He[11] tried to show that copper is a compound of nickel, molybdenum, silica, and a volatile substance. The nitre which he thought he had obtained[12] by strongly heating calcium chloride with manganese dioxide in a retort, and absorbing the gaseous product in caustic potash in the receiver (thus proving, as he thought, the conversion of muriatic into nitric acid) was probably potassium chlorate. He seems to have obtained a thiocyanate, giving a red colour with iron salts, which he thought was due to a peculiar acid (Blutsäure).[13]

Winterl's theoretical views were summarised in 1800–3.[14] He recognised that acids need not contain oxygen, that silica has acidic properties (overlooked by his contemporaries, but known to Tachenius, etc., see Vol. II), and that many metallic calces are acidic. He used the name 'amphoteric bodies'

[1] *Dissertatio de ossium medulla*, Leipzig, 1748.
[2] *Dissertatio de ferro sanguinis aliisque liquidus animalibus*, Göttingen, 1753.
[3] *Dissertatio de acido pinguedinis animalis*, Göttingen, 1754.
[4] Crell's *Chem. J.*, 1778, i, 60; 1779, ii, 112; *Phil. Trans.*, 1780, lxx, I, 109; 1782, lxxii. 8; *Acta Acad. Nat. Curios.*, 1783, vii, 177.
[5] *Ann. Chim.*, 1801, xxxix, 193.
[6] 1794, ii, 368.
[7] *Acta Acad. Mogunt.*, 1778–9, iii, 60.
[8] Crell's *Beyträge*, 1790, iv, 436.
[9] *Ann.*, 1791, I, 225, 327.
[10] *Commentatio de optima Extracta Parandi Methodo*, 4°, Göttingen, 1793.
[11] Crell's *Ann.*, 1787, II, 519; 1788, I, 493.   [12] Crell's *Ann.*, 1789, II, 221, 319.
[13] *Die Kunst Blutlauge zu bereiten*, Vienna, 1790.
[14] *Prolusiones ad chemiam saeculi decimi noni*, Budae, 1800 (pp. xii, 270); *Accessiones novæ ad prolusionem suam primam et secundam*, Budae, [1803] (cont. pag. viii, 272, [iii], with the 1800 work); other works in Poggendorff, (1), ii, 1340; Cuvier, *Rapport historique*, 1828, 74.

(*corporum amphoterorum i.e. acidorum, & basicorum simul*) for substances having both acidic and basic properties, such as oxides of zinc, tin, and lead, and alumina.[1]

Winterl supposed that material atoms, all alike, assume acidic and basic properties by the adherence of immaterial or spiritual acidic and basic principles to the substratum, the different properties being due to more or less complete saturation or 'despiritualisation'; weak acids and alkalis (acida et alcalia fatua) are so formed from strong acids and alkalis. The neutralisation of the acid and basic principles produces heat. Water is an element which, when combined with (spiritualised by) negative electricity (the basic principle) forms hydrogen (water-base), with positive electricity (acid principle) it forms oxygen (water-acid). Winterl obtained a 'new element' *andronia* as a white powder by heating nitre and charcoal and careful neutralisation with acid. In combination with oxygen, water, and the acid principle, it forms carbonic acid, nitrogen and nitric acid; with hydrogen it forms milk, albumin, etc. With lime it gives potash or silica; with lead it forms baryta; with copper, molybdenum; with alumina, glucina. On electrolysis it forms an acid at the positive pole and at the negative ammonia and an acid analogous to putrefying organic matter. The acid at the positive pole is the same as that used in exciting the voltaic pile. Another new element *thelyke* was obtained by dissolving marbles and stalactites in muriatic acid, precipitating with ammonia, and precipitating the filtrate with carbonate of potash. The precipitate was a strong alkali which was converted to fluoric acid at the positive pole on electrolysis.

Chenevix,[2] and Bucholz,[3] found that Winterl's method for the preparation of andronia gave only silica. After a very sceptical review of his book by Guyton de Morveau,[4] Winterl sent specimens of the new earth with a Latin letter to the Paris Institut in order that his discovery could be confirmed. Fourcroy, de Morveau, Berthollet and Vauquelin examined it, and found that it was silica contaminated with lime, alumina, potash and iron (1809).[5] They said: 'M. Vinterl n'a ni notions exactes sur les caractères qui distinguent des corps, ni ces exercices si nécessaires aux chimistes pour reconnoître les substances diverses qu'ils trouvent dans leurs analyses.' This, Kopp[6] said, 'made an end of the whole swindle.' At the time it was proposed, Winterl's system was in agreement with the metaphysical dualism which then passed for philosophy in Germany, and was discussed from this point of view in a long paper on acids and bases by Oersted.[7]

[1] *Prolusiones*, 1800, 10.
[2] *N. Allgem. J. Chem.*, 1804, iii, 105–8; Winterl, *ib.*, 1805, iv, 583; Vilborg, *ib.*, 1806, vi, 605; *J. Chem.* (Gehlen), 1806, i, 313.
[3] *J. Chem.*, 1807, iii, 336.   [4] *Ann. Chim.*, 1802 (An XI), xlvii, 312.
[5] *Ann. Chim.*, 1809, lxxi, 225–53.   [6] (1), ii, 284.
[7] *J. Chem.* (Gehlen), 1806, ii, 509–47 (Die Reihe der Säuren und Basen); R. C. Stauffer, *Isis*, 1957, xlviii, 33.

DOLLFUSS

Johann Caspar Dollfuss of Mühlhausen (particulars of his life are unknown) described[1] the preparation of calomel from mercuric sulphate, mercury, and common salt by sublimation. He published a number of notes in Crell's *Annalen* (those starred being sent from London) saying that Black and Beddoes were not indisposed (nicht abgeneigt) to accept Lavoisier's theory,[2] on Dundonald's experiments on the distillation of coal,[3] on cinchona bark,[4] on the action of nitric acid on the crystals deposited from oil of aniseed and other oils (when nitrogen was evolved),[5] on an acid formed by the action of nitric acid on lard,[6] on a solid sublimate and crystals deposited on distilling sulphuric acid,[7] the freezing of sulphuric acid to an ice-like solid,[8] the absence of nitric acid in chamber sulphuric acid,[9] chlorates,[10] the presence of acid in ordinary ether,[11] and the preparation of sal volatile.[12] His quantitative analysis of a mineral water from Kannstadt[13] is interesting, since he determined the fixed air (CO_2) in solution by boiling, collecting the gas over mercury, and finding the contraction with lime water.

JOHN

Johann Friedrich John (Anklam, Pomerania, 10 January 1782–Berlin, 5 March 1847), M.D., was professor in an institution in Moscow (1804–6), then professor of pharmacy and chemistry at the University of Frankfurt on the Oder, and then in Berlin, where he finally had a private practice. He was particularly interested in physiological and pathological chemistry. His books include one[14] giving analyses of ancient pigments, a monograph on amber, giving full historical data,[15] and tables of the analyses of plant and animal products[16] giving the material in alphabetical order with full references, and valuable in the history of organic chemistry. John also published six volumes of analytical memoirs with varying titles (some with two title-pages) as follows:

I. Chemisches Laboratorium. Oder Anweisung zur chemischen Analyse der Naturalien (with preface by Klaproth), Berlin, 1808 (pp. xii, 522, [ii], 2 copperplates; deals with apparatus and reagents, and analyses);

II. Chemische Untersuchungen mineralischer, vegetabilischer and animalischer Substanzen. Fortsetzung des Chemischen Laboratoriums, Berlin, 1810 (pp. xxvi, 292, ii);

[1] *Pharmaceutisch-chemische Erfahrungen über die neuesten in der praktischen Pharmacie gemachten Entdeckungen und Verbesserungen*, Leipzig, 1787 (R. Irish Acad. Libr.).
[2] *Crell, Ann.*, 1787, II, 60, 160.　　　　　　[3] *Ib.*, 1787, I, 538.
[4] *Ib.*, 1787, II, 147.　　　　　　　　　　　[5] *Ib.*, 1787, I, 443.
[6] *Ib.*, 1788, I, 329, in a paper by Gadolin.　　[7] *Ib.*, 1785, I, 438.
[8] *Ib.*, 1787, II, 445.　　　　　　　　　　　[9] *Ib.*, 1786, II, 208, from Mühlhausen.
[10] *Ib.*, 1788, I, 319: mentioning B. Higgins and Gadolin.　　[11] *Ib.*, 1786, II, 334.
[12] Crell's *Beyträge*, 1786, ii, 198.　　　　　　[13] *Ib.*, 1789, iv, 90.
[14] *Die Maleri der Alten*, Berlin, 1836; Partington, (1), 1935, 47, 111, 118, 136, 138, 140, 154.
[15] *Naturgeschichte des Succins oder des sogenannten Bernsteins; nebst Theorie der Bildung aller fossilen, bituminösen Inflammabilien des organischen Reichs und der Analysen derselben*, 2 vols. 8°, Köln, 1816 (pp. xviii, 438; vi, 120; incl. var. resins).
[16] *Chemische Tabellen der Pflanzenanalysen*, Nürnberg, 1814 (x, 94 v. large pp.); and, uniform in size and set-out, *Chemische Tabellen des Thierreichs*, Berlin, 1814 (pp. viii, 138).

III. Neue Chemische Untersuchungen mineralischer, vegetabilischer und animal-
      ischer Substanzen. Zweite Fortsetzung des Chemischen Laboratoriums, Berlin,
      1811 (pp. xvi, 318, ii);
IV.   Chemische Schriften. Vierter Band. Chemische Untersuchungen mineralischer,
      vegetabilischer und animalischer Substanzen. Dritte Fortsetzung des Chem-
      ischen Laboratoriums, Berlin, 1813 (pp. xvi, 326, ii);
V.   Chemische Schriften Fünfter Band. Chemische Untersuchungen . . . Vierte
      Fortsetzung des Chemischen Laboratoriums, Berlin, 1816 (pp. xx, 246, ii);
VI.   Chemische Schriften. Sechster Band. Chemische Untersuchungen . . . Sub-
      stanzen. Fünfte Fortsetzung des Chemischen Laboratoriums, Berlin, 1821 (pp.
      xx, 365, iii).

He also published a dictionary of chemistry and two works on mineral waters:

VII. Handwörterbuch der allgemeinen Chemie, 4 vols. 8°, Leipzig and Altenburg,
      1817–18–18–19.
VIII. Versuch einer Methode zur Untersuchung der Mineralwasser, mit Darstellung
      einiger Eigenschaften über das Wasser im Allgemeinen, Moscow, 1804 (Bolton,
      (1), 556, gives Moscow and Leipzig, 1805).
IX.   Das Mineralbad zu Gleisen, Berlin, 1821.

John published many papers in various journals,[1] some quite short, dealing
with a wide range of subjects, and he was (like Bucholz) unusually industrious.
The older text-books often refer to him but he is now forgotten.

He isolated metallic manganese in a purer state than previously and investigated its oxides.[2] He thought he had discovered a new metal in a Saxony
manganese ore,[3] investigated metallic and organic chromates,[4] zinc ores,[5] and
agalmatolite (Chinese steatite),[6] and analysed native silver, copper, and
arsenic.[7] His investigation of coloured rock salt showed that the red and yellow
contain ferric oxide and the green basic cupric chloride, but he was unable to
find the cause of the colour in the blue, although he showed that it was not due
to copper.[8]

In meteoric iron John found both nickel and cobalt.[9] He prepared Alexan-
drian blue by fusing powdered quartz, sodium carbonate, and copper filings,[10]
analysed columbite and tantalite,[11] aragonite,[12] tabaschir,[13] and a large number
of minerals, ancient metals, etc. He proposed the name 'klaprothium' for
cadmium,[14] and called racemic acid 'Säure aus den Voghesen'.[15] He proposed
the name 'papeverin' for what he calls the 'very incorrectly named morphium'
(morphine),[16] and investigated a large number of vegetable and animal products. These included fruit gum,[17] opium,[18] ulmin,[19] lichens and Iceland moss,[20]
seaweed (including the iodine content),[21] and pollen.[22] A peculiar substance
pollenin was claimed to exist in lycopodium by Fritsche.[23]

[1] List of 83 items (82 by John alone), in *Roy. Soc. Cat. Sci. Papers*, 1869, iii, 552–4.
[2] *J. Chem. Phys.* (Gehlen), 1807, iii, 452; 1807, iv, 436; *Ann. Phil.*, 1813, ii, 172; 1814, iii, 413; III, 102–200.
[3] III, 200–4.
[4] *J. Chem.* (Schweigger), 1811, iii, 378; *Ann. Phil.*, 1814, iv, 424; III, 243–6.
[5] IV, 272–307, with a history of zinc.
[6] I, 128–51.   [7] I, 269–91, with an interesting history of metals.   [8] VI, 235.
[9] VI, 284.   [10] VI, 351; see Vol. I and Partington, (1), 1935, 117–19.   [11] I, 326–31.
[12] V, 199.   [13] *J. Chem.* (Schweigger), 1811, ii, 260.   [14] VII, iii, 299.
[15] VII, iv; Findlay, *Nature*, 1937, cxl, 22; Delépine, *Bull. Soc. Chim.*, 1941, viii, 463.
[16] VI, p. ix.   [17] *J. Chem.* (Schweigger), 1812, vi, 374.
[18] *Ann. Gén. Sci. Phys.*, 1819, ii, 100.   [19] VI, 23.   [20] VI, 26–50.   [21] VI, 60.
[22] *J. Chem.* (Schweigger), 1814, xii, 244; V, 27.   [23] *Ann. Phys.*, 1834, xxxii, 481.

John[1] separated beeswax into a soluble part (cerin) and an insoluble part (myricin) by the action of alcohol; the composition of wax was further investigated by Brodie,[2] who discovered cerotic acid. An unnamed 'new acid' found in lac by Pearson[3] was investigated and named laccic acid by John.[4] Unverdorben[5] recognised five different resins in grain-lac. John examined various sorts of calculi,[6] amniotic liquid,[7] brain,[8] animal membranes,[9] saliva (in which he found calcium phosphate),[10] isinglass,[11] and ambergris.[12] He found benzoic acid in horses' diabetic urine,[13] and analysed Oriental bezoar.[14] He investigated madder root,[15] extractive,[16] and Peruvian bark and quinic acid.[17] He confirmed H. Davy's discovery of silica in the horsetail and cane,[18] investigated gamboge,[19] prepared imitation indigo by precipitating logwood infusion with a trace of a solution of a copper salt, and found that natural indigo does not form an amalgam with mercury.[20]

John[21] described the red colouring matter of cochineal, soluble in water, alcohol, and ether, and forming lakes, and called it 'cochenilin'. It was further investigated by Pelletier and Caventou,[22] Pelletier,[23] F. Preisser,[24] Warren de la Rue[25] (who called it carminic acid), and Schützenberger.[26] For the starchy constituent of elcampane root[27] John proposed the name helenin, 'or perhaps better inulin.'[28]

KARSTEN

Carl Johann Bernhard Karsten (Bützow, Mecklenburg, 26 November 1782–Berlin, 22 August 1853), a member of a distinguished scientific family, was an inspector of mines; he lectured in Breslau and in 1819 became Ober-Bergrath of the Ministry of the Interior in Berlin.[29] He graduated at Rostock with a dissertation De affinitate Chemica, 1802, and published several memoirs on chemical affinity.[30] He published a book on chemical philosophy[31] criticising the atomic and electrochemical theories, and books on metallurgy and salt manufacture.[32] Karsten[33] found that the mixture rule does not apply to solid

[1] IV, 38. [2] Phil. Trans., 1848, cxxxviii, 147; 1849, cxxxix, 91.
[3] Phil. Trans., 1794, lxxxiv, 383. [4] J. Chem. (Schweigger), 1815, xv, 110; John, V, 1.
[5] Ann. Phys., 1828, xiv, 116. [6] V, 97; VI, 66. [7] VI, 76.
[8] IV, 228; V, 160. [9] VI, 90. [10] VI, 112. [11] VI, 121. [12] VI, 132.
[13] VI, 162. [14] II, 37. [15] IV, 94. [16] IV, 126. [17] II, 294.
[18] IV, 134. [19] IV, 190; cf. Braconnot, Ann. Chim., 1808, lxviii, 19 (33).
[20] VI, 339; cf. Döbereiner, and Schönbein, Vol. IV. [21] IV, 210–24; V, 17.
[22] Ann. Chim., 1818, viii, 250. [23] Ib., 1832, li, 182 (194).
[24] J. Chem., 1844, xxxii, 129–64. [25] Phil. Mag., 1847, xxxi, 471.
[26] Compt. Rend., 1858, xlvi, 47; Ann. Chim., 1858, liv, 52. [27] Inula Helenium L.
[28] IV, 61; inulin was preferred by Thomson, (2), 1817, iv, 75.
[29] G. Karsten, Umrisse zu Carl Johann Bernhard Karsten's Leben und Wirken, Berlin, 1854; Poggendorff, (1), i, 1227.
[30] Über Berthollets chem. Affinitätslehre, J. Chem. (Scherer), 1803, x, 135–56; Über die chemische Verbindung der Körper, 7 memoirs, in Abhl. K. Akad. Wiss. Berlin, math. phys. Kl., 1824 (1826), 1–38; 1831 (1832), 229–68; 1833 (1835), 1–20; 1834 (1836), 1–21; 1839 (1841), 1–29; 1840 (1842), 95–136; 1841 (1843), 4–57; Ostwald, Lehrbuch, 1910, i, 840, 1072.
[31] Philosophie der Chemie, Berlin, 1843 (327 pp.).
[32] Rinman, Versuch einer Geschichte des Eisens, with notes by Karsten, 2 vols., Berlin, 1785; ib., new tr. by Karsten, 2 vols., Liegnitz, 1814; Karsten, Handbuch der Eisenhüttenkunde, 2 vols., Halle, 1816; 2 ed., 4 vols., Berlin, 1827; 3 ed., 5 vols., Berlin, 1841; Metallurgische Reise durch einen Theil von Baiern und durch die süddeutschen Provinzen Österreichs, Halle, 1821; System der Metallurgie, geschichtlich, statistisch, theoretisch und technisch, 5 vols., Berlin, i–iv 1831, v 1832, and Atlas (good historical introduction, i, 17–232); Lehrbuch der Salinenkunde, 2 vols., Berlin, 1846–7.
[33] J. Chem. Phys., 1832, lxv, 394; cf. Boullay, Ann. Chim., 1830, xliii, 266.

compounds, the observed specific gravity being usually greater than the calculated, except for some sulphides and iodides. He investigated the solubility of a salt in a saturated solution of another salt, distinguishing three cases, and he regarded solution as chemical combination in indefinite proportions.[1]

The cases are: (i) salt A separates some of salt B from a saturated aqueous solution and vice versa, when the resulting solution is the same in each case and contains less A and B than a solution in pure water;

(ii) salt A separates solid B from its saturated solution but dissolves in this to the same extent as in pure water, but B dissolves in a saturated solution of A to a less extent than in pure water and does not separate solid A; the solution is the same if A is dissolved in a saturated solution of B or vice versa, or A and B dissolve together in pure water;

(iii) neither A nor B separates the other from a saturated solution, and in some cases more dissolves than in pure water; the solution has a definite composition only if both solid A and B are present.

Karsten found that reaction may occur when pairs of dry solid salts are triturated together, as is shown by a change of colour or taste; in some cases reaction does not occur, even if the salts are triturated with oil, but does so if traces of water are present.[2] He was an independent discoverer of cadmium, for which he proposed the name 'melinum' (melinus, quince yellow) from the colour of the precipitated sulphide.[3]

The uncle of C. J. B. Karsten, Diedrich Ludwig Gustav Karsten (Bützow, 5 April 1768–Berlin, 20 May 1810) was a distinguished mineralogist who published a large number of papers, a catalogue of the Leskean collection (2 vols., Leipzig, 1789; see p. 662), and wrote in Klaproth's *Beyträge* (see p. 598). Gustav Karsten, son of C. J. B., published on the solubility of common salt,[4] but otherwise on physics, of which he was professor in Kiel from 1848.

GOETHE

Johann Wolfgang von Goethe (1749–1832) hardly qualifies for inclusion in a history of chemistry, although he was very interested in the subject and a friend of Döbereiner (see Vol. IV), who owed his career to him. The ideas on chemical affinity in Goethe's novel *Wahlverwandschaften* (1809), taken from Göttling, were out of date. He was very interested in alchemy, from his study with Frl. Klettenberg (an old friend of his mother) in 1768 of the mystical book *Opus Mago-Cabbalisticum et Theosophicum* (1735; in German) of Georg von Welling (1652–1727), which is mentioned in Vol. I.[5]

[1] *Philosophie der Chemie*, 1843, 80–110, 111–31; Ostwald, *Lehrbuch*, 1910, i, 1072.
[2] *Philosophie der Chemie*, 1843, 56–62.
[3] *Archiv für Bergbau und Hüttenwesen*, 1818, i, 209; q. by Herapath, *Ann. Phil.*, 1822, iii, 435.
[4] *Untersuchungen über das Verhalten der Auflösung des reinen Kochsalzes in Wasser*, Berlin, 1846.
[5] Andrade, *Nature*, 1949, clxiv, 338; R. D. Gray, *Goethe the Alchemist*, Cambridge 1952; Grünbaum, *Chem. Ztg.*, 1909, xxxii, 1173; Kopp, (4), ii, 239; *id.*, *Aurea Catena Homeri*, 1880, 5; Lippmann, (1), ii, 439; Lockemann, *Chem. Ztg.*, 1932, lvi, 225; Schneider, *Isis*, 1954, xlv, 117–19; P. Walden, *Goethe als Chemiker und Techniker*, Berlin, 1932 (87 pp.; rev. by Roth, *Z. Elektrochem.*, 1933, xxxix, 336; summary by A. B. Lamb, *J. Amer. Chem. Soc.*, 1934, lxvi, 1003); *Briefwechsel zwischen Goethe und Döbereiner*, ed. Schiff, Weimar, 1914.

CHAPTER XIII

THE LATER PHLOGISTON THEORY

In this chapter some of the modifications of the phlogiston theory in its later phases, some involving combinations of it with the antiphlogistic theory, will be considered.[1] Kopp[2] thought that in the *earlier* theory, phlogiston practically meant negative oxygen, $\phi = - O$, and in the *later* theory it was identified with hydrogen, $\phi = H$, but this scheme is too simple, and from about 1770 the latest developments of the theory agree only in their difference from the opinions of Stahl.[3] This was supposed[4] to show that 'phlogiston must be a very simple body, since opinions are always more in accord about compound and visible bodies'. Dumas[5] said that: 'Lavoisier had no longer to deal with the phlogiston of Stahl, but with a crowd of beings of that name which had no quality in common, unless that of being intangible by any known method.' The so-called 'knock-out blow' delivered in his *Reflexions on Phlogiston* (see p. 462) did not, in fact, demolish the theory, which survived for many years.

It has often been said[6] that the theory served a useful purpose in bringing together many phenomena previously regarded as unrelated, that it was a necessary link in the chain of development of chemical theories, and was 'at least relatively correct'.[7]

It has also been said that this 'crude and clumsy hypothesis . . . led all chemists astray for half a century',[8] and[9] that it was in the line of succession from Paracelsus through Becher to Stahl, and interrupted the beginnings of a truer view of chemical phenomena instituted by Van Helmont and continued by Boyle, Mayow, and Black to Lavoisier. The unfavourable influence of the phlogiston theory was not confined to its applications to combustion and calcination; Stahl's theory of the nature of acids, with its assumption of a 'universal acid', was very unsatisfactory.[10] Many important chemical discoveries were made in the period of the phlogiston theory, but they cannot be shown to have developed from that theory. Nicholson said:[11]

[1] Partington and McKie, *Ann. Sci.*, 1937, ii, 361; 1938, iii, 1, 337; 1939, iv, 113.
[2] (1), i, 150 f.
[3] Fourcroy, (2), iii, 454; Kopp, (1), iii, 142, 155.
[4] Leonhardi, *Macquer's Chymisches Wörterbuch*, Leipzig, 1788, i, 662.
[5] (1), 1837, 161; (2), 1878, 176; (3), 1937, 99; Harcourt, *B.A. Report*, 1839, 8.
[6] E.g. by Thenard, *Traité de Chimie*, 6 ed., 1834, i, 39; Kopp, (1), 1843, i, 264 f.; S. Brown, *Essays*, 1858, i, 200.
[7] Kopp, (2), iii, 230.
[8] Wilson, *Life of Cavendish*, 1851, 35 f.
[9] Delacre, *Rev. gén. sci.*, 1924, xxxv, 708; Guichard, *Essai historique sur les Mesures en Chimie* (*Actualités Scientifiques*, 1937, iii, 46).
[10] E. von Meyer, Entwickelung der Chemie, in *Kultur der Gegenwart*, 1913, Theil III, Abteilung ii, Band 2, p. 6 f.
[11] *Dictionary of Chemistry*, 1795, I, pref. vi.

'It is affirmed that, in Chemistry, even a bad theory is of use to methodise and arrange facts. But this cannot be true; for bad theory, that is to say falsehood, cannot promote the ends of truth. So far as the theory agrees with truth, it will consist of arrangements growing out of the nature of the facts themselves; and so far as it differs from this, it is delusion.'

In what follows, the theory of the levity of phlogiston, a matter not very prominent in the old phlogiston theory (see Vol. II), will first be considered.

The theory of phlogiston ultimately foundered on the fact of the increase in weight of metals on calcination, which was well known throughout the whole period of its use. There are many facts in opposition to generally accepted theories even to-day, and the latter are not, in consequence, abandoned. It is always hoped that some explanation will be found later.

The Weight of Heat

The earlier work on the calcination of metals has been dealt with and it is only necessary here to consider the attitude adopted towards the fact by the followers of Stahl.[1] Boyle explained the increase in weight as due to the fixation of ponderable igneous corpuscles (see Vol. II, p. 529), but Kunckel[2] showed that this was untenable by an experiment in which a mass of metal was found to have the same weight whether red-hot or cold, and the same result was found by Boerhaave,[3] who correctly concluded that heat is imponderable. Boerhaave gives no satisfactory explanation of the increase in weight of metals on calcination, suggesting that it might be due to saline and sulphureous particles present in the air.[4]

Experiments on weighing hot and cold masses of metal are reported in an essay by Mme. de Châtelet,[5] which was unsuccessfully presented in 1737 for a prize offered by the Paris Academy for an essay on 'the nature of fire and its propagation', but was ordered to be printed. She claims to have weighed (no doubt in a Lorraine iron works) hot and cold masses of iron from 1 to 2000 lb., and found the weights the same, as Boerhaave stated. Her friend Voltaire also presented an unsuccessful essay, again ordered to be printed,[6] recording the same experiments but also stating that he had put 100 lb., 35 lb., and 25 lb. of molten cast iron into three thick iron vessels, and found that after six hours the metal in the three vessels had gained 4 lb., 1 lb. $1\frac{1}{2}$ oz., and 1 lb., respectively, on becoming cold. This shows, he says, that fire has no weight, the increase in weight being due to the fixation of something contained in the atmosphere:

il est tres-possible que cette augmentation de poids soit venuë de la matière répanduë dans l'Atmosphere: Donc dans toutes les autres opérations par lesquelles les matières calcinées acquierent du poids, cette augmentation de substance pourroit aussi leur être venuë de la même cause, et non de la matière ignée.[7]

[1] Kopp, (1), iii, 102 f., 119 f.; Leonhardi, 1789, iii, 452 f. (Kalch).
[2] *Laboratorium Chymicum*, 1716, 31.   [3] (2), 1732, i, 259, 362.   [4] (2), i, 493.
[5] Dissertation sur la Nature et la Propagation du Feu . . . par une jeune dame d'un haut rang; in *Recueil des Pieces qui ont remporté le Prix* . . . (*avec les Pieces qui y ont concoru*), Paris, 1752, iv, 85, 102.
[6] Essai sur la Nature du Feu et sur sa Propagation, par un de nos premiers Poètes; *Recueil des Pieces*, 1752, iv, 84, 169 (176–83).
[7] *Ib.*, 178.

He also described the rise in temperature produced on mixing ammonia and vinegar, suggested that heat is the cause of the liquid and gaseous states, and from measurements of the temperature of a mixture of liquids, each at a different temperature, approached the theory of specific heats.[1] Buffon[2] found that large masses of iron were heavier when heated to whiteness, and Roebuck[3] that masses of iron, copper, and silver were slightly heavier when hot than when cold. Marat[4] found that silver and copper spheres are slightly heavier when strongly heated. The theory of ponderable igneous corpuscles was re-adopted by P. van Musschenbroek[5] and Limbourg.[6] Arguments for and against the theory had been summarised by L. Lemery in 1709.[7] Even as late as 1773, Baumé,[8] who says that metals increase by 10 to 12 per cent in weight on calcination, explained it as due to the fixation of igneous particles. Boerhaave's experiment (p. 606) does not disprove this, since in a hot mass of metal the particles of fire do not touch those of the metal; they behave like a bird flying in a cage, and the cage weighs no more than without the bird. When the particles are fixed, as in the calx, it is as though the bird were on the perch, when its weight makes itself felt.

BERAUT

Laurent Beraut, in a dissertation of 1747 which was awarded the prize of the Academy of Bordeaux,[9] pointed out that the calx is less dense than the metal, and that the increase in weight cannot be due to the addition of igneous corpuscles, since although fire as a material body must have some weight yet this must be very slight, like the corpuscles emitted by odorous bodies, and 'nothing can hold it captive'. Molten lead contains much more fire than the calx but weighs less. The increase in weight of calcined metals is not due to air, since 20 lb. of lead yield 25 lb. of calx, and 5 lb. of air occupying 64 cu. ft. must be compressed into a 4 in. cube, this requiring a force of 1728 atm., and there is no adequate explanation as to how this immense compressing force can be produced in the experiment. Beraut argued that the increase in weight is not due to the fixation of light in the experiments with burning lenses, or to material taken up from the vessels, and he comes to the conclusion that the physical phenomenon of increase in weight is caused by the fixation of foreign particles, saline and nitrous, floating about in the air and uniting, by the action of fire, with the parts of the calcined bodies: la véritable et l'unique cause de ce Phénomène physique vient des Corps étrangers répandus dans

---

[1] *Ib.*, 183; cf. Brougham, 1872, 57; E. M. Forster, *Abinger Harvest*, 1936, 199 f.

[2] *Histoire naturelle, Supplément*, Paris, 1775, ii, 11–13.

[3] *Phil. Trans.*, 1776, lxvi, 509; Whitehurst, *ib.*, 575.

[4] *Recherches physiques sur le feu*, Paris, 1780, 30; tr., *Physische Untersuchungen über das Feuer . . . mit Anmerkungen von C. E. Weigel*, Leipzig, 1782, 47.

[5] *Traité du Feu*, §§ MDLXXVIII–MDLXXXVI, in *Cours de Physique Expérimentale et Mathématique*, 4°, Leyden, 1769, ii, 371 f.

[6] *Dissertation sur les affinités chimiques*, Liége, 1761, 42: la materie ignée, ou . . . autre materie subtile.

[7] AdS, 1709, h 6, m 400.

[8] *Chymie expérimentale et raisonnée*, 1773, i, 56; ii, 265.

[9] *Dissertation sur la Cause de l'Augmentation de Poids, que certaines Matières acquièrent dans leur calcination*, 4°, Bordeaux, 1747 (36 pp.); sm. 8°, The Hague, 1748 (98 pp.); see p. 203.

l'air, qui par l'action du feu se réünissent aux parties des Corps calcinez.[1] He refers to the motes seen in sunbeams, and suggests that when the air in which these gross particles of salt and nitre float is rarefied by heat, they fall by their weight on the metal, enter its pores, already greatly dilated by fire, and so increase its weight. Some of the metal is at the same time dissipated in fumes, but very little, on account of the close binding of the metal particles.

VOGEL

Rudolph Augustin Vogel (Erfurt, 1 May 1724–Göttingen, 5 April 1774), professor of medicine in Göttingen,[2] at first thought that antimony did not increase in weight on calcination,[3] but afterwards[4] found that 4 oz. of antimony increased in weight by 60 grains and explained his previous result by his failing to stir the antimony during heating.[5]

WEIGEL

C. E. von Weigel (see p. 594)[6] said that mercury, to be calcined, must be exposed to air and acquires an increase in weight, referring to Lemery, Homberg and Vogel (for lead); he can offer no explanation for this except the fixation of particles of fire:

cuius phaenomeni ego quidem nullam aliam perspicio rationem, quam quod particulae ex igne accesserint et particulis mercurii adhaerentes totius massae pondus maius reddiderunt.

Kunckel's explanation (see Vol. II, p. 374) is wrong, because the volume increases when a metal is calcined:

Kunckelius de pororum maiori gravitate specifica profert, assumere nequeo, cum potius contrarium contingat, dum scil. metalla calcinationis vi in pulverem dilapsa volumine augeri, et poros magnitudine augeri, huic licet grauitas absoluta aucta, tamen specificam imminutam esse, necesse videatur.

Weigel[7] described some experiments on the relative solubilities of calces of mercury made with the burning glass and by fire, which seemed to show that they had different properties, and he concluded that the purest phlogiston exists in sunlight, the next pure in the electric spark, whilst the heat of culinary fires, and combustible matters, contain phlogiston in diminishing purity.

[1] Diss., 1747, 24.   [2] Gmelin, (1), ii, 646, 686; Ferguson, ii, 516.
[3] Experimenta chemicorum de incremento ponderis corporum quorundam calcinatorum examinantur, 4°, Göttingen [1753], 24 pp.; repr. in his Opuscula medica selecta antea sparsim edita, nunc autem in unum collecta recognita aucta et emendata, 4°, Göttingen, 1768, 51–68; in this work (mentioned by Gmelin, (1), ii, 478, and Bolton, (1), 892) Vogel refers to Boyle, Kunckel, etc., but not Rey.
[4] Analecta chemica de vitro antimonii, Göttingen, 1757; in Opuscula, 1768, 147–74, 162.
[5] Vogel's Institutiones chemiae ad lectiones academicas accommodatae, 8°, Göttingen, 1755; Leyden and Leipzig, 1757; Bamberg, Frankfurt and Leipzig, 1762, 1764, 1774, tr. and annotated by J. C. Wiegleb as Lehrsätze der Chemie, Weimar, 1775 and 1785, deals (1775 ed.) with phlogiston (§§ 91 f., pp. 71 f.), calcination (§§ 697 f., pp. 534 f., and Wiegleb's note: matter of fire combines with the metal as phlogiston escapes, since mercury on calcination is 'somewhat increased in weight').
[6] Observationes Chemicae et Mineralogicae, Göttingen, 1771, i, Obs. II, p. 21: Mercurii in pulverem conversio per solum ignem.
[7] Observat., Greifswald, 1773, ii, 1 f.; quotation from Beraut.

Spielmann,[1] mentioning Beraut and Vogel, says physicists are not agreed on the true cause of weight (vera gravitatis causa) and he does not feel able to give a reason for the increase in weight of lead on calcination. In the second edition[2] he adds Rey's name.

The Weight of Phlogiston

Stahl seems generally to have considered phlogiston as a very light substance: 'sulphur, not in weight, but in the number of its most delicate particles (seiner allerzartesten Stäubgen) is completely loaded with it',[3] yet when liver of sulphur is heated with exposure to air until all its phlogiston is expelled, a weighing shows how little fiery substance is contained in it.[4] This method was used to find the proportions of sulphuric acid and phlogiston in sulphur by Brandt (see p. 168), who estimated[5] it to be $\frac{1}{16}$, and Neumann,[6] who concluded that 16 oz. of sulphur contain 15 oz. 6 dr. of acid and only 1 dr. of phlogiston, by which 'the most corrosive acid is in all its properties so surprisingly changed'. Later experimenters concluded that sulphur contains $\frac{1}{7}$ of phlogiston.[7]

Stahl[8] thought that addition of phlogiston could make a body lighter, and Pott[9] that phlogiston, although not volatile of itself, is capable of conferring volatility on the heaviest and most fixed bodies. The view that the accession of inflammable parts made a concrete lighter was enunciated by Stahl separately from its converse that the escape of phlogiston from metals made their calces heavier. The explanation was advanced in its complete form by Scheffer,[10] who reported that he had proved by numerous experiments that metals gain in weight in the proportion in which phlogiston is removed from them, and conversely decrease in weight as phlogiston combines with them: Metallerne öka sin vigt i samma proportion, som de ferlöra af phlogisto, och tvärt om minska vigten, efter som de få phlogiston i förening med sig. Iron cannot be melted in the absence of phlogiston without losing much of its own phlogiston, and thus its weight was increased, since an equal weight was contained in a smaller space.

J. G. Wallerius[11] said the possibility of the increase in weight (which had been certainly established) being due to a loss of inflammable particles which are lighter than air (hoc ipsum deduci posse à particularum inflammabilium, aëre leviorum, separatione) must be taken into account. He regarded phlogiston as a compound of heat matter and a subtle earth (see p. 171).

Mathieu Tillet (Bordeaux, 1714–Paris (?), 20 December 1791), director of

[1] Institutiones Chemiae, Strasbourg, 1763, 239.   [2] Strasbourg, 1766, 275.
[3] Von dem Sulphure, 1718, 83.   [4] Experimenta, etc., 1731, 53 (see Vol. II, p. 662).
[5] Macquer, Dictionnaire, 1766, ii, 506.   [6] Works, 1759, 168.
[7] Erxleben, Anfangsgründe der Chemie, 2 ed., Göttingen, 1784, § 360, p. 256; Kirwan, Phil. Trans., 1782, lxxii, 179 f.
[8] Fundamenta Chymiae, 2 ed., Nürnberg, 1746–7, iii, 374.
[9] Chymische Untersuchungen Welche fürnehmlich von der Lithogeognosia ... handeln, Potsdam, 1746, Versuch ... über die Eigenschaften und Würckungen des Lichts und Feuers, 68; Lithogéognosie, Paris, 1753, 348–51; see Partington and McKie, Ann. Sci., 1937, ii, 368 f.
[10] KAH, 1757, xviii, 314 (321).
[11] Elementa metallurgiæ speciatim chemicæ conscripta, Stockholm, 1768, Sect. II, cap. iv, § 5, p. 208.

the Mint in Troyes, Champagne, who seems to have lived mostly in Paris and became a member of the Academy in 1758,[1] published several memoirs on assaying[2] in one of which (1763) he remarked that lead increases by one-sixth of its weight on calcination, and the Secretary of the Academy, de Fouchy, in discussing this,[3] remarked that the fact is 'a true chemical paradox, which eludes all present physical ideas (un vrai paradox chimique . . . il échappe à toutes les idées physiques que nous avons)'.

CHARDENON

The cause of the increase in weight of metals on calcination was explained by Jean Pierre Chardenon (Dijon; 1714–16 March 1769), a physician, *agregé* of the College of Medicine at Dijon, and one of the secretaries of the Dijon Academy in 1752 (elected *Associé* on 27 March 1744, and *Pensionnaire* on 2 June 1747).[4] Chardenon brought this problem before the Academy of Dijon on 15 July 1763, and at a public séance of the Academy on 9 December 1764. His memoir was published in 1769.[5] Chardenon says the increase in weight of metals on calcination is 'one of the most interesting phenomena in physics', firmly established by numerous experiments and recognised by all physicists. There are two kinds of gravity, specific and absolute, and the latter can increase only by the addition of new substance.

Air is heavier than fire, hence fire, although it may gravitate like other matter, cannot augment the sensible weight of calcined metals. Beraut's theory is rejected for four reasons. Weight is an essential property of matter but lightness is not, as Aristotle thought, a particular quality but is a smaller gravity (une moindre pesanteur). Particles in a compound (mixte) less dense than air will tend to rise, and if they cannot leave the compound 'they will destroy a quantity of the gravitation of the others, proportional to the excess of their lightness to air (ils détruiront une quantité de la gravitation des autres, proportionné à l'excès de leur légéreté sur l'air)', just as a cork buoys up a lead sinker; and phlogiston, 'that light and fugitive part which is removed from calcinable bodies by converting them into calces (cette partie tenue & fugace que l'on enleve aux substances calcinables en les convertissant en chaux)', is in air for these substances what cork is for lead in water.[6]

Chardenon identified phlogiston with fire and says his idea is founded on the common notion of the specific lightness of fire *in air*.[7] He concluded that: (i) the increase in weight is due neither to the fixation of igneous particles nor to the accession of corpuscles from the atmosphere (Beraut's theory); (ii) the principal cause both of the increase in weight of calcined metals and the

---

[1] Poggendorff, (1), ii, 1108.

[2] AdS, 1760, m 361; 1762, h 56, m 10; 1763, h 39, m 1, 38; 1769, h 56, m 153; 1775, m 193; 1776, h 22, m 377; 1778, h 21, m 505.

[3] AdS, 1763 (1766), h 47.

[4] P. Milsand, *Notes et Documents pour servir à l'Histoire de l'Académie des Sciences etc. . . . de Dijon*, 2 ed., Paris, 1871, 323, 367; Partington and McKie, *Ann. Sci.*, 1937, ii, 373; 1938, iii, 57.

[5] *Mém. Acad. Dijon*, 1769, i, 303; Sur l'augmentation de poids des Métaux calcinés.

[6] *Ib.*, 315–16.   [7] *Ib.*, 317.

diminution of weight when they are reduced to the metallic state, 'is nothing else than the change which they undergo, and which constitutes essentially these different states, in the opinion of all physicists, i.e. the absence or presence of phlogiston.'[1]

GUYTON DE MORVEAU

Chardenon's theory that phlogiston is specifically lighter than air (or more strictly than the rarest medium) was developed in detail by Guyton de Morveau.[2] Phlogiston has not an absolute negative weight but is lighter than air, so that a body containing it is buoyed up in the same way as a piece of lead in water weighs less when a cork is attached to it. Calcinable metals, including mercury,[3] contain a volatile phlogiston. A discussion of the reason for the increase in weight on calcination refers to Vogel (see p. 608)[4] and emphasises[5] that the calx is more bulky than the metal. The theories of Boyle,[6] Beraut,[7] and Geoffroy[8] (who thought the calx contained an alkali) are criticised. Gellert[9] thought calces are compounds of the metal with an acid and are formed with loss of a volatile (perhaps mercurial) principle, phlogiston reducing them mainly because it dissolves the acid (hauptsächlich durch die Auflösung der Säure), as is shown by the reduction of horn-silver[10] and calces of lead and antimony by heating with alkali or chalk, which contain no phlogiston. This view is criticised. Chardenon's explanation that the particles of metal are rendered less attractive after calcination would require a change in the law of gravitation.[11]

De Morveau advanced the theory that phlogiston is a light body, lighter than air, which makes bodies lighter, as a cork is buoyant in water:

La comparison du liége dans l'eau au Phlogistique dans l'air, que M. Chardenon n'a donnée que comme explicative, est réellement identique & suffisante.[12]

'Phlogiston is essentially volatile (le Phlogistique est essentiellement volatil).'[13] The volatility of mercury, ethers, alkalis, liver of sulphur, acids of sulphur, odoriferous bodies, oils, sulphur, and even metals in the focus of a burning glass, are all evidence for the volatility of phlogiston, which is supposed to abound in these bodies. The cause of the volatility of phlogiston is 'evidently the excess of gravity of the medium over that of the volatile body'.[14]

'Le corps que j'appelle essentiellement volatil, est celui qui est constamment moins grave que le milieu le plus subtil, soit que nous ne puissons changer sa forme élémentaire, soit que son volume ne puisse être resserré pour qu'il se trouve jamais en rapport égal de densite avec le milieu: tel est le Phlogistique.'[15]

---

[1] Ib., 320.

[2] Digressions Académiques, Dijon, 1772 (see p. 519), 1–267; Sur le Phlogistique considéré comme corps grave, & par rapport aux changements de pesanteur qu'il produit dans les corps auxquels il est uni; see also Ency. Suppl., Amsterdam, 1777, iv, 336; Partington and McKie, Ann. Sci., 1937, ii, 388–401; Meyerson, De l'Explication dans les Sciences, Paris, 1921, ii, 281.

[3] 1772, 41, 53.   [4] Ib., 69.   [5] Ib., 98.

[6] Ib., 92 f.   [7] Ib., 99 f.   [8] AdS, 1720, m 20–34.

[9] Anfangsgründe zur metallurgischen Chemie, Theil II, ch. lxxiii, 2 ed., Leipzig, 1776, 403.

[10] De Morveau, 1772, 120, correctly says this is not a calx.   [11] De Morveau, 1772, 118 f.

[12] Ib., 120; cf.: le Phlogistique ne peut être pesant dans l'air, ib., 135; le Phlogistique est spécifiquement moins grave que l'air, ib., 140 f., 174, 218, 262.

[13] Ib., 136.   [14] Ib., 140.   [15] Ib., 142.

It is on account of its volatility and lightness compared with air that phlogiston reduces the specific gravity (weight) of a body: the specific gravity of phlogiston is less than that of air.[1]

Phlogiston is either a simple body or a compound of the element of fire with a rare body such that the gravity of the compound is less than that of air.[2] De Morveau was convinced that his theory was different from Chardenon's.

He answered in detail four objections to his theory.[3] The objection that the specific gravity of the calx is less than that of the metal is due to a confusion of specific gravity or weight (*gravité spécifique*) or weight in air with absolute gravity (*pesanteur absolue*), and the cause is the random arrangement of the particles after the escape of phlogiston from the metal.[4] The phlogiston in the metal is in some ways like water of crystallisation.[5] The most dense bodies have at least half their volume as empty space, so that the phlogiston can exert its buoyancy even though the metal occupies less space than the calx.[6]

De Morveau showed by experiments that the weight of a metal is increased by calcination with saltpetre or white arsenic, or dissolution in nitric acid, whilst reduction of the calx reduced its weight.[7] Conversion of steel into iron by heating increased the weight, whilst heating the (partly oxidised) iron with charcoal (cementation) gave steel with loss in weight; hence steel is iron plus phlogiston.[8] Reduction of red precipitate *per se* (mercuric oxide) to mercury must be due to a 'metallising principle' passing through the walls of the heated vessel.[9] Prussian blue, which most chemists regarded as iron calx supercharged with phlogiston, *loses* weight on calcination, hence it contains some other substance and is 'une sorte d'hépar' since liver of sulphur also loses weight on calcination and some matter also escapes.[10] Some iron was calcined in a retort containing some litharge in the neck; this was not reduced by the escaping phlogiston, so that 'le seul attouchement du phlogistique libre est incapable de revivifier les chaux'.[11]

At the end of his essay, de Morveau[12] gave a table of the quantities of phlogiston in 1 oz. of metal 'capable de s'opposer dans l'air à la descente d'environ [x] grains de sa terre'; x is for iron 192, tin 157, regulus of antimony 145, zinc 110, copper 88, and lead 85.

An anonymous critic[13] brought up four objections to de Morveau's theory, but de Morveau defended it.[14]

A long abstract and criticism of de Morveau's theory by De la Metherie[15] said it assumed that the light phlogiston can take away and bear up heavy things on its wings; the decrease in weight of lead in water by an attached cork is due to the increase in the total volume, which de Morveau had neglected, as

[1] See *ib.* 136 f.; Ch. iii, 'Preuves que la présence ou l'absence du Phlogistique est la véritable cause de la diminution ou de l'augmentation de pesanteur des corps susceptible de se combiner avec lui'; 140 f., 153, 174, 262; 'Sur la nature du Phlogistique', 234 f.

[2] *Ib.*, 163.   [3] *Ib.*, 152 f.   [4] *Ib.*, 168 f. See p. 203.   [5] *Ib.*, 170.
[6] *Ib.*, 177.   [7] *Ib.*, 179 f., 208.   [8] *Ib.*, 213.   [9] *Ib.*, 233.
[10] *Ib.*, 250 f.   [11] *Ib.*, 240.   [12] *Ib.*, 265.
[13] *J. de Médecine*, 1772, xxxviii, 195; Partington and McKie, *op. cit.*, 395 f.
[14] *Défense de la volatilité du Phlogistique ou Lettres de l'auteur des Digressions Académiques à l'auteur du Journal de Médecine*, 12°, s.l.e.a. [Dijon, 1772].
[15] *Obs. Phys.*, 1772, ii, 281–5 (abstr.), 285–91 (crit.); Crell's *Ann.*, 1784, II, 67; De la Metherie, *Essai Analytique sur l'Air Pur*, Paris, 1785, 360.

well as the ratio of the specific gravity of the cork weighed in air and water; the cork increases the weight of the lead in air and decreases its gravity in water.

Guyton de Morveau[1] later admitted that calces contain a considerable quantity of air:

'Cette hypothèse peut encore obtenir quelque confiance de la part de ceux qui se refuseroient à croire qu'il pût se fixer dix livres d'air pendant la calcination de cent livres de plomb, & qui seroient tentés d'admettre le concours de plusieurs causes dans un effet aussi prodigieux: mais nous avons annoncé que nous serions bientôt connoître les expériences qui démontrent la présence d'une quantité très-considérable de ce fluide, dans les chaux métalliques.'

He then[2] regarded phlogiston as fixed fire (*feu fixe*), or 'nothing but the elementary matter of fire, considered in the composition of bodies'.

Bergman[3] regarded phlogiston as without doubt the lightest material substance (omnium sine dubio materierum levissimi). C. G. Selle[4] after saying that de Morveau had assumed that phlogiston had no weight, or rather that it had a property opposed to weight (vielmehr eine der Schwere entgegengesetzte Eigenschaft), objected to this as too forced (zu gezwungen).

Christian Friedrich Daniel (1753–98), a physician in Halle, in an anonymous work[5] which is essentially a reply to Erxleben's criticism[6] of J. F. Meyer's theory of *acidum pingue*, and a defence of Black's theory, gave a confused account of phlogiston which implied that it makes bodies lighter.

Wiegleb[7] explained that fire always tends to move upwards from the centre of the earth, and gravitates towards the centre of the sun. Phlogiston is the basis of the combustible principle; when combined with an earth fire 'loses all the properties it possessed as pure fire and then has the name phlogiston'.[8] Calcination involves loss of phlogiston and gain of the matter of fire; there is an increase in weight and the full weight of metal is *not* recovered on reduction.[9] In his notes to his translation of Vogel's book[10] Wiegleb attributed the increase in weight of metals (including mercury) on calcination to the fixation of fire matter. In his edition of Erxleben's book[11] Wiegleb mentions the necessity of exposure to air in the calcination of metals, in order to allow the escape of phlogiston. The metals increase in weight. The contraction of the air is probably due to a reduction in elastic force (Spannkraft) of the air by absorption of phlogiston rather than to absorption of part of the air by the metal, which nevertheless increases in weight.

Weigel[12] said: 'No combustion, calcination, etc., can occur without a

[1] *Élémens de Chymie*, Dijon, 1777, i, 172. [2] *Ib.*, i, 164.
[3] De praecipitatis metallicis; *Opuscula*, 1780, ii, 355.
[4] *Neue Beiträge zur Natur- und Arzenei-Wissenschaft*, Berlin, 1782, i, 213.
[5] *Versuch einer Theorie der wichtigsten Beobachtungen aus der Naturlehre, die man zum Theil durch die fixe Luft oder fette Säure zu erklären bemüht war*, Halle, 1777, 134 pp.; Crell's *Ann.*, 1795, I, 287; Partington and McKie, *Ann. Sci.*, 1938, iii, 4.
[6] Ueber die fixe Luft und die fette Säure, in his book, *Physikalisch-chemische Abhandlungen*, vol. i (all published), Leipzig, 1776, pp. 1–279.
[7] *Handbuch der allgemeinen Chemie*, Berlin and Stettin, 1781, i, 183, 372.
[8] *Ib.*, 138, 183. [9] *Ib.*, i, 258 f.; ii, 466 f.
[10] *Lehrsätze der Chemie*, Weimar, 1775, §§ 91 f., 697 f.; pp. 71 f., 534 f.
[11] J. C. P. Erxleben, *Anfangsgründe der Chemie, mit neuen Zusätze vermehrt von J. C. Wiegleb*, Göttingen, 1784, 481 f.
[12] Tr. of de Morveau, Maret, and Durande, *Anfangsgründe der theoretischen und praktischen Chemie*, Leipzig, 1779, i, 134.

decomposition in which parts are volatilised, for the reception of which a solvent [i.e. air] must be present.'

Rinman[1] reported that iron on calcination may increase in weight by over 40 per cent, although there is a limit. Scheffer (see p. 609), if he had had more opportunity, would have shown what de Morveau afterwards conclusively proved, that phlogiston is the lightest known fluid, much lighter than air, and must add to the lightness of bodies such as metals in which it is present. Rinman concluded that his experiments proved that phlogiston is 10 times lighter than air.

The Negative Weight of Phlogiston

Bayen[2] reported that Venel in his lectures at Montpellier from about 1750, and in conversation, asserted without much conviction that:

'Phlogiston is not attracted towards the centre of the earth, but tends to rise; thence comes the increase of weight in the formation of metallic calces and the diminution in weight in their reduction

le phlogistique ne pese pas vers le centre de la terre; il tend à s'élever, de-là l'augmentation de poids dans les chaux métalliques, de-là la diminution de ce même poids dans leur réduction, disoit souvent M. Venel, dans la conversation & dans les leçons de Chymie qu'il donnoit à Montpellier.'

This theory was also taught by Black, as appears from statements by his pupils.[3] Bryan Higgins[4] refers to experiments:

'persuading that phlogiston doth not gravitate, and that it hath a power whereby it counteracts the gravitation of other matter; unless the bodies whose gravitation is encreased whilst they are deprived of phlogiston, attract and combine with the air which cannot be extricated or discovered by any known art.'

Priestley[5] and W. Nicholson[6] rejected the negative weight of phlogiston. Kirwan[7] mentions it as an explanation of the increase in weight of metals on calcination. Lavoisier[8] thought it was 'in contradiction to all the facts avowed and recognised by the disciples of Stahl', but this did not convince everybody. John Elliot (Chard, 19 December 1747–Newgate Prison, London, 22 July

---

[1] *Försök till Järnets Historia*, Stockholm, 1782, § 64, p. 241; tr., *Versuch einer Geschichte des Eisens*, Berlin, 1785, i, § 64, p. 211.

[2] *Obs. Phys.*, 1774, iii, 282; *Opuscules*, Paris, 1797, i, 251.

[3] J. Black, *Lectures on the Elements of Chemistry*, Edinburgh, 1803, i, 237; ii, 398, 401, 750 (cf. McKie, *Ann. Sci.*, 1936, i, 101); William Cleghorn, *Disputatio Physica Inauguralis Theoriam Ignis complectens*, Edinburgh, 1779, 28; J. Elliot, *Philosophical Observations on the Senses of Vision and Hearing; to which are added, A Treatise on Harmonic Sounds, and an Essay on Combustion and Animal Heat*, London, 1780, 217 (from notes of Black's lectures lent to him); Irvine, *Essays, chiefly on Chemical Subjects*, London, 1805, 407–25; P. Dugud Leslie, *A Philosophical Inquiry into the Cause of Animal Heat*, London, 1778, 107 f. See Partington and McKie, *Ann. Sci.*, 1937, ii, 380 f.; Richard Lubbock, *Dissertatio Physico-Chemica Inauguralis, de Principio Sorbili*, 4°, Edinburgh, 1784, 12–13 (see p. 489); Saechtling, *Angew. Chem.*, 1933, xlvi, 754.

[4] *A Syllabus of Chemical and Philosophical Enquiries, composed for the Use of the Noblemen and Gentlemen who have subscribed to the Proposals made for the Advancement of Natural Knowledge*, 1775; repr. in his *A Philosophical Essay concerning Light*, London, 1776, i, xix–liii, xxxviii.

[5] E & O, 1774, i, 267; 1775, ii, 311.

[6] Tr. (anon.) of Fourcroy's *Elements of Natural History and Chemistry*, London, 1790, i, pref. xii.

[7] *Essay on Phlogiston*, 1787, 3; 1789, 3, 311.

[8] *Mémoires de Chimie*, ii, 83; *Oeuvres*, ii, 102.

1787)[1] called phlogiston *electron*.[2] In combustion it unites with air, which has a greater affinity for it than for heat. Phlogiston has negative weight; it is the matter of light in a state of combination with bodies, existing in an elastic state in their pores.[3]

Elliot[4] supposed that the light of flame is phlogiston, and heat is produced from the union of phlogiston and air, the air having a greater affinity for phlogiston than the substance with which the latter is combined in the inflammable body (e.g. vitriolic acid in sulphur). Phlogiston and fire mutually replace one another. These ideas were adopted by Guyton de Morveau.[5]

Phlogiston and Light

Anton Rüdiger (Leipzig; 1720–83), professor of chemistry in Leipzig from 1762, regarded[6] the matter of light as quite different from the inflaming (entzündende) matter of fire. The cause of combustion is a subtle saline nitrous kind of light present in the atmosphere. Phlogiston or combustible matter when combined with the inflaming matter of fire gives actual fire. J. F. Meyer[7] regarded light as pure elementary fire which combined with an unknown acid to form *acidum pingue*, which in motion is ordinary culinary fire. G. C. Morgan[8] thought light is a body subject to gravity but heterogeneous, the same attractive power operating differently on its different parts; it is present in combustibles in a combined form and is expelled when they are decomposed by heat or by other means. Anton Marchand[9] thought inflaming matter (Entzündungsstoff) is light, which is different from fire. A negatively electrifiable body (e.g. resin) contains phlogiston, a positively electrifiable body contains fire. J. H. Voigt[10] had male and female phlogistons with positive and negative weights, viz. ordinary phlogiston and caloric, respectively, which combine to form heat. J. A. Weber[11] regarded phlogiston as a compound of electrical matter and earth, fixed and volatile phlogiston being differentiated by the fineness of the earth.

[1] Partington and McKie, *Ann. Sci.*, 1938, iii, 350; 1950, vi, 262.
[2] The modern negative electron has many of the properties formerly attributed to phlogiston; Partington, *Scientia*, 1938, 121.
[3] Elliot, *Philosophical Observations on the Senses of Vision and Hearing; to which are added, A Treatise on Harmonic Sounds, and an Essay on Combustion and Animal Heat*, London, 1780 (viii, 222 pp.), 85 f., 100 f.; *Elements of the Branches of Natural Philosophy connected with Medicine*, London, 1782, 83 f.
Elliot also wrote a *Medical Pocket Book*, London, 1781, and later eds. (e.g. 1800); *An Account of the Nature and Medicinal Virtues of the Principal Mineral Waters of Great Britain and Ireland*, London, 1781, 2 ed. 1789; Observations on the Affinities of Substances in Spirit of Wine, *Phil. Trans.*, 1786, lxxvi, 155; a paper *On the Blue Colour of the Sky*, submitted to the Royal Society in December 1786, was not published.
[4] 1780, 85 f., 100 f.; 1782, 83 f.
[5] *Ency. Méthod., Chymie*, 1786, i, 255.
[6] *Systematische Anleitung zur reinen und überhaupt applicirten oder allgemeinen Chemie*, Leipzig, 1756, §§ 59–73, pp. 53–64.
[7] *Chymischen Versuche . . . des ungelöschten Kalchs*, Hannover, 1764, 216, 236, 278.
[8] *Phil. Trans.*, 1785, lxxv, 190: on coloured flames.
[9] *Ueber Phlogiston, elektrische Materie, Licht, Luft und die unmittelbare Ursach der Bewegung*, Mannheim, 1787, 23, 33, 41, 59, 78, 95.
[10] *Versuch einer neuen Theorie des Feuers, der Verbrennung, der künstlichen Luftarten, des Athmens, der Gährung, der Electricität, der Meteoren, des Lichts und des Magnetismus*, Jena, 1793, 10 f.
[11] *Neuentdeckte Natur und Eigenschaften des Kalkes und der äzenden Körper*, Berlin, 1778, 65.

Buffon[1] asserted that phlogiston is not a simple principle but a combination of two elements, fire and air, which are fixed in bodies. Phlogiston first becomes the inflammable principle when it is set free by access of air. The increase in weight of metals on calcination is due to the fixation of air. Phlogiston is 'fixed fire animated by air'.[2] The universal pure acid is a compound of air and fire; it acts upon glass to give vitriolic acid and on lime to give the marine acid, and by fermentation it gives nitric acid.[3]

Macquer[4] criticised this theory of phlogiston and included Buffon (without naming him) among those who have written on chemistry without troubling to read what had been written before. Macquer's own theory that phlogiston is the matter of light (see p. 85) was at first adopted by Fourcroy,[5] who combined it with Lavoisier's theory:

'M. Macquer . . . thinks that light . . . is combined in combustible bodies; that its separation is the first cause of combustion; but that it can never be disengaged but by the concourse of air, because air is the precipitant of light, and it unites to combustible bodies in proportion as the light it separates from them is volatilized . . . ; we think . . . that the respectable authority of so great a master constrains us not to reject phlogiston entirely.'

Fourcroy[6] later suggested that a metal is composed of an earth, unknown in the pure state, and phlogiston. On calcination the phlogiston combines with part of the pure air, rendering it incapable of supporting combustion, whilst the other part of the pure air combines with the earth of the metal to form the calx. Guyton de Morveau[7] thought at first that the phlogiston theory and the new theory could be combined, but in 1787 he abandoned phlogiston. Macquer, who never adopted the new theory, suggested[8] that in explaining the reduction of sulphuric acid to sulphur by carbon in Stahl's experiment (see Vol. II, p. 671): 'il est même plus sage de lier ces deux théories & d'admettre la séparation du phlogistique du charbon, en même-tems que celle de l'air de l'acide vitriolique'; he also suspected that 'le gas inflammable . . . pourroit bien n'être que le feu fixé de Stahl', counselling a suspension of judgment till it was seen which opinion would prevail: 'il est plus sage de lier cette dernière [Stahl's theory] avec celle des gas.'[9]

LEONHARDI

Johann Gottfried Leonhardi (Leipzig, 18 June 1746–Dresden, 11 January 1823), associate professor of medicine in Leipzig (1781) and professor of medicine in Wittenberg (1782–91) and at the Sanitary College in Dresden

[1] *Histoire Naturelle, Supplément*, Paris, 1774, i, 44, 58, 72 f., 109; Crell's *Ann.*, 1784, I, 207 f.
[2] *Histoire Naturelle des Minéraux*, 4°, Paris, 1783, ii, 115–26.
[3] *Ib.*, 1783, ii, 145; Crell's *Ann.*, 1786, II, 370.
[4] *Dictionnaire de Chymie*, 1778, iii, 122, 127.
[5] *Leçons élémentaires d'histoire naturelle, et de Chimie*, Paris, 1782, i, 52, 136; tr. T. Elliot, *Elementary Lectures on Chemistry and Natural Philosophy*, Edinburgh, 1785, i, 72, 111, 317, 360.
[6] *Mémoires et Observations de Chimie*, Paris, 1784, 423.
[7] *Obs. Phys.*, 1776, vii, 389; *Élémens de Chymie*, Dijon, 1777, i, 225.
[8] *J. des Savans*, 1782, 792 (review of Fourcroy's *Élémens*); de Morveau, *Ency. Méthod., Chymie*, 1788, i, 628.
[9] *J. des Savans*, 1782, 404.

(1791–1814), in the second edition of the German translation of Macquer's *Chemical Dictionary*,[1] reviewed opinions on the nature of phlogiston. For Stahl it was the basis of fire, of a dry earthy nature; in fire it constituted with other very mobile bodies a vortex motion, and with the help of air and water it constituted flame. Henckel[2] regarded it as the earthy part of inflammable natural bodies and thought it contained an acid as a constituent. Pott[3] thought phlogiston was always found mixed with a subtle earth in motion, and with salt, light, and fire particles; on addition of water it forms flame and heat.

Some (Lavoisier, Bayen, de la Place, Monge, Meusnier, etc.), whose number increases daily, deny that phlogiston is contained in sulphur, phosphorus, metals, plants, sugar, charcoal and fixed air, although they admit a fixed fire in bodies as they admit inflammable air in water and seek a carbon in metals (in den Metallen einen Kohlenstoff suchen). 'They do not at all reject it from conviction but rather from obstinacy (Eigensinn) and love of novelty (Neuerungsliebe).'

Leonhardi gives several reasons why phlogiston is not bound fire or bound matter of heat, or the matter of light, or heat brought into rest by some fixative (Bindemittel) such as earth; although phlogiston converts sulphuric acid to sulphur, and might thus be assumed to contain some fixed part, this process is a mere coagulation, like the production of sal ammoniac from muriatic acid and ammonia. Alcohol and inflammable air burn without depositing soot. It is much more probable that the matter of heat in phlogiston is bound by some saline body, since on burning combustible bodies some acid or alkali nearly always remains. But these may be formed by the destruction of the combustible body, and inflammable air gives no saline residue on combustion, but only tasteless water.

Leonhardi thought it would perhaps be best to accept Westrumb's theory[4] that heat or elementary fire and phlogiston are two different elements, and Kirwan's identification of phlogiston with the basis of inflammable air. The other constituents of inflammable air are mere impurities and can be separated by careful purification, as Fourcroy[5] had shown. Priestley's experiments on the reduction of calces in inflammable air (see p. 268) also support this view.

In his article on calx[6] Leonhardi says the supposition that mere loss of phlogiston makes bodies heavier and addition of phlogiston makes them lighter, 'is not only in itself highly improbable, but is also built on mathematical foundations which have been improperly introduced into chemistry.'[7]

Older theories on the increase in weight on calcination of metals are those of

[1] *Macquer's Chymisches Wörterbuch*, 7 vols., Leipzig, 1788–91; 1788, i, 657–72 (Brennstoff); cf. Gehler, *Physikalisches Wörterbuch*, 1787–91, iii, 460 (Phlogiston).

[2] *Flora Saturnisans*, ch. ix; *Pyritologie . . . on y joint le Flore Saturnisans*, 4°, Paris, 1760, 173.

[3] *Lithogeognosia*, Potsdam, 1746, 67 f.

[4] Crell's *Beyträge*, 1786, I, iv, 35–68 (46); Westrumb, *Kleine phys.-chem. Abhl.*, 1787, II, i, 35.

[5] *Mémoires et Observations de Chimie*, 1784, 151 f., 426 f.

[6] *Macquer's Chym. Wörterbuch*, 1789, iii, 434, 452 (Kalch); cf. Gehler, *Physik. Wörterbuch*, 1787–91, ii, 733 f. (Kalke).

[7] Ref. to Gren, Crell's *Beyträge*, 1788, iii, 241, and against him, Westrumb, *Kleine phys.-chem. Abh.*, 1788, II, ii, 284.

Cardan,[1] that it is due to loss of celestial heat, of Cæsalpinus,[2] who thought a kind of soot was deposited, of Tachenius,[3] who thought something acid was absorbed from the flame, of Hiärne[4] who explained it as due to absorption of acid and fire, and of Boyle and Lemery, who thought only fire was attached to the metal calx. But Crawford had apparently proved that metals contain much less absolute heat than their calces, and Lavoisier found no increase in weight on heating in sealed retorts. J. F. Meyer[5] thought *acidum pingue* or causticum from culinary fire was transferred to metal calces precipitated by caustic lime or alkalis, 'yet Meyer's causticum, if we do not regard it as the matter of heat, is a nonentity [Unding] and the causticity of metallic calces seems to arise principally from dephlogistication [Entbrennstoffung].' It is perhaps also due to the fact that they are fundamentally saline and indeed acid bodies, as was shown in the case of arsenic by Scheele (see p. 218), in the case of zinc by Lassone (see p. 95), and of tungsten and molybdenum by Bergman (see p. 198).

Leonhardi says Rey and Bayen showed that air combines with metals on calcination, and this was confirmed by Priestley, Beccaria (calcination in closed vessels; see p. 401), Lavoisier, and Abich.[6] Kirwan, and Watt,[7] said that aërial acid (carbon dioxide) is formed from the base of vital air combining with the phlogiston in the metal. Scheele[8] had advocated this view, and Watt had gone so far as to allow that water is attracted by calces from the atmosphere. Westrumb[9] found that pyrolusite, calamine, red lead, and zinc calx on heating lose water, and aërial acid, and mercury calx loses water and pure air. The calces of noble metals are formed with only a slight loss of phlogiston, those of other metals with a greater loss. By gentle heat calces lose water, by stronger heat pure air, the source of which is the water in the calx.

In his article on combustion[10] Leonhardi says Priestley[11] at first disclaimed Scheele's view that fixed air is formed from air and phlogiston, but afterwards[12] adopted it. Scheele's and Bergman's theory is that phlogiston in a body, when set in motion on combustion, combines with fire air to form heat, that this heat combines with more phlogiston to form radiant heat, and with still more phlogiston to form light, all capable of passing through the material of a vessel; and that the residual air is partly phlogisticated air and partly aërial acid, the first naturally present in the atmospheric air and the second evolved by the combustion of animal and vegetable matter. Leonhardi says: 'this theory in our days has lost all approbation', since (i) neither air nor phlogiston can pass through glass, and why, therefore, should their compound?, and (ii) there is no change in weight when combustion occurs in closed vessels.

[1] *De Re Subtilitate*, 4°, Nürnberg, 1550, 126; *Opera*, Lyon, 1663, iii, 440.
[2] *De Metallicis libri tres*, bk. iii, ch. 7; Rome, 1596, 184 (incorr. numbered 180).
[3] *Hippocrates Chymicus*, ch. 26; Engl. tr., 1677, 107.
[4] *Tentaminum Chemicorum*, Stockholm, 1753, ii, 112.
[5] *Chymischen Versuche*, Hannover and Leipzig, 1764, 120 f., 127, 168 f.; see p. 145.
[6] Crell's *Ann.*, 1784, I, 399 f.   [7] Crell's *Ann.*, 1786, I, 23, 136.
[8] Crell's *Ann.*, 1785, I, 229 f., 235.
[9] *Kleine phys.-chem. Abh.*, 1787, II, i, 124.
[10] *Macquer's Chym. Wörterbuch*, 1790, vi, 604 f. (Verbrennung).
[11] In Scheele, *On Air and Fire*, tr. Forster, 1780, 256.   [12] E & O *Nat. Phil.*, 1783, iii, 248.

Lavoisier[1] showed that air is necessary for combustion, and Leonhardi[2] accepts this in principle, but says there are difficulties:

'If, however, we assume that part of the matter of heat separated from the respirable air combines with the phlogiston (Brennstoff) in the bodies to form a luminous solution (sich . . . zur leuchtenden Auflösung verbinde), another part acts as free heat, and yet another (as cannot be denied) combines with volatile components of many combustible bodies and is so dissolved in the shape of air, vapour or smoke, then this difficulty disappears.'[3]

HERMBSTÄDT

Hermbstädt[4] modified his earlier views on combustion; he agreed with Kirwan in accepting the existence of phlogiston (ϕ) both in a fixed state and also free as inflammable air. Dephlogisticated air (oxygen) is a compound of a basis and elementary heat. Light is a compound of the basis of dephlogisticated air and the basis of inflammable air (ϕ), and is invisible. Visible fire is produced from light and elementary heat in motion, and light deprived of phlogiston becomes dephlogisticated air. The basis of vital air (oxygen) when combined with heat forms oxygen gas; when combined with phlogiston in different proportions it forms the bases of aërial acid (carbon dioxide), phlogisticated air (nitrogen, which he afterwards called Salpeterstoffgas),[5] and water. Oxygen basis is a peculiar kind of matter of heat which when combined with a larger amount of matter of heat becomes elastic vital air. Acids are compounds of peculiar bases with matter of heat.

Hermbstädt explained the formation of acids by combustion as follows:[6]

$$\text{sulphur} = (\text{S basis}) + \phi,$$
$$\text{vital air} = (\text{O basis}) + \text{matter of heat},$$
$$\begin{cases} (\text{S basis} + \text{matter of heat}) = \text{sulphuric acid} + \text{free heat} \\ (\text{O basis} + \phi) = \text{phlogisticated air} + \text{aërial acid} + \text{water} \end{cases}$$
$$\text{sulphuric acid} + \text{water} = \text{oil of vitriol}.$$

Nitric acid is a compound of a peculiar basis and heat, muriatic acid of a peculiar basis, phlogiston, heat and water, and when muriatic acid is heated with pyrolusite it loses phlogiston, part of the basis combining with the metal calx, and some heat is set free. This heat combines with the dephlogisticated part of the muriatic acid basis to form dephlogisticated muriatic acid air (chlorine), probably containing some phlogisticated air formed from the basis of the vital air (of the pyrolusite) and phlogiston. The vital air which Berthollet obtained by heating salts of dephlogisticated muriatic acid (chlorates) probably came from the water of crystallisation.[7]

Phosphoric acid is a compound of a peculiar basis and matter of heat, and all vegetable acids are composed of one peculiar basis, phlogiston, and matter

[1] AdS, 1777 (1780), m 592.   [2] Op. cit., 621.
[3] See also Leonhardi's articles on 'Feuer', ii, 490 f., 534 f.; 'Flamme', ii, 564 f.; 'Gas', ii, 635 f., 681 f. (saying, 656, that Van Helmont's 'gas ventosum' is atmospheric air, and oxygen could be called 'gas ventosum purissimum'). In his Aerologiae Physico-chemicae Recentiores, 4°, Leipzig, 1781 (10 pp.), Leonhardi gave an account of the known gases.
[4] Phys.-chem. Versuche und Beobachtungen, 1789, ii, 41, 172 f.
[5] Allgemeine Grundsätze der Bleichkunst, Berlin, 1804, 160.
[6] Versuche, ii, 177.   [7] Ib., ii, 181–8.

of heat.[1] The evolution of inflammable air by the action of muriatic acid on zinc is explained by a diagram[2] of double elective affinity:

$$(\text{acid basis} + \text{matter of heat}) + (\text{zinc calx} + \phi) =$$

acid   zinc

$$(\text{matter of heat} + \phi) + (\text{zinc calx} + \text{acid basis})$$

inflammable air   muriate of zinc

Hermbstädt's latest view of combustion[3] was that on burning phosphorus, for example, the combined matter of light in the phosphorus united with some of the caloric or matter of heat (Wärmestoff) of the oxygen gas to form 'pure light', whilst the rest of the caloric escaped as sensible heat. The bases of the phosphorus and oxygen combined to form phosphoric oxide. Light is a compound of the matter of light and caloric.

GREN

Gren (see p. 576) proposed three phlogistic theories in succession. The first theory is explained in his two books: (A) *Handbuch der Chemie*, Halle, 1787, i; 1789, II, i, 1790, II, ii; (B) *Grundriss der Naturlehre*, Halle, (a) 1788, (b) 1793, (c) ed. E. G. Fischer 1808. He assumed that the weight of a body measures only part of its mass (the gravitating part) and there may be material parts which do not gravitate.[4] Older experiments on weighing incandescent pieces of metal (see p. 606) were too crude to prove that heat is weightless. Fordyce[5] found that on freezing 1700 grains of water in a sealed vessel there was an increase in weight of $\frac{1}{16}$ grain, which was lost at the moment of melting of the ice, which proves, says Gren,[6] that matter of heat has absolute levity and tends to rise from the centre of the earth.

Heat and light matters are different and fire is a compound of the two.[7] Matter of light is not subject to gravity; its motion from the sun and stars proves the contrary.[8] Combustible bodies contain a principle of combustibility, of the nature of which various views have been held:[9] as an earthy matter, elementary fire, matter of heat, matter of light, pure combined matter of heat, matter of heat contained in cells or interstitial spaces in the combustible body and set free when these cells are broken, or as a component intimately and chemically combined with the remaining parts of the combustible body which are of a different nature and dissolved by them. There is no such thing as elementary fire, fire being a compound of heat and light which is emitted when phlogiston escapes from a burning body.[10] Phlogiston is thus a compound of the matters of heat and light, and when uncombined is fire or free matter of

---

[1] *Ib.*, ii, 191–2.   [2] *Ib.*, ii, 195; cf. Göttling, p. 632.

[3] *Allgemeine Grundsätze der Bleichkunst*, Berlin, 1804, 162 (on oxygen and fire, 144 f.; on Lavoisier's theory, 152).

[4] Ba, 38; Bb, 32; Bc, 20.

[5] *Phil. Trans.*, 1785, lxxv, 361; Blagden, Crell's *Ann.*, 1786, I, 161 (says Fordyce found a much larger loss with heated gold).

[6] Ba, 225; Leonhardi, *Macquer's Chym. Wörterbuch*, 1790, vi, 622.

[7] Ba, 194 f.   [8] *Ib.*, 296.

[9] *Ib.*, 396–7; Bb, 646–7.   [10] A, i, 205, 216 f.; Ba, 299, 406; Bb, 492, 647.

light and matter of heat.[1] Gren's own theory can be found in two (of fifteen) propositions put forward in his *Dissertation* of 1786:[2]

Prop. xi: 'the increase in absolute weight of the dephlogisticated body which remains in phlogistic processes is to be derived solely from the loss of phlogiston.'
Prop. xii: 'the decrease of the air in phlogistic processes arises solely from the union of the air with phlogiston.'

No one has ever been able to weigh uncombined fire, heat, light and phlogiston, and 'if these materials have not only no gravity but rather possess absolute levity or negative gravity, would they not bring it about that the absolute weight of other bodies with which they combine decreases?' Kirwan[3] said Gren had revived de Morveau's theory 'namely, the absolute levity of phlogiston', but it is rather Venel's theory (see p. 614).

The heavier residue of a body which has undergone a phlogistic process 'contains no part of the air in which it burns'.[4]

All gases contain the matter of heat in intimate combination. Vital air (oxygen) consists of water, the matter of heat and the matter of light,[5] increasing amounts of combined matter of heat converting ice into water, water into steam, and steam into vital air. Every inflammable air requires water for its production, or rather is water in the gaseous form in combination with phlogiston and an acid, the whole owing its gaseous elastic state to the large amount of combined matter of heat.[6]

In the solution of metals in acids, all the inflammable substance is driven out of the metal, which therefore exists in the acid solvent in the form of calx. The inflammable air of metals differs, even after washing, according to the acid used in its preparation, being different in specific gravity and in smell, and hence it cannot be pure phlogiston as Kirwan thought. It contains some of the acid, water and combined matter of heat, as well as phlogiston.

When inflammable air is burnt in respirable air, the latter takes the phlogiston set free by the heat from the inflammable air. The products are water, which contains the acid of the inflammable air (Priestley had found the water to be acid), and also some phlogisticated air (nitrogen) formed from the pure part of the respirable air. The water formed is not a product but an educt. Its weight is greater than that of the inflammable air because of the negative weight of the phlogiston which escaped from the latter. Gren's views on the constitution of gases are summarised by him.[7]

In combustion[8] the phlogiston in a combustible body is decomposed by the free matter of heat supplied in kindling the body by friction or otherwise, and is driven out. If respirable air enters, its strong attraction to phlogiston completely separates this. Since the air cannot combine with the phlogiston immediately, a larger or smaller part becomes free fire, and the matters of light

---

[1] A, i, 216–21; Ba, 406; Crell's *Beyträge*, 1786–7, II, ii, 53.
[2] *Dissertatio . . . circa genesin aëris fixi et phlogisticati*, Halle, *s.a.* [1786], props. xi, xii, pp. 90, 96 (see p. 575); Crell's *Beyträge*, 1788, iii, 241, 247.
[3] *Essay on Phlogiston*, 1789, 311.   [4] A, i, 212; Ba, 344.
[5] Ba, 344, 367, 376; Bb, 632; A, II, ii, 455.   [6] Ba, 358, 360; Bb, 616; A, II, ii, 94–8.
[7] Ba, 360 f.; A, II, ii, 457; Partington and McKie, *Ann. Sci.*, 1938, iii, 17.
[8] A, i, 217 f.; Ba, 407 f.; Bb, 651.

and heat give rise to combustion. The absolute weight of the air supporting combustion is diminished by phlogistication to the same extent as the weight of the combustible is increased, but its elasticity is not increased, so that the volume decreases. This decrease is greater the purer the air. Atmospheric air is 'a dephlogisticated air which is not yet completely saturated with phlogiston but is near the limit of this saturation, so that it will soon be completely phlogisticated or foul air [*Stickluft*]'.[1]

The theory explains the phenomena of calcination:[2]

'it follows from the absolute levity of phlogiston . . . that on its escape the residue must be heavier the greater the amount of phlogiston which has escaped. Suppose 110 parts of heavy lead calx are combined into a regulus with 10 parts of absolutely light phlogiston, then the metallic lead produced will contain only 100 remaining heavy parts which are effective. . . . If now the 100 parts of metallic lead, composed of 110 parts of heavy lead calx and 10 absolutely light parts of phlogiston, has the latter removed by calcination, there must necessarily remain the 110 actually heavy parts, which can now press with their whole force on the balance pan.'

By the action of heat the union of calx and phlogiston in the metal is weakened, and the strong attraction of pure air for phlogiston removes the latter from the metal. The air by combination with absolutely light phlogiston diminishes in weight. Since phlogisticated air has no attraction for phlogiston, calcination in closed vessels ceases when the air is saturated with phlogiston. The air loses just so much weight, according to the phlogiston taken up, as the metal gains weight by loss of phlogiston, and the total weight is unchanged. The calx on reduction regains the phlogiston and loses the previous increase in weight. In the reduction of mercury calx by heat alone[3] the dephlogisticated air comes from the solvent contained in the calx, or watery particles from the atmosphere. Since air is expanded by heat it is hard to understand how it can become fixed on heating mercury in it, and at a higher temperature pure air is reproduced from mercury base and heat, according to Lavoisier. Peart also emphasised this difficulty.[4] Gren says:

'When the quite freshly prepared, still hot mercury calx is reduced without inflammable addition in a retort connected with the pneumatic chemical apparatus, no trace of dephlogisticated air or any other fluid is obtained from it. But if it is wetted with some water, or allowed to lie for some time in the air, then it yields on reduction without inflammable addition dephlogisticated air in greater or less amount.'

Hence those who obtained dephlogisticated air on heating red precipitate must have used calx long exposed to air or made with nitric acid.[5] Similar explanations hold for the evolution of dephlogisticated air on heating minium[6] and pyrolusite,[7] which latter can be used repeatedly if it is exposed to the air or moistened with water after each ignition.

'In general only those bodies which attract phlogiston with sufficient force can allow the water developed from them by ignition to escape as dephlogisticated air, e.g. saltpetre, calces of noble metals, mercury calx, etc.'[8]

[1] A, i, 230.   [2] A, II, ii, 77 f.   [3] *Ib.*, 204.
[4] *The Antiphlogistic Doctrine of M. Lavoisier Critically Examined and Demonstratively Confuted* . . . , London, 1795: review by Crell, *Ann.*, 1796, II, 657.
[5] Gren, A, II, ii, 189–95.   [6] *Ib.*, 255.   [7] *Ib.*, 652.   [8] Cf. B*b*, 377.

Gren's theory was criticised by Westrumb[1] in fourteen propositions, including the following:[2] (4) phlogiston is an element of the second or perhaps of the first order, not active of itself but only along with fire, and never found free; it has weight, although it is lighter than all other bodies; combined with fire it forms inflammable air; (6) water is a compound (an element of the second order) of phlogiston and the basis of moisture or of pure air, together with combined fire; (7) pure air is a compound of the basis of moisture, quite free from phlogiston but intimately combined with a large quantity of fire; (9) aërial acid has the same general composition as water but is poorer in phlogiston and much richer in fire; (10) nitric acid is a peculiar undecompounded substance, perhaps an element; (13) metals are compounds of peculiar earths (perhaps of acid nature) and phlogiston; their calces contain aërial acid or water, and are never free from phlogiston. The water in artificial calces is formed from the phlogiston of the metal and the pure air absorbed in their preparation.

Westrumb[3] rejected the theory that phlogiston is a specifically light element, and Gren replied.[4] Gren said the criticisms of Westrumb and Kirwan,[5] that calces are *specifically* lighter than the metals (as Boyle knew, Vol. II, p. 530), were not relevant, since Gren was dealing with *absolute* weights.

Johann Tobias Mayer (1753–1830), then professor of mathematics and physics at Erlangen, in a letter to Gren[6] said:

'According to your theory, lead calx must necessarily fall faster than lead in the metallic state. . . . Pendulums of matters which contain much phlogiston must, *ceteris paribus*, swing more slowly than those which contain less of it, a lead one, e.g., faster than an iron one, etc. All this, however, seems to contradict experience.'

If lead calx loses ten per cent of its weight when reduced, the gravitational force of lead calx must be to that of lead as $1 : 1-\frac{1}{10}$ or $10 : 9$, if it is not assumed that the mass of the lead, by reason of the phlogiston combined with it, is not greater than that of the lead calx. This criticism was accepted by Gren,[7] who now distinguished between gravity (*Schwere*) and weight (*Gewicht*). He tried to reconcile the pendulum experiments with his theory, but after further objections by Mayer,[8] and correspondence, Gren finally abandoned his first theory.[9] He now thought it was a fact that by loss of phlogiston and matter of heat other heavy atoms combined with these are increased in their absolute weight 'although I . . . admit that I do not know why it so happens'.

Mayer's criticisms were amplified by Karl Friedrich Hindenburg (1741–1808), then professor of philosophy and physics in Leipzig.[10] In a funeral

---

[1] *Kleine physikalisch-chemische Abhandlungen*, Leipzig, 1787, II, i, 1 f.   [2] *Ib.*, 111, 135.
[3] *Ib.*, 1788, II, ii, 288 f.; 1789, III, i, 343.   [4] *Ib.*, 1789, III, i, 415–79.
[5] Crell's *Ann.*, 1787, I, 49; Gehler, *Physikalisches Wörterbuch*, 1787 f., ii, 735.
[6] *J. der Physik* (Gren), 1790, i, 205, 359. Mayer is named by Girtanner in a letter to Van Mons in 1796, given by Fourcroy, (2), iii, 617, as one of the German supporters of the Anti-phlogistic Theory: see also A. Schleebach, *Die Entwicklung der chemischen Forschung und Lehre an der Universität Erlangen von ihrer Gründung 1743 bis zum Jahre 1820*, Bayreuth, 1937. Mayer, *J. der Physik*, 1791, iv, 374, with notes by Gren, defended Lavoisier's theory against a long criticism of Gren (*ib.*, 1791, iii, 437).
[7] *J. der Physik*, 1790, i, 208.
[8] *J. der Physik*, 1790, i, 359.   [9] *Ib.*, 1790, i, 371; 1790, ii, 198.
[10] Stimme, in Ersch and Gruber, *Encyclopädie*, Leipzig, 1831, Sect. II, part viii, pp. 252–3.

oration of J. A. Ernest,[1] Hindenburg remarks that in phlogistic processes the weight of the body left after combustion is increased, whilst at the same time the weight and volume of the surrounding air enclosed in a suitable vessel are diminished. Many theories had been put forward to explain this by 'the ante-phlogistians, phlogistians and anti-phlogistians', and summarised by Leonhardi (see p. 616). Fordyce's experiment had been criticised on the ground that cold decreased the volume of the vessel and the scales if they were near it, and moisture may have condensed around the ice-cold vessel, making it heavier.[2] In all such experiments, and those in which heated metals change in weight, the changes in volume of the body and in the density of the air must be taken into account, and the results are inconclusive.

The argument that matter of heat tends upwards even in a vacuous space is fallacious, since the force of air pressing upwards arises from the gravity of the circumambient air, and this had even been postulated by Bernoulli[3] in the case of ether. Matter receding from the earth on account of its absolute levity must gravitate towards another point or body, such as the Moon or the Sun, and such a repulsive force is merely assumed and has not been demonstrated. Another difficulty, pointed out by Musschenbroek,[4] is that absolutely light matter would ultimately completely disappear from the earth. Gren[5] had said that the levitating matter never becomes absolutely free, because it has an affinity to all other heavy bodies. Yet heat and phlogiston, by reason of innumerable and continual decompositions, would little by little seek higher places on account of their inherent force, and would sooner or later disappear from the lower regions near the earth.

Gravity occurs in all bodies on which we are able to make experiments, hence it must also be assumed by analogy and induction to occur in the matter of heat and to be a universal property of all bodies until the contrary is proved. Newton[6] had proved by accurate experiments with pendulums that the masses of bodies are as their weights, and all agree that weight and mass increase and decrease together, which could not be if absolutely light matters of heat, light and phlogiston were postulated. Gren was convinced by Mayer and Hindenburg that he must give up the hypothesis of the negative weight of phlogiston. He proposed an alternative hypothesis.

---

[1] *Orationem qvæ In Memoriam Ioh. Avgvsti Ernesti D.XI. Sept. A.* clɔlɔcclxxxx *Hora IX In Avditorio Philosophico Habebitvr Indicit et ad eam Avdiendam Invitat Carolvs Fridericvs Hindenbvrg Amplissimi Ordinis H. T. Decanvs-Ostenditur, calorem et phlogiston non esse materias absolute leues,* Lipsiæ, Ex Officina Klavbarthia; mentioned by Scherer, *Grundzüge der neuern chemischen Theorien,* Jena, 1795, 317, who stars it as 'vorzüglichst'; Gmelin, (1), iii, 305; Kopp, (1), iii, 151.
[2] Westrumb, *Abhandlungen,* 1787, II, ii, 286; Gehler, *Physikalisches Wörterbuch,* Leipzig, 1790, iii, 145, 473.
[3] Jac. Bernoulli, *De gravitate ætheris,* in *Opera,* Geneva, 1744, i, 53–163 (108); Boyle, *New Experiments . . . touching the Spring of the Air,* 1660, expts. xxxix f.; *Works,* 1744, iii, 49 f., had tried to 'blow' a vacuum against feathers, etc., by means of bellows under an air-pump receiver — without success.
[4] *Cours de Physique,* Leyden, 1769, ii, § 1585, p. 375.
[5] A, i, § 295; Ba, § 429; Crell's *Beyträge,* 1788, iii, 245.
[6] *Principia,* London, 1687, Lib. iii, Prop. vi, Theor. vi, p. 408: Rem tentavi in auro, argento, plumbo, vitro, arena, sale communi, ligno, aqua, tritico.

Gren's Second Phlogiston Theory

Eimbke[1] weighed a strongly heated glass cylinder inside a well-dried wooden capsule lined with brass, then took out the glass cylinder, allowed it to cool and reweighed. He found the hot cylinder lighter than the cold to the extent of 1 in 1000 or less. He also found a small loss in weight on slaking quicklime in a closed bottle, and concluded that 'a body becomes heavier after the abstraction of its matter of heat'.

Georg Eimbke (Hamburg, 17 December 1771–Eppendorf, nr. Hamburg, 20 April 1843), assistant in the University of Kiel, inspector of salines in Holstein (1797–1806), and apothecary in Hamburg, also published on adipocire (see p. 547),[2] a filtering apparatus,[3] a multiple-wick spirit lamp[4] and a compressing pump.[5] He published a comparative nomenclature.[6]

Gren[7] now assumed that the matters of heat and light are imponderable elastic fluids, expansive by nature, and the fixation of light to phlogiston in bodies decreases their weight, the expansive force of the light being partly removed. Since only combustible bodies revive metallic calces it follows that 'the metals are composed of their calces and the combustible principle, and the reguline properties of the metals depend on the combination of the latter with the calx'. Phlogiston is a compound of the matters of light and heat which have lost their expansive force by union with the calces, but also, in return, change the properties and relations of the latter.

By calcination or removal of combined fire the metal regains the gravity which had been completely removed from one part of its gravitating mass, and all its particles are now again affected by gravity. . . . The respirable air which has taken up the phlogiston of the metal must have its weight reduced. . . . In reduction, the calx has a greater affinity for the phlogiston than the other parts of the combustible body. . . . The other parts of the combustible body are partly evolved by heat as an elastic fluid or partly remain in a changed form.

CRAWFORD

Crawford[8] found that the 'absolute heat' (specific heat) of calx of antimony is to that of metallic antimony as 11·6 to 4·5; hence if phlogiston is added to a body a quantity of absolute heat is extricated and if phlogiston is separated an equal quantity of heat is absorbed. 'In the process of inflammation, the phlogiston is separated from the inflammable body, and combined with the air; the air is converted into fixed and phlogisticated air, and at the same time gives off a very great proportion of its absolute heat.' This appears as flame. Heat and phlogiston are by nature opposite principles.

In the second edition[9] of his book Crawford assumed that pure air (oxygen) contains a large amount of matter of heat, and when a combustible body is

---

[1] *J. der Physik*, 1793, vii, 30: Versuch über den Wärmestoff.
[2] *N. allgem. J. Chem.*, 1805, iv, 439.   [3] *Ib.*, 1806, vi, 250.
[4] *J. Chem.* (Schweigger), 1821, xxxi, 87.   [5] *Ib.*, 90.
[6] *Versuch einer systematischen Nomenklatur für die phlogistische und antiphlogistische Chemie*, Kiel, 1793.
[7] *Bb*, 249, 372, 496; Crell's *Ann.*, 1793, II, 341.
[8] *Experiments and Observations on Animal Heat and the Inflammation of Combustible Bodies*, 1779, 66 f.; Partington and McKie, *Ann. Sci.*, 1938, iii, 347.
[9] 1788, 363.

sufficiently heated, its phlogiston is set free by the attraction of the pure air. The matter of heat in the pure air is expelled by the phlogiston, since all bodies on phlogistication have their capacities for containing bound matter of heat decreased. The burning body, parting with its phlogiston, again takes up part of the heat set free from the air, but part remains over and, according to its quantity, appears as sensible heat, fire, incandescence, and flame. Phlogiston and pure air combine to form fixed air; phlogisticated air is only separated from atmospheric air. Crawford appears to have assumed the following process in calcination (ϕ = phlogiston):

$$(\text{earth} + \phi) + (\text{air} + \text{heat}) = (\text{earth} + \text{some heat})$$
$$\underset{\text{metal}}{} \qquad \underset{\text{air}}{} \qquad \underset{\text{calx}}{}$$
$$+ (\text{air} + \phi) + \text{rest of heat.}$$
$$\underset{\substack{\text{phlogisticated} \\ \text{air}}}{}$$

Venous blood is (blood + ϕ) and arterial blood is (blood + heat), and the change in respiration is:

$$(\text{blood} + \phi) + (\text{air} + \text{heat}) = (\text{air} + \phi) + (\text{blood} + \text{heat}).$$

Crawford emphasised that he did not 'assert that elementary fire is really capable of being chemically combined with bodies; much less do I affirm, as some have supposed, that it is by means of a double elective attraction, that heat is disengaged from the air in the process of respiration'.[1] He had been so misunderstoood by Lubbock (see p. 627). His theory is really based on changes of heat capacity.

CLEGHORN

Cleghorn[2] says phlogiston is never found pure but always combined in bodies. Atmospheric air is necessary for combustion and his 'esteemed friend Crawford' had shown by many experiments that the quantity of fire in bodies of given temperature and weight varies with the quantity of phlogiston; the greater the amount of phlogiston separated from a body the greater the quantity of fire required to maintain it at the same temperature, and when phlogiston is added to a body the temperature is increased and a quantity of fire flows out so that it recovers its former temperature. He found that for equal weights the quantity of fire in atmospheric air is to that in fixed air as 72 to 1. 'He therefore rightly concluded that air gives out fire in its change into fixed air, for phlogiston separated from a burning body and combined with air converts it into fixed air and its temperature is increased, fire flows into the kindled body, more phlogiston is evolved . . . and so it goes on till the body is wholly deprived of phlogiston and the fire is greatly accumulated.' Cleghorn explained the effect by saying that all bodies attract fire but some strongly attract phlogiston. If phlogiston is added the force attracting fire is reduced and much fire will separate. Air contains much fire and attracts phlogiston strongly; if more phlogiston is added to it, the force attracting fire is reduced

[1] 1788, 363; see Partington and McKie, *Ann. Sci.*, 1938, iii, 349.
[2] *Disputatio Physica Inauguralis Theoriam Ignis complectans*, Edinburgh, 1779, 27 f.

and fire is set free and unites with the burning body and other bodies. The volume of the air is also decreased and it is known that when air is compressed, fire is driven out. 'Hence, therefore, it is clear that fire is not generated by burning but merely separated from the air', and not from the burning body. This is essentially the same, minus phlogiston, as Lavoisier's theory (see p. 421).

LUBBOCK

Richard Lubbock (see p. 489), a pupil of Black, in his M.D. Dissertation[1] called oxygen *principium sorbile*. He showed by experiments that fixed air (carbon dioxide) is not formed in such 'phlogistic processes' as the action of nitrous air (nitric oxide) on common air or the combustion of sulphur and phosphorus; 7 gr. of sulphur form 30 gr. of sulphuric acid; 13 gr. of phosphorus form 40 gr. of phosphoric acid, hence 25 gr. of air are absorbed, and the decrease in volume corresponds with 26·04 gr. Fixed air is formed by the combustion of carbon, and by heating alkali sulphate and phosphoric acid with carbon: 2 dr. of sulphuric acid when neutralised and heated with 5 gr. of carbon gave 23 cu. in. of aërial acid (carbon dioxide) weighing 13·110 gr., and 2 dr. of phosphoric acid and 5 gr. of carbon gave 27 cu. in. of aërial acid weighing 15·890 gr.

In a criticism of Crawford's theory (see p. 625) Lubbock[2] examined as a 'mere conjecture' whether:

'Phlogiston, dissociating itself from the other principle or base of the combustible body, combines with the more subtle and rarer principle of the air, and these combined principles appear under the more tenuous form of light and heat. But in the same process by which these things arise, the dense and less subtle principle of the air set free binds itself to the other principle or base of the combustible body, and by this combination there arise the more fixed products of combustion, namely the different acids, which according to this hypothesis are not at all concealed ready formed in the combustible bodies.'

Thus, if phlogiston $= \phi$:

$$\underset{(1)}{\text{combustible body}} + \underset{(2)}{\text{air}} = \underset{(3)}{\text{fixed substance}} + \underset{(4)}{[\text{light and heat}]}$$

$$\underset{(1)}{[\text{base} + \phi]} + \underset{(2)}{[\text{solid principle} + \text{subtle principle}]} = \underset{(3)}{[\text{base} + \text{solid principle}]}$$
$$+ \underset{(4)}{[\phi + \text{subtle principle}]}$$

'This scheme brings combustion into the class of double affinity, which some think is general, but it is a pure hypothesis without experimental foundation. Examples of elective attraction are also known which do not fit the scheme of double affinity, as the expulsion of fixed air from a mild alkali by an acid. But what limit is there to such speculations?'

---

[1] *Dissertatio Physico-Chemica, Inauguralis, de Principio Sorbili, Sive communi Mutationum Chemicarum Causa, Quaestionem, an Phlogiston sit Substantia, an Qualitas, agitans; Et alteram Ignis Theoriam Complectens . . . examini subjicit Ricardo Lubbock, Anglo-Britannus . . . ad 13 Septemb. hora locoque solitis*, 4°, Edinburgh, 1784, Balfour and Smellie, hf. tit., t.p., dedic. to Edward Rigby (errata pasted on *verso*), 137 pp. (BM T. 297. (8.)); Partington and McKie, *Ann. Sci.*, 1938, iii, 356.

[2] *Op. cit.*, 67 f.

Lubbock preferred Lavoisier's theory that pure air (oxygen gas) is a compound of a base, *principium sorbile*, with the matter of heat and light, and that combustion and calcination occur by the combustibles decomposing the air, attracting its *principium sorbile* more than the matter of heat and light does, combining with the *principium sorbile*, and setting free the heat and light. Lubbock calls the matter of heat and light (Lavoisier's caloric) *principium aëri proprium*. He agrees with Lavoisier that combustibles lose no subtle principle on burning and that there is no such thing in nature as phlogiston.

A criticism of Lubbock's dissertation was given by William Scott,[1] who concluded that, 'as the Phoenix rises more beautiful from its ashes, so the oxygen theory will rise again more impregnable after every assault.'

Parkes[2] says that Crichton[3] 'first . . . in his public lectures elucidated the theory, by many appropriate experiments', that oxygen gas = (oxygen + caloric), combustible = (base + light); the product of combustion is (oxygen + base), and fire (caloric + light) is set free. The light does not come from the oxygen, since hydrogen burns with the evolution of much heat but little light.

Black[4] thought that 'Mr. Lavoisier's system did not explain the light which is so characteristic of combustion; and said that some very judicious observations on this subject were to be found in Lubbock's inaugural dissertation, *de Principio Sorbili*, which also professes to give a theory of combustion and acidification'.

James Hutton (1726–97) the geologist[5] asserted that phlogiston is material but weightless, and is of the nature of heat and light. It is evolved as light in combustion, and light acting on plants builds up inflammable matters. (Macquer had said this before, see p. 85.) Combustion is a process of double elective attraction, the action of heat being to weaken the attachment of light or solar matter to the inflammable matter and cause it to separate, the inflammable matter at the same time combining with the atmospheric matter. 'The oxygenous principle of vital air combines with the gravitating matter of the inflammable substance and there is a luminous separation of the hydrogenous matter of the inflammable body.' Bodies on burning lose some substance which can be restored only by another phlogistic body.

GADOLIN

Gadolin (see p. 234) is said to have been the first[6] to propose the scheme:

$$\text{combustible} = \text{base} + \text{phlogiston}$$
$$\text{oxygen} \qquad = \text{base} + \text{heat.}$$

[1] *Tentamen Chemicum Inaugurale de Acido Atmosphericæ sive Aereo*, Edinburgh, 1786 (52 pp.); de Phlogisto, 25 f.; summary in Partington and McKie, *Ann. Sci.*, 1938, iii, 362.

[2] *Chemical Catechism*, 5 ed., 1812, 378–9.

[3] Sir Alexander Crichton (1763–1856) left Edinburgh in 1784 and took the M.D. at Leyden. He was lecturer at Westminster Hospital from 1794 to 1804; Boase, DNB, 1888, xiii, 85.

[4] *Lectures on the Elements of Chemistry*, ed. Robison, Edinburgh, 1803, i, 550; ii, 214.

[5] *Chymical Dissertation concerning Phlogiston, or the Principle of Fire*, in *Dissertations on Different Subjects in Natural Philosophy*, 4°, Edinburgh, 1792, 171–270; summary in Partington and McKie, *Ann. Sci.*, 1938, iii, 366.

[6] Crell's *Ann.*, 1788, I, 15, 417; Kahlbaum and Hoffmann, *Monographien*, 1897, i, 64, 102; Partington and McKie, *Ann. Sci.*, 1939, iv, 125.

'The combustible body consists of a base combined with phlogiston and the vital air of its base combined with heat. When these four bodies attract one another in such a way that the phlogiston can combine with the heat, and the base of the combustible body can combine with the base of the vital air, then a decomposition ensues, which we call combustion or inflammation.

'I am true to the old theory of phlogiston or the combustible principle, but I believe with Mr. Scheele that it is an element, that it has no perceptible weight and that it makes up the principal constituent of light. With him I also believe that the calces of metals separate the phlogiston from glowing fire and can take it to themselves, but at the same time that the vital air produced comes from the calces. I believe with Mr. Kirwan that inflammable air which is emitted in the solution of metals has its phlogiston from the metals, but also I believe with Lavoisier that here a decomposition of water takes place.'

In 1789 in an article on tinning pins[1] Gadolin assumed that in the calcination of metals a common substance unites with and becomes a component part of the calx which, to avoid reference to any theory, he will call the calcining matter (la matière calcinante). A metal is calcinable in different degrees by taking up varying portions of calcining matter, which is contained both in air and in water. The resulting increase in weight proves that 'a metallic calx contains a matter which is not in the metal. The supposition that the metals contain a more subtle matter which is called phlogiston or the reducing matter is not yet proved, which is the reason why it was not adopted'.

In 1790[2] Gadolin again differentiated between the matter of light (ljuramne) and the matter of heat, and says[3] that it is better to suspend judgment on the rival claims of Lavoisier and the phlogiston theory. In 1793[4] he says he does not deny the existence of phlogiston but in the present state of science all the phenomena can be explained just as well without it. In 1796[5] he adopted the antiphlogistic theory. Gadolin's theory of 1788 is the same as that which Lubbock had dealt with in 1784 (see p. 627) and credited to Crawford. It is really the same in principle as Macquer's theory that phlogiston is the matter of light combined with Lavoisier's that oxygen gas contains the matter of heat. The same theory is also given in some later dissertations presented under Gadolin:[6]

nequi nobis vitio quis vertat. . . . Phlogiston . . . ponentes cum nonnullis hodiernorum Chemicorum, combustionem corporum in aëre vitali vi duplicis attractionis perfici, scil. & ejus quæ inter phlogiston corporis inflammabilis & caloricum aëris obtinet, & ejus, quæ ponderabilis corporis inflammabilis pars sive ipsius substratum appetit oxygenium aëris (Erling, 1801).

HOPSON

Charles Rivington Hopson (? –London, 23 December 1796), physician in the Finsbury Dispensary, London, thought[7] fire is a compound of an acid

---

[1] Tr. by Dollfuss in *Obs. Phys.*, 1789, xxxiv, 363 f., 430 f.
[2] Crell's *Ann.*, 1791, I, 448: on affinity and heat.   [3] Crell's *Beyträge*, 1790, iv, 77.
[4] Crell's *Ann.*, 1793, II, 155.   [5] *Ib.*, 1796, II, 282, 626.
[6] *Animadversiones in novam nomenclaturæ chemicæ methodum*, 4°, Åbo, n.d., respondente N. Avellan, 8 f.; and *Animadversiones celeberrime Gmelin in Theoriam Lavoisierianum de Natura Acidi Nitrici examinans*, 4°, Åbo, 1801, respond. J. J. Erling, 7 f.
[7] *An Essay on Fire to which is added, An Appendix*, London, 1781, ch. ii, p. 5 f.; he says the theory was conceived in 1767.

with phlogiston; the fixed matters of heat and light in bodies constitute phlogiston, and (in opposition to Scheele) air cannot form part of heat or light. In his translation of Wiegleb's book,[1] Hopson added a section on specific heats written by Gadolin and an account of gases taken from Fourcroy, and replaced Wiegleb's phlogistic views by a hybrid theory of combustion. Hopson[2] explained that, as an acquaintance, he wished to introduce as many of the teachings of Lavoisier as could be combined with the theory of phlogiston, and he did not hesitate to claim the doctrine that acids are formed by the absorption of air, since it 'occurred to him so early as the year 1768, when he first adopted his present Theory of Fire'. Hopson[3] says: 'the idea of fire being a compound of heat and light . . . seems, in some measure, to pervade all Europe . . . that of phlogiston, being nothing more than light and heat fixed in bodies, appears to gain ground daily with the philosophic world.' On reading Fourcroy's book (presumably *Elementary Lectures on Chemistry and Natural History*, tr. T. Elliot, 1785, see p. 537) in November 1787, Hopson says, he conceived that Lavoisier's theory of combustion could be reconciled with the phlogiston theory and even could not subsist without it. On communicating this to Prof. Gadolin, the latter informed him that in the Spring of 1788 he had sent a paper containing the same theory to Crell.[4] It had, says Hopson, previously been very obscurely hinted at by Fourcroy, and Hopson claims that he first proposed it seriously, the other two proposing it 'doubtingly, and the one having since formally, and the other virtually, renounced it'.

Hopson's theory differs from Gadolin's in making the heat and light come only from the phlogiston, the caloric of the oxygen gas being neglected; it is a modification of Macquer's theory, also adopted by Fourcroy (see p. 537). Hopson[5] says that 'whenever air enters, light or phlogiston flies off'. Atmospheric air consists of pure air (oxygen) and mephitic gas (nitrogen). In combustion[6] the fixed light or phlogiston in combustible bodies becomes converted into light and heat, whilst the base of the combustible unites with the pure air to form fixed air, acids, water or calces, the base of inflammable air being called *hydrophlogium*:

'the basis of inflammable gas with phlogiston forms inflammable gas, and with air, water, which . . . is an incombustible body . . . Heat is generated, not on account of the pure air giving it out in its condensation to water . . . but chiefly, and almost entirely, in consequence of the phlogiston being liberated, and making its escape in the form of light and sensible heat.'

RICHTER

Richter in 1791[7] opposed Lavoisier's theory, and only adopted it in 1793[8] in a modified form, retaining phlogiston as the principle of combustibility

[1] *A General System of Chemistry, Theoretical and Practical, Digested and Arranged, with a Particular View to its Application in the Arts. Taken chiefly from the German of M. Wiegleb*, 4°, London, 1789.

[2] Crell's *Beyträge*, 1790, iv, 441.   [3] *System of Chemistry*, 1789, Pref., iii f., vi.
[4] Crell's *Ann.*, 1788, I, 15, 417.   [5] *System*, 23 f.   [6] *Ib.*, 30 f., 38 f.
[7] *Ueber die neuern Gegenstände der Chymie*, Bresslau and Hirschberg, 1791, i, 87.
[8] *Ib.*, 1793, iii, pref. p. xxi, 53 f., etc.; *id.*, *Anfangsgründe der Stöchyometrie*, 1792, I, i, 233; 1794, I, ii, 31, 139.

(*Brennstof*). This combines with the matter of heat contained in the vital air (oxygen) and forms light (which may not appear as such), whilst the other part (substrate) of the combustible body dissolves in the matter of the vital air and forms the burnt body. Richter's criticism of Lavoisier's theory is very detailed and acute,[1] and raised questions which could only be answered in the light of the later theory of energy.

Elementary fire is material and, like phlogiston, possesses a very small weight, which cannot be detected. Oxygen gas is a compound of oxygen-base and matter of heat. The unknown entity which produces light and heat is phlogiston, 'and where light is present, there is also phlogiston.' Lavoisier regarded combustion as a result of simple affinity, the combustible taking the oxygen-base and letting the heat-matter of the oxygen gas escape; and his theory either regards light as a modification of matter of heat, which is unproved, or else leaves the source of the light unexplained. Richter thought the phenomenon is more probably one of double affinity; phlogiston is present in the combustible along with an unknown substrate, and by combination of this phlogiston with the matter of heat of the oxygen gas, light is formed, perhaps in a definite ratio of its components, and at the same time the ponderable substrates of the combustible and the oxygen gas unite to form the burnt body.

In the decomposition of metallic oxides by heat, the substrate combined in them with oxygen-base combines with the phlogiston streaming in with matter of heat through the walls of the vessel, and forms the metal, the matter of heat combining with the oxygen-base to form oxygen gas. Only light which is absorbed by a body can produce chemical change (this anticipates Grotthuss, see Vol. IV). Nine objections to the phlogiston theory which are proposed in Girtanner's *Anfangsgründe der antiphlogistischen Chemie*, 1792, which Richter says converted him to Lavoisier's theory of oxygen, are answered, and in this, Richter is really directing his criticism at Lavoisier.

Göttling, in the preface to his *Beytrag zur Berichtigung der antiphlogistischen Chemie*, Weimar, 1794, had said that Richter's theory did not agree with Göttling's experiments on the glow of phosphorus in nitrogen gas (really containing an unsuspected trace of oxygen). Richter's reply[2] is dedicated to the Munich Academy of Sciences in respect of their prize question: 'if the matters of light and of fire are the same or different, and if there is a peculiar matter of heat?,' and also an answer to a prize question of the Royal Danish Academy: 'Since light and heat frequently in combination, and often alone, act on the senses, do they arise from one principle (Grundstoff) or must they be considered separate elements?' Richter repeats his theory that light = matter of heat + phlogiston. He gives five arguments in support, including: (i) matter of light is not contained in vital air (oxygen gas),[3] (ii) like its constituents it is weightless;[4] matter of heat and phlogiston must unite in a certain ratio to form light and coloured lights contain them in different ratios.[5] The bending of light towards heavy bodies suggests that it probably has a very small weight.[6]

---

[1] Partington and McKie, *Ann. Sci.*, 1939, iv, 130; Partington, *ib.*, 1951, vii, 173.
[2] *Neuern Gegenstände*, 1796, vii (pp. xxii, 112): Beyträge zur Antiphlogistik in Bezug auf die Göttlingischen Versuche.
[3] *Ib.*, 70 f.   [4] *Ib.*, 82.   [5] *Ib.*, 67, 69, 84 f.   [6] *Ib.*, 87 f.

Göttling

Göttling[1] said Richter's theory of combustion is not altogether satisfactory, since it regards evolution of light and combustion as the same process, and only dependent on varying proportions of phlogiston and matter of heat. Since Göttling[2] thought he had shown that phosphorus will glow and form acid in air in which phosphorus has burnt to extinction (which really still contains a little oxygen), he assumed the existence of a matter of light, oxygen gas being a compound of oxygen basis and matter of heat, and nitrogen gas a compound of oxygen basis and matter of light. Combustibles and metals contain combined light, which unites with the matter of heat combined in the oxygen gas to form fire, by double affinity as Richter assumed, the bases of the combustible (A) and of oxygen gas (B) combining to form a calx or an acid:

$$(A + light) + (B + heat) = (A + B) + (heat + light).$$

Hydrogen is probably not free phlogiston because it does not reduce sulphuric acid. Nitrous gas is a compound of oxygen and the matters of heat and light, hydrogen gas of the two last and the base of hydrogen. Phosphorus glows in nitrogen by uniting with the oxygen base and the light is set free; it does not glow in oxygen because at lower temperatures its affinity for light is greater than that for oxygen, and the affinity of oxygen for matter of heat is greater than its affinity for phosphorus. In air, phosphorus glows with evolution of heat (which is not the case in nitrogen), because both the nitrogen and oxygen of the air are decomposed. Göttling thought he had been able to convert oxygen into nitrogen by the action of light.

Göttling's experiments were refuted by Berthollet,[3] who confirmed, however, that phosphorus does not glow in oxygen; he explained this by saying that phosphorus is dissolved by nitrogen but not by cold oxygen. If oxygen is admitted to nitrogen in which phosphorus has ceased to glow, the glow reappears. If nitrogen is made by exposing air to liver of sulphur, phosphorus does not glow in it even if oxygen is added, perhaps because some sulphur or sulphide is dissolved in the gas. Fourcroy[4] proved that phosphorus does not glow in nitrogen free from oxygen, and that hydrogen in which phosphorus has stood glows when oxygen is added.

Gren's Third Phlogiston Theory

The history of Gren's final adoption of the theory of oxygen and his combination of it with the phlogiston theory throws an interesting light on the experimental competence of the contemporary German chemists in the field of pneumatic chemistry. Chemists in other countries had been preparing

---

[1] *Beytrag zur Berichtigung der antiphlogistischen Chemie auf Versuche gegrundet*, Weimar, 1794, 115, 126; q. in his *Handbuch der theoretischen und praktischen Chemie*, Jena, 1798, pp. x, 19, 131; Fourcroy, (2), iii, 570; Kahlbaum and Hoffmann, *Monographien*, 1897, i, 106.
[2] *Handbuch*, 1798, 49, 111, 118 f., 214, 284.
[3] *J. de l'École Polytechnique*, An IV (1796), 3 cahier, 274; for further refs. see Partington and McKie, *Ann. Sci.*, 1939, iv, 147.
[4] (2), iii, 571.

oxygen by heating red precipitate (mercuric oxide) since 1775. Gren,[1] West-rumb,[2] Schiller[3] and Trommsdorff[4] all reported that on heating calx of mercury (mercuric oxide) in a retort no gas at all is evolved. Westrumb said 'not a single bubble was emitted from the end of the tube in the pneumatic trough' (which shows that his apparatus leaked).

Gren and Westrumb reported that water is formed when red or black (mercurous oxide ?) precipitate of mercury is reduced by heating, which Girtanner[5] said was formed by the burning of organic dust from the atmosphere which had settled on the calx.

Gren[6] denied this, reporting letters from Westrumb and Schiller confirming his own experiment. Peschier (a student from Geneva then in Berlin)[7] and Hermbstädt[8] reported that they had obtained abundance of vital air on heating the calx, and Hermbstädt pointed out that Westrumb's result was too good, since he should at least have obtained some bubbles of air expelled from the retort on heating. Trommsdorff,[9] Westrumb,[10] and Schiller,[11] still failed to obtain any gas, but Lampadius[12] and Hermbstädt[12] obtained it.

Van Mons[13] explained how oxygen could be obtained from red precipitate, and Gren[14] obtained it from the fresh calx (which he thought contained water), but if the calx were first heated until it turned black and was then at once put in this state into a retort and further heated, it gave no gas. A further letter from Van Mons[15] contradicted this, and in a reply of 12 December 1793[16] Gren said that he had at last obtained oxygen by heating ordinary red precipitate. Gren in a letter to Trommsdorff[17] said he had adopted the antiphlogistic theory because of Trommsdorff's experimental proof[18] that the *whole* of a confined volume of vital air (oxygen) is absorbed in the combustion of phosphorus, but Gren did not think he need give up phlogiston.[19] Hildebrandt[20] had achieved the nearly complete absorption of a volume of oxygen by the combustion of a steel spring. Fischer says Lavoisier had never absorbed the whole of a volume of oxygen by the combustion of phosphorus, although the residue, 'nach allen Kennzeichen', was oxygen and not nitrogen.

In his letter to Van Mons (12 December 1793)[21] Gren said he found the phlogiston theory, 'which I formerly made the basis of chemistry, so shaken in its foundations that I should feel myself a base traitor to the truth if I should any longer seek to defend it.' In 1793[22] he said he had adopted an intermediate theory which had been given by Leonhardi[23] and Richter,[24]

---

[1] *J. der Physik*, 1791, iii, 479; 1792, vi, 29, 444; 1793, vii, 146.
[2] Crell's *Ann.*, 1792, I, 252; *J. der Physik*, 1792, vi, 32, 212.   [3] *J. der Physik*, 1792, vi, 419.
[4] *J. der Physik*, 1793, vii, 37; with a certificate of the accuracy of the experiment by Hecker and Meyer, *ib.*, 241, 332.
[5] *J. der Physik*, 1792, vi, 416.   [6] *J. der Physik*, 1792, vi, 418.   [7] *Ib.*, 420.
[8] *Ib.*, 422.   [9] *Ib.*, 1793, vii, 241.   [10] *Ib.*, 148.
[11] *Ib.*, 152, 337.   [12] *Ib.*, 152.   [13] *Ib.*, 338, 343.   [14] *Ib.*, 348.   [15] *Ib.*, 1794, viii, 3.
[16] *Ib.*, 14.   [17] Trommsdorff's *J. der Pharmacie*, 1794, i, II, 271.   [18] *Ib.*, 103.
[19] Westrumb, Crell's *Ann.*, 1793, II, 341, attributes this important experiment to Göttling and Trommsdorff; J. C. Fischer, 1808, viii, 34, to Göttling in 1793, q. Göttling, *Beytrag zur Berichtigung der antiphlogistischen Theorie*, Weimar, 1794, 8.
[20] Crell's *Ann.*, 1793, II, 99.   [21] *J. der Physik*, 1794, viii, 14.
[22] Crell's *Ann.*, 1793, II, 342.
[23] *Macquers Chymisches Wörterbuch*, 1790, vi, 621.
[24] *Ueber die neuern Gegenstände der Chymie*, 1793, III, xxi, 53.

overcoming some of the difficulties in Lavoisier's theory, which Fourcroy had said[1] had been too hastily advanced. Gren gave an account of his new theory in his letter to Van Mons, saying that there were gaps in Lavoisier's system which could be filled only by retaining phlogiston. Gren says his new theory would include the following statements:[2]

(1) The matter of heat is a subtle and radiant fluid which has no weight . . . , capable, by its union with other matters, of having its expansive force modified and of losing its radiant state.

(2) Light is a fluid composed of matter of heat and a base not expansive of itself but capable of becoming so by union with this matter. This base is *inflammable matter* or *phlogiston*, which has no weight.

(3) The absorption of light consists in the absorption and separation of this base with the matter of heat by other bodies.

(4) A combustible body gives phlogiston to the matter of heat (calorique) of vital air; these two matters combine and form light at the same time that the base of the vital air is absorbed by the combustible body.

(5) Vital air is not the acidifying principle.

$$\underset{\text{combustible}}{(\text{base}+\phi)} + \underset{\text{oxygen gas}}{(\text{oxygen base}+\text{caloric})} = (\text{base}+\text{oxygen base}) + \underset{\text{light}}{(\phi+\text{caloric})}$$

Gren explained the theory fully in his books.[3] A combustible body (including a metal) consists of a basis combined with the basis of light-matter; oxygen gas consists of the basis of oxygen combined with heat-matter (caloric). On combustion or calcination, the bases of the combustible and oxygen combine, and at the same time the bases of light and heat combine to form the fire and light emitted. The process is one involving double affinity. Gren applied his theory to explain the combustion of sulphur, phosphorus, and alcohol, the oxidation of liver of sulphur, the explosion of gunpowder, combustion in chlorine, photosynthesis, the calcination of metals, the solution of metals in acids with evolution of hydrogen, the precipitation of one metal by another, and the combustion of metals with sulphur.

Gren[4] thought his theory gave a simple explanation of the difficulty that mercury is oxidised on heating but the oxide is again decomposed at a higher temperature, since in the last case the matter of light is decomposed. Fourcroy[5] claimed that he had pointed out in 1776 that the oxide is only decomposed: 'qu'à l'époque ou les vaisseaux qui le contenoient étoient rouges de feu et pénétrés de lumière . . . la lumière contribuoit au dégagement de l'air vital.'

In the decomposition of steam by heated iron the phlogiston of the metal combines with the base of hydrogen and matter of heat to form hydrogen gas.[6] Nitrous air (Salpetergas) is a compound of phlogiston, oxygen, and nitrogen base; when mixed with oxygen the nitrogen base attracts the base of the oxygen and forms phlogisticated nitric acid. Part of the phlogiston combines

---

[1] *Ann. Chim.*, 1790, iv, 249.   [2] *J. der Physik*, 1794, viii, 14; Fourcroy, (2), iii, 572.
[3] *Handbuch der gesammten Chemie*, 2 ed., Halle, 1794, i, 133 f.; *Grundriss der Naturlehre*, ed. Fischer, Halle, 1808, 473–7; Partington and McKie, *Ann. Sci.*, 1939, iv, 135; for a letter of Humboldt in 1795 on Gren and the antiphlogistic theory see J. Schuster, *A. Nat.*, 1928, x, 303–27.
[4] *Handbuch*, 1795, iii, 79; Göttling, *Handbuch der theoretischen und praktischen Chemie*, Jena, 1798, i, 49, 111, 284.
[5] (2), 1796, iii, 573.   [6] Gren, *Handbuch*, 1794, i, 191 f.

with the matter of heat of the oxygen, but as too little phlogiston is relinquished, there is no production of light but only dark heat. The action of light on colourless nitric acid, producing oxygen and phlogisticated (red) nitric acid is due to absorption of phlogiston from the light.[1]

Nicholson[2] pointed out that 'those who maintained the doctrine of phlogiston are at present returned to the old doctrine of sulphur and oils, though in more general terms', regarding phlogiston not as fixed fire but as some identical combustible principle which unites with respirable air and in doing so extricates heat.

In a letter to Trommsdorff[3] Gren says: 'actually only two systems now hold the field, the purely Lavoisierian and Richter's; all the others are to be looked upon as modifications of these two.' Fourcroy[4] felt that, although their theories still differed in points of detail, the complete harmony between M. Gren and the French chemists was a happy augury for the progress of chemistry, and an example which was calculated to win over a large part of the German chemists. Gren[5] proposed to call the basis of light 'phlogiston', in spite of the objections which would be raised; Suckow[6] thought it would be better to use a new name for this supposed constituent of metals in order to prevent disputes about words.

Crell[7] set out the main principles of the 'older' phlogistic and the antiphlogistic theories, expressing the opinion that it would be possible to adopt parts of each, whilst rejecting others. There was no need to believe in the compound nature of water. In a discussion of 'acids and oxygen'[8] he supposed that vital air is not a constituent of all acids; phosphorus contains an acid concealed by phlogiston. Crell[9] more or less agreed with Gren's view that combustion involves loss of phlogiston and gain of oxygen, and he illustrated this by a large number of examples. This is, apparently, the last time Crell defended the phlogiston theory, although he never openly accepted the new theory.[10]

The long memoir of J. F. Gmelin,[11] criticised by Richter,[12] is based on the idea that combustion and calcination involve double decomposition (wechselseitige Zersetzung), which Gmelin developed in a lecture in 1797.[13] Von Scopoli's 'thoughts on phlogiston'[14] amount to little, and Zauschner's negative answer to his question 'Sollte das Phlogiston wohl Chimäre seyn?'[15] involves the assumptions that phlogiston is the imponderable matter of heat and light, and when it is emitted from a combustible it combines with pure air (oxygen).

[1] Ib., i, 447 f.   [2] Dictionary of Chemistry, London, 1795, ii, 641.
[3] G***, J. der Pharmacie, 1795, iii, I, 314.   [4] (2), 1797, iii, 573.
[5] Grundriss der Naturlehre, ed. Fischer, 1808, 453.   [6] Crell's Beyträge, 1790, iv, 438.
[7] Ann., 1793, II, 346, 406; 1796, I, 24.   [8] Ib., 1795, I, 233.
[9] Crell's Ann., 1799, I, 161, 229, 305; Nachträge zu der Priestley's Betrachtung über die Lehre vom Phlogiston; Priestley's work was published in ib., 1798, II, 308, 376, from Experiments and Observations relating to the Analysis of the Atmospherical Air, etc., London, 1796.
[10] Kahlbaum and Hoffmann, Monographien, 1897, i, 121.
[11] Winke an seine Zeitgenossen, den Streit über den Brennstoff betreffend, Crell's Ann., 1795, I, 287, 391, 479, with copious references.
[12] Ib., 1795, II, 414; id., Ueber die neuern Gegenstände der Chymie, 1796, vii, 51–65.
[13] Göttingischen Journal der Naturwissenschaften, 1798, i, 10–86.
[14] Crell's Beyträge, 1786, iv, 3.   [15] Ib., 1796, iv, 131–83, with masses of references.

Langsdorf supposed that weight is due to the presence of a specific weight-matter (*Schwerstoff*) which combines with inert matter having no gravity of its own.[1]

Most of the English text-books of the early nineteenth century pointed out the weaknesses in Lavoisier's caloric theory of combustion.[2] Thomson,[3] who divided the elements then known into combustibles, supporters of combustion, and incombustibles, removed the objectionable name 'phlogiston' from the theories of Hutton (see p. 628), Richter, and Gren, and proposed a theory that oxygen gas is a compound of oxygen base and caloric, and a combustible a compound of a specific base and light.

'During combustion the base of the oxigen combines with the base of the combustible, and forms the product; while at the same time the caloric of the oxigen combines with the light of the combustible, and the compound flies off in the form of fire. Thus combustion is a double decomposition; the oxigen and combustible divide themselves each into two portions, which combine in pairs; the one compound is the product, and the other the *fire* which escapes.'

This explains why oxygen in products does not produce combustion, as it contains no caloric, and why combustion does not occur when oxygen combines with products or with the base of supporters, as these bodies contain no light. Hence, also, a combustible alone can restore combustibility to the base of a product: 'the oxygen of the product combines with the base of the combustible, while the light of the combustible combines with the base of the product.' The ignition of metals and earths (then regarded as elements) in presence of molten sulphur or phosphorus shows that they contain light: 'the sulphur or phosphorus combines with the metal or earth; while the caloric of the one, uniting to the light of the other, flies off in the form of fire.' The theory was criticised by C. Portal[4] on the ground that oxygen gas must contain combined light. Thomson gave his theory in later editions of his book.[5]

The Last Stand of Phlogiston

It has been seen (p. 293) that Priestley never abandoned phlogiston, and in Germany Wiegleb, to the end, was a champion of the phlogiston theory, which he expressed in various forms at different times. In a review in 1784[6] he remarked on the various opinions held on the nature of phlogiston by Becher and Stahl (an earth), Stahl (elementary fire), Baumé (elementary fire + subtle earth), Macquer (pure fire), de Morveau (fixed fire), Scheele (a peculiar element), Buffon (air + fire), and Kirwan (inflammable air), and he adopted the last. The theory that phlogiston is the same as inflammable air, however, was criticised on the basis of experiments on the calcination of metals, e.g. zinc, in closed vessels by Rudolph Adam Abich (d. 1809), Bergrath and

[1] *J. der Physik*, 1792, v, 49–54, 247–56, 266–71; Mayer, *ib.*, 257–66.
[2] T. Thomson, (2), 1802; 1807, i, 580; Murray, *System of Chemistry*, 1806, ii, 107 f., 116 f., 124 f.; Brande, *Manual of Chemistry*, 1821, i, 317; Henry, *Elements of Experimental Chemistry*, 1823, i, 204, 210.
[3] *Op. cit.*; *Nicholson's J.*, 1802, ii, 10, 92.
[4] *Nicholson's J.*, 1802, ii, 206.
[5] 3 ed., 1807, i, 581; 5 ed., 1817, i, 145.
[6] Lehrbegriffe vom Phlogiston, auf neue Versuche gegründet, Crell's *Ann.*, 1784, I, 207.

inspector of salt-works in Schöningen, who also showed that air in a bladder attached to a retort containing heated zinc or lead contracts.[1]

Wiegleb[2] then adopted Guyton de Morveau's theory of the buoyancy of phlogiston, a body lighter than air, in a memoir intended to convince chemists that the 'purified' (geläuterte) theory of phlogiston was correct, but Scherer[3] thought it contributed to the downfall of the theory. Wiegleb[4] said phlogiston is the lightest of all materials, and Cavendish had found inflammable air 10 times lighter than common air, Kirwan 12 times: 'the combustible principle diminishes the positive gravity of those bodies with which it is combined, and the increased gravity is resumed when it is taken from them.' Wiegleb's ten principles of the 'purified theory of Stahl'[5] include: (1) phlogiston combined with vital air (oxygen) forms phlogisticated air (nitrogen), (2) phlogiston combined with water and fire forms inflammable air (hydrogen), (3) combined with phosphoric and vitriolic acids it forms phosphorus and sulphur, and (4) combined with aërial acid (carbon dioxide), of unknown composition, saline and earthy parts, it forms charcoal. Vital air, of unknown composition, is perhaps the purest water combined with the purest fire. All Lavoisier's results can be explained by supposing that air is necessary to receive the emitted phlogiston.[6]

The decrease in volume of air by the calcination of a metal, said Wiegleb, is due to absorption of phlogiston, since De la Metherie[7] found that vital air when exposed to electric sparks decreases in volume and is converted into fixed air and phlogisticated air; hence vital air decreases in volume when phlogistic vapours are added to it.

De la Metherie was unable to see much difference between Lavoisier's caloric and phlogiston.[8] Westrumb[9] still supported Stahl's theory, and J. Watt junr. wrote from Manchester that, although Kirwan had given it up, Priestley and Keir still held it.[10] Wiegleb abandoned de Morveau's theory in 1796[11] and adopted Macquer's that phlogiston is the matter of light; but in the same year Zauschner[12] regarded it as the imponderable matter of heat and light.

In 1795 Wiegleb[13] had managed to obtained oxygen by heating mercury oxide, an experiment which seems to have offered peculiar difficulties for German chemists (see p. 633), and now agreed that it forms a constituent of metallic calces, believing, however, with Richter (p. 630) that a simultaneous loss of 'some other escaping entity' cannot be denied.

Sulphur and phosphorus do not contain acids, as Stahl thought, but substrates which form the acids with vital air; e.g. in sulphur a compound of sulphuretted hydrogen with the matter of heat and light. Metals are composed of specific calces and light. The new ideas on carbon and on the composition of water Wiegleb cannot accept.

[1] Crell's *Neueste Entdeckungen*, 1782, iv, 69; *id., Ann.*, 1784, I, 408.
[2] Crell's *Ann.*, 1791, II, 387–469.   [3] *Allgem. J. Chem.*, 1800, iv, 701.
[4] Crell's *Ann.*, 1791, II, 401–6.   [5] *Ib.*, 392.   [6] *Ib.*, 411–12.
[7] *Essai Analytique sur l'Air pur et les Différentes Espèces d'Air*, Paris, 1785, 105, 111, 123, 167, 310, 451.
[8] Crell's *Ann.*, 1792, I, 256.   [9] *Ib.*, 1792, I, 3, 152, 252.
[10] *Ib.*, 364.   [11] Crell's *Ann.*, 1796, I, 263.
[12] Crell's *Beyträge*, 1796, iv, 131–85.   [13] Crell's *Ann.*, 1795, II, 516.

In 1796[1] Wiegleb held that phlogiston is the matter of light; he thought the red colour of nitrous fumes proved the presence of fire (cf. Mayow, Vol. II, p. 589). Water is an element and is contained in various gases. Wiegleb proposed a new nomenclature.[2] In some experiments on the reduction of minium by sulphur he concluded that 100 parts of lead increase in weight by 20 parts on conversion into minium.[3] In 1799[4] he still refused to admit the new theory of the composition of water.

HILDEBRANDT

Georg Friedrich Hildebrandt (Hannover, 5 June 1764–Erlangen, 25 March 1816), M.D. and Privatdocent in Göttingen, professor of anatomy in Brunswick (1786), professor of medicine (1793), chemistry (1796), and physics (1799) in Erlangen, published on medicine, chemistry, and physics.[5] He wrote a comparative essay on the old and new theories,[6] and announced in 1793[7] that he had gradually been inclined to become an antiphlogistian (see p. 493). He published:

I. Anfangsgründe der Chemie. Zum Grundriss akademischer Vorlesungen nach dem neuen System abgefasst, 3 vols. 8°, Erlangen, 1794, 2 ed., 2 pts., 8°, Erlangen, 1822.
II. Anfangsgründe der allgemeinen dynamischen Naturlehre, 2 vols. 8°, Erlangen, 1807; 2 ed. 1821 (not in BM or BN).
III. Lehrbuch der Chemie als Wissenschaft und Kunst, 2 vols. 8°, Erlangen, 1816 (completed by G. Bischof) (not in BM or BN).
IV. Encyclopädie der gesammten Chemie, 14 pts. 8°, Erlangen, 1799–1804, 2 ed. Vol. i, 1809 (BN).

He still used[8] Bergman's criterion of a salt by its taste and solubility in boiling water (see p. 191, and Kirwan, p. 667), although it was then recognised that this would exclude lead and barium sulphates, etc. His text-book (I) is based on the antiphlogistic theory, although he says in the preface that this has some minor defects. He regarded heat and light as different.[9] In his book on dynamical natural philosophy (II), although influenced by the ideas of Schelling (see Vol. IV), he recognised that the atomic theory could at least assist in the correct understanding of chemical phenomena, and that the different kinds of matter could hardly be explained without the consideration of atoms.[10]

Hildebrandt published several papers and a book on mercury compounds,[11] on quicklime,[12] ammonium nitrate,[13] the composition of ammonia,[14] the preparation of pure potassium ferrocyanide,[15] on blood, nutrition, and animal heat,[16] and on action at a distance in the restoration (Herstellung) of metals.[17]

He investigated the different coloured lights emitted in electrical discharges

---

[1] Ib., 1796, I, 263.   [2] Ib., 1796, II, 233.   [3] Ib., 1797, I, 213.
[4] Ib., 1799, I, 45, 138, 214 (experimental).
[5] Bischof, J. Chem. (Schweigger), 1819, xxv, 1–16; Poggendorff, (1), i, 1102 (lists of publs.).
[6] Crell's Ann., 1793, I, 536.   [7] Ib., 1793, II, 99.
[8] Crell's Ann., 1795, II, 6.   [9] Ib., i, 108.   [10] Kopp, (1), ii, 326.
[11] Crell's Ann., 1792, II, 54, 196, 291, 398; 1793, I, 12, 141, 195, 296, 376 (rev. of book).
[12] Ib., 1792, II, 113.   [13] Ib., 1794, I, 291.
[14] Ib., 1795, I, 303 (incl. reduction of nitric acid by metals).   [15] Ib., 1798, I, 19.
[16] Ib., 1799, I, 18, 145, 201.   [17] Ib., 1799, II, 10.

in low-pressure air,[1] the gas evolved in the deflagration of nitre and charcoal,[2] double decompositions and separations,[3] the properties of gold,[4] the presence of magnesia in human bones,[5] and the determination of oxygen in air by nitric oxide.[6] He criticised Davy's views on chlorine,[7] and described apparatus for the electrolysis of water and collection of the gases separately,[8] and a voltaic pile of three metals.[9]

[1] *J. Chem.* (Schweigger), 1811, i, 237.

[2] *Ib.*, 1811, i, 391.

[3] *Ib.*, 1811, iii, 274.

[4] *Ib.*, 1812, vi, 369.

[5] *Ib.*, 1813, viii, 1; 1814, xii, 227.

[6] *Ib.*, 1815, xiv, 265.

[7] *Ib.*, 1815, xiii, 72.

[8] *Ann. Phys.*, 1805, xxi, 257 and figs.

[9] *Ib.*, 1808, xxx, 67.

CHAPTER XIV

FOUNDATIONS OF STOICHIOMETRY

The subject of stoichiometry (a name introduced by Richter (p. 680)) comprises the quantitative laws of chemical composition. These are stated in the law of constant composition (Proust), the law of multiple proportions (Higgins and Dalton), and the law of reciprocal proportions or equivalents (Richter). The first and third are dealt with in this chapter, the second in Chapts. XV and XVI. They are all consequences of Dalton's atomic theory, which forms the main topic of Chapt. XVII.

PROUST

Louis Joseph Proust (Angers; 26 September 1754 (not 1755)–5 July 1826), the son of a pharmacist, was a pupil of Rouelle and became chief apothecary in La Salpétrière, Paris. He migrated to Spain and became professor at the artillery school at Segovia (1789), then at Salamanca, and finally at Madrid, where he had a splendid laboratory furnished at the cost of King Charles IV. Even the common apparatus was of platinum, and Fourcroy[1] remarks that the most expensive apparatus made in Paris by Fortin went to Spain. In 1806 Proust obtained leave to visit France, but in 1808 his papers and laboratory were pillaged by the inhabitants of Madrid during the siege by the French army. He was reduced to poverty and was compelled to sell his mineral specimens to buy food. Although invited by Napoleon to found a sugar factory, Proust retired to Craon, where he lived very simply. His memoirs of this period show a sharper tone than early ones. In 1816 Proust was made a member of the Academy by special decree, since he was not resident in Paris, and he was paid the annual grant to members as well as a small pension from King Louis XVIII. He then moved to Angers, his birthplace, where he died. Proust was a man of great independence and originality, of a lively disposition and fond of humorous stories.[2]

Proust was predominantly an accurate and ingenious experimenter. Besides his numerous memoirs on the compositions of minerals and artificial compounds of metals (gold, silver, platinum, copper, mercury, tin, antimony, zinc, iron, cobalt, nickel, etc.), including salts of organic acids, Proust published a

---

[1] (2), 1797, iii, 714.
[2] Cohen, in Diergart, 1909, 602; Dumas, (1), 210; Färber, *Z. angew. Chem.*, 1923, xxxiv, 245; L. V. Godard-Faultrier, *Notice biographique sur L. J. Proust*, Angers, 1852 (30 pp.; BN 8° Ln²⁷. 16723); Kopp, (1), i, 356; ii, 368; (3), 225 f., 234 f., 268; Regnard, NBG, 1862, xli, 104; Tilden, *Famous Chemists*, 1921, 127; list of papers in Poggendorff, (1), ii, 537; summary of Proust's analyses etc. in De la Metherie, *J. de Phys.*, 1804, lx, 95; 1806, lxii, 109.

work in Spanish on tinning copper etc.[1] and a book on the stone.[2] His most important work was on the law of constant proportions. His papers are almost entirely concerned with experimental details; they usually have the title 'Faits pour l'histoire de . . . '. The later papers became more polemical, Thenard's work being rather sharply criticised;[3] in a review of Fourcroy's *Système des Connaissances Chimiques*[4] Proust complained that among so many chemists

FIG. 52. L. J. PROUST, 1754–1826.

there are so few good analysts. His analytical work occupied him from 1797 to 1809 and is mostly published (or abstracted) in the *Annales de Chimie* and the *Journal de Physique*; after the publication of Berthollet's *Statique Chimique* in 1803 it mostly took the form of a controversy on definite proportions, the resulting discussion being[5] a model for scientific polemics in its polite tone and the presentation of new experimental results on both sides. Proust's more important communications are on Prussian blue,[6] on tin,[7] copper,[8] zinc,[9] platinum,[10] the supposed presence of mercury in common salt,[11] nickel in Peruvian native iron[12] and in meteoric iron of Aragon,[13] Peruvian pyrites,[14] oxides of arsenic,[15] nitric acid,[16] nitrous oxide from dilute nitric acid (15° Bé.) and zinc,[16] potassium nitrite,[17] the inflammation of oils by nitric acid,[18] the

[1] *Indagaciones sobre el estando del cobre, la vaxilla de estano y el vidriado*, 4°, Madrid, 1803; summary in *J. de Phys.*, 1804, lix, 412.
[2] *Essai sur une des causes qui peuvent amener la formation du calcul*, Angers, 1824.
[3] *J. de Phys.*, 1815, lxxxi, 263.   [4] *Ib.*, 1802, lvi, 200.
[5] Dumas, (1), 215.   [6] *Ann. chim.*, 1797, xxiii, 85.
[7] *Ib.*, 1798, xxviii, 213.   [8] *Ib.*, 1799, xxxii, 26–54.
[9] *Ib.*, 1799, xxxv, 51.   [10] *Ib.*, 1799, xxxviii, 146, 225.
[11] *J. de Phys.*, 1799, xlix, 153.   [12] *Ib.*, 1799, xlix, 148.
[13] *Ib.*, 1804–5, lx, 185.   [14] *Ib.*, 1799, xlix, 150.
[15] *Ib.*, 151.   [16] *Ib.*, 59.   [17] *Ib.*, 60.   [18] *Ib.*, 62.

explosion of a mixture of ammonia gas and oxygen when inflamed,[1] on tin,[2] detached facts on platinum,[3] on some metallic sulphides,[4] native and artificial sulphides of iron,[5] antimony,[6] nickel,[7] metallic oxidations,[8] sulphate of copper with the minimum of acid found in Peru,[9] green and white muriates of copper (cupric and cuprous chlorides),[10] metallic sulphides,[11] and alkali sulphides,[12] showing, in opposition to Berthollet, that sulphur dissolves in alkalis without addition of sulphuretted hydrogen, and also investigating hydrogen persulphide. He also investigated the hydrates (hydroxides) of copper,[13] the red silver ore (called after him proustite, Ag_3AsS_3),[14] a meteoric stone,[15] verdigris,[16] mosaic gold (stannic sulphide),[17] silver,[18] gold,[19] cobalt ores,[20] cobalt,[21] nickel,[22] zinc blende,[23] showing that it is zinc sulphide but the precipitated form is a hydrosulphide,[24] on oxides of copper (cuprous and cupric oxides),[25] six letters (from Craon) on the uncertainty of some oxidations,[26] on mercury,[27] and the extraction of mercury at Almaden.[28]

Proust in 1775[29] found that the *sal perlatum* obtained by Haupt in 1740 (see p. 67) contains sodium, but in 1781[30] he thought it contained a peculiar acid (which Bergman called *acidum perlatum* and Guyton de Morveau *acide ouretique*),[31] since the salt did not give phosphorus when heated with charcoal. Rouelle junr. in 1776 had correctly concluded that it is a phosphate of soda[32] and this was confirmed by Klaproth and by Scheele (see p. 231) in 1785, and Hermbstädt in 1786.[33] Proust[34] described the deposits of calcium phosphate and wolfram in Estramadura.

Proust showed that the black tarnish forming on silver exposed to air is silver sulphide.[35] He obtained lead dioxide (which he says was discovered by Scheele; see p. 230) by the action of dilute nitric acid on red lead,[36] noticed the evolution of arsenic hydride when impure tin dissolves in acid,[37] showed that the native oxychlorides of copper of Chile and Peru are definite compounds,[38] rediscovered cuprous oxide,[39] and prepared cuprous chloride;[40] he says[41] that Pelletier had discovered stannous chloride and examined its action on solu-

[1] *Ib.*, 63.
[2] *Ib.*, 1800, li, 173–84: introducing the use of hydrogen sulphide in qualitative analysis, p. 174.
[3] *Ib.*, 1801, lii, 409–37.　　　[4] *Ib.*, 1801, liii, 89–97.　　　[5] *Ib.*, 1802, liv, 89–96.
[6] *Ib.*, 1802, lv, 325–44.　　　[7] *Ib.*, 1803, lvii, 169–74.　　　[8] *Ib.*, 1804, lix, 321–43.
[9] *Ib.*, 343–49.　　　[10] *Ib.*, 350–4.　　　[11] *Ib.*, 260–5.
[12] *Ib.*, 265–73.　　　[13] *Ib.*, 393.　　　[14] *Ib.*, 403.
[15] *Ib.*, 1804, lx, 185.　　　[16] *Ib.*, 1804, lxi, 110.
[17] *Ib.*, 338; *Nicholson's J.*, 1806, xiv, 38.　　　[18] *J. de Phys.*, 1806, lxii, 211.
[19] *Ib.*, 131.　　　[20] *Ib.*, 1806, lxiii, 364.　　　[21] *Ib.*, 421.　　　[22] *Ib.*, 442.
[23] *Ib.*, 1807, lxiv, 150.　　　[24] Confirmed by Middleton and Ward, *J. Chem. Soc.*, 1935, 1459.
[25] *J. de Phys.*, 1807, lxv, 80.
[26] *Ib.*, 1814, lxxix, 119, 320, 467 (mentioning Berzelius favourably); 1815, lxxx, 105, 185; 1815, lxxxi, 239, 253.　　　[27] *Ib.*, 1815, lxxxi, 321.　　　[28] *Ib.*, 331.
[29] Sage, AdS, 1777, m 435; *Obs. Phys.*, 1777, x, 377.　　　[30] *Obs. Phys.*, 1781, xvii, 145.
[31] Bergman, *Opuscula*, iii, 380; Guyton de Morveau, *Ency. Méthod.*, *Chymie*, 1786, i, 192, 207, 406.　　　[32] *J. de Médecine*, 1777, xlviii, 299.
[33] In Selle, *Neue Beiträge zur Natur- und Arzenei-Wissenschaft*, Berlin, 1786, iii, 182.
[34] *Obs. Phys.*, 1788, xxxii, 241; letter to D'Arcet.
[35] *Ann. Chim.*, 1789, i, 198.　　　[36] *Ib.*, 1797, xxiii, 98.
[37] *Ann. Chim.*, 1799, xxviii, 215; *J. de Phys.*, 1800, li, 175.　　　[38] *Ann. Chim.*, 1799, xxxii, 48 f.
[39] *Ann. Chim.*, 1799, xxxii, 50 f.; *J. de Phys.*, 1800, li, 182; Lavoisier, *Traité*, 1789, table after p. 202, speaks of 'oxide rouge brun de cuivre'; cf. Scheele, p. 230; Fourcroy, (4), 1793, iii, 324.
[40] *J. de Phys.*, 1800, li, 179–81.　　　[41] *Ib.*, 183.

tions of metallic salts, except those of copper. Cuprous chloride was obtained by Proust, but he maintained that Pelletier should have the honour of the discovery; 'if he does not speak of it, this is because it seemed to him worthy of special attention and because he reserved it for further study.'

Proust prepared cuprous chloride as colourless tetrahedra by keeping plates of copper in a closed bottle of concentrated hydrochloric acid (1799), by precipitating cupric chloride with stannous chloride,[1] and[2] by boiling cupric chloride with copper and concentrated hydrochloric acid and pouring into water. He correctly determined its composition as copper 63, chlorine 35 (100 of 'muriate blanc' gave 142 of silver chloride and 113 of copper carbonate, containing 63 of copper). Proust[3] obtained artificial iron pyrites (FeS_2) by gently heating ferrous sulphide (FeS) with excess of sulphur; he found for 100 of iron, 60 and 90 of sulphur in the two compounds. He recognised clearly the existence of oxychlorides of antimony, bismuth and mercury,[4] and in this paper, one of his most instructive, he swept away as complex mixtures a large number of preparations containing oxides and sulphides which had encumbered chemistry as 'rubies', 'livers', 'crocuses', 'glasses', 'algaroths', 'kermes', etc., of antimony (cf. Lemery, p. 37). He showed[5] that white lead made with vinegar contains no acetate; 100 pts. dissolved in dilute nitric acid and precipitated with alkali carbonate gave 101 pts. of artificial lead carbonate (really basic). Stannous oxide is decomposed by concentrated caustic alkali into metallic tin and a solution of alkali stannate.[6] Purple of Cassius (see Vol. II, p. 370) consists of 76 parts of stannic oxide and 24 of finely-divided metallic gold.[7]

Proust's work in organic chemistry is important. He described the preparation of citric acid,[8] isolated grape sugar from honey and raisins[9] and mannitol from manna.[10] He obtained what he called *caseous oxide* (oxide caséeux), which is leucine, and a *caseic acid*, from the putrefaction of casein (discovered by Berzelius in 1812) in cheese[11] and prepared from barley a bran-like material free from nitrogen which he called *hordëine*.[12] His work on tannin[13] is important. He drew attention in 1802, independently of Davy,[14] to the difference between the tanning principle ('tanin') in oak bark and that in oak galls, a distinction which was not fully realised until 1864.[15]

Proust correctly stated that 'acetous' and 'acetic' acids are identical,[16] but he thought that nitrogen as well as carbon dioxide resulted from fermentation.[17]

---

[1] *Ib.*, 1800, li, 183.   [2] *Ib.*, 1804, lix, 350.   [3] *Ib.*, 1802, liv, 89.
[4] *Ib.*, 1802, lv, 325–44.   [5] *Ib.*, 1802, lvi, 200.   [6] *Ib.*, 1804, lix, 339.
[7] *Ib.*, 1806, lxii, 131.   [8] *Ib.*, 1801, lii, 366–75.
[9] *Ib.*, 1802, liv, 199 (Sur le sucre du miel); 1802, lvi, 113; 1806, lxiii, 257, 340 (Mémoir sur le sucre de raisin); *Mémoir sur le sucre de raisin*, Paris, 1808.
[10] *Ann. Chim.*, 1806, lvii, 131, 225; *Allgem. J. der Chemie* (Gehlen), 1806, ii, 83.
[11] Sur le principe qui assaisonne les Fromages, *Ann. Chim.*, 1818, x, 29, 40.
[12] *Ann. Chim.*, 1817, v, 337.
[13] *Ann. Chim.*, 1798, xxv, 225; 1799, xxxv, 32; 1802, xli, 331 (abstr.); 1802, xlii, 89–98 (summary by Bouillon-Lagrange); AdS, *Mém. div. Sav.*, 1805, i, 184; Nierenstein, *Incunabula of Tannin Chemistry*, 1932.
[14] *Phil. Trans.*, 1803, xciii, 233–73.
[15] Eckert, *Vierteljahresschr. f. prakt. Pharm.*, 1864, xiii, 494, q. by Nierenstein, *The Natural Organic Tannins*, 1934, 235 f.
[16] *J. de Phys.*, 1802, lvi, 205, 211; see p. 544.   [17] *Ib.*, 1802, lvi, 113.

He obtained[1] from urine a 'substance rosacée' as a red sediment which was probably impure uric acid;[2] Vauquelin called it 'acide rosacique'.[3]

The Law of Constant Proportions

When Proust began his work the constancy of composition of chemical compounds was generally accepted and it formed the basis of the quantitative analytical methods of Bergman (p. 187), Wenzel (p. 671), Kirwan (p. 664) and Richter (p. 681). Lavoisier, although he generally assumed that different compounds formed from two elements were definite in composition, and recognised the existence of two oxides of copper (p. 461), said:

'nitrous air [nitric oxide] is capable of taking with oxygen not only two but an infinity of degrees of saturation, and there results an infinity of different nitrous acids, from that which is called dephlogisticated and is white and colourless, to that which is the most red and smoking.'[4]

Also that when a metal is boiled with concentrated sulphuric acid the oxygen of the acid:

'must be considered as obedient to two unequal forces; on the one part it is attracted by the metal which tends to calcination, that is to say, to become an oxide, and on the other hand it is retained by the sulphur, and it is divided into two parts until an equilibrium is obtained.'[5]

Lavoisier also says[6] 'the acidifying and the acidified principle can exist in different proportions, which constitute the points of equilibrium and of saturation'. He seems to have inclined to the idea of indefinite proportions in some special cases, and linked it in an interesting way with the operation of affinity in a manner afterwards developed by Berthollet, who was a co-author and participated in the discussions leading to this publication.

Fourcroy[7] says that each metal and acid 'can remain reciprocally united only within very narrow limits of oxidation. There is a determined proportion of oxygen in the combination of an acid with a metallic oxide' (an idea later developed by Berzelius, see Vol. IV).

The work of Berthollet on affinity in 1799–1803 (see Vol. IV), with its assumption that chemical reactions are usually incomplete, and that one substance is divided between two others in a variable ratio dependent upon the 'mass', as well as his recognition of the importance of reactions in solutions, led him to the conclusion that the composition of a compound is not constant but variable, sometimes between fixed limits. This was a negation of the law of constant proportions. In his first work on affinity Berthollet says he proposes to investigate the circumstances which modify combination, 'or the affections of bodies which favour or diminish their chemical action and which can vary the proportions in the combinations which they can form.'[8]

[1] Ann. Chim., 1799, xxxvi, 258.   [2] Vogel, Ann. Chim., 1815, vi, 306.
[3] J. de Phys., 1811, lxxiii, 157.
[4] Sur l'Affinité du Principe Oxygine; AdS, 1782 (1785), h 39, m 530 (read 1783); Oeuvres, ii, 550; id., in Kirwan, Essay on Phlogiston, 1789, 50.
[5] Lavoisier, in Kirwan, Essay on Phlogiston, 1789, 53.
[6] Méthode de Nomenclature Chimique, 1787, 20.   [7] Philosophie Chimique, 1795, 120.
[8] Recherches sur les lois de l'affinité, 1801, 4; cf. ib., 21, 36.

Berthollet's ideas of variable proportions and affinity actually go back to his earliest memoir on tartaric acid,[1] in which he states:

'It is not that I believe there are no constant laws which bodies obey in their combination, in their union, in their decomposition; but we are very far from being sufficiently advanced to foresee all the circumstances which cause these laws to vary, and to be able to construct a general system of affinities.'

Berthollet's attack on the law of constant proportions was mainly delivered in his book on chemical statics,[2] and some further papers.[3]

According to Berthellot, when substances of definite composition *are* formed, they are either (1) the result of a mutual saturation of an acid by a base, when the powers of each are just neutralised in a certain proportion (the change of reaction proceeding continuously); or (2) they are, exceptionally, due to the interference of other manifestations of the physical forces, such as (*a*) cohesion, when a precipitate of definite composition is formed because it happens to have the maximum density, or (*b*) elasticity, when a gaseous product is formed which escapes from the system, and as the most volatile product is favoured in the reaction. Solutions were regarded as true chemical compounds of variable composition.[4] Salts crystallise out in a neutral state because in that neutral state the insolubility is greatest.[5]

A metal such as tin, lead or copper, when heated in air takes up oxygen in a continuously increasing amount up to a fixed limit (not always the highest known oxide, e.g. in the case of lead), thus producing a continuous series of oxides, as shown in some cases (e.g. lead) by the colour changes.[6]

'I have thus shown that the proportions of oxygen in the oxides depend on the same conditions as those which enter in the other combinations; that these proportions may vary progressively from the term where the combination becomes possible up to that where it attains the last degree; and when this effect does not occur it is only because the conditions which I have indicated become an obstacle to this progressive action.'

Similar results were found for the metallic sulphides,[7] and Berthollet disputed the results of Proust, who had also found[8] that part of the sulphur in iron pyrites and cupreous pyrites can be driven off by heat and regarded this as a 'surplus'. Berthollet says:

'If heat can so easily expel this sulphur, regarded as foreign to the compound, one finds in that a property common to all substances which resist so much the less to the expansive action of heat as they occur in greater proportion in the fixed compound, since the chemical action diminishes with the progress of saturation.'

In his researches on the various oxides of metals (see p. 642), Proust was able to show[9] that each metal forms one or at most two *definite* oxides, and that the supposed continuous series of oxides prepared by Berthollet are mixtures of

---

[1] *Obs. Phys.*, 1776, vii, 140.   [2] *Statique Chimique*, 2 vols., Paris, 1803, i, 334 f.
[3] (1) Observations relatives à differens mémoires de Proust, *J. de Phys.*, 1804, lx, 284–90, 347–51; (2) Sur les lois de l'affinité, *Ann. Chim.*, 1801, xxxvi, 302; (3) Suite de recherches sur les lois de l'affinité, *ib.*, 1801, xxxvii, 151, 221; 1801, xxxviii, 113; 1801, xxxix, 3; *J. de Phys.*, 1804, lxi, 352; 1807, lxiv, 168–87, 193; *Mém. de l'Inst.*, 1806, vii, 229–300; *Ann. Chim.*, 1808, lxvii, 309; see Gilbert, *Ann. Phys.*, 1811, xxxix, 361.
[4] *Stat. Chim.*, 1803, i, 3 f., 10 f., 59, 82, 334 f., 339, 373.   [5] *Ib.*, i, 348.
[6] *Ib.*, ii, 361 f., 370; *J. de Phys.*, 1804, lxi, 352.   [7] *Stat. Chim.*, ii, 433 f.
[8] *J. de Phys.*, 1801, liii, 89.   [9] *J. de Phys.*, 1804, lix, 321 f.

oxide with unchanged metal, or of two definite oxides. The oxides of tin, for example, are:[1]

Oxide	Tin	Oxygen
yellow [SnO]	80	20
white [SnO$_2$]	72	28

(His description of the colour of stannous oxide is noteworthy.) The two oxides of copper are:[2]

	Copper	Oxygen
Black oxide	100	25
Yellow or brown oxide	100	(16) 17–18

Proust clearly distinguished between oxides and hydroxides ('hydrates') of metals, first using the latter name, although he says 'Lavoisier first made known to us the fact, in slaked lime'.[3] Proust found that many supposed oxides of metals were mixtures. Thenard[4] reported six oxides of antimony, but Proust[5] says: ' I fear that the six terms which he recognises are not sanctioned by nature'; he thought there were only two oxides, containing 23 and 30 of oxygen for 100 of antimony, but Berzelius later proved that (apart from a doubtful suboxide) there are three (Sb$_2$O$_3$, Sb$_2$O$_4$, and Sb$_2$O$_5$; see Vol. IV). Thenard later[6] said: 'I am not convinced that there are as many oxides as there are possible degrees of oxidation, and if theory allows them, experience seems to reject them' — obviously referring to Berthollet's theory. There were, however, three oxides of iron[7] (FeO, Fe$_3$O$_4$, Fe$_2$O$_3$), not two only as Proust maintained. Proust later admitted more than two oxides of a metal (e.g. of cobalt) but thought the third oxide was usually a compound of the other two,[8] as is often the case when one oxide is acidic and the other basic; red lead, cited by Proust, may be regarded as Pb$_3$O$_4$ = PbO$_2$ + 2PbO.

In his further experiments with lead, Berthollet[9] concluded that heating the metal in air may not produce a continuous series of oxides, but in this case four different stages of oxidation. Thomson[10] also obtained definite oxides of lead and supported Proust's ideas. In 1801[11] Thomson, who says Proust had definitely proved that 'metals are not capable of indefinite degrees of oxidation', suggested that a higher oxide of a metal is rather a compound of the lower oxide and oxygen, oxygen being 'capable of uniting with metals, or with any other substance for which it has an affinity, only in *one* determinate proportion'.

It has been said[12] that if Proust had calculated the weights of oxygen combining with a fixed weight of metal instead of the percentage composition of two oxides, he would have discovered the law of multiple proportions. Proust

[1] *J. de Phys.*, 1804, lxi, 338.   [2] *J. de Phys.*, 1804, lix, 351; 1807, lxv, 80.

[3] Proust, *Ann. Chim.*, 1799, xxxii, 41, 45 ('hydrate de cuivre . . . une combinaison réelle'); *J. de Phys.*, 1804, lix, 347, 393; 1806, lxiii, 429; 1815, lxxix, 127 (on Lavoisier).

[4] 'Thénart', presented by Guyton-Morveau, *Ann. Chim.*, 1799 (An VIII), xxxii, 257.

[5] *J. de Phys.*, 1802, lv, 331.   [6] *Ann. Chim.*, 1805, lvi, 62.

[7] Thenard, *Ib.*, 1805, lvi, 66, 77.   [8] *J. de Phys.*, 1804, lix, 260; 1806, lxiii, 441.

[9] *J. de Phys.*, 1804, lxi, 352.   [10] *Nicholson's J.*, 1804, viii, 280.

[11] *Ency. Brit. Suppl.*, 1801, I, i, 249.   [12] Kopp, (1), i, 360–1; ii, 370.

actually did this; he generally gives the weights of oxygen combining with 100 of metal, but his analyses are too inaccurate to disclose any simple ratios:[1] he gives for the two oxides of antimony[2] statements in both ways:

Antimony	oxygen	antimony	oxygen
77	23	100	30 (33·05)
81·5	18·5	100	22–23 (19·83)

The correct figures for Sb_2O_3 and Sb_2O_5 are given in brackets. For the 'suboxides' and 'protoxides' of copper and tin he found:

	Copper		Tin	
	suboxide	protoxide	suboxide	protoxide
metal	86·2	80	87	78·4
oxygen	13·8	20	13	21·6
	100·0	100	100	100·0

The proportions of oxygen in the two oxides are 13·8 : 21·5 for copper, and for tin 13 : 24, for a fixed weight of metal, only roughly as 1 : 2. He found that 100 parts of iron combine with 60 of sulphur as a minimum, and 90 as a maximum in natural and artificial pyrites[3] (the correct figures for FeS and FeS_2 are 57 and 114; for Fe_2S_3 86), and he thus recognised two definite sulphides.

The followers of Berthollet were not fully convinced by Proust's work; Murray[4] thought it 'a very strained hypothesis advanced by Proust' that the supposed continuous series of oxides 'arise from the reduction of part of the oxide at the maximum of oxidizement to that at the minimum, and the mechanical intermixture of these two oxides in various proportions'.

Even in the case of the precipitation of one metal by another from solutions of salts of the first, which Lavoisier (p. 460) had referred to varying forces of attraction for oxygen, Berthollet thought the precipitated metal, e.g. silver, contained some of the dissolving metal, e.g. copper.[5]

The law of constant proportions was first stated by Proust as early as 1797[6] in a paper on Prussian blue, in which he clearly recognised that iron forms two definite oxides with 27 and 48 per cent of oxygen, and says:

'I shall conclude by deducing from these experiments the principle I have established at the commencement of this memoir, viz. that iron like many other metals is subject to the law of nature which presides at every true combination, that is to say, that it unites with two constant proportions of oxygen. In this respect it does not differ from tin, mercury, and lead, and, in a word, almost every known combustible.'

[1] Ramsay, *System of Inorganic Chemistry*, 1891, 16.
[2] *J. de Phys.*, 1802, lv, 325 (330–1); Murray, 1807, iii, 480, says this paper shows 'that decision and dogmatism often so conspicuous in the writings of Proust'.
[3] *J. de Phys.*, 1802, liv, 89.   [4] 1807, iii, 42.
[5] *Recherches*, 1801, 96 f.; tr. W. Farrell, *Researches into the Laws of Chemical Affinity*, London, 1804, 117 f.
[6] Recherches sur le Bleu de Prusse; *Ann. Chim.*, 1797, xxiii, 85–101; abstr. in *Bull. Soc. Philomath.*, 1797, No. 3 (June), p. 20; *Nicholson's J.*, 1798, i, 453.

He emphasises that the two definite oxides of iron correspond with two series of salts (ferrous and ferric), also of definite compositions. In 1799[1] he says of copper (basic) carbonate:

'If 100 parts of this [native] carbonate, dissolved in nitric acid and thrown down by alkaline carbonates, give us 100 parts of artificial carbonate; if the base of these two compounds is the [same] black oxide [of copper], one must recognise an invisible hand which holds the balance for us in the formation of compounds and fashions their attributes at its will; one must conclude that nature does not act otherwise in the depths of the earth than on its surface, or in the hands of man. These proportions, these constant attributes which characterise the true compounds (composés) of art or those of nature, in a word this *pondus naturæ* so well seen by Staahl [Stahl], all this, I say, is no more in the power of the chemist than is the law of election which governs (préside à) all these combinations.'

The idea of nature 'holding the balance' had been expressed by Seneca (55 B.C.–A.D. 40): 'Nature weighs her parts as if with a nice adjustment of the balance.'[2]

Antimony attaches oxygen in 'an invariable dose fixed by Nature, and the power of augmenting or diminishing which is not given to man':[3] il s'en attache une dose invariablement fixée par la nature, et qu'il n'est pas donné à l'homme de pouvoir augmenter ou diminuer. In reply to a criticism by Berthollet, Proust says:[4]

'ce n'est pas moi, c'est la nature ou telle puissance qu'on voudra, qui place une barrière entre elle et les efforts de tout chimiste qui se proposeroit de faire du sulfure d'antimoine en-deça ou au-delà de cette proportion.'

'Election and proportion are two poles about which the whole system of true compounds revolves immutably, as much in nature as between the hands of the chemist.'[5]

He calls Berthollet's theory 'la chimie flottante'.[6] According to Berthollet, when a soluble salt of an insoluble basic oxide (e.g. copper sulphate) is precipitated in solution by addition of alkali, the precipitate is not the pure oxide (or hydrate) but a basic salt containing amounts of the acid (e.g. sulphuric) which diminish progressively as more and more alkali is added, the acid being shared between the two bases according to their masses.[7]

Proust[8] thought these were mixtures imperfectly freed from salt by washing, but it is now known that *definite* basic salts can be precipitated, e.g. $CuSO_4,3Cu(OH)_2$, $CuCl_2,3Cu(OH)_2$, and $Cu(NO_3)_2,3Cu(OH)_2$. A basic nitrate of copper was, in fact, prepared by Proust[9] by heating the normal nitrate, and he found that it contained: copper oxide 67, nitric acid 16, water 17. The copper hydrate precipitated from copper nitrate with *excess* of alkali, however, was free from nitric acid and contained copper oxide 74, water 24 (the remaining 2 being probably carbonic acid). With a small amount of potash added to copper sulphate solution a green precipitate containing copper

[1] *Ann. Chim.*, 1799, xxxii, 30.
[2] *Quaest. Nat.*, ii, 10: et natura partes suas velut in ponderibus constitutas examinat.
[3] *J. de Phys.*, 1802, lv, 325.   [4] *J. de Phys.*, 1804, lix, 261.
[5] *Ib.*, 1802, lv, 332.   [6] *Ib.*, 1804, lix, 401.
[7] *Ann. Chim.*, 1801, xxxvii, 221; *Statique Chimique*, 1803, i, 85 f.; ii, 393 f., 447 f. (by A. B. Berthollet); Bayen had noted basic salts of mercury; see p. 395.
[8] *J. de Phys.*, 1804, lix, 393 f.   [9] *Ann. Chim.*, 1799, xxxii, 27.

oxide 68, acid 18 (SO_3) and water 14 was obtained; with more alkali this precipitate became blue.

Berthollet[1] obtained various (basic) sulphates of mercury and concluded that instead of there being only two sulphates, one with the minimum and the other with the maximum of oxygen, these were only the two extremes of a continuous series of salts (between the mercurous and mercuric). Between the salt of mercury obtained by dissolving the metal in cold dilute nitric acid (mercurous nitrate) and that formed with hot nitric acid (mercuric nitrate) all intermediate proportions may exist. He quotes Fourcroy and Bayen. Proust[2] showed that these are all mixtures of two kinds of mercury salts only, which had been recognised by Scheele (p. 230).

When a few bubbles of carbon dioxide are passed into a large excess of caustic alkali solution, only a small portion of the latter is combined and the rest remains free; and in the same way, when a metal is treated with a small amount of oxygen, a small quantity of a definite oxide is formed, whilst the rest of the metal remains unchanged.[3] Berthollet thought salts of a continuous series of oxides of mercury were produced by treating mercury with nitric acid, in which the proportion of oxygen steadily increased. They gave with hydrochloric acid only two chlorides (calomel and corrosive sublimate), and Berthollet[4] assumed that the insolubility of calomel caused the varying oxides to pass to the two end proportions. Proust thought this explanation attributed too much intelligence to the oxides:[5] Il faut convenir ici que voilà des oxides qui se conduisent avec bien d'intelligence. Berthollet[6] rejected Proust's explanation of the action of carbon dioxide on excess of caustic soda; carbon dioxide is evolved from the solution on adding a drop of muriatic acid and a true subcarbonate (sous-carbonate) is formed. By saturating sodium carbonate with carbon dioxide under pressure, Berthollet[7] obtained crystals of a different composition, and by evaporating the solution a salt was obtained containing: soda 31·75, acid 44·40 and water 23·85, whilst the original salt contained soda 20·25, acid 12·15, water 68·60.

The part of Berthollet's theory which gave Proust the most trouble was that denying any distinction between true compounds and solutions; solutions are chemical compounds, produced by the same forces as those operating in any other type (e.g. oxides) but exerted more feebly. When a salt dissolves in water the salt and water are united by affinity; when salt crystallises on cooling it is because cohesion in the solid outweighs the attraction of salt and water, and when it separates on evaporation it is because the elasticity of the vapour of the solvent predominates. Berthollet[8] pressed for precise definitions of 'compounds' (combinaisons) and 'solutions' (dissolutions), and at the same time reminded Proust that Vauquelin and Klaproth, both skilled analysts, had found results differing from those of Proust for substances which the latter regarded as true compounds.

[1] Ann. Chim., 1801, xxxviii, 113–34; Stat. Chim., ii, 393 f.
[2] J. de Phys., 1804, lix, 321 f.   [3] Ib., 329.
[4] Ann. Chim., 1801, xxxviii, 119.   [5] J. de Phys., 1804, lix, 335.
[6] J. de Phys., 1807, lxiv, 181.
[7] Ib., 168 f.; Mém. de l'Inst., 1806, vii, 229 f.   [8] J. de Phys., 1805, lx, 347–51.

Proust found it very difficult to give precise definitions of true compounds which would differentiate them from solutions, alloys and glasses, but he felt that there was a distinction. It is important that he recognised the existence of *solid* solutions.[1] He argued as follows:[2]

'Is the power which makes a metal dissolve in sulphur different from that which makes one sulphide dissolve in another? I shall be in no hurry to answer this question, legitimate though it be, for fear of losing myself in a region not sufficiently lighted up by the science of facts; but my distinction will, I hope, be appreciated all the same when I say: The attraction which causes sugar to dissolve in water may or may not be the same as that which makes a fixed quantity of carbon and of hydrogen dissolve in another quantity of oxygen to form the sugar of our plants, but what we do clearly perceive is that these two kinds of attraction are so different in their results that it is impossible to confound them. . . . Here are, I believe, distinctions which will appear clear to all the world.

'According to our principles . . . a compound is a substance such as the sulphide of silver, of antimony, of mercury, of copper, such as an oxidised metal, an acidified combustible, etc.; it is a privileged product to which Nature assigns fixed proportions, it is, in short, a being which she never creates even between the hands of man otherwise than balance in hand, *pondere et mensurâ*. Let us recognise, therefore, . . . that the characters of true compounds are as invariable as the ratio of their elements. Between pole and pole, they are found identical in these two respects; their appearance may vary owing to the manner of aggregation, but their properties never. No differences have yet been observed between the oxides of iron from the South and those from the North. The cinnabar of Japan follows the proportions of that of Almaden. Silver is not differently oxidised or muriated in the muriate of Peru than in that of Siberia. In all the known parts of the world you will not see two muriates of soda, two muriates of ammonia, two saltpetres, two sulphates of lime, of potash, of soda, of magnesia, of baryta, etc., differing from each other; it is, finally, with the same measure that all the other compounds of the globe have been formed.'

In the introduction to the translation of Thomson's *System of Chemistry*[3] Berthollet repeated that he did not make a distinction between dissolution and combination, both being manifestations of the same chemical action in different degrees. Glasses, alloys, and solutions are chemical compounds of variable composition. The acid sulphate of potash yields products of variable composition on crystallisation, and although there are compounds of fixed composition, their formation is due to influences not contemplated in Dalton's atomic theory. The investigation of solutions, alloys, amalgams and glasses, in fact, awaited the development of the Phase Rule, and Proust was practically driven to the position of defining a true chemical compound as one having a definite composition, independent of its mode of preparation.[4] The existence of *solid* compounds with the components in slightly varying proportions was recognised by Kurnakov,[5] who called them *Berthollide compounds*.

Limited miscibility in the case of alloys had been noticed by Bergman[6] in the case of iron and tin, and by de Morveau[7] in the case of silver and iron. Berthollet[8] also found with two metals which are not completely miscible that

[1] *J. de Phys.*, 1806, lxiii, 364 f.   [2] *Ib.*, 367–9.

[3] *Système de Chimie de M. Th. Thomson . . . traduit . . . par M. Jⁿ. Riffault; précédé D'une Introduction de M. C. L. Berthollet*, Paris, 1809, i, Intr., 20 f., 124–7.

[4] P. J. Hartog, *Nature*, 1894, l, 149; Ostwald, *J. Chem. Soc.*, 1904, 506; Ladenburg, *History of Chemistry*, 1905, 43 f.; Meldrum, *Manchester Mem.*, 1910, liv, No. 7; Partington, *Chymia*, 1948, i, 109.

[5] *Z. anorg. Chem.*, 1914, lxxxviii, 109.   [6] *Opuscula*, 1783, iii, 471.

[7] *Obs. Phys.*, 1778, xii, 135.   [8] *Recherches*, 1801, 36; tr., 1804, 75.

two alloys are formed, one containing a larger proportion of one metal and the second a larger proportion of the second metal, and he correctly compared these with the two immiscible solutions formed with water and ether.

In considering the compositions of neutral salts, Berthollet used the principle of the retention of neutrality on mixing solutions of neutral salts to show that the analyses of Kirwan, etc., are inaccurate,[1] a method previously used by Guyton de Morveau (see p. 528) and Richter (see p. 676). He said:[2]

'Cet état permanent de neutralisation, après les échanges de base qui se sont faits, paraîtrait annoncer que les acides ont des rapports constans de quantité, dans les sels neutres qu'ils forment, avec différentes bases alcaline ou terreuses.'

He mentions that Guyton had made several just and important reflexions on this matter, 'et il cite des observations de Richter dont je ne connais pas encore l'ouvrage' (see p. 528). Berthollet, therefore, concluded that alkaline and alkaline-earth salts (sulphates, muriates, etc.) have definite compositions. The same method was used later by Wollaston,[3] Thomson[4] and Murray.[5]

According to Hartog[6] the usual statement of the Law of Definite Proportions goes back to Davy:[7] 'in all well known compounds, the proportions of the elements are in certain definite ratios to each other'; or 'bodies when they form the same compound always combine in the same proportions, but they may likewise combine in different proportions, and they then form other compounds which are equally definite and invariable'. Hartog thought it should read: If two substances unite chemically, they will do so either in a single ratio or in a series of ratios which are separated by intervals of finite magnitude,[8] but this is unsatisfactory, since it would apply also to a series of solid solutions with limited miscibility.

Dalton's atomic theory and Wollaston's experiments (see p. 701) were criticised by Berthollet[9] and he maintained his theory of indefinite proportions in certain cases.[10] Ladenburg pointed out[11] that the work of Richter, Dalton's atomic theory, Gay-Lussac's law of gaseous volumes, and the work of Berzelius on combining proportions, had by then reinforced Proust's arguments, and nearly all chemists had returned to the view (held, for example, by Bergman) that chemical compounds were of definite composition. Most chemists decided in favour of Proust about 1808. Unfortunately, in rejecting Berthollet's law of indefinite proportions, they also put aside the correct law of mass action, which was not really incompatible with the law of constant proportions and the atomic theory. Chemists then were interested in other matters.[12] Probably the adoption of Dalton's atomic theory was at least as important as Proust's researches in the neglect of Berthollet's theory of variable proportions.[13]

[1] Mém. de l'Inst., 1806, vii, 229 f., 261 f.   [2] Ann. Chim., 1801, xxxviii, 3 (28–9).
[3] Phil. Trans., 1814, civ, 3.
[4] Attempt to Establish the First Principles of Chemistry by Experiment, 1825, i, 106, 200, etc.
[5] Elements of Chemistry, 6 ed., Edinburgh, 1828, i, 519.   [6] Nature, 1894, l, 149.
[7] Elements of Chemical Philosophy, 1812, 112; Works, 1840, IV, vii, 79.
[8] See Mallet, J. Chem. Soc., 1893, lxiii, 1; U. R. Evans, Trans. Faraday Soc., 1923, xix, 420.
[9] In Thomson, Système de Chimie, 1809, i, 21–27.   [10] Mém. Soc. Arcueil, 1809, ii, 470.
[11] History of Chemistry, 1905, 45.   [12] Ostwald, Lehrbuch, 1911, II, ii, 48.
[13] Kopp, (1), ii, 369 f.; R. A. Smith, Manchester Mem., 1856, xiii, 220 f.; Clarke, ib., 1903, xlvii, no. 11; Meldrum, ib., 1910, liv, no. 7.

Dalton[1] criticised Berthollet's 'very obscure view ... that chemical agency is proportional to the mass, and that in all chemical unions, there exist insensible gradations in the proportions of the constituent principles' as inconsistent 'both with reason and observation'. Other chemists were more favourable.

Chaptal[2] gave a clear summary of Berthollet's theory and its consequences, e.g. that salts which can exchange their components will separate from a mixture in solution in the order of their solubility. E. G. Fischer[3] found Berthollet's new view of chemical phenomena so convincing that it is impossible to maintain the old theory; and Karsten reported[4] several conversations with J. B. Richter, who agreed that many salts could be formed with a decided surplus of either ingredient. Gay-Lussac[5] thought the views of Berthollet and Proust could be reconciled by admitting with the former that 'in general we can obtain compounds in very variable proportions', but that 'chemical action is exerted more powerfully when the elements are in simple ratios or in multiple proportions among themselves, and that it then produces compounds which separate most easily'.

Avogadro[6] limited constant proportions to combinations of gases: in liquids and solids there may be more complicated ratios and even 'combination in all proportions'. Davy,[7] who says Berthollet first had 'distinct views of the relations of the force of attraction to quantity' and supposed that glasses and alloys were compounds in indefinite proportions, thought there 'appears no difficulty in reconciling the doctrine of definite proportions, with the influence of quantity', and Berzelius[8] agreed. Thomson, who had given a favourable opinion of Berthollet's law of mass action,[9] and had proposed a view identical with Davy's,[10] in a review of Davy's book[11] said that Berthollet's view of the division of one body between two others 'according to their rate of affinity for it, and that bodies are seldom or never thrown down in a state of absolute purity', are opposed by 'the knowledge of the determinate proportions in which all bodies combine'; yet all his views should not be condemned: 'he has succeeded in demonstrating the inaccuracy of many of the old notions of affinity ... though he has not been so fortunate in establishing his own.'

Murray[12] in a long and detailed account of Berthollet's teachings, thought: 'There can ... be little doubt of the truth of much of Berthollet's theory of complex affinity ... little room to doubt of the great influence of cohesion, elasticity, and proportion, in giving rise to the phenomena of single and double elective attractions'; but the question requires further investigation. Although there are many facts which do not agree with the theory of indefinite propor-

[1] New System, 1808, I, i, 142; Nicholson's J., 1811, xxviii, 81.
[2] Chemistry applied to Arts and Manufactures, London, 1807, i, 4 f.
[3] Allgem. J. Chem. (Scherer), 1801, vii, 503–25.
[4] Ib., 1803, x, 138–43.   [5] Mém. Soc. Arcueil, 1809, ii, 252.
[6] J. de Phys., 1811, lxxiii, 58; ACR, iv, 29, 51.
[7] Elements of Chemical Philosophy, 1812, 117–23.
[8] Ann. Phil., 1813, ii, 443; Traité de Chimie, 1831, iv, 587.
[9] (2), 1802, iii, 134, 143, 189 f., 199, 211 f., 215, 221, 224.
[10] (2), 1807, iv, 14.
[11] Ann. Phil., 1813, i, 371.   [12] 1806, i, 65 f., 83–131; Notes, 1–54.

tions, this is quite favourably received by Murray, who uses it throughout his book. Murray later[1] recognised that the doctrine, although true to a limited extent, 'is certainly erroneous when stated in such broad terms', since it is inconsistent with the well-established law that 'attraction is exerted between bodies with greater force, when they are in certain relative quantities . . . and . . . in a vast majority of cases, combination cannot be established between them in other proportions than these'. Metals, also, form a small number of definite oxides (but not necessarily two as Proust said), Berthollet's opinion being 'now generally abandoned'.[2]

W. Henry[3] gives a good summary of Berthollet's theory of mass action and combination in indefinite proportions and raises five objections against it:

(1) Pfaff[4] found that tartrate of lime and oxalate of lead are completely decomposed by adding just sufficient sulphuric acid to saturate the base.

(2) Berthollet's decomposition of sulphate of baryta by caustic potash was vitiated by the presence of carbonate in the latter.

(3) In some cases acid salts are formed, e.g. potassium hydrogen sulphate when nitric acid acts on sulphate of potash.

(4) In some cases decompositions occur which according to Berthollet should not, and sometimes they do not when they should.

(5) In some cases properties are supposed to operate before bodies are formed, e.g. the cohesion or insolubility of sulphate of baryta, the formation of which is the very thing to be explained.

'Notwithstanding these objections to the theory of Berthollet, when carried so far as has been done by its author, in the explanation of chemical phenomena, it must still be admitted that the extraneous forces, pointed out by that acute philosopher, have great influence in modifying the effects of chemical affinity.'

The theory was criticised by Thenard,[5] Chevreul,[6] and Daubeny,[7] on the ground that the effects of insolubility and volatility were supposed to be exerted[8] by a substance before it came into existence. Berzelius[9] pointed out that the law of mass action is not incompatible with the law of definite proportions.

When concentrated hydrochloric acid is added to a blue solution of copper sulphate, the colour becomes progressively green owing to the formation of copper chloride; if 100 parts of each acid divide 100 of oxide of copper between them so that the sulphuric acid takes 80 and the hydrochloric 20, 'the part of each acid really combined with the oxide is neutralised according to the law of constant proportions', whilst the rest of the acid is free, so that 'the surplus of each of these acids is employed in counterbalancing the surplus of its antagonist'. Berzelius thinks 'this single example is sufficient to show that the principle of Berthollet's theory is not inconsistent with the laws of chemical proportions', and the results of his experiments 'follow as necessary consequences from the views of the corpuscular theory'.

[1] Elements of Chemistry, 6 ed., Edinburgh, 1828, i, 49.   [2] Ib., ii, 126–7.
[3] Elements of Experimental Chemistry, 7 ed., 1815, i, 40–50; 9 ed., 1823, i, 57–72.
[4] Ann. Chim., 1811, lxxvii, 259.   [5] Traité de Chimie, 6 ed., 1836, v, 500 f.
[6] In Pelouze and Fremy, Cours de Chimie générale, 3 vols., Paris, 1848–50; 1850, iii, 875 f., 900.
[7] Atomic Theory, 2 ed., Oxford, 1850, 323.   [8] Berthollet, Stat. Chim., i, 18.
[9] Ann. Phil., 1813, ii, 443; Traité de Chimie, 1831, iv, 513, 586 f.

KLAPROTH

Martin Heinrich Klaproth (Wernigerode, Harz, 1 December 1743–Berlin, 1 January 1817) was from 1759 an apothecary in Quedlinburg. He began to study chemistry from books at Hannover (1766–8) and continued in Berlin (1768–70), where he was assistant in the pharmacy of Valentin Rose, the discoverer of Rose's fusible metal.[1] On the death of Rose, Klaproth took over the pharmacy and educated Rose's two sons, one of whom, Valentin Rose junr., became a chemist of note and collaborated with him.

From 1780, Klaproth published a large number of chemical researches, mainly in analytical chemistry, which was his speciality. In 1786 he opposed Lavoisier's theory,[2] but on 16 September 1792, he successfully repeated Lavoisier's experiments before the Berlin Academy of Science (of which he became a member in 1788); in consequence he adopted the new theory,[3] and was followed by other German chemists. Klaproth was Assessor of Pharmacy to the Collegium Medicum from 1782, professor of chemistry to the Royal Feldartilleriecorps from 1787, and to the Royal Artillerie Academie from 1791, member of the Obercollegium Medici et Sanitatis from 1799, and from its foundation in 1810 until his death he was the first professor of chemistry in the University of Berlin.

Berzelius found Klaproth rather brusque and harsh but Thomson says he was pleasant and rather fond of a joke. He was very conscientious and religious and had many trials which he took calmly and met with fortitude.[4]

Most of Klaproth's numerous publications were collected in his *Beiträge* (I below); he also wrote (II) a good *Dictionary of Chemistry* with Friedrich Benjamin Wolff, professor in the Joachimsthal Gymnasium (Lissa, 7 September 1766–Berlin, 19 January 1845).

I. Klaproth, Beiträge zur chemischen Kenntniss der Mineralkörper, 6 vols. 8°, Posen and Berlin, 1795, 1797, 1802, 1807, 1810; vi with sep. title, Chemische Abhandlungen gemischten Inhalts, Berlin and Stettin, 1815;
IA. English tr. (vol. i and ii only) Analytical Essays towards promoting the Knowledge of Mineral Substances, 2 vols., London, 1801–4;
IB. French tr. by B. M. Tassaert, Mémoires de Chimie, 2 vols., Paris, 1807 (iv ll., 490 pp., i l. errata; ii ll., 476 pp., ii ll.).
II. M. H. Klaproth and F. B. Wolff, Chemisches Wörterbuch, 5 vols., Berlin, 1807–10; supplement, 4 vols., Berlin, 1816–19; first 5 vols. tr. by E. Bouillon-Lagrange and H. A. Vogel, Dictionnaire de Chimie, with portr. of Klaproth, 4 vols., Paris, 1810–11 (Nourry-Thiébaud, *Cat.* 66 (1938), no. 886).
III. Observations relative to the Mineralogical and Chemical History of the Fossils of Cornwall, tr. from the German by J. G. Groschke, London, 1787 (pp. viii, 81, 1 coloured plate).

In 1782 Klaproth investigated two quack remedies (Bestucheff's nerve tincture and Lamott's gold drops, really the same) and found them to be

---

[1] See p. 659.   [2] Crell's *Ann.*, 1786, I, 202; Hermbstädt, *ib.*, 1792, II, 209.
[3] Hermbstädt, *J. der Physik*, 1792, vi, 422.
[4] Berzelius, Selbstbiographische Aufzeichnungen, Kahlbaum's *Monographien*, 1903, vii, 37; Dann, *Pharm. Ztg.*, 1927, lxxii, 549; 1936, lxxxi, 661; Diergart, *Z. angew. Chem.*, 1920, xxxiii, I, 299; Gmelin, (1), iii, 707; Kopp, (1), i, 343; R. Meyer, *Z. angew. Chem.*, 1921, xxxiv, I, 1; Poggendorff, (1), i, 1266; Stöckigt, *Chem. Ztg.*, 1917, xli, 49; Thomson, (1), ii, 136, 192; O. F. Zekert, *Martin H. Klaproth*, Vienna, 1922 (not seen).

solutions of ferric chloride in alcohol.[1] The solutions are reduced to the ferrous state on exposure to sunlight, a reaction later investigated by Grotthuss (see Vol. IV). In 1790 Klaproth analysed the Karlsbad mineral water.[2] Klaproth introduced the practice of drying precipitates to constant weight, igniting if possible, and giving the details of quantitative analyses as actually obtained without rounding them off so as to total 100 per cent. His analyses of minerals are usually more accurate than those of Vauquelin (although chemists did not think so at the time) and led him to the discovery of a few, and the rediscovery of several, new elements.

He introduced fusion with caustic potash in a silver crucible in mineral analysis (1790),[3] and determined alkalis in silicates by fusion with barium nitrate.[4]

The German weights used by most chemists were the Apothecaries' or Nürnberg medicinal weights, divided as follows:

20 grains = 1 scruple	8 drachms = 1 ounce
3 scruples = 1 drachm	12 ounces = 1 pound

as in the English system but the standard pounds are different, and to reduce Nürnberg weights to English they are multiplied by 0·959266. Another system used was the Cologne mark = 8 ounces, 1 oz. = 2 loth, 1 loth = 4 quentchen, 1 quentchen = 4 pfennige, 1 pfennig = 2 heller = 17 eschen = 19 as = 256 richt-pfennige (Richtpfennig or denarius directorius). The Cologne oz. = 0·939018 English Troy oz., the mark = 7·512144 English Troy oz.[5] In Klaproth's publications 1 Unze = 29·23 grams, 1 Gran = 0·061 gram. His weighings are usually accurate to $\frac{1}{2}$ grain, sometimes $\frac{1}{4}$ or $\frac{1}{8}$, and the totals are, for silicates, 1 or 2 per cent low. That for the mineral lepidolite was $6\frac{1}{2}$ per cent short, and he missed the lithium content.[6]

Klaproth discovered the elements uranium and zirconium in the form of oxides. Uranium was discovered in the ore pitchblende (Pechblende) from Joachimsthal in Bohemia and Johann-Georgenstadt in the Saxon Erzgebirge, which had been characterised by B. C. R. Werner. Klaproth found that the solution in acid gives a yellow precipitate with alkali carbonate, soluble in excess. He obtained crystalline yellow uranyl nitrate and acetate, the precipitated phosphate, and the oxide. What he thought was the metal was a lower oxide. He named the element 'Uranium, zu einigem Andenken, dass die chemische Auffindung dieses neuen Metallkörpers in die Epoche der astronomischen Entdeckung des Planeten Uranus gefallen sei'.[7]

[1] Selle, *Neue Beiträge zur Natur-und Arzenei-Wissenschaft*, Berlin, 1782, i, 137; on these remedies, see Model, *Récréations Physiques*, etc., tr. Parmentier, Paris, 1774, i, 362 f.
[2] *Chemische Untersuchung der Mineralquellen zu Karlsbad*, Berlin, 1790.
[3] I, 1795, i, 45.
[4] I, iv, 241 (see Rose, p. 659).
[5] Gren, 1794, i, 124; Guyton de Morveau, *Ann. Chim.*, 1799, xxxii, 225; Thomson, *Ann. Phil.*, 1813, i, 452.
[6] I, i, 279.
[7] *Beobachtungen und Entdeckungen aus der Naturkunde von der Gesellschaft der Naturforschenden Freunde zu Berlin*, Berlin, 1789, iii, 373 (Kurze Anzeige eines neuentdeckten Halbmetalles); *Obs. Phys.*, 1790, xxxvi, 248 (de l'uranit); *Mém. Acad. Berlin*, 1786–7 (1792), 160 (sur l'urane); Klaproth, I, ii, 197.

He discovered zirconium dioxide (zirconia) in Ceylon and Norwegian zircon (1789).[1] Independently of Gregor (1789) he rediscovered titanium dioxide in rutile (Hungarian red schörl; titanite) and ilmenite (menakanit, titaneisen) (1795–7), recognising it as an oxide of a metal which he called titanium.[2] Gregor[3] had really discovered titanium dioxide before Klaproth. William Gregor (Bristol, 1762–Creed, Cornwall, 11 June 1817) was a parish priest,[4] who also analysed wavellite (missing the fluorine) and uranium mica[5] and a zinc ore.[6]

Klaproth confirmed the existence of strontia (1793–4). A peculiar mineral from a lead mine in Strontian, Argyllshire, was brought to Edinburgh about 1787 and examined by Crawford and Cruickshank, who showed quite decisively that it contained a peculiar earth different from baryta.[7] It was independently examined by Hope in 1791, his paper being read to the Glasgow College Literary Society in March 1792, and to the Royal Society of Edinburgh on 4 November 1793.[8] Hope showed by many careful experiments that the mineral was the carbonate of a new earth which he called *strontites*. Klaproth independently examined it in 1793 and came to the same conclusion as Hope, whose paper was not then published.[9] He called the earth *strontian*. Kirwan, who had received a specimen of the mineral from Crawford, also discovered the main properties of the new earth in 1793;[10] his paper, read to the Irish Academy in 1794, was published in full in 1795.[11] Pelletier[12] and Fourcroy and Vauquelin[13] confirmed these results.

In a packet of Hope's lecture notes in the Edinburgh University Library (the Hope Papers) he says of strontia: 'Several chemists had thrown out the suggestion that it was a distinct earth. In 1792 I satisfied myself by a long investigation that it was so.' Haüy[14] had recognised the different crystalline forms of celestine (strontium sulphate) and barytes (barium sulphate) before the discovery of strontia. Strontianite was analysed by Schmeisser.[15]

Klaproth established the identity of tellurium (Latin *tellus*, the earth).[16] Tellurium alloyed with gold had been found in Transylvania and called

[1] I, i, 203 (Zirconerde, terra circonia); *ib.*, iii, 266; IA, i, 175; ii, 211 (jargonia).
[2] I, 1795, i, 233, 245; 1797, ii, 226 (ment. Gregor); IA, i, 200, 211, 496, 499.
[3] Crell's *Ann.*, 1791, I, 55 (Beobachtungen und Versuche über den Menakanit, einen in Cornwall (Kirchspiel Menaccan bei Falmouth) gefundenen magnetischen Sand); the discovery was made in 1789.
[4] J. A. Paris, *A Memoir of the Life and Scientific Labours of the Late Rev. William Gregor, A.M.*, London, 1818; *Ann. Phil.*, 1818, xi, 112.
[5] *Phil. Trans.*, 1805, xcv, 331.   [6] *Trans. Geol. Soc. Cornwall*, 1822, iii, 338.
[7] Crawford, *Medical Communications* (of the Society for Promoting Medical Knowledge), 1790, ii, 301 (On the Medicinal Properties of Muriated Barytes).
[8] *Trans. Roy. Soc. Edin.*, 1794, iii, h 141 (summary); 1798, iv, 3 (in full).
[9] Klaproth, Crell's *Ann.*, 1793, II, 189; 1794, I, 99; I, i, 260; ii, 84, 92.
[10] Crell's *Ann.*, 1795, II, 119, 205.
[11] *Trans. Roy. Irish Academy*, Dublin [1794], v, 243 (the volume is undated); see Ch. Coquebert, *J. des Mines*, No. V, 1794–5 (An III), 61–81 (Sur le witherite et le strontianite); Partington, *Ann. Sci.*, 1942, v, 157; 1951, vii, 95.
[12] *Ann. Chim.*, 1797, xxi, 113; *Mémoires et Observations de Chimie*, 1798, ii, 435 (at first he thought it was barytes, *ib.*, i, 386, ii, 437).
[13] *Ann. Chim.*, 1797, xxi, 276.   [14] *Ann. Chim.*, 1792, xii, 3.
[15] *Phil. Trans.*, 1794, lxxxiv, 418.
[16] *Mém. Acad. Berlin*, 1798 (1801), 117 ('ein neues eigenthümliches Metall, welchem ich, den von der alten Mutter Erde entlehnten Namen Tellurium beilege'); I, 1802, iii, 1; IA, 1804, ii, 1; *Phil. Mag.*, 1798, i, 78–82.

aurum paradoxicum, aurum album, or *aurum problematicum* by mineralogists. The name *sylvanite* was introduced for it by Kirwan.[1] Franz Joseph Müller von Reichenstein (Vienna; 1740–1825) in 1782 concluded that native tellurium was a peculiar metal, similar to but different from antimony and bismuth.[2] Bergman, to whom he sent a specimen, decided that it was not antimony.[3]

According to Tokody[4] tellurium was discovered by the Hungarian chemist Paul Kitaibel in 1788, in a mineral wehrlite (argentiferous bismuth telluride). Kitaibel reported his results to Klaproth; after Klaproth's publication a correspondence between them ensued, the letters being in the Hungarian National Museum.[5]

Paul Kitaibel (Mattersdorf, Hungary, 3 February 1757–Budapest, 13 December 1817 (or 1818); other dates are given) was professor of chemistry and botany (1802–1811), then of botany and director of the Botanic Garden in Buda Pest. He never lectured and made (at the cost of the University) extensive scientific travels in Hungary. He is said to have discovered solid chloride of lime, hydroferrocyanic acid, platinum black, and metallic soaps.[6]

An examination of the red Siberian lead ore led Klaproth to the rediscovery of chromium[7] independently of Vauquelin (see p. 553). He investigated gadolinite (1800),[8] and determined the properties of yttria and beryllia;[9] he adopted the name Beryllerde[10] which he says had already been recommended by Link[11] instead of Vauquelin's name (Glykine, Süsserde) (see p. 553). Klaproth discovered ceria ('ochroïte', from its colour), which he regarded as an earth,[12] independently of Berzelius (see Vol. IV), who regarded it as the oxide of a metal, cerium. Berzelius sent his paper to Gehlen for publication and was told that Klaproth's was to be published in the next number of the *Journal*, Berzelius and Hisinger's appearing in the following number.[13]

Klaproth found that precipitated alumina is soluble in caustic potash (1789).[14] He proved by analysis that anhydrite (then called muriacite) is calcium sulphate free from water[15] and that calcite and aragonite are two different crystalline forms of calcium carbonate;[16] and confirmed that 'bitter spar' (dolomite) is a compound of calcium and magnesium carbonates.[17]

[1] *Elements of Mineralogy,* 1796, ii, 324.
[2] Versuch mit dem in der Grube Mariahilf in dem Gebirge Fazebay bei Salatna vorkommenden vermeinten Spiessglaskönig, in von Born, *Physikalische Arbeiten der einträchtigen Freunde in Wien,* 1783–5, stück i–iii, q. in Abegg, *Handbuch der anorganischen Chemie,* 1927, IV, i, 918; Weeks, *Discovery of the Elements,* 1956, 304; Mellor, xi, 3, gives Born, *Lythophylacium Bornianum,* Prag, 1772, i, 68, but this seems to be too early.
[3] Thomson, (2), 1807, i, 311.
[4] *Centralblatt für Mineralogie, Geologie und Paläontologie,* Stuttgart, 1929, A, 114.
[5] Stöckigt, *Chem. Ztg.,* 1917, xli, 49 (Kitaibel); *J. Chem.* (Gehlen), 1803, i, 460.
[6] L. von Szathmáry, *Chem. Ztg.,* 1931, lv, 645, 784; *id., Chemische Apparatur,* Leipzig, 1932, xix, 49–50; Weeks, *Discovery of the Elements,* 1956, 321–37.
[7] Crell's *Ann.,* 1798, I, 80.
[8] *Mém. Acad. Berlin,* 1801, 13; Klaproth, I, 1802, iii, 52; IA, 1804, ii, 40.
[9] I, iii, 215.   [10] I, iii, 79.   [11] *J. der Chemie* (Scherer), 1799, iii, 603.
[12] *N. Allgem. J. Chem.* (Gehlen), 1804, ii, 303, also describing potassium cerium sulphate; *Mém. Acad. Berlin,* 1804 (1807), 155; I, 1807, iv, 140.
[13] *Ib.,* 397; Berzelius, *Selbstbiographische Aufzeichnungen,* 1903, 37.
[14] I, i, 47; IA, i, 43.   [15] I, i, 307; iv, 224.
[16] *Bergmännische Journal,* 1788, i, 294.
[17] I, i, 300; iv, 204, 236; IA, i, 256; ii, 237; Woulfe, *Phil. Trans.,* 1779, lxix, 11 ('compound spar').

Klaproth analysed datolith,[1] gypsum,[2] and barytes.[3] He missed the fluorine content of apatite,[4] which was detected by Pelletier,[5] but he detected sodium in cryolite[6] and the fluorine content of teeth and fossil ivory,[7] confirmed by Berzelius.[8] He showed that native iron is free from nickel,[9] which is contained in meteoric iron,[10] and analysed chrome ironstone.[11] He described the manufacture of alum at Tolfa.[12] He confirmed (1801)[13] an observation of Kennedy of Edinburgh (1797)[14] that basalt contains soda, and discovered potash (previously regarded as confined to the vegetable kingdom) in the mineral leucite (1797).[15] He made many analyses of ancient metal objects[16] and glazes.[17]

Klaproth also investigated brown coal,[18] green earth,[19] fahl-ore,[20] Graugiltigerz,[21] antimony-lead ore,[22] cinnabar,[23] and made quantitative analyses of sulphate of potash[24] and alum shale.[25] He showed (1799) that the mineral honeystone (mellitite) found in the coal beds of Thuringia, and called Honigstein by Werner in 1790, is the aluminium salt of a peculiar organic acid, mellitic acid (acidum mellilithicum).[26] He investigated the elastic bitumen (mineral caoutchouc) of Derbyshire,[27] found uric acid combined with ammonia in guano from Peru,[28] and rediscovered ulmin (discovered in 1797 by Vauquelin) in a black excrescence on the elm tree.[29] Ulmin was investigated by T. Thomson,[30] and Döbereiner obtained it by exposing a solution of pyrogallic acid in ammonia to oxygen gas and precipitating with acid.[31]

From a saline exudation on the bark of a tree of the white mulberry (*Morus alba*) in Palermo, Klaproth obtained a small quantity of what he called moroxylic acid;[32] it is not identifiable. He prepared ethyl chloride by the action of stannic chloride on alcohol,[33] confirming the observation of the Marquis de Courtanvaux (1762).[34]

[1] *N. Allgem. J. Chem.*, 1806, vi, 107.   [2] *Ib.*, 1804, ii, 355.
[3] *Ib.*, 1805, v, 509.   [4] I, v, 180; Thomson, (2), 1807, iv, 392.
[5] *Mémoires*, 1798, i, 381.   [6] I, iii, 207; Thomson, (2), 1807, iv, 407.
[7] *N. Allgem. J. Chem.*, 1804, iii, 625; I, vi, 214.
[8] *J. Chem. Phys.*, 1807, iii, 2.   [9] I, iv, 98.
[10] *N. Allgem. J. Chem.*, 1803, i, 3–77; *J. Chem. Phys.*, 1809, viii, 461.
[11] *J. Chem. Phys.*, 1806, i, 189.   [12] *N. Allgem. J. Chem.*, 1806, vi, 35.
[13] I, iii, 245; IA, ii, 195.
[14] *Trans. Roy. Soc. Edin.*, 1798 (1805), v, 76: heated with sulphuric acid and obtained sodium sulphate.
[15] I, ii, 39; IA, i, 348.
[16] *Allgem. J. Chem.*, 1801, vi, 227, 245; I, 1815, vi, 21 f.; Caley, *J. Chem. Educ.*, 1949, xxvi, 242.
[17] I, 1815, vi, 136.   [18] *N. Allgem. J. Chem.*, 1803, i, 471.
[19] *Ib.*, 1803, i, 656.   [20] *Ib.*, 1805, v, 3.
[21] *Ib.*, 1805, v, 14.   [22] *Ib.*, 1805, v, 31.
[23] *Ib.*, 1805, v, 432, 437.   [24] *Ib.*, 1805, v, 509.
[25] *Ib.*, 1806, vi, 35.
[26] *Allgem. J. Chem.* (Scherer), 1799, iii, 461; *Mém. Acad. Berlin*, 1801, 3; I, iii, 114; confirmed by Vauquelin, *Ann. Chim.*, 1801, xxxvi, 203; Fourcroy, *Philosophie Chimique*, 1806, 250, called the mellitates 'honigstates'.
[27] I, iii, 107; IA, ii, 83.   [28] I, iv, 299.
[29] *Mém. Acad. Berlin*, 1802 (1804), 21; *N. Allgem. J. Chem.*, 1805, iv, 329; I, vi, 195.
[30] *Ann. Phil.*, 1813, i, 23; 1813, ii, 11.
[31] *Ann. Phys.*, 1822, lxxii, 203; 1823, lxxiv, 410; Murray, *Elements of Chemistry*, 1828, ii, 487.
[32] *Allgem. J. Chem.*, 1803, x, 1; *Nicholson's J.*, 1804, vii, 129; I, vi, 186.
[33] Crell's *Ann.*, 1796, I, 99.   [34] AdS, *Mém. div. Sav.*, 1768, v, 19.

VALENTIN ROSE

Klaproth was associated with Valentin Rose junr. (Berlin; 31 October 1762–10 August 1807), apothecary and from 1797 assessor in the Ober-Collegium-Medicum, Berlin. He found chromium in Saxony serpentine,[1] proved that 'sulphuric ether' contains no sulphuric acid,[2] discovered sodium bicarbonate[3] independently of Hermbstädt (see p. 579) and Berthollet,[4] used barium carbonate in the fusion analysis of felspar (containing silica and potash),[5] made quantitative analyses of chlorides,[6] determined the composition of phosphoric acid[7] and barium sulphate,[8] introduced the method of extracting arsenic by boiling dilute alkali in toxicological analysis,[9] investigated Berthollet's experiments on the action of carbon dioxide on lime water and baryta water,[10] and characterised pyrotartaric acid,[11] confirming Guyton de Morveau's[12] conclusion that it is a definite acid and disproving the statement of Fourcroy and Vauquelin[13] that it is impure acetic acid. Rose remarked that a second distinct acid seems to be formed in the distillation of tartaric acid; this was later isolated by Berzelius who called it pyruvic acid.[14] Rose discovered a substance analogous to starch in the root of elcampane (*Inula helenium*),[15] and named *inulin* by Thomson.[16] Valentin Rose senr., father of the above (Neu-Ruppin, 16 August 1736–Berlin, 28 April 1771) was a pupil of Marggraf, an apothecary in Berlin and from 1770 assessor in the Ober-Collegium-Medicum there. He invented the fusible alloy of bismuth, tin, and lead named after him 'Rose's metal'.[17]

STROMEYER

Another excellent quantitative worker, who also (like Klaproth) made many analyses of minerals, was Friedrich Stromeyer (Göttingen; 2 August 1776–18 August 1835), a pupil of Vauquelin who first studied botany. He became professor of chemistry in Göttingen in 1810.[18] He wrote books on chemistry[19] and published a number of important investigations. He showed that aragonite is a definite crystalline form of calcium carbonate and is not necessarily contaminated with strontium,[20] and recommended starch as a reagent for free

[1] *Allgem. J. Chem.*, 1800, iv, 307. [2] *Ib.*, 1800, iv, 253.
[3] *Ib.*, 1801, vi, 50. [4] AdS, *Mém. de l'Inst.*, 1806, 229; *Ann. Chim.*, 1808, lxv, 316.
[5] *Allgem. J. Chem.*, 1802, viii, 227. [6] *Ib.*, 1806, vi, 22.
[7] *J. Chem. Phys.*, 1806, ii, 309. [8] *Ib.*, 1807, iii, 322.
[9] *Ib.*, 1806, ii, 665. [10] *Ib.*, 1807, iii, 546.
[11] *Ib.*, 1807, iii, 598. [12] *Ency. Méthod., Chymie*, 1786, i, 316.
[13] *Ann. Chim.*, 1800, xxxv, 16. [14] *Ann. Phys.*, 1835, xxxvi, 1.
[15] *Allgem. J. Chem.*, 1804, iii, 217; *Nicholson's J.*, 1805, xii, 97. [16] (2), 1807, v, 54.
[17] *Stralsundisches Magazin*, Berlin, 1776, ii, Stück I, Abhl. 3 (BM 965. d. 1–2; 2 vols., 1767–1776); Gmelin, (1), iii, 519.
[18] Prandtl, *Deutsche Chemiker*, 1956, 153 (portr.).
[19] *Tabellarische Uebersicht der chemischen einfachen und zusammengesetzten Stoffe*, 1806 (Kopp, (1), iv, 124); *Grundriss der theoretischen Chemie*, 2 vols., Göttingen, 1808; *Untersuchungen über die Mischung der Mineralkörper und anderer damit verwandter Substanzen*, Göttingen, 1821 (458 pp.).
[20] *Comment. Gott.*, 1811–13, ii; *Ann. Chim.*, 1814, xcii, 254; *J. Chem.* (Schweigger), 1815, xiii, 362 (with Hausmann), 490; Laugier, *J. des Mines*, 1814, xxxvi, 313; *id.*, *Ann. des Mines*, 1818, iii, 113; Döbereiner, *J. Chem. Phys.*, 1814, x, 217; and Bucholz and Meissner, *J. Chem. Phys.*, 1815, xiii, 1, all found that aragonite may be almost or quite free from strontium.

iodine (1815);[1] the blue colour was first mentioned by Colin and Gaultier de Claubry.[2] Stromeyer investigated arsenic hydride,[3] polyhalite[4] and bismuthates.[5] In the autumn of 1817 he discovered cadmium in a yellow specimen of zinc oxide which was free from iron, and also in metallic zinc.[6] K. S. L. Hermann in Schönebeck also discovered cadmium in May 1818, in a pharmaceutical sample of zinc oxide confiscated at Magdeburg because its solution in acid gave a yellow precipitate with hydrogen sulphide, wrongly attributed to arsenic.[7] Meissner[8] and Roloff[9] confirmed this, and Karsten[10] found it in Silesian zinc ore. Stromeyer published a complete account of the metal, which he called cadmium from the old name for zinc ore or zinc oxide, $\kappa\alpha\delta\mu\epsilon\iota\alpha$, used by Dioskourides (see Vol. I).

KIRWAN

Richard Kirwan (Cloughballymore, Co. Galway, 1 August 1733–Dublin, 22 June 1812) was of English ancestry, the family existing in the time of Henry VI. He studied law in the University of Poictiers for four years from 1750, also reading books on chemistry, then in England and Germany in 1761–6. He was called to the bar in 1766 and practised in London without much success, and changed to Dublin in 1772. He was back in London in 1777 and became F.R.S. in 1780. Most of his chemical work was done in his house at 11 Newman Street, London. He returned to Dublin in 1787 and in 1799 became President of the Royal Irish Academy there, holding office until 1812. Kirwan was at first a Catholic (a Jesuit novitiate in 1764) but became a Protestant. He was a brilliant but eccentric man. On account of his delicate health, he wore his hat and overcoat indoors (as shown in his portrait in the Royal Dublin Society) and because of a weak throat lived on ham and milk. He kept a pet eagle. Kirwan was well known to scientists in Great Britain and Ireland and also on the Continent, and in his time was a man of international reputation. He declined a baronetcy offered him by Lord Castlereagh. Kirwan's first library was captured at sea on the way from Galway to London and disposed of by the privateer captain to the town of Salem, Mass., where it still exists. His second library is mostly in the Royal Irish Academy in Dublin; practically all the title-pagers of the books have the paper cut away to leave the title, author's name, etc., only, and marked in red.[11] Besides scientific papers he published

[1] *Ann. Phys.*, 1815, xlix, 146 (letter to Gilbert).
[2] *Ann. Chim.*, 1814, xc, 87; Andrews and Goettsch, *J. Amer. Chem. Soc.*, 1902, xxiv, 865 (bibl.).
[3] *Comment. Gott.*, 1804–8 (1805), xvi, 141.
[4] *Comment. Gott.*, 1816–18 (1820), iv, 139.   [5] *Ann. Phys.*, 1832, xxvi, 548.
[6] *J. Chem.* (Schweigger), 1817, xxi, 297; 1818, xxii, 362; *Ann. Phys.*, 1819, lx, 193; *Ann. Phil.*, 1819, xiv, 269.
[7] *Ann. Phys.*, 1818, lix, 95, 113 (letter from Stromeyer); 1820, lxvi, 276.
[8] *Ann. Phys.*, 1818, lix, 99.   [9] *Ann. Phys.*, 1822, lxx, 194.
[10] *Archiv für Bergbau und Hüttenwesen*, 1818, i, 209; Herapath, *Ann. Phil.*, 1822, iii, 435.
[11] Agnes M. Clerke, DNB, 1892, xxxi, 228; D. Crowley, *J. Roy. Inst. Chem.*, 1958, lxxxii, 10 (portr.); T. Dillon, *Institute of Chemistry of Ireland Journal*, 1955–6, iv, 11; Donovan, *Proc. Roy. Irish Acad.*, 1847–50 (1850), iv, 480, and Appendix VIII, lxxxi–xcviii (portr.); McLaughlin, *Studies. An Irish Quarterly Review*, Dublin, 1939, xxviii, 461, 593; 1940, xxix, 71, 281; *Phil. Mag.*, 1802, xiv, 353 (frontisp.); Reilly and O'Flynn, *Isis*, 1930, xiii, 298 (portr.); Thomson, (1), i, 347; ii, 137; *id.*, (3), 483; *id.*, *Ann. Phil.*, 1818, xi, 435–6.

FIG. 53. RICHARD KIRWAN (1733–1812).

dissertations on Happiness and on the Origin of Polytheism, Idolatry, and Greek Mythology.[1]

Kirwan drew up the first table of (43) specific heats on the basis of water $= 1$ in 1780.[2] Kirwan's book on mineralogy[3] is based on the 733 specimens in the Leskean Collection.[4] The Leskean Collection of minerals and rocks had belonged to Werner and on his death came into the possession of N. G. Leske (1757–86), professor in Leipzig and Marburg, from whom it was purchased by a grant from the Irish Parliament on the representation of Kirwan. It still exists, but when I saw it the specimens had been partly thrown away and the rest distributed, and some I asked to see could not be traced.

A hardness scale for minerals proposed by Qvist[5] is given by Kirwan with some additions;[6] a shorter table proposed by Mohs[7] is the one now in use.

Kirwan[8] criticised the geological theory of James Hutton,[9] who thereupon expanded his paper into a book of three volumes.[10] Kirwan replied[11] in a temperate and objective way, pointing out that many of Hutton's ideas were inconsistent with chemical facts, e.g. Hutton supposed that iron pyrites could not be formed from aqueous solution but must have had an igneous origin. Kirwan's criticisms seem to have offended Hutton's admirers.

One of Kirwan's most interesting books is his defence of the phlogiston theory:

I. An Essay on Phlogiston and the Constitution of Acids, 8°, London, 1784 (146 pp.), 2 ed. 1789.
II. An Essay on Phlogiston, and the Constitution of Acids. A New Edition. To which are added, Notes Exhibiting and defending the Antiphlogistic Theory; and annexed to the French Edition of this Work; by Messrs. de Morveau, Lavoisier, de la Place, Monge, Berthollet, and de Fourcroy: Translated into English. With additional Remarks and Replies, By the Author, London, 1789 (xviii, 317 pp.).
III. French tr. of I: Essai sur le Phlogistique, et sur la Constitution des Acides, traduit, avec des Notes de MM. de Morveau, Lavoisier, de la Place, Monge, Berthollet, et de Fourcroy, Paris, 1788 (a long summary in Fourcroy, (2), iii, 546–60); the tr. is by Mme. Lavoisier (Grimaux, *Lavoisier*, 1888, 124) and Lavoisier,

---

[1] *Trans. Roy. Irish Acad.*, 1810, xi.

[2] In J. H. de Magellan, *Essai sur la Nouvelle Théorie du Feu Élémentaire, et de la Chaleur des Corps*, London, 1780, 177; Murray, 1806, i, 373 says: 'with regard to these there is considerable obscurity. A number of them are those which were given by Dr. Crawford, in the first edition of his work on heat, and which he afterwards corrected as being erroneous. But there are also several others ... to be presumed ... ascertained by Mr. Kirwan; though ... this is not certain.'

[3] *Elements of Mineralogy*, 8°, London, 1784 (xviii, 412 pp., vi ll. index); 2 enlarged ed., 2 vols., London, 1794–6; tr. by Gibelin, *Élémens de Minéralogie*, Paris, 1785 (xlviii, 432 pp.).

[4] D. L. G. Karsten, *Museum Leskeanum*, 2 vols., Leipzig, 1789; ii, *Regnum Minerale*. See McLaughlin, *Studies*, 1940, xxix, 281; A. G. Werner, *New Theory of the Formation of Veins; with its Application to the Art of Working Mines*, tr. with an Appendix and notes by Charles Anderson, M.D., Edinburgh, 1809.

[5] KAH, 1768, xxix, 55.

[6] *Elements of Mineralogy*, 1784, 171; 1794, i, 38; Grailich and Pekárek, *Wien Ber.*, 1854, xiii, 410.

[7] *Grundriss der Mineralogie*, 2 vols., Dresden, 1822–4; tr. Haidinger, *Treatise on Mineralogy*, 3 vols., Edinburgh, 1825, i, 300; Partington, *Advanced Treatise on Physical Chemistry*, 1952, iii, 231.

[8] *Trans. Roy. Irish Acad.*, 1793, v, 51–81 (Examination of the Supposed Igneous Origin of Stony Substances), read February, 1793.

[9] *Trans. Roy. Soc. Edin.*, 1788, i, 209–304.

[10] *Theory of the Earth*, 1795; Wightman, *The Growth of Scientific Ideas*, Edinburgh, 1950, 398.

[11] *Geological Essays*, London, 1799 (pp. xvi, 502); Essay x, p. 433.

Berthollet, Guyton de Morveau, Fourcroy, and Monge added copious refutations. Kirwan reissued his book as II, the French additions in III being translated by William Nicholson and added, together with short 'Remarks upon the Annotations', by Kirwan.

IV. German tr. by Crell: Versuche und Beobachtungen über die specifische Schwere und die Anziehungskraft verschiedener Salzarten, und über die wahre neuentdeckte Natur des Phlogistons, 2 vols., Berlin, 1783-5.

Kirwan supposed that the basis of inflammable air (hydrogen) is identical with phlogiston.[1] Just as fixed air exists in a free and fixed state, so does phlogiston, but the latter when free is combined with elementary fire to form inflammable air. On dissolving a metal in acid, a 'double decomposition' takes place, 'the dissolving acid yielding its fire to the phlogiston, which then assumes an aërial form, while the phlogiston yields the metallic earth to the acid.' The evolution of heat is due to some fire being set free, to the combination of some phlogiston with the acid, so setting free some of the specific fire of the acid, and to the union of some of the phlogiston to the surrounding atmosphere, setting free part of its specific fire (1782). Kirwan brings forward the following arguments in support of the identity of phlogiston and inflammable air:

(i) Metals which dissolve in acids with evolution of inflammable air displace other metals from solutions of their salts without evolution of this air (see De la Metherie, p. 494);

(ii) calces are reduced to metals by heating in inflammable air, which they visibly absorb (Priestley);

(iii) inflammable air is expelled by heating metals (iron and zinc) in vacuo, — at least with the assistance of moisture (Priestley; Kirwan, 1787);

(iv) calces are never restored to metals except by substances containing the inflammable principle;

(v) inflammable air converts vitriolic acid into sulphur when the concentrated acid is distilled with iron or bismuth, the inflammable air being, 'as Dr. Priestley elegantly expresses it, in its nascent state, before it acquires its whole quantity of specific fire.'

The objection to supposing that phlogiston in inflammable air is combined with some other substance (acid, earth or respirable air) is that the same inflammable air is formed 'from all heterogeneous substances which no way contribute to its inflammability'. It is also set free by alkalis from metals.[2] Kirwan thus assumes that 'inflammable air is nothing else than phlogiston thrown into a fluid form by elementary fire'. When phlogiston is combined with still more fire and is considerably rarefied, it probably constitutes the electric fluid (1783). Metals on calcination:

'lose their phlogiston, which is nothing else but pure inflammable air in a concrete state, and at the same time unite most commonly to fixed air, formed during the

---

[1] *Phil. Trans.*, 1782, lxxii, 179; 1783, lxxiii, 15; I, 1787, 94; II, 1789, 38, 166; Arejula, *Obs. Phys.*, 1788, xxxiii, 273, pointed out that De la Metherie, *Obs. Phys.*, 1781, xviii, 156, 224, 310; 1782, xix, 16, had already identified phlogiston with inflammable air; but this actually goes back to Cavendish (1766; see p. 314).

[2] Lassone, AdS, 1776, h 29, m 686.

operation, but sometimes some of them unite to water and other substances, by whose means they are calcined. The calces of the perfect metals may therefore be reduced by the decomposition of their fixed air, and those of the imperfect, and semi-metals, partly by the decomposition of their fixed air, and partly by its expulsion, and that of the other foreign bodies they had absorbed, and their simultaneous reunion to the inflammable principle.'[1]

Kirwan's paper of 1783 contains corrections of several erroneous experiments of Priestley on inflammable air, e.g. its supposed conversion into common air by agitation with water, but Kirwan was mistaken in supposing that fixed air (carbon dioxide) is formed in the calcination of metals. In 1791 Kirwan[2] attacked the 'logic' of the antiphlogistic theory, but he announced his conversion to Lavoisier's views in a letter to Berthollet, of 26 January 1791,[3] after the publication of the refutation of the theory in his book by the French chemists (see III, p. 662). In a letter to Crell[4] Kirwan says his chief reason for abandoning the phlogiston theory was that: 'I know of no single clear decisive experiment by which one can establish that fixed air is composed of oxygen and phlogiston, and without this proof it seems to me impossible to prove the presence of phlogiston in metals, sulphur or nitrogen (Saltpeter-luft).' Kirwan criticised Cavendish's paper on 'Experiments on Air' (see p. 338).[5]

Many of the arguments used by Kirwan in his *Essay on Phlogiston* depend on apparent contradictions between reactions postulated by the antiphlogistic theory and the regular order of affinities of substances. De Morveau says[6] that Kirwan's questions 'are equally embarrassing on every hypothesis, the solution of which appears to depend upon a concurrence of affinities not yet proved, which offer, in a word, matter for new researches, but are not, for that reason, real objections'. Lavoisier expressly declined to enter upon a discussion of affinities[7] although he gave numerous tables of affinities in his book. It was reserved for William Higgins to show in 1789, by a detailed analysis of Kirwan's book, that the antiphlogistic theory is competent to explain the objections to it on the basis of affinities brought forward by Kirwan (see p. 738).

Kirwan's papers on the combining proportions of acids and alkalis are important. In the first,[8] in which 'Wentzel' (Wenzel) is just mentioned, Kirwan still uses some of Homberg's results of 1699 (see p. 45). He assumed that the weights of nitrous (nitric), vitriolic (sulphuric) and marine (hydrochloric) acids required to saturate (neutralise) a given quantity of fixed alkali (K_2CO_3) were the same. By dissolving marine air (HCl gas), the density of which he took from Fontana as 0·654 grains per cu. in., in water, taking the specific gravities of the solutions, and finding the weights of alkali neutralised by

[1] II, 1789, 168.   [2] Crell's *Ann.*, 1791, II, 1, 103.
[3] Fourcroy, (2), 1796, iii, 560; Reilly and O'Flynn, 307.
[4] Crell's *Ann.*, 1791, I, 425: 'mögten Sie vielleicht ein wenig verwundern dass ich das Stahlische System vom Phlogiston anjetz aufgegeben habe'; see also *ib.*, 1791, II, 348, and Wiegleb's remarks (with sentences ending in triple exclamation marks, !!!), *ib.*, 1791, II, 387 (430), saying 'I can hardly believe my eyes' on seeing Kirwan's announcement.
[5] Kirwan, *Phil. Trans.*, 1784, lxxiv, 154, 178; reply by Cavendish, *ib.*, 119, 170.
[6] II, 1789, 296–7.   [7] *Traité*, 1789, I, xiv.
[8] Experiments and Observations on the Specific Gravities and Attractive Powers of various Saline Substances; *Phil. Trans.*, 1781, lxxi, 7.

solutions of this acid and of the other two acids, Kirwan drew up the first tables of specific gravities of acids.[1] He gave further tables in later papers. He found that there is a contraction of the water on dissolving the acids, which he attributed to affinity.

In the second paper[2] Kirwan pays particular attention to the effect of temperature on the specific gravities of solutions of acids, finding it considerably different from that for water. He gives further experiments on the compositions of salts. The second part of the paper is on phlogiston (see above). The third paper[3] is the most important, since it gives many quantitative experiments on the compositions of salts. The three papers were translated (with an introduction) by Crell,[4] and by L. D. B. and Mme Picardet of Dijon.[5]

Kirwan now recognised that his first assumption (criticised by Berthollet)[6] of equal combining weights of acids was incorrect, and he now assumed that the three acids existing in the strongly dried salts of potash are the 'real acids'. He determined the compositions of some metallic salts by dissolving the metals in the acids and evaporating (when possible), and said that 'chemical affinity or attraction' is 'that power by which the invisible particles of different bodies intermix and unite with each other so intimately as to be inseparable by mere mechanical means'. He concluded that 'the quantity of real acid, necessary to saturate a given weight of each basis, is inversely as the affinity of each basis to such acid', and that 'the quantity of each basis, requisite to saturate a given quantity of each acid, is directly as the affinity of such acid to each basis'. He gives the following table:

Quantity of basis taken up by 100 grs. of each of the mineral acids

	Veg. fixed alkali Grs.	Mineral alkali Grs.	Calcareous earth Grs.	Volatile alkali Grs.	Magnesia Grs.	Earth of alum Grs.
Vitriolic acid	215	165	110	90	80	75
Nitrous acid	215	165	96	87	75	65
Marine acid	215	158	89	79	71	55

These (and the values for metals in the table on p. 666) are really equivalent weights, but Kirwan did not recognise this. He says:

'Thus the affinity of the vitriolic acid to fixed vegetable alkali, that is, the force with which they unite, or tend to unite, to each other, is to the affinity with which that same

[1] Kopp, (1), iii, 11.
[2] Continuation of the Experiments and Observations on the Specific Gravities and Attractive Powers of various Saline Substances, *Phil. Trans.*, 1782, lxxii, 179.
[3] Conclusion of the Experiments and Observations concerning the Attractive Powers of the Mineral Acids, *Phil. Trans.*, 1783, lxxiii, 15.
[4] *Versuche und Beobachtungen über die specifische Schwere und die Anziehungskraft verschiedener Salzarten; und über die wahre neuentdeckte Natur des Phlogistons*, 2 pts., Berlin and Stettin, 1783–5.
[5] *Obs. Phys.*, 1784, xxiv, 134, 188, 356; 1784, xxv, 13; 1785, xxvii, 250, 321, 447; 1786, xxviii, 94.
[6] AdS, 1785 (1788), m 305.

acid unites to calcareous earth, as 215 grs. to 110: and to that which the nitrous acid bears to calcareous earth as 215 grs. to 96, &c.'

He gives a table of 'the affinity of the three mineral acids to metallic substances', containing the weights of metals in the form of wire or powder taken up by 100 grs. of each dephlogisticated (colourless) mineral acid, 'which denote their degree of affinity to each metal':

100 grs.	Fe	Cu	Sn	Pb	Ag	Hg	Zn	Bi	Ni	Co	Sb	As
Vitriolic ac.	270	260	138	412	390	432	318	$\begin{cases}250\\310\end{cases}$	320	360	200	260
Nitrous ac.	255	255	120	365	375	416	304	290	300	350	194	220
Marine ac.	265	265	130	400	420	438	312	$\begin{cases}250\\320\end{cases}$	$\begin{cases}275\\310\end{cases}$	370	198	290

(The modern symbols are substituted for the names used by Kirwan, to save space.) The solutions, he found, often retained an excess of acid.

Kirwan then recalculates the absolute quantities of phlogiston in various metals from Bergman's results (see p. 196) from an experiment on the volume of nitrous air (nitric oxide) evolved by dissolving metallic arsenic in nitric acid, obtaining very different figures from Bergman's; e.g. the quantities of phlogiston in 100 parts of the metals are: copper 19·65, iron 14·67, silver 6·30, lead 2·70. By assuming that 'the affinity of metallic calces to phlogiston is directly as the specific gravity of the respective metals, and inversely as the quantity of calx contained in a given weight of those metals', he drew up a table of these affinities, which he tried to relate to the affinities of acids to bases in a 'homogeneous' series. The assumption, he says, is founded on the 'truth, that the larger the quantity of phlogiston in any metal is, the smaller is the quantity of calx in a given weight of that metal; and that the density which the phlogiston acquires, is as the specific gravity of the metal'. He remarks that this 'is not exactly true . . . yet it is the nearest approximation I can make'. A further paper deals with the effect of temperature on the specific gravity of water.[1]

A continuation of the experiments on the compositions of salts is contained in two papers read to the Royal Irish Academy. In the first[2] Kirwan refers repeatedly to Wenzel's results. He gives new tables of specific gravities of muriatic, sulphuric and nitric acids, taking 1·500, 2·000 and 1·5543 as the 'standards' for these acids, respectively.

'First, I saturate a known quantity of alkali or other basis with an acid whose specific gravity is known, and whose proportion of standard is determined by the tables. I then make another solution of a known quantity of neutral salt of the same species as that formed by saturation [neutralisation],[3] and examine the specific gravity of both

[1] Phil. Trans., 1785, lxxv, 267.
[2] Of the Strengths of Acids, and the Proportion of ingredients in Neutral Salts; Trans. Roy. Irish Acad., 1791, iv, 1 f. (read December, 1790); also separately, 4°, Dublin, 1791 (BM B 468); tr. by Mme. L[avoisier]: De la Force des Acides, & de la Proportion des Substances qui composent les Sels Neutres. Ouvrage traduit de l'Anglois de M. Kirwan par Madame L., s.l.e.a., 108 pp.; mentd. by Grimaux, Lavoisier, 1888, 43.
[3] The term 'neutralization' instead of 'saturation' which is used in a different sense for solutions of salts, etc., was adopted by Murray, 1806, i, 113.

solutions in the same temperature, adding water to the stronger of the two, until their densities become equal, and thence infer that an equal proportion of salt exists in both.'

A standard solution of 120 gr. mild vegetable alkali (calcined tartar) made up to 360 grains was diluted with 518 gr. water. To this 254 gr. of spirit of salt, s.g. 1·466, were added for neutralisation. The 'loss of air' (carbon dioxide) was 34 gr. The s.g. 'of the saturate [neutral] solution' at 56° F. was 1·076 and its total weight 1098 gr. The s.g. of a solution of 100 gr. of salt of Sylvius (potassium chloride) in 720 gr. water at 56° F. was also 1·076, hence the proportion of salt in both solutions was 1/8·2 of the whole. Now 1098/8·2 = 113·902. Of this, 120 − 34 = 86 are pure alkali (potassium oxide) and 113·902 − 86 = 47·902 are acid, or acid + water. But the salt contains practically no water, hence the 47·902 are acid. Hence 100 gr. alkali take up 100 × 47·902 ÷ 86 = 55·7 of 'strongest marine acid', equivalent to 115 of standard, and give 155·7 of salt of Sylvius. Thus 100 gr. of this salt contain 64·2 alkali and 35·8 of strongest marine acid. Kirwan[1] remarks that: 'perhaps water may be essential to the acid properties of all acids, as it certainly is to some of them.'

In his paper of 1800[2] Kirwan refers in detail to Richter,[3] putting forward a long criticism of Richter's numerical results 'to show the inaccuracy of several of his fundamental deductions'.[4] Richter's book must, therefore, have been known then in Dublin. In a letter of April 1797 to Sir Joseph Banks, now in the Natural History Museum, South Kensington, Kirwan says he was delaying publication until he had time to animadvert on a work by Richter. Kirwan now takes the proportions of real acid in the mineral acids as: sulphuric, s.g. 2·000, 89·29 per cent; nitric, s.g. 1·5543, 73·54 per cent; muriatic, s.g. 1·196, 25·28 per cent. Besides his own results, some revised, he considers critically a large number of values found by others and collects the whole in a series of tables, and large folding tables at the end of the paper.

Kirwan's results on the compositions of salts are here collected in a table which includes those given in his book.[5] To save space modern symbols are given. The symbols δ and κ mean 'dry' and 'crystalline', respectively; the small letters refer to Kirwan's different publications by date: $a = 1781$, $b = 1782$, $c = 1783$, $d = 1784$ (*Mineralogy*), $e = 1791$, $f = 1800$.

Kirwan differentiated 'salts' from 'earths' by solubility; a salt is soluble in 1000 times its weight of water, or 100 times in 'a loose and popular sense',[6] or more strictly in 200 times.[7]

Kirwan's important work on the analysis of mineral waters[8] shows the advances made in qualitative analysis. That 'many salts, which are incompatible when in considerable proportion, may nevertheless co-exist when in a very

[1] *Ib.*, 66.
[2] Additional Observations on the Proportion of Real Acid in the Three Antient Known Mineral Acids, and on the Ingredients in Various Neutral Salts and other Compounds (read December 1797), *Trans. Roy. Irish Acad.*, 1800, vii, 163–297; followed, characteristically, by Kirwan's 'Essay on Human Liberty', *ib.*, 305–16.
[3] 'Stochymetrie, 3 theile', on p. 191; 'Stochyometry, 2 theil', on p. 286.   [4] *Ib.*, 286 f.
[5] *Elements of Mineralogy*, 1784, 181–207, 406; also given in the tr. of Bergman's *Essays*, 1788, i, 177 f.; summary in Murray, 1806, ii, 154.
[6] *Elements of Mineralogy*, 1796, i, 2.   [7] *Ib.*, ii, 1.
[8] *An Essay on the Analysis of Mineral Waters*, London, 1799 (pp. vi, 274, 7 folding tables).

		Base	Acid	Water
K₂SO₄	a	66·67	28·51	4·82
	b	64·61	30·21	5·18 δ
				6·18 κ
	e	55	45	—
	f	54·8	45·2	—
Na₂SO₄	b	48·60	29·12	22·28 δ
		21·87	13·19	64·94 κ
	d	22	14	64 κ
	e	24·16	41·3	35·54
	f	44	56	— δ
		18·48	23·52	58 κ
CaSO₄	b	42	39	19 δ
		32	29·44	38·56 κ
	e	34	43	23
	f	41	59	— δ
		32	46	22 κ
MgSO₄	b	36·54	45·67	17·83 δ
		19	23·75	57·25 κ
	d	19	24	57
	e	17	33	50 κ
	f	36·68	63·32	— δ
Alum	b	32·14	42·74	25·05 δ
		18·00	23·94	58·06 κ
	d	18	24	58 κ
	e	29·37	26·63	44
(NH₄)₂SO₄	d	40	42	18
	e	27·42	62·47	10·11
	f	14·24	54·66	32·1
FeSO₄	c, d	25*	20	55
	e	22·32*	38·68	39
	f	12*	26	—
		28†	26	38 (8‡)
NaNO₃	b	52·18	30	17·82 δ
		50·09	28·8	21·11 κ
	d	50	29	21
NH₄NO₃	d	40	46	14
	e	24	76	—
	f	23	57	20
Ca(NO₃)₂	b	32	33·28	34·72
	d	32	33	35
	f	32	57·44	10·56
Mg(NO₃)₂	b	27	35·64	37·36
	d	27	36	37
	f	22	46	22

		Base	Acid	Water
CuSO₄	c, d	27*	30	43
	f	40†	30·3	28·5
ZnSO₄	c, d	20*	22	58
	f	—	20·4	39
PbSO₄	c	73*	17	10
Ag₂SO₄	c	74	17	9
Hg₂SO₄§	c	77	19	4
KCl	a	65·4	28	6·55
	b	63·47	29·68	6·85 δ
				7·85 κ
	d	63	30	7
	e	64·2	35·8	—
	f	64	36	—
NaCl	b	53	35	13 δ
		50	33·3	16·7 κ
	d	50	33	17
	e	53	47	—
	f	53	38·88	—
NH₄Cl	d	40	52	8
	e	27·62	68·49	3·89
	f	25	42·75	32·25
CaCl₂	b	38	42·56	19·44
	d	38	42	20
HgCl₂	c	77	16	6
HgCl	c	86	\{ 14	
AgCl	f	75	16·54	8·46‖
PbCl₂	c	72	18	10
KNO₃	a	66·32	28·48	5·2
	b	66	30·86	3·14 δ
		63·97	28(?9)·89	6·14 κ
	e	46·15	53·85	—
	f	51·8	44	4
Sr(NO₃)₂	f	36·21	31·07	32·72
Ba(NO₃)₂	f	57	32	11
Na₂CO₃	b	35	20	45 κ
(NH₄)₂CO₃	b	39·47	53	5·53
		44		3
KHCO₃		41	43	16 κ
K₂CO₃		60	30	6 δ
CaCO₃	a	55·92	32·42	11·66
Borax	d	17	34	47
KAc	a	32	19	49

* metal.   † calx.   ‡ 8 'of composition'.   § Or HgSO₄?   ‖ Oxygen.

minute proportion to the quantity of water that contains them',[1] was attributed to 'the *resistance* of the particles of water to that *motion* and *separation* from each other, which the action of the devellent [*sic*] powers of the saline particles would necessarily induce',[2] just as particles of gold leaf float on water. (Kirwan used the names 'divellent' and 'quiescent' for affinities in a sense which will be explained in Vol. IV.) This work contains a very complete account of the qualitative and quantitative analysis of various kinds of mineral waters, and although based on the previous researches of Bergman (see p. 182) and Westrumb (see p. 570), it shows Kirwan's chemical skill in a very favourable light. He objects to the practice introduced by Bergman, of stating the quantities of salts with their water of crystallisation, and says a more rational procedure is to give the weights of the anhydrous salts in solution, since when they dissolve their water of crystallisation is no longer differentiated from the mass of water acting as solvent.[3] It contains tables of solubilities of salts in spirits of wine.[4]

In his paper 'On Chymical and Mineralogical Nomenclature',[5] Kirwan criticised the proposals of Guyton de Morveau (see p. 526) and proposed some new names of his own: oxat (oxide), tartarin (potash), hepatule (hydrosulphuret, i.e. hydrosulphide), hepar (sulphuret, i.e. sulphide), which were not adopted by other chemists. His 'Experiments on the Alkaline Substances used in Bleaching'[6] record the weights of ash from various woods and plants,[7] e.g. from 1000 parts: elm 23·5, oak 13·5, beech 5·8, aspin 12·2; and the amounts of alkali in various commercial potashes. Kirwan's agricultural work[8] is important. In discussing Van Helmont's tree experiment (taken by Kirwan from Boyle) he says[9] the earthy matter probably came from the rain water used; he found that 197 lb. of fresh willow wood gave 4·7 lb. of ash.

Kirwan found that a mixture of hydrogen and chlorine explodes when kindled, forming muriatic acid gas: 'inflammable air unites to dephlogisticated marine air, and converts it into common marine acid.'[10] This had been found by Guyton de Morveau (p. 530).

Kirwan determined the densities of eight gases compared with air = 1 with fair accuracy, e.g. oxygen = 1·103, hydrogen = 0·0843, fixed air = 1·500, ammonia = 0·600.[11] He gives a table of the weights in grains of 100 cu. in. at 55° F. and 29·5 in. barometer:

Common air	31	Fixed air	46·5
Dephlogisticated air	34	Hepatic air	34·286
Phlogisticated air	30·535	Alkaline air	18·16
Nitrous air	37	Inflammable air	2·613
Vitriolic air	70·215		

---

[1] *Ib.*, 139.   [2] *Ib.*, 141.   [3] *Ib.*, 152.   [4] *Ib.*, 274.

[5] *Trans. Roy. Irish Acad.*, 1802, viii, 53; S. Dickson, *An Essay on Chemical Nomenclature* . . . *Observations on the same subject by Richard Kirwan*, London, 1796.

[6] *Trans. Roy. Irish Acad.*, 1790, iii, 3; read 1789.   [7] *Ib.*, 35.

[8] What are the Manures most advantageously applicable to the various Sorts of Soils, and what are the Causes of their Beneficial Effect; *Trans. Roy. Irish Acad.*, 1796, v, 129–98 (read 1794); also sep. 4°, Dublin, 1796, and London, 1796; 6 ed., 1806; tr. in Crell's *Ann.*, 1796, I, 63, 139, 221, 367, 459, 553.

[9] *Ib.*, Dublin, 1796, 24.

[10] *Essay on Phlogiston*, 1789, 131–2.   [11] *Ib.*, 1787, 18; 1789, 23 f., 30.

He says he had taken the weights of dephlogisticated air and nitrous air 'somewhat lower than I found them' and that 'others have found their weight still lower'. In 1781[1] he quoted the weights of 1 cu. in. at 55° F. and 29½ in. press. in grains, as follows: air 0·385, CO_2 0·570, HCl 0·654, NO 0·399, SO_2 0·778, NH_3 0·2, H_2 0·035, from Fontana. Fontana[2] determined the density of fixed air by the loss in weight of calamine (zinc carbonate) on heating, and measuring the volume of gas evolved; finding ⅔ grain per cu. in. He points out that this is a general method (see Cavendish, p. 314).

In 1786 Kirwan showed that the gas which he calls *hepatic air*, formed by the action of acids on liver of sulphur, contained no free hydrogen, whilst the hydrogen in that from ferrous sulphide and acids was merely mixed with it.[3] He gives a good account of the properties of sulphuretted hydrogen, including its acid reaction towards litmus, and various coloured precipitates with metals. He concluded (incorrectly) that it consists only of sulphur 'kept in an aërial state by the matter of heat'. He quotes Scheele's observation on the inflammation of hepatic gas mixed with two-thirds of its volume of air, but otherwise does not consider Scheele's earlier work in detail, although an English translation of Scheele's book appeared in 1780 (p. 211), and Berthollet[4] recognised Scheele as the discoverer of the gas. Kirwan later called the gas 'sulphurated hydrogen', and regarded the polysulphides as derived from 'supersulphurated hydrogen'.[5] He found that when hepatic air and nitrous air (nitric oxide) stand over mercury a strong smell of ammonia is developed.[6] In his paper on hepatic air (1786) Kirwan describes phosphoretted hydrogen, which he calls 'phosphoric hepatic air', and thus discovered it independently of Gengembre (1783, see p. 565).[7] Girtanner used the name 'phosphortes Wasserstoffgas'[8] or 'gephosphortes Wasserstoff',[9] translated as 'phosphuretted hydrogen gas';[10] more correct would be 'phosphoretted hydrogen'. Calcium phosphide was discovered by George Pearson, professor in St. George's Hospital,[11] by heating phosphorus with quicklime. The non-spontaneously inflammable gas was obtained in 1790 by Pelletier[12] by heating lower oxy-acids of phosphorus (see Davy, Vol. IV). Guyton de Morveau[13] found that the gas standing over water is decomposed by light.

Kirwan attempted to determine the carbon in bitumens and coals by heating with saltpetre.[14] He found that the 'blind Kilkenny coal', a variety of anthracite, decomposes nearly as much (9·6 parts) of saltpetre as plumbago, and contained 97·3 per cent of carbon and 3·7 of ash. Kirwan assumed that only the carbon 'alkalises' the saltpetre (forms potassium carbonate) and by subtracting

[1] *Phil. Trans.*, 1781, lxxi, 7.

[2] *Obs. Phys.*, 1778, xii, 376 (Sur l'alcali fixe végétal, & sur l'alcali fixe minéral).

[3] *Phil. Trans.*, 1786, lxxvi, 118; tr. by Mme. Picardet in *Obs. Phys.*, 1787, xxx, 133–46, 197–208.

[4] *Obs. Phys.*, 1798, xlvi, 436.   [5] *Analysis of Mineral Waters*, 1799, 10, 11.

[6] *Obs. Phys.*, 1787, xxx, 133 (144); Hausmann, *ib.*, 1787, xxx, 461.

[7] AdS, *Mém. div. Sav.*, 1783 (1785), x, 651; Crell's *Ann.*, 1789, I, 450.

[8] *Anfangsgründe der antiphlogistischen Chemie*, Berlin, 1792, 136.

[9] *Ib.*, 2 ed., Berlin, 1795, 118.   [10] Thomson, (2), 1807, i, 76.

[11] Experiments made with the view of Decompounding Fixed Air, *Phil. Trans.*, 1792, lxxxii, 289.

[12] *Mémoires et Observations de Chimie*, Paris, 1796, i, 312.

[13] Crell's *Ann.*, 1788, I, 118.   [14] *Trans. Roy. Irish Acad.*, 1797, vi, 141.

the carbon and ash the rest was called 'bitumen': the percentages of carbon, bitumen, and ash, respectively, were found to be, for example: compact cannel 75·2, 21·68, 3·1; slaty cannel 47·62, 32·52, 20; Whitehaven 57, 41·3, 1·7; Wigan 61·73, 36·7, 1·57; Newcastle 58, 40, —.

WENZEL

Carl Friedrich Wenzel (Dresden, 1740–Freiberg, 26 February 1793) learnt medicine and surgery in Amsterdam and until 1766 was a ship's surgeon in the service of the Dutch navy. He studied chemistry and metallurgy in Leipzig, in 1780 became director of the Freiberg mines, and in 1786 chemist to the Saxon Meissen porcelain factory.[1] All Wenzel's books are scarce:

I. Lehre von der Verwandtschaft der Körper, 8°, Dresden, 1777; 1782 (identical with 1777 ed. with new t.p.; pp. vi (2 blank), 3–492); ed. D. H. Grindel with notes, 1800 (used by T. Thomson); the book was issued by subscription and is very scarce.
II. Einleitung zur höhern Chymie, Leipzig, 1774 (Bolton, (1), 911; Wiegleb gives 1773) (not seen).
III. Chemische Versuche die Metalle vermittelst der Reverberation in ihre Bestandtheile zu zerlegen (ed. C. G. Kratzenstein), 4°, Copenhagen, 1781 (awarded a prize by the Copenhagen Academy; BM 1034. h. 13).
IV. Chymische Untersuchung des Flussspathes, 8°, Dresden, 1783. (BM 973. b. 20.)

II expresses his belief in alchemy and contains absurd statements which injured his reputation. He regarded metals as composed of phosphorus, a colouring earth, a talc-like earth, and a salt; in gold, mercury, platinum, and iron, the colouring earth is cobalt; in copper it is a red earth. Fanciful compositions of salts are given. A second part of II which was to contain experimental proofs, never appeared, but III took its place.

Thomson says 'Wenzel never obtained the confidence of chemists, nor is his name ever quoted as an authority', and his book (I) 'fell almost dead-born from the press' — yet it was republished twice. I have also found Wenzel quite often quoted, but by later writers in error for Richter (see p. 676). Among his discoveries was the blue mass formed from alumina and cobalt oxide,[2] usually called 'Thenard's blue' (Thenard, 1805, see Vol. IV) but first noticed by Gahn.[3] Wenzel also recognised that iron becomes passive in concentrated nitric acid.[4]

Wenzel's main contribution was a collection of analyses of salts, given in I. His analyses were tabulated (with those of Bergman and Kirwan) by Guyton de Morveau.[5] These values have been checked (with a slide rule) with those in various parts of Wenzel's book and two (marked *) corrected in the table below. Wenzel gives a large number of other analyses in addition to the above,

---

[1] Kopp, (1), ii, 72, 356; id., (3), 250; id., (4), i, 80; Partington, Ann. Sci., 1951, vii, 173 (180); R. A. Smith, Memoir of John Dalton (Manchester Mem., 1856, xiii) 160–6 ('I feel sorry to leave him in this state, and a few kind words will do little good . . . he appears an honest, earnest man'); Thomson, (1), ii, 42, 279; Wiegleb, (2), 1791, ii, 126; Winderlich, J. Chem. Educ., 1950, xxvii, 56 (portr. on p. 29).
[2] II, q. by Mellor, Treatise, v, 300.   [3] Ann. Phil., 1818, xi, 40.
[4] I, 1782, 108.   [5] Ency. Méthod., Chymie, i, 587–9.

e.g. of acetates and phosphates. Modern symbols are used in the table to save space:

	$CaCO_3$	$MgCO_3$	K_2CO_3	Na_2CO_3	Am_2CO_3	$CaSO_4$	$MgSO_4$
Base	55·7	41·7	—	—	—	40·2	16·87
Acid	43·2	32·5	28·4	40	53·7	59·8	30·63
Water	1·1	25·8	—	—			52·5

	$Al_2(SO_4)_3$	K_2SO_4	Na_2SO_4	Am_2SO_4	$ZnSO_4$	$FeSO_4$	$CoSO_4$	$SnSO_4$
Base	11·66	54·75	44·27	41·25	46·19	42·17	38·92	56·43
Acid	9·06	45·25	55·73	58·75	53·81	57·83	61·08	43·57
Water	79·28	—	—	—	—	—	—	—

	$CuSO_4$	$Bi_2(SO_4)_3$	$HgSO_4$	Ag_2SO_4	$Ca(NO_3)_2$	$Mg(NO_3)_2$	$Al(NO_3)_3$
Base	44·4	20·88	37*	31·43	33·82	28	59·25
Acid	55·6	79·12	63*	68·57	66·18	72	40·75
Water	—	—		—	—		

	KNO_3	$NaNO_3$	$AmNO_3$	$Zn(NO_3)_2$	$Fe(NO_3)_2$	$Co(NO_3)_2$	$Pb(NO_3)_2$
Base	48·13	37·5	32·29	34·78	48·28	38·2	76·97
Acid	51·87	62·5	64·96	65·22	51·72	61·8	23·03
Water	—	—	2·75	—	—	—	—

	$Sn(NO_3)_2$	$Cu(NO_3)_2$	$Bi(NO_3)_3$	$Hg(NO_3)_2$	$AgNO_3$	$CaCl_2$	$MgCl_2$
Base	66·1	34·78	50·59	77·55	64·29	49·12	44·97
Acid	33·9	65·22	49·41	22·45	35·71	50·88	55·03
Water	—	—	—	—	—	—	—

	$AlCl_3$	KCl	$NaCl$	$AmCl$	$ZnCl_2$	$FeCl_2$	$CoCl_2$	$PbCl_2$	$SnCl_2$
Base	72·15	64·75	54·4	50·98	57·56	51·35	56·5*	72·69	64·94
Acid	27·85	35·25	45·6	49·02	42·44	48·65	43·5*	27·31	35·06
Water	—				—				—

	$CuCl_2$	$BiCl_3$	$SbCl_3$	$AsCl_3$	$HgCl_2$	$AgCl$
Base	52·22	63·6	49·86	43	72·5	75·24
Acid	47·78	36·4	50·14	57	24·31	24·76
Water	—	—	—	—	3·19	—

Wenzel was credited by Berzelius,[1] apparently by an oversight, with having made very accurate analyses of salts and with the explanation that when solutions of two neutral salts are mixed the resulting solution is neutral, which he says follows from the recognition of the equivalent relation between acids and bases.

Wenzel's analyses are not very accurate, so that (as he himself emphasises) they, in fact, contradict the law of equivalents, which is due to Richter (see p. 676). The observation of the conservation of neutrality on mixing neutral salt solutions was not made by Wenzel but by Guyton de Morveau (see p. 528). Berzelius's error has been copied by nearly every writer on the history of chemistry to the present day; Wenzel's book is rare and was probably not seen by them. The fact that Richter, not Wenzel, was the true discoverer of the law of equivalents was pointed out by Hess in a lecture as long ago as 1840.[2]

[1] Théorie des Proportions Chimiques, Paris, 1819, 2; Traité de Chimie, Paris, 1831, iv, 524; Partington, Ann. Sci., 1951, vii, 173.
[2] J. prakt. Chem., 1841, xxiv, 420 (430); J. S. C. Schweigger, Über die stöchiometrische Reihen, Halle, 1853, 63; R. A. Smith, 1856, 160 f.; Kopp, (3), 251; Löwig, J. B. Richter, Breslau, 1874; Ostwald, Lehrbuch, 1910, i, 12; Partington, Text-Book of Inorganic Chemistry, 1921, 117; id., Ann. Sci., 1951, vii, 173 (180); Walden, Mass, Zahl und Gewicht in der Chemie der Vergangenheit, Stuttgart, 1931, 80 f. (summary); Speter, Chem. Ztg., 1930, liv, 1005; J. F. Moore, History of Chemistry, 1918, 63, says: 'Glauber is credited with the important statement that when two neutral salts are mixed the solution remains neutral whether any chemical reaction is observable or not' (no reference).

Guyton de Morveau[1] and Wollaston[2] pointed out that the analyses of Bergman, Kirwan, and Wenzel are not compatible with the neutrality principle. Murray[3] attributes the principle to Richter and Wenzel and speaks of 'the law of Richter'. F. Döbereiner[4] tabulated Wenzel's results and showed that they are incompatible with reciprocal proportions. Schweigger, who had read Wenzel's books I and II, says he did not find any indication of these in them. Brunner in a letter to Thomas Thomson in 1826[5] says of Wenzel, 'in some examples of mutual decomposition he gives at the end of his work, he calculates the required proportions and finds always that one of the bodies is in excess or in less.'

The fact that Wenzel had no idea of the law of equivalents attributed to him is abundantly clear from a perusal of his book. In one calculation[6] he discusses the reaction now formulated $2AgCl + HgS = Ag_2S + HgCl_2$.

He says that $\frac{1}{2}$ oz. of *luna cornea* (AgCl) contains $180\frac{9}{16}$ grains of silver and in geschwefeltes Silber (Ag_2S) this weight of silver is combined with $26\frac{3}{4}$ grains of sulphur, which in turn would form $125\frac{1}{2}$ grains of cinnabar (HgS), and this amount should decompose $\frac{1}{2}$ oz. of luna cornea (so viel Zinnober wäre also, in Ansehung des Schwefels, zu der Zersetzung einer halben Unze *Luna cornea* hinreichend).

But half an ounce of lunea cornea contains $53\frac{7}{16}$ grains of muriatic acid (Salzsäure, really chlorine).[7] In half an ounce of corrosive sublimate there are $58\frac{1}{4}$ grains of acid and 174 grains of mercury, hence $53\frac{7}{16}$ grains of acid require $159\frac{2}{5}$ grains of mercury. In cinnabar 240 grains of mercury are combined with 65 of sulphur, or $43\frac{1}{4}$ grains of sulphur to $159\frac{2}{5}$ of mercury, giving together $202\frac{1}{2}$ grains of cinnabar. Hence $125\frac{1}{2}$ grains of cinnabar would not separate all the acid in the luna cornea. If the mixture of cinnabar and luna cornea is sublimed, 'the acid of the Hornsilber (luna cornea) rises with the mercury out of $202\frac{1}{2}$ grains of cinnabar as a corrosive sublimate; the silver, on the other hand, remains combined with only so much sulphur as is contained in $125\frac{1}{2}$ grains of cinnabar.'

The inference to be drawn is that an excess of sulphur remains uncombined, and in other cases also Wenzel refers to uncombined residues from double decompositions and suggests that they should be used up by adding other substances. Although he says[8] that 'every possible combination of two bodies stands always in the most exact ratio to every other, and this ratio expresses the degree of combination (ein jede mögliche Verbindung zweyer Körper, mit jeder andern beständig in dem genauesten Verhältnisse stehet, und dieses Verhältniss drücket den Grad der Verbindung aus)', he does not seem to have appreciated the real meaning of this statement.

Wenzel's most important contribution, on the rate of solution of metals in acids,[9] is considered in the history of mass action in Vol. IV: he found that: 'if an acid dissolves one drachm of copper or zinc in an hour, an acid of half the strength requires two hours, when the surfaces and heats remain equal.'

[1] *Ency. Méthod., Chymie*, i, 582, 595 (see p. 528).   [2] *Phil. Trans.*, 1814, civ, 3.
[3] *Elements of Chemistry*, 6 ed., Edinburgh, 1828, i, 518.
[4] In Schweigger, *Über die stöchiometrische Reihen*, Halle, 1853, 63 f.
[5] Anon., *Glasgow Med. J.*, 1857, v, 140.   [6] I, 1782, 453.
[7] The table shows that this amount should be $59\frac{7}{16}$ gr., and $240-180\frac{9}{16}$ is also $59\frac{7}{16}$ and not $53\frac{7}{16}$.
[8] I, 1782, 4.   [9] I, 28.

RICHTER

Jeremias Benjamin Richter (Hirschberg, Silesia, 10 March 1762–Berlin, 4 April 1807) entered the Engineer corps of the army at the age of sixteen but left after seven years. He had been studying chemical books, and in 1785–6 he left Breslau for Königsberg; he studied mathematics (Kant was a professor) and graduated doctor in 1789 with a dissertation *De usu matheseos in chymia*, which contains accounts of the determination of specific gravities of a substance in solution or in its compounds, and with finding the weight of phlogiston.

FIG. 54. J. B. RICHTER, 1762–1807.

He worked for a gentleman near Glogau, where he had a laboratory; then (since he failed to obtain an academic position) as an assayer and secretary of the mining office at Breslau; and finally from 1798 as 'second Arcanist' (chemist) at the Berlin porcelain factory. He carried out (mostly at night) his own experimental investigations, made hydrometers for sale, and occupied himself with literary work. He was a member of the Grossbritannischen Societät of Göttingen and of the Academies of Science of Munich and St. Petersburg.[1] He was criticised in a 130-page article by J. F. Fries, then a

---

[1] C. G. C. Bischof, *Lehrbuch der Stöchiometrie, oder Anleitung die Verhältnisse zu berechnen, nach welchen sich die irdischen Körper mit einander verbinden. Anhang zu Friedrich Hildebrandt's Lehrbuch der Chemie*, etc., Erlangen, 1819, 8, 26, 30 f.; Darmstaedter and Oesper, *J. Chem.*

lecturer in mathematics in Heidelberg, as being too verbose,[1] but made a suitable reply.[2]

Gilbert, the editor of the *Annalen der Physik*, also criticised Richter[3] as being obscure, making mistakes in arithmetic, and failing to take account of Proust's discovery of the different states of oxidation of some metals, yet Richter actually anticipated Proust in this discovery (see p. 678).

Richter was permeated with the idea, which he probably got from Kant in Königsberg, that chemistry is a branch of applied mathematics, and he busied himself in finding regularities among the combining proportions where Nature has not provided any. He combined the phlogistic and antiphlogistic theories (see p. 630). His nomenclature is unusual and he uses symbols freely instead of names,[4] but each symbol represents a combining weight and has a quantitative significance.

Richter's experiments and theories are mainly contained in three large works:

A. Ueber die neuern Gegenstände der Chymie, 11 pts., Bresslau and Hirschberg, and (from part iv) Lissa, Johann Friedrich Korn senr., 1791–1802: i 1791, ii 1792, iii 1793, iv 1795, v 1795, vi 1796, vii 1796, viii 1797, ix 1798, x 1800, xi 1802.

  The title-pages of some parts have the motto: 'Πάντα (ΘΕΟΣ) μέτρῳ καὶ ἀριθμῷ καὶ σταθμῷ διέταξας' from the apocryphal Wisdom of Solomon in the Septuagint; Proust, *J. de Phys.*, 1806, lxiii, 369, quoted 'pondere et mensura' from the Vulgate, omitting 'number'.

B. Anfangsgründe der Stöchyometrie oder Messkunst chymischer Elemente, 3 vols. (in 4), J. F. Korn, Bresslau and Hirschberg, 1792–4: (i) Erster Thiel welcher die reine Stöchyometrie enthält, 1792; (ii) Des ersten Theils zweyter Abschnitt enthaltend die reine Thermimetrie und Phlogometrie, Bresslau, Hirschberg and Lissa, 1794; (iii) Zweiter Theil welcher die angewandte Stöchyometrie enthält; für Mathematiker, Chymisten, Mineralogen und Pharmaceuten, 1793; (iv) Dritter Theil welcher der angewandten Stöchyometrie dritten Abschnitt und einen Anhang zu dem ersten und zweiten Theil enthält, 1793. This work is excessively rare.[5]

C. Chemisches Handwörterbuch nach den neuesten Entdeckungen entworfen von D. Dav. Ludw. Bourguet, Professor der Chemie beym Königlichen Collegio Medico-Chirurgico zu Berlin. Mit einer Vorrede versehen von D. Sig. Fried. Hermbstädt, Berlin. 6 vols., i–ii, 1802; iii–iv, 1803; v, 1804; vi and Anhang [pagination continuous], 1805. Richter (v, 274–6) says his scattered publications if 'joined to unpublished stoichiometric researches, would compose the materials of a small booklet, an intelligible and a useful systematically ordered compendium suitable

Educ., 1928, v, 785; Hess, *J. prakt. Chem.*, 1841, xxiv, 420–38; *Phil. Mag.*, 1842, xxi, 81 (says Richter d. on 4 May); Kopp, (1), ii, 359; *id.*, (3), 1873, 251; Ladenburg, 1905, 51–3; Landolt, *Ber.*, 1890, xxiii, 908 Ref.; C. Löwig, *Jeremias Benjamin Richter, der Entdecker der chemischen Proportionen*, Breslau, 4°, 1874 (publ. for a meeting of the Versammlung deutscher Naturforscher und Aerzte, and containing, 45 f., previously unpublished material showing the depressing circumstances of Richter's life); Partington, *Ann. Sci.*, 1951, vii, 173; 1953, ix, 289; Schwarzkopf, *Chem. Ztg.*, 1907, xxxi, 471; J. S. C. Schweigger, *Über die stöchiometrische Reihen im Sinne Richters*, Halle, 1853; R. A. Smith, *Manchester Mem.*, 1856, xiii, 186 f., with long analysis of, and quotations from, Richter's works; Speter, *J. prakt. Chem.*, 1910, lxxxii, 397 (bibl.); Thomson, (1), ii, 207, 283, 302; Wurtz, *The Atomic Theory*, 4 ed., 1885, 12–23.

[1] *Archiv für die theoretische Chemie*, ed. Scherer, 1801, iii, 315–446.
[2] *Ueber die neuern Gegenstände der Chymie*, 1802, xi, 149, 163: 'die Natur wäre in Wahrheit sehr arm, wenn sie durch meines Kritikers Erkenntnissvermögen beschränkt seyn sollte.'
[3] *Ann. Phys.*, 1811, xxxix, 361 (394).   [4] Löwig, 35.
[5] Thomson, (2), 1807, ii, 559, says he was unable to procure a copy, although he mentions Fischer's extract from it in Berthollet's *Statique Chimique* (1803; see p. 677); in *Proc. Phil. Soc. Glasgow*, 1845, ii, 86 f., Thomson says that he and Dalton knew nothing of what Richter had done until after 1804, when Berthollet's book became available in England.

for chemists ignorant of mathematics, which I will give to the press'. This promise he never fulfilled, and three years after the words were written Richter was dead, at the age of 45.

The Law of Neutrality

The fact that solutions of calcium acetate and potassium tartrate remain neutral on mixing, when calcium tartrate is precipitated and potassium acetate remains in solution, is described by Richter in 1791[1] with the remark that:

'this is found by experience to hold for all decompositions by double affinity, in so far as the compounds used in the decomposition are also neutral' . . .

'it follows that there must be a definite ratio between the masses of each neutral compound, and that the terms (*Glieder*) of ratio are of such a character that they can be determined from the masses of the neutral compounds. . . . If, e.g., the components of two neutral compounds are A – a, a and B – b, b, then the mass ratios of the new neutral compounds produced by double decomposition are unchangeably (*unveränderlich*) A – a : b and B – b : a.'

This is a special case of the law of reciprocal proportions, which appears here for the first time. It was generalised in 1792:[2]

'when two neutral solutions are mixed, and decomposition follows, the new resulting products are almost without exception also neutral; the elements must, therefore, have among themselves a certain fixed ratio of mass.'

This is one of the cases in which statements conveying some beauty and elegance of mathematical relation, or some unexpected generalisations of great significance, stand out from a background of tedious and even irrelevant detail. They pay tribute to Richter's genius.

Berzelius[3] by mistake attributed this result to Wenzel (see p. 671), who:

'proved by singularly exact experiments that this phenomenon is due to the circumstance that the relative ratios between the quantities of the alkalis and earths which saturate a given quantity of the same acid are the same for all the acids.

But it is principally to J. B. Richter . . . that we owe the first positive indication of chemical proportions, founded on numerous experiments. . . . He tried to give chemistry an entirely mathematical form in a work entitled Chemical Stoichiometry (*Steuchiométrie chimique*), in which however, his imagination did not always allow itself to be guided by experiment. . . . When one reads the works of Richter on chemical proportions one is astonished that the study of these ratios should have been neglected for a single instant. However, there is in Richter's works a circumstance which contributes to lessen their impression on the mind of the reader. It is that the numerical results of his experiments are not very exact. . . . Intending to publish an elementary treatise on chemistry, I went through (among other works not usually read) the works of Richter. I was astonished by the light which they threw on the composition of salts and on the mutual precipitation of metals, from which no profit had been drawn. It results from the researches of Richter that, by means of good analyses of some salts, one can calculate the compositions of others.'

Wenzel's analyses were no more accurate than those of his contemporaries, he did not discover, state, or use the principle of maintenance of neutrality in the double decomposition of salts, and so far from drawing the correct con-

[1] A, i, 74.   [2] B, I, i, pp. xx, xxii.
[3] *J. Chem. Phys.* (Schweigger), 1811, ii, 297; *Essai sur la Théorie des Proportions Chimiques*, Paris, 1819, 2 f.; the text is the same in the 2 ed., *Théorie des Proportions Chimiques et Table Synoptique des Poids Atomiques*, Paris, 1835; Berzelius's statements in his *Lehrbuch der Chemie*, Dresden, 1827, III, i, 17 f.; *Traité de Chimie*, Paris, 1831, iv, 524 f.; 2 French ed., 1847, iv, 486–8, are identical.

clusion from it (which he could hardly do, since he does not mention it) he drew from his experiments exactly the opposite conclusion, viz. that mixtures of neutral salts could become acid or alkaline, if his analyses of individual salts are correct. Almost all the discoveries attributed by Berzelius to Wenzel were actually made by Richter.

Richter does not claim to have originated the *fact* of the law of neutrality and Guyton de Morveau in 1787 (see p. 528) used it to prove that some of Kirwan's combining proportions of acids and bases must be incorrect. Berthollet,[1] after mentioning Guyton de Morveau's[2] experiments and arguments, says:

'Richter seems to be the first chemist to draw attention to this remarkable property of saline compounds of not suffering any change whatever in the state of saturation when they are mixed in the same solution.'

He gives an abstract[3] of Richter's views, taken from Fischer's book (see p. 678). Berthollet says[4] Richter's experiments on mixing solutions of neutral salts which form precipitates (sulphate of potash or ammonia with muriate of baryta) seemed:

'to lead necessarily to the consequence which I did not indicate in my researches on the laws of affinity, but which Richter has positively established, viz. that the different acids follow corresponding proportions with different alkaline bases to arrive at a neutral state of combination. This consideration can have a great utility in verifying experiments.'

Berthollet emphasised that the principle is limited to neutral salts which do not form triple salts (e.g. it will not apply to alumina). Richter was aware that some salts which are 'saturated' compounds still have an acid or alkaline reaction, and in some cases may combine with a further definite quantity of alkali or acid to form other salts. He distinguished[5] between *absolute neutrality*, when the acid and base united in the 'ratio of masses' usually give a product neutral to indicators, and *relative neutrality* when only the first condition is satisfied. In relative neutrality a compound can take up an excess of one of the components, as tartar (acid potassium tartrate) can combine with a definite amount of potash or of ammonia to form a neutral salt, or sulphate of alumina can take up potash to form common alum.

Determining Element and Elements Determined

Richter calls acids and bases 'elements', but later extended his idea to other classes of compounds and also to true elements. He determined the weights of various bases reacting with identical weights of one acid, and called the acid the 'determining element' (*elementum determinans*) and the weights of the bases the 'elements determined' (*elementa determinata*):[6]

---

[1] *Statique Chimique*, 1803, i, 116.
[2] Cf. Berthollet, *Ann. Chim.*, 1801, xxxviii, 3 (29): Guyton a déjà fait sur cet objet plusieurs réflexions aussi juste qu'importantes, et il cite des observations de Richter, dont je ne connais pas encore l'ouvrage.
[3] *Statique Chimique*, 1803, i, 134–8.   [4] *Ib.*, i, 120.
[5] C, iii, 154–70, especially 160.   [6] A, 1795, iv, 67–9.

'If P is the mass of a determining element, where the masses of its elements determined are a, b, c, d, e, etc., Q the mass of another determining element, where a, β, γ, δ, ϵ, etc. are the masses of its elements determined, so that a and a, b and β, c and γ, d and δ, e and ϵ shall represent the same elements; and further if the neutral masses P + a and Q + β; P + a and Q + γ, P + c and Q + a, P + a and Q + γ, etc., are decomposed by double affinity, so that the resulting products are neutral, then the masses a, b, c, d, e, etc., have the same quantitative ratio among one another as the masses a, β, γ, δ, ϵ, etc., or conversely.

This rule [the law of neutrality on mixing] is a true touchstone of the experiments instituted with regard to the ratios of neutrality; for if the proportions empirically found are not of the kind that is required by the law of decomposition by double affinity, where the decomposition actually taking place is accompanied by unchanged neutrality, they are to be rejected without further examination as incorrect, since an error has then occurred in the experiments instituted.'

In 1797–8 Richter pointed out[1] that when two metallic salts exchange acids and bases by double decomposition, the metal of one finds in the other exactly the quantity of oxygen necessary to keep it dissolved in the acid; i.e. the quantities of different metals necessary for the formation of neutral salts combine with identical weights of oxygen.

The same result was found independently by Gay-Lussac in 1808,[2] not by analyses but by observing that metals precipitate one another from solutions of salts without the formation of other products: 'puisque le métal précipitant trouve dans celui qui est précipité tout l'oxygène dont il a besoin pour s'oxyder, et neutraliser au même degré l'acide de la dissolution, il s'ensuit que la quantité d'oxygène dans chaque oxyde reste la même.'

Richter anticipated Proust in finding and clearly stating that some metals, e.g. iron and mercury, in forming salts with acids, can combine with two definite proportions of oxygen.[3] He recognised clearly the different degrees of oxidation of many metals and the fact that the highest stages of oxidation are acidic anhydrides.[4] In his investigation of metal oxides Richter showed that quantities of these containing equal amounts of oxygen saturate identical amounts of any acid, the oxygen content of which is immaterial, and he thus concluded that alkalis and earths are oxides of unknown metals.

Fischer's Table of Equivalents

Richter represented the series of combining proportions for each acid and base separately. Ernst Gottfried Fischer (1754–1831), professor of physics and mathematics in the Gymnasium zum grauen Kloster, Berlin, in his translation of Berthollet's *Recherches sur les lois de l'affinité*[5] gives a clear summary of Richter's views (which he says were practically unknown even in Germany) and a table of equivalent weights of acids and bases referred to 1000 parts of sulphuric acid as a single standard:

[1] A, viii, 82 f.; ix, 10 f., 145 f.; see also xi, 84 f.
[2] *Mém. Soc. Arcueil*, 1809, ii, 159–75 (Lu à l'Institut le 5 de décembre 1808).
[3] A, 1798, ix, 116 f., 139 f.   [4] A, 1800, x, 45 f., 86 f., 134 f., 153 f., 168 f., etc.
[5] *Claude Louis Berthollet über die Gesetze der Verwandtschaft*, Berlin, 1802, 229 f.; partly reproduced in French tr. in Berthollet, *Statique Chimique*, Paris, 1803, i, 134–8, which first drew the attention of chemists to Richter's work.

Bases		Acids	
Alumina	525	Fluoric	427
Magnesia	615	Carbonic	577
		Sebacic	706
Ammonia	672	Muriatic	712
Lime	793	Oxalic	755
Soda	859	Phosphoric	979
		Formic	988
Strontia	1329	Sulphuric	1000
		Succinic	1209
Potash	1605	Nitric	1405
Baryta	2222	Acetic	1480
		Citric	1683
		Tartaric	1694

'The meaning of this table is the following: if a substance is taken from one of the two columns, say potash from the first, to which corresponds the number 1605, the numbers in the other column indicate the quantity of each acid necessary to neutralise 1605 parts of potash. . . . If a substance is taken from the second column, the numbers in the first column show how much of each of the substances in this column will be necessary for its neutralisation.'

The basis of Fischer's table is implied in a remark by Richter[1] that determining elements and elements determined may exchange roles; e.g. sulphuric acid (taken as 1000) may be a determining element for a series of alkaline earths, and one of these for a series of acids. (A *determining element* stands at the head of a *mass series* containing the proportions of several *elements determined* by the masses combining with a fixed mass of the determining element.)

Richter determined the equivalent of phosphoric acid as the amount which *neutralises* as much soda as the equivalent of sulphuric acid, i.e. to form Na_2HPO_4. In Fischer's table if sulphuric acid is 1000, phosphoric acid is 979 and with SO_3 and P_2O_5 the correct value is 887.[2]

In 1803 Richter,[3] on the basis of Fischer's table, gave a table of 18 acids and 30 bases (including metal oxides), referred to sulphuric acid = 1000. Richter says 'all numbers of one of the two columns are *specific* in respect of each number of the other column'.

In the preface to his *Anfangsgründe der Stöchyometrie* (1792) Richter says he had often considered how far chemistry was a branch of applied mathematics, and especially through the common experience that two neutral salts, when they mutually decompose each other, again produce neutral compounds: 'this could be no other than that there must be definite ratios of magnitude (*bestimmte Grössenverhaltnisse*) between the constituents of the neutral salts.' This went back before the time of his Königsberg Inaugural Dissertation, *De Usu Matheseos in Chymia*, 1789, in which he said: 'Chemistry belongs unquestionably in its greatest part to applied mathematics (*Die Chymie gehört ohnstreitig einem ihrer grössten Theile nach zu der angewandten Mathematik*).' Even in practical analysis a knowledge of combining proportions (*Grössenverhältnisse*) is necessary.

---

[1] B, I, i, 176; cf. A, 1802, xi, p. xvi f.   [2] Wurtz, *Chem. News*, 1865, xi, 49, 109.
[3] C, 1803, iii, 164; the table was reproduced by Schweigger, *J. Chem. Phys.*, 1815, xv, 498; Partington, 1951, 187.

'Since the mathematical part of chemistry is mostly concerned with bodies which are undecomposable bodies or elements, and teaches how to determine the mass ratios between them, I have been able to find no shorter and more suitable name for this scientific discipline than *Stöchyometry* from στοιχεῖον, which in the Greek language means something which cannot be divided further, and μετρεῖν which means to find out relative magnitudes.'

He distinguishes between *mixtures* and *solutions*; the latter (it is important to notice) include what we call 'chemical compounds'.

'A material in which only uniform parts are assumed we will call an *element*, and it is only a *physical element* in so far as it, without being divided into unlike parts, does not remove the characteristic properties of materials when mixed with them. A *chemical element*, on the contrary, is one which, without being divided into unlike parts, removes the characteristic properties of other materials when mixed with them and gives rise to others. A *chemical element* is *immediate* in so far as it cannot be divided by art into unequal parts, but *mediate* in so far as it is possible to divide it into unequal parts by art.'[1]

Part-wholes (*Theilganze*) are similar parts differing only in figure, size, etc., i.e. what are now called *phases*:[2]

'If materials are such that when mixed together, not every given or perceivable part of the system is a single phase, the system is called a mixture, but if every possible or perceivable part of the system is a single phase, it will be called a solution.

The material or corporeal subject in which the chemical affinity resides I call the mass, principle, or matter of the element. The sum of the masses of the elements which form a neutral solution is the mass or matter of the neutral solution.[3]

A relation or ratio is the reciprocal influence of two things on each other, and thus a chemical relation is the way in which one element enters into solution with another given element, and in which this solution is again removed by a further element.[4]

Stoichiometry is the science of measuring the quantitative proportions or mass ratios in which chemical elements stand to one another.[5]

Every infinitely small phase of the mass of an element contains an infinitely small part of the chemical attractive force or affinity. . . . If a neutral compound is composed from two elements then, provided both elements are in the same state in the two cases, the ratio of the masses is the same in the first case as in the second.'[6]

Richter here approaches very near to the chemical atomic theory of definite proportions, but he makes no use of this theory and believed that matter is divisible without limit.[7]

'The elements must have among themselves a fixed ratio of mass, a determination of which is often provided by the composition of the neutral compounds.

If, therefore, the weights of the masses of two neutral compounds which decompose each other to give a neutral product are A and B, and if the masses of the one element in A is a, and that of the one in B is b, then the masses of the elements in A are $A - a$ and a, those in B are $B - b$ and b. The ratios of the masses of the elements in the neutral compounds before the reaction are $(A - a) : a$ and $(B - b) : b$; after decomposition, however, the masses of the new products formed are $a + B - b$ and $b + A - a$, and the ratios of the masses of the elements are $a : (B - b)$ and $b : (A - a)$. If, therefore, the ratio of the masses in the compounds A and B is known, that in the new products formed is also known.[8] If the mass of one element is assumed to be a definite quantity, e.g. $A = 1000$, then the number of elements of any kind which form neutral compounds with A is called a *series of masses* of these elements. Every mass of such an element is called a *term* of this series of masses. . . . That element on which a series of masses is based will be called the *determining* or *defining* element, the terms of the series the *determined* or *defined* elements.'[9]

[1] B, I, i, 3–7.   [2] B, I, i, 2.   [3] B, I, i, 82.   [4] B, I, i, 86.   [5] B, I, i, 121.
[6] B, I, i, 123.   [7] B, I, i, pp. xx, xxii.   [8] B, I, i, 124.   [9] B, I, i, 176.

The Series of Masses

Richter, with his mathematical outlook on chemistry, had the idea that the combining proportions formed arithmetical or geometrical series. This error permeates the whole of his *Anfangsgründe der Stöchiometrie*, and in finding such numerical relations he 'corrected' his experimental results in a very arbitrary way. The second volume of this book, published in 1793, contains a detailed account of the matter. In the preface he states that:

'the double affinities proceed in arithmetical progression, and after exact observations it is hardly possible to withstand the thought that the whole chemical system consists of such progressions.'[1]

The first part of the text records experiments on the combining proportions of acids and bases.[2] Five oz. of chalk after strong heating gave 2 oz. 6 dr. 22 gr. of quicklime, hence 2400 gr. contain 1342 of earthy matter, or 1000 parts contain 559 of true earth and 441 of water and aërial acid (*Luftsäure*). Twelve oz. or 5760 gr. of muriatic acid (*Salzsäure*) dissolved 4 oz. 7 dr. 53 gr. or 2393 gr. of this chalk and gave 5 oz. 2 dr. 24 gr. or 2544 gr. of fused neutral salt (calcium chloride). The lime in the chalk is $2393 \times 559 \div 1000 = 1337$ and this subtracted from 2544 gives the weight of muriatic acid in the neutral salt as 1207. Richter thus calculated the 'mass ratio' of muriatic acid to lime in the neutral salt as 1000 : 1107.

By similar experiments[3] he found the ratio of magnesia to muriatic acid as 1000 acid to 858 magnesia, of baryta to muriatic acid as 1000 acid to 3099 baryta, of alumina to muriatic acid as 1000 acid to 734 alumina, of lime to vitriolic acid as 1000 acid to 796 lime, of magnesia to vitriolic acid as 1000 acid to 616 magnesia, of baryta to vitriolic acid as 1000 acid to 2226 baryta, and of alumina to vitriolic acid as 1000 acid to 526 alumina in common alum or 1053 in neutral alum. The last two numbers, it will be noticed, are almost exactly in the ratio of 1 : 2, although Richter does not remark on this example of multiple proportions.

He then gives 'the order of the masses of the alkaline earths towards muriatic acid':[4]

1000 muriatic acid

      alumina 734   magnesia 858   lime 1107   baryta 3099.

'In order to see this better we put $734 = a$ and $249/2 = b$, then $734 = a$, $858\frac{1}{2} = a + b$, $1107\frac{1}{2} = a + b + 2b = a + 3b$, $3099\frac{1}{2} = a + b + 2b + 16b = a + 19b$. From this the series of masses appears in the following order:

1000 muriatic acid

      alumina a magnesia $a + b$ lime $a + 3b$ baryta $a + 19b$.

'The mass ratios in which the hitherto known alkaline earths assert neutrality with muriatic acid are therefore terms of a true arithmetical progression, the terms of which arise when to the first term is added a product of a certain magnitude with an odd number, except that many intermediate odd numbers, e.g. 5, 7, 9, 11, 13, 17, are left out.'

He concludes that these represent unknown bases. In a similar way, he tried to arrive at the series of masses of the alkaline earths neutralising 1000 parts of vitriolic acid:[5]

[1] B, ii, p. vii.   [2] *Ib.*, 1–4.   [3] *Ib.*, 6–25.   [4] *Ib.*, 27.   [5] *Ib.*, 33.

1000 vitriolic acid

magnesia 616   lime 796   alumina 1053   baryta 2226.

'Until, therefore, we are able to complete the order, let us make $616 = 616$, $796 = 616 + 2 \times 90$, $1053 = 616 + 5 \times 90 - 13/90$, $2226 = 616 + 18 \times 90 - 10/90$.'

Alumina salt contains 734 alumina and 1000 muriatic acid. If this undergoes double decomposition with Epsom salt, the amount of the latter must be such as contains 858, or rather the corrected amount $858\frac{1}{2}$, of magnesia, since this is the amount combining with 1000 of muriatic acid. But Epsom salt contains 1000 vitriolic acid and 616 magnesia, hence the weight required will contain $616 : 1000 = 858\frac{1}{2} : 1394$ of vitriolic acid. Hence on double decomposition:[1]

'1000 parts of muriatic acid dissolve with $858\frac{1}{2}$ parts of magnesia, and 1394 of vitriolic acid with 734 of alumina. For 1000 parts of vitriolic acid, the proportionate amount of alumina will be $1394 : 734 = 1000 : 526$, which is not the proportion [1053] found with the neutral salt but that in common alum.'[2]

'The quantities of real and possible elements which belong to 1000 parts of muriatic acid belong also to 1394 parts of vitriolic acid.'[3]

'The masses in which the alkaline earths enter into neutrality with muriatic acid are terms of an infinite series which increase by the product of a determinate quantity with consecutive odd numbers. The same relation is found with the alkaline earths in relation to vitriolic acid, only in this case a quantity, which also increases in progression, must be taken from the terms of this last series, the first three excepted.'[4]

Tables comparing Richter's results for the composition of salts with those found by Kirwan, Bergman, Wenzel, and Wiegleb show the great discrepancies among the results. Richter's own values in his tables for the weights of alkalis and alkaline earths neutralising 1000 parts of the stated acids are:[5]

	vitriolic acid	muriatic acid	nitric acid
vegetable alkali	1606	2239	1143
mineral alkali	1218	1699	867
volatile alkali	638	889	453
baryta	2224	3099	1581
lime	796	1107	565
magnesia	616	858	438
alumina	526	734	374

The values are inaccurate, but the idea underlying the table, that the ratios of the figures in the columns are constant, e.g. $1143/867 = 2239/1699$, is correct.

Richter's further publications on stoichiometry are in the parts of A beginning with the sixth, which deals with carbonic acid and seven organic acids (*verbrennliche Säure*). He shows[6] that the masses of baryta, lime and magnesia, and of potash and soda, which neutralise equal weights of acetic acid are in the same quantitative ratio as for other acids, and the same is true for tartaric, citric, oxalic, sebacic, formic, and succinic acids. In a consideration[7] of the

[1] *Ib.*, 37–8.
[2] This is said to be formed by saturating dilute sulphuric acid with alumina in the cold. Richter's 'alums' are aluminium sulphates, not the double salts we now call alums.
[3] This is a clear statement of the law of reciprocal proportions as applied to a special case.
[4] *Ib.*, 41.   [5] B, iii, 282 f.
[6] A, vi, 16, 50, 77, 103, 119, 142, 158, for the acids in the order in the text; a preparation of succinic acid from the lead salt and sulphuric acid is given on p. 165.
[7] *Ib.*, 168 f.

results he gives[1] a table of masses of the acids for 1000 parts of magnesia as determining element, where $b = 1 \cdot 06965$:

	obs.	corrected	
carbonic	939·8	939·8	$a = 937 \cdot 7$
sebacic	1164·1	1126·3	$ab^3 = 1147 \cdot 1$
oxalic	1283·0	1244·0	$ab^4 = 1227 \cdot 6$
formic	1660·0	1607·0	$ab^8 = 1607 \cdot 0$
succinic	2012·9	1966·7	$ab^{11} = 1966 \cdot 7$
acetic	2465·5	2425·5	$ab^{14} = 2407 \cdot 0$
citric	2726·3	2590·0	$ab^{15} = 2574 \cdot 6$
tartaric	2963·8	2815·6	$ab^{16} = 2754 \cdot 0$

The vacant spaces (ab^2, ab^5, etc.) he expected would be filled by yet unknown acids containing carbon. Hence:[2]

'Carbonic acid and all the other acids containing carbon which are at present known are, from the point of view of their neutralisation with alkalis (as well saline as earthy), all terms of a geometrical progression, and there are as many progressions of the same form (but not the same numerically) as there are alkalis.'

The acid tartrates and oxalates belong to the series ab^{26} and ab^{14}; it is disappointing to see that Richter failed to notice the multiple proportions in this case of neutral and acid salts. For a determining mass of acid of 1000 the following abridged table gives his results, the numbers 1 to 12 referring to fluoric, muriatic, vitriolic, nitric, carbonic, sebacic, oxalic, formic, succinic, acetic, citric, and tartaric acids, respectively, the determined earths represented by a to $a + 19b$ being alumina, magnesia, lime, strontia, and baryta, respectively; strontia fits the previously missing term $a + 9b$:

	b	a	$a+b$	$a+3b$	$a+9b$	$a+19b$
1	208·8	1227·2	1436·0	1853·6	3106·4	5194·4
2	125·3	738·7	864·0	1114·6	1866·4	3119·4
3	89·3	525·3	614·6	793·2	1329·0	2222·0
4	63·5	374·0	437·5	564·5	945·5	1580·5
5	154·95	911·5	1066·4	1376·3	2305·1	3855·5
6	126·65	745·1	871·8	1125·1	1884·9	3151·5
7	118·35	696·2	814·6	1051·3	1761·3	2944·9
8	96·4	531·9	622·3	803·1	1345·5	2249·5
9	73·9	434·6	508·5	656·3	1129·7	1838·6
10	60·4	355·1	415·5	536·3	898·7	1502·6
11	56·45	332·0	388·4	501·3	840·0	1404·5
12	52·75	310·3	363·1	468·6	785·0	1312·6

For 1000 parts of alkali the various acids, as numbered above, form two geometrical series having two different values of b.

The rest of the eighth part of the *Gegenstände*[3] deals with 'phlogometric considerations'. A metallic neutral compound is formed from an oxidised (*gelebensluftstoffetes*) substrate and an acid mass such that it cannot undergo chemical reaction unless the mass of the acid element which combines with an added substrate completely leaves the metallic oxide. Richter lays down four laws, condensed as follows:

[1] *Ib.*, 181.   [2] *Ib.*, 182.   [3] A, viii, 82 f.

(i) When an aqueous solution of a metallic neutral salt is so decomposed by another metal that the metal in solution is deposited in a pure state, and neither the solvent nor the water is decomposed, the masses of oxygen which must combine with equal masses of the metals so as to render them soluble in acids are inversely proportional to the masses of the separated and separating metals.

(ii) When a metallic and non-metallic neutral salt exchange principles so that the products are neutral, and no component is decomposed, the degrees of oxidation or dephlogistication of the metallic substrate with respect to the acids are equal, and the two acid masses are in the same ratio as those determined by the alkali.

(iii) If two metallic neutral salts exchange constituents, and the two new products are decomposed by an acid, the degrees of oxidation of each metal are the same for each acid and the degrees of oxidation are inversely proportional to the metallic substrates.

(iv) The masses of metallic oxides combining with a fixed weight of acid form a quantitative order, and as these contain the same amount of oxygen, the masses of the metals also form a quantitative order.

Richter tried to show[1] that the ratio of oxygen to sulphur, nitrogen, hydrogen, phosphorus, and carbon may be expressed in the form $A/(a+nb)$, where $A = 1000$, $a = 1381$, $b = 119$, and the values of n are, respectively, 0, 1, 10, 21, and 36. The latter, however, form part of a series of triangular numbers, viz. 1, 3, 6, 10, 15, 21, 28, 36 . . . . By oxidising a weighed amount of flowers of sulphur with nitric acid, and converting the resulting sulphuric acid into calcined gypsum,[2] Richter found that 222 parts of sulphur gave 947 of calcium sulphate. Since he had found that 947 of gypsum contain 528 of vitriolic acid (SO_3) he calculated that sulphuric anhydride contains 1·0000 of sulphur to 1·3784 of oxygen, i.e. 41·88 per cent sulphur and 58·12 per cent oxygen (the correct figures are 40 and 60), very different from Berthollet's result (see p. 501) of 70 and 30.

Experiments[3] on the neutralising ratios of vitriolic acid and metallic substrates showed that the weights of the metals neutralising 1000 parts of vitriolic acid were in an arithmetical progression $841 + 68n$. The oxides belong to another series[4] of the form $(439 + 841) + 68n$, where 439 is the constant amount of oxygen combining with the metals. The specific oxidations, viz. 439,000 divided by 841, 909, 977, etc., also form arithmetical progressions. The specific oxidation for mercury is found to be 80·3, corresponding with the best analysis of the oxide, 100 mercury to 8 oxygen.[5] Manganese falls into the series as $705 + 68n$. The metals probably have the same quantitative order towards all acids,[6] this order being different from the affinity series,[7] probably that of ease of reduction.[8] The quantities of oxygen taken up by metals on calcination are not necessarily the same as those in salts.

The ninth part of the *Gegenstände* (1798) deals with metals. Richter distinguished clearly two stages of oxidation of mercury[9] and stated clearly[10] that the supposed continuous series of mercury salts assumed by Berthollet (see p. 649) is constituted of mixtures of two definite salts (eine unzählbare Menge von verschiedenen Verhältnissen zwischen Säure und Quecksilber . . . sind nichts als mathematische Functionen, die aus den zwey bestimmten Neutralitätsverhältnissen . . . gemischten sind).

[1] A, viii, 92 f.   [2] A, v, 121 f.   [3] A, viii, 102 f.
[4] A, viii, 115.   [5] Ib., 119.   [6] Ib., 120 f. (manganese), 126.
[7] Ib., 127 f.   [8] Ib., 129.   [9] A, ix, 137 f.   [10] Ib., 141.

He considered,[1] with algebraic equations, some examples of 'indirect analysis', i.e. the analysis of a mixture which is not separated into its components but is completely converted into another mixture. His theory[2] of 'edulcoration' is essentially the same as Bunsen's[3] theory of washing precipitates. If a mixture containing c parts of soluble salt is mixed with so much water that the amount x of water in the mixture is increased m times, then after n washings the amount of c remaining is c/m^n.

The tenth part of the *Gegenstände* (1800) deals with acid-forming metals (chromium, titanium, tellurium, tungsten, etc.). The oxidation ratios are calculated and the table for metals in the ninth part is repeated with some corrections. 1000 parts of metallic arsenic require 349·6 of oxygen to form arsenic acid and 151·2 to form arsenic calx (arsenious oxide). The metallic acids and arsenic calx form an arithmetical series (not, like the other acids, geometrical series) in their specific neutralities with alkalis or metals. The amounts of oxygen combined with 1000 of basis in acids and in water are calculated as $1381 + 119n$, where n is 0, 1, 3, 6, 10, 15, 21, 28, 36.[4] Richter had laid great emphasis on these 'triangular' numbers, $\frac{1}{2}n(n+1)$ where n is an integer,[5] which are well known in the theory of piling spherical shot.

The eleventh part of the *Gegenstände* (1802) mentions in the preface the German translation by Fischer of Berthollet's *Recherches* (see p. 678). Richter says he had already dealt[6] with Fischer's criticism of the series in relation to the geometrical series for acids; in his *Stöchiometrie* and *Gegenstände* he had emphasised that when it is merely a question of numerical ratios and not of order, the metallic calces can be included with the alkalis, and every ratio determined by rule of three; i.e. determining and determined elements can exchange roles. He described[7] the preparation of pure glucina (beryllium oxide) from beryl. The amounts of oxygen combined with 1000 parts of non-metallic elements in acids and in water[8] were supposed to form an arithmetical series of triangular numbers, missing terms perhaps corresponding with unknown elements. This idea foreshadows Mendeléeff's prediction of unknown elements by means of the periodic law.

Bergman, Wenzel, and Kirwan had published experiments on the composition of chemical compounds, and it cannot be said that Richter was working in a field which was neglected, or in which chemists as a whole took little interest. He proved that the analysis of a few neutral salts could furnish by calculation the compositions of many others, and so control the accuracy of analyses. The compositions of neutral salts could be calculated from numbers characteristic of the acids and bases. He proved the constancy of the ratios of the quantities of different acids or bases neutralising the same quantity of any one base or acid, and the constancy of the quantity of oxygen in the quantities of various metal oxides neutralising the same amount of an acid; and by inference that metals combine with fixed amounts of oxygen, which in the case of metals such as mercury, which form two series of salts, are in a fixed ratio. He failed to notice the simple multiple proportions in the last case, not by reason of

---

[1] *Ib.*, 178 f.   [2] *Ib.*, 214 f.   [3] *Ann.*, 1868, cxlviii, 269.   [4] A, x, 184.
[5] Crell's *Ann.*, 1797, II, 15.   [6] A, iv, 66, 69; B, I, i, 124.   [7] A, xi, 12 f.   [8] C, iii, 17.

inaccurate data, although this was sometimes evident (as in the arsenic oxides). He had sound ideas about the use of combining weights in analytical chemistry, and the use of indirect analysis and even the theory of washing precipitates (usually attributed to Bunsen).

It was only after Fischer's summary of Richter's ideas appeared, and their importance was recognised in France by Berthollet, that attention began to be directed to him. Almost at once, however, the unfortunate mistake of Berzelius in attributing to Wenzel what is Richter's property again put his achievements in the shade, and finally when Dalton put forward his atomic theory, Richter's law of reciprocal proportions became a deduction from the theory so obvious that Dalton never took the trouble to state it. Richter was serious and thoughtful, but he lacked the facility of stating his ideas clearly and concisely, and in his obstinate pursuit of mathematical relations which are really non-existent, he failed to see quite simple things which more than once were before his eyes. He was never able to free himself from his early mistake of the fictitious arithmetical and geometrical series of combining ratios.

It would be a mistake to assume that Richter was merely a theoretical speculator. He was an excellent practical chemist and published a large number of experimental researches, some of which are important. His method of preparing absolute alcohol (*absoluten Alkohol*, a name he introduced)[1] consists in preliminary rectification to sp.gr. 0·830–0·835 and then distilling over fused and powdered calcium chloride to a constant sp.gr. 0·792. He gives[2] tables of densities of alcohol-water mixtures from 1·000 to 0·792 and[3] describes a scale for an alcoholometer. The preparation of pure barium salts from heavy-spar[4] depends on fusion of the chlorides, when iron is rendered insoluble. A new method of making citric acid from rotten lemons[5] depends on the precipitation of calcium citrate from a boiling solution and its decomposition with sulphuric acid. In a calorimetric consideration[6] he decides that the water of crystallisation of salts is not in the form of ice, since not only liquids and gases but also solids may contain combined heat. He measured the fall in temperature on dissolving crystallised Glauber's salt, and the rise in temperature on dissolving the anhydrous salt, in water, considered the deviations from the mixture rule, and showed that a melting of ice could not have occurred.

Richter's researches on colloidal gold,[7] made long before Faraday's (see Vol. IV), are of great interest. He says the purple precipitate (purple of Cassius, see Vol. II, p. 370) formed by mixing solutions of gold and tin salts, is 'nothing but an intimate mixture of extremely finely divided gold with tin calx'. That the gold in purple of Cassius is metallic was confirmed by Proust[8] and by Marcadieu, an assistant in the Paris Mint.[9]

Richter noticed that in very dilute solutions iron vitriol and gold solution

---

[1] A, viii, 67. Cardan, *De Subtilitate*, 8°, Basel, 1560, 1048, called weaker spirit 'aqua ardens non absoluta'.
[2] *Ib.*, 74.
[3] *Ib.*, 81; these were superseded by the tables of Tralles, *Ann. Phys.*, 1811, xxxviii, 349–431 (386), who gave the compositions by volume and included the results of experiments by Gilpin, *Phil. Trans.*, 1794, lxxxiv, 275.
[4] A, ix, 222.   [5] *Ib.*, 224.   [6] A, x, 250.
[7] A, 1802, xi, 91.   [8] *J. de Phys.*, 1806, lxii, 131.   [9] *Ann. Chim.*, 1827, xxxiv, 147.

form a purple colour which immediately changes to yellowish-brown (etwas Purpurfarbe, wie ich sehr oft bemerkt, zum Vorschein kommt, welche augen-blicklich in das Gelbbraune übergehet). He obtained a more stable red col-loidal solution of gold by dissolving in water the red mass formed by heating fulminating gold with borax.[1] On standing, a dark precipitate separated which could be washed free from borax but still gave a coloured solution with water. He gives a long and detailed description of the colour phenomena observed with different gold preparations. He says:[2] 'With metallic gold it depends entirely on the grade of sub-division whether it has a metallic lustre or a purple colour, or different gradations between metallic lustre and a purple colour' (es bey dem metallischen Golde bloss auf den Grad seiner Zertheilung ankommt, ob Metallglanz oder eine Purpurfarbe oder verschiedene Abstuffungen zwischen Metallglanz und Purpurfarbe entstehen). Gold in ruby glass is metallic gold. To bring gold into the finest state of subdivision 'depends principally on an intimate mixture of it with a large amount of such a sub-stance as can again easily be separated from it'.

Richter observed[3] that ignited metallic oxides dissolve in acids with diffi-culty. From experiments on fulminating gold and ammonium nitrate,[4] he calculated the composition of ammonia as 19·11 hydrogen and 80·89 nitrogen; Berthollet, by decomposing the gas by sparking had found 19·33 and 80·67. Richter[5] thought he had discovered a new metal, *niccolanum*, in nickel ores, but later experiments by Trommsdorff, Gehlen, Hisinger, and Murray showed that it was impure nickel, containing cobalt, iron and arsenic.

Other publications by Richter, mostly short papers (those in Crell's *Annalen* are often included in the volumes of his *Neuern Genenstände*) are: a criticism of Rettenberg on a hydrostatic law,[6] the inflammation of metals by sulphur in the absence of oxygen (saying that the phlogistic and antiphlogistic theories are compatible),[7] the specific gravities of aqueous alcohols, with tables,[8] new observations on phlogiston (a reply to Gmelin),[9] the preparation of succinic acid by the action of sulphuric acid on lead succinate,[10] the purification of barium salts,[11] a new quantitative order of the elements (discussing strontia),[12] metallurgical phlogometry (dealing with the absolute weight of phlogiston, the mutual displacement of metals and its relation to the law of neutrality),[13] an analysis of an ironstone,[14] freeing alcohol from water (with calcium chloride; density of absolute alcohol 0·791),[15] the purification of manganese from iron (with potassium tartrate),[16] the preparation of pure citric acid (by decomposing calcium citrate with sulphuric acid) and on iron tartrate,[17] the preparation of concentrated formic and acetic acids (by distilling the potassium salts with sulphuric acid; formic acid was still made by distilling ants),[18] observations on phlogometry (the 'triangular series'),[19] reduction of platinum salts by mer-cury (and relation to the series),[20] the reduction of red lead by sulphur (with

[1] A, xi, 185. [2] *Ib.*, 195 f. [3] *Ib.*, 98. [4] *Ib.*, 118, 124.
[5] *N. allgem. J. Chem.*, 1805, iv, 392. [6] Crell's *Ann.*, 1793, II, 108.
[7] *Ib.*, 1794, II, 291. [8] *Ib.*, 1795, II, 17. [9] *Ib.*, 1795, II, 414.
[10] A, 1796, vi, 165. [11] Crell's *Ann.*, 1796, I, 333. [12] *Ib.*, 1796, I, 442.
[13] *Ib.*, 1796, I, 448. [14] *Ib.*, 1796, I, 540. [15] *Ib.*, 1796, II, 211.
[16] *Ib.*, 1796, II, 300. [17] *Ib.*, 1796, II, 380.
[18] A, 1796, vi, 1. [19] Crell's *Ann.*, 1797, II, 15. [20] *Ib.*, 1797, II, 202.

calculations of the reacting quantities and the proof that Wiegleb's data are inconsistent),[1] the detection of arsenic in refined sulphur (with a discussion of the law of proportions),[2] the determination of the contents of aqueous solutions and mean specific gravity (with a reply to Jäger's criticism),[3] the substrate of oxygen in fluoric acid (with a reply to criticisms),[4] the distillation of fuming nitric acid (with a calculation of reacting quantities),[5] on agust earth (see p. 588),[6] on palladium (refuting Chenevix's claim that it was platinum amalgam),[7] on pure nickel as a noble metal and on pure nickel and cobalt salts,[8] on the need for using excess of sulphuric acid in the preparation of nitric acid,[9] the analysis of a salt from a vitriol mother-liquor,[10] the purification of uranium salts,[11] metallic chromium,[12] the purity of reduced nickel,[13] and a theory of liquation.[14] Richter was no mere theorist; his extensive experimental work was frequently quoted by contemporary and later chemists, although his theories were neglected.

LINK

Heinrich Friedrich Link (Hildesheim, 2 February 1767–Berlin, 1 January 1851), professor of natural history, botany and chemistry in Rostock (1792), of chemistry and botany in Breslau (1811), and of botany in Berlin (1815), published on botany, geology, and chemistry.[15] He discussed phlogiston,[16] chemical affinity,[17] Berthollet's theory of affinity,[18] and attraction and affinity.[19] He investigated the action of sulphuric acid on vegetable matter,[20] double salts and acid sulphates,[21] chemical reactions of solids produced by trituration,[22] considered fluidity, solidity, and the solution of bodies,[23] and made some of the earliest observations on the mode of separation of crystals from solutions, in some cases finding that they first formed as 'globulites'.[24] He published a book on antiphlogistic chemistry.[25]

[1] *Ib.*, 1797, II, 287.   [2] *Ib.*, 1798, II, 449.   [3] *Ib.*, 1799, II, 13.
[4] *Ib.*, 1799, II, 105.   [5] *Ib.*, 1799, II, 199.
[6] *N. allgem. J. Chem.*, 1803, i, 445; 1805, v, 352.   [7] *Ib.*, 1803, i, 547.
[8] *Ib.*, 1804, ii, 61; 1804, iii, 244, 444; 1805, v, 311. Richter's work on nickel was very good. R. Tupputi, *Ann. Chim.*, 1811, lxxviii, 133–76; 1811, lxxix, 153–98, also published some excellent experiments on nickel and its compounds.
[9] *Ib.*, 1805, iv, 194.   [10] *Ib.*, iv, 564.   [11] *Ib.*, iv, 402.
[12] *Ib.*, 1805, v, 352.   [13] *Ib.*, v, 699.   [14] *Ib.*, 1806, vi, 355.
[15] Poggendorff, (1), i, 1469; *Roy. Soc. Cat. Sci. Papers*, 1870, iv, 35.
[16] Crell's *Ann.*, 1790, II, 473: on his pamphlet, *Bemerkungen über das Phlogiston*, 1790 (19 pp.).
[17] *Ib.*, 1791, I, 484–90.   [18] *J. Chem.* (Gehlen), 1807, iii, 232–47.
[19] *Ann. Phys.*, 1808, xxx, 12.   [20] *J. Chem.* (Schweigger), 1814, xi, 249.
[21] Crell's *Ann.*, 1796, I, 26.   [22] *J. Chem.* (Schweigger), 1815, xiv, 193.
[23] *Ann. Chim.*, 1798, xxv, 113–25.
[24] *Ann. Phys.*, 1839, xlvi, 258 (Ueber die erste Entstehung der Kristalle); Partington, *Advanced Treatise on Physical Chemistry*, 1952, iii, 25, and refs.
[25] *Die Grundwahrheiten der neueren Chemie, nach Fourcroy, etc.*, 8°, Leipzig and Rostock, 1806, 2 ed. 1815.

CHAPTER XV

CHEMISTRY IN GREAT BRITAIN AND IRELAND

After Priestley's departure for America and Cavendish's abandonment of chemistry there was no prominent figure in the science in Great Britain, and it was said there were only ten chemists in the country.[1] Before the emergence of Davy and Dalton, however, there were several British and Irish chemists whose researches and publications are most decidedly worthy of mention.

DOBSON

Matthew Dobson was the son of a nonconformist minister in Yorkshire. He graduated in Edinburgh and was physician in the Liverpool Infirmary (1770–1780), but retired owing to ill-health and went to Bath, where he died on 25 July 1784.[2] He assisted Cullen in his experiments on the cold produced by evaporation.[3] He published on the medicinal use of fixed air[4] and in 1776,[5] before Cruickshank in 1797 (see p. 530), showed that diabetic urine on evaporation gives a solid mass looking and tasting like raw sugar, and capable of alcoholic and acetous fermentation. From the sweet taste of the blood serum of diabetic patients, he concluded that the sugar is present in the blood and accumulates owing to failure in assimilation (it is present in small amounts, he found, in normal serum), and also to an abnormal fermentation similar to that occurring in grain on malting. He was, however, unable to isolate the sugar from serum. Crystalline sugar, identified by alcoholic and acetous fermentation and oxidation to oxalic acid, was separated in a pure state from diabetic urine by Johann Peter Frank (Rotalben, 19 March 1745–Vienna, 21 April 1821).[6] The identity of diabetic sugar and glucose was established by E. Peligot.[7] Dobson published an account of 'the annual evaporation in Liverpool' dealing with the humidity of the air; he thought air and heat were the causes of evaporation.[8]

---

[1] *Allgem. J. Chem.* (Scherer), 1801, v, 126.

[2] O. T. Williams, *Liverpool Medical and Chirurgical Journal*, 1912, xxxii, 245–54; F. W. Lowndes, *ib.*, 1916, xxxvi, 127–9.

[3] Black, *Lectures on Chemistry*, 1803, i, 162.

[4] *A Medical Commentary on Fixed Air . . .*, Chester, 1779; 2 ed., 1785, with an appendix *On the Efficacy of the Solution of Fixed Alkaline Salts Saturated with Fixable Air, in the Stone and Gravel*; 3 ed., enlarged, 1787.

[5] Experiments and Observations on the Urine in Diabetes Mellitus in *Medical Observations and Enquiries. By a Society of Physicians in London*, London, 1776, v, 298–316.

[6] *De Curandis Hominum Morbis Epitome*, Mannheim, 7 pts., 1792–1825; 1794, V, i, 46 f.; Papaspyros, *History of Diabetes Mellitus*, 1952.

[7] *Ann. Chim.*, 1838, lxvii, 113 (136); Lippmann, (1), i, 326.

[8] *Obs. Phys.*, 1779, xii, 81; 'tr. from English'.

PERCIVAL

Thomas Percival (Warrington, 29 September 1740–Manchester, 30 August 1804), student at Warrington Academy and friend of Priestley, then at Edinburgh, toured the Continent, M.D. Leyden 1765 with a dissertation *De frigore*, F.R.S. 1765, began to practise in Manchester in 1767. His publications are contained in the *Philosophical Transactions* and in his *Essays Medical and Experimental*, 1767, 2 ed., 2 vols. 1772–3; and *The Literary, Moral and Medical Works*, 4 vols., 1807. He was much interested in vital statistics and proposed legislation for factories. From weekly meetings in his house the Manchester Literary and Philosophical Society was founded in 1781 with Percival as president.

The Manchester Literary and Philosophical Society originated from meetings of scientists and industrialists in the Nonconformist Academy in Warrington. The meetings of the Manchester Society were regularly recorded from 1781 and papers read at Meetings were published from 1785. It is laid down in Law VIII that 'the subjects of conversation comprehend natural philosophy, theoretical and experimental chemistry, polite literature, general politics, commerce, and the arts'. Some of its members supported the French Revolution, Thomas Cooper and James Watt jr. being elected deputies of the French National Assembly, but the Society refused to be involved in politics and they resigned.[1]

Percival attempted in 1783 to found a Dissenting Academy in Manchester on the lines of the Warrington Academy and Dalton was one of the teachers. Percival made much use of cod-liver oil, raw and also emulsified with soap, in the Manchester Hospital. He condemned tea but praised coffee. His papers included experiments on Peruvian bark (the strength of decoctions of which he measured by the colour produced by iron salts), ink, cantharides, columbo and orris roots, calculi, and hard water (which he knew produced goitre). He could not confirm Boyle's observation that hard water became soft on exposure to air for a few days; he found (to his surprise) that soft water attacked lead more than hard; he measured the hardness roughly by the curdling of soap. He made a great number of experiments on the arrest of putrefaction by various substances, and investigated Buxton and Matlock waters.[2]

THOMAS HENRY

Thomas Henry (Wrexham, 26 October (O.S.) 1734–Manchester, 18 June 1816)[3] was descended from a family long settled in Antrim in Ireland; he was apprenticed to an apothecary in Wrexham in Wales, then served in Knutsford and Oxford, starting on his own account in Knutsford in 1759; he moved to Manchester in 1764, where he met Percival. Henry became F.R.S. in 1775, and president of the Manchester Literary and Philosophical Society in 1807.

---

[1] W. H. Brindley, *J. Roy. Inst. Chem.*, 1955, 61 (portrs.).   [2] *Phil. Trans.*, 1772, lxii, 455.
[3] Faujas Saint-Fond, *Voyages en Angleterre*, etc., 1797, ii, 302; W. Henry, *Manchester Mem.*, 1819, iii, 204; read 1817 (also as a pamphlet, with the funeral sermon, Manchester, 1819); id., *Ann. Phil.*, 1819, xiv, 161; Sutton, DNB, 1891, xxvi, 127; Partington, *J. Soc. Chem. Ind.*, 1933, lii, 478.

In 1771 he published an improved method of preparing magnesia.[1] 'Henry's magnesia' was long a favourite domestic remedy. A solution of magnesium bicarbonate ('liquid magnesia') was introduced as a medicine by Dr. Murray of Belfast.[2]

Henry found that lead dissolves in water impregnated with nitrous air (nitric oxide),[3] investigated the effect of fixed air (carbon dioxide) on plants,[4] and the preservation of sea water from putrefaction by quicklime.[5] He published on the advantages of literature and philosophy,[6] on magnesia,[7] and on fermentation (including a substitute for yeast).[8] He published *Memoirs of Albert de Haller*, Warrington, 1783 (price 2s. 6d.). Some of Henry's writings were collected and published (price 2s. 6d.) as:

Experiments and Observations on the following subjects. 1. On the preparation, calcination and medicinal uses of Magnesia Alba. 2. On the Solvent Qualities of Calcined Magnesia. 3. On the variety in the Solvent Powers of Quick-Lime, when used in different quantities. 4. On Various Absorbents, as promoting or retarding putrefaction. 5. On the comparative Antiseptic Powers of Vegetable Infusions prepared with Lime, etc. 6. On the Sweetening Properties of Fixed Air; London, 1773, xvi (errata), 142 pp.

He translated Lavoisier's *Opuscules* as *Essays* (1776), with notes and corrections (see p. 372). He found that fixed air in the pure state killed vegetation but promoted it when diluted; he thought that fixed air 'is the exciting cause as well as the product of fermentation' and used soda-water mixed with spirit as a drink. Bewley first made 'soda-water' by saturating a solution of carbonate of soda with fixed air, Priestley having used water only (see p. 247). Priestley[9] printed a letter from Henry of 13 December 1776, reporting experiments made in December 1775, and January and December 1776, on the antiseptic properties of fixed air in preserving fruits and milk (which, he suggested, should be churned with it). Henry published an interesting memoir on dyeing:

Considerations relative to the Wool, Silk, and Cotton, as Objects of the Art of Dying [sic]; on the various Preparations, and Mordants, requisite for these different Substances; and on the Nature and Properties of Colouring Matter. Together with some Observations on the Theory of Dying in general, and particularly the Turkey Red.[10]

Turkey red dyeing was introduced by John Wilson of Ainsworth in 1762, and bleaching was generally introduced into the Manchester district in 1763. Henry adopted the chemical theory; the unequal powers of wool, silk, linen, and cotton for taking up and fixing dyes he regarded as due to different chemical attractions. Mordants have affinities for the fabric and the colour and

---

[1] *Med. Trans. Coll. of Physicians London*, 1772, ii, 226–34 (read Sept. 1771); repr. in *Experiments and Observations*, 1773; *A Letter to Dr. Glass, containing a reply to his examination of Mr. Henry's Strictures on the Magnesia sold under the name of the late Mr. Glass. To which are added some further testimonies in support of the truth of those strictures*, 8°, London, 1774, 31 pp.

[2] Thomson, (4), 1831, ii, 531.

[3] Letter in Priestley, *Experiments and Observations on Air*, 1774, i, 323.

[4] *Manchester Mem.*, 1785, ii, 341.

[5] *Ib.*, 1785, i, 41.

[6] *Ib.*, 1785, i, 7.

[7] *Ib.*, 1785, i, 448.

[8] *Ib.*, 1785, ii, 257.

[9] E & O, 1777, iii, 369.

[10] *Manchester Mem.*, 1790, iii, 343–408.

so link them together. A solution of acetate of alumina, he found, is preferable to alum since the acetic acid is volatile and also has a smaller affinity for alumina than has sulphuric acid. Henry lectured to practical men on dyeing, bleaching, and calico-printing in the Manchester College of Arts and Sciences, and petitioned Parliament successfully against a monopoly of foreign dyers attempting to exploit bleaching by chlorine.

FORDYCE

George Fordyce (Aberdeen, 18 November 1736–London, 25 May 1802), M.D. Edinburgh 1758, a pupil of Cullen, settled in London in 1759 and began a course of lectures on chemistry which he continued for 30 years, materia medica and medicine being added in 1764. The lectures were from 7 to 10 a.m. six days a week for four months. Fordyce was a slow, hesitating lecturer, using no notes, and was careless in dress and manner: fond of society, he frequently began his lecture without having had any sleep. In 1770 he became physician to St. Thomas's Hospital.[1] Besides an *Elements of Agriculture and Vegetation* (Edinburgh, 1765, 2 ed., London, 1771, 3 ed. 1779), and medical works, he published a *Syllabus of Lectures on Chemistry* (12°, n.d.). Several full manuscript copies of his lectures are extant; I have seen one (4 vols. 8°, of 100 lectures written from August 1784 to December 1785; 745 pp. and index). He became F.R.S. in 1776, and communicated papers on experiments on living in a strongly heated room,[2] on the light produced by inflammation,[3] an examination of ores in William Hunter's Museum,[4] a new method of assaying copper ore,[5] experiments on heat,[6] and on the cause of the additional weight which metals acquire by calcination.[7] In the last he describes experiments on dissolving zinc in acid, precipitating, and calcining the oxide, and he concluded that the increase in weight and the inflammable air evolved both come from water. In his chemical lectures, illustrated by experiments, he defines chemistry as 'that Science or part of Natural Philosophy which points out the properties of particular Substances in as far as depends upon their internal structure'. There is a mechanical limit at the smallest integral parts of matter, with which chemistry deals, since they possess the properties of the larger masses. Air and water are the most simple substances known. A table of elements includes:

I. Salts soluble in water and not inflammable:
   (1) acids (vitriolic, nitrous, muriatic, acetous, tartar, native vegetable, distilled vegetable, of borax, native animal, of benzoin, phosphoric, of amber, of spar, volatile vitriolic), (2) alkalis (fixed vegetable, fixed fossil, volatile).
II. Inflammables:
   (1) oils (expressed, essential, empyreumatic, fossil, aether, oleum dulce, phosphorus), (2) alcohol, (3) sulphur.
III. Metals of great specific gravity but opaque:
   (1) malleable (gold, silver, lead, tin, copper, iron, mercury — to which the student

[1] [Wells], *Gentleman's Magazine*, 1802, lxxii, I, 588; Chalmers, *General Biographical Dict.*, 1814, xiv, 474; Payne, DNB, 1889, xix, 432; *Phil. Trans.* abgd., 1809, xiv, 93.
[2] In Blagden, *Phil. Trans.*, 1775, lxv, 111.
[3] *Ib.*, 1776, lxvi, 504.   [4] *Ib.*, 1779, lxix, 527.   [5] *Ib.*, 1780, lxx, 30.
[6] *Ib.*, 1787, lxxvii, 310 (see p. 620).   [7] *Ib.*, 1792, lxxxii, 374.

has added platina), (2) not malleable (zinc, antimony, cobalt, arsenic, bismuth, platina — struck out by the student — nickel, magnesius).

IV. Earths, which by fusion with 'fixt alkalies' form glasses (absorbent, calcareous, magnesia, of alum, crystalline, argillaceous, heavy spar, talk, asbestes, serpentine stone, shirl, zeolites &c.).

V. Water.

VI. Airs, vapours in the common heat of the atmosphere (respirable, gas or fixt air, inflammable, nitrous, foetid or hepatic, phlogisticated).

VII. Animal and vegetable mucilages soluble in water, decomposed by fire.

Fordyce then considers 'the powers by which substances act upon one another', distinguishing mechanical mixture from chemical attraction which combines the smallest integral particles of one body with the smallest integral particles of another body so as to form an integral particle of a substance different from either. The elements are not destroyed in this process. Attraction and repulsion constitute all the properties of matter. A *menstruum* and a *solvend* form a solution. Attraction is elective; one metal precipitates another from a solution in acid because it attracts the acid more. He gives a table of elective attractions similar to Geoffroy's (see p. 52). Compound elective attraction operates in the case of two compounds which decompose one another. Heat tends to diminish or destroy attractions.

He then deals with solution, precipitation, fermentation, crystallisation, and diffusion (which occurs on dilution of a solution). One integral particle of one body may unite with one or two particles of another body. This extended Bryan Higgins's one to one ratio (see p. 734) before the publication by William Higgins (1789; see p. 742). A candle ceases to burn in a confined volume of air when it saturates it with phlogiston. Water may be converted into earth by distilling in a glass retort. He describes the lead chamber process for oil of vitriol but hardly mentions chlorine in dealing with muriatic acid. He mentions sodium acetate as 'a crystallisable salt not yet named'. The compounds of acetous acid with phlogiston are alcohol, ether, and oleum dulce. He describes the preparation of acid of tartar from tartar by way of calcium tartrate, citric and oxalic acids by way of the lead salts. The distilled vegetable acid is used in medicine as 'tar water', and he mentions the acid of ants. The volatile vitriolic acid is a compound of vitriolic acid and phlogiston. Every acid will unite with an alkali to form a neutral salt but only in a certain proportion: they unite by the first mode of saturation, forming perfect chemical compounds, but tartar seems to be a compound of a neutral salt and an acid. An alkali is separated from its gas by quicklime, which attracts gas more readily and forms chalk, the alkali being rendered quite pure or caustic. The older processes of separating fossil alkali (soda) from salt are given.

Fordyce (Lecture 11) pointed out that 'since each of the smallest integral parts of one body unites with the smallest integral parts of another body it is clear . . . that two substances can only combine with one another in one proportion'. One of the smallest integral particles of one body may unite with only one of the smallest integral parts of another body (see above). 'Saturation is of three kinds, 1st when we have dissolved a solvend in a menstruum in one proportion so that it cannot be diffused through either of its elements: we call that the first mode of Saturation: but when the Compound may be diffused thro' one of the elements then there is an appearance as if you might take the elements in as large a quantity as you please. We call this the second mode of saturation. The third case is when the compound may be diffused thro' either of its elements. In this case it has been called the third mode of saturation.'

The increase in weight of a metal on calcination has been explained by some by supposing that 'phlogiston was light and when it was separated the metal had its full weight. Others have supposed that there was respirable air or Gas absorbed, or something we could not know any thing at all about' (Lecture 90). 'Formerly every thing that distilled in drops were called phlegm and those that did not distil in drops but ran down the sides of the vessel they were distilled in and formed stria were called spirits' (Lecture 55). 'We may have the same elements in the same proportion in two compounds totally different from one another' (an anticipation of isomerism). In fermentation there is a 'separation of the elements of a compound and the recombination of them in a different mode so as to form a new compound' (Lecture 60).

In discussing fermentation Fordyce distinguishes 'gas' and 'an intoxicating vapour called Gas Sylvestre' (Lecture 63). The brass alcoholometer is described (Lecture 68).

Inflammable substances contain phlogiston and another substance. 'Inflammation is a decomposition of an inflammable substance by means of respirable air', the air uniting with the phlogiston and detaching the other element. In inflammation there is a compound elective attraction (see p. 628). The flame produced by inflammation is of a blue colour, and the bottom of a candle flame, 'when the flame is not tinged with the yellowness of the Empyreumatic Oil is of a blue colour' (Lecture 44). In the treatment of phlogiston the statements are intentionally vague and cautious (Lecture 45). Fordyce repeats his statement (see p. 620) that water gains $\frac{1}{2000}$ of its weight on conversion into ice (Lecture 48).

PEARSON

George Pearson (Rotherham, 1751–London, 9 November 1828), a pupil of Black, M.D. Edinburgh 1773, F.R.S. 1791, also studied in France, Germany, and Holland, practised as a physician in Doncaster and London, and became head-physician in St. George's Hospital, London.[1] Pearson was one of the first to accept the antiphlogistic theory, and translated the *Nomenclature Chimique* in 1794 (see p. 481). He introduced the use of sodium phosphate in medicine in 1787.[2] He prepared it from phosphoric acid made from phosphorus and nitric acid, and sold it at what he considered the low price of 8s. per lb. He investigated James's powder,[3] an Indian wax resembling Chinese *pé-la* (tree wax)[4] and Indian *wootz* steel.[5] He analysed ancient copper, iron, etc.

[1] Hartog, DNB, 1895, xliv, 165; Faujas Saint-Fond, *Voyages en Angleterre*, etc., Paris, 1797, ii, 310 f.; portrs. in *Phil. Mag.*, 1804, xvii, and (from a drawing in the Royal Society) in Sir R. Hadfield, *Faraday and his Metallurgical Researches*, 1931, 37.

[2] *Obs. Phys.*, 1788, xxxiii, 147; Chaptal, (1), 1791, iii, 342; Thomson, (2), 1807, ii, 569 f.

[3] *Phil. Trans.*, 1791, lxxxi, 317.

[4] *Ib.*, 1794, lxxxiv, 383.   [5] *Ib.*, 1795, lxxxv, 322.

arms, utensils, and implements, finding tinned copper and Roman soldering with pure tin (no lead); no zinc was found in the alloys.[1] He published on the constituents of potatoes,[2] and analysed Buxton water.[3] Pearson demonstrated the presence of carbon in carbonates, obtaining it[4] in a quantitative experiment in which phosphorus was heated with sodium carbonate, at the same time discovering calcium phosphide by heating phosphorus with quicklime and finding that it gave off a spontaneously inflammable gas when treated with water. He collected this gas and called it 'phosphoric air', showing that it lost its property of spontaneous inflammability on standing over water, when some phosphorus was deposited. In 1797 he decomposed water into hydrogen and oxygen by electric sparks (see Vol. IV).[5] Pearson also investigated urinary concretions (calculi),[6] expectorated matter,[7] pus and mucus,[8] and black spots on the lungs and the black bronchial glands,[9] due to soot. He recommended green vitriol as a manure.[10]

WOLLASTON

William Hyde Wollaston (East Dereham, Norfolk, 6 August 1766–London, 22 December 1828),[11] of a Staffordshire family, was one of seventeen children of the Rev. Francis Wollaston, F.R.S. (1731–1815) and great-grandson of William Wollaston (1659–1724), author of *The Religion of Nature Delineated* (1722).[12] He was admitted pensioner in 1782 in Caius College, Cambridge, graduated M.B. in 1787 and M.D. in 1793. In 1789 he left for London. In 1792 he began to practise as a physician in Bury St. Edmunds, after a few months in Huntingdon. He returned to London in 1797 and was a candidate for the position of physician to St. George's Hospital, but the post was given to Pemberton. This is said to have disappointed Wollaston, and in 1800 he abandoned practice (probably because of his sensitiveness) and devoted himself to applied science and research. He was elected F.R.S. in 1793 (while he was at Bury St. Edmunds), became Secretary in 1804, and Vice-President (1821–8), and acted as President in 1820 on the death of Sir Joseph Banks but stood down in favour of Davy. He became an associate of the Paris Institut in

[1] *Ib.*, 1796, lxxxvi, 395.
[2] *Experiments on the Constituent Parts of the Potatoe Root*, London, 1795.
[3] *Experiments and Observations for investigating the Chemical History of the Tepid Springs of Buxton*, 2 vols., London, 1784.
[4] *Phil. Trans.*, 1792, lxxxii, 289.
[5] *Phil. Trans.*, 1797, lxxxvii, 142 (abstr.); *Nicholson's J.*, 1797, i, 241, 299, 349 (in full); *Ann. Phys.*, 1799, ii, 154.
[6] *Phil. Trans.*, 1798, lxxxviii, 15.   [7] *Ib.*, 1809, xcix, 313.
[8] *Ib.*, 1810, c, 294.   [9] *Ib.*, 1813, ciii, 159.
[10] *Nicholson's J.*, 1805, x, 206.
[11] Anon., *Amer. J. Sci.*, 1830, xvii, 159; Anon., *Brit. Quart. Rev.*, 1846, iv, 81; Sir J. Barrow, *Sketches of the Royal Society and the Royal Society Club*, 1849, 54; Brande, 1848, I, cii; S. Brown, *Essays*, 1858, i, 42; F. L. Gilbert, *Notes and Records of the Royal Society*, 1952, ix, 311; 1955, xi, 256; id., in *Platinum Metal Exhibition, The Institution of Metallurgists*, London, 1953 [anon. art., pp. 3–26]; Gordon, *Nature*, 1934, cxxxiv, 86; Hadfield, *Faraday and his Metallurgical Researches*, 1931, 43, plate x (fine portr.); W. Henry, *Elements of Experimental Chemistry*, 11 ed., 1829, i, p. ix; Thomson, (1), ii, 247; *Proc. Phil. Soc. Glasgow*, 1850, iii, 135; Thorpe, *Essays*, 1902, 557; W. Walker, *Memoirs of the Distinguished Men of Science*, etc., 1862, 216; Wayling, *Science Progress*, 1927, xxii, 81 (portr.); id., *Nature*, 1928, cxxii, 970; G. Wilson, *Religio-Chemici*, London and Cambridge, 1862, 253.
[12] Saverien, 1761, ii, 297 and portr. in 1763, iii, at end.

1823. He was associated with Smithson Tennant in a process for malleable platinum (see p. 703) which Wollaston published shortly before his death, after a long and painful illness, a tumour of the brain.

Wollaston was a careful and accurate experimenter, inventing many useful pieces of apparatus. He was perhaps too cautious and meticulous and he had the misfortune to be outshone by the brilliance of Davy, and to be anticipated by Dalton in the enunciation of the chemical atomic theory. Thomson[1] says

FIG. 55. W. H. WOLLASTON, 1766–1828.

Wollaston 'had been struck with the proportions of oxygen in my table of metallic oxides[2] and he had begun to study the subject when my account of the Daltonian theory[3] prevented him from proceeding with his investigations', the result of which, otherwise, 'would have been the discovery of the atomic theory.' It is very doubtful if Wollaston would ever have had the courage to publish this theory, even if it had occurred to him. Wollaston was a personal friend of Berzelius, who greatly admired him.[4]

Wollaston never admitted even his friends to his laboratory. When a foreign scientist called on him and asked to see this, Wollaston merely showed him a tea-tray containing a blowpipe, some platinum foil, a few watch-glasses and some test-tubes. He was able to work with small and simple apparatus. Soon after a great voltaic battery had been constructed by Children, the Secretary

[1] Ann. Phil., 1814, iii, 331 f.   [2] (2), 2 ed., 1804, i, 272–3.   [3] (2), 3 ed., 1807, iii, 425 f.
[4] Berzelius, Bref, Uppsala, 1914, I, iii (correspondence with Marcet).

of the Royal Society, which produced brilliant deflagrations of metallic wires, Wollaston met a friend in the street 'and seizing his button (his constant habit when speaking on any subject of interest) he led him into a secluded corner; when, taking from his waistcoat pocket a tailor's thimble, which contained a galvanic arrangement, and pouring into it the contents of a small phial, he instantly heated a platinum wire to a red heat',[1] no doubt a fine 'Wollaston wire' (see p. 700).

J. Davy[2] says 'some accidental annoyance in the medical profession made him, I think, jealous and reserved in the earlier part of his life; but latterly he became far more agreeable and confiding, and was a warm and kind friend and a pleasant social companion'.

Besides being one of the most accomplished chemists of his time, Wollaston was eminent in other fields. His 39 papers in the *Philosophical Transactions* (out of a total of his 56 publications) deal with astronomy, optics, mechanics, acoustics, mineralogy (he was a keen geologist), crystallography, physiology, pathology, and botany as well as chemistry. Thomson[3] said: 'Dr. Wollaston's knowledge was more varied, and his taste less exclusive than any other philosopher of his time, except Mr. Cavendish.'

In 1809[4] Wollaston invented what he calls the 'reflective goniometer' for the measurement of crystal angles, and by means of this instrument he was able to show[5] that the rhombohedral cleavage angles of calcite ($74°\ 55'$), bitter spar or dolomite ($73°\ 45'$), and iron spar or spathic iron ore ($73°\ 0'$), were not identical. He invented a reflexion refractometer for determining the refractive indices of liquids.[6] The dark lines in the solar spectrum, afterwards carefully mapped by Fraunhofer, were discovered by Wollaston in 1802, and he also discovered, independently of Ritter, that invisible rays extend beyond the violet in the solar spectrum, which are capable of blackening silver chloride.[7] His paper on the action of a diamond in cutting glass[8] is interesting, and his cryophorus 'for freezing at a distance'[9] is still familiar in good lectures on physics. Wollaston's cryophorus was much smaller than those now used; it is the same as the 'pulse glass' described by Franklin for boiling water under reduced pressure,[10] but Franklin does not mention its use for freezing water. Leslie froze water by evaporation under an air-pump receiver and absorbing the vapour in sulphuric acid or oatmeal in a dish.[11] In 1801[12] Wollaston

[1] Paris, *Life of Davy*, 1831, i, 147.   [2] *Life of Sir H. Davy*, 1836, i, 258.
[3] (1), ii, 248.   [4] *Phil. Trans.*, 1809, xcix, 253.   [5] *Phil. Trans.*, 1812, cii, 159.
[6] *Phil. Trans.*, 1802, xcii, 365; Partington, (6), iv, 27.
[7] *Phil. Trans.*, 1802, xcii, 365, *Ann. Phys.*, 1811, xxxix, 291; Ritter, *Ann. Phys.*, 1801, vii, 527; 1802, xii, 409.
[8] *Phil. Trans.*, 1816, cvi, 265.
[9] *Phil. Trans.*, 1813, ciii, 71 (the name *cryophorus* is given).
[10] Franklin, *Experiments and Observations on Electricity*, London, 1769, 489 (letter of 1768), not named; Black, *Lectures on Chemistry*, Edinburgh, 1803, i, 179 and plate ('pulse glass'); Partington, *Advanced Physical Chemistry*, 1952, iii, p. lix.
[11] *A Short Account of Experiments and Instruments depending on the Relations of Air to Heat and Moisture*, Edinburgh, 1813, 140, plate figs. 9 and 10, referring, on p. 137, to Wollaston's recent proposal of 'a very simple and portable apparatus, by which a small portion of water, at a short distance from a freezing mixture, may at any time be visibly converted into ice'. An interesting illustration showing Leslie's, Wollaston's and Marcet's (p. 707) apparatus, is given in Mrs. Marcet's *Conversations on Chemistry*, 1817, i, 138, plate v; see also Brande, 1848, i, 83.
[12] *Phil. Trans.*, 1801, xci, 427.

established the identity of frictional and voltaic electricity (see Vol. IV). By observations on the satellites of Jupiter, he concluded (incorrectly) that this planet has no atmosphere, and that the atmosphere of the earth is limited. He thought that this proved that the atmosphere contains only a finite number of repelling molecules, and hence that matter is not indefinitely divisible.[1]

Whilst in practice in Bury St. Edmunds Wollaston published an important memoir 'on urinary and gouty concretions',[2] which he showed contained in different cases uric acid ('lithic acid') combined with soda, phosphate of magnesia and ammonia 'in the fusible calculus', already noticed by Tennant, and oxalate of lime in the 'mulberry calculus'. He found that the second and third species were separately infusible before the blowpipe but when mixed were fusible. It is said[3] that he was once performing a blowpipe experiment on a calculus, and finding it infusible and requiring a little calcium phosphate, he supplied it from a few shavings of his ivory paper knife, when the specimen instantly fused. In 1810 he discovered cystine ('cystic oxide') in a rare calculus.[4] The name cystic oxide was changed to cystin by Berzelius,[5] since 'with very few exceptions all organic bodies are oxides'. It was analysed by Prout[6] and Lassaigne[7] with very different results, but both found carbon, hydrogen, oxygen, and nitrogen. Prout's analysis gave $C_3H_6NO_4$. Baudrimont and Malaguti[8] first showed that it contains sulphur. Other publications on calculi are by Pearson,[9] Brande,[10] Fourcroy and Vauquelin[11] and Yelloly.[12] Another rare constituent of calculi, xanthine, was discovered by Marcet (p. 707). Brande denied that ammonium urate could occur in calculi, but it was shown to be present by Prout.[13]

Wollaston became interested in platinum metals by Smithson Tennant (see p. 704) whilst a student in Cambridge, and his most useful discovery and one which brought him considerable wealth (£30,000 is mentioned but may be too high), is that of making platinum malleable. The invention was made after 1801, probably about 1804; it was kept secret, Wollaston engaging in the manufacture himself in a shed at the bottom of his garden, but he published it in 1829 shortly before his death, and it is the earliest application of powder metallurgy.[14] This was effected by dissolving native platinum in aqua regia, precipitating ammonium chloroplatinate with ammonium chloride, decomposing it by heat, washing the finely divided residue of platinum, compressing a mud of the moist powder, heating white hot, and hammering to an ingot which could be beaten into foil or drawn into wire.

[1] Phil. Trans., 1822, cxii, 89.   [2] Phil. Trans., 1797, lxxxvii, 386; see Pearson, p. 695.
[3] Paris, Life of Davy, 1831, i, 148.
[4] Phil. Trans., 1810, c, 223; Ann. Chim., 1810, lxxvi, 21; Nicholson's J., 1811, xxviii, 222; cystine is $CO_2H.CH(NH_2).CH_2.S.S.CH_2.CH(NH_2).CO_2H$.
[5] Lehrbuch der Chemie, 1831, IV, i, 399.
[6] Med. Chirurg. Trans., 1817, viii, 526, urea, uric acid; 1818, ix, 472, uric acid, cystic oxide.
[7] Ann. Chim., 1823, xxiii, 328.   [8] Compt. Rend., 1837, v, 394.
[9] Phil. Trans., 1798, lxxxviii, 75.
[10] In Hatchett, ib., 1806, xcvi, 372; 1808, xcviii, II, 223; 1810, c, 136.
[11] See p. 549; Fourcroy, (1), 1801, x, 204 f., cites Pearson but not Wollaston.
[12] Phil. Trans., 1829, cxix, 55.   [13] Ann. Phil., 1820, xv, 436.
[14] Bakerian Lecture, 'On a method of rendering Platina malleable': Phil. Trans., 1829, xcix, 1; Partington, (6), iii, 3.

The first platinum apparatus was made by Count von Sickingen,[1] Austrian ambassador in Paris, whose father (1702–86) was an alchemist.[2] According to Nordenskiöld,[3] the first to fuse pure platinum, with the oxy-hydrogen blow-pipe, was Erik Swartz (1762–84) in the Bergs-Collegium in Stockholm in 1784,[4] and there is a thick platinum spoon (sp.gr. 20·89 at 19°) in the mineral-ological collection in the National Museum in Stockholm, made in 1788 by Anders Niclas Tunborg, who was respondent for Bergman's dissertation *De diversa phlogisti quantitate in metallis*, 1780 (see p. 196), and became professor in a college in Vergara, Spain. Jeanety, a Paris jeweller, was making platinum apparatus from about 1787, and Guyton de Morveau used a platinum crucible (see p. 533). It was so expensive and difficult to obtain that German chemists were unable to procure platinum crucibles; in 1801 Rose and Karsten were unable to examine the statements of Guyton de Morveau and Desormes that potash consists of lime and hydrogen, and soda of magnesia and hydrogen, for want of a platinum crucible.[5]

Jeanety used a process tried by Marggraf (Vol. II) and investigated by Achard,[6] of fusing platinum with arsenic and then driving off the arsenic by ignition, when malleable platinum remained, from which Achard made the first platinum crucible. Jeanety's process was described in some detail by Pelletier[7] and Berthollet and Pelletier.[8] Pelletier[9] used phosphorus instead of arsenic, and Mussin-Pushkin[10] used mercury.

Richard Knight[11] ignited the dry precipitate of ammonium chloroplatinate in a conical fireclay mould and obtained a coherent metal which could be worked up by hammering and drawing. Strauss[12] proposed plating copper with platinum. Tilloch[13] wrapped the platinum powder in platinum foil, or put it into a platinum tube, heated it to redness, and hammered it until an ingot was formed. According to Matthey[14] a process of refining and consolidating plati-num was in use from 1800 to 1809 and had been devised and worked out by Thomas Cock, a man of independent means at first working in Allen's laboratory. At Allen's request he communicated his results to Wollaston (who was not employing him), and Wollaston has 'generally been accorded the credit of having discovered it'. Cock was assistant to his brother-in-law Percival Norton Johnson, who made the first large sheet of pure platinum at 79 Hatton Garden. Cock's process was published by A. and C. R. Aikin.[15] He used the dry powder of platinum compressed into an iron mould, the aggregated

[1] *Versuch über die Platina*, Mannheim, 1782, q. by Ingen Housz, *Vermischte Schriften*, tr. Molitor, Vienna, 1784, i, 419; Crell's *Ann.*, 1785, II, 372.
[2] Brater, *A. Med.*, 1931, xxiv, 329 (352).
[3] *Scheele; Nachgelassene Briefe*, Stockholm, 1892, 339.
[4] B. R. Geijer, KAH, 1784, v, 122, 283–6.
[5] Roscoe and Schorlemmer, *Treatise*, 1923, ii, 1453.   [6] Crell's *Ann.*, 1784, I, 1.
[7] *Obs. Phys.*, 1789, xxxiv, 193; *Mémoires de Chimie*, 1798, ii, 128.
[8] *Ann. Chim.*, 1792, xiv, 20: report from Jeanety.   [9] *Ann. Chim.*, 1792, xiii, 101.
[10] *Ann. Chim.*, 1797, xxiv, 205; Crell's *Ann.*, 1797, II, 26; *Allgem. J. Chem.*, 1800, iv, 411; *Nicholson's J.*, 1804, ix, 65. Some early Russian work on platinum is described by B. N. Men-schutkin, *J. Chem. Educ.*, 1934, xi, 226.
[11] *Phil. Mag.*, 1800, vi, 1–3 (On a new expeditious process for rendering platina malleable).
[12] *Nicholson's J.*, 1804, ix, 303.
[13] *Phil. Mag.*, 1807, xxi, 175 (read 1804–5 to the Askesian Society).
[14] *J. Chem. Soc.*, 1867, xx, 395; Powell, *Nature*, 1953, clxxii, 700.
[15] *A Dictionary of Chemistry and Mineralogy*, 1807, ii, 233–4 ('original communication').

bar being heated strongly in a charcoal fire and then hammered, heated to whiteness, and quenched. Wollaston started with a moist mud, but the difference is unimportant. Another important earlier worker on malleable platinum was Chabaneau (Notron; 21 April 1754–January 1842).[1]

Wollaston[2] showed that extremely fine wires of platinum could be drawn inside a silver sheath, and the silver afterwards dissolved off in dilute nitric acid.[3]

The first large piece of platinum apparatus was a boiler or still used for concentrating sulphuric acid, of a deep cylindrical form, weighing 423 oz. and capable of holding 300 lb. of sulphuric acid. It was made in December 1809 for Sandemann, who had a small chemical works at Thames Bank (the Borough), at a price of 16s. per oz. of metal. In 1816–20 the works was run for soap-making by Sandemann's widow and Andreas Kurtz, whom she married.[4] In 1817 platinum apparatus of all kinds was available in London and Paris. The price in Paris was 24 fr. per ounce of metal with 15 fr. per ounce for working it up; in London the price was rather lower. In 1846 the price had risen to 30s. an ounce; at the present day it is enormously dearer.[5]

Wollaston's discovery of palladium was announced in anonymous handbills in April 1803, stating that 'palladium, or new silver . . . a new noble metal' was on sale in London, using such names as 'spirit of nitre', 'calx', etc., and composed in crude language as if written by a tradesman. The literature says it was sold at 'Mrs. Foster's', but the original handbill[6] (in the Mineralogy Department, Cambridge) says: 'It is sold by Mr. Foster, at No. 26, Gerrard Street, Soho, London. In Samples of Five Shillings, Half a Guinea, & One Guinea each.'[7] Chenevix (see p. 712), who suspected fraud, bought the whole stock. He described the properties of the metal, but concluded that it was an amalgam of platinum and mercury, although only four experiments in a thousand gave the expected metal from these materials. Soon after Chenevix published his paper in 1803, an anonymous advertisement, in very poor style, appeared,[8] offering a reward of £20 for a grain of the metal prepared by the process of Chenevix or in any other way, and Wollaston finally[9] announced that he was the discoverer of palladium and described its preparation from native platinum; in the same paper he announced the discovery of rhodium. He must have written the handbill and advertisement.[10]

[1] Howe, Chem. News, 1914, cix, 229; Schofield, Endeavour, 1947, vi, 125.

[2] Phil. Trans., 1813, ciii, 114.

[3] An improved method, electrolysing off the silver in a cyanide bath, was described by Partington, Proc. Roy. Soc., 1921, c, 27; Z. Phys., 1930, lx, 420.

[4] Information from Johnson, Matthey and Co. Ltd., 1944; the statement in Roscoe and Schorlemmer, Treatise, 1923, ii, 1455, that the still was made by Johnson and Matthey is wrong, since Percival Norton Johnson did not start his business until 1817 and it did not become Johnson and Matthey until 1851. It was probably made by Wollaston, who made five large platinum boilers for concentrating sulphuric acid in 1805–18.

[5] Klaproth and Wolff, Supplement zu dem chemischen Wörterbuch, Berlin, 1817, iii, 168; Wilson, Religio-Chemici, 1862, 268.

[6] Reproduced by Gunther, Early Science in Cambridge, 1937, 234.

[7] The text of the handbill is given by Roscoe and Schorlemmer, Treatise, 1923, ii, 1406, who have 'Forster' in mistake for 'Foster'.

[8] Nicholson's J., 1804, vii, 75, 79.   [9] Phil. Trans., 1804, xciv, 419.

[10] Chenevix, Phil. Trans., 1803, xciii, 290; 1805, xcv, 104 (dated from Freyberg); N. allgem. J. Chem., 1803, i, 108, 174; V. Rose and Gehlen, ib., 529; Chenevix, Nicholson's J., 1803, v, 136; 1804, vii, 75 (where 'Mrs. Foster' is given), 159; 1810, xxv, 65; Ann. Chim., 1808, lxvi,

Thomson[1] says Chenevix's paper was read to the Royal Society by Wollaston, who told Thomson that he had done all in his power to stop Chenevix sending in his paper, even writing to him to say he had tried unsuccessfully to repeat his experiments. Chenevix probably annoyed Wollaston by his justifiable statement that the discovery of a new metal 'was shamefully announced'. It is incorrect to say that the paper passed through Wollaston's hands as Secretary of the Royal Society, since he did not assume this office until November 1804, Chenevix's paper being read in May 1803.[2]

The Journal Book of the Royal Society contains a very sarcastic account of Chenevix's paper, saying that 'the singular fact that an alloy of two metals should be produced, the specific gravity of which is little more than one-half of what it ought to be by calculation is, no doubt, worthy of particular attention'; and that 'those who cultivate chemistry with any degree of ardour will be gratified to see in this paper the pains taken by the author, and the various modes he has devised, to produce this compound metal in its most perfect state of combination'. The account of Wollaston's paper of 1804 in the Journal Book refers to the 'concise delineation of its character' in the advertisement of the metal, in which Wollaston 'avoided directing the attention of chemists to the source from which it had been obtained, and thereby reserved to himself a more deliberate examination'.[3] Whatever were Wollaston's motives, his behaviour was certainly very peculiar for a scientific man, and an advertisement by him of the metal for sale seems hardly conducive to a reservation of the subject for his own investigation.

In 1808[4] Wollaston showed that the amounts of carbonic acid (CO_2) combined with identical weights of potash (K_2O) in the carbonate (bicarbonate $KHCO_3$, i.e. $K_2O, 2CO_2, H_2O$) and sub-carbonate (normal carbonate, K_2CO_3, i.e. K_2O, CO_2) of potash were in the ratio 2 : 1. (The normal salt, which is strongly alkaline, was regarded as a compound with excess of base.) The experiment was made by passing 2 grains of 'carbonate' ($KHCO_3$) wrapped in tissue paper into hydrochloric acid in a tube over mercury, and repeating with 4 grains after heating to redness, when the same volume of carbon dioxide was evolved in both cases. The same ratio 2 : 1 was found to obtain for the sulphuric acid (SO_3) in the super-sulphate ($KHSO_4$, i.e. $K_2O, 2SO_3$, H_2O) and sulphate (K_2SO_4, i.e. K_2O, SO_3) of potash. Wollaston also obtained a third oxalate (quadroxalate) of potash, and showed that the relative weights of oxalic acid (C_2O_3) in the three salts were in the ratio 1 : 2 : 4. Wollaston said his experiments were made before he had read Thomson's account of Dalton's atomic theory in 1807 (see p. 796), which would require the multiple proportions:

'I thought it not unlikely that this law might obtain generally in such compounds, and it was my design to have pursued the subject with the hope of discovering the

---

82; Wollaston, *Phil. Trans.*, 1804, xciv, 419; 1805, xcv, 316; *Nicholson's J.*, 1805, x, 204; Vauquelin, *Ann. Chim.*, 1813, lxxxvii, 167; *Ann. Phil.*, 1814, iv, 216.
    [1] *Proc. Phil. Soc. Glasgow*, 1850, iii, 135.   [2] Gilbert, *Chem. and Ind.*, 1952, 17.
    [3] Thorpe, *Essays*, 1902, 560–3.
    [4] On Superacid and Subacid Salts; *Phil. Trans.*, 1808, xcviii, 96 (read 28 January); *Nicholson's J.*, 1808, xxi, 164–9; ACR, ii, 34; Ostwald's *Klassiker*, iii, 21; Thomson, (1), ii, 249.

cause to which so regular a relation might be ascribed. But since the publication of Mr. Dalton's theory of chemical combination . . . the enquiry which I had designed appears to be superfluous, as all the facts that I had observed are but particular instances of the more general observation of Mr. Dalton.'

Wollaston attempted to explain the formation of compounds by the arrangement of spherical atoms, and in particular he suggested that 4 atoms (or radicals) are arranged about a central atom at the corners of a regular tetrahedron in the most stable arrangement. Seven years before Wollaston's publication Thomas Thomson[1] had explained the 'saturation' of sulphuric acid by potash by supposing that 'the integrant particle' of sulphuric acid is a tetrahedron and 'the particles of potass are of such a form, that one of them can attach itself to each of the sides of the acid particle: In that case, an integrant particle of sulphate of potass would be composed of five particles, one of acid and four of alkali . . . and . . . the acid would then be saturated, or . . . incapable of receiving any more alkaline particles in combination with it'. Dalton[2] says:

'Dr. Wollaston's lecture of 1813[3] is an expansion of the ideas I published in 1808. (Chemistry, vol. I, p. 210.) When he mentioned these ideas to me in conversation, (I think in 1810,) he could scarcely credit that I had entertained and published the same, until he brought my book out of his library, and I shewed him the page. He had probably seen it before, but had forgotten it.'

The passage[4] deals with the formation of crystals from elementary particles and the relation between crystal form and the packing of the particles.

The quadroxalate of potash was really discovered by F. P. Savary in 1773[5] by crystallising the binoxalate (salt of sorrel) from dilute sulphuric or nitric acid, but his publication was little known. The salt was later investigated by Anderson.[6]

A little before Wollaston, Thomas Thomson[7] gave the first example of the law of multiple proportions, by showing that in the normal and acid oxalates of potash and strontia, one salt, for the same amount of acid 'contains just double the proportion of base contained in the second', and he drew attention to Dalton's theory.

In his paper on equivalents[8] Wollaston evidently thought he is proposing an alternative system independent of the atomic theory:

'When we estimate the real weights of equivalents, Mr. Dalton conceives that we are estimating the aggregate weights of a given number of atoms, and consequently the proportion which the ultimate single atoms bear to each other. . . . I have not been desirous of warping my numbers according to an atomic theory, but have endeavoured to make practical experience my sole guide.'

He says Gay-Lussac's law of volumes was anticipated by William Higgins (see p. 752), who 'in his conception of union by ultimate particles clearly pre-

---

[1] Ency. Brit. Suppl., 1801, I, i, 343.
[2] Letter of 1831 (?) to Daubeny, in Daubeny, Atomic Theory, Oxford, 1850, 479.
[3] Phil. Trans., 1813, ciii, 57.   [4] Dalton, New System, 1808, I, i, 210.
[5] Dissertatio de sale acetosellae, Strasbourg, 1773; Kopp, (1), iv, 354.
[6] J. Chem. Soc., 1849, i, 231.   [7] Phil. Trans., 1808, xcviii, 63 (read 14 January).
[8] Phil. Trans., 1814, civ, 1 (read 4 November 1813); Ann. Phil., 1814, iv, 176; Ann. Chim., 1814, xc, 138–74.

ceded Mr. Dalton in his atomic views of chemical combination'. Wollaston, in fact, uses Dalton's ideas, not Higgins's, and the theoretical foundations for Wollaston's 'equivalents' are very obscurely given. He takes oxygen $= 10$, and says[1] that since 1 vol. of oxygen gives 1 vol. of carbon dioxide and the specific gravities of the gases are as $10 : 13\cdot77$ 'or 20 to $27\cdot54$', the weight of carbon which 'is combined with 2 of oxygen' is $7\cdot54$, which is the equivalent. He does not explain why *two* of oxygen are chosen, and the same careless and arbitrary procedure runs through the paper. By making use of the results of others, including those of 'the very industrious and very accurate Berzelius',[2] Wollaston arrives at a long table of 'equivalents' of elements and compounds, including the following:

hydrogen	$1\cdot32$	$(1\cdot06)$	phosphorus	$17\cdot40$	$(13\cdot92)$	copper	40	$(32\cdot0)$
oxygen	$10\cdot00$	$(8\cdot00)$	nitrogen	$17\cdot54$	$(14\cdot03)$	zinc	41	$(32\cdot8)$
carbon	$7\cdot54$	$(6\cdot03)$	chlorine	$44\cdot1$	$(35\cdot3)$	mercury	$125\cdot5$	$(100\cdot4)$
sulphur	$20\cdot00$	$(16\cdot00)$	iron	$34\cdot5$	$(27\cdot6)$	lead	$129\cdot5$	$(103\cdot6)$
sodium	$29\cdot1$	$(23\cdot3)$				silver	135	$(108\cdot0)$

The values recalculated to $O = 8$ are given in brackets.

Wollaston describes a 'synoptic scale of chemical equivalents'[3] in the form of a logarithmic slide-rule. These scales, and tables of equivalents accompanying them, were sold by Newman, Regent St., London, and some are still in existence.[4]

Wollaston's paper on equivalents and his slide-rule introduced confusion into chemical theory, since some of his numbers are not equivalents at all, and they no doubt popularised the use of Gmelin's equivalents (Vol. IV) instead of Berzelius's true atomic weights.[5] Wollaston mentions Richter[6] and points out that Wenzel's results are incompatible with the law of neutrality.

In 1822[7] Wollaston found very hard crystals in the slag of a blast furnace at Merthyr Tydfil which he thought were metallic titanium, but Wöhler in 1849 showed that they contain carbon and nitrogen (Vol. IV).

TENNANT

Smithson Tennant (Selby, Yorkshire, 30 November 1761–Boulogne, 15 February 1815) studied under Black in Edinburgh (1781), and chemistry, mathematics, and botany in Cambridge (1782). He travelled in Denmark and Sweden (1784), France and Holland (1786–8). He became F.R.S. in 1785. After further travels, he became professor of chemistry in Cambridge in May 1813. He was killed in an accident on a horse on an insecure drawbridge at Boulogne (where he is buried); his mother had been killed when riding with

---

[1] *Phil. Trans.*, 1814, civ, 8 f.   [2] *Ib.*, 13.
[3] See Klaproth and Wolff, *Supplement zu dem chemischen Wörterbuch*, 1819, iv, 192–200; Faraday, *Chemical Manipulation*, 1842, 564.
[4] A. Scott, *J. Chem. Soc.*, 1917, cxi, 288.   [5] Ladenburg, 1905, 64.
[6] Previously mentioned by Thomson, (2), 1807, iii, 624–6.   [7] *Phil. Trans.*, 1823, cxiii, 17.

him in his youth.[1] He published in the *Philosophical Transactions* on the nature of the diamond,[2] the composition of dolomite[3] and emery,[4] and the discovery of osmium and iridium.[5]

Tennant began in 1803 to work on the residue remaining when crude platinum is dissolved in aqua regia, and believed then that it contained a new metal. Fourcroy and Vauquelin,[6] and Collet-Descotils,[7] simultaneously concluded that the solution of crude platinum contains a new metal, and they should rank with Tennant as independent discoverers of iridium.

In 1789[8] Guyton de Morveau reported that all attempts to decompose carbonic acid gas (e.g. Achard's of passing it over fused nitre) had failed. Although Monge, and Van Marum and Landriani, had found that the gas expands and becomes combustible on sparking, the latter concluded that the result was due to moisture. In 1791 Smithson Tennant showed that carbon is formed when phosphorus is heated with powdered marble,[9] and Pearson[10] obtained carbon on heating sodium carbonate with phosphorus.

In experiments in 1797[11] Tennant burnt diamonds in nitre fused in a gold tube, showing that the gas evolved contained no fixed air (carbon dioxide). The residue was dissolved in water and precipitated with calcium chloride solution. The liquid was decanted from the precipitated chalk (calcareous earth), the vessel filled with mercury, and the fixed air liberated by muriatic acid was measured. It was found that $2\frac{1}{2}$ grains of diamond gave 10·1 to 10·3 oz. water volume of fixed air at 55° F. and 28 in. barometer, which 'does not differ much from that which, according to M. Lavoisier, might be obtained from an equal weight of charcoal'. The precipitate gave charcoal when heated with phosphorus. It is said that Tennant used to ride at a fixed hour of the day and once, when an experiment with a diamond and nitre was unfinished at the time, he abandoned it and sacrificed the diamond.

Experiments confirming Tennant's and Pearson's, made by Vauquelin, Fourcroy, Sylvestre, and Brongniart, are reported by Fourcroy,[12] and the question of the affinities, 'déjà indiquée par M. Tennant, mais mal entendue & presque combattue par M. Pearson', is fully considered. Since carbon has a greater affinity for oxygen than any other combustible, carbonic acid cannot be decomposed by simple affinity, and the 'affinité prédisposante de l'acide phosphorique pour la chaux' is necessary to bring about the reaction. If the affinity of oxygen for carbon is 7, that of oxygen for phosphorus is 6, and that of phosphoric acid for lime is 9, then the two forces are 15. But the carbon and oxygen are united with lime by a force 8, and $7+8$ also $=15$. No decomposition occurs in the cold. On heating, the affinity of lime for carbonic acid is partly destroyed and becomes 2, and $7+2=9<15$, hence decomposition occurs. The cases of sodium carbonate, etc., are set out in tables.

[1] Thomson, *Ann. Phil.*, 1815, v, 312; 1815, vi, 1, 81; *id.*, (1), ii, 232; [J. Whishaw], *Some Account of the late Smithson Tennant, Esq.*, 1815 (46 pp.); Barrow, *Sketches of the Royal Society*, 1849, 156.

[2] *Phil. Trans.*, 1797, lxxxvii, 123.   [3] *Ib.*, 1799, lxxxix, 305.

[4] *Ib.*, 1802, xcii, 398.

[5] *Ib.*, 1804, xciv, 411.

[6] *Ann. Chim.*, 1803, xlviii, 177; 1804, xlix, 188, 219; 1804, l, 5.

[7] Sur la cause des couleurs différentes qu'affectent certains sels de Platin; *Ann. Chim.*, 1804, xlviii, 153.

[8] *Ency. Méthod., Chymie*, 1789, i, 750.   [9] *Phil. Trans.*, 1791, lxxxi, 182.

[10] *Ib.*, 1792, lxxxii, 289.

[11] *Ib.*, 1797, lxxxvii, 123.   [12] (2), 1796, iii, 591 f.

Tennant also investigated the action of fused nitre on gold and platinum,[1] both of which he found to be corroded. He found[2] that magnesian limestone acts prejudicially when used as a fertiliser. He described a method of producing a double distillation with the same heat,[3] and a simple method of preparing potassium by heating caustic potash and iron in a tube and condensing the vapour in a vessel in a cooler part of the tube.[4] He described native boric acid of the Lipari Islands.[5]

HATCHETT

Charles Hatchett (London; 2 January 1765–10 March 1847) was the son of a wealthy man who, it is said, offered him £3000 and a place in parliament if he would give up chemistry.[6] He observed the formation of iron pyrites in a mere at Diss, Norfolk,[7] analysed lead molybdate from Carinthia,[8] and investigated the alloys of gold.[9] In his paper on bones and shells[10] he described the solution of calcium phosphate and carbonate from these by dilute nitric acid and the properties of the organic residues, and also proved that the enamel of teeth is similar in composition to bone, the mineral part being mostly calcium phosphate. In his 'Chemical Experiments on Zoophytes; with some Observations on the Component Parts of Membrane'[11] he described the organic residue obtained in a similar way from shells, and distinguished it as a 'cartilaginous body', different from gelatin, glue, or mucilage.

Hatchett obtained 'an artificial substance possessing the properties of tannin' by boiling charcoal powder with dilute nitric acid and evaporating the solution.[12] The last three papers contain important observations on resins, in which he recognised that they dissolve in alkalis and some in alkali carbonates, forming soaps.[13] R. Jameson[14] had previously obtained 'a brown, bitter, somewhat deliquescent mass, soluble in water, spirit of wine and alkalies' by the action of nitric acid on charcoal, but he thought it was suberic acid and that it was present in a water extract of peat.

Hatchett published privately a pamphlet on spikenard.[15] He proposed the use of copper ferrocyanide as a brown pigment. In a paper 'Observations on the Change of some of the proximate Principles of Vegetables into Bitumen'[16] Hatchett gives a long description of Bovey coal, which had been mentioned by J. Milles[17] from specimens found in Devonshire. Hatchett also described

[1] Phil. Trans., 1797, lxxxvii, 219.   [2] Ib., 1799, lxxxix, 305.
[3] Ib., 1814, civ, 587–9.   [4] Ib., 1814, civ, 578.
[5] Trans. Geol. Soc., London, 1811, i, 389.
[6] Walker, Memoirs of Distinguished Men of Science, 1862, 83; Sir J. Barrow, Sketches of the Royal Society and the Royal Society Club, 1849, 189; Poggendorff, (1), ii, 1031 (says d. 10 February 1847); Weeks, J. Chem. Educ., 1938, xv, 153 (portrs.); id., Discovery of the Elements, 1956, 369.
[7] Phil. Trans., 1798, lxxxviii, 572.   [8] Ib., 1796, lxxxvi, 285.
[9] Ib., 1803, xciii, 43; he acknowledges assistance by Cavendish.
[10] Ib., 1799, lxxxix, II, 315.   [11] Ib., 1800, xc, II, 327.
[12] Ib., 1805, xcv, 211, 285; 1806, xcvi, 109.   [13] Thomson, (2), 1807, v, 146.
[14] An Outline of the Mineralogy of the Shetland and of the Island of Arran, Edinburgh, 1798, 167; Thomson, Ency. Brit. Suppl., 1801, I, i, 332; the expt. is not in Jameson's Mineralogy of the Scottish Isles, Edinburgh, 1800, which, i, 120 f., describes experiments on peat.
[15] On the Spikenard of the Ancients, 4°, London, 1836 (ii ll., 21 pp., fold. pl. from Blane, Phil. Trans., 1790, lxxx, 284).
[16] Phil. Trans., 1804, xciv, 385–410.   [17] Phil. Trans., 1760, li, 534.

mineral caoutchouc (elastic bitumen) which seems to have been mentioned by Lister as a 'fungus', found in a forsaken mine in Derbyshire.[1] It had been described by De la Metherie[2] and Klaproth.[3]

In 1801 Hatchett in the investigation of a mineral from North America found it to contain a new metal which he called *columbium*.[4] The mineral was described as 'a heavy black stone with golden streaks . . . from Mr. Winthrop', in the catalogue of the collection of minerals belonging to Sir Hans Sloane, which afterwards passed to the British Museum. John Winthrop was the grandson of the first Governor of Connecticut, from whence the mineral came.[5] In 1802 Ekeberg[6] discovered a new metal in some rare-earth minerals (afterwards called yttrotantalite) and called it *tantalum* since it does not combine at all with acids (midt i öfverflödet af syra, däraf taga något ät sig och mättas), being like Tantalus, unable to drink. Wollaston[7] then claimed that he had shown that columbium and tantalum were identical, and Ekeberg's work was discredited.[8] Further investigations were made by Berzelius,[9] Wöhler[10] and several other chemists, the position being finally clarified by H. Rose,[11] who showed that there are two elements, Hatchett's columbium, which he renamed niobium, and Ekeberg's tantalum, and Wollaston was mistaken.

PARKES

Samuel Parkes (Stourbridge, 26 May 1761–London, 23 December 1825), owner of a circulating library at Stourbridge, soapmaker at Stoke-on-Trent (1793–1803), then technical chemist in London, published a popular 'catechism'[12] and some essays[13] which contain much interesting historical information. He published a list of periodicals printed in Great Britain and Ireland from 1681 to 1749.[14] His essay on the manufacture of tin-plate[15] is especially interesting.

[1] Lister, *Phil. Trans.*, 1673, viii, 6179.
[2] *Obs. Phys.*, 1787, xxxi, 311: elastic bitumen from Derbyshire, referring to Woulfe.
[3] *Beiträge*, 1802, iii, 107; who quotes an earlier publication by Hatchett ('Scherers Journ. d. Chemie. 21 Heft. S. 282').
[4] *Phil. Trans.*, 1802, xcii, 49: Analysis of a Mineral Substance from North America, containing a metal unknown; Murray, *Elements of Chemistry*, 6 ed., Edinburgh, 1828, ii, 278, thought the mineral really came from Sweden.
[5] Brooks, *Sir Hans Sloane*, 1954, 197, says it was the specimen used by Hatchett.
[6] KAH, 1802, xxiii, 68; *Ann. Chim.*, 1802, xliii, 276; *Nicholson's J.*, 1802, iii, 251.
[7] *Phil. Trans.*, 1809, xcix, 246.
[8] On the discovery of columbium and tantalum, see Berzelius, *Ann. Phil.*, 1814, iv, 467, with Thomson's remark that 'Christopher Columbus has as good a claim to give his name to a metal as King Tantalus'.
[9] *Ann. Chim.*, 1807, lxi, 256.   [10] *Ann. Phys.*, 1839, xlviii, 83 (91).
[11] *Ann. Phys.*, 1844, lxiii, 317; 1846, lxix, 115; 1859, xc, 456; see Vol. IV.
[12] *Chemical Catechism*, 1806; 5 ed. 1812, 9 ed. 1819, 10 ed. 1822 (with plate), 11 ed. 1824 (f'piece and plate), 12 ed. 1825; new ed. by W. Barker, 1854; *An Elementary Treatise on Chemistry; upon the Basis of the Chemical Catechism; originally published under the Title of Rudiments of Chemistry . . .* , 1839.
[13] *Chemical Essays*, 5 vols., 12°, 1815; 2 ed., 2 vols. 8°, 1823.
[14] *Quart. J. Sci.*, 1822, xiii, 36, 289.   [15] *Chemical Essays*, 1823, ii, 551–79.

MARCET

Alexander John Gaspard Marcet (Geneva, 1770–London, 19 October 1822), M.D. Edinburgh 1797, F.R.S. 1815, was from 1807 lecturer on chemistry at Guy's Hospital. He retired to Geneva and equipped a laboratory in his house but did not live to use it much.[1] He was a friend of Berzelius[2] and of A. A. De la Rive; with the latter he carried out measurements of the specific heats of gases.[3]

Marcet discovered in a urinary calculus[4] a substance which he called *xanthic oxide*, since it was soluble in alkalis and on evaporation with nitric acid gave a yellow substance. Its correct formula, $C_5H_4O_2N_4$, was first found by Wöhler and Liebig,[5] and since it contains one atom of oxygen less than uric acid, Berzelius[6] called it urous acid (Harnige Säure). It is now called xanthine; it can be obtained by reducing uric acid with sodium amalgam and is colourless when pure.[7]

Marcet and Berzelius (working in Marcet's private laboratory) showed that 'alcohol of sulphur' is a compound of sulphur and carbon (carbon disulphide),[8] a result which was anticipated in publication by Vauquelin.[9] Marcet froze mercury by the rapid evaporation of ether under an air pump;[10] later he used carbon disulphide. He described an alcohol-oxygen blowpipe flame;[11] the oxy-hydrogen blowpipe had been described by Hare.[12] Marcet's paper[13] on the analysis of sea and lake waters contains a great number of results. In a later paper[14] he showed that sea water does not contain mercury, as Rouelle had stated (see p. 77); he noticed the crystallisation from the residual brine of the double salts carnallite ($KMgCl_3$, $6H_2O$) and schönite ($K_2Mg(SO_4)_2$, $6H_2O$), but did not determine the quantitative compositions.

Marcet's publications on body fluids, including cerebro-spinal and dropsical fluids,[15] are of biochemical importance, but his most interesting discovery in this field concerned a specimen of urine turning black[16] in a case of alcaptonuria; the substance involved was called *alkapton* (from alkali, and κάπτειν to drink up) by Boedeker (1859).[17] It is homogentisic acid, 2:5-dihydroxy-

[1] Moore, DNB, 1893, xxxvi, 122; Garrod, *Guy's Hospital Reports*, 1925, 373 (portr.); W. Babington and W. Allen, *A Syllabus of a Course of Chemical Lectures read at Guy's Hospital*, London, 1802; Babington, Allen, and Marcet, same title, 1816; *The Life of William Allen with Selections from his Correspondence*, 3 vols. London, 1846, i, 59, 67, 73, 85.

[2] Berzelius, *Bref*, 1914, I, iii (correspondence with Marcet); Bourquelot, *J. Pharm. Chim.*, 1916, xiii, 230.

[3] De la Rive and Marcet, *Bibl. Brit.*, 1827, xxxvii, 100, 174; *Ann. Chim.*, 1827, xxxv, 5; 1840, lxxv, 113.

[4] *An Essay on the Chemical History and Medical Treatment of Calculus Diseases*, London, 1817, 45 f., 95 (xanthic oxyd); 2 ed. enlarged, 1819 (BM).

[5] *Ann.*, 1838, xxvi, 340.   [6] *Lehrbuch der Chemie*, 1840, ix, 489.

[7] Roscoe and Schorlemmer, *Treatise*, 1890, III, ii, 369.

[8] Berzelius and Marcet, *Phil. Trans.*, 1813, ciii, 171; *Ann. Phil.*, 1814, iii, 185.

[9] *Ann. Muséum d'Hist. Nat.*, 1812, xix, 396; Berthollet, Thenard, and Vauquelin, *Ann. Chim.*, 1812, lxxxiii, 252 — quoting experiments of Cluzel; see p. 597.

[10] *Nicholson's J.*, 1813, xxxiv, 119.   [11] *Ann. Phil.*, 1813, ii, 99.

[12] *Phil. Mag.*, 1802, xiv, 238, 298.   [13] *Phil. Trans.*, 1819, cix, II, 161.

[14] *Phil. Trans.*, 1822, cxii, 448–56.   [15] *Med. Chirurg. Trans.*, 1811, ii, 343; 1815, vi, 618.

[16] *Med. Chirurg. Trans.*, 1823, xii, 37; Prout, *ib.*, 43 (melanic acid).

[17] *Ann.*, 1861, cxvii, 98.

phenylacetic acid, $C_6H_3(OH)_2.CH_2.COOH$, a product of protein metabolism.[1]

Rouelle had found that the alkalinity of blood serum is due to soda and this was confirmed by Marcet;[2] this led to a controversy with Pearson.[3] Marcet defended the presence of sugar in diabetic urine against the denial of Wollaston.[4]

MRS. MARCET

In 1799 Marcet married Jane Hallimand (London; 1769–28 June 1858), also of Swiss parentage and later very wealthy.[5] She wrote a very popular *Conversations on Chemistry*[6] which first appeared anonymously, her name being given first in the 13 ed. (1837), and there were many American editions, by 1853 more than 160,000 copies were sold there. The book first interested Faraday in chemistry when he was binding a copy in his early days as a bookbinder's apprentice. In it two young ladies carry on conversations and perform experiments with 'Mrs. B.' (Bryan ?). Mrs. Marcet also wrote: *Conversations on Natural Philosophy*, 1819, 1824, 1827, 13 ed. 1858, 14 ed. 1872; and *Conversations on Vegetable Physiology*, 1829. A *Conversations on Botany* (anon.), 1817, 1820, is also attributed to E. and S. M. Fitton. She also wrote some children's books. It is notable that there is no account of Dalton's atomic theory in the *Conversations on Chemistry*; this perhaps was a reflexion of Davy's prejudice against it (see p. 798). Harriet Martineau, who borrowed her opinions freely without acknowledgment, but later became her good friend, said Mrs. Marcet 'had a great opinion of the great'.

MRS. FULHAME

Mrs. Elizabeth Fulhame, of whom nothing seems to be known except that she was the wife of a doctor, was an early convert to Lavoisier's theory. In 1794 she published a very interesting *Essay on Combustion* (now very scarce), which attracted general attention.[7] She was elected an honorary member of the

---

[1] Wolkow and Baumann, *Z. physiol. Chem.*, 1891, xv, 228–85; Garrod, *The Inborn Errors of Metabolism*, 2 ed., 1923, 43; Neubauer, Vogel, and Huppert, *Analyse des Harns*, 10 ed., Wiesbaden, 1898, 243, 789; 11 ed., 1913, ii, 850; Hoppe-Seyler and Thierfelder, *Handbuch der physiologisch-pathologisch-chemischen Analyse*, 6 ed., 1893, 365; 9 ed., 1924, 303; Beilstein, *Handbuch der organischen Chemie*, 1927, x, 407; *ib.*, I Ergw., 1932, x, 197.

[2] *Med. Chirurg. Trans.*, 1813, ii, 342 (370).

[3] *Nicholson's J.*, 1812, xxxi, 145; 1812, xxxii, 37; 1812, xxxiii, 285; Marcet, *ib.*, 1812, xxxi, 230; Bostock and Marcet, *ib.*, 1812, xxxiii, 147.

[4] *Phil. Trans.*, 1811, ci, II, 96.

[5] Elizabeth Lee, DNB, 1893, xxxvi, 122; Eva V. Armstrong, *J. Chem. Educ.*, 1938, xv, 53 (portr.); Read, (2), 176.

[6] 2 vols., 1806 (Royal Institution Library), 1807, 1809, 1813, 1817, 1819, 10 ed. 1825, 13 ed. 1837, 15 ed. 1846, 16 ed. 1853 (18 eds. in all); French tr. *Conversations sur la Chimie*, 3 vols. 12°, Paris, 1809 (BM); *La Chimie enseignée en 26 leçons*, 12°, Paris, 1825.

[7] *An Essay on Combustion, with a view to a New Art of Dying [sic] and Painting. Wherein the Phlogistic and Antiphlogistic Hypotheses are Proved Erroneous*, 8°, London, Printed for the Author, by J. Cooper, Bow Street, Covent Garden, 1794 (pref. dated 5 November), pp. xiii (v. blank), contents (v. blank), 182; German tr. by A. G. W. Lentin, *Versuche über die Wiederherstellung der Metalle durch Wasserstoffgas, Phosphor, Schwefel, Schwefelleber, geschwefeltes Wasserstoffgas, gephosphortes Wasserstoffgas, Kohle, Licht und Säuren*, 12°, Göttingen, 1798 (Sotheran *Cat.* 800 (1926) No. 10848). The book was reviewed by Ritter, in Scherer's *Journal*

Philadelphia Chemical Society, her book being reprinted there in 1810.[1] James Woodhouse, professor of chemistry in Philadelphia (1795), called her 'the celebrated Mrs. Fulhame'.[2] Priestley[3] mentions the book and the experiments of Mrs. Fulhame, who 'was so obliging as to shew me the results of some in London'. Of her statement about the 'phenix' (see below), he says her theory is 'fanciful, and fabulous, as the story of the phenix itself'. The experiments of 'the ingenious and lively Mrs. Fulhame' on the reduction of gold salts by light were repeated by Count Rumford[4] who thought, however, that the changes are produced 'not by any chemical combination of the matter of light with such bodies, but merely by the heat which is generated, or excited by the light that is absorbed by them'.

Mrs. Fulhame says:[5] 'I shall endeavour to show, that the hydrogen of water is the only substance, that restores oxygenated bodies to their combustible state; and that water is the only source of the oxygen, which oxygenates combustible bodies.' In the reduction of metallic oxides the hydrogen gas combines with the oxygen of the water, and the hydrogen of the water unites with the oxygen of the oxide, reducing the latter to metal.[6] In the reduction of oxides by carbon, the latter is really oxidised by the oxygen of the water which must be present: 'The carbone of the charcoal attracts the oxygen of the water, while the hydrogen of the latter unites, in its nascent state, with the oxygen of the metal, and reduces it.'[7] 'In like manner during the combustion of charcoal, in vital air, the carbone attracts the oxygen of the water, and forms carbonic acid, while the hydrogen of the water unites with the oxygen of the vital air, and forms a new quantity of water equal to that decomposed.'[8] This theory of the gifted authoress, insufficiently supported by the numerous experiments described in her book, is a foreshadowing of that proposed by H. B. Dixon[9] on the basis of experiments. Her theories were forgotten until attention was directed to them by J. W. Mellor.[10] The same theory had been given to explain why iron does not rust in dry oxygen but does so in presence of water, by William Higgins,[11] and Mrs. Fulhame is one among the many who, he later said, appropriated his views as their own.

Mrs. Fulhame poetically concludes her essay[12] by saying:

'This view of combustion may serve to show how nature is always the same, and maintains her equilibrium by preserving the same quantities of air and water on the surface of our globe: for as fast as these are consumed in the various processes of combustion, equal quantities are formed, and rise regenerated like the Phenix from her ashes.'[13]

---

der Chemie, 1798, i, 443; Coindet, Ann. Chim., 1798, xxvi, 58–85 (theory on p. 63); and De la Metherie, J. de Phys., 1798, xlvi, 392; it is mentioned by Thomson, (2), 1817, ii, 253.
[1] Miles, Chymia, 1950, iii, 95 (107). [2] Trans. Amer. Phil. Soc., 1799, iv, 465.
[3] The Doctrine of Phlogiston Established, 1800, 58 f.; 1803, 79.
[4] Phil. Trans., 1798, lxxxviii, 449; Complete Works, London, 1876, v, 73.
[5] Essay, 8. [6] Ib., 40. [7] Ib., 137. [8] Ib., 166.
[9] B.A. Rep., 1880, 503; J. Chem. Soc., 1902, lxxxi, 1272.
[10] J. Phys. Chem., 1903, vii, 557; id., Chemical Statics and Dynamics, 1904, 303, corrected in id., Treatise, 1940, v, 812; Mrs. Fulhame says nothing about the combustion of carbon monoxide.
[11] Comparative View of the Phlogistic and Antiphlogistic Theories, 1789, 13. [12] 1794., 180.
[13] The phoenix, it may be noted, was a fabulous bird regarded as sexless.

SMITHSON

James Smithson (France, 1769–Genoa, 27 June 1829; his remains are now in Washington), was the natural son of the Duke of Northumberland and Elizabeth Hungerford (niece of the Duke of Somerset). By his will he founded the Smithsonian Institution in Washington (10 August 1846, after lawsuits).[1] The male line of Percy had become extinct in 1670 and the Earldom of Northumberland passed in 1750 to a son-in-law, Sir Hugh Smithson, who assumed the name of Percy. James Smithson is sometimes referred to as James Louis Macie Smithson, probably because he matriculated at Pembroke College Oxford in 1786, aged 17, as James Louis Macie, his mother's surname, and he used this name in his paper on tabaschir,[2] which he found was mostly silica.

He analysed zinc minerals,[3] distinguishing calamine (zinc carbonate) from native zinc silicate, which he called 'electric calamine' from its pyro-electric properties. Beudant (1824) proposed the name smithsonite for calamine, the latter name having been used for the silicate by Brongniart (1807). British mineralogists call the carbonate 'calamine' and the silicate 'electric calamine' or 'hemimorphite'; American mineralogists call the two minerals 'smithsonite' and 'calamine', respectively. Smithson also identified native minium (Pb_3O_4),[4] and in an analysis of zeolite[5] he recognised that silica is acidic: 'quartz itself considered an acid.' He investigated ulmin,[6] some Egyptian colours (finding the blue to be a copper silicate composition),[7] some vegetable colours and aphis-fly green,[8] confirmed the presence of fluorine in topaz and some other minerals,[9] and published a letter (dated 18 September 1790) from Black describing a simple small balance.[10]

YOUNG

Thomas Young (Milverton, 13 (or 16) June 1773–London, 10 May 1829), the famous physicist,[11] who had studied chemistry under Black, published some old-fashioned affinity tables,[12] which he thought worth summarising in

[1] W. J. Rees, The Smithsonian Institution. Documents relative to its Origin and History, 1835–99, in *Smithsonian Misc. Coll.*, Washington, 1901, xlii, xliii; J. B. Goode, *The Smithsonian Institution*, Washington, 1897; Langley, *Biographical Sketch of James Smithson*, Washington, 1914; *The First Hundred Years of the Smithsonian Institution*, Washington, 1946; Smithson's copy of Rey's *Essay* (see p. 397) is in the Institution Library; Rhees, *James Smithson, Scientific Writings*, Washington, 1880; *James Smithson and his Bequest*, Washington, 1880; W. P. True, *The Smithsonian*, New York, 1950; *Nature*, 1951, clxviii, 888.
[2] *Phil. Trans.*, 1791, lxxxi, 368; *Obs. Phys.*, 1792, xl, 122.
[3] *Phil. Trans.*, 1803, xciii, 127.   [4] *Ib.*, 1806, xcvi, II, 267.
[5] *Ib.*, 1811, ci, 171.   [6] *Ib.*, 1813, ciii, 64.
[7] *Ann. Phil.*, 1824, vii, 115.   [8] *Phil. Trans.*, 1818, cviii, 110.
[9] *Ann. Phil.*, 1824, vii, 100.
[10] *Ann. Phil.*, 1825, x, 52–4; for other publications see Poggendorff, (1), ii, 946–7.
[11] Arago, Éloge (1832), AdS, 1835, XIII, lvij–c; Pettigrew, *Medical Portrait Gallery*, 1844, iv; Barrow, *Sketches of the Royal Society and the Royal Society Club*, 1849, 162; Bence Jones, *The Royal Institution*, 1871, 223; Tyndall, *New Fragments*, 1892, 248–306; F. Oldham, *Thomas Young, Physician and Philosopher*, 1933; A. Wood (and F. Oldham), *Thomas Young*, Cambridge, 1954.
[12] *Phil. Trans.*, 1809, xcix, 148 (numerical table of elective attractions); Young, *Miscellaneous Works*, ed. Peacock, 1855, i, 563.

Latin hexameters,[1] and was joint author of a work on Greek caligraphy.[2] His bibliographical work[3] includes the affinity tables,[4] a summary of parts of Berzelius on Animal Chemistry,[5] and on the rules of chemical combination.[6] In it he first used the name 'combining weights'.[7]

BOSTOCK

John Bostock (Liverpool, 1773–London, 6 August 1846, of cholera), pupil of Black, was a physician in Liverpool and lecturer on physiology in the Liverpool Institution, then from 1822 lecturer on chemistry at Guy's Hospital. He wrote on respiration, galvanism, and physiology.[8] He was also a translator of Pliny, a botanist and a geologist.[9] In his *Essay on Respiration* he criticised Lavoisier's theory that animal heat is produced by the oxidation of a 'hydrocarbonous humour', denied that hydrogen is oxidised in the lungs, and supposed that carbon dioxide is also formed in digestive processes.

In his important publications on body fluids[10] he distinguished three primary constituents of animal fluids: albumen (coagulated by heat and by mercuric chloride), jelly (gelatin) (liquefied by heat, becoming solid again on cooling, not precipitated by mercuric chloride but precipitated by tannin), and mucus (present in saliva, not coagulated by heat or concreted by cold, not precipitated by mercuric chloride or tannin but copiously precipitated by basic lead acetate). If albumen is first precipitated from blood serum by mercuric chloride, the remaining liquid gives no precipitate with tannin, hence blood serum does not contain gelatin; this was confirmed by Berzelius,[11] and disproved the assertion of Fourcroy[12] that blood serum contains gelatin (veritable matière gélatineuse).

Bostock also investigated 'vegetable muciliges' (e.g. cherry-tree gum),[13] vegetable astringents,[14] and the precipitation of gelatin (jelly) by tannin.[15] He showed that urine in a case of insipid diabetes did not contain sugar, but another sample of diabetic urine contained sugar, since it gave crystals of oxalic acid when oxidised with nitric acid.[16] Bostock investigated the formation and properties of beeswax, myrtle wax, adipocire (see p. 547) and biliary calculi.[17] He analysed the acetate and basic acetate of lead,[18] and Dalton[19] in his

---

[1] *Nicholson's J.*, 1809, xxii, 304.

[2] J. Hodgkin and T. Young, *Caligraphia Graeca*, London, 1794 (plates).

[3] *An Introduction to Medical Literature . . . together with detached Essays, . . . on Chemical Affinities, on Animal Chemistry . . .*, London, 1813, 2 ed., 1823.

[4] 1823, 507.   [5] 1823, 523.

[6] 1823, 561, from Berzelius's *Lärbok* (1812, ii, 561).   [7] Kopp, (3), 345.

[8] *An Essay on Respiration*, Parts 1 and 2, Liverpool, 1804 (chemistry, 69 f.); *An Account of the History and Present State of Galvanism*, London, 1818; *An Elementary System of Physiology*, 3 vols., London, 1827; 3 ed., 1836.

[9] Pettigrew, *Medical Portrait Gallery*, 1844, iii (portr.); Lord Northampton, *Proc. Roy. Soc.*, 1846, v, 636; S. G. Smith, *M.Sc. Dissert.*, London, 1953.

[10] *Nicholson's J.*, 1805, xi, 244; 1806, xiv, 140; *Med. Chirurg. Trans.*, 1815, i, 47 (read 24 Dec. 1806); 1813, iv, 53, and table opposite p. 73, 'Synopsis of albuminous fluids.'

[11] *Med. Chirurg. Trans.*, 1812, iii, 198.   [12] *Ann. Chim.*, 1790, vii, 146 (156).

[13] *Nicholson's J.*, 1807, xviii, 28.   [14] *Nicholson's J.*, 1809, xxiv, 204, 241.

[15] *Nicholson's J.*, 1809, xxiv, 1.   [16] *Med. Chirurg. Trans.*, 1812, iii, 107.

[17] *Nicholson's J.*, 1803, iv, 129–39.

[18] *Nicholson's J.*, 1805, xi, 75.   [19] *Ib.*, 1811, xxix, 143.

controversy with Bostock (see p. 806) pointed out that the results agree with the law of multiple proportions.

CHENEVIX

Richard Chenevix (Dublin, 1774–Paris, 5 April 1830), of Huguenot ancestry, was imprisoned in Paris during the Terror with some French chemists. On regaining his freedom he studied the subject and became an expert analyst. His opposition to the 'Naturphilosophie' of Germany made him many enemies in that country. In 1802 he published *Remarks upon Chemical Nomenclature, according to the Principles of the French Neologists* (containing a symbol for liquid hydrogen). After the unfortunate dispute with Wollaston (see p. 700) Chenevix lived mostly in France, but he did not (as Thomson says) abandon chemistry.[1]

Chenevix[2] obtained chlorine dioxide by the action of sulphuric acid on potassium chlorate, but he did not determine its composition. He analysed corundum[3] and examined the chemical nature of the humours of the eye.[4] Nicolas[5] found phosphate of lime in them, but this was not found by Chenevix or by Berzelius.[6] Chenevix analysed native cuprous oxide ('red octahedral copper ore') from Cornwall,[7] finding its composition more correctly than Proust (see p. 646), and several other minerals, and examined the magnetism of nickel and cobalt.[8] He criticised the mineralogical systems of Werner and Haüy.[9]

Chenevix[10] determined the composition of sulphuric acid as $61\frac{1}{2}$ sulphur to $38\frac{1}{2}$ oxygen, which are very inaccurate. He oxidised sulphur to sulphuric acid by boiling with nitric acid and precipitated barium sulphate, which he found to contain 14·5 per cent of sulphur. He synthesised calcium sulphate from lime and sulphuric acid, finding it to contain 43 per cent sulphuric acid. He then found that 100 calcium sulphate gave 183 barium sulphate. These results gave the figures quoted. He mentions that Thenard ('Ann. Chim. no. 96') by a similar method had found 44·44 sulphur to 55·56 oxygen, and that Guyton de Morveau (same ref.) had found that barium sulphate contains 74·82 of baryta (BaO) to 25·18 sulphuric acid (SO_3). A good result (41·88 sulphur and 58·12 oxygen) had been found by Richter (see p. 684) but was overlooked. The correct figures are 40 and 60.

Chenevix investigated the *esprit pyro-acétique* (acetone) produced by distilling acetates and concluded that it contained less oxygen than acetic acid.[11]

[1] Thomson, (1), ii, 215; Hunt, DNB, 1887, x, 185 (an unusual account).
[2] *Phil. Trans.*, 1802, xcii, 126: Observations and experiments upon oxygenized and hyper-oxygenized muriatic acid.
[3] Count de Bournon, *Phil. Trans.*, 1802, xcii, 233.
[4] *Phil. Trans.*, 1803, xciii, 195; *Phil. Mag.*, 1803, xvi, 268.
[5] *Ann. Chim.*, 1805, liii, 307.
[6] Thomson, (6), 1843, 513; Pierre François Nicolas (Saint-Mihiel, 26 December 1743–Caen, 18 April 1816), professor of chemistry at Grenoble, Nancy, and Caen: P.L. in NBG, 1863, xxxvii, 991; Poggendorff, (1), ii, 284.
[7] *Phil. Trans.*, 1801, xci, 193.   [8] *Ann. Chim.*, 1802, xliv, 221.
[9] *Ann. Chim.*, 1808, lxv, 51, 113, 225.
[10] *Trans. Roy. Irish Acad.*, 1802, viii, 233 (read 4 May 1801); *Phil. Mag.*, 1801, xi, 112 (in full); *Nicholson's J.*, 1803, v, 126.
[11] *Ann. Chim.*, 1809, lxix, 5; *Nicholson's J.*, 1810, xxxvi, 225, 340.

PROUT

William Prout (Horton, Gloucestershire, 15 January 1785–London, 9 April 1850), M.D. Edinburgh 1811, F.R.S. 1819, physician in London,[1] is best known for his hypothesis that atomic weights are whole multiples of that of hydrogen, which is the primary matter ($\pi\rho\acute{\omega}\tau\eta$ $\H{\upsilon}\lambda\eta$),[2] which he discussed in his Bridgewater Treatise.[3] Thomson early formed a high opinion of Prout, saying in 1820:[4] 'if Dr. Prout persevere in the career which he has begun with so much ardour, the science of chemistry will be indebted to him for discoveries of a far higher and more important kind than have hitherto been made.' Daubeny (1852) says Prout's experimental work was greatly admired by his contemporaries. He developed a method for the analysis of organic compounds by combustion.[5]

Prout made some accurate determinations of the density of air[6] by weighing in a glass globe, with 'a counterpoise of glass, as nearly as possible of the same size and weight as the balloon in which the air is weighed', to eliminate buoyancy. He found 100 cu. in. of dry air freed from carbon dioxide, at 32° F. in 30 in. barometer 'in the latitude of London', to weigh 32·7958 grains, very constant except on one day when it was 32·8218, perhaps due to the presence in the air of 'malaria' since an epidemic broke out then. The effect of temperature did not agree with Gay-Lussac's coefficient of expansion. The result at 60° F. gave 32·8206 calculated for 32° F. instead of 32·7900 (sic) observed.

Most of Prout's investigations were in the field of physiological and pathological chemistry. He analysed urea, uric acid, and cystine (overlooking the sulphur in the latter)[7] and found that a calculus was composed of ammonium urate (lithate of ammonia).[8] He found uric acid in serpent and bird excrements, that of the boa constrictor containing 90 per cent of it.[9] By heating uric acid with dilute nitric acid he found it dissolved with effervescence, and on neutralising with ammonia and evaporating, a deep purple solution was obtained, depositing red crystals, which Prout called purpurate of ammonia. On heating with caustic potash solution, the red colour disappeared, and on adding to dilute sulphuric acid a cream-coloured insoluble powder called *purpuric acid* separated. Most of its compounds with bases are red, some are green and some yellow. By combustion analyses with copper oxide Prout found the

---

[1] Daubeny, *Atomic Theory*, 2 ed., 1850, 471; *id.*, *Edin. N. Phil. J.*, 1852, liii, 98; Hartog, DNB, 1896, xlvi, 426; analysis of publs. in *Edin. Med. J.*, 1851, lxxvi, 126–83.

[2] Anon., *Ann. Phil.*, 1815, vi, 321, 472; 1816, vii, 111; Thomson, *ib.*, 1816, vii, 343, announced that the author was Prout, who later, *Med. Chirurg. Trans.*, 1817, viii, 534, admitted this.

[3] *Chemistry, Meteorology and the Functions of Digestion considered with reference to Natural Theology*, two eds. 1834, 3 ed. 1845, 4 ed. 1855.

[4] *Ann. Phil.*, 1820, xvi, 167.

[5] *Med. Chirurg. Trans.*, 1817, viii, 526; *Ann. Phil.*, 1815, vi, 269; 1818, xi, 352; 1820, xv, 190; 1822, iv, 424; *Phil. Trans.*, 1827, cxvii, 355 (On the ultimate composition of simple alimentary substances; with some preliminary remarks on the analysis of organized bodies in general); Prout's earlier combustion apparatus is described by Henry, *Elements of Experimental Chemistry*, 1829, ii, 195.

[6] *B.A. Rep.*, 1832 (1833), 566–71: Abstract of Observations on Atmospheric Air; the lecture was illustrated by charts of the results.

[7] *Med. Chirurg. Trans.*, 1817, viii, 526; 1818, ix, 472; *Ann. Phil.*, 1818, xi, 352.

[8] *Ann. Phil.*, 1820, xv, 436.   [9] *Ann. Phil.*, 1815, v, 413; 1819, xiv, 363.

equivalent formula $C_2H_2NO_2$ ($=C_4H_4NO_2$).[1] Liebig and Wöhler afterwards showed that purpuric acid did not give red salts with bases and was a decomposition product of the supposed salt, which they named *murexide* (see Vol. IV). Taylor[2] supposed that purpurate of ammonia was present in a banded calculus. Purpuric acid was investigated by Fritsche.[3] Prout's experiments on urinary sediments and calculi are included in his book.[4] The work of Prout is praised in the book by Golding Bird (c. 1815–54), lecturer on materia medica at Guy's Hospital.[5]

Prout discovered free hydrochloric acid in gastric juice,[6] investigated the chemical changes in eggs during incubation,[7] vine sap,[8] the liquor amnii of a cow,[9] ink of the cuttle fish,[10] sanguification and the blood in general,[11] pulmonary and other concretions,[12] pink sediment of urine,[13] excrement of the chamaeleon (ammonium urate),[14] urine of the horse,[15] and fluid of hydrocephalus.[16] He devised a portable hydrometer for determining the specific gravity of urine,[17] described the preparation of pure potash,[18] and made experiments on the varying quantity of carbon dioxide emitted in respiration at different times,[19] in which he found that alcohol and all fermented liquors diminish the amount of carbon dioxide formed, a result confirmed by Fyfe,[20] who is quoted by Prout.

ALLEN. PEPYS. BABINGTON

William Allen (London, 29 August 1770 (or 19 August 1776)–Lindfield, Surrey, 30 December 1843), a Quaker, was lecturer on chemistry at Guy's Hospital and later conducted a pharmacy (from which the firm of Allen and Hanbury is descended).[21]

William Haseldine Pepys junr. (London; 23 March 1775–17 August 1856), F.R.S. 1808, also a Quaker, was director of the Imperial Continental Gas Association, and of General Steam Navigation; he also invented a well-known gas-holder.[22] Pepys was the son of a cutler and followed this trade for a time.[23]

[1] *Phil. Trans.*, 1818, cviii, I, 420.   [2] *Phil. Mag.*, 1838, xii, 412.
[3] *J. prakt. Chem.*, 1839, xvii, 42.
[4] *An Inquiry into the Nature and Treatment of Gravel, Calculus and other Diseases connected with a Deranged Operation of the Urinary Organs*, London, 1821 (227 pp. and coloured illustration; pref. dated 12 December 1820); 2 ed. 1825 (318 pp.), 3 ed., *On the Nature and Treatment of Stomach and Urinary Diseases: Being an Inquiry into the Connexion of Diabetes, Calculus, and other Affections of the Kidney and Bladder, with Indigestion*, 1840 (483 pp.); 4 ed., *On the Nature and Treatment of Stomach and Renal Diseases*, 1843 (593 pp.); 5 ed., 1848 (595 pp.); American ed. (from 2 ed., enlarged), Philadelphia, 1826.
[5] *Urinary Deposits, their Diagnosis, Pathology, and Therapeutical Indications*, 3 ed. 1851, 4 ed. 1853, 5 ed. 1857.
[6] *Phil. Trans.*, 1824, cxiv, 45 (read 11 December 1823): On the nature of the acid and saline matters usually existing in the stomachs of animals; *Isis*, 1925, vii, 239.
[7] *Phil. Trans.*, 1822, cxii, 377.   [8] *Ann. Phil.*, 1815, v, 109.
[9] *Ib.*, 1815, v, 416.   [10] *Ib.*, 1815, v, 417.   [11] *Ib.*, 1819, xiii, 12, 265.
[12] *Ib.*, 1819, xiv, 232–3.   [13] *Ib.*, 1820, xv, 155.   [14] *Ib.*, 1820, xv, 471.
[15] *Ib.*, 1820, xvi, 150.   [16] *Ib.*, 1820, xvi, 151.   [17] *Ib.*, 1825, ix, 334.
[18] *Ib.*, 1820, xvi, 150.   [19] *Ib.*, 1813, ii, 328; 1814, iv, 331.
[20] *Ib.*, 1814, iv, 334.
[21] *William Allen. Life with selections from his Correspondence*, 1846; J. Sherman, *Memoir of William Allen*, 1851; Daniel Hanbury (London; 11 September 1825–24 March 1875), *Science Papers, chiefly Pharmacological and Botanical*, London, 1876.
[22] *Phil. Mag.*, 1802, xiii, 153, and plate; *Allgem. J. Chem.*, 1802, vi, 171, pl. III.
[23] Hadfield, *Faraday and his Metallurgical Researches*, 1931, 47 (portr.).

He supervised the construction of the voltaic battery of 2000 double plates for the Royal Institution.[1] He analysed human teeth[2] and Shetland iron ore and iron pyrites,[3] but his most notable research was the 'steelification' of iron by electrically heating a wire of pure soft iron in a notch in which was a pinch of diamond powder,[4] the iron in contact with which was converted into 'perfect blistered steel'. Allen and Pepys published three papers on respiration (see p. 478).[5]

William Babington (Portglenone, nr. Coleraine, Antrim, 1756–London, 29 April 1833), apothecary in Guy's Hospital, lectured on chemistry and materia medica in the Medical School; M.D. Aberdeen 1795, physician to Guy's Hospital, F.R.S. 1805, and president of the Geological Society; the mineral babingtonite (a complex silicate) was named after him by Levy of Paris. His son, Benjamin Guy Babington (London; 1794 (Guy's Hospital)–1866) was a London physician.[6]

CHILDREN

John George Children (Ferox Hall, Tunbridge, 18 May 1777–Halstead Place, Kent, 1 January 1852), F.R.S. 1807, Secretary of the Royal Society 1826–7 and 1830–7, the son of a wealthy banker in Tunbridge, had a laboratory there in which Davy sometimes worked. The bank failed in 1816 and Children lost his fortune in paying its debts. He then became librarian in the British Museum (where in 1821 he discovered the book by Jean Rey, see p. 397), transferring on Davy's recommendation to the zoology department in 1823 (he was very interested in natural history).[7] Together with his father he set up in Tunbridge an enormous battery of 21 sets of zinc and double copper plates, each 6 ft. by 2 ft. 8 in., or 32 sq. ft., in vessels containing in all 945 gallons of dilute acid, also a *couronne de tasses* of 200 half-pint jugs with zinc and copper plates 2 in. square, with which he made some impressive experiments.[8] Children published mostly in the *Annals of Philosophy*, of which he was joint editor with Richard Phillips, although his name does not appear on the title-pages. He translated Berzelius's book on the blowpipe[9] and part of Thenard's *Traité*.[10] He defended the Davy lamp,[11] and Davy's method of protecting the coppering of ships from corrosion, against criticisms.[12] He worked on the newly-discovered element cadmium,[13] analysed an Egyptian pigment (blue copper frit),[14] and diaspore,[15] described the examination of minerals with

---

[1] *Phil. Mag.*, 1803, xv, 94.   [2] *Ib.*, 1803, xv, 313.
[3] *Ib.*, 1804, xix, 86.   [4] In Children, *Phil. Trans.*, 1815, cv, 363.
[5] *Phil. Trans.*, 1808, xcviii, 249; 1809, xcix, 404; 1829, cxix, 279.
[6] Paine, DNB, 1885, ii, 311, 315; Levy, *Ann. Phil.*, 1824, vii, 275.
[7] Bettany, DNB, 1887, x, 249; Hadfield, *Faraday and his Metallurgical Researches*, 1931, 47 (portr.).
[8] *Phil. Trans.*, 1809, xcix, 32–8; 1815, cv, 363–74 (An account of some experiments with a large voltaic battery); *Life of William Allen with Selections from his Correspondence*, 1846, i, 107.
[9] *The use of the Blowpipe in Chemical Analysis . . . with numerous notes and additions*, 1822.
[10] *An Essay on Chemical Analysis, chiefly translated from . . . the Traité de Chimie Élémentaire, with additions*, 1819 (pp. xvii, 494).
[11] *Phil. Mag.*, 1816, xlviii, 189–96; *Ann. Phil.*, 1816, viii, 265–9.
[12] *Ann. Phil.*, 1824, viii, 141–3, 362–5.   [13] *Quart. J. Sci.*, 1819, vi, 226–30.
[14] *Ann. Phil.*, 1821, ii, 389–90.   [15] *Ib.*, 1822, iii, 434; 1822, iv, 146–8.

the blowpipe,[1] and the minerals baryto-calcite, brochantite, and roselite,[2] and discovered selenium in Anglesey pyrites,[3] and silica in sponges.[4] The mineral childrenite, a basic phosphate of manganese, aluminium, and iron, was named after him by H. J. Brooke, F.R.S., a London wool merchant;[5] the mineral brookite (titanium dioxide) was named after Brooke by Levy.[6] Children criticised Berzelius's atomic theory and symbols (see Vol. IV). In 1824 Children (who travelled extensively) derived a considerable profit by selling to several South American mining companies the right to use a new method he had discovered for extracting silver from its ores without amalgamation.

THOMSON

Thomas Thomson (Crieff, Perthshire, 12 April 1773–Kilmun, Argyllshire, 2 July 1852) entered the University of St. Andrews in 1788. Moving in 1791 to Edinburgh with the intention of studying medicine, he attended in 1795–6 the lectures on chemistry of Joseph Black (of which he left three volumes of notes), and he graduated M.D. in 1799 with a dissertation *De Aere Atmospherico*. Thomson was a good linguist, mathematician, mineralogist and geologist. He studied theology and contemplated entering the Church, but gave up this project about 1798.

In 1796, aged 23, he succeeded his elder brother James as Editor of the *Supplement* to the *Encyclopædia Britannica*, to which he contributed articles on 'Chemistry', 'Mineralogy', and 'Vegetable and Animal Substances and Dyeing'. From about 1800 until 1811 he lectured on chemistry at Edinburgh, prepared his famous *System of Chemistry*, carried out research work, and, at least as early as 1807, opened a laboratory for practical instruction in chemistry (a class-list being extant); this must have been the earliest laboratory of its kind in Great Britain. Thomson became F.R.S. in 1811. At the end of the session 1810–11 he moved to London, where he founded the *Annals of Philosophy*[7] in 1813. This contained original articles (including the two papers by Prout (1815–16) on atomic weights), translations of foreign memoirs (including many by Berzelius), notes on current affairs and reports of meetings of learned societies, and annual reports on the progress of science. In the autumn of 1812 Thomson paid a visit to Sweden, of which he wrote an interesting account.[8]

In October 1817 Thomson was appointed Lecturer in Chemistry in the University of Glasgow on the recommendation of Sir Joseph Banks. At the instance of the Duke of Montrose a Regius Professorship of Chemistry was instituted by George III, and Thomson, as the first incumbent, took up the appointment on 17 March 1818, with an annual salary of £50. Thomson's devotion to pure research in the first ten years of his professorship is noteworthy in view of the salary and the opportunities he had of doing more remunerative work. He had no laboratory until the summer of 1818; it was a

[1] *Ib.*, 1824, viii, 36–9.   [2] *Ib.*, 1824, viii, 115, 243, 441.   [3] *Ib.*, 1825, ix, 52–3.
[4] *Ib.*, 1825, ix, 431.   [5] *Ib.*, 1824, vii, 316.   [6] *Ib.*, 1825, ix, 140–2.
[7] *Annals of Philosophy*, Vols. 1–16, London, 1813–20; continued by Richard Phillips, vols. 17–28, 1821–6; then merged into the *Philosophical Magazine*.
[8] *Travels in Sweden in the Autumn of 1812*, London, 1813.

damp ground-floor room. The chemistry lectures were given daily except
Sunday, and 'even practical experimenting is not neglected'. His statements
that for some years before 1825 he 'had been engaged in teaching practical
chemistry', and that a manuscript manual of quantitative analysis was available to students in his laboratory, show that he gave practical instruction in
Glasgow as well as, earlier, in Edinburgh.

FIG. 56. T. THOMSON, 1773–1852.

The new buildings for the Chemistry Department, opened in 1831, included a laboratory. When London University was founded in 1827 Thomson
was invited to occupy the chair of chemistry, but declined and Edward
Turner was appointed.

Thomson knew personally, or corresponded with, most of the eminent
scientists of the time, and took part in the foundation of the Wernerian Society
of Edinburgh and the Geological Society of London. From 1841 he was
assisted in his teaching work by his nephew, Robert Dundas Thomson.
Thomas Thomson continued to give the lectures on inorganic chemistry until
1846, when R. D. Thomson assumed all the duties of the chair. Thomas
Thomson was succeeded as Regius Professor by Thomas Anderson.[1]

[1] Anon., *Glasgow Med. J.*, 1857, v, 69, 121 (portr.); Crum, *Proc. Phil. Soc. Glasgow*, 1855,
iii, 250; Harden, DNB, 1898, lvi, 271; H. S. Klickstein, *Chymia*, 1948, i, 37 (portr.); Partington, *Ann. Sci.*, 1949, vi, 115; *id.*, in A. Kent (ed.), *An Eighteenth Century Lectureship in
Chemistry*, Glasgow, 1950, 176 (portr.); Poggendorff, (1), ii, 644, 1097–1100; R. D. Thomson,
Edin. N. Phil. J., 1852–3, liv, 86; list of 201 papers in *Roy. Soc. Catal. Sci. Papers*, 1871, v, 970.

Sir Robert Christison says[1] Thomson 'was a very little, well-made man, with small, sharp, handsome features, a calm, contemplative eye, and smooth untroubled brow'. Although warm-hearted and good-natured, he was reserved and often adopted a rather cynical pose, but he was no intriguer and was very open, fearless, and independent, not hesitating to express his views and convictions. When Berzelius complained that Thomson had altered 'kalium' and 'natrium' into 'potash' and 'soda' in a paper printed in his *Annals*, he was told: 'The chemical nomenclature in the English language is too well established to be altered either by your opinion or by mine and if we wish to be read we must conform ourselves to it.'[2]

His first paper[3] on 'Experiments to determine whether or not Fluids be Conductors of Caloric', showed that, contrary to the results of Count Rumford, liquids are conductors of heat. He discovered sulphur chloride[4] ('sulphuretted muriatic acid'), but failed to determine its composition correctly: if he had followed up his analyses he could have anticipated Davy in disclosing the elementary nature of chlorine, which view Thomson was one of the first to accept.[5] The determination of the density of a solid by flotation in a liquid was, apparently, first described by him.[6]

In an investigation of the action of hydrogen sulphide on sulphur dioxide in presence of water, he suspected the presence in the precipitate of sulphur of a new oxyacid of sulphur which he called *hydrosulphurous acid*.[7] This was afterwards recognised as pentathionic acid by Wackenroder in 1845, who was unaware of Thomson's work, which, if he had followed it up, would have given him the credit of the discovery. In Thomson's paper[8] 'On some Compounds of Chromium', he describes the discovery ('about a year and a half ago') of chromyl chloride ('chlorochromic acid', which he thought was a compound of '1 atom chromic acid' and '1 atom chlorine'), of chromium chromate, some new chromates and dichromates, and some double and complex compounds of chromium. Some compounds he described were mixtures, and 'carbonate of chromium' and 'disulphuretted oxide of chromium' are non-existent.

He described many new salts, without claim to discovery, in his *System of Chemistry*. He analysed a large number of minerals, and described some new species, such as *allanite* and *sodalite*; the mineral *thomsonite*, a species of zeolite, was named after him. He introduced[9] the names *protoxide*, *deutoxide*, *tritoxide*, and *peroxide*, and later[10] used Greek and Latin prefixes for the numbers of atoms of radical and oxygen, respectively.

---

[1] *The Life of Sir R. Christison*, 1885, i, 366.   [2] Berzelius, *Bref*, 1918, III, i, 24.
[3] *Nicholson's J.*, 1801, iv, 529.   [4] *Nicholson's J.*, 1803, vi, 92 (104).
[5] *Ann. Phil.*, 1814, iv, 11.
[6] *System of Chemistry*, 1804, i, 353 (not in the first ed., 1802); as pointed out by E. Cohen, *Chem. Weekbl.*, 1933, xxx, 191, and again by H. Irving, *Sci Progr.*, 1937, xxxi, 654; this precedes the use of the method by Davy, *Phil. Trans.*, 1808, xcviii, 21, mentioned by Ostwald, *Z. phys. Chem.*, 1893, xii, 94; it is usually attributed to Dufour, *Compt. rend.*, 1860, l, 1039; 1862, liv, 1079.
[7] *Ann. Phil.*, 1818, xii, 441; Berzelius in letters of 1846–7 gave Thomson credit for this work (*Briefwechsel zwischen J. Berzelius und F. Wöhler*, ed. O .Wallach, Leipzig, 1901, ii, 637, 664).
[8] *Phil. Trans.*, 1827, cxvii, II, 159.   [9] *Nicholson's J.*, 1804, viii, 280.
[10] *An Attempt to Establish the First Principles of Chemistry*, etc., 1825, i, Pref.

In 1807 Thomson,[1] in considering salts other than neutral salts, containing an excess of acid (supersalts) or of base (subsalts), said:

'The simplest way of considering these bodies is, to conceive the supersalts to be compounds of two atoms of acid with one of the base, and the subsalts of two atoms of base with one of acid. Thus supersulphate of potash is composed of one atom of potash united to two of sulphuric acid . . . borax, on the other hand, is composed of two atoms of soda united to one of boracic acid.'

In an important paper[2] 'On Oxalic Acid', Thomson gave the first experimental example (before Wollaston, see p. 702) of the law of multiple proportions by showing that in the normal and acid oxalates of potassium and strontium, one salt, for the same amount of acid, 'contains just double the proportion of base contained in the second', and he drew attention to the bearing of the result on Dalton's atomic theory. In this paper he uses chemical symbols in a *quantitative* sense.[3] The atoms of oxygen, carbon, and hydrogen, are denoted by w, c and h, and the formulae of carbon dioxide, methane, carbon monoxide, water, oxalic acid and sugar by $2w+c$, $c+h$, $w+c$, $w+h$, $4w+3c+2h$, and $5w+3c+4h$. In 1818 he used[4] the symbols o, h, c, ch, p, etc., for the atoms of oxygen, hydrogen, carbon, chlorine, phosphorus, etc.

On the basis of his *Encyclopædia* articles,[5] Thomson, while lecturer in Edinburgh, composed his famous text-book, *A System of Chemistry*.[6] The first edition appeared in 1802. The only previous comparable work was the large treatise by Fourcroy (see p. 538), which lacked an adequate use of important and numerous English sources. An elementary work in one volume[7] was published in 1810; it contains no reference to the atomic theory, compositions being given in percentages. The *System* was finally split into separate works on Inorganic Chemistry (see ref. 6 below), Organic Chemistry,[8] Mineralogy[9] and Heat and Electricity.[10]

[1] (2), 1807, iii, 626.

[2] *Phil. Trans.*, 1808, xcviii, I, 63 (read 14 January); *Phil. Mag.*, 1808, xxxi, 102, 244; 1808, xxxii, 39 (in full); ACR, ii.

[3] For his earlier qualitative symbols, see *Ency. Brit. Suppl.*, 1801, II, i, 193 f.; *System of Chemistry*, 1802, iii, 431; J. R. Partington, *J. Soc. Chem. Ind.*, 1936, lv, 759.

[4] *Ann. Phil.*, 1818, xii, 338, 436.

[5] *Supplement to the Encyclopædia Britannica*, 3 ed., Edinburgh, 1801, I, i, 210 f. (this part appeared before 10 December 1800); 1801, II, i, 193 f. (this part is said to have appeared in 1798); 1801, II, ii, 529 f.

[6] T. Thomson, *A System of Chemistry*, 4 vols., Edinburgh, 1802; 4 vols., 1804; 5 vols., 1807 (interesting as containing the first account of Dalton's atomic theory); 5 vols., 1810; London, 4 vols., 1817; 4 vols., 1820; *A System of Chemistry of Inorganic Bodies. Seventh Edition*, London, 2 vols., 1831. French tr. [of the fifth ed.] by J[ea]n [René Denis] Riffault [des Hêtres], *Système de Chimie . . . Précédé D'une Introduction de M. C. L. Berthollet*, 9 vols., Paris, 1809 (interesting for Berthollet's comments); another French ed., 4 vols., 1818 and supplement, 1822, which I have not seen, contained original communications on light by A. Fresnel. German tr., *System der Chemie in vier Bänden. Nach der zweiten Ausgabe* [1804] *aus dem englischen übersetzt von Friederich Wolff*, Berlin, 4 vols., 1805, and a fifth volume in two parts, *Zusätze und Erweiterung der Wissenschaft seit 1805*, Berlin, 1811 (Bolton, (1), 871, who lists two American eds.: *A New System of Chemistry, including Mineralogy and Vegetable, Animal and Dyeing Substances, comprehending the latest Discoveries and Improvements of the Science*, Philadelphia, 1803 (4°, 364 pp.); and with notes by Thomas Cooper, from the fifth London Edition, Philadelphia, 4 vols., 1818).

[7] T. Thomson, *The Elements of Chemistry*, Edinburgh, 1810.

[8] *Chemistry of Organic Bodies. Vegetables*, London, 1838; *Chemistry of Animal Bodies*, Edinburgh, 1843.

[9] *Outlines of Mineralogy, Geology and Mineral Analysis*, London, 2 vols., 1836.

[10] *An Outline of the Sciences of Heat and Electricity*, London and Edinburgh, 1830; 2 ed., London, 1840.

The arrangement of the *System* is first into imponderable bodies and ponderable bodies, the latter being divided into simple supporters of combustion and simple combustibles, the combustibles being acidifiable or alkalifiable; then follow compounds of various classes, theoretical sections on affinity and states of aggregation, and accounts of meteorology, minerals, and vegetable and animal chemistry. The treatment is mostly historical, which Thomson says lends interest and assists the memory of the student.

Thomson also published long reports on the progress of chemistry which show extensive reading of the literature, including French, German, and Swedish.[1] He published a treatise on brewing and distillation.[2] His *History of the Royal Society*[3] gives an account of the history of each science as nearly as possible from its origin, and a summary of the contents of the Royal Society papers arranged under subjects with biographical accounts of the authors. Thomson's *History of Chemistry*,[4] written in a very interesting style, gives a large amount of valuable information, is largely based on original sources and is still of value. A curious error in the work[5] is the attribution of the discovery of the law of equivalents to Wenzel instead of to Richter, a mistake which had been pointed out to Thomson by Professor Brunner in a letter[6] in 1826.

Thomson was a most successful author, taking great pains to acquire and systematise his material, and the popularity of his books was well deserved. They undoubtedly exercised a very good influence on the progress of chemistry in Great Britain. His style is clear, concise and positive; the material is well arranged and the numerical data are tabulated, the last feature being characteristic.

Thomson was greatly attracted by the hypothesis of William Prout, put forward anonymously in two papers[7] in Thomson's *Annals of Philosophy* in 1815–16, to the effect that atomic weights are whole multiples of that of hydrogen. Thomson took oxygen $= 1$ as his standard, but since he took $O = 8$ when $H = 1$, the same whole number ratio would follow. He thought all other atomic weights were whole multiples of *twice* the atomic weight of hydrogen, *i.e.* of $2 \times 0.125 = 0.25$.[8] For ten years, Thomson made a large number of

---

[1] *Ann. Phil.*, 1814, iii, 1–32; 1815, v, 1–53; 1816, vii, 1–71; 1817, ix, 1–89; 1818, xii, 1–43; 1819, xiii, pp. ix–xcii; 1820, xvi, 1–46, 81–102.

[2] *Brewing and Distillation. With Practical Instructions for Brewing Porter and Ales according to the English and Scottish Method*, by W. Stewart, Edinburgh, 1849 (from his *Encyclopædia* article).

[3] *History of the Royal Society, from its Institution to the end of the Eighteenth Century*, London, 1812. This was intended as a supplement to the *Abridgement of the Philosophical Transactions*, 18 vols., London, 1809.

[4] *The History of Chemistry*, 2 vols., London, 1830–1 (Gleig's *National Library*, Nos. 3 and 10); 2 ed., n.d. (Sotheran *Cat.* 773 (1919), 205 (no. 2633) dates *c.* 1835) in one volume, London.

[5] *Ib.*, ii, 279–82: the numerical examples given are not from Wenzel's book, *Lehre von der Verwandtschaft der Körper*, Dresden, 1777; see p. 672.

[6] Anon., *Glasgow Med. J.*, 1857, v, 140: letter (in English) of 1 November 1826, saying he had read Wenzel's book and 'could not find in it any hint belonging to the theory of atoms . . . in some examples of mutual decomposition he gives at the end of his work, he calculates the required proportions and finds always that one of the bodies is in excess or in less'.

[7] Anon. [W. Prout], *Ann. Phil.*, 1815, vi, 321; 1816, vii, 111; for authorship, see Prout, *Phil. Trans.*, 1827, cxvii, II, 355; Thomson, *Ann. Phil.*, 1820, xvi, 327.

[8] *Ann. Phil.*, 1820, xvi, 1 (16), 321.

experiments with the object of testing Prout's hypothesis, publishing[1] the results in 1825. The experimental methods involved the determination of weight ratios, the determination of the weights of salts giving complete precipitation reactions in solution, and (in the case of organic compounds) combustion analyses by heating with copper oxide in a copper tube, as 'originally suggested by Gay-Lussac'.[2] Unfortunately, Thomson used a method of mixing solutions of known weights of potassium sulphate and barium chloride so that the filtrate from the barium sulphate gave no turbidity with a sulphate or a barium salt, when he assumed that equivalent weights of the two salts had reacted. The barium sulphate carries down some potassium sulphate and hence many of Thomson's results were vitiated, as Turner showed (see Vol. IV).[3] The history of Thomson's experimental work in relation to Prout's hypothesis is taken up in Vol. IV.

Determinations of the densities of gases,[4] made in Thomson's laboratory by Harvey, were claimed to be accurate to 1 part in 1000 (the fully loaded balance was sensible to 0·001 grain). Thomson 'corrected' the values (found with reference to air = 1) on the assumption that air is a definite compound N_4O, and also with reference to Prout's hypothesis. Although the relative density of oxygen was found in three experiments to be 1·1117, he took the theoretical value 1·1111, and for nitrogen instead of the observed value of 0·9728 he took 0·9722. The observed and adopted (on the basis of Prout's hypothesis, in brackets) values were:

Air	1·0000	HCl	1·2844 (1·2847)	SO_2	2·2216 (2·2222)
O_2	1·1117 (1·1111)	CO_2	1·52673 (1·5277)	H_2S	1·17906 (1·1805)
N_2	0·9728 (0·9722)	CO	0·9698 (0·9722)	PH_3	0·90325 (0·90277)
H_2	0·06940	C_2H_4	0·9709 (0·9722)	HI	4·37566 (4·375)
N_2O	1·5269 (1·5277)	CH_4	0·5576 (0·55555)		
NO	1·04096 (1·04166)	C_2N_2	1·80395 (1·8055)		
NH_3	0·5931 (0·59027)	$COCl_2$	3·4604 (3·4722)		

The great discrepancies found with euchlorine, which he supposed (on the basis of Davy's analyses) was an oxide Cl_2O, could if followed up have led Thomson to the discovery that the gas is a mixture in varying proportions of chlorine dioxide and chlorine.

HOPE

Thomas Charles Hope (Edinburgh; 21 July 1766–13 June 1844), at first professor of medicine in Glasgow, succeeded Black as professor of chemistry in Edinburgh in 1799 (he had acted as assistant professor from 1795), although

---

[1] *An Attempt to Establish the First Principles of Chemistry by Experiment*, 2 vols., London, 1825. Bolton, (1), 871, lists a French tr., 2 vols., Paris, 1825.

[2] Thomson, *Ann. Phil.*, 1820, xvi, 1.

[3] Turner, *Phil. Trans.*, 1829, cxix, 291; John Prideaux, *Phil. Mag.*, 1830, vii, 276; 1830, viii, 161 (defending Thomson); Turner, *Phil. Mag.*, 1832, i, 109; *Phil. Trans.*, 1833, cxxiii, 523; Thomson, *Records of General Science*, 1836, iii, 179 (188); R. Phillips, *Phil. Trans.*, 1839, cxxix, 35; Mallet, *J. Chem. Soc.*, 1893, lxiii, 1 (19 f.) for Thomson's method.

[4] *Ann. Phil.*, 1820, xv, 161, 241; for method, see Thomson, *Mem. Wernerian Nat. Hist. Soc.*, 1811, i, 504.

it was expected that Rutherford would obtain the chair. His lectures (he taught Lavoisier's theory) and lecture experiments were very good; in 1823 he lectured to 575 students, but he did not encourage research and had no practical classes for students.[1] He rediscovered strontia (some of Hope's strontium preparations are still in Edinburgh),[2] investigated barium compounds,[3] obtaining baryta by heating the carbonate in a plumbago crucible in a smith's forge, and invented the well-known 'Hope's experiment' on the maximum density of water.[4] Hope noted that the existence of a point of maximum density of water had been demonstrated by William Croune (1683),[5] but it had been observed previously by the Florentine Academicians;[6] it was denied by Hooke. It was investigated by J. J. de Mairan and by J. A. De Luc[7] who fixed it at 41° F. Dalton[8] found it $41\frac{1}{2}$° F. and later (1808) 36° F. Hope's apparatus is independent of the change of volume of a containing vessel.

Hope's assistant, Dr. David Boswell Reid, conducted an extra-mural laboratory course for students in Edinburgh in 1833–4, and George Wilson (Edinburgh; 21 February 1818–22 November 1859), at first Graham's assistant in London, from 1855 professor of technology in Edinburgh, who had lectured previously in Edinburgh, also conducted such a course.[9]

URE

Alexander Ure (Glasgow, 18 May 1778–London, 2 January 1857)[10] studied in Glasgow (M.D. 1801) and Edinburgh, practised medicine, then became professor of chemistry and physics in the Andersonian Institution, Glasgow, and astronomer (through his efforts Glasgow Observatory was founded in 1809); moved to London 1830, from 1834 chemist to the Board of Customs. He was greatly interested in applied chemistry and industries. He was the author of several works.[11] Ure at first supported the oxymuriatic acid theory,[12] made measurements of vapour pressures,[13] the mediate analysis of vegetable

[1] Traill, Trans. Roy. Soc. Edin., 1849, xvi, 419 (read 1847); Life of Sir Robert Christison by his Sons, 1885, i, 54; Life of William Allen with Selections from his Correspondence, 1846, i, 355; Dobbin, in Edinburgh's Place in Scientific Progress (British Assoc.), Edinburgh, 1921, 50; Kendall, in Kent, An Eighteenth Century Lectureship in Chemistry, Glasgow, 1950, 157 (portr.); 4 vols. of MS. of Hope's lectures are in Chemical Society Library, London, and some in Edinburgh University Library.
[2] Trans. Roy. Soc. Edin., 1794, iii, h 141; 1795, iv, m 3.   [3] Ib., 1794 (1798), iv, 34.
[4] Ib., 1805, v, 379 (read in 1804); see also Rumford, Essays, 1800, ii, 281.
[5] Birch, History of the Royal Society, 1757, iv, 253, 263.
[6] Saggi di Natvrali Esperienze, Florence, 1666, 137; Phil. Trans., 1670, v, 2020.
[7] Recherches sur les Modifications de l'Atmosphère, 4°, Geneva, 1772, i, 225.
[8] Manchester Mem., 1802, v, 374 (read April 1799); New System of Chemical Philosophy, 1808, I, i, 134.
[9] Dobbin, op. cit., 1921, 54.
[10] Pharm. J., 1857, xvi, 437; Hartog, DNB, 1899, lviii, 40.
[11] A Dictionary of Chemistry on the basis of Mr. Nicholson's, 8°, London, 1821, 2 ed. 1823, 1824, 3 ed. 1828; Philosophy of Manufactures, 8°, London, 1835, 1861; Dictionary of Arts, Manufactures, and Mines, London, 1839, 3 ed. (2 vols.) 1843, 4 ed. 1853, 5 ed. (3 vols., ed. E. Hunt) 1860 and 1861, 6 ed. 1867, 7 ed. (by E. Hunt and F. W. Rudler) 1875; The Revenue in Jeopardy, 1843.
[12] Trans. Roy. Soc. Edin., 1818, viii, 329, 343, with, ib., 338, a description of a U-shaped eudiometer.
[13] Phil. Trans., 1818, cviii, 338.

matter[1] and organic analyses by combustion with copper oxide;[2] invented a 'thermostat' (bimetallic strip for 'opening dampers', etc.),[3] confirmed the safety of the Davy lamp,[4] worked out the process of manufacturing iodine from kelp in Glasgow,[5] investigated the manufacture of bleaching powder (chloride of lime),[6] the composition of textiles,[7] indigo,[8] caoutchouc,[9] the preparation and analysis of ammonium salts and ammonium amalgam,[10] supersaturation of salt solutions (including crystallisation by an electric current; he showed that the atmosphere has no action),[11] and the preparation of sodium alum[12] and prussic acid.[13] He made measurements of the densities of solutions of hydrochloric acid,[14] sulphuric acid,[15] and nitric acid,[16] and the contraction on diluting the acids.[17] He also made extensive use of volumetric methods of acidimetry and alkalimetry,[18] determined the atomic weight of silver[19] as 111, and investigated the density and uses of wood spirit (pyroxylic spirit).[20] A. Ure junr. found that benzoic acid when taken is excreted in the urine as hippuric acid.[21]

Ure also published some gruesome experiments on the movements of a corpse exposed to galvanism,[22] in the course of which several spectators ran out of the theatre and 'one gentleman fainted'; and on disinfection and quarantine, in which apparatus for producing chlorine gas is described.[23] In the *Dictionary of Chemistry* (1821) Ure adopted Berzelius's notation and in the article on 'Equivalents' showed discernment in dealing with contemporary theories. Dalton[24] had a poor opinion of Ure as a chemist.

John Anderson (Rosmarth, Dunbartonshire, 1726–Glasgow, 13 June 1796), professor of oriental languages (1756) and later (1790) of natural philosophy in the University of Glasgow, lectured on scientific subjects to artisans from about 1760 and left all his effects for the founding of a college for the education of artisans in practical subjects. Anderson's Institution (1796), one of the earliest mechanics' institutes, later became the Royal Technical College.[25] The professor of physics was George Birkbeck (Settle, Yorkshire, 10 January 1776–London, 1 December 1841), who in 1804 moved to London and gave courses of scientific lectures, leading to the foundation in 1823 of the London Mechanics' Institute, which later became Birkbeck College, University of London.

[1] *Ann. Chim.*, 1823, xxiii, 377.   [2] *Phil. Trans.*, 1822, cxii, 457.
[3] *Proc. Roy. Soc.*, 1831, iii, 67.   [4] *Phil. Mag.*, 1816, xlviii, 81, with figure of lamp.
[5] *Phil. Mag.*, 1817, l, 161.
[6] *Quart. J. Sci.*, 1822, xiii, 1, also on at. wt. of manganese.
[7] *Ib.*, 1826, xxi, 28, 297.   [8] *Ib.*, 1830, xxix, 160.
[9] *Phil. Mag.*, 1839, xv, 76.   [10] *Ann. Phil.*, 1817, x, 203.
[11] *Quart. J. Sci.*, 1818, v, 106.   [12] *Ib.*, 1822, xiii, 276.
[13] *Ib.*, 1822, xiii, 312.   [14] *Ann. Phil.*, 1817, x, 269, 369.
[15] *Quart. J. Sci.*, 1818, iv, 114.
[16] *Ib.*, 1818, iv, 291; 1819, vi, 242 (criticising R. Phillips' 'insolence').   [17] *Ib.*, 1818, iv, 151.
[18] *Ib.*, 1821, xi, 401; *Ann. Phil.*, 1821, ii, 15; complaining of the publication of his method by Henry, *Elements of Chemistry*, 1818, ii, 51.
[19] *Quart. J. Sci.*, 1822, xii, 286.   [20] *Phil. Mag.*, 1841, xix, 511.
[21] *J. de Pharm.*, 1841, xxvii, 646.
[22] *Quart. J. Sci.*, 1819, vi, 283: An Account of some Experiments made on the Body of a Criminal immediately after Execution.
[23] *J. Roy. Inst.*, 1831, ii, 83.   [24] *Manchester Mem.*, 1819, iii, 446.
[25] J. Muir, *John Anderson. An Address to the Andersonian Chemical Society*, Glasgow, October 1930.

FYFE

Andrew Fyfe (Edinburgh; 18 January 1792–31 December 1861), M.D. 1814, F.R.S. 1823, lecturer in chemistry in Edinburgh, professor of medicine and chemistry in Aberdeen (1844–61),[1] analysed the water of the North Polar Sea and made experiments on the occurrence of iodine in sponges, kelp, etc.[2], on coal gas and oil gas, and a form of Döbereiner's lamp,[3] and on silver phosphate as sensitive material in photography.[4] He analysed a specimen of 'tutenag or white copper of China',[5] and this led to the European development of the white alloy.

Butini[6] found that carbonate of magnesia is more soluble in cold than in hot water. Fyfe confirmed this by quantitative determinations, and found the same behaviour with magnesium oxide and magnesium carbonate.[7] He used iron in place of zinc in voltaic batteries.[8] He published a text-book of chemistry.[9] Fyfe's M.D. dissertation was on respiration[10] and some of Fyfe's experiments on respiration are quoted by Prout.[11]

HARE

Although this chapter is devoted to British and Irish chemists, it seems appropriate also to include in it an account of a contemporary American, Robert Hare (Philadelphia; 17 January 1781–15 May 1858), professor of chemistry in the university of Pennsylvania, Philadelphia.[12] He invented 'Hare's apparatus' (the 'litrameter') for determining the specific gravities of liquids, also a hydrostatic balance similar to Mohr's,[13] a cryophorus ('palm glass'),[14] a gas density balance on the principle of the much later Lux's balance,[15] a method of burning metals in chlorine by shaking the powdered metal into the gas in a jar,[16] and eudiometers for exploding gases,[17] as well as a number of other pieces of apparatus.

He invented an oxy-hydrogen blowpipe supplied with the mixed gases under pressure,[18] and an apparatus of this kind in which the mixed gases contained in a bladder were compressed into a strong copper box, from which they were

[1] A. Findlay, The Teaching of Chemistry in the University of Aberdeen, Aberdeen University Studies, cxii, Aberdeen, 1935, 57 (portr.).
[2] Edin. Phil. J., 1819, i, 160, 254. [3] Ib., 1824, xi, 171, 367; 341.
[4] Ib., 1839, xxvii, 144. [5] Ib., 1822, iv, 69: Cu 40·4, Zn 25·4, Ni 31·6, Fe 2·6.
[6] Nouvelles Observations et Recherches Analytiques sur la Magnésie du sel d'Epsom, suivies de Réflections sur l'Union Chimique des Corps, Geneva, 1781.
[7] Edin. Phil. J., 1821, v, 305–8. [8] Phil. Mag., 1837, xi, 145.
[9] A Manual of Chemistry, Edinburgh, 1826 (Bolton, (1), 465); Elements of Chemistry, 2 vols., Edinburgh, 1827, 2 ed. 1830, 3 ed. 1833 (BM), including a discussion of caloric, light, electricity, and galvanism. His Compendium of Anatomy, 2 vols., Edinburgh, 1800, reached an eighth edition, 4 vols., Edinburgh, 1823.
[10] Dissertatio de copia acidi carbonici e pulmonibus inter respirandum evoluti, Edinburgh, 1814 (BM 1184. b. 16. (9.)).
[11] Ann. Phil., 1814, iv, 331 (334).
[12] E. F. Smith, Archeion, 1927, viii, 330–5 (poor portr.); Isis, 1928, xi, 473; picture of Hare's lecture room and laboratory in Amer. J. Sci., 1831, xix, 26; Poggendorff, (1), i, 1018.
[13] Amer. J. Sci., 1826, xi, 121. [14] Ib., 1828, xiii, 1; 1838, xxxiii, 244.
[15] Ib., 1829, xvi, 293. [16] Ib., 1828, xiv, 354.
[17] Ib., 1829, xv, 260. [18] Phil. Mag., 1802, xiv, 238, 298.

burnt at a jet, was invented and sold by the London instrument maker John Newman.[1] This apparatus was improved by E. D. Clarke, professor of mineralogy in Cambridge (Willingdon, Sussex, 5 June 1769–Cambridge, 9 March 1822), who tried to prevent the flame passing back into the box and exploding the gases by fitting capillary tubes in a safety jet, but since explosions sometimes occurred he worked with the apparatus behind a strong wall in the laboratory, through which the jet of the blowpipe passed.[2] There are some blowpipes of this kind in the Old Ashmolean Museum, Oxford.

What he called the 'lime-light' was described by Lieut. Thomas Drummond, R.E., F.R.S. (Edinburgh, October 1797–Ireland (Dublin ?), 15 April 1840),[3] who used an alcohol flame directed by a jet of oxygen on to a piece of lime. Drummond later[4] used hydrogen and oxygen supplied through separate tubes. Drummond had been anticipated by Goldsworthy Gurney, lecturer in the Surrey Institution, who used the mixed gases in a bladder (which did little harm if it exploded), passing them through a water trap before kindling them at a jet, and allowed the flame to play on a piece of lime, when a most intense light was produced. He also used magnesia (as did Drummond) and even suggests that 'the light produced in this way . . . will be used with great advantage in light-houses, &c.', and that the blowpipe could be used in fusing platinum (he had fused 6 oz. at one time).[5] Gurney received the gold medal of the Society of Arts for his invention and it is surprising that Drummond did not mention him.[6] The lime-light was often called the 'Drummond light'. Gurney also suggested a hydrogen-chlorine blowpipe.

The oxy-hydrogen blowpipe with a tube supplying oxygen inside one supplying hydrogen, suggested but not used by Lavoisier,[7] was described by Daniell,[8] who also used coal-gas, and applied it to the melting of platinum and to the lime-light.

John Hemming[9] invented a safety-jet for the mixed gases containing a tight bundle of brass wires. W. Maugham improved the Daniell apparatus for lime-light, the jet being bent over so as to project the flame on a piece of lime.[10]

[1] Newman, *Quart. J. Sci.*, 1816, i, 65; H. J. Brooke, *Ann. Phil.*, 1816, vii, 367; Newman, *Description of a New Blow-Pipe, with Cautions and Instructions for its Use, when containing a mixed Atmosphere of Explosive Gases*, 1817 (8 pp. and frontispiece); other suggested oxy-hydrogen blowpipes, G. Gray, *Ann. Phil.*, 1817, ix, 479; J. T. Beale, *ib.*, 481; Spilsbury, *ib.*, 483; see Berzelius, *Lehrbuch der Chemie*, 1831, IV, ii, 863; Berzelius-Wöhler, *Briefwechsel*, 1901, i, 353; ii, 222.

[2] Clarke, *Quart. J. Sci.*, 1816, ii, 104; *Ann. Phil.*, 1816, viii, 313, 357; 1817, ix, 7, 89, 162, 194, 326 (capillary tubes in safety jet); 1817, x, 76, 133, 373; *Ann. Phys.*, 1819, lxxii, 339–98 (with notes by Gilbert); *The Gas Blow-Pipe, or Art of Fusion by Burning the Gaseous Constituents of Water*, 1819 (109 pp. and plate of the apparatus); he mentions that Thomson called it the 'oxy-hydrogen blow-pipe'. On Clarke, see [W. Otter], *The Life and Remains of the Rev. Edward Daniell Clarke, Ll.D., Professor of Mineralogy in the University of Cambridge*, 4°, 1824; 2 vols. 8°, 1825 (portr., list of publications). Clarke published *A Syllabus of Lectures on Mineralogy*, Cambridge, 1807, London, 1818.

[3] On the means of facilitating the Observation of distant Stations in Geodetical Operations, in *Phil. Trans.*, 1826, cxvi, 324–37.

[4] On the Illumination of Light-Houses, in *Phil. Trans.*, 1830, cxx, 383–98 ('lime-light').

[5] Gurney, *Trans. Soc. Arts*, 1823, xli, 70–7, plate IV; *A Course of Lectures on Chemical Science, as delivered at the Surrey Institution*, 1823, 272–310, and plate.

[6] Niemann, *A. Nat.*, 1913–15, v, 202.　　[7] AdS, 1782 (1785), m 457; *Oeuvres*, ii, 423 (430).

[8] *Phil. Mag.*, 1833, ii, 57–60; Winderlich, *A. Nat.*, 1928, x, 427–31.

[9] *B.A. Rep.*, 1832 (1833), 572–3; *Trans. Soc. Arts*, 1833, xlix, 41.

[10] *Trans. Soc. Arts*, 1836, l, Pt. II, 41–9.

DONOVAN

Michael Donovan (Dublin; 15 May 1790–notice of death, 19 April 1876), who was William Higgins's successor as professor of materia medica and chemistry in Apothecaries' Hall, Dublin, published: I *Essay on the Origin, Progress and Present State of Galvanism*, Dublin, 1816; II *A Treatise on Chemistry*, London, 3 ed., 1832 (Cabinet Cyclopaedia) — no earlier edition is known. He proposed the name 'dose (from δεδοται, of διδωμι, I give), a determinate or definite quantity of a thing given' instead of atom, equivalent, proportion, or combining weight.[1] He does not mention Higgins but says Dalton 'first distinctly conceived that, from the relative weights of the elements in the mass of any compound body, the relative weights of the ultimate particles or atoms of the bodies might be inferred'.[2] He gives Avogadro's hypothesis,[3] mentioning his name and giving a reference to his paper.

Donovan discovered in mountain-ash berries what he called sorbic (malic) acid,[4] which he found in rhubarb stem;[5] he afterwards[6] admitted the identity of sorbic and malic acids. He described the preparation of pure potash from carbonate and slaked lime,[7] investigated whether alcohol is a product of fermentation or distillation,[8] preparation of pure silver[9] and of phosphorus,[10] and denied the identity of ordinary (frictional) electricity, voltaic electricity, magneto-electricity, and thermo-electricity.[11] He wrote on alchemical and chemical physicians[12] and the use of hyoscyamus[13] — both in titles only, and on smelting lead,[14] as well as on pharmaceutical and medical subjects in the *Dublin Journal of Medicine and Chemistry* (1839–46). Donovan invented a gas lamp,[15] a gas table-lamp,[16] a hygrometer, and an apparatus for filtration out of contact with air.[17] 'Donovan's solution' is a 1 per cent solution of equal weights of arsenious and mercuric iodides used in the treatment of skin diseases.

[1] II, 368.   [2] II, 390.   [3] II, 379.
[4] *Phil. Trans.*, 1815, cv, 231; *Phil. Mag.*, 1816, xlvii, 16; *Ann. Chim.*, 1816, i, 281.
[5] *Ann. Phil.*, 1817, ix, 103.   [6] *Proc. Roy. Irish Acad.*, 1850, iv, 502.
[7] *Ann. Phil.*, 1825, x, 72.   [8] *Phil. Mag.*, 1814, xliv, 207, 317.
[9] *Phil. Mag.*, 1816, xlvii, 204 (pp. by copper from silver nitrate solution).
[10] *Proc. Roy. Irish Acad.*, 1850, iv, 316; *Phil. Mag.*, 1851, ii, 202.
[11] *Ann. Phil.*, 1814, iv, 401; *Phil. Mag.*, 1852, iii, 117, 198, 290, 335, 445; 1852, iv, 33, 130, 210.
[12] *Proc. Roy. Irish Acad.*, 1851, v, 81.   [13] *Pharm. J.*, 1861, iii, 618; 1871, i, 907.
[14] *Proc. Roy. Irish Acad.*, 1850, iv, 136.   [15] *Dingler's Polytechn. J.*, 1831, xl, 345.
[16] *Proc. Roy. Irish Acad.*, 1848 (1850), iv, 75, 91.   [17] *Ann. Phil.*, 1825, x, 115.

CHAPTER XVI

BRYAN AND WILLIAM HIGGINS

BRYAN HIGGINS

Bryan Higgins (Collooney, Co. Sligo, 1737 or 1741–Walford, Staffs., 1818) took the external M.D. of Leyden and practised as a physician in London, where he opened a School of Practical Chemistry on 5 July 1774 in Greek Street, Soho, giving a course of lectures and demonstrations.[1] He was assisted for a time by his nephew William Higgins, who calls him 'a phlogistian'.[2] The syllabus of the lectures was issued first in 1775 (I), then reprinted with many slight changes of wording and omissions in 1776 (II). In I Higgins says many subscribers had asked for a previous course of practical chemistry in which a didactic order would be preserved, and a syllabus of this was published as III:

I. A Syllabus of the Discourses and Experiments, With which the Meetings of the Subscribers are to be opened, after the Course of Chemistry is concluded; undated. On p. 2: Advertisement. The following Proposals, altho' formerly published, are inserted with a view to express the purposes for which the approaching meetings are to be held.

II. A Syllabus of Chemical and Philosophical Enquiries, composed for the Use of the Noblemen and Gentlemen who have subscribed to the Proposals made for the Advancement of Natural Knowledge; in IV, pp. xix–liii, and separately (same title): London, printed for J. Robson and Co., New Bond Street, and B. Law, Ave Maria Lane, 1776.

III. Syllabus of Dr. Higgins's Course of Philosophical, Pharmaceutical, and Technical Chemistry, 112 pp., n.d.; Zeitlinger, Sotheran *Cat.* 839 (1934), no. 511, dated it 1778. This pamphlet has XXVII complete sections, ending on p. 111 and the beginning of Section XXVIII, 'Vulgar Analytic Chemistry', on p. 112. This breaks off after a complete sentence and at the bottom of the blank half-page is the statement 'The author has not time at present to announce the particulars of this part of his course'.

III is quite different from I. It begins without introduction with: Section I, 'Introductory Lectures', in which 'The author's sense of the words element, atom, molecule, and particle; with cursory observations on these subjects, illustrated by experiments', and 'the author's sense of the word attraction' and 'the word repulsion', are included, also 'the distinguishing characters of phlogiston' and 'experiments and observations, shewing that phlogiston, whether combined or detached, is a kind of matter different from that of Light'. Sections II to XXVII then deal with vitriolic acid, nitrous acid, marine acid; acetous acid, vinous liquors, and argol; anomalous acids, and phosphoric acid; tincal and sedative salt, fixed vegetable alkali, mineral alkali, volatile

---

[1] Goodwin, DNB, 1891, xxvi, 366; B. Higgins, IV, viii; Lippmann, (3), ii, 248; and the literature cited under William Higgins, p. 737.

[2] W. Higgins, *A Comparative View of the Phlogistic and Antiphlogistic Theories*, 1789, xii, 249.

alkali, calcareous earths, silicious earth, argillaceous earth (including manganese), arsenic, cobalt, nickel, bismuth, antimony, zinc, tin, lead, copper, iron, mercury, silver, gold, and platina. The course was obviously detailed and practical and embraced technical and pharmaceutical chemistry. Higgins often mentions his own discoveries and theories and the errors of other chemists.

In I (p. 27) Higgins speaks of 'Conceits of acid air, vitriolic air, acetous air, nitrous air, &c.', obviously referring to Priestley, who attended some of the lectures, and the latter issued an 86-page pamphlet (with a price-list of his books at the end) devoted to dealing with the matter,[1] in which he calls Higgins's theories of the negative weight of phlogiston, etc., 'suchlike long exploded and crude notions.'[2] Higgins had made verbal claims to the discovery of some gases, but Priestley says he had told Higgins about these, and had shown him some experiments. He gives some information on Higgins's personal manner and about his lectures. In 1775, Priestley[3] spoke of being 'favoured' with the use of chemicals by Dr. Higgins, but probably not gratuitously as Meldrum suggested,[4] since Priestley says the red precipitate he bought in Paris from Cadet was cheaper than that supplied by Higgins. Priestley[5] told Higgins: 'the Council of the Royal Society, wanting the wisdom of your advice, had been so infatuated, as to have conferred upon me their annual prize-medal [the Copley Medal, 1773] for about one half of those [discoveries] that are contained in that first volume' (of his *Experiments and Observations on Air*). It is perhaps a pity that Dalton later did not deal in a similar way with the aggressive claims of William Higgins (see p. 749), but Dalton (a Royal Medallist) was cast in a different mould from Priestley.

Bryan Higgins also published:

IV. A Philosophical Essay concerning Light, Vol. I (all publ.), 8°, London, 1776, liii, 256 pp, i l. errata, plate; pp. xix–liii reprint (modified) of I.
V. Experiments and Observations relating to Acetous Acid, Fixable Air, Dense Inflammable Air, Oils and Fuel; the Matter of Fire and Light, Metallic Reduction, Combustion, Fermentation, Putrefaction, Respiration, and other Subjects of Chemical Philosophy, 8°, London, 1786 (pp. xvi, 1 l. errata, 353).

In 1779 Higgins took out a patent for a cement composed of washed sand, slaked lime, lime water, and bone ash, and he described a large number of experiments in a book:

VI. Experiments and Observations made With the View of Improving the Art of Composing and Applying Calcareous Cements And Of preparing Quicklime: Theory of these Arts; And Specification of the Author's cheap and durable Cement, for Building, Incrustation or Stuccoing, and artificial Stone, 8°, London, 1780, pp. xi, 233.

The 'Society for Philosophical Experiments and Conversations' was established on the basis of proposals issued in November 1793, in the Greek Street Laboratory on 25 January 1794 with a subscription of five guineas. The Chairman was Field Marshal Conway, a friend of Horace Walpole, one of the

[1] *Philosophical Empiricism: containing Remarks on a Charge of Plagiarism respecting D^r H-s, interspersed With various Observations relating to different kinds of air*, London, 1775.
[2] *Ib.*, 59.   [3] *Experiments and Observations on Air*, 1775, ii, 23, 70 ,76, 80, 82, 86, 114.
[4] See ref. on p. 737.   [5] *Philos. Empiricism*, 70.

Assistants in Experiments was Thomas Young, and one of the members of the publication committee was Thomas Partington, of the Temple. The Society met weekly during the Session of Parliament at 8 p.m. over a period of six months. Some of the apparatus used was quite complicated and expensive. The experiments, lectures, and discussions were, on the direction of the publication committee, published by Higgins in 1795:

VII. Minutes of the Society for Philosophical Experiments and Conversations, London, Cadell and Davies, 1795, pp. 355 (+ 1 errata) and iv folding plates; a second t.p. with the same title adds 'Instituted in London 25th Jan. 1794'.
German tr. by A. N. Scherer: Protokolle der Verhandlungen einer Privat-Gesellschaft in London über die neuern Gegenstände der Chemie. Geführt unter der Anleitung von Bryan Higgins, Halle, 1803 (Bolton, (1), 1129); often q. in Gmelin's Handbuch.

In 1797 Higgins visited the West Indies and, for large fees, advised on sugar and rum manufacture:

VIII. Observations and Advices for the Improvement of the Manufacture of Muscovado Sugar and Rum, 3 pts. St. Jago de la Vega, 1797–1800–1801; Fragment of the Fourth Part of Dr. Higgins's Observations and Advices . . . Sugar and Rum, Jamaica, 1803 (BM 7954. bb. 12. (1.), pts. 1, 2; BN S. 14839–14841; *Cat. Gén.*, 1920, lxxi, 1202), Fragment, 1803, BM 7945. bbb. 12. (2.); Lippmann, (3), ii, 248, gives 5 pts., St. Jago de la Vega, 1799–1803; Higgins, *Phil. Mag.*, 1806, xxiv, 308–22.

Before Higgins's theoretical speculations are dealt with, some of his practical observations will be mentioned. He says[1] that he showed in his lectures in 1776 that red-hot charcoal 'cooled in vessels into which nothing ponderable but air was admitted' increased greatly in weight, owing to the 'attractive powers which draw air into bodies, and condensed in them', so that he discovered gaseous adsorption before Scheele and Fontana (see pp. 231, 296), who, however, published earlier. In 1781 Higgins was granted a patent for making caustic soda from common salt by converting this into sodium sulphate, reducing this to sulphide by heating with coal, and fusing the sulphide with lead, when caustic soda floated to the surface.[2]

The *Minutes of the Society* begins with theories of caloric and attraction and then describes a series of experiments. Lavoisier's experiment for the analysis of air by heated mercury (see p. 417) was modified[3] by using an improved apparatus consisting of a wider tube connecting the retort containing the mercury, and a funnel-shaped receiver containing air, loosely floating in mercury; the composition of air by weight was found to be 27 oxygen and 73 nitrogen (the correct figure is 23·2 of oxygen).

In an experiment on the respiration of a sparrow 'the gentlemen unanimously demanded that he should be set at liberty',[4] but in another experiment in which a sparrow was expected to survive 'he fell dead in a second . . . neither did blowing gently into his lungs avail'.[5] A simple apparatus for finding the combining volumes of hydrogen and oxygen is described, Lavoisier's being 'liable to many objections',[6] a jet of hydrogen ignited electrically being burnt in oxygen in a glass globe. It was found that 416·5 grains of oxygen

[1] VI, 16.　　　　　[2] Mellor, *Treatise*, ii, 729.　　　[3] VII, 97.
[4] *Ib.*, 132.　　　　[5] *Ib.*, 134.　　　　　　　　[6] *Ib.*, 174 f., Plate I.

combined with 72·5 grains of hydrogen (total 489 gr.) to form 487 gr. of water which, 'contrary to all expectation, had no sensible acidity.'[1] Some experiments with Lavoisier's ice calorimeter are described.[2] The descriptions of an improved method of making phosphorus,[3] and the preparation of black crystalline fulminating silver, deposited from a solution of silver oxide in ammonia on exposure to air,[4] are interesting, and Higgins was obviously a clever experimenter, Goodwin's statement[5] that he was more successful as a speculator than as an experimenter being incorrect.

Bryan Higgins discovered acetamide by distilling ammonium acetate, and described its properties, including its precipitation by silver nitrate, and its m.p. 170° (correctly 177°).[6] He devised the experiment of wrapping moist copper nitrate in tinfoil, when nitrous fumes are evolved, then fire is produced which bursts and fuses the tinfoil in several places.[7] The 'chemical harmonica', in which a jet of hydrogen burning in a vertical glass tube produces a musical note,[8] was shown to Sir Joseph Banks in 1777 and frequently later to others. It was described by J. A. De Luc[9] and Hermbstädt.[10]

Pictet and De la Rive[11] thought it was caused by the vibration of the tube, but Faraday[12] showed that it is due to the vibration of the flame by a series of small explosions. Higgins described a gasometer.[13] In his course[14] he had a 'Digression concerning alchemistic enquiries; vindication of alchemists, and cautions against the dangers of alchemy'. His *Syllabus*[15] has a long section on phlogiston, which is:

'a matter subtile, elastic, invisible, incommutable, indestructible, incapable of decomposition . . . is a distinct element; and there is but one phlogistic element. . . . Experiments, shewing that many non-phlogistic bodies, accurately weighed, and then combined with considerable quantities of phlogiston, acquire no additional absolute gravity . . . the absolute gravity of many non-phlogistic bodies, is considerably counteracted or in effect lessened by combining these bodies with phlogiston . . . phlogiston doth not gravitate, and that it hath a power whereby it counteracts the gravitation of other matter.[16] . . . Fire is a compound consisting of phlogiston and some other matter . . . it is phlogiston combined with light.[17] . . . Blaze is a mixture of Fire and phlogistic matter which hath not yet formed fire [been decomposed, so as to contribute to the formation of Fire].[18]

The elements are earth, water, alkali, acid, air, phlogiston, and light; fire, the ethereal fluid, and the mercurial principle being rejected.[19] Higgins in the *Syllabus* often refers to 'diagrams' of globular atoms which he no doubt showed in his lectures, where they were seen by William Higgins. It mentions:

'Experiments observations, and arguments, persuading that each primary element consists of atoms homogeneal; that these atoms are impenetrable, immutable in figure,

[1] *Ib.*, 194.   [2] *Ib.*, 243.   [3] *Ib.*, 254 f., 261.
[4] *Ib.*, 324 f.   [5] DNB, 1891, xxxvi, 366.   [6] V, 1786, 192 f.
[7] *Phil. Trans.*, 1773, lxiii, 137; Wasserberg, *Institutiones Chemicae*, Vienna, 1778, i, 239.
[8] Higgins, *Nicholson's J.*, 1802, i, 129.
[9] *Idées sur la Météorologie*, 8°, London, 1786, i, 170: c'est donc une Vibration dans l'Air même; no mention of Higgins.
[10] Crell's *Ann.*, 1793, I, 356.   [11] *Nicholson's J.*, 1803, iv, 23.
[12] *Quart. J. Sci. and Arts*, 1818, v, 274; *Experimental Researches*, 1859, 21.
[13] *Allgem. J. Chem.*, 1801, vi, 175, 188, pls. IV, V.   [14] I, 45; IV, xxxvii.
[15] I, 35–65; IV, xxxii–xlvii; Partington and McKie, *Ann. Sci.*, 1938, iii, 342.
[16] I, 47; IV, xxxviii.   [17] I, 49, 68; IV, xl, xlviii f.
[18] I, 54; II, 54; IV, xlii.   [19] I, 9; IV, xix.

inconvertible, and that in the ordinary course of nature they are not annihilated, nor newly created, . . . the atoms of each element are globular or nearly so; and the spiral, spicular, and other figures ascribed to these atoms, are fictitious, unnecessary, and are inconsistent with the uniformity and simplicity of nature, and repugnant to experience.[1] There is but one species [cause] of attraction operating with great force between the similar [homogeneal] or dissimilar [heterogeneal] atoms of certain elements; and with less force between those of other elements, in gradations; but in all affected by distance and polarity[2] . . . fire pervades all known bodies . . . produces effects on bodies diametrically opposed to the power and effects of attraction[3] . . . the atomary repulsion of the alkaline element [fluid] so much overpowered by the attraction of other interposed matter, that solid ponderous masses are formed therewith.'[4]

This refers to Priestley's experiment (1773–4)[5] in which a mixture of alkaline air (ammonia gas) and acid air (hydrochloric acid gas) condensed to solid sal ammoniac ($NH_3 + HCl = NH_4Cl$). Priestley probably showed this experiment to Higgins (see p. 728), on whom it made a great impression. Newton had imagined (see Vol. II, p. 476) that the particles of air (the only gas known to him) were self-repulsive, but Priestley's experiment showed that the particles of two different gases could exert an attraction on one another, resulting in chemical combination (see p. 732). Higgins continued:

'The doctrine of the repulsion of the homogeneal atoms of all elements except earth and water . . . the attraction causing the aggregation and gravitation of earth considered in opposition to the action of fire.[6] . . . Probable suggestions that repulsion and attraction, which are forcible in contact . . . universally extend to distances indefinite.[7] Repulsion is the cause of elastic fluids and attraction of solid bodies.[8] Experiments and diagrams, explaining the phenomena of invisible fluids formed by two or more elements [fluids] which attract and saturate each other.[9]

'The true cause of saturation investigated. Experiments, shewing that no element doth saturate, nor can saturate the like element; that no element, whose atoms attract each other, can saturate any other element whose atoms attract each other; that a repellent element doth saturate non-repellent elements, and *vice versa*; that repellent elements do saturate reciprocally; and that attraction and repulsion, operating adversely, are the cause of saturation {and saturation is not a distinct or primary law of nature but only an effect}.[10]

'The theory of saturation further confirmed. Experiments in order to analyse the nitrous acid compleately [and to exhibit the air contained in it].[11] Fire is matter and . . . is an elastic fluid.

'Fire pervades all bodies and this property of fire is no exception against the doctrine of saturation, that doth not teach that the size of elementary atoms can be altered, nor that molicules [molecules] can be formed until the atoms are in contact. Solid bodies, which are expanded by a small charge of fire, are softened by a greater charge of fire; are rendered fluid or fused by a charge of fire still greater; and are thrown into vapour by a charge of fire much greater. Fire hath the power of counteracting attraction, by reason of its capacity to remove contiguous atoms of bodies to a distance from each other.'[12]

Higgins took over Newton's idea of mutually repulsive atoms in air and applied it to the particles of all gases, simple and compound:

'The atoms of air repel reciprocally.[13] Air and all other known matters attract at every distance those bodies which they attract at any distance, and repel at every

---

[1] I, 9–10; IV, xix.   [2] I, 12; IV, xxi (words in brackets).

[3] I, 13; IV, xxi.   [4] I, 21; IV, xxv.   [5] E & O, 1774, i, 170.

[6] I, 16; IV, xxiii.   [7] I, 21; IV, xxv.   [8] I, 22; IV, xxvi.

[9] I, 23; IV, xxvi.   [10] I, 23; IV, xxvi; the words in { } are in I only.

[11] I, 34; IV, xxxi; cf. W. Higgins, p. 742.

[12] I, 56–8; IV, xliii–xliv; the mis-spelling of 'molicule' and its subsequent correction to 'molecule' reappear in W. Higgins.

[13] I, 30; IV, xxx.

distance those bodies which they repel at any distance.[1] Light is an elementary matter consisting of atoms of the smallest size . . . which repel each other and . . . every known matter except phlogiston.[2] . . . The electrical fluid contains [consists chiefly of] light.'[3]

In his *Essay Concerning Light* (1776), Higgins repeatedly quotes Newton. He says the atoms of each element are accurately or nearly globular; a 'molecule' is the name given, 'after the example of the modern chemists', to a body consisting of *two* coherent and heterogeneous (different) atoms. (The *name* is much older but the restriction to an aggregate of two different atoms is peculiar to Bryan Higgins.) The attraction and repulsion of atoms and their polarity are dealt with at great length, with quotations from Newton.[4]

'A body whose parts repel cannot be saturated by a body whose parts attract each other', but 'a compound whose parts attract each other, so as to be held in contact, can be saturated by, or can unite with only a determinate quantity of a repellant element . . . the excess of the repulsive above the attractive forces is truly the cause of saturation.'[5]

In a long section (xii) 'Of Saturation'[6] Higgins gives some details of his views on chemical combination, including 'queries' in imitation of Newton's *Opticks*. When volatile alkali (ammonia) dissolves in water there ensues a regular arrangement of particles:

'the parts of the water must be arranged alternately with parts of the alkali; because each atom of water which attracts alkaline atoms, must be drawn into the line between them, whilst it draws them towards each other, contrary to their repulsive force . . . the sum of the attractive forces must be nearly equal to the repulsive forces of a certain number of alkaline atoms; and . . . so much water, ought to condense or hold in combination, so much alkali, and no more.[7] And as attractive powers manifestly cause combination in any proportions of the bodies, whose parts all attract each other; so the excess of repulsive, above the attractive forces, is truly the cause of saturation.'[8]

For Bryan Higgins 'saturation' means combination in *definite* proportions, which he says had not previously been explained.[9] Acid fluid (hydrochloric acid gas) and alkaline fluid (ammonia gas), when mixed 'in the quantity necessary for their reciprocal saturation' condense to solid sal ammoniac (he fails to mention Priestley):

'shewing that divers repellent matters saturate each the other; whilst any one of these saturates attractive matter; such as earth or water, but is not saturable thereby.
'In order to illustrate this subject; let the circles *a a a*, &c. and the circles *b b b*, &c. Fig. I. represent several atoms of acid and of alkali. And since the acid atoms *a a a*, &c. repel each other, and attract alkaline atoms *b b b*, &c. . . . the arrangement of the atoms must . . . be accurately or nearly that which is represented in the figure; wherein atoms of acid are shewn to intercede and touch atoms of alkali, which stand distant from each other; and atoms of alkali appear interposed between, and in contact with atoms of acid. . . .
'In this compound, if the forces wherewith *a a a*, &c. attract the atoms . . . *b b b*, &c. be nearly equal to the forces wherewith the homogeneal atoms *a a a*, and the homogeneal atoms *b b b*, repel each other: it follows from our principles, that no additional number of acid or alkaline atoms can adhere to, or combine with the compound thus formed: for whether an alkaline atom *c* be applied, so as to touch the like alkaline atom *b*; or whether an alkaline atom *d* be applied, so as to touch an acid atom *a* or an alkaline atom *b*; or whether the alkaline atom *e* be applied such as to touch only an acid

[1] I, 32; IV, xxx.   [2] I, 65-7; IV, xlvii-xlviii.   [3] I, 73; IV, li.
[4] IV, 3-4, 20, 115, 150 f.   [5] IV, 199.   [6] IV, 185-229.
[7] IV, 195.   [8] IV, 200.   [9] IV, 187.

atom a; the sum of the forces, whereby the alkaline atom so applied is repelled by the contiguous, and by all the alkaline atoms $b\ b\ b$, &c. being equal, by the hypothesis, to the sum of the forces wherewith it is attracted by the contiguous, and by all the acid

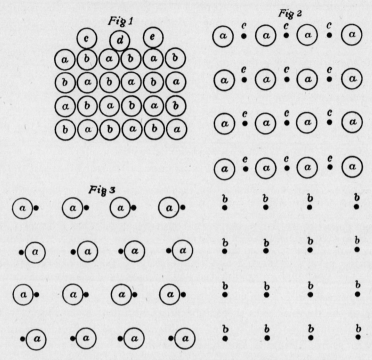

FIG. 57. PARTICLES OF GASES ACCORDING TO BRYAN HIGGINS.

atoms $a\ a\ a$, &c. There is no unrestrained agent to cause the alkaline atom c, or d, or e, to adhere to the compound in any plane or section thereof represented by this figure.'[1]

Even when the attractive forces of a for b are greater in sum and detail than the repulsive forces of a to a and b to b, as must be the case if a compound is formed, an aggregate $ababab$, &c. will be formed and will be incapable of combining with additional separate atoms.

'For, when the attractive forces, of equal numbers of acid and alkaline atoms, are prevalent over the repulsive forces of the homogeneal atoms, the prevalent attractive power, will enable the compound to draw and hold a certain quantity of acid, or of alkali, beyond the equal quantities of these; but this will be a limited quantity, because the attractive force which was prevalent, must be equalled and counteracted by the repulsive forces of a certain number of the superadded repellent atoms.'[2]

Combinations in fixed or 'determinate proportion' are 'easily explained according to the foregoing principles; and afford additional proofs of the truth of this theory of saturation'.[3]

In a discussion of the formation of inflammable air from acid elastic fluid and phlogiston (which he thought were its constituents) Higgins[4] considers the atoms $a\ a\ a$ of acid held equidistant 'by repulsive powers decreasing in any

[1] IV, 202–4.   [2] IV, 205.   [3] IV, 207.   [4] IV, 210 f.

reciprocal ratio of the distances between them'; and similarly an 'equal number of phlogistic atoms *b b b* &c' also repelling each other in a reciprocal ratio
'not widely different' from the first ratio, whilst the atoms are separate (Fig. 2).
Now if the atoms *a* attract the atoms *b* with forces less than the repulsive for
the same distances, it follows that the atoms *b b b* &c. thrown amongst the
atoms *a a a* &c.:

'must arrange themselves so that an atom of the one fluid shall intercede two atoms of
the other in every series of atoms lying in the same right line; and if they do not arrange
themselves precisely in the order expressed in Fig. 3 . . . they must arrange themselves
in . . . such order as is suitable to our present illustration.'[1]

In this, the repellent atoms are equidistant, each *a* touches a *b*, and the *a* and *b*
atoms occur alternately in any line to form solitary molecules *ab*, *ab* . . . An
arrangement in which *a* and *b* are equidistant under equal powers of attraction
would be unstable like a piece of iron suspended in the air by a magnet. Hence:

'whenever two elastic fluids whose homogeneal parts repel each other, and whose
heterogeneal parts attract each other according to the foregoing laws, are blended
together; the homogeneal atoms *a a a* &c. Fig. 3 will remain equidistant; and the
homogeneal atoms *b b b*, will remain equally distant from each other; whilst the heterogeneal atoms *ab*, *ab*, *ab*, &c. will form the solitary molecules *ab*, *ab*, *ab*; And these
molecules will recede from each other by how much force the repulsive powers exceed
the attractive powers . . . a compound fluid consisting of such molecules will be compressible, and indefinitely expansible, by virtue of these repulsive powers.'[2]

The attractive forces, however, 'must necessarily cause a reduction of the
volume of the fluid *ab*, *ab*, *ab*, &c.' because these forces co-operate with the
atmospheric pressure, 'and render it equivalent to a greater force of atmospheric pressure.'[3] Higgins says these results hold whenever the attractive and
repulsive forces be as the reciprocal of any power of the distance ($1/r^n$), 'provided only that the heterogeneous atoms attract each other less forcibly than
the homogeneal atoms repel each other at any given distance between them.'[4]
The hypothesis will explain the decrease in volume of air on phlogistication by
any process.[5]

Bryan Higgins confined chemical combination of two elements to union of
particle with particle; his binary molecules contain one atom of each element.
Fordyce (see p. 693) considered union of one particle with *two* particles;
William Higgins considered the combination of one particle of one element
with two *or more* particles of another element (see p. 742).

Bryan Higgins described[6] a quantitative experiment of distilling lead acetate
and concluded that:

'when the acid matter of acetous acid is employed *in excessive quantity* to form fixable
air [carbon dioxide] with the empyreal air [oxygen] of litharge, the fixable air may
consist of a little more than one part of the acid matter combined with two of the
empyreal air . . . the proportions would be found to be accurately two to one, provided
fixable air, like other acids, may not subsist with various proportions of the empyreal
air.'

He further develops his idea of the combination of particles:

[1] IV, 211–12.   [2] IV, 213–14.   [3] IV, 215. This anticipates van der Waals's idea.
[4] IV, 215–16.   [5] IV, 217–20.   [6] V, 232.

'The matter of fire, by virtue of the repulsion subsisting between its homogeneal parts, and of their attraction to the parts of other matter, is the cause of the elasticity of aeriform fluids.[1]

'The charges of repellent matter, by which attractive and gravitating particles form elastic fluids, are distinct atmospheres of fiery matter, in which the densities are reciprocally as the distances from the central particles, in a duplicate or higher ratio.[2]

'The matter of fire limits the quantity, in which aeriform fluids, and bodies containing it, can combine chemically.[3]

'By the same law it is determined that elastic fluids shall unite with each other in limited proportions only, to form denser fluids or solid bodies, and that the superfluous quantities shall remain elastic and unaltered[4] . . . we must ascribe to this only competent and manifest agent [the matter of fire], all those limitations which we experience, in regard to the proportions in which bodies can be chemically united, and which we briefly express by the word *saturation*.'[5]

In elastic fluids the bulk 'is the measure of the atmospheres, compared with the gravity, which is the measure of the gross particles'.[6] In a vague statement Bryan Higgins approaches Dalton's idea of the atoms of elements having different weights, and Avogadro's hypothesis that equal volumes of all gases contain equal numbers of particles. These generalisations eluded him, as they did William Higgins both then and later. Bryan says:[7]

'I consider the specific gravity as a safe guide in our investigation of these affinities and of their order, in regard only to the elastic fluids which seem to consist of no more than one kind of gravitating matter engaged in the repellent atmospheres.'

This does not hold for compound gases such as fixable air (carbon dioxide), dense inflammable air (carbon monoxide, or methane), acid airs (sulphur dioxide, hydrogen chloride), the phlogisticated alkaline air (ammonia) 'and others', in which:

'the atmospheres include molecules instead of solitary ultimate parts; for without this chemical union of heterogeneal parts, and the formation of molecules, an elastic fluid of the kind that I now speak of, could not differ, as it does, from either kind of matter of which it is composed.'

A consideration of the attractive forces which tend to form molecules, and of the atmospheres of fire which surround the molecules of compound gases 'but not the ultimate parts severally', can explain the conversion of a substance by heating, not into one but into two or three different elastic fluids,[8] e.g. acetous acid, a compound of the gravitating parts of empyreal air, phlogiston, and the acid principle of vegetables, forms fixable air and dense inflammable air.[9]

'The aerial form is maintained, not by the mere interposition of the matter of fire, but by the intervention of it in the described state of density near the gross particles and extreme rarity at the coincidence or contiguity of the atmospheres.[10]

'Therefore, to destroy the elasticity, and to effect the aggregation and union of the gross parts of an aeriform fluid, or of any mixture of different airs, nothing more is necessary than to break or blend the atmospheres into a medium of equal density in the spaces between the particles . . . by replenishing the minute spaces, in which the atmospheres extend, with a denser fiery fluid . . . the smallest spark . . . or a larger spark, whether of the electric fluid, or from a burning body. . . . The ignition necessary towards the accension . . . is directly as the density of the repellent atmospheres, and inversely as the attraction of the gravitating parts to each other.'[11]

[1] V, 303.   [2] V, 306.   [3] V, 307-8.   [4] V, 309.   [5] V, 310.   [6] V, 315.
[7] V, 317.   [8] V, 317-18.   [9] V, 319-20.   [10] V, 323.   [11] V, 326-7.

The *Minutes of the Society* (VII) dwells in tedious detail on the nature of 'caloric'. The matter of light and caloric are identical, light being caloric in rapid motion.[1] Compound 'molecules' contain the central particles of the elements combined and charged with caloric.[2] Attempts were made to weigh caloric, including weighing a supersaturated solution of Glauber's salt before and after crystallisation, the latter being supposed to be brought about by the pressure of the atmosphere (although an experiment in which the pressure was developed by a column of mercury without exposure to the air was suggested it was not tried).[3] No loss in weight was found, but in slaking quicklime in a tinned iron vessel there was a loss of more than a grain.[4] Higgins[5] returned to his speculations about 'particles' with their atmospheres of caloric, which resist their approach. In a mixture of hydrogen and oxygen, when an electric spark is passed, the atmospheres are 'blended and confounded in the Calorific fluid', and when the caloric is 'excluded from the uniting faces of such particles', these particles, 'pressed or drawn on all sides by contrary and equal powers of this fluid, necessarily obey the attractive forces which ever tend to the union of them.'

R. Angus Smith[6] says Bryan Higgins's writings 'are mostly in the first stage of thought before opinion is formed. . . . His opinions on atoms might have been held by the ancients . . . his theory was not clear, or he would have been led by it to decide on the necessity of fixed constitution as a result'. Meldrum[7] thought this judgment was defective, since Smith had not read the *Essay concerning Light* and failed to appreciate the influence of Newton on Higgins, and I agree to a large extent with this.

WILLIAM HIGGINS

William Higgins (Collooney, Co. Sligo, 1762–3–Dublin, end of (30 ?) June 1825), nephew of Bryan Higgins, was educated (1787–August 1788) at Pembroke College, Oxford (matriculating at Magdalen Hall in 1786), which he left without a degree. He is said to have been 'operator' to Beddoes, who seems to have succeeded Austin (the professor) as Reader in 1787; on leaving Oxford Higgins went to London; since he says he assisted his uncle in some of the experiments described in Bryan Higgins's *Experiments and Observations relating to Acetous Acid* (1786), he must have been in London before he went to Oxford. It is said he worked again with Bryan Higgins, a phlogistian, but since William published his book defending the antiphlogistic theory in 1789, and was probably writing it in Oxford, his uncle may have withdrawn his support and in consequence William left Oxford.

In January 1792 William Higgins was appointed Chemist at Apothecaries' Hall in Dublin, with a salary of £200 p.a. with apartments, coals and candles, taking over 'a small back room' in May, and he fitted out a laboratory. His salary came into arrears and in 1795 he asked for payment in such terms that

[1] VII, 29, 62, 290 f., 302 f.   [2] VII, 35 f., see the diagrams on plates III, IV.
[3] VII, 86 f., 213.   [4] VII, 221 f.   [5] VII, 292–6, plates III, IV.
[6] Memoir of Dalton; *Manchester Mem.*, 1856, xiii, 170 f.
[7] *Manchester Mem.*, 1910, lv, no. 4, p. 13.

his employment was terminated, the Governors borrowing £200 to pay him off. In 1795 he was appointed 'chymist' to the Irish Linen Board at a salary of £100 p.a., and held this until 1822. He did a considerable amount of good work for the Board and published an *Essay on Bleaching*:

I. An Essay on the Theory and Practice of Bleaching, wherein the Sulphuret of Lime is recommended as a Substitute for Pot-Ash By William Higgins, M.R.I.A. Professor of Chemistry and Mineralogy at the Expository of the Dublin Society. Dublin: Printed by B. and J. Williamson, Grafton Street, Printers and Stationers to the Right Hon. and Hon. the Trustees of the Linen Board. 1799.

A London issue, same title, but London: printed for the Author; and sold by Vernor and Hood, No. 31, Poultry. 1799. Price Two Shillings (Manchester Central Library). Both issues pp. xxxii, 71.

Higgins also published on this in the Royal Dublin Society.[1] His merits were appreciated by Kirwan (whose theories Higgins had attacked in his book *A Comparative View* . . . , 1789), who recommended him in 1795 for appointment as Supervisor of the Leskean Collection of minerals of the Royal Dublin Society. He was appointed in 1796, becoming professor of chemistry and mineralogy by an act of the Irish Parliament. He began to lecture in 1797.[2] He had been elected a Member of the Royal Irish Academy in 1794, and was elected F.R.S. in 1806 (his certificate being signed by Davy), but first signed the charter book and obtained admittance in May, 1817.

Higgins was eccentric and many anecdotes of him were current. He seems to have been kept busy in his various appointments. He lived in rooms in Dublin but left a considerable amount of property when he died, purchasing lands for £2000 and £6800 in 1821–3.

Higgins did not suffer from excess of modesty; in 1799[3] he claimed that in his system of chemistry 'I have connected the whole, and reduced it to a system, and made use of demonstrations, which in my opinion are not to be invalidated or contradicted, until the order of natural things assume a different aspect . . . assumed modesty upon such an occasion as this, would be weakness indeed, and affected diffidence downright folly'. By some of his pronouncements, it is to be feared, some of his recent admirers have been sadly misled.[4]

William Higgins's most important work is his *Comparative View* (II); his other publication, *Experiments and Observations* (III) is polemical, attacking Dalton (it reproduces parts of II):

II. A Comparative View of the Phlogistic and Antiphlogistic Theories. With Inductions. To which is annexed, an Analysis of the Human Calculus, with

---

[1] Essay on the Sulphuret of Lime, as a Substitute for Pot-Ash; or a new method of Bleaching. . . , in *Trans. Roy. Dublin Soc.* for 1799, Dublin, 1800, i.

[2] Higgins, *Phil. Mag.*, 1819, liii, 405.   [3] I, xx–xxi.

[4] Atkinson, *J. Chem. Educ.*, 1940, xvii, 3; T. Dillon, *Institute of Chemistry of Ireland Journal*, 1955–6, iv, 11; Goodwin, DNB, 1891, xxxvi, 366 (Bryan), 371 (William); Kopp, (3), 282; Meldrum, 'Two Great Irish Chemists: B. and W. Higgins', *New Ireland Review*, 1909–10, xxxii, 275, 350; Partington, *Nature*, 1951, clxvii, 120, 735; 1955, clxxvi, 8; J. Reilly and D. T. MacSweeney, *Sci. Proc. Roy. Dublin Soc.*, 1929, xix, 139; R. A. Smith, *Manchester Mem.*, 1856, xiii, 175, 184–5; W. K. Sullivan, *Dublin Quart. J. Medical Sci.*, 1849, viii, 465 (incl. other Irish chemists); T. S. Wheeler, *Endeavour*, 1952, xi, 47; id., *Studies*, Dublin, 1954, liv, 78, 207, 327; id. and J. R. Partington, *The Life and Work of William Higgins, Chemist*, London, 1960 (with reprints of II and III); J. H. White, *Sci. Progr.*, 1929, xxiv, 300; see also p. 749.

Observations on its Origin, &c. By William Higgins, of Pembroke College, Oxford. London: Printed for J. Murray, 8°, 1789 (Manchester University Library); 2 ed. (same title), London, 1791 (Chemical Society Library), probably the same sheets with a new t.p.; both eds. [vi], i–xiv, 316 pp. Motto on t.p. from Horace, Ep. i, 1, 32: Est quodam prodire tenus, si non datur ultra (there is some point we may reach, if we cannot go further).

III. Experiments and Observations on the Atomic Theory, and Electrical Phenomena. By William Higgins, Esq. F.R.S. & M.R.I.A. Professor of Chemistry to the Dublin Society. Dublin: Printed by Graisberry and Campbell, 10, Back-Lane, and Sold by Gilbert and Hodges, Dame Street. 1814, pp. vi, 180; dedicated to the Right Honorable and Honorable the Dublin Society.

A syllabus of his course of 41 lectures at the Royal Dublin Society was published:

IV. A Syllabus of a Course of Chemistry for the Year 1802, Dublin, 1801 (pp. v, 88), promising a text-book which never appeared. In III, 18, he says: 'I had it in contemplation, for some years past, to publish a system of chemistry on a new arrangement, which I am now determined upon.' This never appeared. He mentions 'phosphoric matches' (p. 34) and calls glucina 'glucen' (p. 50). The statements about 'theory' (pp. 20–4, etc.) give the ordinary explanations of chemical reactions and his own theory (in II) is hardly mentioned.

Higgins's *Comparative View* is mostly concerned with a clever refutation of Kirwan's *Essay on Phlogiston* (1787), the French edition (see p. 662) being also mentioned[1] as seen first after the section on the marine acid was completed. The sections deal with: the composition and decomposition of water (p. 1), the composition of acids (p. 8), vitriolic acid (p. 18), nitrous acid (p. 82), marine acid (p. 179), the calcination of metals *via sicca* (p. 219), the calcination of metals by steam and the decomposition of water (p. 240), the reduction of metallic calces by charcoal and the formation of fixed air (p. 249), the solubility of metals (p. 254), the precipitation of metals by each other (p. 259), and (as an appendix) an analysis of the human calculus with observations on its origin (p. 283), which the preface (p. xiii) says was sent to the Royal Society in 1787 and read in Spring 1788 (it was not published and is in the archives of the Royal Society).

Higgins[2] said he 'adopted the antiphlogistic theory four years ago' (i.e. in 1784–5) and claimed[3] to be the first chemist in England to do this, saying that his book was perhaps neglected when a discussion on the relative merits of the phlogistic and antiphlogistic theories had ceased to be of interest. 'For a considerable time I stood alone in England, where I then resided, being the first who adopted the antiphlogistic doctrine, and the only man who had expressly written in favour of it in the English language.'[4] Black (in Scotland) he classed among phlogistians,[5] and he does not mention Lubbock (1784), who wrote in Latin (see p. 489).

Since the phlogistians and antiphlogistians could not reach conviction by experiments, he had recourse to 'reasoning rather novel in chemistry', considering phlogiston as 'a substance chemically united to bodies in a solid state', and also 'whether the same phenomena were as explicable by supposing the different bodies which unite to dephlogisticated air to attract it,

---

[1] II, 281.   [2] II, xi.
[3] *Phil. Mag.*, 1819, liii, 405–6.   [4] I, xi.   [5] II, xi.

independent of a common principle or phlogiston'.[1] He was 'obliged to introduce several diagrams, in order to render what I meant to convey the more intelligible . . . , and the most effectual means to come at truth'.[2] His arguments are really directed against Kirwan's *Essay on Phlogiston*, which the French chemists had translated and criticised in 1787 (see p. 662).[3] He thought that the phlogiston theory is full of inconsistencies, led into a wilderness, and every single fact is in favour of the antiphlogistic theory.[4] He gives[5] from Kirwan[6] a table of the weights in grains of 100 cu. in. of various gases, adding 34 for 'heavy inflammable air':

Common air	31	Fixed air (CO_2)	46·5
Dephlogisticated air (O_2)	34	Hepatic air (H_2S)	34·286
Phlogisticated air (N_2)	30	Alkaline air (NH_3)	18·16
Nitrous air (NO)	37	Light Inflammable air (H_2)	2·613
Vitriolic air (SO_2)	70·215	Heavy Inflammable air (CO?)	34

He says:[7]

'I frequently inflamed several cubic inches of light inflammable [hydrogen] and dephlogisticated [oxygen] air, and never observed, by the nicest test, the presence of an acid, when the airs worked upon were pure, and when the inflammable air prevailed. But when I reversed the proportion, I always obtained nitrous acid in a single charge. When the dephlogisticated air contained one-eighth phlogisticated air [nitrogen], I obtained nitrous acid in great abundance. Hence I infer, if we could procure dephlogisticated air entirely free from phlogisticated, that not a particle of acid would be produced.[8] I condensed . . . half a gallon of dephlogisticated air by the continual flame of light inflammable air, and I could not detect the smallest vestige of any sort of acid.'

No fixed air was formed, and nitric acid cannot contain fixed air, as Kirwan supposed.[9] Higgins says:[10]

'It is generally allowed, and justly, that nitrous air [nitric oxide] consists of dephlogisticated air and phlogistic in the proportion of two of the former and one of the latter . . . therefore every ultimate particle of phlogisticated air must be united to two of dephlogisticated air; and these molicules combined with fire constitute nitrous air. Now if every of these molicules were surrounded with an atmosphere of fire equal in size only to those of dephlogisticated air, 100 cubic inches of nitrous air should weigh 98,535 grains; whereas according to Kirwan, they weigh but 37 grains. Hence, we may justly conclude, that the gravitating particles of nitrous air are thrice the distance from each other that the ultimate particles of dephlogisticated air are in the same temperature, and of course their atmospheres of fire must be in size proportionable; or else some other repelling fluid must interpose.'

It is not clear why nitrous air (nitric oxide) should be composed of 'two' of oxygen and 'one' of nitrogen, since this is true neither by weight (16 to 14) nor by volume (1 to 1). Here, as elsewhere, Higgins omits to say whether he means the ratio of volumes or weights.

'The decomposition of nitrous air, by the light inflammable air of the hepatic gas [H_2S], is equally extraordinary, considering . . . the inflammable air is not in a condensed state; and, therefore, combined with its natural portion of fire. Do atmospheres of equal density favour the union of their respective gravitating particles? Or, do a

---

[1] II, viii.   [2] II, ix–x.   [3] II, x.   [4] II, x, 29–30, 218.
[5] II, xiv.   [6] *Essay on Phlogiston*, 1789, 30.   [7] II, 4–5, 82 f.
[8] This is in opposition to Priestley, *Phil. Trans.*, 1788, lxxviii, 313.
[9] II, 82 f., 93.   [10] II, 14–15; III, 54.

dense and a rare atmosphere, by easily blending, promote their chemical union, by suffering them to approach nearer? Or does the electric fluid interfere? . . . it seems to me that the attractive forces of bodies are not to be estimated by the facility of compounding, but rather by the difficulty of decompounding these again.'[1]

This is obviously based on the speculations of Bryan Higgins (see p. 735); William's indebtedness to him was overlooked by previous writers except Meldrum. Higgins[2] says:

'I have often combined sulphur rendered perfectly dry, and dephlogisticated air likewise, deprived of its water by fused marine selenite[3] in large proportion over mercury, and could never observe that water was produced . . . 100 grains of sulphur, making an allowance for water,[4] require 100 or 102 of the real gravitating matter of dephlogisticated air to form volatile vitriolic acid [sulphur dioxide]; and as volatile vitriolic acid is very little short of double the specific gravity of dephlogisticated air, we may conclude, that the ultimate particles of sulphur and dephlogisticated air, contain equal quantities of solid matter; for dephlogisticated air suffers no considerable contraction by uniting to sulphur in the proportion merely necessary for the formation of volatile vitriolic acid. Hence we may conclude, that, in volatile vitriolic acid, a single ultimate particle of sulphur is intimately united only to a single particle of dephlogisticated air; and that, in perfect vitriolic acid [sulphur trioxide] every single particle of sulphur is united to 2 of dephlogisticated air, being the quantity necessary to saturation.'

Higgins, therefore, took the formulae of sulphur dioxide and trioxide as SO and SO_2 and the quantities of oxygen for a given *weight* of sulphur as in the ratio 1 : 2 instead of 2 : 3. How he could arrive at the composition of sulphur dioxide without assuming equality in weights of the atoms of sulphur and oxygen is not clear. His name 'saturation' is taken from Bryan Higgins.

'As 2 cubic inches of light inflammable air [H_2] require but 1 of dephlogisticated air to condense them, we must suppose that they contain equal number of divisions, and that the difference of their specific gravity depends chiefly on the size of their ultimate particles; or we must suppose that the ultimate particles of light inflammable air require 2 or 3, or more, of dephlogisticated air to saturate them. If this latter were the case, we might produce water in an intermediate state, as well as the vitriolic or the nitrous acid, which appears to be impossible; for in whatever proportion we mix our airs, or under whatsoever circumstance we combine them, the result is invariably the same. This likewise may be observed with respect to the decomposition of water. Hence we may justly conclude, that water is composed of molicules[5] formed by the union of a single particle of dephlogisticated air to an ultimate particle of light inflammable air, and that they are incapable of uniting to a third particle of either of their constituent principles.'

In 1819[6] Higgins claimed that the above words could bear the following interpretation:

'Although a cubic inch of oxygen gas is fourteen times heavier (some make it more) than a cubic inch of hydrogen gas; yet, as there are but half the number of particles in the latter that the former contains, the particles of oxygen can be no more than seven times heavier.'

This claim is quite unjustified, as the words quoted above show.

---

[1] II, 15–16.   [2] II, 35–6; III, 58–9.
[3] Calcium chloride, Priestley's 'fixed ammoniac', see p. 269.
[4] Assumed to be contained in the 143 gr. of dephlogisticated air which Kirwan found to be necessary; Higgins is using weights here.
[5] Corrected in errata to 'molecules', 'and so elsewhare'.
[6] *Phil. Mag.*, 1819, liii, 401 (408–9); ref. to II, 37, and III, 146.

Higgins made use of diagrams and symbols in discussing the supposed forces between particles.[1] The use of the initial letters of names as symbols (emphasised by Reilly and McSweeney[2] and Wheeler[3]) was not consistent; I stands both for iron and inflammable air,[4] and volatile vitriolic acid (a compound) is V.[5] Higgins also has a symbol for oil, and did not confine the single letters to symbols for *elements*.

Higgins made use of the idea of *attraction* of particles, and the symbols for the particles are joined by lines, which in a way have the same meaning as valency bonds, and the forces exerted along them are represented by numbers. The attractions constitute his exclusive interest. Higgins wrote the formula of

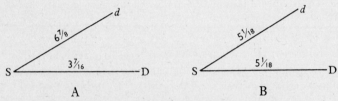

FIG. 58. FORCES IN MOLECULE OF VITRIOLIC ACID.

water I—*d* and of volatile sulphureous acid (sulphur dioxide) S—*d*, the forces between the particles being $6\frac{5}{8}$ in the first and $6\frac{7}{8}$ in the second. As the attraction of bodies is mutual, Higgins supposed that S and *d* each have $3\frac{7}{16}$. If S unites with another particle of *d* to form perfect vitriolic acid (sulphur trioxide), S must relax its attraction for *d* by a half. 'That is, the force of $3\frac{7}{16}$ will be divided and directed in two different points, which will reduce the attachment of dephlogisticated air and sulphur in perfect vitriolic acid to $5\frac{1}{18}$' (Fig. 58). The diminution of force as successive particles are added 'seems to be a general law'.[6] It should be noticed that, whereas Bryan Higgins considered only the combination of *two* particles, William Higgins extends this to compounds of one particle with two or more others. He had been anticipated in this by Fordyce (see p. 693), whose ideas, though not published, were probably well known.

Higgins[7] attempts to explain why iron dissolves in dilute sulphuric acid but not in concentrated, and dissolves in sulphurous acid without evolution of gas ($2Fe + 3H_2SO_3 = FeSO_3 + FeS_2O_3 + 3H_2O$). Iron (I) with a close texture presents a greater number of ultimate particles to a given surface than vitriolic acid, especially when the latter is diluted with water. If I attracts *d* with a force of 7, S with a force of $5\frac{1}{18}$,

'the force of 7, exerted at once by a number of the martial particles on D *d*, suddenly snatches them as it were from S, which cannot move with the same pace towards I; because being in contact with water, it exerts its whole force on that compound. Therefore it is the violence and suddenness of the pull from the metal, and the velocity of the motion of D *d* towards it, that leaves S so circumstanced as to be able to decompose water in the manner already described.'

[1] II, 39, 44–9, 59–61, 66, 133–5, 171–2, 190–3, 262, 271–3.
[2] *Proc. Royal Dublin Soc.*, 1929, xix, 139 (148).
[3] *Endeavour*, 1952, xi, 47.   [4] II, 46, 48, 262–3; on p. 192 I stands for both.
[5] *Ib.*, 273.   [6] II, 39–41; III, 63. It should be $5\frac{5}{32}$.   [7] II, 59–62.

If iron I is put into sulphurous acid S—d in which S is attracted to d with a force $6\frac{7}{8}$, there is a small attraction of $\frac{1}{8}$ between S and I, so that $6\frac{7}{8} + \frac{1}{8} = 7$, and

'the force of 7, subsisting between I and d, will influence S and d equally the same; so that S and d will move with equal pace to unite to I. Hence no decomposition takes place, and of course no inflammable air is produced.'

Higgins devotes particular attention to the oxygen compounds of nitrogen. In describing experiments on the decomposition of nitre by heat[1] he says:

'According to Mr. Lavoisier, 100 grains of nitrous [nitric] acid contain $79\frac{1}{2}$ of dephlogisticated air, and $20\frac{1}{2}$ of phlogisticated air, which is not quite four to one. But his experiments contradict this; for whatever mode he adopted to decompose nitrous acid, it appeared that the proportion of dephlogisticated air was nearly as five, to one of phlogisticated air.'[2]

Whatever Higgins may have said later,[3] it is clear that he was speaking of proportions by *weight*, and when he formulated nitric acid (anhydride) as NO_5 (see p. 743) he must have assumed that the particles of oxygen and nitrogen were equal in weight. He says:[4]

'The red nitrous vapour contains three parts of nitrous air [nitric oxide] and one part of dephlogisticated air, or one of phlogisticated air and three of dephlogisticated air.[5] . . . The common straw coloured nitrous acid contains more dephlogisticated air than the red nitrous acid or vapour; the proportion appears to be four to one; but the colourless contains about five of dephlogisticated to one of phlogisticated air.[6]
'I did not hesitate to conclude, but that which is called dephlogisticated nitrous air, is common nitrous air, deprived only of a portion of its dephlogisticated air . . . $P - a$ [$= N_2O$] imperfect nitrous air.'[7]

Higgins, therefore, assumed five oxides of nitrogen, NO, NO_2, NO_3, NO_4, and NO_5. The compositions of NO (nitrous oxide), NO_3, and NO_4 were guessed, and the identities of NO_3 and NO_4 remain obscure.

'In my opinion, the purest nitrous [nitric] acid contains 5 of dephlogisticated to 1 of phlogisticated air. Nitrous air [NO], according to Kirwan, contains 2 of dephlogisticated to 1 of phlogisticated air. According to Lavoisier, 100 gr. of nitrous air contain 32 gr. of phlogisticated air, and 68 of dephlogisticated air [i.e. 2·16 to 1]. I am myself of the former philosopher's opinion: I likewise am of opinion, that every primary particle of phlogisticated air is united to two of dephlogisticated air, and that these molecules are surrounded with one common atmosphere of fire.'[8]

Higgins then proceeds[9] to discuss the five oxides of nitrogen in a passage which has been supposed to have anticipated Dalton's atomic theory and his law of multiple proportions. He gives diagrams in the text, but for convenience these have been grouped in Fig. 59.

'To render this more explicable, let us suppose P to be an ultimate particle of phlogisticated air [nitrogen], which attracts dephlogisticated air with the force of 3; let a be a particle of dephlogisticated air [oxygen], whose attraction to P we will suppose to be 3 more, by which they unite with the force of 6: the nature of this compound will be hereafter explained.
'Let us consider this to be the utmost force that can subsist between dephlogisticated and phlogisticated air. Let us suppose another particle of dephlogisticated air b to

[1] II, 82 f.   [2] II, 83.   [3] III, 109.   [4] II, 84.
[5] He assumed the formula NO_2 for nitric oxide and $3NO_2 + O$ will not give NO_3.
[6] II, 84 , 157.   [7] II, 165, 171–2.   [8] II, 132–3.   [9] II, 133–5.

unite to P, they will not unite with the force of 6, but with the force of $4\frac{1}{2}$; that is, the whole power of P, which is but 3, will be equally divided and directed in two points towards a and b; so that P and $a\,b$ will unite with the forces annexed to them; for the attraction of a and b to P meeting with no interruption, will suffer no diminution. This I consider to be the true state of nitrous air. Let us now suppose another particle of dephlogisticated air c to unite to P, it will combine only with the force of 4, whereby $a\,b\,c$ and P will gravitate toward one another. Such is the state of the red nitrous vapour, or the red nitrous acid.

'Let us again suppose a fourth particle of dephlogisticated air d to combine with P, it will unite only with the force of $3\frac{3}{4}$. This I think is the state of the pale or straw-coloured nitrous acid.

'Lastly, let us suppose a fifth particle of dephlogisticated air e, to unite to P, it will combine with the force of $3\frac{3}{5}$, so that $a\,b\,c\,d$ and e will each gravitate towards P as their common centre of gravity. This is the most perfect state of colourless nitrous [nitric] acid; and in my opinion no more dephlo-

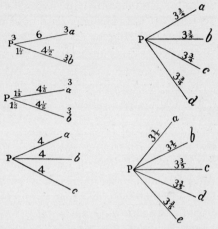

FIG. 59. OXIDES OF NITROGEN ACCORDING TO WILLIAM HIGGINS.

gisticated air can unite to the phlogisticated air, as having its whole force of attraction expended on the particles of dephlogisticated air, $a\,b\,c\,d\,e$. This illustrates the nature of saturation.'

This is all Higgins said in 1789. In 1814,[1] long after Dalton's theory was known, he said: 'a measure of oxygen gas contains twice the number of ultimate particles, that are contained in the same volume of azotic gas,' that[2] in nitrous gas (nitric oxide) 'every primary particle of azote is united to 2 of oxygen, and that the molecule thus formed, is surrounded with one common atom of caloric', that[3] dephlogisticated nitrous air (nitrous oxide) consists of 1 atom of azote and 1 atom of oxygen, and[4] 'the specific gravity of oxygen gas is very little more than that of azotic, and this I attribute to the dimensions of their respective atmospheres of caloric, those of the latter gas being more extensive and less dense'. Finally:[5] 'Nitric acid was known to consist of azote and oxygen some time before I wrote my *Comparative View*, and the volumes of the gases, which compose it, were ascertained by Lavoisier and myself', thus implying that in 1789 his formulae of oxides of nitrogen were referred to *volumes*, whilst the wording quoted on p. 742 shows clearly that they referred to *weights*.

Higgins obtained phlogisticated air [N_2] by dissolving iron filings in dilute nitric acid (1 : 16),[6] and remarked that 'we can never obtain dephlogisticated nitrous air [N_2O] from nitrous acid [HNO_3] until it is nearly saturated with a metal; and then by introducing more of the same metal, or a different metal, we obtain dephlogisticated nitrous air'.[7] The puzzling fact that nitrous oxide, which contains less oxygen than nitric oxide,[8] is more soluble and is a much better supporter of combustion, he could not explain on his theory of affinity

[1] III, 146.   [2] *Ib.*, 119.   [3] *Ib.*, 132.   [4] *Ib.*, 145.
[5] *Ib.*, 117.   [6] II, 140.   [7] II, 170.   [8] II, 166.

(since he had chosen a wrong formula for it), and he fell back on a weak supposition of the difference in their atmospheres of fire, which 'unites chemically to bodies, and of course must gravitate towards them. Can we therefore doubt but that fire is a substance, and not a quality, as some philosophers are pleased to suppose?'[1] Higgins could not have chosen the correct formulae N_2O, NO, N_2O_3, NO_2, as Dalton did, because these would not have suited his force diagrams.

It has been claimed[2] that Higgins in 1789 could not have deduced the formula HS_2 for sulphuretted hydrogen unless he knew the weights of the atoms. This is wrong in two ways. First, Higgins did not regard sulphuretted hydrogen (hepatic gas) as a definite compound at all but[3] as a solution of sulphur in light inflammable air, like that of water in gases and salts in water, 'occasioned by a sort of intermediate attraction, not differing from chemical attraction but in its degree of force, and not at all different from that power whereby the heavenly bodies influence one another'; and secondly he did not assume the ratio 2 : 1 but 9 : 5. It was only in 1814[4] that he says 'according to the experiment, they are as 18 to 9', instead of 9 to 5, and describes an experiment showing that when sulphur burns in oxygen there is a contraction in volume of $\frac{1}{11}$. He claimed that his first experiment showed 'the weight of an atom' of sulphur dioxide and 'the comparative diameter of its calorific atmosphere. And lastly, the proportion of the ultimate particles of hydrogen, and of sulphur, in sulphuretted hydrogen gas'. These claims cannot be admitted.

In the experiment[5] he found that a mixture of $4\frac{1}{2}$ vols. of hepatic gas and $4\frac{1}{2}$ vols. of dephlogisticated air gave $2\frac{1}{2}$ vols. of volatile sulphureous acid (sulphur dioxide). Austin had found that 'the solution of sulphur in light inflammable air neither contracts nor expands it', hence $4\frac{1}{2}$ vols. of hepatic gas contain $4\frac{1}{2}$ vols. of hydrogen, which require 'at least $2\frac{1}{4}$' vols. of oxygen. Of the rest, 2 vols. burnt the sulphur to sulphur dioxide and $\frac{1}{4}$ vol. was used to burn nitrogen as an impurity. Hence the 2 vols. of volatile vitriolic acid (SO_2) contain 2 of oxygen.

From the table of specific gravities (grains per 100 cu. in.) on p. 739:

Dephlogisticated air	34
Volatile vitriolic acid	70·215
Hepatic air	34·286
Light inflammable air	2·613

if the weight of hydrogen is taken from that of hepatic gas the remainder $34\cdot286 - 2\cdot613 = 31\cdot673$ is the weight of sulphur in it. The specific gravity of dephlogisticated air is 34 and half that of volatile vitriolic acid is $35\cdot107$. If the weights of the sulphur and oxygen particles are *assumed* to be equal, volatile vitriolic acid, therefore, contains 1 particle of sulphur and 1 particle of oxygen (see p. 740). Higgins inferred that:

2 vols. of volatile vitriolic acid were formed from 2 vols. of hepatic gas and the sulphur in $2\frac{1}{2}$ vols. of hepatic gas was precipitated; if the precipitated sulphur had been

[1] II, 175.   [2] Soddy, *Nature*, 1951, clxvii, 735.
[3] II, 13, 72–3, 77–8, 80.   [4] III, 84.   [5] II, 78–81.

burnt he would have got $2+2\frac{1}{2}=4\frac{1}{2}$ vols. of volatile vitriolic acid from $4\frac{1}{2}$ vols. of hepatic gas, and these would contain $4\frac{1}{2}$ particles of sulphur.

The inflammable air in $4\frac{1}{2}$ vols. of hepatic gas used the rest of the dephlogisticated air, viz. $4\frac{1}{2}-2$ vols. $=2\frac{1}{2}$ vols. (This does not agree with his statement that $2\frac{1}{4}$ vols. were used, but he says 'at least $2\frac{1}{4}$ vols.'.) But 2 vols. of inflammable air require 1 vol. of dephlogisticated air for combustion, and since he assumed that water contains 1 particle of inflammable air and 1 particle of dephlogisticated air, the $4\frac{1}{2}$ vols. of hepatic gas contain $2\frac{1}{2}$ particles of inflammable air. Hence hepatic gas contains $4\frac{1}{2}=\frac{9}{2}$ particles of sulphur and $2\frac{1}{2}=\frac{5}{2}$ particles of inflammable air, or 9 particles of sulphur to 5 particles of inflammable air. (The reaction in the experiment was: $2H_2S+2O_2=2H_2O+SO_2+S$).

In 1799[1] Higgins claimed to have shown by this experiment that 'sulphuric acid consists of one part of sulphur and two of oxygen chemically united', and that 'the sulphureous acid contains equal parts of oxygen and sulphur', but he does not explain what he means by 'parts'.

Higgins had a fairly clear idea of the formation of 'molecular compounds' by residual affinities.[2]

'Let I be iron; D dephlogisticated air (Fig. 60) united with the force of 7; let us suppose D to be the quantity necessary to saturate I, so as to form a perfect calx; let S be sulphur, d dephlogisticated air attached with the force of $6\frac{7}{8}$. Let us suppose S to have a tendency to unite with more dephlogisticated air; and let us likewise suppose, which is well known to be the case, a small attraction to exist between S and I. Let us state the whole sum of these forces between S, D, and I, to be 2; which power, though it will not separate I from D, or d from S, yet is sufficient to combine I—D to S—d when in contact, and when no other power is to counteract it.

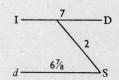

FIG. 60. COMBINATION OF OXIDE OF IRON AND SULPHUREOUS ACID.

He also had a rudimentary idea of a transition state in a reaction.[3] He assumed that marine acid (hydrochloric acid) is a compound of an unknown base B combined with two particles of dephlogisticated air (oxygen) D and d with a force of 6. When iron is placed in it, it attracts oxygen from B which, owing to its great affinity for it, removes oxygen from water Id, so that no gas but hydrogen is evolved. Bd (muriatic acid) and calx of iron IdD then unite to form muriate of iron (Fig. 62, in which I on the top is inflammable air and I on the right is iron).

'When the iron influences the dephlogisticated air of the marine basis with so superior a force as $3\frac{1}{2}$ to 2; B, or the marine basis, being in contact with water, which retains its dephlogisticated air with the force of $6\frac{5}{8}$, or, laying aside reciprocal attraction, with only the force of $3\frac{5}{16}$, yields its own dephlogisticated air to the iron, and directs the whole force of its attraction, which is 4, towards the dephlogisticated air of the water; by which it is decomposed, and inflammable [air] is produced. The marine basis being thus furnished with half the quantity of dephlogisticated air which is necessary to the formation of common marine acid, unites to the calx, and dissolves it . . . is it not reasonable to suppose, as soon as I, or iron, should influence dD, that B would re-act on d, or the dephlogisticated

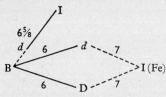

FIG. 61. HIGGINS'S IDEA OF A TRANSITION COMPOUND.

[1] I, xv–xvi.
[2] II, 47–8; Schützenberger, art. 'Affinité' in Wurtz, *Dictionnaire de Chimie*, Paris, 1869, i, 75.
[3] II, 192–3; Wheeler, *Endeavour*, 1952, xi, 47; *Proc. Chem. Soc.*, 1959, 221.

air of the water, and disengage I, or inflammable air. I make no doubt but a good mathematician (for I acknowledge my own deficiency) would demonstrate this to a degree of certainty.'

Higgins claims[1] that he 'frequently repeated almost the whole of the different experiments quoted' from other authors, and he made a number of new ones, leading to discoveries which he later claimed as important. He noted the solution of iron nails by 'strong volatile vitriolic acid' (sulphurous acid) without evolution of gas; on standing the solution became dark, deposited sulphur and carbon, and had a 'strongly chabybeat' taste but no smell.[2] He later[3] claimed that he had then discovered a method of determining carbon in steel (which he does not mention in 1789) and so anticipated Vauquelin (1797, see p. 543). The discovery of the solution of iron in sulphurous acid really belongs to Stahl (see Vol. II, p. 680).

Higgins found,[4] when he was 'busy in assisting at a public course of chemistry, at Oxford', that on heating animal blood with nitric acid and $\frac{1}{5}$ of the whole of water it became of the colour of bile and very bitter, and on dilution with water deposited a bright yellow solid. He afterwards[5] claimed that he had thus anticipated Fourcroy in showing the presence of bile in blood (see p. 550).

Iron is not affected by dry dephlogisticated air (oxygen) and 'it appears, that iron has no effect on air in a common temperature, but that it is the water which is decomposed, and that the dephlogisticated air and inflammable air unite at the very instant of its liberation, and re-compose water'.[6] Higgins[7] says Mrs. Fulhame[8] 'boasts very much of her discovery', but 'cautiously omitted mentioning the work from which she borrowed her ideas'. But what he said in 1799,[9] that 'the fair author' had probably not read his book, is more correct.

Higgins[10] claimed that in March 1785 he had found that when nitric acid acts on tin and an alkali is then added, ammonia is evolved. Austin[11] gives this experiment without naming Higgins, Berthollet[12] and Guyton de Morveau[13] who attributed it to William Higgins. Austin said gaseous nitrogen and hydrogen combine only when:

'they part with a certain quantity of that fire to which they owe their elasticity; and that, unless their attraction to each other exceed their attraction to fire, they will not unite. . . . When they are not in an aëriform state their attraction to each other is greater, on account of the proximity of their parts; it is then superior to their attraction to fire, and therefore they combine.'

William Austin (Wotton-under-Edge, Glos., 28 December 1754–London, 21 January 1793), was a student at Wádham College, Oxford, where he became proficient in Hebrew. Although of medium stature, he showed feats of strength and used to walk from Oxford to London in a day. He became M.D. 1783, practised in Oxford, was physician to the Radcliffe Infirmary, and was

[1] II, ix.   [2] II, 49 f.   [3] I, xiii; III, 73.   [4] II, 162 f.   [5] I, 1799, xii.
[6] II, 13.   [7] III, 53; Phil. Mag., 1819, liii, 401 (407).
[8] An Essay on Combustion, 1794, 40: 'water is the only source of the oxygen, which oxygenates combustible bodies,' etc.; see p. 708.
[9] I, xxvii, xxxii.   [10] II, 309.   [11] Phil. Trans., 1788, lxxviii, 379.
[12] AdS, 1785 (1788), m 316 (325).   [13] Crell's Ann., 1788, II, 118 (127).

appointed professor of chemistry in Oxford in 1785, but resigned on 10 August 1786 to become physician to St. Bartholomew's Hospital, London, where he improved the teaching of chemistry.[1] He was succeeded in Oxford in 1787 by Beddoes (see Vol. IV), who was Reader and not Professor.

In the same paper (Experiments on the Formation of Volatile Alkali, and on the Affinities of the Phlogisticated and light Inflammable Airs) Austin also showed that gaseous nitrogen forms ammonia when confined over mercury with moist iron filings: 'a double decomposition takes place: one part of the water is attracted by the iron; the other is attracted by the phlogisticated air; and the water seems by these compound affinities to be much more rapidly decomposed, than when iron and water are mixed by themselves.'

Iron, water, and sulphur in presence of atmospheric air also form ammonia, and this misled Scheele, who found too much absorption of oxygen, since some nitrogen was also absorbed. In 'Experiments on the Analysis of the Heavy Inflammable Air',[2] Austin proposed a number of erroneous ideas.

Higgins's most important discovery, which neither he nor his later admirers claimed or emphasised, was that *dry* chlorine and nitric oxide do not react when mixed:[3] 'when the airs are perfectly dry, and mixed over mercury, no decomposition seems to take place until water is produced. Hence I infer, that water assists the decomposition from its attraction to marine acid' (which he thought was formed when nitric oxide withdraws oxygen from dephlogisticated marine acid or chlorine). This experiment later played an important part in the controversy between Murray and John Davy on the nature of chlorine (see Vol. IV). Higgins, it is seen, failed to interpret it correctly.

Higgins argued that since only one kind of water exists (see p. 740) it must be composed of fixed numbers of particles of hydrogen and oxygen and (perhaps influenced by Bryan Higgins) he chose the simplest assumption that it contains one particle of each (is HO). Since the gases combine in the volume ratio 2 : 1, two volumes of hydrogen contain the same number of particles as one volume of oxygen. Higgins also says[4] that Lavoisier found that water contains 87 of dephlogisticated air and 13 of light inflammable air, 'which is nearly seven to one' ($87/13 = 6 \cdot 7$). Kirwan's densities[5] give the ratio 34 to $2 \cdot 613$ and if Higgins's assumption is used the particle of oxygen can be calculated to be $34/(2 \cdot 613 \times 2) = 6 \cdot 5$ times as heavy as a particle of hydrogen. After Dalton's theory had been published, Higgins claimed[6] that this calculation is an obvious one. But the same data were available to Bryan Higgins, who did not draw this conclusion. Grotthuss, a much abler man than either Bryan or William Higgins, formulated water as HO in 1805 (Fig. 62 A: + = hydrogen, − =

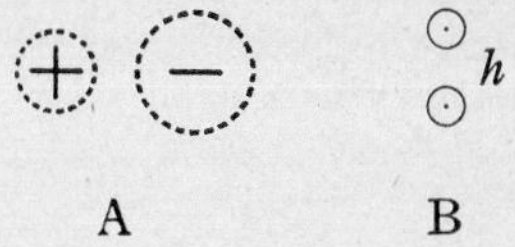

A   B

FIG. 62. DIAGRAMS OF WATER MOLECULES ACCORDING TO GROTTHUSS.

[1] Moore, DNB, 1885, ii, 272.   [2] *Phil. Trans.*, 1790, lxxx, 51.   [3] II, 212.
[4] II, 2, 148.   [5] II, xiv.
[6] *Phil. Mag.*, 1816, xlviii, 363, 408; 1819, liii, 401 (408).

oxygen) and HO_2 in 1807 (Fig. 62 B: $\odot$ = oxygen, h = hydrogen).[1] But in 1818,[2] pointing out that the figures he had given were practically the same as Dalton's symbols, he says the beautiful idea of Dalton of deducing the weights of atoms from the compositions of bodies had not, remarkably, occurred to him:

Merkwürdig ist es dass ich der Daltonschen Entdeckung, das Gewicht der Atome betreffend, . . . damals sehr nahe gewesen bin. Ich gestehe aber, dass mir der herrliche und verwegene Gedanke, das Gewicht der Atome aus den Zusammensetzung der Körper relativ zu bestimmen, *nicht* eingefallen ist.

William Higgins refers to 'ultimate particles' as something well known; although he does not *explicitly* say they are all equal in weight, yet he seems to imply this in the only cases where he discusses it. He says they are combined in definite proportions; although the idea of multiple proportions *by weight* follows from his diagrams (p. 743) he never states it in so many words. Higgins[3] says:

'metals will unite with dephlogisticated air in various proportions, until saturated. If 100 grains of a metal are capable of uniting to 15 gr. of dephlogisticated air only, they will attract and retain 5 gr. of dephlogisticated air with greater force than they will 10 gr. and 10 gr. with greater force than 15 gr. Let us suppose every 100 gr. of tin, when in perfect solution, to be united to 15 gr. of dephlogisticated air with the force of $5\frac{1}{2}$. Let iron attract dephlogisticated air with the force of 7, and let us suppose this force to be reduced to 6, by the accession of $7\frac{1}{2}$ gr. of dephlogisticated air, and the attraction of the tin to its dephlogisticated air to be increased by losing its $7\frac{1}{2}$ of dephlogisticated air: in this case, iron cannot precipitate tin in its metallic state, although it may have a greater attraction to dephlogisticated air than the tin has.'

The figures $7\frac{1}{2}$ and 15 are purely hypothetical numbers (the correct figures are 13·4 and 26·8), and although they agree with the law of multiple proportions it does not seem to me justifiable to assume, as Meldrum[4] did, that Higgins saw clearly that the *atoms* of tin and oxygen have different weights, that of tin much larger than that of oxygen. Higgins said later:[5]

'We have every reason to suppose that the ultimate particles of every substance in nature possess the same specific gravity and that the difference in the weight of metals depends upon the distance of their respective ultimate particles from each other. This I have shown to be the case in respect to some gases. See pages 14, 15, of my Comparative View.[6]

'. . . this suggested the first effort of ascertaining the weights of the particles of different elementary matter, and that the weight of the atoms and molecules which they produced, might readily be ascertained, those facts being once established. This part of my theory Mr. Dalton strictly attended to.'

In a reply to a criticism of his claims by Murray,[7] Higgins[8] regarded the remarks on the oxidation of tin as an anticipation of Berthollet's views on mass-action: '. . . Dalton, Gay-Lussac, Berthollet and Dr. Wollaston, . . . have

[1] Grotthuss, *Mémoire sur la Décomposition de l'Eau*, Rome, 1805; *Ann. Chim.*, 1806, lviii, 54; 1807, lxiii, 5 (20).
[2] *J. Chem. Phys.*, 1818, xx, 225 (269); Ostwald's *Klassiker*, clii, 92.
[3] II, 275. [4] *Manchester Mem.*, 1910, lv, no. 4, 14. [5] III, 12, 60.
[6] This is the passage about 'the gravitating particles of nitrous air are thrice the distance from each other that the ultimate particles of dephlogisticated are', quoted on p. 739.
[7] *System of Chemistry*, 4 ed., Edinburgh, 1819, i, 127.
[8] *Phil. Mag.*, 1819, liii, 401 (409).

written long after me on these interesting subjects, and of course have no claims to originality.'[1]

Austin[2] in discussing hydrogen and nitrogen in relation to experiments in which Higgins[3] claimed to have collaborated, assumed that if 'the elementary particles of the 2 airs be of equal magnitude', the ratio of the specific gravities being 11 to 1, then the distances of the particles in the two gases are in the ratio $\sqrt[3]{11}$ to 1. Higgins,[4] long after Dalton's theory had been published, said:

'In my opinion, the ultimate particles of azote are larger, and of course, heavier than those of oxygen. I also conceive that a measure of oxygen gas contains twice the number of ultimate particles, that are contained in the same volume of azotic gas,'

and still later:[5]

'The ultimate particles of azotic gas are almost twice as heavy as those of oxygen gas, yet the latter gas is heavier in volume. . . . I should presume that the specific gravity of the ultimate particles of all bodies is the same, their size constituting the difference of their weight.'

The statement by Roscoe and Schorlemmer,[6] referring to Dalton's theory, that: 'all previous upholders of an atomic theory, including even Higgins, had supposed that the relative weights of the atoms of the various elements are the same', was criticised by Meldrum[7] on the basis of the single statement by Higgins about tin (see p. 748).

HIGGINS AND DALTON

Higgins's claims to have anticipated Dalton, put forward seven years after the publication of Dalton's theory, really originated in statements by Davy in 1811. They would perhaps more correctly be dealt with in the chapter on Dalton, but since he took no part in discussion of them it seemed undesirable to encumber that chapter with them and they will be disposed of here.

In 1810 and 1811 Humphry Davy lectured to the Royal Dublin Society, receiving fees of 400 guineas and £750 and the degree of Ll.D., and no doubt met William Higgins. Davy was the first to draw attention to him in a Bakerian lecture to the Royal Society, 15 Nov. 1810:[8]

'In my last communication to the Society,[9] I have quoted Mr. Dalton as the original Author of the hypothesis, that water consists of 1 particle of oxygen, and 1 of hydrogen; but I have since found that this opinion is advanced, in a work published in 1789 — *A Comparative View of the Phlogistic and Antiphlogistic Theories*, by William Higgins. In this elaborate and ingenious performance, Mr. Higgins has developed many happy sketches of the manner in which (on the corpuscular hypothesis) the particles or molecules of bodies may be conceived to combine; and some of his views, though formed at this early period of investigation, appear to me to be more defensible, assuming his data, than any which have since been advanced; for instance, he considered nitrous gas as composed of two particles of oxygen, and one of nitrogen.'

[1] See also his remarks in *Phil. Mag.*, 1816, xlviii, 363, 408; 1817, l, 401 (406); 1818, li, 81, 161, on Wollaston.
[2] *Phil. Trans.*, 1788, lxxviii, 379. [3] II, 77, 312. [4] III, 146; see p. 735.
[5] *Phil. Mag.*, 1819, liii, 401 (408–9). [6] *Treatise*, 1920, i, 35.
[7] *Manchester Mem.*, 1910, lv, no. 4, 14.
[8] *Phil. Trans.*, 1811, ci, 1 (15); *Works*, 1840, v, 326.
[9] *Phil. Trans.*, 1810, c, 231; *Works*, v, 298.

Davy criticises many results of his 'learned friend' Dalton; he feels 'obliged to dissent from most of them, and to protest against the interpretations that he has been pleased to make of my experiments'. The tone is harsh and unfriendly. This statement circulated throughout Great Britain and on the Continent.

Meldrum[1] thought that Dalton's paper on affinity and particles,[2] written on 19 December 1810, only a month after Davy's lecture, in which Dalton distinguishes between an 'atom' and a 'particle' and is 'careful not to mention Higgins', was intended as a reply to Davy's remarks. Meldrum failed to mention the testimony of William Henry, quoted by his son W. C. Henry,[3] which seems to negative Meldrum's conclusion (he did sometimes omit unfavourable material known to him). W. Henry in a memorandum written in 1833 states that 'calling on Mr. Dalton, I found him in the act of reading the note to Davy's paper in the *Phil. Trans.*, 1811, p. 15. He expressed his surprise and asked me if I had seen Higgins's book. I told him that I had not only seen it, but quoted it,[4] and lent him the volume'. Dalton, therefore, was not aware of the existence of Higgins's *Comparative View* until after the *publication* of Davy's paper in 1811. W. C. Henry says: 'I have heard my father affirm, on various occasions, and to various persons, that Dalton had never seen Mr. Higgins's work, till some years subsequently to the publication of the *New System*, when it was lent to him by my father.'

Davy in 1812[5] said:

'Mr. Higgins is, I believe, the first person who conceived that when gasses [*sic*] combined in more than one proportion, all the proportions of the same elements were equal; and he founded this idea, which was made public in 1789, on the corpuscular hypothesis, that bodies combine particle with particle, or one with two, or three, or a greater number of particles. Mr. Dalton, about 1802, adopting a similar hypothesis, apparently without the knowledge of what Mr. Higgins had written, extended his views to compounds in general.'

Davy in his obituary notice of 1825 on William Higgins[6] said:

'he brought forward no new experiments and endeavoured to establish a loose kind of dynamic hypothesis . . . it is impossible not to regret that he did not establish principles which belong to the highest department of chemistry, and that he suffered so fertile and promising a field of science to be entirely cultivated by others; for though possessed of great means of improving chemistry, he did little or nothing during the last thirty years of his life.'

Davy, as President of the Royal Society, in presenting the Royal Medal to Dalton in 1826, said[7] that many ideas of William Higgins had been anticipated by Bryan Higgins in 1786, and as these were known to William:

'it is difficult not to allow the merits of prior conception, as well as of very ingenious illustration, to the elder writer. . . . Mr. Dalton, as far as can be ascertained, was not

---

[1] *Manchester Mem.*, 1911, lv, no. 22.   [2] *Nicholson's J.*, 1811, xxviii, 81 (see p. 807).
[3] *Memoirs of the Life and Scientific Researches of John Dalton*, 1854, 78–9.
[4] In Henry's *An Epitome of Chemistry*, 1801, 65, on the reduction of nitric acid by tin to ammonia.
[5] *Elements of Chemical Philosophy*, 1812, 107; *Works*, 1840, iv, 78.
[6] *Works*, 1840, vii, 75–6.   [7] *Works*, 1840, vii, 95.

acquainted with any of these publications,[1] at least he never refers to them: and whoever will consider the ingenious and independent turn of his mind, and the original
tone prevailing in all his views and speculations, will hardly accuse him of wilful
plagiarism. . . . He first laid down, clearly and numerically, the doctrine of multiples;[2]
and endeavoured to express, by simple numbers, the weights of the bodies believed to
be elementary.'

In February 1829, in Rome, shortly before his death from a long illness,
Davy wrote[3] of Dalton:

'It is difficult to say how he gained his first notion of atoms, but I strongly suspect
that *Researches Chemical and Philosophical*,[4] published in 1801, . . . gave him his first
ideas. . . . He had probably seen the works of the two Higginses, but I do not think he
was acquainted with the views of Richter. . . . Whatever came into his mind, from any
source, he seemed always to consider his own property. . . . He was a very coarse
experimenter and always found the results he required, trusting to his head rather than
to his hands.'

I believe this judgment is almost wholly incorrect. Davy's brother[5] said:
'He always respected and esteemed Mr. Dalton, and never thought lightly of
any of his views.'

Thomas Thomson[6] said that Higgins's book was meritorious and 'states
some striking facts respecting the gases and anticipated Gay-Lussac's theory
of volumes', but Dalton 'first generalized the doctrine, and thought of determining the weight of the atoms of bodies'. This annoyed Higgins, who
arranged for John Nash to reply to it.[7] Nash drew attention to Higgins's statements that 'the gravitating particles of nitrous air are thrice the distance that
the ultimate particles of dephlogisticated air are in the same temperature',[8] to
the compositions of the 'molecules' of sulphurous (SO) and sulphuric (SO_2)
acids and water (HO),[9] and especially the difficult passage[10] on the composition of sulphuretted hydrogen (S_9H_5) mentioned on p. 744. In a reply to
Nash, Thomson[11] says he had possessed Higgins's book:

'since the year 1798 and had perused it carefully; yet I did not find anything in it
which suggested to me the atomic theory. That a small hint would have been sufficient
I think pretty clear from this, that I was forcibly struck with Mr. Dalton's statement in
1804, though it did not fill half an octavo page.'

Thomson thought the discussions on the compositions of water[12] and sulphuretted hydrogen,[13] and the account of the oxides of nitrogen,[14] showed that
Higgins 'had an idea of the atomic theory when he wrote his book'.

In 1814 Higgins, six years after the publication of the first volume of
Dalton's *New System*, put forward his claim that he anticipated Dalton and
that Dalton based his theory on Higgins's *Comparative View* of 1789. He
says the 'ultimate particle' of 1789 is the same as Dalton's 'atom', and the

[1] Of Bryan and William Higgins, and Richter.
[2] This was actually implicit in Higgins's work of 1789; see p. 742.
[3] Henry, *Life of Dalton*, 1854, 217: communicated by John Davy.
[4] Davy, *Researches, Chemical and Philosophical; chiefly concerning Nitrous Oxide*, London,
1800 (not 1801 as Davy stated).
[5] John Davy, *Memoirs of the Life of Sir Humphry Davy*, 1836, i, 440.
[6] *Ann. Phil.*, 1813, ii, 445.
[7] *Phil. Mag.*, 1814, xliii, 54: 'The Discovery of the Atomic Theory claimed for Mr. Higgins.'
[8] II, 15.   [9] *Ib.*, 36 f.   [10] *Ib.*, 80–1.   [11] *Ann. Phil.*, 1814, iii, 331.
[12] II, 36–7.   [13] II, 81.   [14] II, 132 f.

'molecule' of 1789 was the same as that of 1814.[1] Dalton derived his information from Higgins; he 'cannot . . . directly say Mr. Dalton is a plagiarist, although appearances are against him'.[2] Higgins says: 'I cannot discover any improvement made in my doctrine'; he had used the atomic theory in 'abstruse and difficult researches', whilst Dalton had applied it 'in a general and popular way'.[3] He quotes[4] passages from his work of 1789, sometimes, he says, modernising and shortening them so as to make them more perspicuous; the changes are slight and consist mainly in using 'oxygen' and 'hydrogen' instead of 'dephlogisticated air' and 'light inflammable air', additions being distinguished by italics (but see p. 744). Higgins valued his numerical estimates of affinity: 'chemical philosophy will never reach its meridian splendour except by means of such principles.'[5] He recognised implicitly that he had paid too little attention to the weights of the particles but says: 'Mr. Dalton may weigh these molecules, but he must allow that they were first *identified* by me';[6] Dalton's 'attempt to weigh a few atoms, no matter how, or whether he is correct or not, gives him no claim whatever to the system which I established several years before'.[7] Higgins quotes[8] a large section from Dalton's *New System*[9] and says: 'It will be found very nearly the ditto of the principles which I established, excepting his omission of numbers, which represent the relative force of chemical attraction of particles and atoms to each other, and which appears to me to be one of the most important features of my system.'

Thomson[10] in a review of the book denied that 'there is the slightest allusion to the weight of a single elementary atom' in the book of 1789, or 'the slightest reason to induce us to believe that the idea of ascertaining the weights of these atoms has so much as entered into the conception of the writer'. Thomson says Higgins's book of 1789 was unknown in Edinburgh and London until Davy (when he visited Dublin) had his attention drawn to it by Higgins as containing the outline of the atomic theory. Thomson read the book again after Davy's statement and told him that he could not find the atomic doctrine in it.

Wollaston[11] suggested that:

'Higgins conceived, rather than actually observed to occur, certain successive degrees of oxidation of azote, . . . at the same time added his opinion, that such are the proportions in which these gases unite to each other in *bulk*.' He 'clearly preceded Mr. Dalton in his atomic views of chemical combination', but 'he appears not to have taken much pains to ascertain the actual prevalance of that law of multiple proportions by which the atomic theory is best supported'.

Higgins in 1819[12] claimed that 'what is called the atomic theory formed a part of my annual course of lectures' given since 1796 at the Royal Dublin Society, but the syllabus of the course which was printed (see p. 738) in 1801 gives no indication that he regarded it as of particular importance. Extracts from the book of 1814 by Gaultier de Claubry[13] made it known in France; Klaproth and Wolff[14] thought it was the publication of Dalton's theory which caused Higgins

[1] III, 8.   [2] III, 9–10.   [3] III, 17.   [4] III, 46 f.   [5] III, 71.
[6] III, 115.   [7] III, 178.   [8] III, 165–71.   [9] 1808, I, i, 211 f.
[10] *Ann. Phil.*, 1814, iv, 52–66.   [11] *Phil. Trans.*, 1814, civ, 5; but see p. 743.
[12] *Phil. Mag.*, 1819, liii, 401–10 (405).   [13] *J. de Phys.*, 1817, liii, 392.
[14] *Supplemente zu dem chemischen Wörterbuch*, Berlin, 1819, iv, 155.

to read into his book of 1789 what he imagined was his anticipation of it, and W. J. Macneven (an Irishman)[1] thought Higgins's 'own experiments were too few, and there were not data enough furnished by others to supply sufficient materials for the construction of the atomic theory . . . with more industry he might, perhaps, have secured to himself the reputation for which he is now so solicitous'. W. C. Henry[2] gives a long and fair summary of Higgins's work and praises his 'uncommon sagacity'; he thought that the compositions of sulphur and nitrogen compounds were based on the assumptions of equality in weight of the atoms of oxygen, nitrogen, and sulphur. R. Angus Smith,[3] who also gives long extracts from his book, says Higgins 'for a moment laid hold of the idea that bodies which are atomically constituted must be formed of the union of one or more bodies, and of no intermediate atoms', that 'he expressed the fact of atomic simple and multiple proportions', but 'in his mind it was not raised to the dignity of a great law'.

Others have been more favourable to Higgins. Thomas Graham[4] answers the question: 'Who first made use of the atomic hypothesis in chemical reasonings?' quite definitely: 'A Mr. Higgins, of Dublin — in a book of his published in the year 1789'; and Sir John Herschel,[5] in a dialogue 'On Atoms' written in 1860, has:

'*Hermione.* Do tell me something about these atoms. I declare it has quite excited me; 'specially because it seems to have something to do with the atomic theory of Dalton.
Hermogenes. Higgins, if you please.'

Later advocates are Meldrum (see p. 737), Atkinson,[6] and especially Soddy,[7] whose intemperate statements were dealt with by the author.[8] T. Dillon[9] says 'To me, however, it seems that he failed to go as far as Dalton, whose real achievement was to attribute a definite and characteristic weight to the atom of each element'; but Dillon thought Dalton had read the *Comparative View*, whilst Wheeler thought he had not.

Roscoe,[10] after mentioning that Kirwan (1783) and Higgins (1789; he does not mention Bryan Higgins) had expressed 'the belief that chemical combination consists in the approximation of unlike particles', said Dalton 'was the first to propound a truly *chemical* atomic theory, the only one hitherto proposed which co-ordinates the facts of chemical combination in a satisfactory manner . . . a *quantitative* theory respecting the constitution of matter, whereas all others are simply qualitative views'. An attempt to review the matter temperately and impartially was made by Wheeler and Partington,[11] who give

[1] *Ann. Phil.*, 1820, xvi, 195 (199).   [2] *Life of Dalton*, 1854, 77.
[3] *Manchester Mem.*, 1856, xiii, 175 f., 184–5.   [4] *Chemical Catechism*, 1829, 35.
[5] *Familiar Lectures on Scientific Subjects*, London and New York, 1866, 453.
[6] *J. Chem. Educ.*, 1940, xvii, 3.
[7] *The Story of Atomic Energy*, London, 1949; Paneth, *Nature*, 1950, clxvi, 799; Soddy, *ib.*, 1951, clxvii, 735.
[8] Partington, *Nature*, 1951, clxvii, 120, 735 (I had some abusive letters from Prof. Soddy, who evidently felt strongly on the matter).
[9] *Institute of Chemistry of Ireland Journal*, 1955–6, iv, 11 (17).
[10] *Treatise*, 1920, i, 35.   [11] *The Life and Work of William Higgins*, 1960.

all the sources and conclude that Dalton was led to his atomic theory quite independently of Higgins, and that Higgins (as he himself admits, see p. 752) did not attach any importance to the atomic *weights*, which are a cardinal feature of Dalton's theory, nor did he propose any methods by which they could be determined. Higgins deserves credit for his ingenious views on forces between particles, for his implicit recognition of multiple proportions, and his rudimentary foreshadowing of some aspects of modern views on reaction mechanism.

CHAPTER XVII

DALTON

John Dalton (Eaglesfield, 6 September 1766–Manchester, 27 July 1844) was born at Eaglesfield, a village near Cockermouth in Cumberland in a situation apart from the main centres of commerce and learning. He was the son of a wool weaver, his ancestors being artisans and not peasants. The family was in modest but not poor circumstances, owning a small estate ('statesmen' in local description). His father seems to have been of somewhat timid disposition, but his mother, Deborah Greenup of Caldbeck, of a yeoman family, was energetic and lively, and Dalton's characteristics were inherited from her. Both parents were Quakers, to which sect Dalton belonged all his life. In consequence, there is no record of his birth in the parish registers, the date 6 September 1766 being recovered long afterwards from the memories of neighbours of his parents. His father taught him arithmetic and navigation and was apparently a man of some education. At the age of 10 he was given evening lessons in mathematics by Elihu Robinson, a wealthy Quaker of scientific attainments, who probably also first interested Dalton in meteorology.

At that time Dalton was attending a school kept by John Fletcher, and it is said that as a pupil he was not brilliant but steady and persevering, being especially capable in arithmetic. When Fletcher retired, Dalton (then aged 12) set up a school, at first in a barn and later in the Quaker meeting house. This was closed in 1780 and in 1781 John and his brother Jonathan went as assistants in a school in Kendal, which they took over in 1785 on the retirement of the headmaster, their cousin George Bewley. Their sister Mary acted as housekeeper. They taught Greek, Latin, French and mathematics as well as English subjects; the languages and mathematics were acquired by Dalton by hard study, in which he was encouraged and helped by Mr. John Gough (1757–1825), a blind Quaker of Kendal of high intellectual attainments.[1]

---

[1] Boulger, DNB, 1890, xxii, 277. On Dalton, see: Anon., *British Quarterly Review*, 1845, i, 157–98 (says b. 5 September); Anon., *Quarterly Review*, 1855, xcvi, 43–75 (the author, an Edinburgh man, Geo. Wilson, knew Dalton); Anon., *Nature*, 1946, clviii, 193 (memorial of Dalton in Padshaw Hall graveyard, nr. Eaglesfield); J. Bostock, *Nicholson's J.*, 1811, xxviii, 280–92 (criticism of Dalton's atomic theory); E. M. Brockbank, *John Dalton: some unpublished letters of personal and scientific interest*, Manchester, 1944 (62 pp.) (says b. 5 September); S. Brown, *Lectures on the Atomic Theory and Essays Scientific and Literary*, 2 vols., Edinburgh and London, 1858; F. W. Clarke, *Manchester Mem.*, 1903, xlvii, no. 11 (general); C. Clay, *Chem. News*, 1884, l, 59–60 (reminiscence of Dalton, 1816–17); Agnes M. Clerke, DNB, 1888, iii, 428; E. Cohen, *Chem. Weekbl.*, 1905, ii, 97 (caricature of Dalton by Moll); H. F. Coward, *J. Chem. Educ.*, 1927, iv, 22 (portr.); J. Dalton, Autobiography (22 October 1822) in W. C. Henry, 1854, 2 (facsim.; see also Duveen and Klickstein, *J. Chem. Educ.*, 1955, xxxii, 333–4); C. Daubeny, *An Introduction to the Atomic Theory*, Oxford, 1831 (147 pp.); 2 enlarged ed., Oxford, 1850 (502 pp.); H. Davy, *Works*, 1840, iv, 78; v, 326; vii, 93; H. Debus, *Z. phys. Chem.*, 1896, xx, 359; 1897, xxiv, 325; 1899, xxix, 266; 1899, xxx, 556; *id.*, *Phil. Mag.*, 1896,

In 1784–94 Dalton contributed solutions of mathematical problems to the *Gentleman's Diary* (obtaining two prizes) and answers to scientific and general questions (including one on love) to the *Ladies' Diary*, two periodicals then in repute.[1] Dalton kept a meteorological journal, studied zoology and botany, and delivered in the winters of 1787 and 1791 two courses of lectures on natural philosophy, the second including some lectures on the chemistry of

xlii, 350; M. Delacre, *Monit. Scientif.*, 1921, xi, 328 (Dalton's symbols); *id.*, *Histoire de la Chimie*, Paris, 1920, 215–43; E. Divers, *B.A. Rep.*, 1902, 557 (atomic theory without hypotheses); J. N. Friend, *Nature*, 1944, cliv, 103 (pictures of Dalton's birthplace); H. Garnett, *Nature*, 1931, cxxvii, 201 (photographs of Dalton); W. W. H. Gee, with H. F. Coward and A. Harden, *Manchester Mem.*, 1914–15, lix, No. 12 (66 pp. and plates; 150 diagrams for Dalton's lectures found in a cupboard, probably prepared in 1810–15); F. Greenaway, *Manchester Mem. and Proc.*, 1958–9, c, 1–98 (The Biographical Approach to John Dalton; see review by Partington, *Nature*, 1959, clxxxiii, 1765); R. Harrington, *The Death-Warrant of the French Theory of Chemistry, signed by Truth, Reason, Common Sense, Honour and Science . . . Likewise, Remarks upon Mr. Dalton's late Theory . . .*, London: Printed for the Author, 1804; W. C. Henry, *Memoirs of the Life and Scientific Researches of John Dalton*, 1854. (In a letter of January 1838, Henry says Dalton's papers came into his hands before that date, and he was then working on them, not first in 1844 as he says in the preface to his book: see Loewenfeld, 10); A. Hopwood, *J. Chem. Educ.*, 1926, iii, 485; G. L. Hume, *Chemical Attraction. An Essay in Five Chapters*, Cambridge, 1835 (laws of combination, electrochemical theory, Dalton's atomic theory (112 f.), theory of volumes of Gay-Lussac, agents opposing chemical attraction; dedic. to E. Turner); F. Jones, *Manchester Mem.*, 1904, xlviii, no. 22 (Dalton's apparatus; portr. Dalton opp. t.p.); G. W. A. Kahlbaum, *Z. phys. Chem.*, 1899, xxix, 700 (crit. Debus); W. Kirkby, *Chemist and Druggist*, 1931, cxv, 16 (Dalton's lectures on pharmaceutical chemistry in Manchester in 1793, and on the atomic theory in 1824); H. Kopp, (3), 1873, 285–300; K. Loewenfeld, *Manchester Mem.*, 1913, lvii, no. 19 (illustr., incl. Dalton's birthplace); H. Lonsdale, *John Dalton*, in *Worthies of Cumberland*, 1874, v (portr. and unpubl. letters); H. McLachlan, *Manchester Mem.*, 1943–5, lxxxvi, no. 7, 165 (Dalton in Manchester, 1793–1844); W. J. Macneven, Exposition of the Atomic Theory of Chymistry; and the Doctrine of Definite Proportions, in *Ann. Phil.*, 1820, xvi, 195–214, 289–93, 338–50; *J. de Phys.*, 1821, xcii, 274, 376, 444 (on him see D. Reilly, *Chymia*, 1949, ii, 17); A. N. Meldrum, *Avogadro and Dalton. The Standing in Chemistry of their Hypotheses*, Edinburgh, 1906; extended in a series of papers on 'The Development of the Atomic Theory' as follows: (1) Berthollet's Doctrine of Variable Proportions, *Manchester Mem.*, 1910, liv, No. 7; (2) The various Accounts of the Origin of Dalton's Theory, *Chem. News*, 1910, cii, 1; *Manchester Mem.*, 1910–11, lv, No. 3; (3) Newton's Theory, and its Influence in the Eighteenth Century, *Manchester Mem.*, 1910, lv, No. 4; (4) Dalton's Physical Atomic Theory, *ib.*, 1910–11, lv, No. 5; (5) Dalton's Chemical Theory, *ib.*, 1910–11, lv, No. 6 (summarising, with bibliography, a long controversy between Debus and Divers, Kahlbaum, and Roscoe and Harden (see these)); (6) The Reception of the Theory advocated by Dalton, *ib.*, 1911, lv, No. 19; (7) The rival claims of William Higgins and John Dalton, *ib.*, 1911, lv, No. 22; (8) *The Development of the Atomic Theory*, Bombay, Oxford University Press, n.d. [1920] attacking A. Scott, see below (on Andrew Norman Meldrum (Alloa, 19 March 1876–Edinburgh, 12 March 1934) see Forster, *J. Chem. Soc.*, 1934, 1476; and bibl. of papers in *Isis*, 1929, xii, 379); J. V. Millington, *John Dalton*, in *English Men of Science* Series, London, 1906; M. M. P. Muir, *Heroes of Science. Chemists*, 1883, 106–54; *id.*, *History of Chemical Theories and Laws*, New York, 1907, 76–87; L. K. Nash, *Isis*, 1956, xlvii, 101 (origin of atomic theory); L. J. Neville-Polley, *John Dalton*, London, 1920 (pp. 63); F. Nicholson, *Manchester Proc.*, 1911, lv, p. xii (bust of Dalton); W. Ostwald, in G. Bugge, *Das Buch der Grossen Chemiker*, 1929, i, 378–85 (portr.); J. R. Partington, *Ann. Sci.*, 1939, iv, 245; *id.*, *Endeavour*, 1948, vii, 54; *id.*, *Nature*, 1951, clxvii, 120, 735; 1959, clxxxiii, 1765; *id.*, *Scientia*, July 1955; Ritchie, *Manchester Mem.*, 1945, lxxxvi, 189 (history of atomic theory); H. E. Roscoe, *Nature*, 1874, xi, 52 (Dalton's first table of atomic weights); *id.*, in *Science Lectures for the People*, Manchester, 1874, vi; *id.*, *John Dalton and the Rise of Modern Chemistry*, 1901; *id.*, and A. Harden, *A New View of the Origin of Dalton's Atomic Theory*, 1896; *id.*, *Z. phys. Chem.*, 1897, xxii, 241; *id.*, *Phil. Mag.*, 1897, xliii, 153 (crit. Debus); *id.*, *Die Entstehung der Dalton'schen Atomtheorie in neuer Beleuchtung*, in Kahlbaum's *Monographien*, Leipzig, 1898, ii (with notes by Kahlbaum); A. Scott, *J. Chem. Soc.*, 1917, cxi, 288 (see Meldrum, 8); R. Angus Smith, Memoir of John Dalton and History of the Atomic Theory up to his Time, in *Manchester Mem.*, 1856, xiii, 1–298, and sep.; T. Thomson, (1), ii, 285; (2), 1807, iii, 424; A. D. Thorburn, *Ind. Eng. Chem.*, 1924, xvi, 190 (illustr., memorials in Manchester); W. A. Tilden, *Famous Chemists*, 1921, 104; T. T. Wilkinson, *Manchester Mem.*, 1855, xii, 1–30 (Dalton's earliest publications); G. Wilson, *Religio Chemici*, London and Cambridge, 1862, 304.

[1] Wilkinson, *op. cit.*

gases.[1] In a letter of 1790[2] Dalton says he had read Boerhaave, Watson's *Essays* (see Vol. II, p. 765), and Boyle — whom he found tedious and verbose.

In 1793 Dalton, on Gough's recommendation to Dr. Barnes, was appointed tutor in mathematics and natural philosophy in New College, Manchester, a dissenting institution in Mosley Street which was the outcome of the Warrington Academy (p. 758). He had a very modest salary. In addition he also taught

FIG. 63. JOHN DALTON, 1766–1844.

chemistry in 1794, using Lavoisier's *Elements* and Chaptal's *Chemistry* as text-books.[3] Dalton remained for the rest of his life in Manchester. In 1796 Dalton himself attended a course of twelve lectures on natural philosophy and thirty on chemistry given in Manchester by Dr. Thomas Garnett of Harrogate,[4] who was later Davy's predecessor (in 1799–1800) at the Royal Institution in London (see Vol. IV).[5]

On the invitation of Robert Owen, Dalton in 1794 joined the Manchester Literary and Philosophical Society, founded in 1789. He was Secretary in 1800, Vice-President in 1808, and President from 1817 till his death in 1844.[6] He read 116 papers to the Society, many of little importance and designed to provide material for meetings which, as President, he insisted should be held

[1] R. A. Smith, 1856, 15; Coward, 1927, 25. [2] Brockbank, 1944, 10.
[3] R. A. Smith, 1856, 18. [4] Henry, 1854, 47.
[5] R. Garnett, DNB, 1890, xxi, 7; Thorpe, *Humphry Davy*, 1901, 68.
[6] Henry, 1854, 24.

regularly. He resigned from his post in New College in June 1800; he supported himself for the rest of his life by giving private tuition and some courses of lectures, and doing some consulting work, at the same time carrying out research.

A Manchester College of Arts and Science, with Thomas Percival as President, was established in June 1783, but was dissolved after a little more than two years. A second Academy was established in 1786, and it was in this (called New College) that Dalton was tutor. It was moved to York in 1803, back to Manchester in 1840, to London in 1853 and finally to Oxford as Manchester College in 1889, occupying its own buildings from 1893, its existence being continuous.[1]

Dalton never pretended that his teaching work interfered with his research, saying that 'teaching was a kind of recreation, and if richer he would not probably spend more time in investigation than he was accustomed to do'.[2] As an experimenter he was self-taught. His apparatus (some of which still exists in Manchester University and some in the Science Museum, South Kensington)[3] was simple but effective; he had a predilection for empty penny ink-bottles, which contributed to some of his fundamental discoveries.[4] Dalton's home-made barometer, with a paper scale in his writing, 'agrees very closely with a modern barometer.'[5] The crudeness of his analytical results has been over-emphasised and many of them are remarkably accurate. In the difficult field of gas analysis he obtained very good results.

Unlike Priestley, Dalton 'probably never instituted a single experiment without a clearly preconceived object'.[6] He had the true investigator's gift of finding the right result almost by intuition, which is worth much more than tedious refinement and elaboration without inspiration. In the preface to the second part of Vol. I of his *New System* (1810) Dalton says: 'Having been in my progress so often misled, by taking for granted the results of others, I have determined to write as little as possible but what I can attest by my own experience', which is a perfectly reasonable attitude.

In the period 1804–30 Dalton lived with the Rev. W. Johns, his laboratory being in the rooms of the Philosophical Society. After leaving the Johns, Dalton lived the rest of his life at 27 Falkner St., Manchester, having a housekeeper. He gave lessons in grammar, arithmetic and science, his fee being 1/- an hour, later raised to 1/6 and (when he had become famous) 2/6; he also did a little analytical work at correspondingly low fees.[7] He was very conscientious in these duties and his strict truthfulness is reflected in an anecdote that when a pupil who missed one lecture of a course asked for a certificate, Dalton would not give it, but said: 'If thou will come to-morrow I will go over the lecture thou hast missed', and as a result he gave the certificate. One of his pupils was Joule. In 1824 he lectured to medical students in the medical school

[1] Anon., *Brit. Quart. Rev.*, 1845, i, 157; McLachlan, 1943–5; Brockbank, 1944, 13; letter from Dr. W. H. Brindley, 18 Oct. 1956.

[2] Wilson, 1862, 348.　　　　[3] F. Jones, 1904 (plates); Coward, 1927, 23 (figs.).

[4] Lonsdale, 1874, 247; Anon., *Quart. Rev.*, 1855, xcvi, 46: 'his laboratory, which we once visited, might well, in its slovenly arrangements, provoke a smile from the modern adept in analysis.'

[5] F. Jones, 1904, 2.　　　　[6] Henry, 1854, 229.　　　　[7] Lonsdale, 229.

in Pine Street. His discovery in 1792 of colour-blindness in himself was announced in 1794[1] and there are some amusing anecdotes of the results of this defect of vision. He mentions the earlier account of colour-blindness by Huddart.[2]

Although it is said[3] he was 'ungainly and inelegant' as a lecturer and 'unattractive and uncouth' in society (perhaps an impression of his North-Country and Quaker manners) he wore good clothes and was careful of his personal appearance. He was much in request as a lecturer, giving courses in Manchester, in London at the Royal Institution in 1803–4 and 1809–10,[4] in Edinburgh,[5] in Glasgow (1807) — where he had a very good reception,[6] and Birmingham and Leeds. His harsh and indistinct voice ('gruff and mumbling') and lack of elegance in diction — he gave offence in London by calling the chemical elements 'articles'[7] — occasioned unfavourable comment, but the material was attractive and original.

In 1816 Dalton was made a corresponding member of the Paris Institut, a very signal honour. He visited Paris in 1822 and was very well received by Laplace, Berthollet and other distinguished savants. In 1830 he was awarded Davy's place as one of the eight foreign associates of the Institut. In 1822 he became F.R.S. (he had declined Davy's offer of nomination in 1810) and in 1826 received the Royal Medal, with a eulogy from Davy, the President.[8] In 1832 he became D.C.L. of Oxford (Mayow's degree), on the occasion of a meeting there of the British Association, Dr. Daubeny having proposed him to the governing body. In 1833, as a result of representations to the Government by Mr. Babbage, then Lucasian professor of mathematics in Cambridge (not Dr. Chalmers, as Wilson says), Dalton was awarded a Civil Pension of £150 per annum (increased to £300 in 1836 — a large sum in those days) and he was presented at Court,[9] wearing his doctor's gown to conceal the absence of the customary sword, and apparently pleased the King. The award of the pension was announced, with an extempore eulogy, in the presidential address to the British Association in Cambridge in 1833 by Professor Sedgwick, Dalton being present. On the occasion of the Association meeting in Edinburgh in 1834 the degree of Ll.D. was conferred upon Dalton. In 1833 a subscription of £2000 was raised in Manchester for a marble statue by Chantrey, now in the entrance to the Town Hall, in which building there is also a fresco by Ford Madox Brown finished in 1886 and showing Dalton collecting marsh gas from a ditch.[10] There is a marble bust by Cardwell in the Christie Library of the University of Manchester.

Dalton enjoyed robust health till nearly seventy; in 1837 he had an attack of

[1] *Manchester Mem.*, 1798, v, I, 28 (read 31 October 1794).   [2] *Phil. Trans.*, 1777, lxvii, 260.
[3] Clerke, DNB, 1888, iii, 438; John Davy's account in Henry, 1854, 217.
[4] See his interesting letters to Rothwell and his brother, in Henry, 1854, 47–50.
[5] '. . . to a scanty audience'; Anon., *Quart. Rev.*, 1855, xcvi, 49; but cf. Thomson, *Ann. Phil.*, 1814, iv, 165.
[6] Dalton, *New System*, 1808, I, i, dedic. and pref.
[7] Anon., *Quart. Rev.*, 1855, xcvi, 49; Dalton, *New System*, 1808, I, i, 220.
[8] Davy, *Works*, 1840, vii, 93.   [9] Wilson, 351; Henry, 174 f., 181.
[10] F. M. Hueffer, *Ford Madox Brown. A Record of his Life and Work*, 1896, plate opp. p. 379; Thorburn, *Ind. Eng. Chem.*, 1924, xvi, 190; the portrait is from a small bust of Dalton which was in Joule's possession.

paralysis, from which he partially recovered. He was abstemious, though not a total abstainer, and fond of a pipe of tobacco. His habits were extremely regular; every Thursday he went to the 'Dog and Partridge' for a game of bowls. He went to his laboratory every week-day and lighted his own fire, shutting up at nine o'clock at night. One of Dalton's friends, who acted as his literary assistant, was Peter Clare (1781–1851), an instrument and clock maker in Manchester.[1]

Dalton was alive at 6 a.m. on the morning of 27 July 1844, and made an entry in his diary: 'little rain this day', the last word being feebly written; soon after he was found dead. He was given a public funeral on 12 August, attended by marks of the deepest respect, all the shops and warehouses on the route, and many others, being closed. His remains are in Ardwick Cemetery in Manchester, but it was proposed to move the two-ton granite tombstone to make way for playing fields.[2] A dry shrivelled eye of Dalton (examined on account of his colour blindness) is still in existence in Dalton Hall (one of the University residential halls) in Manchester.

Dalton never married (he says he never found time), but throughout his life he was fond of the society of educated women; at one time, soon after going to Manchester, he seems to have been attracted by a widow lady of great intellectual ability and personal charm. 'During my captivity, which lasted about a week,' he later wrote to a friend, 'I lost my appetite and had other symptoms of bondage about me, as incoherent discourse, etc., but have now happily regained my freedom.'

Dalton was somewhat above middle height, with a robust and muscular frame, capable even in his later years of great physical exertion, but with a slight stoop. His face had some resemblance to Newton's, especially in later life: this was noticed when he visited Cambridge in 1833.[3] The portrait in Henry (from the statue by Chantrey) is good and shows Dalton's 'austere gentleness of expression'.[4]

Dalton's mind was bold, self-reliant, and capable of wide sweeps of generalisation,[5] although careful, slow, and laborious.[6] He relied little on the work of others, he said (as Paracelsus had long before) that he had few books and 'could carry his library on his back'.[7] He was indifferent to 'public opinion', never intervening e.g. in the controversy among others on the relative merits of Higgins and himself. Although now little known for anything but his atomic theory, he actually published nearly 150 communications to various journals.[8] In personality, Dalton differed as greatly from each of his famous contemporaries, Davy and Faraday, as these differed from each other.

Dalton's lecture and laboratory notes, bound in 12 volumes of MS., were preserved in the Manchester Literary and Philosophical Society.[9] Dr. Harden informed me in 1938 that some had then disappeared, and the rest were lost when the Society's premises and its contents were destroyed as a result of a

[1] Brockbank, 1944, 36 f. [2] *Chem. Age*, 1960, lxxxiii, 764.
[3] Anon., *Quart. Rev.*, 1855, xcvi, 53. [4] Lonsdale, 223.
[5] Wilson, 341. [6] Henry, 1854, 236.
[7] *Ib.*, 79, 224; Delacre, *Histoire de la Chimie*, 1920, 242: 'Dalton ne complète rien; il fonde. . . .'
[8] List in R. A. Smith, 1856, 253 f. [9] Roscoe and Harden, 1896, 12.

German air-raid in the night of 23–4 December 1940, when Joule's barometers and thermometers, a secretaire of Newton's, and a library of 50,000 volumes, were also destroyed.[1]

In his early days in Cumberland Dalton had begun to study air and water, and it was by a continuation of these studies that he arrived at his atomic theory; cheap materials used in simple apparatus. The meteorological observations were begun at Kendal (where he had ample opportunities for studying rainfall) in 1788 and were continued to the day of his death — his last entry in his diary is an unfinished sentence on the weather (see p. 760). The observations were published in 1793:

A (1). Meteorological Observations and Essays. By John Dalton, Professor of Mathematics and Natural Philosophy, at the New College, Manchester. London: printed for W. Richardson, under the Royal Exchange; J. Phillips, George Yard; and W. Pennington, Kendal. 1793. Price Four Shillings. The t.p. has the same quotation from Horace as Higgins's book (p. 738): 'Est quodam prodire tenus, si non datur ultra. Horace.' 8°, pp. xvi, 208. Another probably later issue with a new t.p., without date is: London: Printed for T. Ostell, No. 3, Ave-maria-lane. Price Five Shillings; text otherwise the same (pref. dated 1793); Sotheran *Cat.* 868 (1941), nos. 458–9.

A (2). Second ed., printed verbatim from the first, apart from an appendix of notes, pp. 197–244, a list of Dalton's publications, and the omission of the quotation from Horace on the t.p.: Meteorological Observations and Essays. By John Dalton, D.C.L., F.R.S. . . . Second Edition. Manchester: printed by Harrison and Crosfield, for Baldwin and Cradock, London. 1834. Pp. xx, 244, [iv].

For convenience of reference the short title of Dalton's second book is given here, the full description being given on p. 799:

B. A New System of Chemical Philosophy. Part I, Manchester, 1808; Part II, Manchester, 1810; Part First of Vol. II (all printed), Manchester, 1827. These are denoted by I, i; I, ii, and II, respectively. Second ed. of I, i, London, 1842.

Dalton says he had been anticipated in the theory of the aurora as due to magnetic matter in the atmosphere by an author calling himself 'Amanuensis' in an obscure journal in 1792, whom he quotes in full.[2] Dalton concluded that 'The aurora borealis is a magnetic phenomenon, and its beams are governed by the earth's magnetism'.[3] The 'elastic fluid of magnetic matter' producing the aurora is not the same as the 'magnetic fluid or effluvium'. 'Whether any of the various kinds of air, or elastic vapour, we are acquainted with, is magnetic, I know not, but hope philosophers will avail themselves of these hints to make a trial of them.'[4] In the preface (p. vii) he says he found, after the book had been printed, that he had been anticipated in the relation between the aurora and magnetism by Halley.[5] Dalton maintained his estimate of the height of the aurora, 150 miles, much later.[6] A similar theory was proposed by Biot,[7] who mentions Dalton. After his discovery of the paramagnetism of oxygen, Faraday[8] published a long discussion of 'atmospheric magnetism' and

---

[1] *The Observer*, 19 January 1941; Fleure, *Endeavour*, 1947, vi, 147.
[2] A (1), 159. [3] *Ib.*, 175. [4] *Ib.*, 186–7.
[5] *Phil. Trans.*, 1716, xxix, 406. [6] *Phil. Trans.*, 1828, cxviii, II, 291.
[7] *J. de Phys.*, 1821, xciii, 5–19.
[8] *Phil. Mag.*, 1847, xxxi, 401–21; oxygen is magnetic in air or hydrogen; *Phil. Trans.*, 1851, cxli, 7–28 (oxygen is strongly paramagnetic), 29–84, 85–122.

its relation to the aurora, 'which can hardly be independent of the magnetic constitution of the atmosphere.' He mentions neither Dalton nor Biot.

Dalton said in 1793[1] that he was:

'confirmed in the opinion that *the vapour of water (and probably of most other liquids) exists at all times in the atmosphere, and is capable of bearing any known degree of cold without a total condensation and that the vapour so existing is one and the same thing with* steam, *or vapour of the temperature of 212° or upwards.* The idea, therefore, that vapour cannot exist in the open atmosphere under the temperature of 212°, unless chemically combined therewith, I consider as erroneous; it has taken its rise from a supposition, that *air* pressing upon *vapour* condenses the vapour equally with *vapour* pressing upon *vapour*, a supposition we have no right to assume. When a particle of vapour exists between two particles of air, let their equal and opposite pressures upon it be what they may, they cannot bring it nearer to another particle of vapour, without which no condensation [of vapour] can take place.'

He gave a table of vapour pressures of water at different temperatures from his own observations.[2] This statement is clearly a criticism of Lavoisier's views (see p. 769).

In 1793[3] Dalton asserted that pure air is: 'an intimate mixture of various elastic fluids or *gasses*', that the question whether the water vapour in it 'is ever chymically combined . . . or . . . exists . . . as a fluid *sui generis*, diffused among the rest' had not been clearly answered. 'If we adopt the opinion, which to me appears the more probable, that water evaporated is not chymically combined with the aerial fluids, but exists as a peculiar fluid diffused amongst the rest', the phenomena of rain and dew are easily explained. Dalton[4] claims that this 'theory of the state of vapour in the atmosphere . . . is entirely new', and that it will 'solve all the phenomena of vapour we are acquainted with'. In the preface to the second edition (1834)[5] Dalton says:

'I have been the more anxious to preserve the first edition unchanged, as I apprehend it contains the germs of most of the ideas which I have since expanded more at large in different Essays, and which have been considered discoveries of some importance. For instance, the idea that steam or the vapour of water is an independent elastic fluid . . . and hence that all elastic fluids, whether alone or mixed, exist independently.'

On 1 March 1799 Dalton read a paper to the Manchester Philosophical Society on 'Experiments and Observations to determine whether the Quantity of Rain and Dew is equal to the Quantity of Water carried off by the Rivers and raised by Evaporation; with an Enquiry into the Origin of Springs';[6] this paper contains the earliest definition of dew-point (in the added footnote) and the conclusion that springs are fed by rain. Dalton[7] repeated his assertion of 1793 that aqueous vapour is not chemically combined in the atmosphere, that the pressure of it is determined by the temperature alone, and defined the dew-point, which he calls the 'extreme temperature':

'aqueous vapour is an elastic fluid *sui generis*, diffusible in the atmosphere, but forming no chemical combination with it . . . whatever quantity of aqueous vapour may exist in

[1] A (1), 201; A (2), 188; italics in original.   [2] A (1), 134.
[3] A (1), 76, 132, 138, 144.   [4] *Ib.*, Pref. vi.   [5] A (2), xv.
[6] *Manchester Mem.*, 1802, v, II, 346–72; the footnote on pp. 351–2 was added after the paper was read.
[7] *Ib.*, 351.

the atmosphere at any time, a certain temperature may be found, below which a portion of that vapour would unavoidably fall or be deposited in the form of rain or dew, but above which no such diminution could take place, chemical agency apart . . . whenever any body colder than the extreme temperature of the existing vapour is situated in the atmosphere, dew is deposited upon it.'

Dalton measured the temperature of cold spring water which caused the deposition of dew on the outside of a glass cup; if necessary a pinch of saltpetre was added to the water. This simple apparatus is the basis of Daniell's hygrometer (Vol. IV).

Dalton not only had to contend with the theory that atmospheric air is a chemical compound of oxygen and nitrogen (see p. 744), but had also to meet a much older theory of the state of water vapour in the atmosphere, viz. that it was not merely physically mixed with the air but was in a state of solution, similar to that of salt in water, and could even, in some circumstances, be actually transformed into air. Newton[1] said Nature '. . . seems delighted with Transmutations. Water, which is a very fluid tasteless Salt, she changes by Heat into Vapour, which is a sort of Air . . . '. Halley[2] explained the spontaneous evaporation of water into the atmosphere as analogous to the solution of salts in water, also increasing with the temperature. He says (p. 470):

'I take it, that it would follow that the Air of it self would imbibe a certain quantity of Aqueous Vapours, and retain them like Salts dissolved in Water; that the Sun warming the Air and raising a more plentiful Vapour from the Water in the day time, the Air would sustain a greater proportion of Vapour, as warm Water will hold more dissolved Salts, which upon the absence of the Sun in the Nights would be all again discharged in Dews, Analogous to the precipitation of Salts on the cooling of the Liquors.'

Halley also supposed that the particles of water in the atmosphere exist as minute hollow bubbles, a theory held by Le Roy, Hamilton, Franklin, etc.[3] The solution theory was favoured, as a chemical one, by Berthollet[4] and Murray.[5]

Evaporation as a 'solution' of water in air by a combination of fire with water particles was discussed by Hamilton,[6] who rejected the much earlier physical theory proposed by Desaguliers[7] that the water vapour assumes an elastic state by repulsive forces between its particles (as in Newton's theory of the air, Vol. II, p. 475). Most Continental authors[8] attribute Halley's 'solution' theory to Le Roy,[9] who found that air can be saturated with water vapour (just as water can be saturated with salt), the degree of saturation depending on the temperature. The solution theory was opposed by Nils Wallerius, who proved that water can evaporate into a vacuum.[10] The solution theory was favoured by H. B. de Saussure,[11] who thought that evaporation was less in a

---

[1] *Opticks*, Qu. 30; 1730, 349.

[2] *Phil. Trans.*, 169$\frac{4}{7}$ (t.p. dated 1693), xvii, 468–73, No. 192.

[3] Waller, *Phil. Trans.*, 1847, cxxxvii, 23; Whewell, (1), 1857, ii, 409; Dyment, *Ann. Sci.*, 1937, ii, 465; Partington, (6), iv, 241.

[4] *Statique Chimique*, 1803, i, 288.

[5] *System*, 1806, i, 10; *Elements of Chemistry*, 1828, i, 430.   [6] *Phil. Trans.*, 1765, lv, 146.

[7] *Phil. Trans.*, 1729, xxxvi, 6.   [8] E.g. Rosenberger, 1884, ii, 349.

[9] AdS, 1751, m 481.   [10] KAH, 1747, viii, 214, 251; J. C. Fischer, 1804, v, 63–71.

[11] *Essais sur l'Hygrometrie*, Neuchâtel, 1783, 274, 312, 361.

vacuum than in air. Berthollet[1] deduced from Saussure's results that 'the weight of aqueous vapour is the same in the same space, whatever the quantity of air with which it is united', and that 'the temperature alone determines this quantity'; but he still maintained that the 'solution' of water vapour in air is due to a feeble chemical affinity.

De Saussure[2] says he found that water also 'dissolves' in inflammable air (hydrogen). He assumed that water vapour is a compound of water and the matter of fire, and that evaporation consists in the intimate union of water with elementary fire, and it can occur in a vacuum; when evaporation occurs in air there is a combination of water and air to form a 'true dissolution'.

Saussure's theory was opposed by De Luc, who asserted[3] that the pressure of water vapour is the same in a vacuum as in air. De Luc, however, was far from clear in his views. He thought[4] that evaporation occurs 'by means of fire (l'evaporation se fait par le moyen du feu)', giving an expansible fluid or vapour which rises in the air because of its specific lightness. De Luc[5] also thought that water vapour could be converted into air by electricity, and that air could be reconverted into water, since only by the latter process could the sudden appearance of clouds on mountain tops be explained. De Luc[6] supposed that water vapour is merely mixed or diffused in the air by the repulsive force of heat, and it was known that water evaporates in a vacuum, so that the phenomenon was not due to a 'solvent' effect of air. De Luc[7] asserted that whenever water is in a state of evaporation an expansible fluid called steam, composed of water and fire, is produced; that steam has (like air) a power of pressure, but is not a permanent fluid as it may be decomposed by a certain degree of pressure or cooling, according to determined laws. De Luc had anticipated some of Dalton's ideas, but the latter were arrived at independently; Dalton[8] says: 'Since writing the above, I have met with an account of Mr. De Luc's elaborate work on the modifications of the atmosphere, (vid. the Appendixes to the 49th and 50th vols. of the Monthly Review) . . . his idea of *vapour* too seems not unlike mine. — It is a favourable circumstance to any theory, when it is deduced from a consideration of facts by two persons independently.'

Dalton's theory of the state of aqueous vapour in the atmosphere was not well received by physicists;[9] Johann Friedrich Benzenberg (1777–1846)[10] was one of the few who defended it.

On 12 April 1799 Dalton read a paper on 'Experiments and Observations on the Power of Fluids to conduct Heat'.[11] He disproves by several experiments

---

[1] *Statique Chimique*, 1803, i, 285, 288, 292.
[2] *Op. cit.*, 1783, 240, 272 f., 361 f.
[3] *Idées sur la Météorologie*, London, 1786, i, 20.
[4] *Recherches sur les modifications de l'Atmosphère*, Geneva, 1772, ii, 182–99 (§§ 691–721); *Idées sur la Météorologie*, 1786, i, 13; 1787, ii, 129 f., 202; Rosenberger, 1887, iii, 106 f.
[5] *Idées sur la Météorologie*, 1787, ii, 203 f., 281, 425 f.; cf. de Saussure, *Essais sur l'Hygrometrie*, Neuchâtel, 1783, 310.
[6] *Recherches*, 1772, ii, 182–99; §§ 691–721.
[7] *Phil. Trans.*, 1792, lxxxii, I, 400–24: 'On Evaporation.'
[8] A (2), pref. xii.   [9] Rosenberger, 1887, iii, 108.
[10] *Ueber die Dalton'sche Theorie*, Düsseldorf, 1830 (xvi, 192 pp., 3 lithogr. plates).
[11] *Manchester Mem.*, 1802, v, II, 373–97.

the theory of Rumford[1] that heat circulates in fluids by convection only. Water is a very poor conductor of heat, as Dalton showed. Although Dalton's paper was read in 1799 it was not published until 1802, and in 1801 Thomas Thomson[2] had independently disproved Rumford's theory. In this paper Dalton describes experiments on 'the precise degree of cold at which water ceases to be further condensed' and found $42\frac{1}{2}°$ F. In a letter to his brother of 28 March 1799, Dalton said water has a maximum density at 42° F., expanding below this exactly as it does above, so that the density at 32° is the same as at 52°;[3] but in his published paper he gives $42\frac{1}{2}°$ F. After Hope's experiments[4] Dalton[5] adopted 36° F.;[6] Hope found 39·5° F. The correct temperature of maximum density (4° C. or 39·27° F.) was first found by Lefèvre-Gineau in connexion with work on the metric system, the kilogram being defined as the mass of a cubic decimetre of water at its temperature of maximum density. His value was reported by Haüy.[7]

On 18 April 1800, Dalton read 'Experimental Essays to determine the Expansion of Gases by Heat, and the Maximum of Steam or Aqueous Vapour which any Gas of a given temperature can admit of; with observations on the common and improved Steam Engines'. This was passed for publication but never appeared as such[8] and nothing remains of the observations on steam engines. The experiments were probably incorporated into the papers of 1801 (see p. 766), and the title suggests that the law of expansion of gases by heat (p. 769) was already discovered by April 1800.

On 27 June 1800, Dalton read 'Experiments and Observations on the Heat and Cold produced by the Mechanical Condensation and Rarefaction of Air'.[9] Joule (a pupil of Dalton) says[10] that Dalton 'ascertained that about 50° of heat are evolved when air is compressed to one-half its original bulk; and that, on the other hand, 50° are absorbed by a corresponding rarefaction'; and this result can be inferred from what Dalton says, although it is not explicitly stated. The method (of adiabatic expansion) was afterwards adapted by Clement and Desormes to the determination of the ratio of specific heats of a gas.[11]

Theory of Mixed Gases

A 'New Theory of the Constitution of Mixed Aeriform Fluids and particularly of the Atmosphere', dated 14 September 1801,[12] is the first published statement of the important theory (based on Newton's theory, as is stated) of

[1] The Propagation of Heat in Fluids, *Phil. Trans.*, 1786, lxxvi, 273; 1792, lxxxii, 48; *Essays*, 1800, ii, 199–386; Chree, *Phil. Mag.*, 1887, xxiv, 1.
[2] *Nicholson's J.*, 1801, iv, 529.   [3] Henry, 1854, 28.
[4] *Trans. Roy. Soc. Edin.*, 1805, v, 379 (read 1804); see p. 722.
[5] *Nicholson's J.*, 1805, x, 93; 1806, xiii, 278; 1806, xiv, 380; B, I, i, 30.
[6] Correspondence of Hope and Dalton, in Roscoe and Harden, 1896, 130–41, 152.
[7] *Traité Élémentaire de Physique*, 1803, i, 181 (q. by Riffault); 2 ed., 1806, i, 256: J. N. Riffault, *Ann. Chim.*, 1805 (An XIII), liii, 272–306 (273), in a tr. of Hope's paper said: 'le travail de M. Lefebvre-Gineau, dont on le trouve le précis dans le traité de physique de Haüy, tome 1, page 181', preceded Hope's 'depuis plusieurs années'.
[8] Meldrum, (4), 10, 18.
[9] *Manchester Mem.*, 1802, v, II, 515; on earlier experiments made about 1775 (with the assistance of Warltire), see Erasmus Darwin, *Phil. Trans.*, 1788, lxxviii, 43.
[10] *Phil. Mag.*, 1845, xxvi, 369–70.
[11] *J. de Phys.*, 1819, lxxxix, 321, 428.   [12] *Nicholson's J.*, 1801, v, 241.

mixed gases, afterwards expanded in Dalton's first essay of 1801 (see below), and in all probability this was arrived at not earlier than August 1801.[1] Dalton gives four hypotheses on the constitution of the atmosphere and adopts one; he points out that Lavoisier's statement:[2] 'our atmosphere is a compound of all the fluids which are susceptible of the vaporous or permanently elastic state, in the usual temperature, and under the common pressure', is incorrect unless the last five words are omitted.

In 1801 Dalton read four essays to the Manchester Philosophical Society which gave him a European reputation and contain results of the greatest importance: he said in a letter to his brother in February 1804[3] that they 'excited the attention of philosophers throughout Europe'. These are: 'Experimental Essays (1) On the Constitution of Mixed Gases (read 2 October); (2) on the Force of Steam or Vapour from Water and other Liquids in different temperatures, both in a Torricellian Vacuum and in Air (read 16 October); (3) on Evaporation (read 30 October); and (4) on the Expansion of Gases by Heat.'[4] Between April 1800 and October 1801, it appears from the titles that Dalton had extended his experimental work on vapour pressures to liquids other than water and had formulated his law of mixed gases; he says[5] that the latter was 'hit upon' in 'the autumn of 1801'.

(1) In the essay 'On the Constitution of Mixed Gases', after giving a summary of the four essays, Dalton says[6] two opinions had been put forward to explain the 'mode of combination' of the 'two distinguishable elastic fluids of different specific gravities' (oxygen and nitrogen) composing the atmosphere. Of these, 'the one supposes that the two fluids are merely mixed together, without any chemical combination; but assigns no reason why they do not separate. . . . The other supposes a true chemical union to exist between the two, and thus obviates the difficulty arising from the consideration of specific gravity.' Two other hypotheses which are rejected are that (i) 'the particles of one elastic fluid may repel those of another with the same force as they repel those of their own kind', and (ii) there are variable repulsive forces between the various kinds of fluids. These, he says, would require that the elastic fluids should separate into layers according to their specific gravity, which does not happen. Dalton[7] states as a 'first law, which is as a mirror in which all the experiments are best viewed', but was '*last* detected', the following proposition:

'When two elastic fluids, denoted by A and B, are mixed together, there is no mutual repulsion amongst their particles; that is, the particles of A do not repel those of B, as they do one another. Consequently, the pressure or whole weight upon any one particle arises solely from those of its own kind.'

This is equivalent to what is now called the Law of Partial Pressures; Dalton later[8] stated it more practically as follows:

[1] Meldrum, (4), 13.   [2] *Traité de Chimie*, 1789, i, 31.   [3] Henry, 1854, 48, 50.
[4] *Manchester Mem.*, 1802, v, II, 535, 550, 574, 595 (the numbering is not in the original); the three dates are given *together* at the head of the first page; *Phil. Mag.*, 1805, xxiii, 351; Meldrum, (4), 11, 19, thinks the fourth essay (undated) was not read in October, as were the others, but the dates of reading of the others are given in the Minute Book of the Society.
[5] B, I, i, 153.   [6] *Manchester Mem.*, 1802, v, II, 538.   [7] *Ib.*, 536.   [8] B, I, i, 191.

'When any two or more mixed gases acquire an equilibrium, the elastic energy of each against the surface of the vessel or of any liquid, is precisely the same as if it were the only gas present occupying the whole space and all the rest were withdrawn.'

In the essay (1) Dalton does not use the word 'atom' but always 'ultimate particle'. At the end[1] he gives a diagram of the structure of the atmosphere in which the particles of oxygenous gas are shown as small diamonds, those of azotic gas by dots, those of carbonic acid by black triangles, and those of aqueous vapour by asterisks. There is every probability that the statement about the two gases A and B given above was a development of Newton's demonstration, with its mutually repulsive particles,[2] which Dalton mentions five times.

Newton says that if the particles of an elastic fluid repel one another so that the density is proportional to the pressure (Boyle's law) the centrifugal forces of the particles are inversely proportional to the distances between their centres (Si Fluidi ex particulis se mutuo fugientibus compositi densitas sit ut compressio, vires centrifugæ particularum sunt reciproce proportionales distantiis centrorum suorum), and vice versa, adding cautiously that the question whether the particles of an elastic fluid behave like this is a physical, not a mathematical one. Bryan Higgins, it will be remembered, had made use of Newton's idea.

That Dalton began to study Newton only in 1801[3] is doubtful; he probably read the *Principia* with Gough at Kendal,[4] and perhaps when he was contributing mathematical articles to the *Ladies' Diary* in the period 1784–94.[5]

Beside the influence of Newton, that of Lavoisier was strong: much of the first volume of Dalton's *New System* is taken up with the properties of the imaginary caloric or the matter of heat, the assumption of the existence of which, and the view that the gaseous state was a combination of the material principle with caloric, he took over unchanged from Lavoisier. In surrounding the atoms with self-repelling atmospheres of caloric, Dalton combined the views of Newton and Lavoisier and provided a plausible hypothesis of the cause of the supposed repulsion of gaseous particles which Newton had postulated but never explained. Dalton then[6] pictured a gaseous particle as 'constituted of an exceedingly small central atom of solid matter, which is surrounded by an atmosphere of heat, of great density next the atom, and gradually growing rarer according to some power of the distance'.

Dalton in 1801[7] says Newton had demonstrated 'for homogeneous [elastic] fluids only' that the particles 'repel one another with a force decreasing directly as the distance of their centres from each other',[8] and that 'it follows too that the distances of the centres of the particles, or which is the same thing, the diameters of the sphere of influence of each particle, are inversely as the cube root of the density of the fluid'. In Newton's time only one elastic fluid, common air, was known, and since it was supposed to be an element, it was 'homogeneous', i.e. its particles were all of the same kind. For an atmosphere composed of different kinds of particles, as the atmospheric air in Dalton's time was known to be, Newton's demonstration failed.

[1] *Ib.*, 602.   [2] *Principia*, book ii, prop. 23, theorem 18; London, 1687, 301; see Vol. II.
[3] Meldrum, (4), 13.   [4] Cf. Dalton, *Nicholson's J.*, 1804, ix, 274.
[5] Henry, 1854, 6 f.   [6] B, I, i, 147.   [7] Essay (1), 540.
[8] Newton's statement of his result is actually much more cautious; see above.

In his lectures in London in 1810 Dalton explained[1] how he 'set to work to combine the atoms on paper' so as to represent the composition of the atmosphere. He found there were not enough 'atoms' of water to form groups of three particles with oxygen and azote. He then tried combining the oxygen and azote in pairs, but the oxygen failed; 'I then threw all the remaining particles of azote into the mixture, and began to consider how the general equilibrium was to be obtained.' The triple particles of water, oxygen and azote would sink to the bottom, the double particles of oxygen and azote would take the middle station, and the azote would float, on account of the different weights. 'I remedied this defect by lengthening the wings of my heavy particles, that is, by throwing more heat around them', but this made the whole specific gravity equal to that of azote.

'In short, I was obliged to abandon the hypothesis of the chemical constitution of the atmosphere altogether, as irreconcilable to the phenomena. There was but one alternative left, namely, to surround every individual particle of *water*, of *oxygen*, and of *azote*, with heat, and to make them respective centres of repulsion, the same in a *mixed* state as in a *simple* state.'

This introduced the difficulty of stratification, so in 1801 he:

'hit upon an hypothesis which completely obviated these difficulties. According to this, we were to suppose that the atoms of one kind did *not* repel the atoms of another kind, but only those of their own kind.'

In making up his diagrams of the atoms in the atmosphere Dalton probably assumed that the numbers of particles of oxygen, azote, carbonic acid and aqueous vapour were proportional to their partial pressures, since he had then no other means of finding these numbers.

(2) The second essay, 'On the Force of Steam', describes measurements of the vapour pressure of water from 32° to 212° F. (see p. 308), and *calculated* values for other temperatures, given in a long table, and describes a dew-point hygrometer (see p. 763). Dalton says the water vapour in the atmosphere behaves like any other gas in a mixture of gases, and he showed that the maximum pressure of water vapour is the same in air as in a vacuum. He thought he had established the result that:

'the force of steam from all liquids is the same, at equal temperatures above or below the several temperatures at which they boil in the open air. . . . Thus, the force of *aqueous* vapour of 212° is equal to 30 inches of mercury; at 30° below, or 182°, it is of half that force; and at 40° above, or 252°, it is of double that force; so likewise the vapour from sulphuric ether which boils at 102°, then supporting 30 inches of mercury, at 30° below that temperature it has half the force, and at 40° above it, double the force: and so in other liquids.'[2]

Air in which water vapour has not the maximum pressure can be cooled till the maximum is reached, and then, on further cooling, it deposits dew. This work laid the foundations of scientific meteorology and raised hygrometry to 'the rank of an exact science'.[3] Dalton says:[4]

[1] Roscoe and Harden, 1896, 14 f.   [2] *Ib.*, 536–7, see table on p. 559.
[3] Henry, 1854, 226.   [4] *Ib.*, 550; this had been said by Lavoisier, see p. 426.

'There can scarcely be a doubt entertained respecting the reducibility of all elastic fluids of whatever kinds into liquids; and we ought not to despair of effecting it in low temperatures and by strong pressure exerted upon the unmixed gases.'

Dalton calculated vapour pressures for temperatures above the boiling point by a rule which T. Young[1] showed was theoretically unsound, and these values were widely different from those found experimentally by Ure.[2] Experiments on vapour pressure and boiling were also made by Volta (1784–95);[3] those of Cavendish (see p. 308) were not published.

Dalton later admitted[4] that his rule, and also another proposed in 1808,[5] that the vapour pressure increases in geometrical progression as the temperature increases in arithmetical progression, which is equivalent to the formula: $\log p = AT + B$, where T is the absolute temperature and A and B are constants, were erroneous. His experimental results, although generally confirmed by Ure,[6] were much later shown by Regnault[7] to be lacking in precision. Dalton says that Lavoisier's 'notion of pressure preventing the evaporation of liquids, which seems to have been taken as an axiom by modern philosophers, has been the cause of more error and perplexity perhaps than any other ungrounded opinion'.[8]

Dalton[9] gives the formula for the volume of a moist gas; 1 vol. of gas at a given temperature and under a pressure p becomes $1 + f/(p - f)$, or $p/(p - f)$, when saturated with water vapour of pressure f:

'In short, in all cases the vapour arises to a certain force according to temperature, and the air adjusts the equilibrium by expanding and contracting as may be required.... The notion of a chemical affinity subsisting between the gases and vapours of different kinds cannot at all be reconciled to these phenomena, ... we must on this ground suppose that all the gases have the same force of affinity for any given vapour; a supposition that cannot be admitted as having any analogy to other established laws of chemical affinity.'

(3) In the essay 'On Evaporation' Dalton showed that the quantity of water evaporating in a given time is proportional to the vapour pressure.

Expansion of Gases by Heat

(4) In experiments described in the essay 'On the Expansion of Gases by Heat' Dalton used a straight tube sealed at one end, containing *dry* air confined by a pellet of mercury.[10] He says:[11]

'I have repeatedly found that 1000 parts of common air of the temperature of 55° [F.] and common pressure, expand to 1321 parts in the manometer; to which adding 4 parts for the corresponding expansion of glass, we have 325 parts increase upon 1000 from 55° to 212° or for 157° of the thermometric scale.'

[1] *Lectures on Natural Philosophy*, 1807, ii, 398.   [2] *Phil. Trans.*, 1818, cviii, 338.
[3] *Opere*, Milan, 1929, vii, 83, 141, 393 f.: 'law of vapour pressures.'
[4] *Manchester Mem.*, 1819, iii, 446 (470); B, II, 298–304.
[5] B, I, i, 13–14, 19, 218 (plate 2).
[6] *Phil. Trans.*, 1818, cviii, 338 (dated Glasgow, July 1817); Ure showed that Dalton's theory was faulty.
[7] *Ann. Chim.*, 1844, xi, 273; AdS, 1847, xxi, m 465; 1862, xxvi, m 339; Taylor's *Scientific Memoirs*, 1846, iv, 559.
[8] *Manchester Mem.*, 1802, v, II, 535 (548–9).
[9] *Ib.*, 572–4.   [10] *Ib.*, 595 f.   [11] *Ib.*, 598.

He found that 1000 of air at 55° expanded by 167 at 132½° and only by 158 between 132½° and 210°, whereas Dalton thought it should have expanded more, not less, at the higher temperature.

'The results of several experiments made upon hydrogenous gas, oxygenous gas, carbonic acid gas and nitrous gas, which were all the kinds I tried, agreed with those on common air not only in the total expansion, but in the gradual diminution of it in ascending: the small differences never exceeded 6 or 8 parts on the whole 325; and differences to this amount will take place in common air, when not freed from aqueous vapour, which was the situation of all my factitious gases.

'Upon the whole therefore I see no sufficient reason why we may not conclude, that *all elastic fluids under the same pressure expand equally by heat* — and that *for any given expansion of mercury, the corresponding expansion of air is proportionally something less, the higher the temperature*' (italics in original).

Thomson[1] says it is to Dalton that 'the honour of the discovery of the law of the dilatation of gaseous bodies is due: for Mr. Gay-Lussac did not publish his dissertation on the expansion of the gases till more than six months after'.[2] Thomson says:

'from the experiments of Gay-Lussac we learn, that air, by being heated from 32° to 212°, expands from 100 to 137·5 parts: the increase of bulk for 180° is then 37·5 parts; or, supposing the bulk at 32° to be unity, the increase is equal to 0·375 parts: this gives us 0·00208, or $\frac{1}{480}$th part, for the expansion of air for 1° of the thermometer. Mr. Dalton found that 100 parts of air, by being heated from 55° to 212°, expanded to 132·5 parts: this gives us an expansion of 0·00207, or $\frac{1}{483}$th part, for 1°, which differs as little from the determination of Lussac as can be expected in experiments of such delicacy.'

Thomson has divided the increase in volume from 55° to 212°, i.e., 32·5, by the rise in temperature, 157°, whereas to make the result comparable with Gay-Lussac's the initial volume should be at 32° F. Assuming that the expansion is uniform, Dalton's result shows that 100 volumes *measured at 32° F.* become 139·1 volumes at 212°, and his value for the coefficient of expansion is 0·00391 per 1° C. as compared with Gay-Lussac's 0·00375, and is considerably less accurate, the correct value being 0·00366.

Joule[3] pointed out that in 1801 Dalton says the volume at 55° F. is 1000 and at 212° F. is 1325, whilst in 1808[4] Dalton says: 'The volume at 32° is taken as 1000 and at 212°, 1376 according to Gay-Lussac's and my own experiments.' He says that in 1801: 'I had not then an opportunity of having air at 32°. By more recent experiments I am convinced that dry air of 32° will expand the same quantity from that to 117° or 118° of the common scale, as from the last term to 212°.' Joule says 'The experiments which Dalton states to agree with Gay-Lussac's are clearly some unpublished ones made subsequently [to 1801]'.

Dalton and Gay-Lussac share the honour for the *publication* of the law of equal expansion of different gases by heat, but this law for oxygen, nitrogen, hydrogen, and carbon dioxide was discovered about 1787 by Jacques Alex-

[1] (2), 1817, i, 65.
[2] Gay-Lussac, *Ann. Chim.*, 1802, xliii, 137 f. (Recherches . . . lues à l'Institut national le 11 pluviôse, an 10); Cuvier, *Rapport*, (2), 1828, 40; *Histoire*, (3), 1837, i, 19; mentions Dalton and Gay-Lussac in this order as having found the expansion equal all for gases.
[3] *Manchester Mem.*, 1860, xv, 143 (read 1858); *Scientific Papers*, 1884, i, 384; cf. H. B. Dixon, *Manchester Proc.*, 1891, iv, 36.
[4] B, I, i, 19.

andre César Charles (Beaugency, 12 November 1746–Paris, 7 April 1823), professor of physics in the Conservatoire des Arts et Métiers, Paris.[1] His results were not published but communicated verbally to Gay-Lussac.[2] Other experimenters had found the expansions to be very different.[3] According to Dalton[4] these 'arose from the want of due care to keep the apparatus and materials free from moisture'. Both Dalton's and Gay-Lussac's apparatus was probably moist, although they attempted to dry the glass.[5] Desormes and Clement,[6] before Gay-Lussac's publication, determined the expansion of carbon monoxide by heating it in a graduated tube inverted over mercury and surrounded by a water-jacket, and found it the same as that of air from 15° C. to 51° C., but the coefficient of expansion found was much too large (0·0058).

Volta[7] was the first to *publish* the law of expansion for *air*; he found the coefficient 0·003662. Guillaume Amontons[8] found in 1699 that the *pressure* of air at constant volume increases by one-third when heated from room temperature to that of boiling water; in 1702 he confirmed this, and inferred from Mariotte's (Boyle's) law that at constant pressure the volume would increase by the same amount; he then used his apparatus as 'une nouvelle thermomètre'. Air under 28 in. pressure increased in pressure by 9 in. 4 lines, that under 28 × 2 in. pressure by 18 in. 9 lines, which is $\frac{1}{3}$ of 56. He says that: 'masses inégales d'air chargées de poids égaux augmentoient également la force de leur ressort par des degrez de chaleur égaux' (he distinguished between degrees of heat and temperature). Lambert,[9] who drew attention to the work of Amontons, calculated the absolute zero as −293·5° C. from his results. Lambert himself calculated −274° C.[10]

Neither Amontons nor Volta discovered the law of Charles, Dalton, and Gay-Lussac, the essence of which is that *all gases* expand in the same way on heating; the first two obtained a good result for *air* only, but Charles, Dalton, and Gay-Lussac found practically the same coefficient for *all* the gases they used. Guareschi's suggestion that the law should be called 'Volta's law' is, therefore, unacceptable.

Dalton[11] says the equal expansion of gases by heat 'plainly shews that the expansion depends *solely* upon heat', the unequal expansions of liquids and solids being due to a variable attractive force of chemical affinity between their

[1] Poggendorff, (1), i, 421; Fourier, AdS, 1829, VIII, h lxxiij–lxxxvij.
[2] *Ann. Chim.*, 1802, xliii, 157: le cit. Charles avait remarqué depuis 15 ans la même propriété de ces gaz.
[3] De Morveau, *Ency. Méthod., Chymie*, 1788, i, 677 f.
[4] *Manchester Mem.*, 1802, v, II, 596.
[5] Ostwald's *Klassiker*, 1894, xliv; Balfour Stewart, *Elementary Treatise on Heat*, 5 ed., Oxford, 1888, 63; James, *Sci. Progr.*, 1929–30, xxiv, 57.
[6] *Ann. Chim.*, 1801, xxxviii, 26 (56).
[7] *Annali di Chimica*, 1793, iv, 227; *Opere*, 1816, iii, 329; *Opere*, 1929, vii, 345, 437 f. (for a letter on it of 1791, *ib.*, 321): Memoria sulla uniforme dilatazione Dell' Aria per ogni grade di calore, cominciando sotto la temperture del ghiacco fin sopra quella dell' ebolizione dell' acque; Guareschi, *A. Nat.*, 1914–15, v, 142–54, 209–25; Guye, *J. Chim. Phys.*, 1917, xv, 471; Aumerio, *Nuov. Cim.*, 1928, v, 39.
[8] AdS, 1699, h 103, m 114; 1702 (1704), h 1, m 155; 1703 (1704), h 6, m 50.
[9] *Pyrometrie, oder vom Maasse des Feuers und der Wärme*, Berlin, 1779, 29, 40, 74.
[10] Gerland, in Diergart, 1909, 357, who does not mention Dalton; Partington, (6), 1949, i, 592.
[11] *Op. cit.*, 600.

particles. If 'the repulsive force of each particle is exactly proportional to the whole quantity of heat combined with it', reckoned from an absolute zero, then since 'the diameter of each particle's sphere of influence is as the cube root of the space occupied by the mass we shall have $\sqrt[3]{1000} : \sqrt[3]{1325}$ (10 : 11, nearly) :: the absolute quantity of heat in air of 55°: the absolute quantity in air of 212°. This gives the point of total privation of heat, or absolute cold, at 1547° below the point at which water freezes', whilst Crawford had deduced 1532°. (The loss of heat from 212° to 55° (157°) is $\frac{1}{11}$; hence a loss of $\frac{11}{11}$, or all the heat, requires a cooling of $11 \times 157° = 1727°$ from 212°, or $(1727 - 212) + 32° = 1547°$ below 32° F.)

Dalton later[1] devoted much attention to 'the natural zero of temperature, or absolute privation of heat', which had occupied Crawford, and Lavoisier and Laplace (see p. 429). He gives nine methods of finding it; the fusion of ice, mixing sulphuric acid and water, slaking lime, the action of nitric acid on lime, and the combustion of hydrogen, phosphorus, charcoal, oil, etc., and ether. The results varied from 4150° to 11,000° below 32° F., the mean being 6150°.

Dalton[2] also supposed, as a result of experiments, that all pure homogeneous liquids expand from their point of congelation or greatest density as the square of the temperature from that point, but this required a new scale of temperature T differing from the Fahrenheit mercury scale F except at 32° F., 212° F. and − 40° F. (taken as the f.p. of mercury):

$$T = \left\{ \frac{\sqrt{(F + 40)} - \sqrt{72}}{\sqrt{252} - \sqrt{72}} \times 180 \right\} + 32.$$

Dalton[3] thought that the vapour pressure of a pure liquid increases in geometrical progression as the temperature increases in arithmetical progression, that the expansion of permanent elastic fluids is in geometrical progression to equal increments of temperature, and that the law of cooling of bodies is that the temperature descends in geometrical progression in equal intervals of time.[4] Dulong and Petit[5] disproved all these hypotheses, and Dalton later[6] admitted that the difference between the air and mercury scales was less than he had supposed, and that he had not taken into account the expansion of the glass of the thermometer.

Diffusion of Gases

Priestley[7] found that mixtures of gases of very different densities, such as air and carbon dioxide and air and hydrogen, do not separate on standing, but he thought that: 'if two kinds of air, of very different specific gravities, were put into the same vessel, with very great care, without the least agitation that might mix or blend them together, they might continue separate ... but when once they have mixed, they will continue to be so.'

On 28 January 1803 Dalton read his memoir 'On the tendency of Elastic

[1] B, I, i, 56 f., 82–97.
[2] B, I, i, 7 f., 13, 29, 43, 107; Gee, Coward, and Harden, 1914–15, 25 f.
[3] B, I, i, 13.
[4] B, I, i, 13.   [5] *Ann. Chim.*, 1818, vii, 113, 225, 337.
[6] B, II, 288 f.   [7] E & O, 1777, iii, 301; 1790, ii, 441.

Fluids to Diffusion through each other'[1] in which he describes experiments on gaseous diffusion with very simple apparatus. The two gases were contained in two phials separated by a narrow vertical tube, the lighter gas being in the upper phial. On standing, the gases mixed uniformly, thus establishing 'the remarkable fact, that a lighter elastic fluid cannot rest upon a heavier'. Dalton concluded that:

'The facts, stated above, taken together, appear to me to form as decisive evidence for that theory of elastic fluids which I maintain, and *against* the one commonly received, as any physical principle which has ever been deemed a subject of dispute, can adduce.'

The experiments were repeated and confirmed by Berthollet,[2] who found that hydrogen diffuses fastest. In 1834[3] Dalton said:

'It has been long known, that if a tall jar, of two or more inches   FIG. 64. DALTON'S in diameter, be filled with a *heavy* elastic fluid, and held with its   GASEOUS DIFFUSION mouth *downward*, it will be emptied in a moment or two, and   EXPERIMENT. at the same time filled with common air; but if placed with its mouth *upward*, it will remain for a considerable time in the jar, and be *gradually* diluted with common air, till at length it becomes filled with the same; and vice versâ, if filled with a *light* elastic fluid. But it was not known, I believe, until I published my Chemistry in 1810,[4] that if a vessel of any shape be filled with either light or heavy gas, and it be made to communicate with the atmosphere by a tube of one tenth of an inch diameter, it matters little whether the tube be held up or down, as regards the time of exit of the gas. It will be slow and gradual, in both positions.'

Criticisms of Dalton's Theory of Mixed Gases

To avoid disturbing the summaries of Dalton's early papers some reactions of other chemists to them have been omitted. These will now be taken up.

William Henry at first opposed Dalton's theory of mixed gases, but when he discovered the law of solubility of gases that, at a given temperature, 'water takes up the same volume of condensed gas as of gas under ordinary pressure',[5] Dalton was able to point out to him (and Henry agreed) that this is a strong argument in favour of the view that solution is 'purely a mechanical effect'; if the dissolved gas is retained wholly by the incumbent pressure, there is no need to bring in chemical affinity.[6] Henry (in reply to Gough) also found that from a mixture of gases 'each gas when dissolved in water, is retained in its place by an atmosphere of no other gas but its own kind',[7] which is in excellent agreement with Dalton's law of partial pressures, and Dalton's 'theory' is not merely a 'hypothesis'. A letter from Henry to Dalton, read to the Manchester Philosophical Society on 20 June 1804,[8] says that

'the doctrine of mixed gases was opposed by every member interested in such subjects, and by no one more strenuously than myself. I am now satisfied that . . . your theory is better adapted than any former one, for explaining the relation of mixed gases to each

[1] *Manchester Mem.*, 1805, i, 259; *Phil. Mag.*, 1806, xxiv, 8; B, 1808, I, i, 151; 1810, I, ii, 230–1; A (2), 1834, 212.
[2] *Mém. Soc. Arcueil*, 1809, ii, 463.   [3] A (2), 212.
[4] B, I, ii, 230–1.   [5] *Phil. Trans.*, 1803, xciii, 29 (41).
[6] Henry, *Phil. Trans.*, 1803, xciii, 274; Dalton, B, I, i, 202.
[7] *Nicholson's J.*, 1804, ix, 126 (13 September 1804).   [8] *Nicholson's J.*, 1804, viii, 297.

other, and especially the connection between gases and water. *All* gases equally *completely* displace carbonic acid dissolved in water; hence there can be no question of different affinities of various gases for water, and solution is "a purely mechanical effect".'

Henry then expressed Dalton's law of partial pressures in the concise form: 'every gas is a vacuum to every other gas.'

The most serious objection to Dalton's theory of mixed gases was the view that atmospheric air is a compound, not a mixture, of nitrogen and oxygen. This was held by F. Humboldt,[1] Morozzo,[2] and at first by Davy,[3] who later changed his opinion[4] although he was not satisfied with Dalton's theory of mixed gases. The compound theory was also held by Thomas Thomson,[5] Berthollet,[6] who said Dalton's diagram of mixed gases was 'un tableau d'imagination',[7] Bostock,[8] Murray,[9] and Gough.[10]

Murray[11] says Dalton is mistaken in supposing that if chemical attraction is exerted between particles it must always cause their intimate combination with the production of a new substance. The attraction may still be exerted although the elasticity of the gases may prevent the production of a different substance:

'the attraction is not exerted merely when it is effective, but before this . . . its being effective is owing rather to the powers acting against it being overcome . . . *and . . . between mixed gases, which are capable, under any circumstances, of combining, an attraction must always be exerted.*'

This is the point of view of Berthollet,[12] who had distinguished between the 'dissolution' and the 'combinaison' of the gases; and, says Murray, there are 'numerous shades of combination'.

In the atmosphere the attraction between the nitrogen and oxygen may 'be sufficient to counteract the slight difference in their specific gravities, and prevent them from separating from each other'. Dalton's assumption that 'mixed gases neither attract nor repel each other' is *ad hoc* and not made probable by any reasoning; the caloric atmospheres on *different* particles should also repel one another. 'If oxygen and nitrogen can exert a mutual attraction at a red heat . . . they may exert the same attraction at lower temperatures with diminished force.' Murray thought that the same reasoning as showed that oxygen, nitrogen and even carbonic acid are combined by weak chemical forces in the atmosphere could be applied to the watery vapour. Water, which evaporates in a vacuum, would perhaps not evaporate under the pressure of the atmosphere unless aided by chemical attraction.

Dalton's hypothesis that atmospheric gases do not repel one another is 'contradictory to the soundest principles of chemistry' (!), and his theory of

[1] *Ann. Chim.*, An VI (1797–8), xxvii, 141.
[2] *J. de Phys.*, 1798, xlvii, 203; Humboldt, *ib.*, 205.
[3] *Researches . . . concerning Nitrous Oxide*, 1800, 279 f., 286, 326 f.
[4] Lecture 'on the chemical composition of the atmosphere', 1807; in *Works*, 1840, viii, 252 f.
[5] (2), 1802, iii, 270–1, etc.; see p. 776.   [6] *Statique Chimique*, 1803, i, 274, 485 f., 502 f.
[7] *Ib.*, 499.   [8] *An Essay on Respiration*, Liverpool, 1804, 219.
[9] 1806, i, 94; ii, 49, Notes, 3; *Elements of Chemistry*, 6 ed., Edinburgh, 1828, i, 418 f.
[10] *Phil. Mag.*, 1806, xxiv, 103.   [11] 1806, ii, Notes, 3.   [12] 1803, i, 277.

the effect of pressure on boiling point is defective. The objection that equal volumes of different gases (presumably having different affinities) take up the same amount of moisture, even in a vacuum, had been derived from vapour pressure measurements, and Gough (see p. 756) had objected that these *assume* that the aqueous vapour is uncombined. Clement and Desormes[1] had determined the amount of moisture by absorption with calcium chloride and found it the same (0·3 gm. per cu. ft.) in five cases; but in their experiments, says Murray, not all the water was removed and the amount remaining may be different in the different gases; in any case, the differences need only be small. The different quantities of gases absorbed by liquid water show that the affinities are different.

The positive arguments for the theory of combination are, says Murray: (1) the generality of the action of chemical affinity; (2) water absorbs gases and the attraction must be mutual (Henry's law does not necessarily prove that the solution is mechanical, since the pressure serves to overcome the elasticity of the gas); (3) some gases (muriatic and fluoric acids, and ammonia) have an undoubted affinity for water; carbonic acid may have, and hence the probability can be extended to nitrous gas, oxygen gas, etc., the solubilities of the very soluble gases being also increased by pressure, 'and, I have no doubt, according to the same law'; (4) the solubilities of sparingly soluble gases are different at the same pressure, and oxygen is preferentially absorbed from air; (5) one gas tends to separate another from solution; (6) ice below the melting point is dissolved by air (as Boyle showed), though the temperature is not high enough to form vapour; (7) water of crystallisation of salts, bound by chemical affinity, is lost to air and must have been separated by a superior chemical power. Dalton replied to Murray in 1808.[2]

A very persistent critic of Dalton's theory of mixed gases was his old friend Gough, to whose numerous papers[3] replies were made by Dalton[4] and by W. Henry.[5] Dalton sent some of his early papers to Gough for criticism, but as this was uniformly unfavourable, he wisely discontinued the practice. One of Gough's objections was that if oxygen and nitrogen exist uncombined in the atmosphere and do not act upon one another, each should transmit a sound wave separately, with its own velocity, and hence at a sufficient distance two successive sounds should be heard from the same source:[6]

'If then our atmosphere consisted of two independent masses of these fluids mutually pervading each other, every momentary report would have been double to sense, at a sufficient distance from the seat of sound; because such a report would arrive at the ear more expeditiously through the medium of the azote, than it would through that of the oxigen.'

[1] *Ann. Chim.*, 1802, xlii, 121 f.; *Phil. Mag.*, 1802, xiii, 67, 155; Berthollet, *ib.*, 1802, xiii, 276.
[2] B, I, i, 176 f.
[3] *Manchester Mem.*, 1805, i, 296 (read November 1803), 405 (read January 1804); *Nicholson's J.*, 1804, viii, 243 (written 16 July); 1804, ix, 52 (written 23 August), 107, 160; 1805, x, 20; 1809, xxiii, 182.
[4] *Nicholson's J.*, 1804, ix, 89 (written 8 September), 269; *Manchester Mem.*, 1805, i, 425 (October 1805); *Phil. Trans.*, 1826, cxvi, II, 174; 1837, cxxvii, 347.
[5] *Nicholson's J.*, 1804, ix, 126 (13 September).
[6] *Nicholson's J.*, 1804, viii, 246; 1804, ix, 107.

Dalton thought this objection was serious and he quoted[1] some old experiments of Derham[2] in which a double report from a cannon was heard at a distance (which Derham correctly explained as due to echo). Another objection was that light would be scattered by refraction in the heterogeneous atmosphere and would not reach the earth. Gough regarded Dalton's theory of mixed gases not as a 'theory' but as a 'hypothesis', and said it should have been worked out mathematically.[3] Gough's own theory was that the gases break up into 'parcels' which then blend together by agitation.

Dalton[4] thought 'geometry has nothing to do with the business' and mentions his experiment of the mixing of two gases in phials connected by a narrow tube (see p. 773). Gough[5] tried to show (from inaccurate data) that the density of a mixture of oxygen and nitrogen is different from that of air (although, curiously, the calculated density was *greater* than that of air), and concluded that air is 'a gaseous oxide of azote'. Dalton[6] pointed out that the densities of gases used in Gough's calculations were inaccurate. Gough had complained[7] that Dalton had ridiculed him, and had failed to give a mathematical demonstration of his theory. He[8] repeated his specific gravity calculations, and also[9] brought forward some crude experiments on water vapour in air.

The mathematical demonstration which Gough asked for was later given[10] by Dalton's pupil Peter Ewart (Troquaire Manse, Dumfriesshire, 14 May 1767–Woolwich, 15 September 1842), a civil engineer, later owner of a cotton-mill in Manchester, and finally Inspector of the Royal Dockyards, Woolwich.

Thomas Thomson in his influential text-book[11] expressed the opinion that:

'Even Mr. Dalton's ingenious supposition, that they neither attract nor repel each other, would not account for this equal distribution [of the two gases in the atmosphere]: for undoubtedly, on that supposition, they would arrange themselves according to their specific gravity. . . . We must therefore consider air as a chemical compound.'

Dalton replied,[12] stating his theory more fully so as to meet this objection and quoting Newton again. There is no physical objection to the supposition that the particles of a gas should repel particles of that gas and not particles of other gases; like poles of magnets repel one another but the presence of other (non-magnetic) bodies would offer a mere mechanical resistance to them. The gases need not separate any more than shot and sand filling its interstices, and into 'the vacuity of one gas' we can throw another gas.

In the second edition of his book[13] Thomson brings forward four arguments for regarding air as a chemical compound: (i) its composition is constant, (ii) a mixture of oxygen and nitrogen is more diminished by nitric oxide than is air, (iii) different combustible bodies absorb different amounts of oxygen from air, corresponding with their affinities for oxygen, e.g. phosphorus 22 per cent,

[1] B, I, i, 185.   [2] *Phil. Trans.*, 1708, xxvi, 2, no. 313.
[3] *Nicholson's J.*, 1804, ix, 52.   [4] *Nicholson's J.*, 1804, ix, 89 (written 8 September 1804).
[5] *Ib.*, 1804, ix, 107 (written 5 September).   [6] *Ib.*, 1804, ix, 269 (written 15 November).
[7] *Ib.*, 1804, ix, 160 (written 16 October).
[8] *Ib.*, 1805, x, 20 (written 13 December 1804).
[9] *Ib.*, 1809, xxiii, 182 (written 22 May).   [10] *Ann. Phil.*, 1815, vi, 376.
[11] (2), 1802, iii, 270–1; repeated in *ib.*, 1807, iii, 441–50.
[12] *Nicholson's J.*, 1802, iii, 267 (written 18 November).   [13] (2), 1804, iii, 316 f.

sulphur 8 per cent, and gold none, (iv) a gas corresponding in composition with air is formed on the decomposition of nitrous oxide by electric sparks, and in one stage of the preparation of nitric acid from saltpetre and sulphuric acid.[1]

To these arguments Dalton replied as follows:[2] (i) this agrees with either theory, (ii) is incorrect, (iii) is due to the dilution of the oxygen, and iron would probably burn in air under 5 atm. pressure, (iv) the composition is variable, Priestley found more, and Davy less oxygen in the gas than in air, and it is a mixture.

In 1807[3] Thomson proposed some objections to Dalton's 'very ingenious hypothesis' of mixed gases: (i) one gas ought to rush into the space occupied by other gases almost as fast as into a vacuum, (ii) if particles of hydrogen and oxygen do not repel each other in a mixture, why do they not unite on contact, and similarly hydrogen and nitrogen?, (iii) two gases stratified mix only slowly, and it seems as if they are mutually elastic. We must thus conclude:

'however problematical it may appear at first view, that the gases not only mutually repel each other, but likewise mutually attract, and that all gases, as Berthollet states it, have the property of *dissolving* the other elastic fluids. . . . Thus, notwithstanding the ingenuity of Mr. Dalton's hypothesis, and the elegant way in which it explains most of the facts, there are several circumstances which render it hazardous for us to adopt it.'

Even in 1817,[4] for Thomson, air was still 'a compound of oxygen and azotic gas', and in 1825 Laplace[5] said that Dalton's supposition that 'l'action répulsive réciproque de deux gaz différens' is 'bien peu naturelle: elle est d'ailleurs contraire à plusieurs phénomènes' — which he does not specify.

Dalton had to press his correct opinions in the face of very formidable opposition from most of the leading scientists and from the text-book writers of the time, and this chorus of disapproval might well have overawed a less determined and original man. Only Henry was, at first, in favour of Dalton's views; nearly everybody else was against them, but Davy in 1802 was impressed by them, saying in a letter to Davis Giddy that in his papers Dalton 'appears to me to have executed them in a very masterly way'.[6] It has been said[7] of the ideas on mixed gases, 'unless we knew that they were first published by Dalton and were initially received with incredulity, we might think [they] are self-evident.'

Dalton's experiments on gaseous diffusion (p. 773) did not seem to have the force which we now attribute to them, even when the quantitative law was established by Graham.[8] Graham[9] objected that cold should be produced by the expansion and that the mixing of different gases by diffusion occurs at different rates: 'Something more, therefore, must be assumed than that gases are vacua to each other, in order to explain the whole phenomena observed in diffusion.' T. S. Thomson[10] attempted to reconcile Dalton's theory of mixed

[1] Davy, *Researches . . . concerning Nitrous Oxide*, 1800, 279 f., 327.
[2] *Nicholson's J.*, 1804, viii, 145.   [3] (2), 1807, iii, 440 f.; *Ann. Phil.*, 1814, iv, 5.
[4] (2), 1817, iii, 174.   [5] *Traité de Mécanique Céleste*, 1825, v, 109–10.
[6] Paris, *Life of Sir H. Davy*, 1831, i, 157.   [7] Partington, *Nature*, 1959, clxxiii, 1765.
[8] *Quart. J. Sci.*, 1829, xxviii, 74; *Phil. Mag.*, 1833, ii, 175, 269, 351.
[9] *Elements of Chemistry*, 1842, 70 f.; 2 ed., 1850, i, 88–9.
[10] *Phil. Mag.*, 1844, xxv, 51 (11 June).

gases with Graham's law of diffusion. He regarded the structure of a system of two gases as $\begin{smallmatrix} A\,B \\ A\,B \end{smallmatrix}$ before diffusion and as $\begin{smallmatrix} A\,B \\ B\,A \end{smallmatrix}$ after diffusion, and considered the supposed forces between the particles.

The whole subject of mixed gases could not be properly understood until the statical theory of repulsions introduced by Newton and adopted by Dalton had been abandoned, and a gas regarded as composed of particles *in motion*, exerting practically no forces on one another. This was a suggestion proposed by Descartes and mentioned by Boyle (Vol. II, p. 523); a formal demonstration of the production of gaseous pressure by molecular bombardment was given by Daniel Bernoulli in 1738.[1] The kinetic theory was definitely proved to be necessary as a result of some experiments of Dalton's pupil, James Prescott Joule (1818–89),[2] which showed that: 'no change of temperature occurs when air is allowed to expand in such a manner as not to develop mechanical power.'[3] This removed the first of Graham's objections.

Dalton[4] speaks of: 'interstitial heat amongst the small globular molecules of air, . . . [which] scarcely can be said to belong to them, because it is equally found in a vacuum or space devoid of air, as is proved by the increase of temperature upon admitting air into a vacuum', i.e. his experiments of 1800.[5] A diagram which he made to illustrate this[6] shows the heat in small particles, i.e. as atomic in structure, as Black had also assumed (p. 154).

The Structure of Gases

The point of departure of Dalton's theory of mixed gases, which led ultimately to his atomic theory, was his attempt to adapt Newton's theory, in which air was regarded as an element, to air as a mixture of gases. In his 1810 lectures at the Royal Institution, Dalton said:[7]

'Newton had demonstrated clearly . . . that an elastic fluid is constituted of small particles or atoms of matter, which repel each other by a force increasing in proportion as their distance diminishes. But modern discoveries having ascertained that the atmosphere contains three or more elastic fluids of different specific gravities, it did not appear to me how this proposition of Newton would apply to a case of which he, of course, could have no idea.'

Meldrum[8] pointed out that Dalton entertained two different hypotheses to explain gaseous diffusion. The first, formulated (p. 780) between April 1800 and September 1801, made no reference to the *size* of particles. In the notes for Dalton's lectures at the Royal Institution in 1810, he says[9] he arrived in 1801 at a hypothesis explaining why mixed gases did not stratify in layers on standing, viz. that 'the atoms of one kind did *not* repel the atoms of another kind, but only those of their own kind'. On reconsidering the subject he realised that he had not 'contemplated the *difference of size* in the particles of

[1] *Hydrodynamica*, Strasbourg, 1738, 200, Fig. 56; Guareschi, *Atti R. Accad. Torino*, 1910, xlv, 641; see Vol. II, p. 477.
[2] *Phil. Mag.*, 1845, xxvi, 369; Joule, *Scientific Papers*, 2 vols., 1884–7, i, 172.
[3] *Phil. Mag.*, 1845, xxvi, 377; see Gay-Lussac, Vol. IV.   [4] B, 1808, I, i, 73.
[5] *Manchester Mem.*, 1802, v, II, 515; see p. 765.
[6] Gee, Coward and Harden, 1914–15, plate VIII.   [7] Roscoe and Harden, 1896, 13.
[8] (4), 13 f.   [9] Roscoe and Harden, 1896, 15.

elastic fluids. By *size* I mean the hard particle at the centre and the atmosphere of heat taken together'. He reflected that if the sizes were different, then (on the supposition that the repulsive power is heat) 'no equilibrium can be established by particles of different sizes pressing against each other'. Meldrum showed that this second theory of mixed gases was evolved only in September 1804, a year after the chemical atomic theory had been arrived at. Dalton says this second theory was to be illustrated by diagrams. These are not in the original notes, but the matter is illustrated and explained in the *New System*:[1]

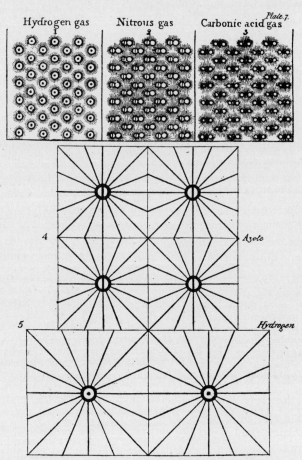

FIG. 65. PARTICLES OF GASES SURROUNDED BY REPELLING ATMOSPHERES OF CALORIC ACCORDING TO DALTON.

'Plate 7. Fig. 1, 2, and 3. represent profile views of the disposition and arrangement of particles constituting elastic fluids, both simple and compound, but not mixed; it would be difficult to convey an adequate idea of the last case, agreeably to the principles maintained, page 190.[2] The principle may, however, be elucidated by the succeeding figures.

'Fig. 4 is the representation of 4 particles of azote with their elastic atmospheres,

---

[1] B, 1810, I, ii, 548, and plate 7; see Fig. 65. [2] B, 1808, I, i, 190.

marked by rays emanating from the solid central atom; these rays being exactly alike in all the 4 particles, can meet each other, and maintain an equilibrium.

'Fig. 5. represents 2 atoms of hydrogen drawn in due proportion to those of azote, and coming in contact with them; it is obvious that the atoms of hydrogen can apply one to the other with facility, but can not apply to those of azote, by reason of the rays not meeting each other in like circumstances; hence the cause of the intestine motion which takes place on the mixture of elastic fluids, till the exterior particles come to press on something solid.'

In plate 8 the particles are 'drawn in the centres of squares of different magnitude, so as to be proportionate to the diameters of the atoms as they have been herein determined'. Dalton assumed that the number of particles in unit volume of a gas is proportional to the weight of that volume, or the density of the gas, divided by the weight of a single particle, its atomic weight. The diameter of a particle is inversely proportional to the cube root of the number of particles in a given volume. If the atomic weight of hydrogen is taken as 1, the diameter d of the particle of any gas compared with that of one of hydrogen is $d = \sqrt[3]{(w/s)}$, where w is the relative weight of the ultimate particle and s the relative density of the gas. Five out of the sixteen gases in the table have their particles of the same diameter, and it is not clear how Dalton reconciled this with his theory of diffusion.[1] In a table given in his notebook on 19 September 1803[2] Dalton uses the above method of calculation, but with reference to the standard of liquid water instead of hydrogen; the diameters of the particles are mostly different.

Dalton made much use of diagrams in his lectures explaining the atomic theory,[3] and cubical wooden blocks to represent atoms.[4] The student's definition: 'atoms are blocks of wood, painted in various colours, invented by Dr. Dalton', was no doubt based on such visual aids to memory.[5] Dalton[6] says:

'My friend Mr. Ewart, at my suggestion, made me a number of equal balls, about an inch in diameter, about 30 years ago; they have been in use ever since, I occasionally showing them to my pupils.' One had 12 equidistant holes in it, another 8; the holes had pins inserted connecting other balls. The 12 added were $\frac{1}{10}$ in. apart, the 8 were $\frac{3}{10}$ in. apart. He says 7 is 'an awkward number to arrange around 1 atom. The 6 are an equidistant number of atoms, 90° asunder, 2 at the poles, and 4 at the equator. The 5 are a *symmetrical* number, 2 at the poles [90° from the equator] and 3 at the equator 120° asunder. The 4 is a split of the 8, a regular number and equidistant. The 3 are around the equator and 120° asunder. The 2 at two opposite poles, &c.'

About 1810, therefore, Dalton had constructed many of the models familiar in modern stereochemistry.

In 1808[7] Dalton had given the substance of the remarks in his lecture of 1810 as follows:

'At the time [1801] I formed the theory of mixed gases, I had a confused idea, as many have, I suppose, at this time [1808], that the particles of elastic fluids are all of the same size; that a given volume of oxygenous gas contains just as many particles as the same volume of hydrogenous; or if not, that we had no data from which the

[1] Roscoe and Harden, 1896, 25.   [2] *Ib.*, 41.

[3] Gee, Coward and Harden, 1914–15, plates.   [4] F. Jones, 1904, 5, pl. IX, No. 5.

[5] Schorlemmer, *Rise and Development of Organic Chemistry*, 1894, 117.

[6] *On the Phosphates & Arseniates . . . and a New and Easy Method of Analysing Sugar*, Manchester, 1840–2, last section, p. 3.

[7] B, I, i, 187.

question could be solved . . . different gases have *not* their particles of the same size; and the following may be adopted as a maxim, till some reason appears to the contrary: namely, —

'That every species of pure elastic fluid has its particles globular and all of a size; but that no two species agree in the size of their particles, the pressure and temperature being the same.'

Dalton says he arrived at the conclusion that 'different gases have *not* their particles of the same size' by 'a train of reasoning, similar to that exhibited at page 71', and here[1] he says:

'if equal measures of azotic and oxygenous gases were mixed, and could be instantly united chemically, they would form nearly two measures of nitrous gas [nitric oxide], having the same weight as the two original measures; but the number of ultimate particles could at most be one half of that before the union. No two elastic fluids, probably, therefore, have the same number of particles, either in the same volume or the same weight.'

The experimental result is Davy's,[2] but (as Davy says) had previously been found by Priestley,[3] who heated iron in nitrous gas by a burning glass and found that the gas was diminished about $\frac{1}{2}$, and converted into nitrogen: $7\frac{1}{2}$ oz. measures was reduced to 3·7 oz. measures of 'perfectly phlogisticated air'. It is probable that Davy drew attention to this during Dalton's first lectures at the Royal Institution in 1803–4, but Dalton had reached the conclusion from the volumetric composition of steam on 6 September 1803 (see p. 783). Dalton thus in 1801 had what he calls the 'confused idea' that equal volumes of different gases at the same temperature and pressure contain equal numbers of particles, so that Debus thought Dalton in 1801 had anticipated Avogadro in 1811. Roscoe and Harden point out, however, that Dalton held this view only for a very short time, and then finally abandoned it, for reasons which are explained above. It is difficult to understand what Dalton meant by 'confused', since the 'idea' is perfectly definite. From the 'maxim' mentioned, Dalton said in 1810: 'we arrive at the reason for that diffusion of every gas through every other gas, without calling in any other repulsive power than the well known one of *heat*.'[4] It is important to remember that Dalton had reached the conclusion about different 'sizes' in September 1803 on *chemical* evidence (the formation of steam).[5] Dalton's own statements that the second diffusion theory was arrived at in 1805, and that he then went on to 'a train of investigation . . . for determining the *number* and *weight* of all chemical elementary principles', are incorrect, since his table of atomic weights was in existence in September 1803 (see p. 784), whilst his second diffusion theory was evolved in September 1804, as Meldrum[6] showed from an entry in Dalton's notebook, then previously unpublished, near a table of weights and diameters of atoms dated 14 September 1804:

'On the ultimate atoms of elastic fluids.

There are but three positions that are anyway likely to be true on this head.

1. The ult. atoms of all gases are of the same weight

[1] B, I, i, 70–1.
[2] *Researches . . . concerning Nitrous Oxide*, 1800, 122 f.
[3] E & O, 1790, ii, 50.
[4] Roscoe and Harden, 1896, 15–17, 25.
[5] Meldrum, (2), 9; (4), 13 f.
[6] (4), 15–16.

2. The ult. atoms are of the same relative weight as the gases themselves.

3. That neither of these positions is accurate.

'According to the first the gases of greatest specific gravity are those whose particles are closest and the diameters of the elastic particles will be the same as the cube root of the sp. gr.[1] This cannot be true for nit. gas which is made up of azot and oxygen is lighter than oxygen itself; and so is aq. vapour than oxygen one of its constituents.

'According to the 2nd position all gases will have the same number of particles, and consequently the same distances of each in a given volume, under like circumstances.[2] This position is contradicted by facts: for all compounds would be heavier than the simples upon this principle, which is contrary to experience.

'The two former positions being disproved, it follows that when two gases of like force, &c., are presented to each other, the number of particles in a given surface of one of them will not be the same as in the other; consequently, no proper equilibrium can take place.'

Meldrum thinks the new theory was put forward in consequence of Thomson's objections (p. 776); Thomson visited Dalton in August 1804, and Dalton says[3] the new view 'obviates the objections which Dr. Thomson has brought against the former'. The two diffusion hypotheses are explained in the *New System*;[4] in 1826[5] Dalton returned to the first one:

'It appears to me . . . that whenever two or more such gases or vapours . . . are put together they will finally be arranged each as if it occupied the whole space and the other were not present.'

Meldrum in 1906[6] regarded Dalton's 'physical' and 'chemical' atomic theories as identical, but in 1910[7] he concluded that Dalton put forward *two* 'physical' theories, the first formed in the period April 1800 to September 1801 (see p. 778), and the second before September 1804, as well as a 'chemical' theory which was evolved in September 1803. It seems to me[8] that Meldrum has overlooked Dalton's argument on difference in 'size' reached on chemical evidence in September 1803 in supposing that this conclusion was first reached on physical evidence in September 1804. I think Dalton's 'first' physical theory was formed in 1801 and that he modified it on the basis of the 'chemical' theory of 1803.

Dalton's Chemical Atomic Theory

In a paper read 12 November 1802,[9] Dalton took for the specific gravities of gases:

Atmospheric air	1·000	Carbonic acid gas	1·500
Azotic gas	·966	Aqueous vapour	·700
Oxygenous gas	1·127	Hydrogenous gas	·077

These are from Kirwan and Lavoisier except for oxygen, which is Davy's figure,[10] and aqueous vapour, which Dalton determined himself. He remarks that the figure for hydrogen is probably too low and it should be about 0·10.

---

[1] Austin's assumption, *Phil. Trans.*, 1790, lxxx, 51, see p. 749.
[2] This is Avogadro's hypothesis.   [3] B, I, i, 192; cf. *ib.*, 156.
[4] B, I, i, 187 f.   [5] *Phil. Trans.*, 1826, cxvi, II, 174.
[6] *Avogadro and Dalton*, 1906, 57.   [7] *Id.*, (4), (5).
[8] See also Nash, 1956.   [9] *Manchester Mem.*, 1805, i, 244 (255).
[10] *Researches . . . concerning Nitrous Oxide*, 1800, 565.

On 6 September (his birthday) 1803, Dalton has an entry in his notebook (pp. 244 f.) giving the earliest known table of atomic weights:[1]

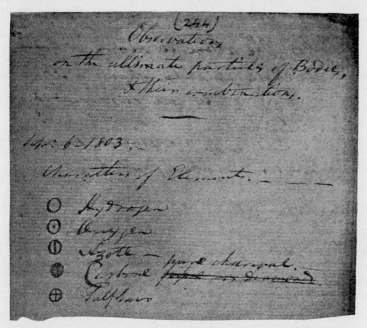

FIG. 66. DALTON'S FIRST TABLE OF SYMBOLS FOR ATOMS.

p. 245. N.B. The ultimate atoms of bodies are those particles which in the gaseous state are surrounded by heat; or they are the centres or *nuclei* of the several small elastic globular particles.

p. 246. Enquiry into the specific gravity of the ultimate particles or elements.

Though it is probable that the specific gravities [*sic*] of different elastic fluids has [*sic*] some relation to that of their ultimate particles, yet it is certain that they are not the same thing; for the ult. part. of water or steam are certainly of greater specific gravity than those of oxygen, yet the last gas is *heavier* than steam.

p. 247. From the composition of water and ammonia we may deduce ult. at. azot 1 to oxygen 1·42:—

Ult. atom of nit. gas should therefore weigh 2·42 azot.
Ult. atom of oxygen   „   „   „   1·42 oxygen.

According to this 1 oxygen will want 1·7 nitrous.

	Sulph.	Oxy.
Chenevix —	$61\frac{1}{2}$ + $38\frac{1}{2}$	=sulphuric A.
Then	$61\frac{1}{2}$ + $19\frac{1}{4}$	should be sulphureous.

This gives ult. part. of sulphur to oxy. 3·2 : 1 nearly.

	Sulph.	Oxy.
Thenart [*sic*]	56 + 44	
	56 + 22	sulphureous.
Fourcroy says	85 + 15	=sulphureous.

[1] Roscoe and Harden, 1896, 27.

p. 248.

Ult. at. Hydrogen	1		Ult. at. Nitrous Oxide	13,66
Oxygen	5·66		Nitric Acid	15·32
Azot	4·—		Sulphur	17
Carbon (Charcoal)	4·5		Sulphureous acid	22·66
Water	6·66		Sulphuric acid	28·32
Ammonia	5·—		Carbonic Acid	15·8
Nitrous Gas	9·66		Oxide of Carbone	10,2.

These values are inaccurate but Dalton took all the experimental results from publications of famous chemists, as Roscoe[1] showed: *oxygen* from Lavoisier's result for water, 85 p.c. oxygen, $\therefore 85/15 = 5\cdot66$; *nitrogen* from Austin's analysis of ammonia (1788) 80 p.c. nitrogen and 20 p.c. hydrogen, $\therefore 80/20 = 4$; *carbon* from Lavoisier's synthesis of carbonic acid gas, 72 p.c. oxygen and 28 p.c. carbon (Dalton assumed the formula CO_2 and with oxygen 5·66 this gives carbon 4·4; 4·5 is either a miscalculation or rounded off); *sulphur*, Chenevix's result gives $5\cdot66 \times 3\cdot2 = 18\cdot1$, Thenard's $56 \times 5\cdot66 \times 2/44 = 14\cdot4$, Dalton took 17, assuming sulphuric acid to be SO_2 (see p. 785).

The entry in Dalton's notebook on 6 September 1803 contains, explicitly or implicitly, the following principles:[2]

(i) Matter consists of small ultimate particles or atoms. (ii) Atoms are indivisible and cannot be created or destroyed (law of indestructibility of matter, or of conservation of mass). (iii) All atoms of a given element are identical and have the same invariable weight. (iv) Atoms of different elements have different weights. (v) The particle of a compound is formed from a fixed number of atoms of its component elements (law of fixed proportions). (vi) The weight of a compound particle is the sum of the weights of its constituent atoms. (vii) If more than one compound of two elements is known, the numbers of atoms of either element in the compound particles are in the ratio of whole numbers (law of multiple proportions). (viii) The weight of an atom of an element is the same in all its compounds, so that the composition of a compound of two elements a and c may be deduced from the compositions of compounds of each with a third element b (law of reciprocal proportions). Dalton used this in finding the composition of nitric oxide (NO) from those of ammonia (NH) and water (HO). (ix) If only one compound of two kinds of atoms A and B is known, it is, unless there is some reason to the contrary, $A + B$. If there is more than one compound, one is $A + B$ and the other $2A + B$ or $A + 2B$, and so on. This 'rule of greatest simplicity' was also used by William Higgins (1789; see p. 740). Dalton assumed the more complicated ratio $2A + 3B$ in October 1803, to explain the results of experiments on the oxides of nitrogen, and his clarification of these was notable. Even so, he regarded 'nitrous acid' as a 'compound of the second order', a binary compound of two particles, $NO + NO_2$, rather than N_2O_3. Dalton took nitrous and nitric oxides as N_2O and NO, rather than NO and NO_2 as Higgins did, but Dalton's formula for nitric acid, $NO_2(4 + 11\cdot32 = 15\cdot32)$ is wrong and Higgins had the formula NO_5 (see p. 742). (x) If the numbers of atoms m and n of two elements in a particle of a compound $mA + nB$ are assumed, the relative weights of the atoms can be

[1] *Nature*, 1874, xi, 52; *Manchester Mem.*, 1876, v, 269–75; Roscoe and Harden, 1896, 81.
[2] Partington, *Scientia*, 1955, xlix, 221–5.

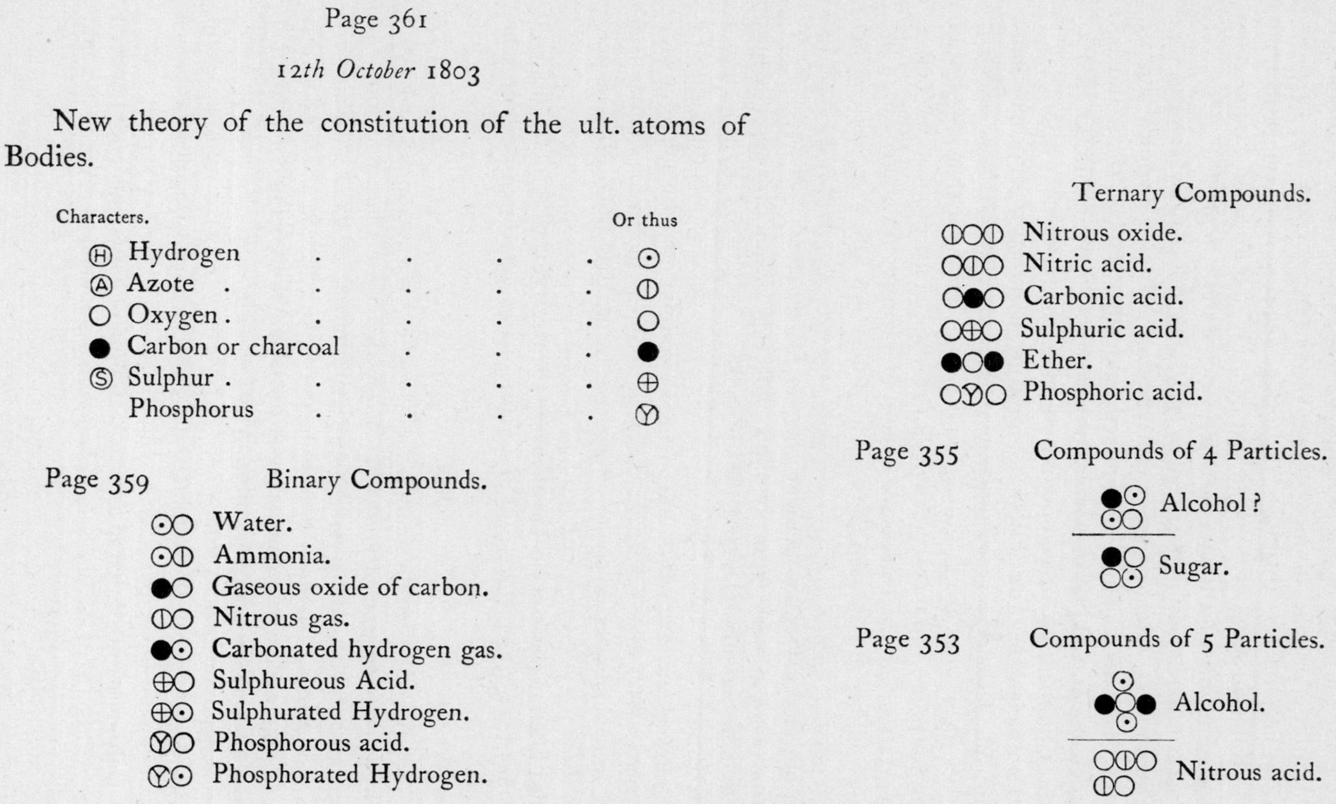

Page 361

12th October 1803

New theory of the constitution of the ult. atoms of Bodies.

Characters.   Or thus

⊕ Hydrogen   .   .   .   .   ⊙
Ⓐ Azote   .   .   .   .   ⊖
○ Oxygen   .   .   .   .   ○
● Carbon or charcoal   .   .   ●
Ⓢ Sulphur   .   .   .   ⊕
Phosphorus   .   .   ⊗

Page 359   Binary Compounds.

⊙○   Water.
⊙◐   Ammonia.
●○   Gaseous oxide of carbon.
⊖○   Nitrous gas.
●⊙   Carbonated hydrogen gas.
⊕○   Sulphureous Acid.
⊕⊙   Sulphurated Hydrogen.
⊗○   Phosphorous acid.
⊗⊙   Phosphorated Hydrogen.

Ternary Compounds.

○○○   Nitrous oxide.
○○○   Nitric acid.
○●○   Carbonic acid.
○⊕○   Sulphuric acid.
○●○   Ether.
○⊗○   Phosphoric acid.

Page 355   Compounds of 4 Particles.

⊙○/●●   Alcohol?
○/⊙●○   Sugar.

Page 353   Compounds of 5 Particles.

○●○/●●   Alcohol.

○○○/⊖○   Nitrous acid.

FIG. 67. DALTON'S SYMBOLS OF ELEMENTS AND COMPOUNDS.

calculated from the ratio of the weights mA/nB of the elements found by analysis. Dalton chose the atomic weight of hydrogen as unity and gave the weights of other atoms on this basis, assuming m and n from (ix). (xi) Equal volumes of different gases at the same temperature and pressure cannot contain the same number of ultimate particles, since water vapour, the particle of which must contain at least one atom of oxygen, is lighter than oxygen gas.

These statements, which contain the whole of Dalton's chemical atomic theory, were arrived at completely in September to October 1803, and remained unchanged in all Dalton's later publications. The symbolic representation of the compositions of compounds used by Dalton (his 'symbol law') contained implicitly the laws of definite, multiple, and reciprocal proportions, and Dalton does not give verbal statements of these laws.[1] It was asserted[2] that the 'law of *constant* proportions' would be a better name than the 'law of *definite* proportions' and that a further 'law of compound proportions' (vi) is necessary, stating that the combining weight of a compound is the sum of the combining weights of its components, which does not follow from the other laws of chemical combination.

Dalton has an entry of 12 October 1803 in his notebook (see Fig. 67).[3] It is seen that Dalton uses letter symbols before Berzelius (but see Higgins, p. 741), that he has interchanged the symbols ⊙ and ○ for hydrogen and oxygen used on 6 September, that alcohol is formulated as a compound of a hydrocarbon CH and water HO, and sugar as a compound of carbon monoxide CO and water HO. The first anticipates the etherin theory of Dumas (see Vol. IV), and alcohol is given an alternative formula C_2H_2O. Nitrous acid (N_2O_3) is shown as a binary compound of NO and NO_2.

How did Dalton arrive at his chemical atomic theory of 1803? This difficult question has been much discussed and some of the suggestions will now be considered.

The Solubility of Gases

On 21 October 1803 Dalton read to the Manchester Philosophical Society a paper 'On the Absorption of Gases by Water and other Liquids' which was printed in 1805.[4] His experiments on the solubilities of gases in water are recorded in his diary in January to March, and in August, 1803.[5] He asks: 'is it not two atmospheres pressing one against the other: both being constituted of geometrical progressions of very different ratios?' These are the 'atmospheres' of the gas and a hypothetical atmosphere of the dissolved gas, and Roscoe and Harden say pp. 96–120 of the notebook are 'entirely filled with speculations as to the arrangement of the particles of a gas dissolved in water, especially at its surface'. Dalton assumed[6] that in a vertical column of gas the distance between the centres of the particles increases upwards in a geometrical progression, and

---

[1] Henry, 1854, 87; Rau, *Grundlage der modernen Chemie*, Brunswick, 1877, 15; Delacre, *Moniteur Scientif.*, 1921, xi, 3; *Histoire de la Chimie*, 1920, 215 f.
   [2] Anon., *Brit. Quart. Rev.*, 1845, i, 157.   [3] Roscoe and Harden, 1896, 45–6 (see p. 785).
   [4] *Manchester Mem.*, 1805, i, 271–87; ACR, no. 2, 15–26.
   [5] Roscoe and Harden, 1896, 55 f.
   [6] See notes by Roscoe and Harden, and Kahlbaum, 1898, 51–3 (not in the English ed.); Dalton, B, I, i, 200–6.

hence the 'diameters' of the particles; also that the dissolved gas is distributed in a similar way, the ratio for the two series being different. The distances between the particles he found by taking the cube-root of the volumes.[1]

In the printed paper Dalton has reached the conclusion that the volume of any gas absorbed by one volume of air-free water, which does not combine chemically with the water (i.e. can be completely expelled from solution by reducing the pressure), is a fraction which is a reciprocal of the cube of a natural number, the volume of gas being measured at the temperature and pressure of the experiment:

Bulk absorbed,
the bulk of water
being unity

$$\frac{1}{1^3} = 1$$ $\quad$ {Carbonic acid gas, sulphuretted hydrogen, nitrous oxide

$$\frac{1}{2^3} = \frac{1}{8}$$ $\quad$ Olefiant gas, of the Dutch chemists

$$\frac{1}{3^3} = \frac{1}{27}$$ $\quad$ {Oxygenous gas, nitrous gas, carburetted hydrogen gas, from stagnant water

$$\frac{1}{4^3} = \frac{1}{64}$$ $\quad$ Azotic gas, hydrogenous gas, carbonic oxide

$$\frac{1}{5^3} = \frac{1}{125}$$ $\quad$ None discovered.

Dalton says: 'I had the results of Mr. William Henry's experience before me, an account of which has been published in the Philosophical Transactions for 1803.[2] By the reciprocal communications since, we have been enabled to bring the results of our Experiments to a near agreement.' Dalton then describes his own experiments on the solubility of gases. He states the important result that when water is 'agitated with a mixture of two or more gases (such as atmospheric air) the water will absorb portions of each gas the same as if they were presented to it separately in their proper density'. Thus,

$$\frac{1}{64} \times \frac{79}{100} = 1 \cdot 234 \text{ of azotic gas and } \frac{1}{27} \times \frac{21}{100} = 0 \cdot 778 \text{ of oxygen gas, from air.}[3]$$

'The density of the gas in water has a special relation to that out of the water, the distance of the particles within being always some multiple of that without. Thus, in the case of carbonic acid, &c. the distance within and without is the same . . . ; in olefiant gas the distance of the particles in the water is twice that without; in oxygenous gas, &c. the distance is just three times as great within as without; and in azotic, &c. it is four times.'[4]

Dalton later noticed that the results of Theodore de Saussure[5] did not agree with his theory, but he says[6] the four examples given by de Saussure which seemed to militate against Dalton's law of the solubility of mixed gases 'coincide as near as anyone can expect with the views which I have all along taken of this subject'.

[1] Roscoe and Harden, 56–7.
[2] Henry, *Phil. Trans.*, 1803, xciii, 29 (read 23 December 1802).
[3] *Manchester Mem.*, 1805, i, 273. [4] *Ib.*, 281; this is seen from his table.
[5] *Bibl. Brit.*, 1812, l, 39–61, 127–51; *Ann. Phys.*, 1814, xlvii, 113–83; *Ann. Phil.*, 1815, vi, 241, 331.
[6] *Ann. Phil.*, 1816, vi, 215–23; B, II, 309.

If the absorption is purely mechanical 'it may be expected that all liquids having an equal fluidity with water, will absorb like portions of gas. In several liquids I have tried no perceptible difference has been found; but this deserves further investigation'.[1] Dalton later[2] admitted that Saussure's results (see above) showed that this conclusion had been 'too hasty'.

Dalton then gives in eight numbered paragraphs a 'Theory of the Absorption of Gases by Water, &c.':[3]

'1. All gases that enter into water and other liquids by means of pressure, and are wholly disengaged again by the removal of that pressure, are *mechanically* mixed with the liquid, and not *chemically* combined with it.

'2. Gases so mixed with water, &c. retain their elasticity or repulsive power amongst their own particles, just the same in the water as out of it, the intervening water having no other influence in this respect than a mere vacuum.[4]

'3. Each gas is retained in water by the pressure of gas of its own kind incumbent on its surface abstractedly considered, no other gas with which it may be mixed having any permanent influence in this respect.

'4. When water has absorbed its bulk of carbonic acid gas, &c. the gas does not press on the water at all, but presses on the containing vessel just as if no water were in. [In water saturated with $\frac{1}{27}$ of its bulk of oxygen] the exterior gas presses on the surface of the water with $\frac{26}{27}$ of its force, and on the internal gas with $\frac{1}{27}$ of its force, which force presses upon the containing vessel and not on the water. With azotic and hydrogenous gas the proportions are $\frac{63}{64}$ and $\frac{1}{64}$ respectively.'

5–6. Dalton then discusses the results in terms of particles pressing on piles of shot.

Appended to this paper are three plates: (1) View of a square pile of shot, (2) Horizontal View of Air in Water, (3) Profile View of Air in Water. The diagrams are drawn in Dalton's notebook in September 1803, the pages preceding that containing the table of atomic weights. In the notebook only oxygen and nitric oxide appear for particles at distances 3 : 1; 'carburetted hydrogen gas' (marsh gas) in the table printed in 1805 must have been added after the experiments with it in August 1804 (see p. 796).[5] Speculations on 'atmospheres pressing one against the other' etc., go back to March and April 1803.[6]

By considering a square pile of shot Dalton concluded that the single particle at the apex distributes its pressure among all the shots in a lower layer, and 'so the particle of gas distributes its pressure equally amongst every successive horizontal stratum of particles of water downwards till it reaches the sphere of influence of another particle of gas'. The numbers of particles in successive layers of the pile are, 1, 4, 9, 16, . . . i.e. 1^2, 2^2, 3^2, 4^2. . . . Suppose one particle presses on the surface of the water and let the distance of the particles of gas from each other be to those of water as 10 to 1:

'then each particle of gas must divide its force equally among 100 particles of water, as follows:— It exerts its immediate force upon 4 particles of water; these 4 press upon 9, the 9 upon 16, and so on according to the order of square numbers, till 100 particles of water have the force distributed amongst them; and in the same stratum each square of 100, having its incumbent particle of gas, the water below this stratum is uniformly pressed by the gas, and consequently has not its equilibrium disturbed by that pressure.'

[1] *Ib.*, 275, 282.   B, 1827, II, 309.   [3] *Ib.*, 282 f.
[4] This is a striking anticipation of van't Hoff's gaseous theory of solution (see Vol. IV). It seems as if Dalton supposed that the particles of the gas retain their heat envelopes even when they are in solution.
[5] Roscoe and Harden, 59.   [6] *Ib.*, 56–7.

If water absorbs $\frac{1}{27}$ of its bulk of a gas, the stratum of gas on the surface of the water presses with $\frac{26}{27}$ of its force on the water and $\frac{1}{27}$ of its force upon the uppermost stratum of gas in the water. The distance of the two strata of gas must be nearly 27 times the distance of the particles in the incumbent atmosphere and 9 times the distance of the particles in the water. When $\frac{1}{64}$ is absorbed the distance of the atmospheres becomes 64 times the distance of two particles in the outer, or 16 times that of the inner. ($9 = 27^{2/3}$ and $16 = 64^{2/3}$.)

'7. An equilibrium between the outer and inner atmospheres can be in no other circumstance than that of the distance of the particles of one atmosphere being the same or some multiple of that of the other; and it is probable the multiple cannot be more than 4. For in this case the distance of the inner and outer atmospheres is such as to make the perpendicular force of each particle of the former on those particles of the latter that are immediately subject to its influence, physically speaking, equal; and the same may be observed of the small lateral force.

'8. The greatest difficulty attending the mechanical hypothesis, arises from different gases observing different laws. Why does water not admit its bulk of every gas alike? — This question I have duly considered, and though I am not yet able to satisfy myself completely, I am nearly persuaded that the circumstance depends upon the weight and number of the ultimate particles of the several gases: those whose particles are lightest and single being least absorbable and the others more according as they increase in weight and complexity.[1] An enquiry into the relative weights of the ultimate particles of bodies is a subject, as far as I know, entirely new: I have lately been prosecuting this enquiry with remarkable success. The principle cannot be entered upon in this paper; but I shall just subjoin the results, as far as they appear to be ascertained by my experiments.'

On the next page, just filling it,[2] is a 'Table of the relative weights of the ultimate particles of gaseous and other bodies':

Hydrogen	1	Nitrous oxide	13·7 [13·9]
Azot	4·2	Sulphur	14·4
Carbone	4·3	Nitric acid	15·2
Ammonia	5·2	Sulphuretted hydrogen	15·4
Oxygen	5·5	Carbonic acid	15·3
Water	6·5	Alcohol	15·1
Phosphorus	7·2	Sulphureous acid	19·9
Phosphuretted hydrogen	8·2	Sulphuric acid	25·4
Nitrous gas	9·3 [9·7]	Carburetted hydrogen	
Ether	9·6	from stag. water	6·3
Gaseous oxide of carbone	9·8	Olefiant gas	5·3

This table ends the paper. There are no symbols. Kopp[3] and Roscoe[4] pointed out that the figures for nitrous gas and nitrous oxide do not agree with those for nitrogen (4·2) and oxygen (5·5) but should be 9·7 and 13·9. Meldrum[5] said: 'There is no reason to doubt that the paper contained a table of atomic weights when it was read, but Dalton certainly extended the table before going to press.' The last two entries were added after experiments on the composition of marsh gas and olefiant gas made by explosion with oxygen on 24

[1] *Ib.*, 286. In a footnote Dalton says: 'Subsequent experience renders this conjecture less probable.'
[2] *Ib.*, 287. [3] (3), 1873, 293. [4] *Manchester Mem.*, 1876, v, 269. [5] (6), 3.

August 1804.[1] Dalton later[2] referred to the ether atom 'published in the table on the absorption of gases in 1803', and most of the table probably dates from that year.

L. K. Nash[3] suggested that it was in thinking over the solubility results that Dalton arrived at the chemical atomic theory. Nash discussed in detail the alternative explanations of Roscoe and Harden and of Meldrum, and concluded that the atomic weight table is introduced logically into the solubility paper in order to provide some explanation of the fact, difficult to understand on the mechanical hypothesis, that different gases have different solubilities. The experiments on solubility were begun early in 1803, perhaps in January, but the first mention of atomic weights was on 6 September 1803.

There is a difficulty here. In this paper on solubilities of gases[4] Dalton, in footnotes, speaks of 'oxygen in the water, each measure of which takes $3\frac{1}{2}$ of nitrous gas to saturate it'; also:

'One part of oxygenous gas requires 3·4 of nitrous gas to saturate it in water. It is agreeable to this that the rapid mixture of oxygenous and nitrous gas over a broad surface of water, occasions a greater diminution than otherwise. In fact, the *nitrous* acid is formed in this way; whereas when water is not present the *nitric* acid is formed which requires just half the quantity of nitrous gas, as I have lately ascertained.'

The words suggest that this was in the paper as read. The theoretical ratios $(4NO + O_2 = 2N_2O_3$ and $2NO + O_2 = 2NO_2)$ are 4 : 1 (instead of 3·5 or 3·4) and 2 : 1; Dalton then thought nitric acid was NO_2. He had been working on the subject since 21 March, soon after his first solubility experiments, and he continued the experiments with oxides of nitrogen simultaneously with those on solubilities.

Composition of Oxides of Nitrogen

Dalton adopted the composition of nitric acid found by Lavoisier and formulated it in his table as 15·2, i.e. $4·2 + 2 \times 5·5$, corresponding with NO_2. In his notebook for 21 March 1803 he says: 'Nitrous gas — 1·7 or 2·7 may be combined with oxygen, it is presumed', and again on 1 April there is a list of results showing that Dalton then appreciated that more nitrous gas is absorbed when the mixture is made rapidly over water.[5] On 4 August 1803 he had discovered that there is a simple relation: 'It appears, too, that a very rapid mixture of equal parts com. air and nitrous gas, gives 112 or 120 residuum. Consequently that oxygen joins to nit. gas sometimes 1·7 to 1, and at others 3·4 to 1.' Roscoe and Harden say[6] that Dalton 'did not include the composition of nitrous acid (N_2O_3) in any of the earlier atomic weight tables, although nitrous oxide and nitrous gas, about the composition of which he had made no experiments, both found a place in all of them'; and hence it is 'very unlikely that the atomic theory was suggested by this particular experiment about nitrous gas and oxygen'. The results depend on the fact that nitric oxide is only half oxidised in rapid mixing, as in a wide jar, and the absorption reaction is: $NO_2 + NO + H_2O = 2HNO_2$; the oxidation of the second half (by a

[1] Roscoe and Harden, 62–3.　　　　　[2] *Ann. Phil.*, 1820, xv, 117 (133).
[3] *Isis*, 1956, xlvii, 101–16.　　　　　[4] *Manchester Mem.*, 1805, i, 272, 274.
[5] Roscoe and Harden, 1896, 34 f.　　　[6] 1896, 38.

termolecular reaction) is slow and in a narrow tube the absorption reaction is $2NO_2 + H_2O = HNO_2 + HNO_3$ (Dalton thought only nitric acid is formed).

Dalton on 12 November 1802 read to the Manchester Philosophical Society a paper on an 'Experimental Enquiry into the Proportion of the several Gases or Elastic Fluids, constituting the Atmosphere'. This was printed in 1805[1] in the volume containing the paper on the solubility of gases and preceding this. The experiments described in it were made between 10 October and 13 November 1803,[2] so that it was revised before it was printed, and Dalton probably wished the two papers to appear in this order for some reason. In the paper as printed there is a description of some experiments on mixing nitric oxide (nitrous gas) and air over water, both in narrow tubes (9 in. by $\frac{3}{10}$ in.) and in wide jars. In the tube, 100 measures of air were mixed with 36 of nitrous gas and left 80 measures of nitrogen; in the jar, 100 measures of air mixed with 72 measures of nitrous gas left 80 measures of nitrogen. Hence Dalton concluded that:

'the elements of oxygen may combine with a certain portion of nitrous gas or with twice that portion, but with no intermediate quantity. In the former case *nitric* acid is the result; in the latter *nitrous* acid: but as both these may be formed at the same time, one part of oxygen going to *one* of nitrous gas, and in another to *two*, the quantity of nitrous gas absorbed should be variable, from 36 to 72 per cent. for common air.'

The result implies the law of multiple proportions, and since I found it difficult to obtain Dalton's results I thought he probably had this law in mind in reporting them. Nash found that only 'a few trials out of many' gave 'a reasonable approximation to the ratio in question'. Meldrum, who was not aware of the experimental difficulties, said:[3] 'the author, after a careful consideration of the evidence, can come to no other conclusion than that it was Dalton's experiments on the combination of nitric oxide and oxygen that aroused his attention, and made him apply his physical theory to the purposes of chemistry.' Dalton then had his physical theory in mind; 'these experiments simply served to give the impulse needed to set his mind working.' Meldrum agreed with Larmor[4] that the idea of a combination of atoms in the proportion 1 : 1 must forthwith lead to other cases such as 1 : 2; 'once it is postulated that only one kind of aggregation into molecules occurs, e.g. that in water there is only one way in which the hydrogen attaches itself to the oxygen, the laws of definite and multiple proportions are self-evident.'

In August 1803 Dalton gives the values 1·7 and 3·4 to 1 for the volumes of nitrous gas; in the paper of 1805 the values are 1·8 (36 : 20) and 3·6 (72 : 20). Meldrum suggested that nitrous acid was omitted from the earlier tables because it had, apparently, too complicated a formula (N_2O_3). He thought that Dalton already had in mind the necessity for a simple multiple combining ratio for the gases before he reached the result of 4 August 1803, derived by an extension of the 1 : 1 ratio which was suggested by Newton's theory. After

[1] *Manchester Mem.*, 1805, i, 244–58; ACR, ii, 5–15.
[2] Roscoe and Harden, 35.   [3] (5), 12.
[4] Wilde Lecture, the 'Physical Aspect of the Atomic Theory', *Manchester Mem.*, 1908, lii, no. 10, 9.

reading Nash's paper (which he kindly submitted to me before publication) I feel less sure of the cogency of Meldrum's arguments.

In his first table Dalton assumed the formulae N_2O for nitrous oxide, NO for nitric oxide, and NO_2 for nitric acid. Just before and just after he drew up this table he had been experimenting on mixing air and nitric oxide over water (see p. 791), and on 9 September 1803 he repeated Cavendish's experiment of sparking nitrogen and oxygen over alkali (see p. 339) and found that 'about 20 grs. measure of air were reduced to 16; remainder $2\frac{1}{3}$ oxygen'; and on 9 and 10 September again, on sparking '17 grain measures of air $\frac{1}{3}$ azotic, and $\frac{2}{3}$ oxygenous, in a glass tube $\frac{1}{8}$ inch diameter' for 4 to 5 hours, 4 gr. measures, of which $2\frac{1}{3}$ were oxygen, were left, and Dalton calculated that nitrogen and oxygen in the ratio 4 to 9 by volume, or in ratio of 'individual particles' 4 to 11·3, had disappeared. The volume ratio found is 2 : 4·5; Cavendish[1] had found 2 : 4·4 and 2 : 5·05 in two experiments.

Dalton wished to find the formula of nitrous acid, and on 12 October 1803 he gave it as $\frac{ONO}{NO}$ (in modern symbols; see p. 785), which is the first correct statement of it based on experiment (Higgins had guessed NO_3, see p. 742).

Something may now be said about the other parts of Dalton's paper on the composition of the atmosphere (see p. 791). Beginning with Priestley's observation[2] that when 1 vol. of common air is mixed over water with $\frac{1}{3}$ vol. of nitrous air, $\frac{1}{5}$ of the common air and all the nitrous air disappear, the method had been used extensively in 'eudiometry' (see p. 323) but was found liable to give erratic results. Henry[3] gives details of the method as used by Dalton, who 'constantly employs nitrous gas in determining the purity of air, and with perfect satisfaction as to the accuracy of the results'.

Berthollet[4] found that when 15 vols. of oxygen were added gradually to 46 vols. of nitric oxide over water, only 2 vols. of gas were left which contained 1 vol. of nitrogen. When 12 vols. of oxygen were placed in a wide cylinder and 24 vols. of nitric oxide added, the product was absorbed by water, but in a narrow tube, 3 vols. of oxygen absorbed 5 vols. of nitric oxide. He recognised clearly the effects of the size of the vessel and the manner of mixing.

Dalton determined the amount of carbon dioxide in air[5] by first adding enough standardised lime-water to precipitate the carbon dioxide in the air in a 7-litre bottle after shaking. Two of his pupils, Hadfield (1828–30)[6] and Watson,[7] improved the process, which is essentially the same as that used by Pettenkofer, who used baryta water.[8] Dalton,[9] using densities from Lavoisier and Kirwan, Davy for oxygen, and his own determination for aqueous vapour, gave the gravimetric percentage composition of air as: azotic gas 75·55, oxygenous gas 23·32, aqueous vapour 1·03 (variable), carbonic acid gas 0·10. He found the proportion of oxygen to decrease at higher altitudes, but only slightly; air from the summit of Helvellyn (1100 yards) had the same com-

[1] *Phil. Trans.*, 1785, lxxv, 372.   [2] *Phil. Trans.*, 1772, lxii, 210 f.; E & O, 1774, i, 110.
[3] *Elements of Experimental Chemistry*, 1815, i, 369.
[4] *Statique Chimique*, 1803, ii, 171–2.   [5] *Manchester Mem.*, 1805, i, 254.
[6] *Ib.*, 1842, vi, 10.   [7] *B.A. Rep.*, 1835, iv, 583.
[8] *J. Chem. Soc.*, 1858, x, 292; F. Jones, 1903.   [9] *Manchester Mem.*, 1805, i, 257.

position as Manchester air. In 1826,[1] however, he found much less oxygen in a specimen of air brought for him from the summit of Helvellyn than in air from the ground level, but Henry[2] said this air had probably been kept over water containing organic matter.

Gay-Lussac[3] found that the composition of a specimen of air which he collected in a balloon ascent to the great height of 21,785 ft. above sea level was the same as that of air at the surface of the earth. In 1837[4] Dalton gave analyses of air from Helvellyn and Switzerland, finding hardly any difference at ground level (20·95 oxygen) and 3000, 9600, and 15000 ft. (20·62 oxygen). He says: 'In elevated regions the proportion of oxygen to azote is somewhat less than at the surface of the earth, but not nearly so much as the Theory of Mixed Gases would require', and he gives the correct explanation that it is the effect of mixing by 'the increasing agitation of the atmosphere by currents and counter-currents', which was proposed again (in ignorance of Dalton's statement) as new over a century later.[5]

Dalton used the nitric oxide process eudiometrically, mixing the gas with the air in a narrow tube without agitation. To 100 of air he added about 36 of nitric oxide and multiplied the contraction by $\frac{7}{19}$ to find the volume of oxygen.[6] Besides using nitric oxide, and absorption of oxygen in a solution of sulphuret of lime, Dalton found that:

'Volta's eudiometer is very accurate as well as elegant and expeditious: according to Monge (see p. 453), 100 oxygen require 196 measures of hydrogen; according to Davy[7] 192; but from the most attentive observations of my own, 185 are sufficient. In atmospheric air I always find 60 per cent. diminution when fired with an excess of hydrogen; that is, 100 common air with 60 hydrogen, become 100 after the explosion, and no oxygen is found in the residuum; here 21 oxygen take 39 hydrogen.'[8]

Dalton thus takes the composition of air as a mixture of 21 oxygen and 79 nitrogen by volume. He found 1 vol. of carbonic acid in 1460, instead of Humboldt's 1 per cent by weight; the proportion by weight is 1 in 1000, and even in a crowded room the air contained little more than 1 per cent of this gas.

On 26 October 1802 Davy wrote to Davies Giddy mentioning Dalton's papers in vol. 5 of the *Manchester Memoirs*. 'As far as I can understand his subjects, the author appears to me to have executed them in a very masterly way. I wish very much to have your judgment upon his opinions, some of which are new and singular.' Probably as a result of Davy's recommendation, Dalton gave a course of lectures at the Royal Institution in London, beginning on 22 December 1803 and returning to Manchester on 1 February. He gave an interesting account of these,[9] saying that he was introduced to Davy, 'a very agreeable and intelligent young man . . . the principal failing in his character as a philosopher is that he does not smoke.' Dalton left an account of his theory

[1] *Phil. Trans.*, 1826, cxvi, II, 174.   [2] 1854, 156.
[3] *Ann. Chim.*, 1805, lii, 75; *Ann. Phys.*, 1805, xx, 19 (33).
[4] *Phil. Trans.*, 1837, cxxvii, II, 347.   [5] Paneth, *Nature*, 1937, cxxxix, 181.
[6] *Phil. Mag.*, 1805, xxiii, 349 (351); Thomson, (2), 1807, iv, 59.
[7] Davy, *Researches . . . concerning Nitrous Oxide*, 1800, 291, gives 40 hydrogen and 20·8 oxygen, corresponding with 100 : 192.
[8] *Manchester Mem.*, 1805, i, 251–2, 255.   [9] Henry, 1854, 47 f.

for publication in the *Quarterly Journal*, but 'was not informed whether that was done'.[1] It was not.

Two unpublished lectures to the Manchester Philosophical Society on 'A Review and Illustration of some Principles in Mr. Dalton's course of lectures on Natural Philosophy at the Royal Institution in January, 1804', and 'On the Elements of Chemical Philosophy', given in 1804,[2] were probably to fill up vacant programmes.[3] Dalton probably gave the first fairly complete account of his chemical atomic theory in his first lecture at the Royal Institution on 22 December 1803.[4] There is an entry in his notebook for that date:

'Proportions of compounds according to theory:—   Davy's Expts.

	Azote	Oxy.		Azote	Oxy.
Nitrous oxide	62	38	Nitrous oxide	63·3	36·7
Nitrous gas	42·1	57·9	Nitrous gas	44·05	55·95
Nitric acid	26·7	73·3	Nitric acid	29·5	70·5'

Davy probably gave Dalton the results of his experiments, published in 1800 (see p. 751). Dalton has made a mistake in his calculation for nitrous oxide, taking azote $= 4 \cdot 5$ instead of 4, and the figures should be azote 59·2, oxygen 40·8.

In 1811 Dalton[5] said: 'I remember the strong impression which at a very early period of these inquiries was made by observing the proportions of oxigen to azote, as 1, 2 and 3, in nitrous oxide, nitrous gas, and nitrous acid, according to the experiments of Davy.' Davy in 1829[6] said: 'It is difficult to say how he [Dalton] gained his first notions of atoms, but I strongly suspect that *Researches Chemical and Philosophical*, first published in 1801 [actually 1800] in which it is stated that nitrate of ammonia becomes water and nitrous oxide, and perhaps Cruickshank's [see p. 273] discovery of gaseous oxide of carbon gave him his first ideas.' Davy's analyses of the oxides of nitrogen[7] give for the ratios of oxygen to nitrogen in the three compounds mentioned by Dalton, 1, 2·2, and 3·9, so that multiple relations are not apparent, and in any case we know that Dalton himself had been experimenting on oxides of nitrogen, and had arrived at his chemical atomic theory, more than three months before he met Davy.

Analyses of Hydrocarbons

In 1804 Thomas Thomson travelled from Glasgow to Greenock and thence by sea to Liverpool. From Liverpool he went to Manchester to visit his former pupil Dr. William Henry. In his diary for 1804 Thomson wrote:[8]

'Aug. 26, Sunday. Called on Mr. Henry, and found him; dined with his father and drank tea in Mr. Henry junior's, in company with Mr. Dalton. Mr. Dalton had been lately occupied with experiments on the carburetted hydrogen. He finds three species.

[1] B, I, i, pref. v.   [2] Meldrum, *Manchester Mem.*, 1911, lv, No. 19, 4.
[3] Gee, Coward, and Harden, 1915, 5.   [4] Roscoe and Harden, 43–4.
[5] *Nicholson's J.*, 1811, xxix, 144.
[6] Henry, 1854, 217; from an unpublished fragment.   [7] *Researches*, 1800, 328–9.
[8] Anon., *Glasgow Medical J.*, 1857, v, 69, 121; sep. reprint, 1857, 23.

1. Olefiant gas, composed of an atom of hydrogen and an atom of carbon. 2. Gas of marshes, composed of two atoms of hydrogen and one of carbon. 3. Oxide of carbon, composed of an atom of carbon and one of oxygen [*sic*]. He has suggested the following ingenious method of ascertaining the constituents of bodies.'

The symbols used by Dalton follow. In 1825[1] Thomson said: 'Unless my recollection fails me, Mr. Dalton's theory was originally deduced from his experiments on olefiant gas and carburetted hydrogen.' In 1831[2] Thomson said Dalton told him that:

'the atomic theory first occurred to him during his investigations of olefiant gas and carburetted hydrogen gases, at that time imperfectly understood, and the constitution of which was first fully developed by Mr. Dalton himself.' Dalton found that 'if we reckon the carbon in each the same, then carburetted hydrogen gas contains exactly twice as much hydrogen as olefiant gas does. This determined him to state the ratios of the constituents in numbers, and to consider the olefiant gas as a compound of one atom of carbon and one atom of hydrogen; and carburetted hydrogen of one atom of carbon and two atoms of hydrogen.'

If $H=1$ and $C=6$, ethylene is $C_4H_4=CH$ and methane is $C_2H_4=CH_2$. In 1850, however, Thomson said[3] Dalton founded his theory on analyses of nitrous and nitric oxides (which Dalton never seems to have made; perhaps he means Davy's). Angus Smith,[4] puzzled by Thomson's two statements, adopts both of them (the analyses of the oxides of nitrogen being replaced by the experiments on mixing air and nitric oxide). Henry,[5] who suspected the real origin from the theory of mixed gases (see p. 778), could not omit Thomson's account, particularly as it seemed to agree with Dalton's statement in 1810[6] that:

'No correct notion of the constitution of the gas [light carburetted hydrogen, methane] . . . seems to have been found till the atomic theory was introduced and applied in the investigation. It was in the summer of 1804, that I collected at various times, and in various places, the inflammable gas obtained from ponds . . . 100 measures of this gas require rather more than 200 measures of oxygen, and give rather more than 100 carbonic acid. . . . Hence, then, we may conclude that the diameter of an atom of carburetted hydrogen is nearly equal to that of hydrogen, but rather less.'

This really implies that the theory was in existence before the experiments in 1804. In 1808[7] Dalton said:

'Various essays of his were read before the Literary and Philosophical Society of Manchester, chiefly on heat and elastic fluids, and were published in 1802 [see p. 766]. The author was not remiss in prosecuting his researches, in which he was considerably assisted by the application of principles derived from the above essays. In 1803, he was gradually led to those primary Laws, which seem to obtain in regard to heat, and to chemical combinations, and which it is the object of the present work to exhibit and elucidate.'

Thomson's account, which was based on a conversation with Dalton, although its accuracy was suspected in 1845,[8] undoubtedly gives what he was told by Dalton. Thomson's memory was good; he gave[9] a long account of

[1] *An Attempt to Establish the First Principles of Chemistry by Experiment*, 1825, i, 11.
[2] (1), ii, 289–91.   [3] *Proc. Phil. Soc. Glasgow*, 1850, iii, 135; notice on Wollaston.
[4] 1856, 231 f.   [5] 1854, 80.   [6] B, 1810, I, ii, 444.
[7] B, 1808, I, i, Pref. v.
[8] Anon., *Brit. Quart. Rev.*, 1845, i, 157.   [9] (2), 1807, iv, 553–605.

Werner's unpublished geological system from conversations with Prof. Jameson, and in reporting meetings of the Royal Society in his *Annals of Philosophy* he had to rely on memory. Thomson's account of the origin of Dalton's atomic theory was accepted for a very long time (it is still found in some fairly modern books), but Roscoe and Harden showed that it is incorrect by publishing the account of the theory in Dalton's notebook on 6 September 1803. They also showed that the experiments on the hydrocarbons are first recorded in his notebook on 6 August 1804,[1] and the values for carburetted hydrogen and olefiant gas were added to the table as published in 1805 (see p. 789). Dalton[2] in describing the determination of the composition of ether vapour by explosion with oxygen in a eudiometer says, however, that he first used this method in September 1803.

First Publication of Dalton's Chemical Atomic Theory

On the basis of his conversation with Dalton in 1804 Thomas Thomson prepared a short account of the atomic theory which was published in the third edition of his *System of Chemistry* in 1807.[3] It begins quite abruptly in a section on the densities of gases and is not mentioned in the undated preface. It says:[4] 'we have no direct means of ascertaining the density of the atoms of bodies, but a hypothesis lately contrived by Mr. Dalton, if it prove correct, will furnish us with a method of ascertaining that density with great precision . . . this hypothesis . . . furnishes us with a ready method of ascertaining the relative density of those atoms that enter into such combinations', going on to show that he meant 'relative weight'. In his notebook in 1803 (see p. 783) Dalton himself had referred to 'ultimate particles' and 'ultimate atoms', and the 'specific gravity' of an ultimate particle as the weight of the atom. He probably used the last name in his conversations with Thomson in August 1804 (p. 794) and since Dalton also used it for the relative density of a gas, Thomson felt the need of making a distinction and used the name 'density'. Dalton long afterwards[5] said:

'It is rather amusing to me to observe the different manners in which a cursory view of the atomic system strikes different persons. Dr. Thomson was the first who, from some hints I gave him, published an outline of the system in the third edition of his chemistry. He used the phrase *density of the atoms* indifferently for *weight of the atoms*, thereby implying that all atoms are of *the same size*, and differ only in *density*; but he has since very properly discontinued the use of the phrase.'

Thomson says: 'when two elements unite to form a third substance, it is to be presumed that *one* atom of one joins to *one* atom of the other, unless when some reason can be assigned for supposing the contrary.' He gives Dalton's symbols for oxygen, hydrogen, and azote, and his formulae for water and ammonia (HO and NH in modern symbols), thence, from the quantitative compositions, finding the atomic weights ('relative densities') hydrogen 1, azote 4, oxygen 6. If there is more than one compound, one is one atom to one and 'the next simple combination must . . . arise from the union of *one* atom

---

[1] Roscoe and Harden, 1896, 31, 62.   [2] *Manchester Mem.*, 1819, iii, 446.
[3] (2), 1807, iii, 424–9; other references to the theory, 515 f., 523, 540, 614; ACR, ii, 42–8.
[4] *Ib.*, 425–6.   [5] *Ann. Phil.*, 1814, iii, 175; a criticism of Berzelius.

of one with *two* atoms of the other'. He gives Dalton's formulae for nitrous gas (NO), nitrous oxide (NON) and nitric acid (ONO), one binary and two ternary compounds. Thomson gives a table of 'densities of the atoms' of hydrogen (1), azote (5), oxygen (6), muriatic acid (9), water (7), ammonia (6), nitrous gas (11), nitrous oxide (16), nitric acid (17), oxymuriatic acid (2 muriatic acid + 1 oxygen, 24), and hyperoxymuriatic acid (1 muriatic acid + 3 oxygen, 27). Thomson also gives carbon = 4·4,[1] phosphorus 8,[2] sulphur 15,[3] and several metals and salts,[4] as calculated by himself. In discussing the compositions of neutral salts, Thomson[5] says:

'If we apply Dalton's hypothesis, we may find the relative density of the constituents of those neutral salts which have been analysed. This will afford a test of considerable importance of the degree of confidence to be put in the hypothesis. . . . The acids and alkaline bases, indeed, may be capable of uniting with each other in various proportions; but the neutral combination must be constant: it must likewise be the most intimate. We may therefore suppose, that in it the acid and base unite atom to atom . . . the very near coincidence between the preceding table of densities, and the results of analysis, must appear something more than accidental, and affords a very strong presumption in favour of the truth of Dalton's hypothesis.'

Thomson, therefore, some time before Berzelius (see Vol. IV), had extended Dalton's atomic theory to the metals and to acids and bases. W. C. Henry[6] says his father William Henry and he were told by Dalton that the atomic theory was deduced to explain Richter's table of equivalents published in Berthollet's *Statique Chimique* in 1803 (see p. 678). Dalton's early atomic weight tables, however, never mention the combining weights of acids and alkalis, the compounds investigated by Richter, whose name first occurs in Dalton's diary on 19 April 1807.[7] Thomson, in his account of Dalton's theory in 1807,[8] says it explains Richter's law of equivalents and it was probably Thomson who drew Dalton's attention to Richter, since Dalton was in Edinburgh when he first mentions Richter in his diary. Higgins also had developed his views in relation to gaseous compounds, as Dalton did (see p. 739).

Dalton's lectures in Edinburgh (where he repeated the course) and Glasgow in the spring of 1807 were very well attended and he had a very good reception,[9] for which he probably had Thomson to thank. On his return to Manchester, Dalton began to write his *New System*,[10] which is dedicated to the 'Professors of the Universities, and other residents, of Edinburgh and Glasgow, who gave their attention and encouragement' to his lectures, as well as 'to the Members of the Literary and Philosophical Society of Manchester, who have uniformly promoted his researches'. Hope, in Edinburgh, did not accept the theory, saying in a letter of 2 January 1811 to Dalton that: 'I am by no means a convert to your doctrine, and do not approve of putting the results of speculative reasoning as experiment', whilst 'I admire the ingenuity of your speculations'.[11]

Besides the account in his book, which made Dalton's theory known to Berthollet and Avogadro, Thomson also explained it in his paper on oxalic

[1] *Ib.*, 515. [2] *Ib.*, 518. [3] *Ib.*, 519. [4] *Ib.*, 614, 617 f. [5] *Ib.*, 617 f.
[6] 1854, 84. [7] Roscoe and Harden, 7 f., 46, 79, 91 f. [8] (2), 1807, iii, 622.
[9] Smith, 1856, 58. [10] B, I, i, preface, vi. [11] Roscoe and Harden, 153.

acid,[1] and Wollaston[2] then mentioned it very favourably. Thomson[3] gives an amusing story of the attempts he and Wollaston made to convert Davy to the theory in the autumn of 1807; they were unsuccessful, but Wollaston soon after converted Davies Gilbert, who, says Thomson, 'had the merit of convincing Davy that his former opinions on the subject were wrong', and Davy 'ever after was a strenuous supporter of the theory'. But in 1811[4] Davy said: 'it is not, I conceive, on any speculations upon the ultimate particles of matter, that the true theory of definite proportions must ultimately rest.' He and Wollaston (see p. 702) inclined to the view that the use of equivalent or combining proportions was sufficient, without the hypothesis of atoms, but Thomson[5] said:

'unless we adopt the hypothesis with which Dalton set out, namely, that the ultimate particles of bodies are *atoms* incapable of further division, and that chemical combination consists in the union of these atoms with each other, we lose all the new light which the atomic theory throws upon chemistry.'

The Origin of Dalton's Atomic Theory

Meldrum[6] showed that all the accounts of the origin of Dalton's theory go back to Dalton himself: (1) Thomson's account of 1804 (p. 795), (2) the influence of Richter (p. 797), (3) the 'amended' theory of mixed gases (p. 781), and others. 'Apparently, Dalton never had in his mind a precise view of how the theory developed, and when invited to give one he produced, on the spur of the moment, an account to which he did, or did not, adhere on the next occasion.'

In 1845[7] it had been argued that Dalton arrived at his atomic theory from physical speculations about the atmosphere, beginning in his work on meteorology. In 1854, Henry[8] said: 'I am even inclined to suspect that the framing of the atomic hypothesis may have been the antecedent, and the discovery of multiple proportions the consequence, rather than the converse.' Wilson in 1862[9] emphasised the 'great unity and the impress of intellectual consistency ... stamped on all Dalton's labours', and from a careful analysis of the sequence and contents of Dalton's *published* memoirs and their relation to his early meteorological studies, inferred that Dalton was probably led to his atomic theory 'in the course of a purely physical enquiry into certain of the properties of a single class of bodies, the gases', the 'first glimpse' being in the work on solubilities in 1803. Nash adopted the last suggestion (see p. 790).

In his lectures of 1810 at the Royal Institution Dalton himself attributed the origin of the theory to his attempts to explain the phenomena of mixed gases,[10] and it seems certain that his earliest, 'physical', theory arose in this way. The 'chemical' theory was in existence on 6 September 1803; whether it developed from Dalton's work on the solubility of gases (p. 790) or on the composition of oxides of nitrogen (p. 791) is, I think, still uncertain.

[1] *Phil. Trans.*, 1808, xcviii, 63.   [2] *Ib.*, 96.   [3] (1), ii, 293.
[4] *Works*, 1840, v, 326.   [5] (1), ii, 294.
[6] *Chem. News*, 1910, cii, 1; *Manchester Mem.*, 1901–11, lv, no. 3.
[7] Anon., *Brit. Quart. Rev.*, 1845, i, 157.   [8] 1854, 222, 230.
[9] *Religio Chemici*, 1862, 331 f.   [10] Roscoe and Harden, 13 f.

A New System of Chemical Philosophy

Dalton's own book, *A New System of Chemical Philosophy*, was published in three parts in 1808 (2 ed. 1842), 1810, and 1827. Dalton sent out a prospectus dated 12 May 1808: 'In the Press (and will be ready for publication in June, price Seven Shillings, in Boards) Part I of a New System of Chemical Philosophy. By John Dalton', 4°, 2 ll. (printed on one side only); and on 22 June 1808 he sent 4 copies to Dr. Bostock of Liverpool, with a letter saying: 'you will find several things in it that have not been published before; when you will see how happily the atomic system in the sequel, will accommodate itself to the neutral salts, the oxides, &c. I think you can hardly withold your assent.'[1]

In his notebook in July 1808, Dalton speaks of his *New System of Chemistry*, and according to Kahlbaum[2] the title on the cover of the book as issued was: 'Dalton's New System of Chemistry. Part I. Price 7s.' My copy of the first part of Vol. II has: 'Dalton's New System of Chemistry. Vol. II (Part First). Bds. 10s. 6d.'

For Stahl everything was 'fundamental' (see Vol. II, p. 655), for Dalton it was 'new'. His little-known book on grammar is also a 'new system'.[3]

A full description of Dalton's book will now be given:

B (1). A New System of Chemical Philosophy. Part I. By John Dalton. Manchester: Printed by S. Russell, 125, Deansgate, for R. Bickerstaff, Strand, London, 1808 (referred to as Vol. I, pt. i), dedic. ('inscribed') to the 'Professors of the Universities, and other Residents of Edinburgh and Glasgow' and to the 'Members of the Literary and Philosophical Society of Manchester'; 8°, vi, [ii], 220 pp., 4 plates. (2) Part II (referred to as I, ii), Manchester: Printed by Russell and Allen, Deansgate, for R. Bickerstaff, Strand, London, 8°, 1810, 'inscribed' to Humphry Davy, Esq. Sec. R.S. and William Henry, M.D. F.R.S. Vice President of the Literary and Philosophical Society, Manchester, &c. &c., pagin. cont. with Pt. I, [viii], 221–548, Appendix, 549–60, plates 5–8. (3) Part First of Vol. II. By John Dalton, F.R.S. President of the Literary and Philosophical Society, Manchester; Corresponding Member of the Royal Academy of Sciences, Paris; Member of the Royal Academy, Munich, and of the Cæsarean Natural History Society, Moscow; Honorary Member of the Royal Society, Edinburgh, and of the Philosophical Societies of Bristol, Cambridge, Leeds, Sheffield and Yorkshire. Manchester: Printed by the Executors of S. Russell, for George Wilson, Essex Street, Strand, London, 8°, 1827, 'inscribed' to John Sharpe, Esq. F.R.S. of Stanmore, Middlesex, and Peter Ewart, Esq., pp. xiii, 357, [iii, list of Dalton's 'Books, Essays, &c'.] This third part was begun in 1817 and held up while Dalton made experiments; it was nearly completed in 1821 but was finally ready for publication only in 1827, when Dalton had finished his experiments on the metallic oxides, sulphides, and phosphides, and on alloys. By the time this part appeared much of it was out of date.

B (2). Second ed. of Part I. By John Weale, Architectural Library, High Holborn. Printed by Simpson and Gillett, Brown St., Manchester, 1842, on better paper and with better typography than the first edition, with a list of Dalton's titles: D.C.L., Ll.D., F.R.S.S.L. and E., M.R.I.A., Member of Royal Acad. of Sci. Paris, . . . &c &c.

[1] R. D. Gurney, *Cat.* 11 (1955), no. 118; R. G. Neville, *Ambix*, 1960, viii, 42.
[2] *Monographien*, 1898, ii, 76.
[3] *Elements of English Grammar: or a New System of Grammatical Instruction for the Use of Schools & Academies*, 12°, London (printed in Manchester), 1801 (120 pp.); 2 ed., 12°, London (printed in Birmingham), 1803 (123 pp.); dedicated to J. Horne Tooke, M.P.; the example 'phenomenon, phenomena' of gender marked by termination remains in the 2 ed.; the prefaces are dated Manchester, 10 March 1801, and 27 Sept. 1803.

In the preface Dalton says: 'The first Edition of this part of the work having been out of print for some years, the Author has been induced at the request of several of his friends to publish a second Edition, without making any material alterations in it. The feeble state of the Author's health, resulting from a long and severe illness which he experienced about five years ago has greatly interfered with his scientific pursuits; but he is now preparing for publication the following Essays, viz.:—

    1. On Microcosmic Salt.
    2. On the Sulphate of Magnesia, and the Biphosphate of Soda.
    3. On the Acid, Base and Water, of different Salts.
    4. On a simple and easy method of analysing Sugar.
    March, 1842.'

C. On the Phosphates & Arseniates, Microcosmic Salt, Acids, Bases, and Water, and a new and easy Method of Analysing Sugar. By John Dalton, D.C.L., F.R.S., &c. Manchester: John Harrison, Printer, Market Street, 1840–2; pp. [ii], 21 (1 plate), i [ii blank], 14, 10. On p. 21 *v* he says he proposed to publish three essays: (1) On the Mixture of Sulphate of Magnesia and Biphosphate of Soda. (2) On the Mixture of Biphosphate of Soda and Ammonia; — making Microcosmic Salt. (3) *Acid, Base* and *Water,* &c. *Solid* and *liquid* in all atoms. J.D.

The French chemists took an interest in the *New System.* Dalton wrote to his brother[1] that they 'speak very respectfully of the first part'. It was well received in Germany, and a translation of the first two parts was made by F. Wolff.[2] A large part of the first volume of the *New System* concerns heat, which Dalton (following Lavoisier) called caloric and believed to be material. He criticised the ordinary calorimetric method of determining specific heats; it assumes that the specific heat is constant and that the mercury thermometer gives a true measure of temperature. The ice calorimeter requires an accurate value of the latent heat of fusion, and some of the water formed on melting remains entangled in the ice. He used the method of cooling for liquids and the calorimetric method for solids.[3] His results[4] for solids are fairly good. The section on the specific heats of gases[5] gives only Crawford's results; Dalton considers, on the basis of them, whether (i) equal weights or (ii) equal bulks have the same quantity of heat, and concludes that neither is true. He says that: 'the quantity of heat belonging to the ultimate particles of all elastic fluids, must be the same under the same pressure and temperature', and that 'the specific heats of any two elastic fluids are inversely as the weights of their atoms or molecules'. This is not true, and it is curious that Dalton did not try a similar hypothesis with solids, when he might have anticipated Petit and Dulong's law of atomic heats (1809).

Dalton then[6] deals with heats of combustion, explaining the evolution of heat as due 'to the diminished capacities of the products' (Crawford's theory). In his experiments with gases, a known quantity in a bladder was burnt at a jet and the flame allowed to touch the concave bottom of a metal calorimeter containing water. Liquids were similarly burned in a lamp. Solids were burned on a stand under the calorimeter, except charcoal, which was burned by 'a gentle blast from a blow-pipe, directing the heat as much as possible upon the bottom of the vessel'. He gives tables of results for 1 lb. of each, with

[1] Henry, 1854, 64.
[2] *Ein neues System des chemischen Theiles der Naturwissenschaften,* 2 vols., Berlin, 1812–13.
[3] B, I, i, 54–66.   [4] Table, *ib.* 62.   [5] *Ib.,* 66–75.   [6] *Ib.,* 75–82.

the weight of oxygen combining with it, and compares them with the results of Lavoisier and Crawford; the weight of ice in lb. melted was calculated:

	Dalton	Lavoisier	Crawford
1 lb. Hydrogen melts	320	295	480
Phosphorus	60	100	—
Charcoal	40	96·5	69
Wax	104	133	97
Oil	104	148	89

Dalton remarks that 'both Crawford and Lavoisier have been, in some degree, led away by the notion, that oxygenous gas was the sole or principal source of the light and heat produced by combustion', whereas Crawford should have seen that 'hydrogenous gas, one of the most frequent and abundant combustibles, possessed nearly five times as much heat as the same weight of oxygenous gas'. Both the combustible and oxygen contribute and 'for aught we know to the contrary, in proportion to its specific heat before combustion'. A long section[1] is devoted to attempts to calculate the absolute zero of temperature (see p. 772).

Observations on the three states (solid, liquid, elastic fluid) of many bodies, e.g. water, had:

'tacitly led to the conclusion which seems universally adopted, that all bodies of sensible magnitude, whether liquid or solid, are constituted of a vast number of extremely small particles, or atoms of matter bound together by a force of attraction, which is more or less powerful according to circumstances, and which as it endeavours to prevent their separation, is very properly called in that view, *attraction of cohesion*; but as it collects them from a dispersed state (as from steam into water) it is called, *attraction of aggregation*, or more simply, *affinity* . . . we may conclude that *the ultimate particles of all homogeneous bodies are perfectly alike in weight, figure, &c* . . . every particle of water is like every other particle of water; every particle of hydrogen is like every other particle of hydrogen, &c.'

Besides the force of attraction we find another universal force acting on matter, viz. repulsion, which:

'is now generally, and I think properly, ascribed to the agency of heat. An atmosphere of this subtile fluid constantly surrounds the atoms of all bodies, and prevents them from being drawn into actual contact.'[2]

The brief account of the chemical atomic theory, 'On Chemical Synthesis',[3] lays down that the atoms of elements are unchanged in chemical processes:

'Chemical analysis and synthesis go no farther than to the separation of particles one from another, and to their reunion. No new creation or destruction of matter is within the reach of chemical agency. We might as well attempt to introduce a new planet into the solar system, or to annihilate one already in existence, as to create or destroy a particle of hydrogen;[4] it is one great object of this work, to shew the importance and advantage of ascertaining *the relative weights of the ultimate particles, both of simple and compound bodies, the number of simple elementary particles which constitute one compound particle, and the number of less compound particles which enter into the formation of one more compound particle*'.[5]

[1] *Ib.*, 82–99.   [2] B, I, i, 141–4; ACR, ii, 27 f.
[3] *Ib.*, 211–20; ACR, ii, 28 f.   [4] *Ib.*, 212.   [5] *Ib.*, 213; italics in original.

His attempts to realise these aims constitute what we may call *Dalton's* Atomic Theory. The recognition of compounds of different 'orders', afterwards so largely extended by Berzelius (see Vol. IV), is clear from the last words of the passage. Dalton proceeds, without any preamble, to say how the relative weights may be calculated:

'If there are two bodies, A and B, which are disposed to combine, the following is the order in which the combinations may take place, beginning with the most simple: namely,

1 atom of A + 1 atom of B = 1 atom of C, binary.
1 atom of A + 2 atoms of B = 1 atom of D, ternary.
2 atoms of A + 1 atom of B = 1 atom of E, ternary.
1 atom of A + 3 atoms of B = 1 atom of F, quaternary.
3 atoms of A + 1 atom of B = 1 atom of G, quaternary.
&c. &c.

The following general rules may be adopted as guides in all our investigations respecting chemical synthesis.

1st. When only one combination of two bodies can be obtained, it must be presumed to be a *binary* one, unless some cause appear to the contrary.

2d. When two combinations are observed, they must be presumed to be a *binary* and a *ternary*.

3d. When three combinations are obtained, we may expect one to be *binary*, and the other two *ternary*.

4th. When four combinations are observed, we should expect one *binary*, two *ternary*, and one *quaternary*, &c.

5th. A *binary* compound should always be specifically heavier than the mere mixture of its two ingredients.

6th. A *ternary* compound should be specifically heavier than the mixture of a binary and a simple, which would, if combined, constitute it; &c.

7th. The above rules and observations equally apply, when two bodies, such as C and D, D and E, &c. are combined.'

Dalton then gives a reference to his Plate 4 (Fig. 68), which 'contains the arbitrary marks as signs chosen to represent the several chemical elements or ultimate particles':

Fig.			Fig.		
1	Hydrog. its rel. weight	1	11	Strontites	46
2	Azote,	5	12	Barytes	68
3	Carbone or charcoal,	5	13	Iron	38
4	Oxygen,	7	14	Zinc	56
5	Phosphorus,	9	15	Copper	56
6	Sulphur,	13	16	Lead	95
7	Magnesia,	20	17	Silver	100
8	Lime,	23	18	Platina	100
9	Soda,	28	19	Gold	140
10	Potash,	42	20	Mercury	167

'Soda and potash . . . according to Mr. Davy's very important discoveries . . . are metallic oxides, potash a compound of an atom of metal 35 and one of oxygen 7, and soda of an atom of metal 21 and one of oxygen 7.'

21 An atom of water or steam, composed of 1 of oxygen and 1 of hydrogen, retained in physical contact by a strong affinity, and

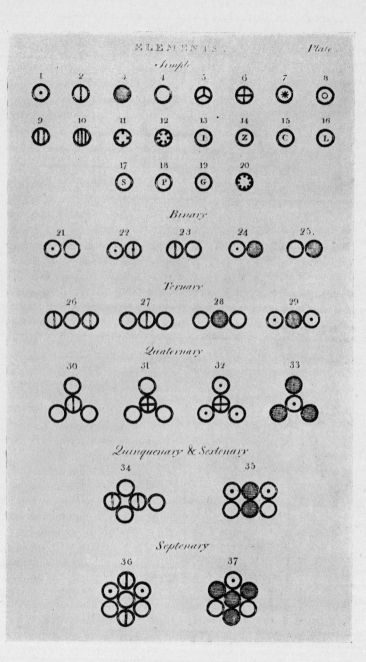

FIG. 68. DALTON'S SYMBOLS FOR ELEMENTS AND COMPOUNDS.
(*New System of Chemical Philosophy*, Vol. I, 1808.)

	supposed to be surrounded by a common atmosphere of heat; its relative weight =	8
22	An atom of ammonia, composed, of 1 azote and 1 of hydrogen	6
23	An atom of nitrous gas, composed of 1 of azote and 1 of oxygen	12
24	An atom of olefiant gas, composed of 1 of carbone and 1 of hydrogen	6
25	An atom of carbonic oxide composed of 1 of carbone and 1 oxygen	12
26	An atom of nitrous oxide, 2 azote + 1 oxygen	17
27	An atom of nitric acid, 1 azote + 2 oxygen	19
28	An atom of carbonic acid, 1 carbone + 2 oxygen	19
29	An atom of carburetted hydrogen, 1 carbone + 2 hydrogen	7
30	An atom of oxynitric acid,[1] 1 azote + 3 oxygen	26
31	An atom of sulphuric acid, 1 sulphur + 3 oxygen	34
32	An atom of sulphuretted hydrogen, 1 sulphur + 3 hydrogen	16
33	An atom of alcohol, 3 carbone + 1 hydrogen	16
34	An atom of nitrous acid, 1 nitric acid + 1 nitrous gas	31
35	An atom of acetous acid, 2 carbone + 2 water	26
36	An atom of nitrate of ammonia, 1 nitric acid + 1 ammonia + 1 water	33
37	An atom of sugar, 1 alcohol + 1 carbonic acid	35

In the second part of the *New System*[2] Dalton adds several new symbols and atomic weights:

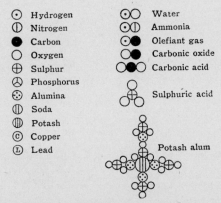

FIG. 69. DALTON'S SYMBOLS AND FORMULAE.
(From his *New System of Chemical Philosophy*, Vol. I, Part i, 1808; Part ii, 1810.)

1	Oxygen	7	8	Platina	100?
2	Hydrogen	1	9	Silver	100
3	Azote	5	10	Mercury	167
4	Carbone	5·4	11	Copper	56
5	Sulphur	13	12	Iron	50
6	Phosphorus	9	13	Nickel	25? 50?
7	Gold	140?	14	Tin	50

[1] What Dalton calls oxynitric acid, here formulated as NO_3, is 'formed by mixing nitrous gas with excess of oxygen'; Diary, 2 November 1806, where it is formulated N_2O_5; Roscoe and Harden, 75.

[2] B, 1810, I, ii, 546, Plates 5 and 6.

15	Lead	95	26	Potash	42
16	Zinc	56	27	Soda	28
17	Bismuth	68?	28	Lime	24
18	Antimony	40	29	Magnesia	17
19	Arsenic	42?	30	Barytes	68
20	Cobalt	55?	31	Strontites	46
21	Manganese	40?	32	Alumine	15
22	Uranium	60?	33	Silex	45
23	Tungsten	56?	34	Yttria	53
24	Titanium	40?	35	Glucine	30
25	Cerium	45?	36	Zircone	45

The 'symbols of compound elements' (*sic*) in Plate 6 include (38) fluoric acid (regarded as HO_2), (39) muriatic acid (regarded as HO_3) and (40) oxymuriatic acid (chlorine, regarded as HO_4). Potash and soda are elements, (2) potasium (*sic*) is 'hydruret of potash', (5) sodium is hydruret of soda. The alkaline earths (28–31), alumina (32), silica (33) and other earths are elements. (20) is potash alum (see Fig. 69), 21 is 'potasiuretted silex or glass', 25 is 'fluate of silex' (silicon fluoride) and 27 is 'oxymuriate of olefiant gas' (ethylene dichloride). 26 'subpotasiuretted ammonia' is potassamide.

The formulae of other compounds, in modern symbols, are:

sulphurous oxide	SO	phosphuretted hydrogen	PH
sulphurous acid	SO_2	phosphorous acid	P_2O_2
sulphuric acid	SO_3	phosphoric acid	PO_2
sulphuretted hydrogen	HS	phosphorus sulphides	PS and P_2S
persulphuretted hydrogen	HS_2	oxymuriate of olefiant gas	$2CH + HO_4$

Dalton gives reasons for regarding potassium and sodium as hydrides of potash and soda.[1]

Gay-Lussac and Thenard, and Berthollet, had proved that caustic potash and soda contain water in a definite proportion, but as Davy had obtained only the metal and oxygen by electrolysis of them, the metals must contain anhydrous soda or potash combined with the missing hydrogen. 'Mr. Davy still adheres to his original views, the only rational ones' as long as the fused alkalis were thought to be oxides, but they are now known to contain water. Davy had found that on heating potassium in fluoric acid vapour, fluate of potash and a little hydrogen are formed, and Dalton said he found on sparking fluoric acid vapour and hydrogen there is a diminution, but much greater in the hydrogen, and this formed water with oxygen in the fluoric acid. Since 1 at. H and 2 at. O make $1 + 14 = 15$, the at. wt. of fluoric acid, the latter is probably HO_2.[2] For muriatic acid[3] Dalton relied on Henry's experiments on sparking the gas over mercury, when a little hydrogen was formed, and Davy's on heating potassium in it, when muriate of potash and hydrogen were produced, and by a quantitative argument Dalton reached the conclusion that the acid was $HO_3 = 22$. The hypotheses are not just mere assumptions by Dalton.

[1] *Ib.*, 484, 502; *Nicholson's J.*, 1811, xxix, 129.   [2] B, I, ii, 283–6.   [3] *Ib.*, 288–94.

Dalton gives[1] a table containing 'diameters of atoms', and 'number of atoms in a given volume', air being taken as 1 and 1000, respectively:

	Wt. of 100 cu. in. in grains	Diam.	No. of atoms		Wt. of 100 cu. in. in grains	Diam.	No. of atoms
Air	31	—	—	Carbonic oxide	29	1·020	940
Hydrogen	2·5	1·000	1000	Carbonic acid	47	1·00	1000
Oxygen	34	·794	2000	Sulphurous acid	71	·95	1170
Azote	30·2	·747	2400	Olefiant gas	29·5	·81	1890
Muriatic acid	39·5	1·12	700	Carburetted hyd.	18·6	1·00	1000
Ammonia	18·6	·909	1330	Sulphuretted hyd.	36	1·00	1000
Oxymuriatic acid	76	·981	1060	Phosphur. hyd.	26	1·00	1000
Nitrous gas	32·2	·980	1060	Superflu. of silex	130	1·15	658
Nitrous oxide	50	·947	1180				

He also gives the volume and weight percentage compositions of 17 gases and vapours, the volumes of the constituents in 100 vols. being:

ammonia	$52N + 133H$	carb. oxide	$47O$ + charcoal
water	$100O + 200H$*	carb. acid	$100O$ + charcoal
nitrous gas	$46N + 55O$	carbur. hyd.	$200H + 1$ pt. charcoal
nitrous oxide	$99N + 58O$	olefiant gas	$200H + 2$ pts. charcoal
nitric acid	180 nit. gas $+ 100O$	sulph. hyd.	$100H$ + sulphur
nitrous acid	360 nit. gas $+ 100O$	muriate of am.	100 mur. ac. $+ 100NH_3$ gas
sulphs. acid	$100O$ + sulphur	carb. of am.	100 carb. acid $+ 80$ NH_3 gas
sulph. acid	100 sulphs. ac. $+ 50O$		

* 'I believe 197 is nearer the truth.'

The figures only rarely agree with Gay-Lussac's law of combining volumes, which Dalton never accepted (see Vol. IV).

Nitrous anhydride (N_2O_3) was regarded by Dalton (since 12 October 1803, see p. 785) as a binary compound of two binary compound atoms ($NO + NO_2$), and similarly some other complex compounds (e.g. alcohol). Dalton used to say, in his Quaker turn of speech: 'Thou knows ... no man can split an atom', and when referred to the sesquioxides (such as N_2O_3), apparently containing $1\frac{1}{2}$ atoms of oxygen to 1 of the other element, he said: 'Yes, but *they* are 3 atoms to 2.'[2]

In his criticism of Dalton's atomic theory, Berthollet[3] points out that the assumption of combination one atom with one atom is arbitrary:

'it seems that one takes a more certain route by importing greater exactness in experiment, by seeking means of multiplying it, and of evaluating all the circumstances; in making more rigorous analyses and drawing general consequences immediately from the facts, or by an induction more or less direct, more or less combined (*combinée*), more or less probable, from well determined properties, than by engaging in hypothetical speculations on the number, arrangement and figure of the molecules, which escape all experience.'

Bostock[4] also criticised Dalton's rule that in case only one compound is known it is binary (1 atom of each), and his other rules of combination; Bostock says that the atomic theory is not in agreement with analyses quoted by Thomson. 'Mr. Dalton must first prove, that the analyses are incorrect, and must rectify

[1] *Ib.*, 560.   [2] Henry, 1854, 222.
[3] Introd. to Riffault's French tr. of T. Thomson, *Système de Chimie*, 1809, i, 26–7.
[4] *Nicholson's J.*, 1811, xxviii, 280–92; cf. Dalton, *ib.*, 81.

them.' Bostock prefers the name 'particle' to atom and a note by 'C.' says the name 'molecule' is objectionable, as it gives rise to a ridiculous suggestion (mollycoddle ?).

Although Dalton[1] himself had said (before the discovery of hydrogen peroxide by Thenard in 1818): 'After all, it must be allowed to be possible that water may be a ternary compound', either H_2O or HO_2, when the atomic weight of oxygen would be $2 \times 7 = 14$, or $7 \times \frac{1}{2} = 3\frac{1}{2}$, he replied in full to Bostock, with whom he was on friendly terms (see p. 799):[2]

'When an element A has an affinity for another B, I see no mechanical reason why it should not take as many atoms of B as are presented to it, and can possibly come into contact with it (which may probably be 12 in general), *except so far as the repulsion of the atoms of B among themselves are more than a match for the attraction of an atom of A.* Now this repulsion begins with 2 atoms of B to one of A, in which case the two atoms of B are diametrically opposed; it increases with 3 atoms of B to 1 of A, in which case the atoms of B are only 120° asunder; with 4 atoms of B it is still greater, as the distance is then only 90°; and so on in proportion to the number of atoms.'

In a footnote he says if the repulsion of 2 atoms of B opposite is 1, that of 3 atoms is 2 and that of 4 atoms is 3, if the force is inversely proportional to the distance.

In 1808[3] Dalton had stated that a binary compound is specifically heavier than a mixture of its ingredients (see p. 802); according to Meldrum[4] he saw this was not true for hydrochloric acid and in 1810[5] he says: 'Carbonic acid is of greater specific gravity than carbonic oxide; and on that account, it may be presumed to be the ternary or more complex element [*sic*]'; hence Meldrum thinks Dalton changed his mind in the interval. This is not the case, since Dalton is here comparing two *compounds*, not a compound and a *mixture* of its elements. Dalton maintained his original statement in 1811,[6] saying that it was 'based on a principle recognised by chemists as *general* if not *universal*; namely that condensation of volume is a necessary consequence of the expulsion of heat by the exertion of affinity', referring to water and ammonia as examples.

In 1824[7] Dalton said nitrous gas (nitric oxide, NO) is a binary compound $(N + O)$ because, when compared with other *compounds* of oxygen and nitrogen, 'its having the least specific gravity of any of them' shows that it is less complex than nitrous oxide, which Dalton correctly represented as N_2O. In 1811[8] he emphasised that he had said in 1808 that if only one compound of two elements is known 'it must be presumed to be a binary one *unless some cause appear to the contrary*'. Even if carbonic acid gas were the only known compound of carbon and oxygen it would still have been represented as OCO (CO_2) by analogy with other acids; 'like them it ought to contain at least two atoms of oxygen to one of base', and here 'some cause' was apparent 'to the contrary'.

Dalton could not agree with Bostock that the rule of binary compounds is arbitrary:

[1] B, 1810, I, ii, 276.   [2] *Nicholson's J.*, 1811, xxix, 147; italics in original.
[3] B, I, i, 214.   [4] (5), 7.   [5] B, I, ii, 369.
[6] *Nicholson's J.*, 1811, xxix, 148.
[7] Henry, 1854, 140.   [8] *Nicholson's J.*, 1811, xxix, 149.

'I hope such remarks will be no more advanced; and farther, that if any one should inquire, for instance, why 1 part of carbon, which takes 1·28 oxigen, or 2·56, does not also occasionally take 3·84 and 5·12 parts of oxigen, it will be understood, that the reason I should assign is, that in the state of carbonic acid there are two atoms of oxigen combined with one of carbon, and a third or fourth atom of oxigen, however it may be attracted by the carbon, cannot join it without expelling one or more of the atoms of oxigen already in conjunction. The attraction of the carbon is able to restrain the mutual repulsion of two atoms of oxigen, but not of three or more.'

This argument is reproduced by William Henry,[1] and was provided with a detailed proof based on Newton[2] by Peter Ewart.[3] William Higgins's ideas (see p. 743) seem to me to be different, since they are based mainly on the weakening of the *attractive* force due to its subdivision on the successive addition of particles to one particle of an attracting element.

Dalton says:[4] 'Though I am fully persuaded we are in possession of data sufficient to decide upon the relative *weight* of atoms, we are not in regard to their *size*.' The mercury atom is larger than the hydrogen atom but not in such a large ratio as the weights of 170 to 1. He agrees with Newton who had said:[5] 'God is able to create Particles of Matter of several Sizes and Figures, and in several Proportions to Space, and perhaps of different Densities and Forces.' This shows, says Dalton, that Newton had already suspected that the 'densities' (weights) of the atoms are different (see Vol. II, p. 475).

The second primary object of his researches stated in 1808 by Dalton,[6] viz. the determination of formulæ, was not successfully achieved. He had to confess in 1827[7] that there were two possible sets of formulae for the oxides of nitrogen, the choice between which might be possible from a study of compounds of carbon, hydrogen, oxygen and nitrogen; 'but it will be seen that I am not satisfied on this head, either by my own labour or that of others, chiefly through the want of an accurate knowledge of combining proportions.' A new *theoretical* principle (Avogadro's hypothesis) was, in fact, required (Vol. IV).

In a long undated (1831 ?) letter to Daubeny[8] Dalton refers to the multiple proportions exhibited by the oxides of nitrogen, says the atomic weight of nitrogen is 7 and not 14 ('too hastily adopted by Drs. Wollaston, Thomson, &c.' from Berzelius), gives four reasons why nitrous gas (NO) is 'the most simple of the combinations of azote and oxygen', and correctly formulates these oxides as N_2O, NO, N_2O_3, NO_2 and N_2O_5, with Berzelius, who 'now agrees with me'. (Berzelius was actually the first to give the correct formula N_2O_5 for nitric anhydride, which Dalton had formulated as NO_2.)

Dalton's Atomic Weights

Dalton varied the numbers he took for the atomic weights from time to time; the table[9] on pages 810 and 811 gives the values of these. The sources of many of these (those for col. II were given on p. 784) were

[1] *Elements of Experimental Chemistry*, 7 ed., 1815, i, 85.
[2] *Principia*, Bk. ii, prop. 23, theorem 18; London, 1687, 301.
[3] *Ann. Phil.*, 1815, vi, 376.   [4] *Nicholson's J.*, 1811, xxix, 150.
[5] *Opticks*, Query 31; 1730, 379.   [6] B, I, i, 213; see p. 801.
[7] *Ib.*, II, i, 351.   [8] *Atomic Theory*, Oxford, 1831, 133 f.; 2 ed., 1850, 475–9.
[9] Gee, Coward, and Harden, 1914–15, 46.

given by Roscoe and Harden.[1] In 1805 (the first published table) Dalton changed azote to 4·2 from Berthollet's analysis of ammonia.[2] The value 5 (cols. VIII–XVI) was based on Davy's analyses of oxides of nitrogen (giving 5·6 for $O = 7$) and ammonia 4·7 with $H = 1$.[3] Dalton did not see that the formula NH is incompatible with his (correct) formulae for the oxides of nitrogen and took an average 5·1, rounded off to 5. The values for carbon are all from Lavoisier's result for carbon dioxide, with the different values for oxygen, the value 7 for oxygen being the 6·93 from Gay-Lussac and Humboldt's figure from the synthesis of water (87·4 p.c. oxygen) rounded off. The values for sulphur are varying; that in XV is based on the formula SO_3 for sulphuric acid $3 \times 7 + 13 = 34$, giving 38·3 p.c. sulphur (correct is 40). Phosphorus is based on Lavoisier's composition of P_2O_5 (39·4 p.c. P) assuming PO_2, with oxygen 5·5, giving $P = 7·2$ in VII. The values in VIII–XVIII are based on the incorrect result that phosphoretted hydrogen contains its own volume of hydrogen, has the density 10 ($H = 1$) and the formula PH. The sources of the values for alkalis, alkaline earths, and metals are considered by Roscoe and Harden. A table of atomic weights, undated, but probably written by Dalton some time between 1818 and 1827, includes hydrogen peroxide and 'oxymuriatic acid (chlorine) 29 or 30'.[4] Many of Dalton's atomic weights are improved if they are recalculated on the basis oxygen = 8 instead of oxygen = 7 (which he used in his later tables).[5]

In Vol. II, pt. i of his *New System* (1827) Dalton records a number of experiments on the atomic weights of metals, made over a period of years. He gives four methods in use for the analysis of oxides (i–iv) and adds two new ones (v–vi):

(i) Burn a known weight of metal in air or oxygen and weigh the oxide.

(ii) Dissolve a known weight of metal in acid, precipitate the hydrated oxide by an earth or alkali, ignite and weigh (Dalton does not seem to have recognised hydroxides or hydrated oxides as definite compounds).

(iii) Transfer oxygen from the oxide to another metal.

(iv) Find the volume of hydrogen evolved by solution of the metal in an acid and allow half that volume for the equivalent of oxygen.

(v) Treat the lower oxide in solution with a solution of oxymuriate of lime (bleaching powder) to precipitate a higher oxide.

(vi) Find the volume of nitrous gas (NO) evolved during the solution of a given weight of metal in nitric acid.

Method (vi), which might seem unpromising, gave Dalton some accurate values, better than those of most contemporary analysts. With platinum and gold he used aqua regia. He assumed the reactions:

$$Me + N_2O_5 = MeO_3 + 2NO, \qquad 2Me + MeO_3 = 3MeO,$$

[1] 1896, 81–98; for the values reported by Thomson in 1807, see p. 797.
[2] *Obs. Phys.*, 1786, xxix, 175; 121N to 29H, 121/29 = 4·2.
[3] Davy, *Researches*, 1800, 61, gave 4.   [4] Loewenfeld, 1913.
[5] Marsh, *The Origins and Growth of Chemical Science*, 1929, 74.

2D

	I	II	III	IV	V	VI	VII	VIII	IX
Hydrogen	1	1	1	1	1	1	1	1	1
Oxygen	7	5·66	5·66	5·5	[5·5]	5·5	5·5	7	7
Azote	5	4	4	4		4·2	4·2	5	5
Carbone	5·4	4·5	4·4			[4·3]	4·3	5	5
Sulphur	12	17	14·4			[14·4]	14·4	22	22 –
Phosphorus	9		7·2				7·2	9⅓	9 +
Potash	42							18?	22 +
Soda	28							28	26 28 }
Lime	23							22	22 10? }
Magnesia	20							20?	20±
Strontian	46							38 42 }	44?
Barytes	68							76?	48
Alumine	—							(11) 36?	30 40 60 }
Gold	140				105			140	
Platina	100								
Silver	100				105			63	
Mercury	167				105			133 112 }	
Copper	56				44			56	
Iron	40				16			19? 38? }	33? 66 }
Tin	—				22			36	
Lead	95				105			63	
Zinc	56				22			50 +	
Bismuth					22			60	
Antimony									
Arsenic								25 50 } ?	
Manganese					16			56	

I. Lecture Sheet (1806–7?).
II. 6 Sept. 1803 (Notebook, I, 248).
III. 19 Sept. 1803 (Notebook, I, 258).
IV. Sept. 1803 (Notebook, I, 260).
V. March 1804 (Notebook, I, 381–2).
VI. 14 Sept. 1804 (Notebook, II, 107).
VII. 1805 (*Manch. Mem.*, 1805, vi, 287).
VIII. 14 Aug. 1806 (Notebook, II, 284).
IX. 23 Aug. 1806 (Notebook, II, 282).
X. 16 Sept. 1806 (Notebook, II, 247).

X	XI	XII	XIII	XIV	XV	XVI	XVII	XVIII	XIX
1	1	1	1	1	1	1	1	1	
7		7	7		7	7		7	7
5		5	5		5	5		5± or 10?	
5		5	5·4		5	5·4		5·4	
12		12			13	13		13 or 14	
		9⅓			9	9		9	10
42		42	42		42	42			42
28		28	28		28	28		28	28
23		23	23		23	24		24	24
20		20	20		20	17		17	17 or 17½
46		46	46		46	46		46	
68		68	68		68	68		68	
		11?				15		20	
	140–50				140	140?	90} 45}	60±	
	90–100				100	100?	90	73	
115	100±	100±		100	100	100	90	90	
		166		166	167	167	167	167 or 84	167
		56		56	56	56	56	56 or 28	
29} 58}		40		50	38	50	50} 25}	25	
	70			50–60		50	52	52	
106} 90}		95		95	95	95	90	90	
52		56		56	56	56	29	29	
	117±			62		68?	62	62	
	32–44			37? 50? 40		40	40	40	
	40–48			42?		42?	21	21	21
	58?			63		40?	25	25	

XI. Sept. 1806 (Notebook, II, 255).
XII. 22 Oct. 1806 (Notebook, II, 256).
XIII. Spring, 1807 (Edinb. and Glasgow lects.).
XIV. July, 1807 (Notebook, II, 421).
XV. *New System*, 1808.
XVI. *New System*, 1810.
XVII. 2 May, 1815 (Notebook, VI, 227).
XVIII. *New System*, 1827.
XIX. *On the Phosphates & Arseniates*, etc. (C, p. 800), 1840–2 (I have added this column).

hence (taking $O = 7$, $N = 5$) 3×7 pts. of oxygen go to the metal and $2(5 + 7)$ pts. of nitrous gas are evolved; $\frac{7}{8}$ of the weight of nitrous gas is thus the weight of oxygen combined with the metal. Dalton took the specific gravity (air $= 1$) of nitrous gas as $1 \cdot 04$, the correct figure being $1 \cdot 038$. If Dalton's results are recalculated with the correct atomic weights of oxygen and nitrogen they are surprisingly good,[1] and the common opinion that he was an inaccurate quantitative worker is without foundation.

Reception of Dalton's Atomic Theory

The atomic theory was adopted with great enthusiasm by Thomas Thomson and by Berzelius (see Vol. IV). Thomson gave the first published account of the theory in 1807 (see p. 796), which was followed by a series of papers[2] 'On the Daltonian Theory of Definite Proportions in Chemical Combination', in which he surveys, tabulates, recalculates and criticises all the available experimental material (including that of Berzelius). His own work on the oxalates (see p. 719) had given an experimental background, and he was very near the theory before Dalton. Thomson calculated a number of atomic weights on a standard oxygen $= 1$, rather than Dalton's hydrogen $= 1$, explaining that oxygen forms a larger number of compounds than any other element, and atomic weights had mostly been deduced from analyses of oxygen compounds. In Thomson's table on this standard the atomic weights of at least eight elements are whole numbers, whilst on the standard $H = 1$ they would mostly contain fractions. In his first set of papers Thomson[3] gave the following values, those in brackets[4] referring to oxygen $= 8$:

O	1·000 (8·00)	K	5·000 (40·00)	Cu	8·000 (64·00)
H	0·132 (1·06)	Na	5·882 (47·06)	Fe	6·666 (53·33)
C	0·751 (6·01)	Ca	2·620 (20·96)	Sn	14·705 (117·64)
N	0·878 (7·02)	Ag	12·618 (100·94)	Pb	25·974 (207·79)
P	1·320 (10·56)	Hg	25·000 (200·00)	Zn	4·315 (34·52)
S	2·000 (16·00)				

The weight of the oxygen atom is $7 \cdot 5$ times that of the hydrogen atom, and the combining volumes show that a given volume of hydrogen contains only half as many atoms as an equal volume of oxygen.

Thomson assumed that all compounds contain a single atom of one of the elements, e.g. the nitrogen oxides $2N + O$, $N + O$, $N + 2O$ (nitrous acid) and $N + 3O$ (hyponitric acid), ammonia $N + H$, potash $K + O$ and a superoxide $K + 3O$, soda $Na + 2O$ and a superoxide $Na + 3O$, oxides of lead $Pb + 2O$, $Pb + 3O$, $Pb + 4O$, and zinc $Zn + O$, etc. Thomson's formulae for oxides (unlike Dalton's) are not equivalents in neutralising acids; in neutral salts of potash and zinc oxide, 1 atom of base takes 1 atom of acid, while soda and lead oxide take 2 atoms of acid.

---

[1] Trengrove, *M.Sc. Dissert.*, London, 1954.
[2] *Ann. Phil.*, 1813, ii, 32, 109, 167, 293; 1814, iii, 134, 375; 1814, iv, 11, 83; 1818, xii, 338, 436.
[3] *Ann. Phil.*, 1813, ii, 42, 46–7.   [4] Calculated by Kopp, (3), 361.

Apart from William Henry, who was at first rather sceptical, Thomson was the only British chemist to support Dalton without reservation in the years immediately following the enunciation of the atomic theory. Henry in 1810,[1] with a reference to Dalton's *New System* (1808), said:

'This doctrine, it must be confessed, cannot at present be regarded in any other light than that of an hypothesis . . . which has been developed with great ingenuity and patience of investigation, and which is supported by many striking and daily increasing analogies. The hypothesis, therefore, although its leading principle be a gratuitous assumption, must stand or fall by the results of analysis. The instances in which it agrees with these results, are already very numerous; and none have hitherto been shown to be directly contradictory to it.'

He gives some diagrams, including one of 'an atom of water or steam, composed of one oxygen and one hydrogen, retained in physical contact by a strong affinity; and supposed to be surrounded by a common atmosphere of heat' (Dalton's description, see p. 804). The much longer account in 1815[2] is distinctly more favourable, yet:

'it would be claiming too much . . . for the theory of Mr. Dalton to assert that, in its present state, it is to be considered as fully established in all its details. In the further progress of chemical discovery, it is probable that it will receive considerable modifications, and that the relative weights of the atoms of bodies will, in many cases, be essentially changed . . . the universality of its application to chemical phenomena will be scarcely inferior to that of the law of gravitation in explaining the facts of chemical philosophy.'

An account of the atomic theory appeared in America in 1819, written by the Irishman William James Macneven (Co. Galway, 21 March 1763–New York, 12 July 1841).[3]

The Composition of Inflammable Air

Reference has been made (p. 271) to the confusion of different inflammable gases by Priestley, Watt, Lavoisier, and Berthollet by calling them 'inflammable air'. The name 'light inflammable air' was used fairly early for hydrogen, also called by Cavendish 'inflammable air from metals'. The name 'heavy inflammable air' was used indifferently for carbon monoxide, water-gas (a mixture of hydrogen and carbon monoxide, called by Berthollet 'oxycarburetted hydrogen'), and methane. Methane and ethylene (olefiant gas) were also called 'light' and 'heavy' carburetted hydrogen, respectively.[4] William Higgins[5] correctly said that 'neglecting to discriminate between the light and heavy inflammable airs, has been the chief cause of all the errors and confusion that at present prevail in the science of chemistry'. The clarification occurred in

[1] *Elements of Experimental Chemistry*, 6 ed., 1810, i, 81–2; ii, 475–8; in i, 72–81, he gives a much longer account of Berthollet's theory of mass action and combination in *indefinite* proportions.

[2] *Elements of Chemistry*, 7 ed., 1815, i, 27–38.

[3] *Exposition of the Atomic Theory of Chymistry, and the Doctrine of Definite Proportions, with an Appendix of Chymical Exercises by the Pupils at the Laboratory*, New York, 1819, 103 pp.; *Ann. Phil.*, 1820, xvi, 195, 289, 338; *J. de Phys.*, 1821, xcii, 274, 376, 444; Reilly, *Chymia*, 1949, ii, 17.

[4] See Murray, 1806, ii, 376 f.; Henry, *Elements of Chemistry*, 1815, i, 304 f.; Murray, *Elements of Chemical Science*, London, 1818, 151 (light inflammable air, obtained by heating wet charcoal to redness, composed of 72 carbon and 28 hydrogen; it really consists of carbon monoxide and hydrogen).

[5] *Comparative View of the Phlogistic and Antiphlogistic Theories*, 1789, 250.

stages: the discovery of marsh-gas (methane) and of its composition by Volta (1776), the discovery of the composition of carbon monoxide by Cruickshank and by Clement and Desormes (1801), and the clear distinction between methane and ethylene (olefiant gas) by Dalton (1804). These stages will now be considered in detail separately.

The Discovery of Marsh Gas

The collection of inflammable marsh gas is described by Volta in some letters to Carlo Giuseppi Campi, dated from Como the 14, 21 and 26 November, and 18 December 1776.[1] Campi had observed the source of inflammable air in S. Colombet; Volta found it in Lake Como, etc., and collected it by stirring the mud with a stick and letting the bubbles pass into an inverted bottle filled with water. He distinguished it from the 'inflammable air from metals' (hydrogen) by its azure-blue flame and slower combustion, and by its requiring 10–12 vols. of air for detonation. A much larger electric spark was necessary to ignite marsh gas than to ignite hydrogen. Volta, who invented the 'electric pistol', thought detonating gas could be used as a propellant. He found that when a mixture of air and hydrogen is exploded over water there is a diminution in volume greater than the volume of hydrogen added, and phlogisticated air remains; and he proposed to determine the proportion of vital air in this way in 1778. In a letter of 1778 Volta supposed that the flames of wood, paper, wax, oil, pitch, alcohol, ether, and even sulphur are due to marsh gas or inflammable air, which he supposed was a compound of phlogiston with an acid, or sometimes with the volatile alkali, since Priestley had obtained inflammable air by sparking the latter (see p. 265), and Austin[2] called this gas 'heavy inflammable air'.

In 1778 Le Roi[3] described some of Volta's experiments as shown to the Paris Academy by Dietrich, on the properties of marsh gas, including the explosion with 9 to 10 parts of air in a graduated tube. In a letter to Priestley[4] Volta described the inflammation of common and inflammable airs in a closed

[1] *Lettre del Signor Don Alessandro Volta . . . sull' aria infiammabile nativa delle paludi*, Milan, 1777; *Lettres de Mr. A. Volta . . . sur l'air inflammable des marais; aux quelles ou a ajouté trois lettres du même auteur tirées du Journal de Milan*, Strasbourg, 1778; Volta, *Opere*, 1816, iii, 1 f., 131 f., 176, 195; letters to Priestley, in Priestley, E & O, 1777, iii, 380 (letters of 8, 14, and 15 January 1777); Volta, *Briefe über die entzündbare Luft der Sümpfe*, tr. C. H. Köstlin, Strassburg, 1778 (t.p. v ll. 226 pp., 1 plate); Volta's letters and papers on marsh gas and the eudiometers will be found in *Le Opere di Alessandro Volta. Edizione Nazionale*, Milan, 1928, Vol. vi, 15–102 (*Lettre*, Milan, 1777), 103 (summary in Amoretti, *Scelte di Opuscoli interessante*, 4°, 1784, iii, 153–67), 121 (3 letters on electric pistol), 151 (4 letters on inflammable and dephlogisticated airs to Landriani), 171 (2 letters to Priestley on inflammable air and a new eudiometer, in Amoretti, *Scelte*, 1784, iii, 432–9), 176 (facsimile and plate of eudiometer type A, from *Obs. Phys.*, 1778, xii, 365 and plate III; see p. 326), 255 (2 letters to Senebier on inflammable air), 269 (3 letters to Senebier on species of airs), 291 (on inflammable air eudiometer, sketch on p. 294), 329 (on different kinds of air, lectures in 1783–4 in Pavia), 345 f. (extracts on airs by Volta in Italian ed. of Macquer's *Dictionary*, Pavia, 1783), opp. p. 392 (photograph of Volta's eudiometer, in Como); *Opere*, 1929, vii, 3 (art. on heat in Macquer, 1783), 49 (art. on phlogiston in do.), 61 (art. on eudiometer in do.), 173 (eudiometer type B, from Brugnatelli's *Annali di Chimica*, 1790–1, and *J. de Phys.*, 1805, xiii, 151; see p. 327), 257 (phosphorus eudiometer of 1796); see F. Scolari, *Alessandro Volta, Guide Bibliographique*, Rome, 1927, nos. 33–40, pp. 77 f., also pp. 198 f. for other letters on inflammable air; Fourcroy, (2), 1796, iii, 493 f.; Roscoe and Schorlemmer, *Treatise*, 1885, III, i, 190.

[2] *Phil. Trans.*, 1790, lxxx, 51.
[3] *Obs. Phys.*, 1778. xi. 401.   [4] *Obs. Phys.*, 1778, xii, 365 and Plate III (November).

graduated glass eudiometer provided with stopcocks and a brass wire for passing the electric spark, in this way measuring the 'goodness' of the air: he points out its advantages over the nitric oxide method. A second long letter to Priestley[1] describes experiments on the limits of inflammation of mixtures of air and oxygen with hydrogen, and the diminution on explosion, with explanations based on the phlogiston theory. Neret[2] distinguished inflammable oil gas from hydrogen and from marsh gas by its luminous flame and greater density.

An improved graduated glass eudiometer (type B) (Fig. 31) with a funnel and metal stopcock below and a metal cap with an insulated sparking wire at the top, was described by Volta in 1790.[3] Excess of hydrogen was added to a known volume of air, the mixture exploded by a spark, and one-third of the contraction gave the volume of oxygen.

What were called 'Volta's eudiometers' by English workers varied considerably in shape and were usually different from those described by Volta. Some were pear-shaped vessels of thick glass with a stopcock and provided with firing wires; others were thick glass cylinders with sparking wires sealed through the closed top; others straight tubes with a single sealed-in wire for sparking to the mercury inside the tube.[4] Dalton's eudiometer (Fig. 70) bequeathed to W. C. Henry, was a thick pear-shaped glass globe with a stopcock in the lower neck and copper wires for sparking fitted into the upper part (see p. 333).[5]

Bryan Higgins[6] by heating potassium acetate obtained fixable air (carbon dioxide) and a 'heavy inflammable air', which was methane. W. Austin[7] found on sparking 'heavy inflammable air' that he obtained an increase in volume, and he supposed that phlogisticated air (nitrogen) and hydrogen were formed. He made some experiments on exploding heavy inflammable air and light inflammable air (hydrogen) with dephlogisticated air (oxygen), finding that the first gave fixed air (carbon dioxide) and the second water. From various experiments Austin concluded that 'the phlogisticated and heavy inflammable airs combined, constitute charcoal', but he confused methane and carbon monoxide. William Henry[8] found that methane after sparking gives the same quantity of carbonic acid with oxygen as before and that when dried it is only slightly decomposed on

FIG. 70. DALTON'S EUDIOMETER.

sparking; the hydrogen formed in Austin's experiments came from moisture in the gas.

[1] *Obs. Phys.*, 1779, xiii, 278, and Plate I (April).   [2] *Obs. Phys.*, 1779, xiv, 126, 292.
[3] *Annali di Chimica*, 1790, i, 171; *Opere*, 1816, iii, 195 and plate II; *J. de Phys.*, 1805, xiii, 151; Lowry, *Historical Introduction to Chemistry*, 1915, 122, Fig. 27.
[4] See figs. 29*a* and *b*, plate II; fig. 34, plate IX; fig. 1, plate X; in Henry, *Elements of Experimental Chemistry*, 7 ed., 1815, i; 9 ed., 1823, ii.
[5] F. Jones, 1904; see Dalton's description of Volta's eudiometer in B, I, ii, 274.
[6] *Experiments and Observations relating to Acetous Acid, Fixable Air, Dense Inflammable Air,* etc., 1786, 31 f., 147, 285 f.
[7] *Phil. Trans.*, 1790, lxxx, II, 51.   [8] *Phil. Trans.*, 1797, lxxxvii, 401; 1800, xc, 188.

Carbon Monoxide

The composition of various combustible gases was given by Cruickshank[1] in the paper in which he established the identity of carbon monoxide and determined its composition by exploding it with oxygen (see p. 273), the same result being independently found by Desormes and Clement.[2] Although the poisonous character of the gas from burning charcoal was well known in antiquity (Vol. I) and had been emphasised by Van Helmont and Hoffmann (Vol. II), it was later thought to be due to carbon dioxide (which is not poisonous but asphyxiating) until Félix Leblanc, demonstrator in the École polytechnique and then head of the laboratory in the École centrale des arts et manufactures, showed that it is due to carbon monoxide.[3]

Desormes and Clement showed that carbonous gas (gaz carboneux) is formed by passing carbon dioxide over red-hot charcoal, as well as by strongly heating charcoal with zinc oxide or barium carbonate. By exploding it with oxygen in a eudiometer they found, from the known composition of carbonic acid, that it contained 44 parts of carbon and 56 of oxygen (the correct figures are 43 and 57).

Dalton,[4] who called it 'carbonic oxide', found that 100 vols. required 47 of oxygen and gave 94 of carbonic acid, saying: 'I always find the oxygen fully equal to half the carbonic acid, whether fired over mercury or water.' That the oxygen in carbonic acid was found to be 'just double of that in the carbonic oxide for a given quantity of carbone' by Clement and Desormes is noted by Dalton, who adds: 'This most striking circumstance seems to have wholly escaped their notice.'

Monge[5] found that carbonic acid gas sparked with iron wires over mercury expanded, the mercury became black, and the iron was 'calcined'; the gas, after removal of carbonic acid by alkali, was combustible and Monge thought it was hydrogen from water present in the gas. Saussure,[6] who used copper wires, showed that it was carbonic oxide, formed from carbonic acid by removal of oxygen by the copper. He found that a mixture of carbon dioxide and hydrogen when sparked with iron wires forms carbonic oxide. William Henry[7] found that dry carbonic acid gas expands when sparked with platinum wires, and if the excess of carbonic acid was absorbed with alkali, the residual gas was exploded by a spark, and was thus a mixture of oxygen and carbonic oxide.

The Combustion of Hydrocarbons

Desormes and Clement[8] found that on burning a hydrocarbon with a deficiency of oxygen, hydrogen is set free, but they do not say that carbon monoxide is formed. They made the 'hydrogène carboné' by heating charcoal with hydrogen in a red-hot iron tube (methane), or passing alcohol vapour

---

[1] *Nicholson's J.*, 1801, v, 1 (on 'hydrocarbonate' and compounds of carbon and oxygen); Murray, 1806, ii, 395.

[2] *J. de l'École Polytechn.*, 1810, iv, 322; *Ann. Chim.*, 1801, xxxviii, 285; 1801, xxxix, 26.

[3] *Ann. Chim.*, 1842, v, 223.   [4] B, 1810, I, ii, 375.

[5] AdS, 1786, m 430; On the effect of electric sparks excited in fixed air.

[6] *J. de Phys.*, 1802, liv, 450.

[7] *Phil. Trans.*, 1797, lxxxvii, 401; 1800, xc, 188 (203).   [8] *Ann. Chim.*, 1801, xxxix, 26 (55).

through a red-hot iron tube containing charcoal (ethylene, although the gas burnt with a flame red inside and blue outside, 'donnant de petites étincelles'), and say:

'si l'on n'en met pas une suffisante quantité [of oxygen] pour brûler et le charbon et l'hydrogène, le charbon seul se brûle et l'on obtient alors une augmentation de volume qui va quelquefois à plus d'un tiers, ce qui vient de ce que dans l'hyrogène (sic) carboné, l'hydrogène est condensé, et qu'il reprend son état élastique lorsque ce principe lui est enlevé.'

Berthollet[1] also experimented on the explosion of methane with a quantity of oxygen insufficient for complete combustion and found that hydrogen is formed, but he mistook the carbon monoxide for carbon dioxide (which is also formed):

'When carburetted hydrogen is inflamed in the eudiometer of Volta, if there is not enough oxygen for total combustion, only the carbon burns; the hydrogen recovers its elasticity which it had lost by its combination with the carbon and the volume of the gas is dilated. It is then a mixture of carbonic acid and hydrogen, which burns with a blue flame like carbonic oxide (gaz carboneux), but which after washing with lime water diminishes and leaves a residue of pure hydrogen.'

Berthollet thought that water gas was a compound of carbon, hydrogen and oxygen (oxycarburetted hydrogen) and that all charcoal contained hydrogen. He criticised Guyton de Morveau's view that charcoal is an oxide of carbon. He argued that when a solid such as carbon combines with carbonic acid gas it could not produce a gas much less dense than the latter:[2] no other gaseous compound is lighter than the lightest of its elements, and the supposition would be contrary to all chemical facts, since it would require that the combination is not due to an attraction but to a repulsion.

Berthollet[3] found that when a mixture of 4 vols. of ethylene and 3 vols. of oxygen is exploded, carbon is deposited and the volume increases to 11 volumes. If the gaseous product is exploded with a suitable quantity of oxygen it is found to be 'composed of the carbon which existed in a corresponding quantity of the primitive gas, less the small portion which formed the carbonaceous deposit, of its hydrogen except a very small part which has produced water, and the oxygen used in the previous detonation, less the small quantity which entered into the composition of the water'.

Cruickshank[4] found in the same experiment a residue of 17·75 vols., $2\frac{1}{4}$ of carbon dioxide and $10\frac{1}{2}$ of carbon monoxide. Thomson[5] thought these experiments:

'demonstrate . . . the truth of Berthollet's notion, that there really exists a gas entitled to the name of oxycarbureted hydrogen; for it is not possible to doubt the existence of hydrogen in this residual gas . . . the evolution of pure hydrogen gas by combustion, while oxygen gas is present, and the combination of this oxygen in preference with carbon, are absolutely inconceivable, and cannot therefore be admitted.'

---

[1] *Phil. Mag.*, 1802, xiii, 276; *Mém. de l'Inst.*, 1803, iv, 269–324, 325–33 (Observations sur le charbon et les gas hidrogènes carbonés); *Statique Chimique*, 1803, ii, 71–3.
[2] *Statique Chimique*, ii, 61 f., 92.
[3] *Statique Chimique*, 1803, ii, 71; *Mém. Soc. Arcueil*, 1809, ii, 68; 1817, iii, 148; *J. Chem. Phys.*, 1820, xxix, 490.
[4] *Nicholson's J.*, 1801, v, 1.   [5] (2), 1807, iii, 476.

Thomson[1] by explosion with oxygen of marsh gas (containing 12·5 per cent of
air as collected) and olefiant gas gave the compositions: marsh gas 72 carbon +
28 hydrogen, olefiant gas 85 carbon and 15 hydrogen, in fairly good agreement
with Dalton's theory and with the densities of the gases (air = 1, marsh gas
= 0·5554, olefiant gas = 0·9745), but he still thought that an oxycarburetted
hydrogen exists as an individual gas.

Some important investigations on the combustion of hydrocarbons were
made by Dalton in 1805.[2] In his notebook for 5 July 1805 Dalton said:[3]

'It appears that stag. Gas requires ½ of its share of oxigen, namely cent per cent before
it will fire. It then becomes same bulk of gas without acid, that is gas. oxid. of carb. and
hyd. It again appears that olefiant gas requires its bulk of oxigen to fire — 1 measure
then becomes nearly 4, and requires ½ its bulk of oxigen and produces half its bulk of
acid. No oxigen or acid after the first firing.'

In modern symbols these results are:

$$1. \qquad CH_4 + O_2 = CO + H_2 + H_2O \text{ (condensed)}$$
$$2a. \qquad C_2H_4 + O_2 = 2CO + 2H_2$$
$$b. \quad 2CO + 2H_2 + 2O_2 = 2CO_2 + 2H_2O \text{ (condensed).}$$

The experiments were described in 1810 as follows:

'If 100 measures of oxygen be put to 100 of olefiant gas, and electrified, an explosion
ensues, not very violent; but instead of a diminution, as usual, there is a great increase
of gas; instead of 200 measures, there will be found about 360; some traces of carbonic
acid are commonly observed.' On removal of this by lime water, 350 measures of gas
remain, 'yielding by an additional dose of oxygen, carbonic acid and water.' The 350
measures consist of 'carbonic oxide and hydrogen mixed together, an equal number of
atoms of each. . . . One third of the oxygen requisite for the complete combustion,
suffices to convert the carbone into carbonic oxide, and the hydrogen at the instant is
liberated'.[4]

Of carburetted hydrogen (methane) obtained from stagnant ponds Dalton
says:

'If 100 measures of carburetted hydrogen be mixed with 100 measures of oxygen
(the least that can be used with effect), and a spark passed through the mixture, there is
an explosion, without any material change of volume.' After removing a small amount
of carbon dioxide by lime water the residual gas 'is found to possess all the characters
of a mixture of equal volumes of carbonic oxide and hydrogen. Upon adding 100
measures of oxygen to this residue and passing a spark, nearly 100 measures of carbonic
acid are produced, and the rest of the produce is water'.[5]

Dalton remarks that although a mixture of carburetted hydrogen and air in
coal mines 'exhibits some dreadful explosions in the large way; yet when
mixed with common air, in Volta's eudiometer, it does not explode by a spark,
unless the gas be to the air, as 1 to 10 nearly, and then feebly'.

Carburetted hydrogen gas (methane) 'is a compound of one atom of charcoal and two of hydrogen; the compound atom occupies the same space
(nearly) as an atom of hydrogen; and 4 atoms of oxygen are necessary for its
complete combustion'. For Dalton $C = 5$, $H = 1$, methane is CH_2, or for $C = 12$

[1] Mem. Wernerian Soc., 1811, i, 504; Nicholson's J., 1811, xxviii, 321.
[2] Bone, J. Chem. Soc., 1933, 1599; Partington, Ann. Sci., 1945, v, 229.
[3] Roscoe and Harden, 68.   [4] B, I, ii, 442.   [5] B, I, ii, 446.

it is CH_4, occupying the same space as H_2, or CH_2 the same space as H. For combustion: $CH_2 + 4O = CO_2 + 2HO$ if $O = 8$ (Dalton took $O = 7$).

'This conclusion derives a very elegant confirmation, from the facts observed by exploding the gas with one half of the oxygen requisite for complete combustion. In this case, each atom of the gas requires only 2 atoms of oxygen; the one joins to one of hydrogen and forms water; the other joins to the carbone to form carbonic oxide, at the same moment the remaining atom of hydrogen springs off.'[1]

Dalton,[2] referring to Berthollet's idea of 'oxycarburetted hydrogen', says:

'there is one circumstance which M. Berthollet has not explained in regard to this gas, and it turns upon a point which he and I acknowledge, but which is not perhaps generally received; namely that when two gases unite to form a third, this last is specifically heavier than the lighter of the two.' But the gas formed by exploding equal volumes of olefiant gas and oxygen (i.e. $CO + H_2$) is 'lighter by one half nearly than the lighter of the two'.

In 1819[3] Dalton correctly found that 10 vols. of ether vapour on explosion in a eudiometer required 60 vols. of oxygen for combustion and gave 40 vols. of carbon dioxide. (This corresponds with: $C_4H_{10}O + 6O_2 = 4CO_2 + 5H_2O$.) He remarks that he first used this method of analysis of hydrocarbons in September 1803. Dalton showed from explosion analyses and vapour density that 'the atom of ether weighs 20·8, and is compounded of 1 atom of water and 2 of olefiant gas', whilst 'alcohol ... is constituted of 1 atom carburetted hydrogen and 1 of water, as it seems to give carbonic acid = half the volume of oxygen consumed, or very little more', although combustion in a lamp in ordinary air 'would imply alcohol to be 1 water and 1 olefiant gas'. He determined the vapour density of ether by evaporation in a vacuous globe and measuring the pressure on a mercury manometer.

In 1820 Dalton[4] in a memoir 'On Oil and the Gases Obtained from it by Heat', reported that the gas formed on 'cracking' whale oil and spermaceti contains a hydrocarbon which exploded with oxygen like olefiant gas but only about half of which combined with chlorine like olefiant gas. 100 vols. of gas required on an average 500 of oxygen to give 300 of carbonic acid gas. The part not combining with chlorine seemed to be carburetted hydrogen (methane).

'The portion which is acted upon by oxymuriatic acid is either a gas hitherto not described, or a mixture of olefiant gas and one or two other gases that have not yet been characterized ... this new gas ... for the present I shall call superolefiant. ... In order to form a gas of this character it would only be required to combine an atom of olefiant gas with 1 of carburetted hydrogen, and to condense them both into the space of 1 atom of olefiant gas. Another supposition might be made, of two atoms of olefiant gas united and comprised in the space of one. In this case, 100 measures would give 400 carbonic acid and require 600 oxygen. This supposition would fall within the compass of the results. [This would be correct] ... it would seem the most simple way of accounting for the phenomena to suppose that part of the gas from oil which we have called superolefiant gas to be a mixture of ordinary olefiant gas, and a new one of double its power, ... at present the subject must remain in uncertainty.' The note added in May 1823[5] says: 'I think it is nearly demonstrable that oil gas is a mixture of

[1] Ib., 447–8.   [2] Ib., 443.   [3] Manchester Mem., 1819, iii, 446 (read 16 April).
[4] Ib., 1824, iv, 64 (read 6 October 1820, with a dated note added May 1823), 527 (note of July 1824); q. by Henry, Phil. Trans., 1821, cxi, 136.
[5] Op. cit., 78 (80–1).

carburetted hydrogen [CH_4], carbonic oxide and hydrogen, together with a greater or less portion of a gas *sui generis*, consisting of the elements of olefiant gas united in the same proportion, but differing in the number of atoms. Most probably the atom of the new gas consists of two of olefiant gas; and the density or specific gravity of the new gas is greater than that of olefiant gas in the ratio of 4 to 3; or its specific gravity is 1·293, atmospheric air being 1.'

Dalton showed that the latter assumption agreed with his experiments, and hence must be regarded as a discoverer of butylene, C_4H_8; he is mentioned by Faraday,[1] who isolated pure butylene from oil gas.

In 1821, William Henry[2] had said that oil gas contains 'a new gas *sui generis*, consisting of hydrogen and charcoal in proportions that remain to be determined'. In a paper 'on olefiant gas', Dalton[3] said the new gas is 'compounded of three volumes of vapour of carbon and three volumes of hydrogen condensed into one volume and its specific gravity . . . [is] 1·458'. It is 'a modification of olefiant gas, constituted of the same elements as that fluid, and in the same proportions, with this difference, that the compound atom is *triple* instead of *double*'. Dalton's first assumption, however, repeated in 1823 (see above) that the 'atom' is double that of ethylene, was correct.

Dalton assumed that vegetable substances are formed from a 'vegetable atom', CHO.[4] If modern atomic weights are used, this corresponds with formaldehyde, HCHO, which was supposed by Baeyer to polymerise to carbohydrates (Vol. IV). Dalton's recognition of polymerism (C_2H_4 and C_4H_8) was accompanied by a recognition of isomerism; he wrote the formula of albumin (I Fig. 71) and gelatin (II Fig. 71) as C_2H_2ON with different

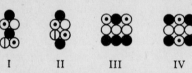

I   II   III   IV

FIG. 71. ISOMERIC MOLECULES.

arrangements of the atoms, and also had a tetrahedral formula for oxamide, CHON.[5] Thomson[6] gave the formulae of acetic acid (III Fig. 71) and succinic acid (IV Fig. 71) as $C_4H_2O_3$, saying that 'these two arrangements would produce a great change in the nature of the compound'. Berzelius first generalised such examples (Vol. IV).

Dalton's Miscellaneous Observations

Among the many papers read by Dalton to the Manchester Literary and Philosophical Society, but not all published,[7] are those on winds (1802), a review of his lectures to the Royal Institution (1804), on the elements of chemical philosophy (August 1804), on heat (October 1804), on respiration and animal heat (March 1806), on the specific heat of bodies and of gases (1808), respiration (1808), compounds of sulphur and sulphuric acid (1809), oxymuriate of lime (1812), phosphoric acid and phosphates (1813), on many compounds of metals (1813 on), compounds of azote and oxygen (1816), alum (1820), remarks on the notation of Berzelius (1830), arseniates and phosphates

[1] *Phil. Trans.*, 1825, cxv, 440; *Experimental Researches*, 1859, 154.
[2] *Phil. Trans.*, 1821, cxi, 136; dated Manchester, January 1821; read 27 February 1821.
[3] *Ann. Phil.*, 1822, iii, 37; dated 29 September 1821.
[4] Gee, Coward and Harden, 1914–15, 42, 57.   [5] Gee, Coward, and Harden, 42, plate VII.
[6] (1), ii, 304.   [7] Angus Smith, 1856, 253.

(1838), Graham's work on phosphates (1839), the quantity of acid, bases and water in different salts, with a new method of measuring the water of crystallisation (1840), and on organic acids (1841). The last paper he read (16 April 1844) was, appropriately enough, 'On the fall of Rain, &c. &c., in Manchester, during a period of 50 years.' Of those published the most important are:

'Experiments and Observations on Phosphoric Acid, and on the salts denominated Phosphates',[1] 'Experiments and Observations on the Combination of Carbonic Acid and Ammonia'[2] — the first preparation of normal ammonium carbonate,[3] and 'On Sulphuric Ether'.[4] In 1827 he gave a simple description of the rock strata near Manchester.[5]

In his papers on 'oxymuriate of lime' (bleaching powder) Dalton[6] assumed that it is a compound of hydrate of lime and chlorine (oxymuriatic acid), or 'hyperoximuriate of lime', whilst Ure[7] denied that it had any definite composition, supposing that 'the molecules of chlorine are loosely clustered round the hydrate' (i.e. the slaked lime).

A memoir 'On the Phosphates and Arseniates' was declined publication by the Royal Society in 1839, so Dalton had it printed with essays 'On Microcosmic Salt', 'On the Quantity of Acids, Bases and Water in different varieties of Salts', and 'On a New and Easy Method of Analysing Sugar', in 1840–2.[8] Dalton uses his old circular symbols and his old atomic weights (see p. 811). Soda is still an element, and phosphoric acid is PO_2, although he refers to Graham and Berzelius. The essays are mostly written in a disjointed way, and Dalton mentions 'my present state, afflicted with Paralysis'. He says:

'I sent the account of the *Phosphates* and *Arseniates* to the Royal Society, for their insertion in the Transactions. They were *rejected*. Cavendish, Davy, Wollaston, and Gilbert are no more (p. 12). . . . In 1810 I was solicited by Davy to offer myself as a candidate to the Royal Society, but declined it. In 1816, I was elected a *Corresponding* Member of the Institute of France . . . upon the death of Davy, in 1830, I was introduced as an *Associate* Member of the French Institute. In 1822 some of my friends proposed me, without my knowledge, as a Candidate to the Royal Society; I do not know who they were . . . : I was elected, and paid the usual fee' (pp. 20–21).

This was unworthy of Dalton, a Royal Medallist in 1826. The paper on phosphates and arsenates could not have been printed in the form in which it was written, particularly after Graham's memoir of 1833 in which the compositions were correctly given.[9] The Royal Society acted correctly and, we may be sure, regretfully. It did, it is true, reject Joule's fundamental paper shortly afterwards, but made amends later. As Joule said, Manchester was 'a remote place to the gentlemen of the Royal Society'.

Of the four short papers two, 'On a new and easy Method of Analysing Sugar', and 'On the Quantities of Acids, Bases and Water in the different Varieties of Salts', are quite important. They announced the discovery,

[1] *Manchester Mem.*, 1819, iii, 1; read 22 Jan. 1813.
[2] *Ib.*, 1819, iii, 18: read 19 March 1813.   [3] Divers, *J. Chem. Soc.*, 1870, xxiii, 171.
[4] *Manchester Mem.*, 1819, iii, 446: read 16 April 1819.   [5] *Ib.*, 1831, v, 148: read 1827.
[6] *Ann. Phil.*, 1813, i, 15; 1813, ii, 6; *Phil. Mag.*, 1825, lxv, 122 (on indigo).
[7] *Quart. J. Sci.*, 1822, xiii, 1.
[8] C, p. 800; Manchester (John Harrison), 1840–2; the essays are paginated separately: 1–22; 1–14, 1–10.
[9] *Phil. Trans.*, 1833, cxxiii, 253.

extended by Playfair and Joule[1] that certain anhydrous salts do not increase the volume of water on solution, the salts 'enter the pores' of the water. In the 'Method of Analysing Sugar' (p. 3) Dalton says: 'It is my opinion that the simple atoms are *alike, globular*, and all of the same *magnitude* or *bulk*, whether *hydrogen* 1, or *lead*, 90.' He gives descriptions (but not figures) of the arrangements of the atoms of the elements in the 'atoms' of sugar, tartaric acid, acetic acid, vinic acid, and citric acid (see p. 820).

Dalton found that steel contains little or no free carbon, left as a residue after solution in acid, and he supposed the peculiar hardness was due to a crystalline state of the iron.[2] In a paper, 'Remarks tending to facilitate the Analysis of Spring and Mineral Waters',[3] Dalton introduced volumetric analysis. He proposed the 'use of tests', i.e. standard solutions:

'the exact quantities of the ingredients in each test should be previously ascertained and marked on the label of the bottle. . . . We should then drop in certain quantities of each from a dropping tube graduated into grains till the required effect was produced; then from the quantity of the test required, the quantity of saline matter in the water might be determined without the trouble of collecting the precipitate; or if this was done the one method might be a check upon the other.'

He gives directions for determining the alkalinity of water by the use of acids and 'these acids may be considered as sufficient for tests of the quantity of lime in such waters, and nothing more is required than to mark the quantity of acid necessary to neutralize the lime'. Dalton's pupil, Henry Hough Watson, told Angus Smith[4] that Dalton used the volumetric method constantly. Dalton also used a very small hydrometer (scale $1\frac{1}{2}$ long divided into $25°$, the difference between distilled and common spring water being about $1°$) in water analysis, and 'particularly in determining minute proportions of residual salt after precipitation'. He noticed with surprise that water 'containing carbonate or supercarbonate [bicarbonate] of lime, is essentially *limy* or alkaline by the colour tests'. He showed by titration with standard acid that the solubility of calcium hydroxide decreases with rise of temperature.[5]

In a letter of July 1809 to William Allen[6] Dalton refers to experiments on respiration made two or three years before, 'which will perhaps appear in our next volume', showing that 'all the oxygen which disappears is to be found in the carbonic acid', but his results differed in some respects from Allen's.[7] In a paper on indigo[8] Dalton altered Crum's formula[9] $C_{16}H_4NO_2$, which is nearly correct (it should be $C_{16}H_5NO_2$), to C_8H_2ON with Dalton's atomic weights.

W. HENRY

William Henry (Manchester; 12 December 1774–2 September (or 30 August) 1836)[10] entered Percival's house to study medicine, practised five years

[1] *Mem. Chem. Soc.*, 1845, ii, 401; 1848, iii, 57; *J. Chem. Soc.*, 1849, i, 121, 139; Joule, *Scientific Papers*, 1887, ii, 11, 117, 180, 203.
[2] B, II, 217.   [3] *Manchester Mem.*, 1819, iii, 52; read 1 April 1814.   [4] 1856, ix, 251.
[5] B, I, ii, 509.   [6] *Life of William Allen with Selections from his Correspondence*, 1846, i, 113.
[7] See p. 478.   [8] *Manchester Mem.*, 1824, iv, 427–40.   [9] *Ann. Phil.*, 1823, v, 81.
[10] W. C. Henry, *Manchester Mem.*, 1842, vi, 99 (read 1837); Walker, *Memoirs of Distinguished Men of Science*, 1862, 86; Sutton, DNB, 1891, xxvi, 129; Partington, *J. Soc. Chem. Ind.*, 1933, lii, 478.

with Dr. Ferriar in Manchester Infirmary, and studied under Black in Edinburgh (1795–6), M.D. Edinburgh 1807, F.R.S. and Copley Medal, 1809. He then directed the chemical works (making 'Henry's magnesia', etc.) established by his father Thomas Henry (p. 690). Thomson[1] refers to Henry's analytical skill; his reputation was very high, 'even under the disadvantage of being a manufacturing chemist.' Henry's dissertation for the M.D.[2] in a chapter 'De acido urico ex aliis innotuerint', contains a short history of uric acid. In an early essay, 'A Review of Some Experiments which have been supposed to Disprove the Materiality of Heat' (i.e. Rumford's and Davy's), written in 1799,[3] Henry says caloric occupies space because it enlarges other bodies, is impenetrable, for otherwise no expansion would occur, has no gravitational attraction, and need not have form or figure. He argues that it cannot be pure motion, since it traverses a vacuum, and that its properties suggest that it possesses the kind of attraction called chemical affinity.

In 1800[4] he found that mercury over which muriatic acid gas was sparked became converted into the muriate. His most important publication was on 'Henry's law':[5] 'under equal circumstances of temperature water takes up in all cases the same volume of condensed gas as of gas under ordinary pressure'; or by combining this result with Boyle's law, 'it follows that water takes up, of gas condensed by one, two or more additional atmospheres, a quantity which, ordinarily compressed, would be equal to twice, thrice, etc., the volume absorbed under the common pressure of the atmosphere.' He used a kind of Boyle's-law tube with a small graduated bottle at the closed end, into which, by stopcocks, measured quantities of water and gas could be introduced over mercury. By pouring mercury into the graduated open arm of the tube the pressure could be raised to 58 in. of mercury, nearly 3 atm. The greatest difficulty, pointed out to him by Dalton, was the presence of less soluble impurities in the gases, which accumulated as the pressure increased. His results, however, were good. The experiments convinced Henry that the solution of a gas is 'purely a mechanical effect'[6] and of the truth of Dalton's theory of mixed gases[7] (see p. 773).

Henry[8] published analyses of British and foreign common salt which showed that the first was much purer than the foreign salt then preferred by the Irish provision curers. Londons, a Northwich firm, purified rock salt by fusion in a reverberatory furnace,[9] a process patented in 1903 by Lee in Ireland.[10]

The most notable chemical researches of W. Henry were on hydrocarbon gases and on the combustion of ammonia with oxygen. In the second[11] he determined the composition of ammonia gas by exploding it with a small

[1] (1), ii, 232.
[2] *Dissertatio chemico-medica de Acido Urico et Morbis a nimia ejus Secretione ortis*, Edinburgh, 1807 (pp. v, 47); Sotheran *Cat.* 925 (1959), 67, no. 1002.
[3] *Manchester Mem.*, 1802, v, 603–21; read June 1801.   [4] *Phil. Trans.*, 1800, xc, 188.
[5] *Phil. Trans.*, 1803, xciii, 29; read 23 December 1802.   [6] *Phil. Trans.*, 1803, xciii, 274.
[7] Henry, *Nicholson's J.*, 1804, viii, 297 (20 June); 1804, ix, 126 (12 Sept.).
[8] *Phil. Trans.*, 1810, c, 89–122.   [9] Parkes, *Chemical Essays*, 1823, ii, 590.
[10] Partington, *The Alkali Industry*, 1925, 15.
[11] *Phil. Trans.*, 1809, xcix, 430; a letter to Davy.

amount of oxygen; the ammonia was decomposed into its elements, hydrogen and nitrogen, and these may be determined by adding more oxygen and exploding. Dry ammonia is decomposed on sparking for some time, 100 vols. becoming 180·6 vols. When ammonia is exploded with excess of oxygen, appreciable amounts of oxides of nitrogen are formed.[1]

Henry, in work begun in Thomson's laboratory in Glasgow, analysed various specimens of coal gas, wood gas, etc., and found that they contained hydrogen, methane, olefiant gas, and carbonic oxide as combustibles, together with carbonic acid; he gives an account of Murdoch's (*sic*) experiments.[2] In 1808[3] Henry found that the combustible constituent of fire-damp is methane (light carburetted hydrogen), which he clearly distinguished from olefiant gas. He remarks on the great violence of the explosion and the danger of bursting the vessel when hydrocarbons are exploded with oxygen in a closed eudiometer, and devised an apparatus in which the gas was burnt quietly from a jet inside a receiver of oxygen, being kindled by an electric spark. He gives the following table:

Cruickshank and Dalton Gas	Sp. gr. of gas (air = 1000)	Vols. of oxygen for 100 vols.	Vols. of carbonic acid formed	Diminution of air on firing
Olefiant	907	300	200	200
Carbonized hydrogen from stag. water	600	200	100	200
Carbonic oxide	967	45	90	55
Hydrogen	84	50	—	154

Henry	O_2 for 100 vols.	Vol. CO_2 produced
Pure hydrogen	50–54	—
Gas from moist charcoal	60	35
,, ,, oak wood	54	33
,, ,, dried peat	68	43
,, ,, coal or cannel	170	100
,, ,, lamp oil	190	124
,, ,, wax	220	137
Pure olefiant gas	284	179

He assumed that 1 vol. oxygen was used to produce 1 vol. carbonic acid, hence:

'we shall learn, by deducting the numbers in the third column from the corresponding one in the second, what proportion of the consumed oxygen has been allotted to the

---

[1] See Partington and Prince, *J. Chem. Soc.*, 1924, cxxv, 2018; Partington and Beeson, *ib.*, 1925, cxxvii, 1146.

[2] *Nicholson's J.*, 1805, xi, 65–74.

[3] *Ib.*, 1808, xix, 148–53 (dated 10 January); *Phil. Trans.*, 1808, xcviii, 282: Description of an Apparatus for the Analysis of Compound Inflammable Gases by Slow Combustion; with Experiments on the gas from Coal, explaining its Application.

saturation of the hydrogen of each hydro-carburet . . . the quantity of hydrogen . . . may be ascertained . . . by subtracting the number in the third from the corresponding one in the second column, in each instance, and doubling the remainder.'

In later experiments[1] Henry determined the olefiant gas in coal gas from the contraction when the gas in a narrow tube is mixed with chlorine, with the exclusion of direct sunlight, when liquid ethylene chloride is formed. He described the preparation, purification, and analysis of coal gas. He says the factory of Philips and Lee in Manchester was lighted by gas, and Mr. Lee's private residence by gas brought two miles daily from the factory in a portable gas-holder on a cart. Henry estimated the hydrogen sulphide in gas by test-papers coated with white lead, the colour being compared with a standard. Analyses of coal gas were made by Thomas Thomson.[2]

Henry followed Dalton in clearly distinguishing methane from ethylene, the two gases being confused even as late as 1820 by Brande.[3] Henry in 1824[4] described a method of analysing gas mixtures by fractional combustion in presence of finely-divided platinum as a catalyst. He refers to Döbereiner, Davy, and Dulong and Thenard (see Vol. IV). The platinum was used in the form of platinum sponge, or a mixture of platinum black and clay was made into a ball supported by a wire, as in Döbereiner's experiments.[5] He noticed that ethylene prevents the catalytic union of hydrogen and oxygen, carbon monoxide does so to a less extent, whilst methane exerts practically no influence. From a mixture of hydrogen, methane, ethylene, and carbon monoxide, ethylene was first removed by adding chlorine in the dark. The residue was mixed with oxygen and passed over platinum sponge at 340° F., when hydrogen and carbon monoxide were burnt. From the contraction, and the absorption in alkali, the two gases were determined. Methane did not react until the temperature was above the boiling point of mercury.

Henry wrote some elementary works on chemistry which ultimately formed an enlarged and frequently revised text-book:

A. A General View of the Nature and Objects of Chemistry, and of its Application to Arts and Manufactures, Manchester, 1799 (44 pp., errata slip; repr. at the beginning of the Elements of Experimental Chemistry, except the last ed. of 1829);

B. Syllabus of a Course of Lectures on Chemistry, Manchester, n.d. (40 pp.; price 1/–; back of t.p. says the last sheet was not yet printed but will be delivered as soon as completed);

C. An Epitome of Chemistry, in Three Parts. Part I, intended to facilitate, to the Student, the Acquisition of Chemical Knowledge, by Minute Instructions for the Performance of Experiments. Part II, Directions for the Analysis of Mineral Waters; of Earths and Stones; of Ores of Metals; and of Mineral Bodies in general. And Part III, Instructions for applying Chemical Tests and Reagents to various useful Purposes, sm. 8°, London, 1801 (printed in Manchester, 216 pp.), 2 ed. 1801 (xv, 221, [iii] pp., with description and prices, 15, 11, and 6½ guineas, of 'Portable

[1] Experiments on the Gas from Coal; *Manchester Mem.*, 1819, iii, 391.
[2] *Proc. Phil. Soc. Glasgow*, 1843–4, i, 165.
[3] *Phil. Trans.*, 1820, cx, 11–28 (assisted by Faraday): Analysis of the Inflammable Gaseous Compounds from Coal and Oil, etc.
[4] *Phil. Trans.*, 1824, cxiv, 266 (On the Action of finely divided Platinum on Gaseous Mixtures and its Application to their Analysis).
[5] Mittasch and Theis, *Von Davy und Döbereiner bis Deacon*, 1932, 53, and figure.

Chemical Chests, invented by William Henry, And sold by him at his Laboratory in Manchester'), 3 ed. 1805, 4 ed. 1806, 5 ed. 1808 (xxii ll., 502 pp., 8 fold. plates).
    This was expanded and issued (the ed. numbers being continued) as:
D. The Elements of Experimental Chemistry, 2 vols. 8°, London, 6 ed. 1810, 7 ed. 1815 (9 fold. plates engr. by Lowry), 8 ed. 1818; 9 ed. 1823 (10 fold. pts.), 10 ed. 1826, 11 ed. 1829; dedic. to John Dalton; also American ed., 2 vols. Philadelphia, 1819, etc. French tr. (from 1810 ed.) by H. F. Gaultier de Claubry, Élémens de Chimie Expérimentale, 2 vols. 8°, Paris, 1812; German tr. (from 5 ed. of Epitome) by F. Wolff, Grundriss der theoretischen und praktischen Chemie, 2 vols., Berlin, 1812; Danish tr. by S. C. Salling, Odensee, 1805 (Bolton, (1), 524).

Coal Gas

The use of coal gas as an illuminant was introduced by William Murdock (Old Cumnock, Ayrshire, 1754–Soho, 1839), an employé of Boulton and Watt, who began experiments at Redruth, Cornwall, in 1792. The works of Boulton and Watt at Soho, near Birmingham, were illuminated outside by gas on the Peace of Amiens in 1802 and plant for manufacturing coal gas was installed in 1803.[1] Experiments by Clayton and Hales on the preparation of coal gas were mentioned in chapter IV. George Dixon[2] in County Durham, about 1759, heated coal in an old kettle with a clay tobacco-pipe fixed to the spout; a larger apparatus exploded. R. Watson in 1767 made coal gas by distilling 96 oz. of Newcastle coal in an earthen retort, the gas being estimated by difference as weighing 28 grains.[3] Jan Pieter Minckelers, professor of physics in Louvain, it is alleged, lighted his class-room with coal gas in 1785, or 1787, and sent up a balloon filled with coal gas in Louvain on 21 November 1783. In 1784 he published in Louvain a *Mémoire sur l'air inflammable tiré de differentes substances* (49 pp.).[4]

Zacharias Andreas Winzler in 1802 in Vienna gave lectures on gas lighting and installed it in three places. Friedrich Albert Winzer on his return from Paris in 1802, demonstrated a 'thermolamp' of Phillipe Lebon, which burned wood-gas, in Brunswick and obtained a privilege from George III. He changed his name to Winsor and in 1804–9 took out patents in London for gas lighting, street lighting being attempted in 1808. Samuel Clegg senr. in Manchester introduced purification by milk of lime and introduced gas lighting in Stonyhurst College in Lancashire. The first public gas-works was in Salford, Lancashire, in 1805, gas being supplied to factories. The use in private houses came later.[5] On 1 January 1837 there were 30 gas-works in London and the suburbs, using annually about 180,000 tons of coal and producing about 1460

[1] Murdock, *Phil. Trans.*, 1808, xcviii, 124; Henry, *Nicholson's J.*, 1805, xi, 65; W. Matthews, *An Historical Sketch of the Origin, Progress, & Present State, of Gas Lighting*, 1827; Parkes, *Chemical Essays*, 1823, i, 379; Smiles, *Lives of the Engineers. Boulton and Watt*, 1904, 226, 399; Thomson, (2), 1807, i, 50; Polack, *Chem. and Ind.*, 1956, 252, says Murdock until 1797 wrote his name 'Murdoch', thereafter (perhaps because Boulton and Watt wrote it so) 'Murdock', and perhaps the first was more correct (Thomson wrote 'Murdoch' in 1807).
[2] J. Bailey, *General View of the Agriculture of Durham*, 1810, 291; J. Macfarlan, *Trans. Newcomen. Soc.*, 1926, v, 53.
[3] *Chemical Essays*, 6 ed. 1793, ii, 317.
[4] C. Morren, *Bull. Acad. Bruxelles*, 1835, ii, 162; L. Darmstaedter, *Handbuch zur Geschichte der Naturwissenschaften und der Technik*, 1908, 238; Feldhaus, (1), 1914, 355; J. Macfarlan, *loc cit.*
[5] Feldhaus, (1), 1914, 355 f.; Samuel Clegg, junr., *A Practical Treatise on the Manufacture and Distribution of Coal-Gas*, 4°, London, 1841, 1853, 1859, 1866.

million cu. ft. of gas.[1] J. Murray[2] suggested the use of iron instead of copper pipes for coal gas, as the copper pipes were soon stopped by corrosion.

ACCUM

An important early worker on coal gas was Friedrich Christian Accum (Bückeburg, 29 March 1769–Berlin, 28 June 1838) who came to England in 1793. He became engineer to the Chartered Gas Light and Coke Co., formed in 1810 (Royal privilege had been granted to Winsor on behalf of this in 1812),[3] and was also lecturer in chemistry at the Surrey Institution, Blackfriars Bridge, and librarian of the Royal Institution, where he came under suspicion of damaging and purloining books. He was acquitted but at once left England for Berlin in 1822, and became professor in the Gewerbe-Institut there.[4] His chief work was in founding the gas industry and in the chemistry of foods; he wrote a sensational book on food adulteration, with the quotation from Lucan (*Pharsalia*, ix, 617): pocula morte carent (There is Death in the Pot) on the title-page. Chaptal[5] says vast quantities of vinegar sweetened with litharge were sold as wine in 1750 in Paris. Accum published:

A System of Theoretical and Practical Chemistry, 2 vols., 1803, 2 ed., 1807; A Practical Essay on the Analysis of Minerals, 1804; Analysis of a Course of Lectures on Mineralogy (given at the Surrey Institution), 1809; Manual of a Course of Lectures on Experimental Chemistry and on Mineralogy, etc., 1810; Elements of Crystallography, after the method of Haüy, 1813 (lxiii, 396 pp. 4 copperplates); A Practical Essay on Chemical Re-Agents or Tests. Illustrated by a Series of Experiments. A Descriptive Catalogue of the Apparatus and Instruments employed in Experimental and Operative Chemistry, in Analytical Mineralogy, and in the Pursuits of the recent Discoveries of Voltaic Electricity, 1816, 1818 (enlarged), 1826 (ed. W. Maugham), 1828; French tr. by Riffault, 1819; Italian tr. by G. Pozzi, 2 vols., Milan, 1819; Chemical Amusements, comprising a Series of Curious and Instructive Experiments in Chemistry, etc., 1817, 3 ed. 1818, 4 ed. 1819; Spanish tr. by Casaceda, 2 vols. 12°, Perpignan, 1836; The Use and Application of Chemical Tests, 1818; A Practical Treatise on Gas-Light, 1815 (1 and 2 eds.), 3 ed. 1816, 4 ed. 1818; German tr. by Lampadius, Weimar, 1816, 1819; French trs. by Winsor and anon. (Chez l'Auteur et Nepveu), Paris, 1816; Description of the Process of Manufacturing Coal Gas, 1819, 1820; Death in the Pot: A Treatise on the Adulteration of Food, and Culinary Poisons, 1820 (1 and 2 eds.); Culinary Chemistry . . . with the chemical Constitution and nutritive Qualities of different Kinds of Food, 1821; A Treatise on the Art of Brewing, 1820, 1821; A Treatise on the Art of Making Bread, 1821; A Treatise on the Art of Making Wine from Native Fruits, etc., 1820, French ed., 1851, 1872; Explanatory Dictionary of the Apparatus and Instruments employed in the various Operations of Philosophical and Experimental Chemistry, By a Practical Chemist, 1824 (vii, 295 pp., 17 double copperplates; Bolton, (1), 38, gives an ed. of 1821); Physische und chemische Beschaffenheit der Baumaterialen, 2 vols., Berlin, 1826.

Accum had a large private laboratory in London, in which he gave practical instruction. Benjamin Silliman senr. studied there in 1804–5, and later another famous American, the mineralogist James Freeman Dana.

[1] Brande, 1848, i, 493.   [2] *Elements of Chemical Science*, London, 1818, 153.
[3] Everard, *The History of the Gas Light and Coke Company*, London, 1949.
[4] Rodwell, DNB, 1885, i, 57; C. A. Browne, *J. Chem. Educ.*, 1925, ii, 829, 1008, 1140; *id.*, *Isis*, 1927, ix, 164; *id.*, *Nature*, 1938, cxli, 1153; Cole, *Ann. Sci.*, 1951, vii, 128; F. A. Filby, *History of Food Adulteration*, 1934; Gunther, (1), 1923, i, 73.
[5] *Elements of Chemistry*, 1791, ii, 310.

INDEX OF NAMES

(Pages containing biographical notices or full treatments are in heavy type)

INDEX OF SUBJECTS

PRINTED IN GREAT BRITAIN
BY ROBERT MACLEHOSE AND CO. LTD
THE UNIVERSITY PRESS, GLASGOW